EGON R
Cellnet G

Hotels & Restaurants

)00 establishments in Great Britain and Ireland

cellnet

Egon Ronay's Guides
73 Uverdale Road
London SW10 OSW

Consultant **Egon Ronay**
Editorial Director **Bernard Branco**
Managing Editor **Andrew Eliel**
Publishing Director **Angela Nicholson**

First published 1993 by Pan Macmillan Publishers Ltd, Cavaye Place, London SW10 9PG

987654321

The contents of this book are believed correct at the time of printing. Nevertheless, the publisher can accept no responsibility for errors or omissions or changes in the details given.

ISBN 0 330 329 22 4

Typeset in Great Britain by Spottiswoode Ballantyne, Colchester, Essex.
Printed and bound in Great Britain by BPCC Hazell Books Ltd

All restaurant and hotel inspections are anonymous and carried out by Egon Ronay's Guides' team of professional inspectors. Inspectors may reveal their identities at hotels in order to check all the rooms and other facilities. The Guide is independent in its editorial selection and does not accept advertising, payment or hospitality from listed establishments.

Contents

cellnet
The nearest phone.

Welcome to the 1994 edition of the Egon Ronay's Cellnet Guide to Hotels and Restaurants.

Our long term commitment to this guide underlines our trust in its impartiality as an invaluable reference to over 3000 establishments throughout the U.K. Now in its 36th year of publication, it is regarded as the authoritative directory of a wide spectrum of hotels and restaurants to suit the needs of all travellers. An entry is something to be strived for, as it sets the standard for value and quality.

Just as the guide offers choice and value, so we at Cellnet share the same aims in our business. We constantly strive to improve our service and provide more choice and value. Once the preserve of business people, the mobile phone is now an accepted part of everyday life. We have opened up the market with our Lifetime initiative to make mobile telephony affordable for the occasional user as well as the frequent user. It is my aim to bring the benefits of our services to many more people and we will continue to offer our customers a choice so that you have the tariff to suit your lifestyle.

I hope you enjoy using the guide and will agree that this year's edition is the best yet.

Stafford Taylor
Managing Director, Cellnet

Cellnet – making more of the mobile phone.

Since the launch of cellular communications in the UK in 1985, Cellnet, with the support of its parent companies BT and Securicor, has invested more than £700 million in the continuous development of its network and customer services.

More support for handportable phones.

If you've bought, or are considering a handportable phone you'll need to be connected to Cellnet – the mobile communication network that offers in-depth coverage, locally and nationwide.

We are investing over £30million on 230 new local network base stations, which will bring the total number of Cellnet cellular stations to over 1,000 and help to ensure Cellnet continues to offer handportable users the best possible service nationwide.

More coverage nationwide.

Embracing over 98% of the UK population and stretching the length and breadth of the nation (including exclusive coverage of the Channel Islands and the Isle of Man), you can make calls on Cellnet, nationally and internationally, from almost anywhere in the UK.

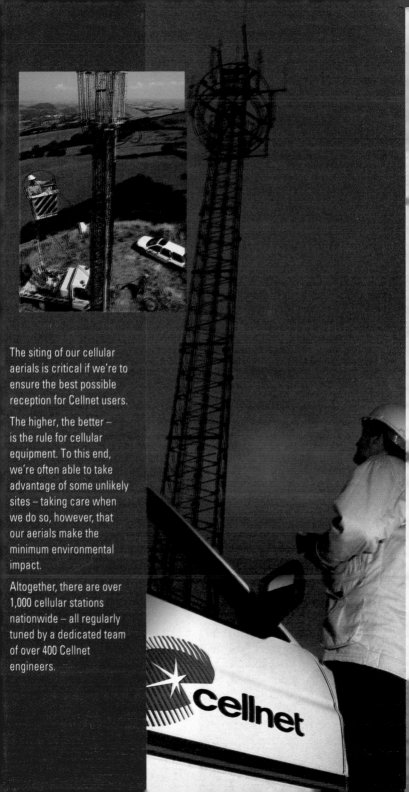

The siting of our cellular aerials is critical if we're to ensure the best possible reception for Cellnet users.

The higher, the better – is the rule for cellular equipment. To this end, we're often able to take advantage of some unlikely sites – taking care when we do so, however, that our aerials make the minimum environmental impact.

Altogether, there are over 1,000 cellular stations nationwide – all regularly tuned by a dedicated team of over 400 Cellnet engineers.

More commitment to service quality.

Our mastery of the advanced technology which supports mobile communications, and our commitment to customer service, is reflected in our Network Management Centre at our headquarters in Slough.

From here a unique monitoring service operating 24 hours a day, 365 days a year, keeps watch over every aspect of the Cellnet network. It enables us to anticipate any problems that may arise, and resolve them long before they can affect our customers. Our aim is to provide an uninterrupted service. A service that you can rely on.

In the unlikely event of experiencing any difficulty with the network, corporate customers with CallAccess links can, with the agreement of their Service Provider, phone directly into Cellnet. No other mobile communications network offers UK businesses support on this scale.

And the widest choice of tariffs to suit your lifestyle.

Recognising that different users have very different needs, Cellnet offers a choice of tariff packages designed to offer high volume and less frequent users – not only in London, but throughout the country – more flexibility and greater value for money.

More services. More support.

Cellnet offers a comprehensive range of sophisticated services, too. Supporting both business and personal needs, including International Calls, Information Lines (such as AA Roadwatch, Cellnet Weathercall and Talking Pages), and intelligent messaging.

With Cellnet, personal communications can mean so much more than personal efficiency and peace of mind. With Cellnet, your mobile phone will not only make life easier – it will help to make life more enjoyable, too. Keeping you in touch, wherever life takes you.

Introduction by Managing Editor Andrew Eliel

All change

After several years in the doldrums there are signs that the hotel and restaurant industry is recovering, albeit patchily, and at a price. In order to attract what little business there has been and to counteract the recession, many hotels and restaurants have actually had to reduce their charges; this perhaps highlights overcharging in the greedy 80s, which gave way to what we have dubbed the needy 90s. There's a price war going on, and however it is waged (discounts, added value, special offers, corporate rates etc) the customer benefits. Only the strongest have survived and, sadly, many have fallen by the wayside (or into the hands of receivers). 'Executive' spending has been greatly reduced and when it's your own money you're parting with, you're naturally more careful and particular about where it goes. To attract more customers restaurants have had to adapt their style: bargain set meals, less expensive lunches (and on that subject, why not cheaper dinners as well?), cutting down on luxury ingredients and in many cases staff as well – the latter more apparent in hotels, where service is often stretched.

When the country's second largest group of hotel operators are administrative receivers (often not apparent until your bill marked "in administrative receivership", so don't be afraid to ask when booking), how heartening it is to see new restaurants and hotels still being opened. With sound financing, now is indeed the right time to buy, although the luxury end of the market in the capital is looking top heavy. London's *Mirabelle* and *Les Saveurs* restaurants (both Japanese-backed, incidentally) will probably be the last 'luxurious' ones to open and it is doubtful that we will ever see their likes again. The future appears to lie in the new route pioneered by Forte, with proven star chefs cooking in de luxe hotels, and it's good to see our major hotel operators finally showing serious interest in their food and beverage operations (*Chez Nico at Ninety Park Lane* is now well established in Grosvenor House, and Marco Pierre White of *Harveys* fame is seeking further acclaim when he opens at the Hyde Park Hotel). Even one of the greatest of them all – Robuchon in Paris – is taking a similar route. By the end of the decade it seems likely that the great restaurants will once again be found in major hotels; thus a full circle will have been turned in little more than twenty years, for it was in the early 70s that a major challenge was mounted to the grand hotels: the Roux brothers opened the original *Le Gavroche*, and led the way for others to follow, not least *La Tante Claire*, *Chez Nico*, *Le Manoir aux Quat'Saisons*, *L'Ortolan* and *Harveys*. While there will always be a place for this style of restaurant (though regrettably some of the great names are no longer consistently performing at their peak), our tastes, not to mention the depth of our pockets, continue to change.

New developments

Throughout the country we continue to see the opening of basic bedroom factories (the Regent London may turn out to be the last luxury hotel to open in the capital, which must surely have reached saturation point in the top bracket) and more casual restaurants serving less complicated dishes with the emphasis perhaps not so much on the actual food on the plate, as on a combination of relaxed ambience, value-for-money cooking and fun. Out has gone the reverence of food, in has come enjoyment. Our long-established and renowned star system is based first and foremost on excellence of cooking, with only secondary consideration given to other factors. When these factors – setting, ambience, decor, service, value-for-money – are taken into account, other results emerge; where the cooking is supported by at least one other outstanding attraction a restaurant's popularity can surge out of proportion to the quality of its culinary offerings.

And – as was the case on one of our visits – does it matter any longer if the star chef is sitting in his flat above the restaurant watching television, if his brigade cooks well and to the standards the proprietor has set? He may no longer put in an appearance in gleaming whites after service, working the tables for comments and compliments, but do we really need that? Do we want chefs to be the media darlings of the 90s (shades of fashion photographers in the 60s)? After all, it's the restaurant we are recommending, not the kitchen supremo.

Northern lights

Encouragingly, our Chef of the Year Paul Heathcote is at the forefront of revitalised cooking in the north of England (though some will say it was never anything but vital). Returning to his Lancastrian roots, he has swiftly put Longridge on the map. Likewise Terry Laybourne at *21 Queen St*, Newcastle, Kevin Mangeolles at *Michael's Nook*, Grasmere and Tessa Bramley at *The Old Vicarage*, Ridgeway. And still going strong are *The Chester Grosvenor*, *Fischers*, *McCoys*, *Normandie*, *Pool Court*, *Restaurant 19*, and *Yang Sing*. Ones to watch include *Brasserie 44*, *Northcote Manor*, *Winteringham Fields* and *The Box Tree* at Ilkley, which has very recently undergone further changes in the kitchen as we went to press (and does not appear in the Guide this year); the constant movement of chefs throughout the country continues apace – we endeavour, as ever, to offer praise where it is rightfully due.

Taste

The Brussels bureaucrats may appear to be destroying all semblance of taste by introducing punitive regulations regarding the transport and import of food produce, but the good news is that here in Britain we are partly benefiting by focusing attention on our own producers to supply our needs. A wide selection of first-rate British cheeses, for instance, is regularly appearing on trolleys, boards and menus; innovative breads are once again being home-made, and we're less inclined to cross the Channel, though we still rely on France (too heavily perhaps?) for many of the ingredients that chefs require. Similarly, one need look no further than the coffee we drink in restaurants, which has improved tenfold over the last few years. The Real Coffee Association's aim is not only to educate the consumer in how to make real coffee, but to give him the information required to enjoy perfect coffee every time.

And finally...

On the subject of assessing establishments by more than our usual methods, here are a few interesting lists of some of our favourite places; they show that we have in this country many hotels and restaurants that are worthy of their world-wide reputations. All are listed in the same order as the Guide's gazetteer, with London establishments first.

Top Ten

Due recognition must be given to the following restaurants not only for raising standards in general, but also for their dedication to training and encouraging the new generation of chefs, many of whom are British and all of them ready to take on the mantle of young pretender. Our all-time top ten (all of which have been open for at least ten years) is as follows, *in gazetteer order*:

London W1	The Connaught
London W1	Le Gavroche
London SW3	La Tante Claire
Bray-on-Thames	Waterside Inn
Dartmouth	Carved Angel
Great Milton	Le Manoir aux Quat'Saisons
Ullswater	Sharrow Bay
Fort William	Inverlochy Castle
Abergavenny	Walnut Tree
Shanagarry	Ballymaloe House

Instant Nostalgia

London E1 & NW11, Blooms
London W1, Claridge's
London SW1, Ebury Court, Tophams
London W1, L'Etoile
London WC2, Simpsons-in-the-Strand
London W1, White Tower
Horton, French Partridge
Knutsford, Belle Epoque
Oxford, Restaurant Elizabeth
Edinburgh, Caledonian Hotel, Carriages
Glasgow, Rogano
Ballina, Mount Falcon Castle
Dublin, Oisins

Romantic

London SW7, Blakes
London W1, Dorchester Terrace
London W8, Launceston Place
London W1, Mirabelle
London W1, Odin's
London WC2, Savoy River Room
Cambridge, Midsummer House
Dedham, Le Talbooth
Goring-on-Thames, Leatherne Bottel
Grasmere, Michael's Nook
Melbourn, Pink Geranium
Whimple, Woodhayes
Nairn, Clifton Hotel
Auchterarder, Auchterarder House
Fort William, Inverlochy Castle
Llansanffraid Glan Conwy, Old Rectory
Rozel Bay, Chateau la Chaire
Gorey, Marlfield House

Classic British Cooking

London W1, The Dorchester Grill
London W1, Greenhouse
London WC2, Savoy Grill Room
Amberley, Amberley Castle
Castle Cary, Bond's
Handforth, Belfry
Haworth, Weavers
Taplow, Cliveden
Taunton, Castle
Banchory, Raemoir House
Edinburgh, The Balmoral, Grill Room
Linlithgow, Champany Inn

Great Setting

London SE1, Le Pont de la Tour
Bray-on-Thames, Waterside Inn
Gulworthy, Horn of Plenty
Helford, Riverside
Mawnan Smith, Nansidwell
Oakham, Hambleton Hall
Taplow, Cliveden
Achiltibuie, Summer Isles
Eriska, Isle of Eriska
Glenborrodale, Glenborrodale Castle
Portpatrick, Knockinaam Lodge
Scarista, Scarista House
Ullapool, Altnaharrie
Tresco, Isles of Scilly, Island Hotel
Kenmare, Sheen Falls Lodge

Busy & Buzzy

London SW7, Bistrot 190
London SW10, The Canteen
London W1, dell'Ugo
London W1, The Ivy & The Caprice
London W8, Kensington Place
London SW1, Quaglino's
Liverpool, Armadillo
Manchester, Yang Sing
Leeds, Brasserie 44
Edinburgh, The Atrium
Glasgow, Ubiquitous Chip

One of a kind

London NW1, Belgo
London SW7, Blakes
London EC1, Quality Chop House
London WC1, Wagamama
Fressingfield, Fox & Goose
Huntsham, Huntsham Court
Ledbury, Hope End
Leeds, 42 The Calls
Padstow, Seafood
Penzance, Abbey Hotel
Staddle Bridge, McCoys
Stapleford, Stapleford Park
Thornton-le-Fylde, River House
Ballater, Tullich Lodge
Portmeirion, Hotel Portmeirion
Ahakista, Shiro
Baltimore, Chez Youen

Farewell

London SW8, L'Arlequin
London SW11, Polyanna's
London W1, Rue St Jacques
Blackwater, Long's
Easton, Clarke's
Glemsford, Barrett's
Grimsthorpe, Black Horse
Llanrwst, Meadowseet
North Huish, Brookdale House
Rozel Bay, Granite Corner
Scarborough, Holbeck Hall
St Lawrence, Jersey, Little Grove
Whitwell-on-the-Hill, Whitwell Hall
Wootton Common, Lugley's

How to use this Guide

As well as our recommended establishments this Guide includes many interesting features and a wealth of useful quick reference lists designed to help you select the hotel or restaurant that best suits your requirements. A list of hotels by county, with key statistics and prices, will allow you to see at a glance what is available in the area where you intend to stay. Conference and banqueting capacities are included – a boon to organisers of business meetings or functions. Places of interest are listed after the London gazetteer and under the nearest relevant location throughout the Guide. For details of all listings consult the contents pages.

Order of Entries

London appears first, in alphabetical order by **establishment name**. Listings outside London are in alphabetical order by **location** within divisions of England, Scotland, Wales, Channel Islands, Isle of Man, Northern Ireland and the Republic of Ireland. See contents page for specific page numbers, and the index for individual entries.

Map References

Map references alongside each hotel or restaurant entry are to the map section at the back of the book. Use this section in conjunction with the county lists to select establishments in areas you wish to visit.

Hotels

Hotel entries are identified by the letter '**H**'.

Percentage ratings

According to their percentage rating, hotels are classified as:

De luxe 80% and over

Grade 1 70-79%

Grade 2 50-69%

Prices

These are based on current high-season rates at the time of going to press and include VAT (also service if applicable), for a *double room for two occupants with private bath and cooked breakfast*. Prices are shown above the '**H**' or '**PH**' or '**I**' symbol.

The Percentage shown on a hotel entry is an individual rating arrived at after careful testing, inspection and calculation according to our unique grading system.

We assess hotels on 23 factors, which include the quality of service and the public rooms - their cleanliness, comfort, state of repair and general impression. Bedrooms are looked at for size, comfort, cleanliness and decor. The exterior of the building, efficiency of reception, conduct and appearance of the staff, room service and leisure facilities are among other factors. The percentage is arrived at by comparing the total marks given for the 23 factors with the maximum the hotel could have achieved.

The Size of a hotel and the prices charged are not considered in the grading, but the food is, and *if we recommend meals in a hotel a separate entry is made for its restaurant.*

The category of chain hotels offering cheap, practical accommodation and not much else is denoted by the letter '**L**'.

Certain other hotels are ungraded. These may be private house hotels ('**PH**') which are de luxe 'bed and breakfast' hotels offering comfortable, often luxurious accommodation and personal service, but do not have a restaurant or public rooms - although some have a drawing room.

Inns, identified by the letter '**I**', are ungraded, being distinguished from hotels proper by their more modest nature, usually with respect to the day rooms. For our purposes an inn is normally either a pub with hotel-style accommodation or a small hotel with a bar and the atmosphere of a pub.

Also ungraded are some of the more modest London hotels and hotels undergoing major construction or refurbishment programmes at the time of research, and those which opened too late for the fullest inspection.

The major characteristics of the leading hotel groups are covered in a special section at the back of the Guide.

Bargain breaks. Almost all hotels now offer bargain breaks of some kind. Specific details regarding the availability and price of such breaks should be checked with individual establishments. In addition to bargain breaks many hotels are offering price reductions more or less throughout their range. Phone the hotels in the area you're visiting and see what they have to offer.

Restaurants

Restaurants are identified by the letter '**R**'.

★★★ ★★ ★

We award one to three stars for excellence of cooking. One star represents cooking much above average, two outstanding cooking, and three the best in the land.

↑ beside stars indicates a restaurant at the top of its star range.

↑ by itself indicates a restaurant approaching star status.

The symbol '**RR**' denotes a restaurant with rooms, a category based on *restaurants avec chambres* in France. Food is the main attraction, but overnight accommodation is also available. A list of these restaurants appears at the back of the Guide.

We only include restaurants where the cooking comes up to our minimum standards, however attractive the place may be in other respects. We take into account how well the restaurant achieves what it sets out to do as reflected in the menu, decor, prices, publicity, atmosphere – factors that add up to some sort of expectation.

Crowns are awarded to restaurants offering a degree of traditional luxury [ ] or some striking modern features. [ ] They have nothing to do with the quality of the cooking.

This symbol represents a wine list that is outstanding.

Signifies a wine list featuring good-quality California wines.

Signifies a restaurant serving a selection of good-quality wines by the glass.

Signifies a restaurant serving notable desserts.

Signifies a restaurant serving good British cheeses.

Restaurant prices, correct at the time of going to press, are for a *three-course meal for two including one of the least expensive bottles of wine, coffee, service and VAT. Prices are shown alongside the restaurant entry.*

Set-price menus. Prices quoted will often not include service and usually exclude wine. They are not necessarily of three courses. Where two prices are given thus – £14.50/£17.75 – it indicates that there is a 2 or 3-course option; prices given thus – £17.95 & £24.95 – indicates that there are two different set-price menus. A great number of restaurants around the country now *only* offer a set-price menu (although this will usually include a choice).

Many restaurants offer at least one main course for vegetarians; tell them your requirements when you book. There is a list of no-smoking restaurants in the quick reference list section, as well as a list of hotels with wheelchair access.

Starred Restaurants

London ★★★

Chez Nico at Ninety Park Lane **W1** ↑

Le Gavroche **W1**
Les Saveurs **W1**
La Tante Claire **SW3**

England ★★★

Bray-on-Thames Waterside Inn
Great Milton Le Manoir aux Quat'Saisons
Shinfield L'Ortolan

Scotland ★★★

Ullapool Altnaharrie Inn

London ★★

Inter-Continental Hotel, Le Soufflé **W1** ↑

Alastair Little **W1**
The Connaught **W1**
The Dorchester, Terrace **W1**
Mirabelle **W1**

England ★★

Chagford Gidleigh Park
Dartmouth Carved Angel

Wales ★★

Abergavenny Walnut Tree

London ★

Bibendum **SW3** ↑
The Capital Hotel Restaurant **SW3** ↑
Hilaire **SW3** ↑
Le Meridien Oak Room **W1** ↑
Nico Central **W1** ↑

Al San Vincenzo **W1**
Bistrot Bruno **W1**
Blakes Hotel Restaurant **SW7**
Bombay Brasserie **SW7**
Café Royal Grill Room **W1**
The Canteen **SW10**
Clarke's **W8**
Fung Shing **WC2**
The Halkin Hotel Restaurant **SW1**
The Ivy **WC2**
Kensington Place **W8**

London ★ continued

The Lanesborough, Dining Room **SW1**
Ming **W1**
Museum Street Café **WC1**
Neal Street Restaurant **WC2**
Panda **W1**
Pied à Terre **W1**
The Savoy, Grill Room **WC2**
The Savoy, River Restaurant **WC2**
Simply Nico **SW1**
The Square **SW1**
Le Suquet **SW3**
Tatsuso **EC2**
Turners **SW3**

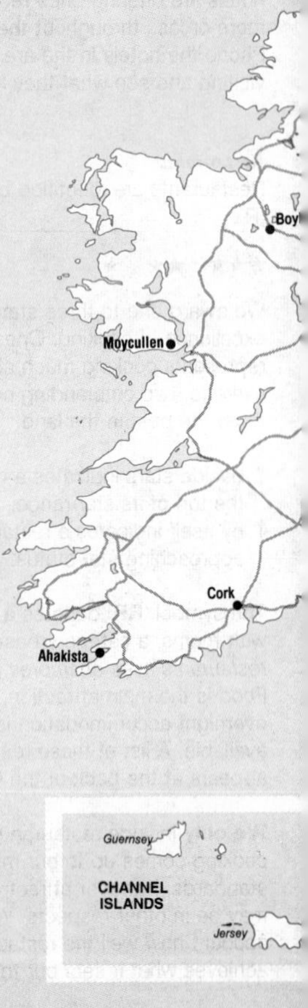

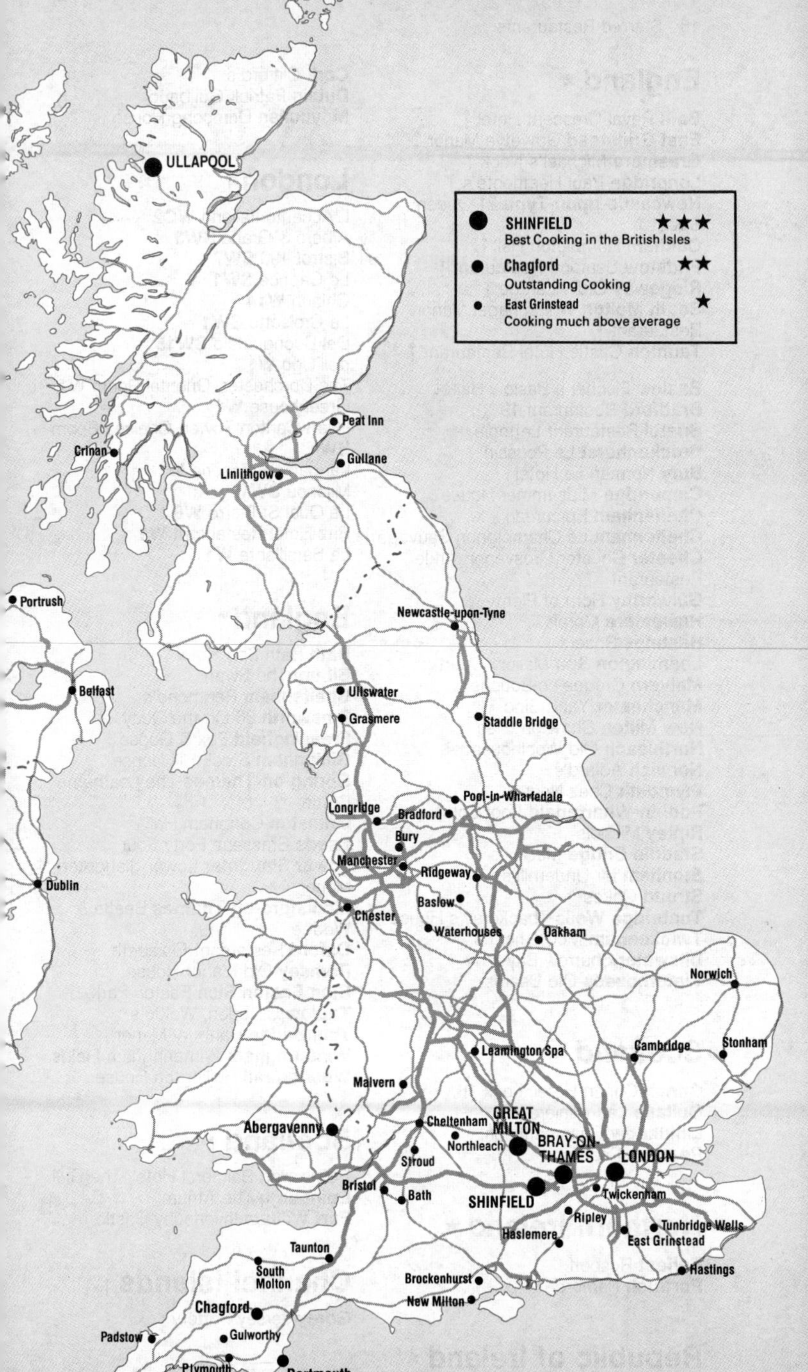

SHINFIELD ★★★
Best Cooking in the British Isles
Chagford ★★
Outstanding Cooking
East Grinstead ★
Cooking much above average
ULLAPOOL
Peat Inn
Crinan
Gullane
Linlithgow
Portrush
Newcastle-upon-Tyne
Belfast
Ullswater
Grasmere
Staddle Bridge
Pool-in-Wharfedale
Longridge
Bradford
Bury
Manchester
Ridgeway
Dublin
Baslow
Chester
Waterhouses
Oakham
Norwich
Leamington Spa
Cambridge
Stonham
Malvern
GREAT MILTON
Abergavenny
Cheltenham
Northleach
BRAY-ON-THAMES
LONDON
Stroud
Bristol
Bath
SHINFIELD
Twickenham
Ripley
Tunbridge Wells
Haslemere
East Grinstead
Taunton
South Molton
Hastings
Brockenhurst
New Milton
Chagford
Padstow
Gulworthy
Plymouth
Dartmouth

England ★

Bath Royal Crescent Hotel ↑
East Grinstead Gravetye Manor ↑
Grasmere Michael's Nook ↑
Longridge Paul Heathcote's ↑
Newcastle-upon-Tyne 21 Queen Street ↑
Oakham Hambleton Hall ↑
Padstow Seafood Restaurant ↑
Ridgeway Old Vicarage ↑
South Molton Whitechapel Manor Restaurant ↑
Taunton Castle Hotel Restaurant ↑

Baslow Fischer's Baslow Hall
Bradford Restaurant 19
Bristol Restaurant Lettonie
Brockenhurst Le Poussin
Bury Normandie Hotel
Cambridge Midsummer House
Cheltenham Epicurean
Cheltenham Le Champignon Sauvage
Chester Chester Grosvenor, Arkle Restaurant
Gulworthy Horn of Plenty
Haslemere Morels
Hastings Rösers
Leamington Spa Mallory Court
Malvern Croque-en-Bouche
Manchester Yang Sing
New Milton Chewton Glen
Northleach Old Woolhouse
Norwich Adlard's
Plymouth Chez Nous
Pool-in-Wharfedale Pool Court
Ripley Michels'
Staddle Bridge McCoy's
Stonham Mr Underhill's
Stroud Oakes
Tunbridge Wells Thackeray's House
Twickenham McClement's
Ullswater Sharrow Bay
Waterhouses Old Beams

Scotland ★

Crinan Crinan Hotel, Lock 16
Gullane La Potinière
Linlithgow Champany Inn
Peat Inn Peat Inn

Northern Ireland ★

Belfast Roscoff
Portrush Ramore

Republic of Ireland ★

Ahakista Shiro
Boyle Cromleach Lodge
Cork Clifford's
Dublin Patrick Guilbaud
Moycullen Drimcong House

London ↑

L'Accento Italiano **WC2**
Albero & Grana **SW3**
Bistrot 190 **SW7**
Le Caprice **SW1**
Chinon **W14**
La Croisette **SW1**
Del Buongustaio **SW15**
dell'Ugo **W1**
The Dorchester, Oriental Room **W1**
Greenhouse **W1**
Hyatt Carlton Tower, Chelsea Room **SW1**
Langan's Brasserie **W1**
Mijanou **SW1**
Le Quai St Pierre **W8**
Ritz Hotel Restaurant **W1**
La Sémillante **W1**

England ↑

Bath Bath Spa Hotel
Bibury The Swan
Cheltenham Redmond's
Emsworth 36 On the Quay
Fressingfield Fox & Goose
Gillingham Stock Hill House
Goring-on-Thames The Leatherne Bottle
Grimston Congham Hall
Leeds Brasserie Forty Four
Lower Slaughter Lower Slaughter Manor
Moulsford-on-Thames Beetle & Wedge
Oxford Restaurant Elizabeth
Romsey Old Manor House
Ston Easton Ston Easton Park
Taplow Cliveden, Waldo's
Thundridge Hanbury Manor
Winteringham Winteringham Fields
Woolton Hill Hollington House

Scotland ↑

Edinburgh Balmoral Hotel, The Grill
Edinburgh The Atrium
Fort William Inverlochy Castle

Channel Islands ↑

Gorey Jersey Pottery

Republic of Ireland ↑

Shanagarry Ballymaloe House

De Luxe Hotels

London

91% The Connaught **W1**
The Dorchester **W1**
The Savoy **WC2**
89% Four Seasons Hotel **W1**
The Lanesborough **SW1**
88% Claridge's **W1**
Hyatt Carlton Tower **SW1**
86% The Berkeley **SW1**
47 Park Street **SW1**
Halkin Hotel **SW1**
The Ritz **W1**
85% Hotel Conrad **SW10**
84% Inter-Continental Hotel **W1**
Le Meridien **W1**
83% Grosvenor House **W1**
The Regent London **NW1**
The Waldorf **WC2**
82% Hyde Park Hotel **SW1**
Royal Garden Hotel **W8**
81% The Capital **SW3**
Howard Hotel **WC2**
80% Churchill Hotel **W1**

England

91% **Taplow** Cliveden
89% **New Milton** Chewton Glen
88% **Ston Easton** Ston Easton Park
87% **Bath** Bath Spa Hotel
86% **Aylesbury** Hartwell House
Stapleford Stapleford Park
85% **Great Milton** Le Manoir aux Quat'Saisons
84% **Bath** Royal Crescent Hotel
Chester Chester Grosvenor
East Grinstead Gravetye Manor
Oakham Hambleton Hall
83% **Colerne** Lucknam Park
82% **Ashford** Eastwell Manor
Chagford Gidleigh Park
Hintlesham Hintlesham Hall
Ullswater Sharrow Bay
81% **Amberley** Amberley Castle
Torquay Imperial Hotel
80% **Cheltenham** Greenway
Leamington Spa Mallory Court
Linton Wood Hall
Thornbury Thornbury Castle

Scotland

90% **Fort William** Inverlochy Castle
86% **Auchterarder** Gleneagles Hotel
84% **Turnberry** Turnberry Hotel
83% **Edinburgh** The Balmoral
82% **Dunblane** Cromlix House
Glasgow One Devonshire Gardens
St Andrews St Andrews Old Course Hotel
81% **Alexandria** Cameron House

Wales

80% **Llyswen** Llangoed Hall

Channel Islands

80% **St Saviour** Longueville Manor

Republic of Ireland

86% **Cong** Ashford Castle
Kenmare Sheen Falls Lodge
Straffan Kildare Hotel
85% **Kenmare** Park Hotel
81% **Gorey** Marlfield House
Thomastown Mount Juliet Hotel
80% **Waterford** Waterford Castle

Hotel of the Year

One Devonshire Gardens
Glasgow, Strathclyde, Scotland

For sheer style, there are few town hotels that can compete with Ken McCulloch's; it comprises three separate Victorian terraced houses, cleverly designed to feel more like a private home. Indeed, each of the original houses still has its own front door, and guests in Numbers Two and Three walk to Number One to eat. Interior designer Amanda Rosa has assisted in creating a hotel of stunning impact and elegance, and general manager Beverly Payne leads a team of engaging staff who provide faultless service.

The hotel receives a unique hand-painted Wedgwood plate

Previous Winners

1993 **The Chester Grosvenor**
Chester

1992 **The Dorchester**
London

1991 **Longueville Manor**
St Saviour, Jersey

1990 **Gidleigh Park**
Chagford

1989 **The Savoy**
London

1988 **Park Hotel**
Kenmare

1987 **Homewood Park**
Freshford

Restaurant of the Year

Le Soufflé Restaurant, Inter-Continental Hotel
London

A restaurant of impeccable style and elegance whose sophisticated modern decor is the perfect backdrop for the culinary talents emanating from the kitchens. Peter Kromberg, now in his 18th year at *Le Soufflé*, continues (together with a team of brilliant sous-chefs) to produce menus of outstandingly well-constructed complexity. Individual dishes, true creations, engender genuine frissons of delight. Service, too, under the direction of Joseph Lanser, himself here for 10 years, is executed with a professionalism that is the epitome of unobtrusive attentiveness.

The restaurant receives a unique hand-painted Wedgwood plate

Previous Winners

1993 The Carved Angel
Dartmouth

1992 Bibendum
London

1991 L'Ortolan
Shinfield

1990 Waterside Inn
Bray-on-Thames

1989 L'Arlequin
London

1988 Morels
Haslemere

1987 Walnut Tree Inn
Abergavenny

Chef of the Year

Paul Heathcote
Paul Heathcote's Restaurant, Longridge, Lancashire

At the forefront of Northern cooking, and after textbook training (*Sharrow Bay*, *The Connaught* and *Le Manoir aux Quat'Saisons* to name but three), Paul has returned to his Lancastrian roots. The newly expanded restaurant goes from strength to strength, due in no small part to the loyalty of all the staff, most of whom have been with Paul since the outset. If the cooking here is an example of the talents of the next generation of British chefs, it is indeed in safe hands.

Paul receives a unique hand-painted Wedgwood plate

Previous Winners

1993 Shaun Hill
Gidleigh Park, Chagford

1992 Marco Pierre White
Harveys London SW17

Dessert of the Year

L'Ortolan
Shinfield, near Reading, Berkshire

John Burton-Race's *assiette chocolatière* (foreground) is a perfect example of his attention to detail. Long a favourite among the involved carte of desserts, it combines a clever mix of white and dark chocolate tastes heightened by exquisite artistry in its presentation on the plate. A fitting end to a glorious meal in a peaceful setting.

Previous Winners

1993 Jean-Christophe Novelli
Le Provence at Gordleton Mill, Lymington

1992 Roger Pizey
Harveys, London SW17

Dessert of the Year Regional Winners

London
Les Saveurs W1

Joël Antunès is quietly causing a stir in Mayfair. His style is worldly, the setting stylish and the presentation of dishes nothing short of perfection on a plate. Simple descriptions such as pineapple sorbet in a spicy bread pyramid, chocolate madeleine with an almond sauce or croquant of rhubarb with cream praline give no indication of the technical mastery and creativity behind such spectacular desserts. Perhaps best of all is his coffee tart with whisky cream.

Home Counties
Michels' Ripley

Erik Michel's sweets show the same dedication to detail as his preceding courses. Typical is a wonderfully light savarin ring moistened with syrup and set on a vanilla pastry cream and topped with almost transparent slivers of fruit and crisp caramel.

South of England
Angel Midhurst

Peter Crawford-Rolt's revitalised 16th-century coaching inn features a lovely, light restaurant where poached pear in puff pastry leaves with butterscotch sauce, rhubarb fool, dark chocolate terrine with caramelised oranges or individual summer pudding might feature among the desserts.

West Country
Seafood Restaurant Padstow

A master's hand gives a touch of class to the desserts: lemon tart, warm date and apple pudding with hot fudge sauce, pears baked with port and vanilla and served with crème brulée ice cream. Small choice, perhaps, but unlikely to disappoint.

Midlands/Heart of England
Epicurean Cheltenham

No one tries harder than Patrick MacDonald, who has stars in his eyes. His desserts are wonderful creations, quite simply described on the menu: perhaps hazelnut or peach soufflé, raspberry condé, hot pear and caramel tart or lemon tart. Pictured: Hazelnut parfait, chocolate sauce.

East of England
Duxford Lodge Duxford

Home-made ice creams (including English lavender) and sorbets are a particular speciality and feature strongly among a selection of delectable desserts.

North of England
21 Queen Street Newcastle

Terry Laybourne's skills extend right to the end of a meal – leave room for almond tuiles with crème Chantilly, a chocolate extravaganza or praline-filled crepe with glacé tangerines and white chocolate ice cream. Pictured: Tarte tatin of mango with passion fruit syrup and mango sorbet.

Scotland
Inverlochy Castle Fort William

A civilised setting in which to enjoy one's choice from a small selection of desserts: raspberry crème brulée, hot chocolate tart with an orange sauce, trio of sorbets with fresh fruit and lime syrup or nougatine ice cream in a brandy snap with citrus salad. Uncomplicated, well executed and thoroughly enjoyable.

Wales
Walnut Tree Inn Abergavenny

Franco and Ann Taruschio's white-painted roadside inn is a gourmet haven. A long, long 'sweet menu' offers over 20 desserts to suit all tastes – from Italian regional favourites like dolce pugliese or torinese to chocolate brandy loaf with coffee bean sauce, strawberry pavlova and the most wonderful and refreshing fruit soup.

Northern Ireland
Roscoff Belfast

Paul and Jeanne Rankin's restaurant is the best place to eat in town. Jeanne is responsible for the divine desserts - from lemon tart with a berry coulis to apricot cheesecake with marinated apricots and a Cointreau jus or snow eggs with a lavender anglaise.

Republic of Ireland
Cromleach Lodge Boyle

Imaginative desserts served on smart Rosenthal china: Moira Tighe's 'tonight's (alcoholic) delights' might be brandy and Bailey's soufflé, home-made ice creams with butterscotch and rum sauce or poached meringue with Malibu cream.

British Cheeseboard of the Year

The Lygon Arms
Broadway, Hereford & Worcester

The cheese trolley offers only British and Irish cheeses from small producers, supplied by Longman's, Stratford-upon-Avon and Poupart of Sedgeberrow near Evesham. Most of the cheeses are unpasteurised giving a fuller flavour, and at least two are made with vegetarian rennet. Some of the more unusual cheeses featured are Celtic Promise (cow's milk – wash rind with cider, matured by James Aldridge), Golden Cross (goat's milk – log-shaped coated in ash, again matured by James Aldridge), the semi-hard and mild-tasting Swaledales from Yorkshire, and Devon Ticklemore, a mature hard cheese made from goat's milk. Cheddar is an 18-month-old Montgomery from Somerset, and the Colston Bassett Stilton and Blue Shropshire come from Nottingham, from one of the best producers in the area.

The restaurant receives a unique hand-painted Wedgwood plate

Previous Winner

1993 Old Vicarage
Witherslack

British Cheeseboard of the Year Regional Winners

London
Simpson's-in-the-Strand WC2

You would expect one of London's longest-established English restaurants to have an excellent cheese trolley, and you will not be disappointed here: Tornegus (a Somerset Caerphilly) from Glastonbury, Wedmore with chives, Cornish Yarg, Stilton from Cropwell Bishop and Cheddar from Quickes in Devon being just some of the examples. New restaurant manager Brian Clivaz will provide knowledgeable assistance, and this is one of the few places where you can get Welsh rarebit.

Home Counties
Leatherne Bottel Goring-on-Thames

Cheese merchant James Aldridge supplies many of the British cheeses that you will find here, including the unique Abbeywell, a soft rind-washed cheese made from cow's milk. Another rare find is the Dunlop from Devon, a hard Cheddar type, also made from cow's milk. Blues include Lanark, Beenleigh and Jersey; the Jersey cows also provide both the Brother David and St David cheeses. Regular appearances are made by Cornish Yarg, Blue Shropshire, Bonchester, Tornegus and Wedmore. As you can see, cheese is treated seriously here - try the unlikely-named smoked Rook's Nest from Cumbria.

South of England
Le Poussin Brockenhurst

Cheeses such as Dorset Blue Vinney, mature Cheddar from Bridport, Buxton Blue and the quite salty Lanark Blue come from a variety of suppliers, including Vin Sullivan of Abergavenny and Alan Porter in Boroughbridge, North Yorkshire. Chef-patron Alex Aitken particularly recommends the Rosary goat's cheese from Landford, Salisbury.

West Country
Castle Hotel Taunton

You can choose some splendid cheeses in prime condition here. They are expertly described, and include Appleby's Cheshire and Double Gloucester (both from Shropshire!), a Lancashire from the Kirkham's farm in Goosnargh, the local Montgomery Cheddar, and two unpasteurised cheeses from Mary Holbrook near Bath – Tymsboro', a soft ripened goat's milk, and Tyning made from ewe's milk. The Stilton comes from Colston Bassett. Look out also for the Cornish Yarg and Capricorn goat's cheese from Crewkerne in Somerset.

East of England
Three Horseshoes Madingley

Neal's Yard Dairy deliver cheeses weekly here, so you can rely on their quality. Try the Little Rydings, a young goat's cheese, from Emlett in Somerset, a hard Spenwood from Gloucestershire, or Ducket's Caerphilly. There's a Bonchester Brie from Hawick, Montgomery's Cheddar, Kirkham's Lancashire and a Stilton, once again from Colston Bassett.

Midlands/Heart of England
The Lygon Arms Broadway

see **British Cheeseboard of the Year Winner**

North of England
Wordsworth Hotel Grasmere

The main supplier is Porter's (Boroughbridge, North Yorkshire), though the Stilton is purchased locally from Halls of Kendal. Try Mr Appleby's Cheshire, or a Devon Blue in the Roquefort style made by Robin Congden in Totnes. The Ribblesdale, a pasteurised goat's cheese comes from North Yorkshire, as does the Whitby Jet, an unpasteurised cheese made from the milk of mountain sheep. The Waterloo, a mild Guernsey milk cheese, on the other hand, comes from Berkshire.

Scotland
Clifton Hotel Nairn

Sadly, some of the local cheesemakers who have been supplying J. Gordon Macintyre's hotel for many years have gone out of business. Nevertheless, the cheeses (all Scottish except for the Stilton) offered here are always in prime condition. Try the Lanark Blue and Banchory Black, a full-fat hard cheese with a black peppercorn coat, both made from ewe's milk, or the rich Bonchester and Brie-style Howgate that come from Jersey cows. Then there's a Stitchell from Kelso, similar to a Cheshire, or Inverloch, a hard goat's cheese made on the island of Gigha.

Wales
Maes-y-Neuadd Talsarnau

A selection of two Welsh cheeses plus a blue is served as a course each evening with home-made oatcakes and bread. About a dozen are regularly stocked, and include a white crumbly hard Caerphilly, a strong Cheddar-type Caws Llyn, Pencarreg, a full-fat creamy cheese similar to Brie, and the lovely-named Y Fenni, made with real ale and mustard seeds. There's usually a Stilton, as well as several other Welsh cheeses that are much too hard to spell correctly!

Cellar of the Year

Are wine lists in British restaurants getting better? Sadly I have to say that in my opinion they are not. Time was when restaurant wine lists set the agenda for serious wine drinkers' aspirations. Restaurants – or some restaurants at least – did much of wine lovers' work for them, making discriminating and judicious selections from a catholic choice culled from the offerings of many independent wine merchants.

It would be difficult to argue that restaurants play any leading role in wine exploration nowadays. That role has been superseded by supermarkets, whose worldwide choices restaurant wine list compilers all too often nowadays tamely imitate. There are two problems there. First supermarket wines are, quite necessarily because of the bulk quantities involved in satisfying the mass market, no more than mediocre or fair-to-average stuff. Second, for hotels and restaurants to list wines that are readily seen on retail shelves all round the country makes their markups all too painfully obvious.

Wine that is cheap and cheerful from a supermarket is likely to seem expensive and cheerless when it has to be paid for in a restaurant dining room. Most restaurant wine lists still fall all too easily into one of two categories: short, simplistic and uninformative on the one hand, or unmanageably weighty, compendious and unselective on the other. Places that make no attempt to identify the wine they are trying to sell (no maker's or supplier's name, and often no vintage) are still numerous. At least, though, they make no pretence of being interested.

Quite as annoying, to me, are the album-makers who stuff page after page of some biblical tome with hundreds of different wines, with never a trustworthy tasting note beside any of them. Their lists are catalogues of wine collections which have usually been compiled without rhyme or reason. One thing both sorts of place all too often have in common is that when the wine is ordered, it is not that wine but something different which is brought to the table.

In the off-hand place which lists wines by *appellation* alone, Beaujolais is out of stock and a red *vin de pays* or a Cotes-du-Rhone is offered instead. In the place with encyclopedic lists – oh dear! the last bottle of what you want has just been sold, and something else will have to do. Usually quite a few quid more expensive, too. And just because the wine list shows vintages, that does not mean those are the vintages you will get. In a July week alone, at three top-rated British hotels in succession I was brought bottles which were of a different vintage from that shown on the list.

How annoying, too, the inability of so many restaurants to list wines appropriate to the sort of food they serve. Why should chop houses expect to sell classed growth clarets at £50 a bottle, just because they refuse to list the fruity, quaffing reds that should be on the list at a fifth of the price? Where are the Mediterranean wines to complement the voguish Mediterranean cuisine, and how can so-called "French" restaurants go on failing to list wines whose presence the French would regard as axiomatic? Fresh pink wines in summer, red wines to drink cool or chilled ready for service at those temperatures, dry white Bordeaux of quality, and the quintessential food wines from Alsace are the four categories I most regularly (well, almost invariably in fact) deprecate the lack of.

Finally, now that there are so many practical and inexpensive ways of protecting wines from oxidation, there is no excuse for restaurants not to offer a good selection of wines by the glass. With drink-driving regulations and health concerns making many customers anxious to limit their intake, it makes sense to give guests the chance of drinking something better than plonk if they want to order by the glass rather than the bottle. Drinking less but better is a motto restaurateurs should be encouraging too.

You may take it, then, that even when regional winners of the Cellar of the Year awards do not meet each and every requirement I would seek in an ideal wine list, they remain exceptional places. They, and previous winners of the Egon Ronay's Guide's awards, set the standards which their neighbours should be striving to better. Their wine lists are interesting, balanced, helpful, well-presented, appropriate, and not hideously over-priced. Would that the competition they faced for pride of place in our winners' listings were a bit keener, that's all.

Judging Panel (L to R). Charles Metcalfe: Associate Editor, *Wine Magazine* **Andrew Eliel:** Managing Editor, *Egon Ronay's Guides* **Andrew Montague:** UK Director, *The Wine Institute of California* **Robin Young:** *The Times, Country Homes & Interiors*

Robin Young

Cellar of the Year

Gravetye Manor
East Grinstead, West Sussex

The judges had to overcome a smidgeon of editorial reluctance (not true! – Ed) about giving the Cellar of the Year award to a hotel which still insists on showing wine prices exclusive of VAT, but Peter Herbert is determined he should not be blamed for the amount the VAT-man adds to his customers' bills. Since Mr Herbert overcame a long-standing antipathy to Italian wines, which he long claimed were impossible to sell, Gravetye's patrician list has been one of the most catholic in the whole country. Gravetye was last year's Home Counties regional winner and our California Wine Cellar of the Year, but its selections from the Antipodes, from Germany, from the Loire, and from Alsace also put most competitors to shame. The whole list, which includes a rich endowment of champagnes and classic vintages of top clarets and burgundies, is discriminatingly chosen at all levels, with the aid of a tasting panel made up of staff and regular guests, without whose approval no purchases proceed. The list is well-larded with half-bottles and curiosities. It pre-empts objections about changed vintages in the "smaller" wines by promising Stephan Le Rouge, "our wine waiter will advise on any such changes", and apologises in advance for any deletions in sections where "some of the rare wines listed are available only in limited quantities". That, for once, leaves few grounds for complaint.

The winner receives a unique hand-painted Wedgwood plate

Previous Winners

1993 Croque-en-Bouche
Malvern

1992 The Cross
Kingussie

1991 White Horse Inn
Chilgrove

1990 La Potinière
Gullane

1989 Old Bridge Hotel
Huntingdon

1988 Champany Inn
Linlithgow

Cellar of the Year Regional Winners

London
Gilbert's 2 Exhibition Road, SW7

Six nicely chosen house wines are offered by glass or bottle; Pilsner Urquell gets on the same page as the five champagnes and sparkling wines; half-bottles (about 50) and wines under £15 (more than 30) are helpfully listed on pages of their own; and five pages of "fine wines" are distinguished from perfectly honourable choices which only qualify as "red" or "white", and are then listed (mostly, but not invariably) according to grape variety. Not the easiest list to find your way around in, but at least its contents support the feeling that the search will be richly rewarded. The background and tasting notes are sensible, helpful and accurate.

Home Counties
Dundas Arms Kintbury

Not the best balanced or lengthiest list in the Home Counties but one of the most keenly priced and enthusiastically compiled. David Dalzell-Piper is plainly most interested in truly excellent clarets and burgundies, but there are bottles from the lesser French regions in the £12 to £16 bracket, and a page for the "New World" where the Antipodes and California get their show.

South of England
The Three Lions Stuckton

Karl Wadsack gives a good display to Australia, Germany, Alsace, the Rhone and the Loire as well as Bordeaux and Burgundy, and his is an enterprising, well-chosen list in which most customers will have no difficulty finding something desirable, delicious and affordable. There are bin-ends for wines in short supply, and changes of vintage are signalled on the list.

West Country
Harveys Restaurant Bristol

Bordeaux-lovers stand a better chance of finding it here than most places, whether "it" be a better-than average off-vintage *cru bourgeois* under £20 or legendary historic vintages from the back-list of Chateau Latour (1945, £420). As befits a restaurant belonging to leading wine merchants, the list is well-endowed in most other areas too, but especially so in port and sherry. The list's notes, though, are of more academic interest than practical use.

Midlands/Heart of England
Stonor Arms Stonor

Most of the well-chosen house recommendations come in under £20, and the overall balance of the list (dipping into the New World) has been carefully worked out. Note the Chateau Batailley collection, the Olivier Leflaive burgundies, and the really excellent 1991 Chiltern Valley "Noble Bacchus" English dessert wine, which shows an uncanny balance of sweetness and acidity.

East of England
The George of Stamford, Stamford

"Interesting" here means "characterful, individual, intriguing – not simply classic". Pricing favours the better bottles, too. The percentage mark-up is lower on more expensive wines. The "house list", of two dozen wines arranged by style, is self-professedly biased towards Italy, but is notably economical, as are the prices generally. Tasting notes encourage experimentation. The list also gives advance notice of the month in which the vintages of lesser wines can be expected to change. Special features include good numbers of half-bottles, a page of bin-ends, lots of dessert wines and a selection of magnums.

North of England
Winteringham Fields, Winteringham

One must, perhaps, not be too surprised that a Swiss chef/proprietor lists more Swiss wines than wines from the Loire and Alsace. In a northern context the Schwabs' list at Winteringham Fields is testimony that recessionary gloom at least never got this corner of Humberside down. Fifteen champagnes, a strong hand in growers' burgundies, some notable Australians and a page of great bottles headed The Patron's Reserve add interest to an eclectic list (as, it has to be said, do some of the typing errors).

Scotland
La Potinière, Gullane

A regular among the gongs in this contest and past winner of the Cellar of the Year award, David Brown is an enthusiast, and one restaurateur who can still be counted a wine explorer. His list includes the trophies brought home from his personal wine-shopping expeditions to the wine-producing regions of France. Especially strong, original and tempting are the country wines of the south-west (Madiran etc.), a richly ripe selection of Sauternes, and judiciously chosen, well-made wines from less favoured vintages in the classic regions. A happy hunting ground indeed for wine-loving bargain-seekers.

Wales
Llangoed Hall, Llyswen

To complement the talents of the chef, Llangoed's managers have built a cellar of over 350 wines. To help customers toward a speedy choice they have also short listed "especially recommended" wines chosen for "interesting characteristics", which cover such assorted virtues as less familiar grape varieties, peculiarly high production standards, and better-than-average value for money. South Africa, Israeli and Lebanese wines have joined New Zealand and Chile; there is even one wine from Wales, and more than 70 wines are available in halves.

Ireland
Arbutus Lodge, Cork

Arbutus Lodge promises not to chill white wines in advance, and divides its list, Gaul-like, into three parts. The first is a ready-reference list, the second picks out wines under £17 (punts) a bottle, and the third repeats the first but adds details of growers, shippers and some rather over-enthusiastic tasting notes. The very stong hand in wines of the traditional classic regions does not preclude an adequate show for the rest.

California Cellar of the Year

Lower Slaughter Manor
Lower Slaughter, Gloucestershire

With some score of California reds from five grape varieties, eight regions, a fistful of leading producers and vintages back to 1985, plus a dozen whites and a trio of sparklers, Lower Slaughter Manor makes a braver show of California than many places with less vinous élan manage even with Bordeaux or Burgundy. The choices are not always predictable, but suggest a personal palate at work in the selection. It is good to see Santa Barbara, Sonoma, Monterey and Carneros getting in here alongside the more inevitable Napa Valley, and the prices (£22.50 for Ridge's Geyserville Zinfandel 1989) are not unreasonable in such surroundings.

Previous Winners

1993 **Gravetye Manor**
East Grinstead

1992 **190 Queen's Gate**
London SW7

1991 **Croque-en-Bouche**
Malvern

1990 **Gidleigh Park**
Chagford

Photograph by kind permission of Martin Brigdale - Good Housekeeping.

Food styles for California Wine

Some people use food just as a fuel. The readers of this Guide surely want more out of their meals than that. A top-up of energy reserves, perhaps, but pleasure as well. And most pleasure-seeking lovers of fine cooking will look to accompany their meal with a good bottle of wine.

Wine's natural vocation is to enrich and enhance the pleasure of eating. Wine buffs may pore and sniff over rare pre-phylloxera vintages. Wine critics may agonise over the relative qualities of a line-up of supermarket wines. Indeed, you may enjoy a glass or two of warming red after a windy walk, a cooling sip after a game of tennis in the sun, but most bottles of wine are served with food. And much of the time we don't think very hard about what goes best with what.

No, I'm not suggesting a rule-book. Wine and food are so much matters of personal taste that inflexible rules can never work for everyone. You need a laid-back, liberated approach, and where better to look for a relaxed attitude to the pleasures of life than California? Leisure is important to the Californians – surfing, tennis, aerobics, partying. And, of course, good food and wine. They think about which of their wines goes with which dishes. They even write books about it, and most major California wineries have chefs specially employed to create dishes to accompany their wines.

For some of them, it becomes almost an obsession. Wine is the centre of their working world, and the search for just the right flavours to go with their company's wines is quite understandable. Having found answers, some California wineries used to have an alarming tendency to write didactic back-labels along the lines of 'this wine has been specially crafted to accompany broiled swordfish served with a chanterelle risotto and nasturtium-leaf salad'. Those days, happily, are gone.

In their place has come an era of experiment. All over California cooks are exploring the full range of fresh foods their state has to offer. A new style of California cookery has evolved, drawing on the rich heritage of European, Central American and Asian cuisines. And California's winemakers are honing and refining their many and varied wine styles.

The evolution of California wine and California cooking has been in separate directions. While the winemakers have opted for increasing subtlety in the flavours they are conjuring from their grapes, the cooks have developed a cuisine in which high-quality meat, fish, vegetables and fruits are presented with clear, bright flavours. And the quality of the fresh ingredients is dazzling. Whatever California cannot supply is flown in, but the state-produced seafood, game, fruits and vegetables compete with the world's best. The organic herb, fruit and vegetable garden at wine producers Fetzer in Mendocino County is one of the world's great produce gardens.

And the harmony possible between California wine and food has been increased. Most of us look to match foods with wines, rather than the other way round, and this is far easier to do if the flavours in the wines are complex and subtle, rather than brash and direct. You decide the main ingredient of your dish, you choose the wine to set it off well, then you adjust the way you cook or sauce your dish to enhance the subtleties of your wine. Strong, straightforward flavours in wine such as the intense blackcurrant of a young Cabernet Sauvignon, the aromatic, grassy, gooseberry character of some Sauvignon Blancs, powerful oakiness or high acidity make a wine more difficult to match with food. Subtler flavours are easier, whether the subtlety comes from more sophisticated winemaking or the maturity of the wine.

It's not unreasonable to consider the wine as an extra element in the saucing of a dish, in fact. For that very reason, the very American way of describing the dishes on the menu and how they are cooked in minute detail is reassuring if you are going to be the one who chooses the wine in a restaurant. If, of course, your main reason for going to a particular restaurant is because it has a wonderful wine list, your priorities change. In these circumstances, if, say, you have made an appointment with a bottle of mature Heitz Martha's Vineyard Cabernet Sauvignon from Paul Henderson's fabulous list at Gidleigh Park, choose simple food. Let the wine take centre stage and play the starring role, without too much upstaging from the food.

Whether wine or food takes precedence, though, it is still worth bearing certain guidelines (not rules – notice) in mind. The best matches are either between wines and foods similar in flavour, or quite strongly opposing. Similar flavours might include well-hung game dishes with the wild, slightly 'dangerous' flavours of mature Pinot Noir or Syrah, smoked salmon with a toasty, oaky Chardonnay, or fresh goat's cheese with a steely, young Sauvignon Blanc. Examples of opposing flavours, on the other hand would be foie gras with a young acidic Chardonnay to cut through the richness, or blue cheese with a sweet wine.

These are the two general principles of pairing wines with food. Then there are certain key elements of the taste of food and wine that have to be matched or balanced. Sweetness and acidity are the two components common to food and wine; tannin is the tongue-furring substance in young red wine that has to be tamed if it's too obtrusive.

Sweetness is not just confined to fruit, puddings and desserts: many vegetables are naturally sweet as well. A lot of processed foods – savoury as well as obviously sweet – have sugar added to make them more attractive, particularly in the USA. Consequently, there has to be more sugar in food before American consumers perceive it than is true in Europe. Some wine styles, too, in California – cheaper Chardonnays, for instance – are made slightly sweeter than they would be in France, since they are still perceived as dry by the locals, and actually balance much American food better that way.

And balance is the key. In order to make a good match with a sweet course, for instance, you must find a sweet wine that has a similar or higher sweetness than the food you are eating. A late-harvested Riesling that may taste sweetly delicious as an aperitif could easily come to grief when paired with a tart filled, say, with blueberries and a light apricot jam glaze. Sweet wines have to be much sweeter than you expect before they can cope with most desserts. You need to venture into the botrytised wines or fortified Muscats before you come to wines that have a high enough level of sweetness.

The same applies to acidity. Everyone knows that citrus fruits have acidity; most fruit has some natural acidity unless it is over-ripe. Apples, strawberries, raspberries, pineapples all have high acidity. So do tomatoes. So if you're looking for a match for a starter of sun-ripened tomatoes with Mozzarella and basil, consider the acidity level of your wine. A crisp Sauvignon could be a good choice.

Wine with good acidity can also be used to balance rich, oily dishes. The current fashion of cooking in California has veered away from this style of cooking, but it's always worth bearing in mind when next confronted by a plate of fish and chips. A crisp, dry white is a much more pleasing prospect than vinegar and a mug of tea.

And so to tannin. The bitter taste from a tea-bag stewed for too long is the same type of substance as is extracted from the skins, pips and stalks of black grapes during fermentation. Tannin is essential to the structure of a red wine destined for long ageing, but can be harsh and aggressive when such a wine is young. Time in the bottle softens tannins, as they group together to form larger, less spikey molecules, and eventually drop out of solution in the form of sediment. But, for those who enjoy the flavours of young red wine, the tannin levels of some California Cabernet Sauvignons can be pretty daunting in their youth.

However, there is an acceptable solution – for meat-eaters. Red meat cooked rare reacts with tannin in red wine at least partly to neutralise it. So, if you want to enjoy the glorious fruit of a young Cabernet Sauvignon but fear for the inside of your mouth, make sure your meat comes undercooked.

And that's just about it. One or two little points are still worth noting, however. It is almost impossible to match fish with red wine unless the fish has had red wine incorporated into the sauce. Even then, the best red wines to accompany such fish dishes are very light Pinot Noirs, not the richly fruity, savoury Pinots of Carneros and Santa Maria Valley. And red wines are totally out for very oily fish (herring, mackerel, sardines, for instance).

Finally, moving towards the end of the meal, chocolate and cheese. Chocolate is notoriously difficult to pair with wine. The only wines that come anywhere near coping are made from the Muscat grape. Frankly, it's hardly worth bothering: if you want to enjoy a fine, botrytised Riesling to finish the meal, steer clear of chocolate. Or, you could finish with cheese. Cheese is not as easy to match with wine as is often suggested, and a sweet white wine makes a more successful pairing than a red. Gewurztraminer wines can be good, too. If you definitely want to have a red wine with cheese, Pinot Noir is usually better than Cabernet Sauvignon.

Armed with these general guidelines, you are free to experiment as imaginatively as you wish. Have fun testing out which wines go with which foods. With the wines and cookery styles of California there is so much more freedom to experiment than with those of Europe. California is a region where much has changed – much still is changing – in winemaking and cooking. The classic European wine regions not only have their rigid systems of wine legislation, but also a whole system of gastronomy built up over the centuries to complement (and incidentally bolster the reputation of) the local wines. Suggest to a French sommelier that you would like something a bit out of the ordinary with a particular dish, and he will, more (or, often, less) politely inform you that your choice is wrong. California is not bound by these centuries of restrictive legislation and suffocating gastronomic rules. You can just do your own thing and have a nice day.

Occasionally the California spirit of experimentation gets a little out of control, and the imaginative creation of dishes goes over the top. Tim Hanni, an American chef and Master of Wine who works for Beringer, talks about a puzzle he was once posed. What could he select to drink with 'Hawaiian Mahi-Mahi garnished with New Zealand greenlip mussels and kiwi fruit in a blood orange beurre blanc'. Umm ......Mineral water?

Charles Metcalfe

Hosts of the Year

Francis Coulson and Brian Sack
Sharrow Bay
Ullswater, Cumbria

Well into their fifth decade as the pioneers of country house hotels, Francis and Brian are as enthusiastic as ever, and show no signs of either slowing down or relinquishing their position as leaders in their profession. Sharrow Bay is still, and always has been, a shining example of British hospitality at its very best, thanks to the indomitable spirit and sheer hard work of Francis, Brian and their loyal staff. They set standards that others have tried hard to follow.

Previous Winners

1993 Stock Hill House
Gillingham

1992 Woodhayes
Whimple

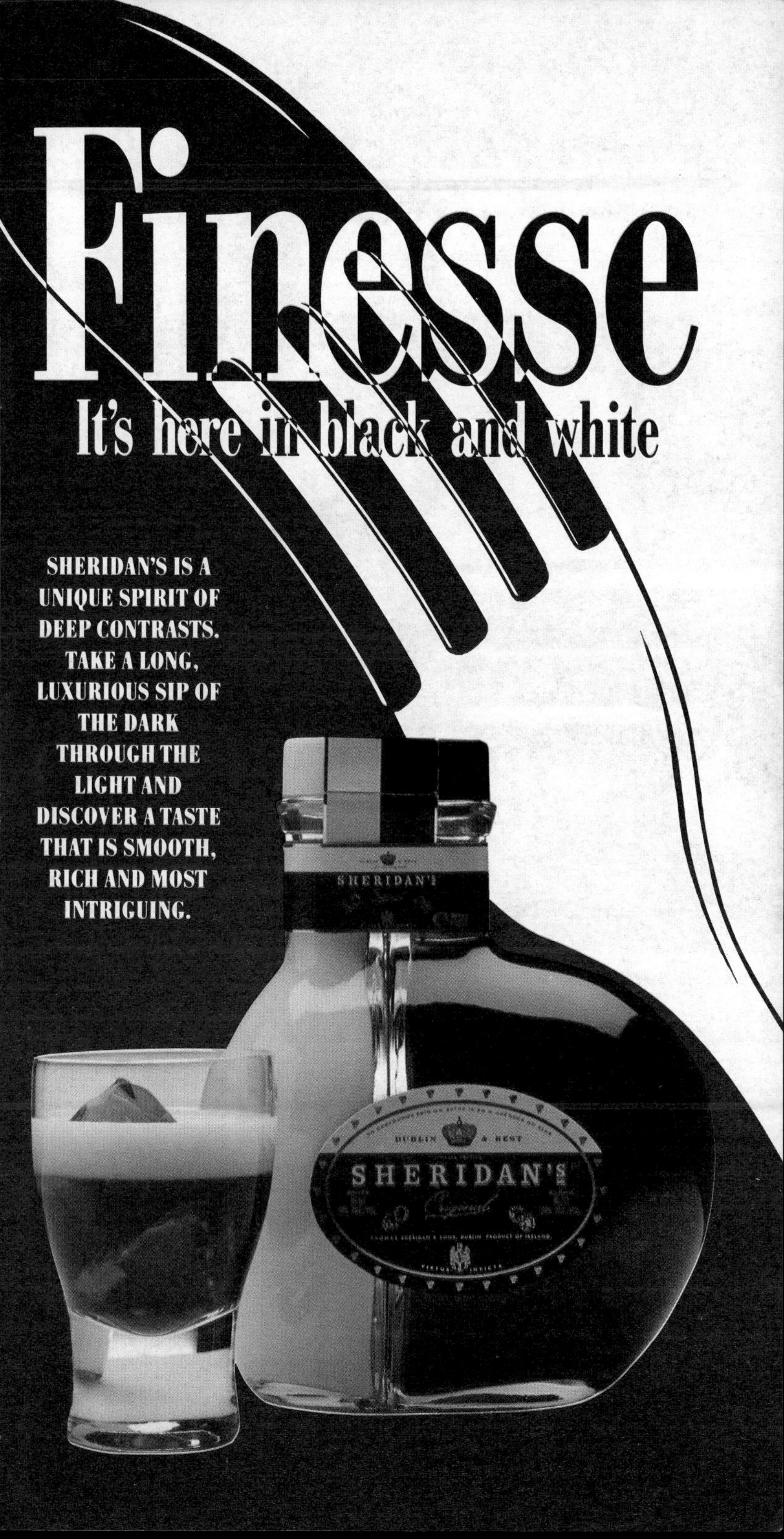
Finesse
It's here in black and white
SHERIDAN'S IS A UNIQUE SPIRIT OF DEEP CONTRASTS. TAKE A LONG, LUXURIOUS SIP OF THE DARK THROUGH THE LIGHT AND DISCOVER A TASTE THAT IS SMOOTH, RICH AND MOST INTRIGUING.
SHERIDAN'S
DUBLIN
BEST
SHERIDAN'S

No othe

cellnet
The nearest phone.
primetime™
Primetime is the tariff for those who use a mobile phone frequently during the day. The fixed costs (connection charge and monthly subscription) are higher than Lifetime but calls are cheaper during peak business hours.
Primetime features a wide range of useful call handling services and information lines that can help you to increase business efficiency and productivity, and enables you to make international calls.
Choose Cellnet.
You'll have more choice.
For further details call Cellnet on
0800 21 4000
Primetime is a registered trademark of TCSR Ltd.

London

W2 Abbey Court

£148

Tel 071-221 7518 Fax 071-792 0858

PH

20 Pembridge Gardens W2 4DU

Map 18 A3

Efficient staff, good-quality furniture and eye-catching flower arrangements are the hallmarks of good hotel-keeping in this friendly establishment. It's a five-storey Victorian town house in a quiet street only a few minutes from Notting Hill Gate. Public rooms are limited to a smart reception area and a conservatory where cooked breakfast is served. The individually styled and decorated bedrooms have Italian marble, whirlpool baths and towelling robes. Top of the range are the four-poster rooms. No children under 12. ***Rooms*** *22.* AMERICAN EXPRESS *Access, Diners, Visa.*

W2 L'Accento ↑

£50

Tel 071-243 2201

R

16 Garway Road W2 4NH

Map 18 A3

A starkly decorated little restaurant with a front that is all plate glass, and walls that are a uniform grey apart from one which is sandblasted and coloured yellow ochre and gold. The overall concept is of modish rusticity and this is reflected in the food, which is modern Northern Italian.
To begin a basket of wonderful bread comes with a dip of herb-infused virgin olive oil. Starters are typified by tagliatelle verdi with a duck ragu, cappellacci (large pasta trinagles) filled with pumpkin and dressed in sage and butter or pan-fried sardines stuffed with parsley and garlic. Main dishes could include osso buco, bollito misto – a classic dish of mixed boiled meats accompanied by a parsley sauce – or pan-fried calf's liver in a balsamic vinegar sauce. The cooking is first-rate with exquisite flavours exemplifying Italian cuisine at its best. ***Seats*** *42. Parties 12. L 12.30-2.30 D 6.30-11.30. Closed L Sat, all Sun. Set meals from £10.50. Access, Visa.*

W12 Adam's Café

£25

Tel 081-743 0572

R

77 Askew Road W12

Map 17 A4

Jekyll and Hyde in W12. By day this is an English café, by night a pukka restaurant serving Mediterranean cuisine and Tunisian specialities. It's a popular place, and recently almost doubled its seating capacity. Couscous is *the* speciality – a bed of steamed durum wheat with a spicy bouillon sauce and a choice of vegetarian, lamb, royale (lamb, chicken and merguez) and impériale (all those plus beef). Lamb soup, briks or rolls of filo pastry filled with minced beef to start, patisserie or hot lemon pancake to round things off. Wines from Tunisia and Morocco accompany the robust food.
Seats *60. Parties 36. Private Room 24. D only 7.30-10.30. Closed Sun, Bank Holidays. No credit cards.*

SW7 Adelphi Hotel 62%

£112

Tel 071-373 7177 Fax 071-373 7720

H

127 Cromwell Road SW7 4DT

Map 19 A5

Smart white-painted period-style hotel on a busy corner of Cromwell Road, with its main entrance in Courtfield Gardens. Three conference suites hold up to 80. Rooms not vacated by 11am are charged by the hour. ***Rooms*** *68.* AMERICAN EXPRESS *Access, Diners, Visa.*

WC2 Ajimura

£60

Tel 071-240 0178

R

51 Shelton Street WC2H 9HE

Map 21 B1

Sushi and sashimi are the specialities at a popular Japanese restaurant (the oldest-established in Britain) which sticks mainly to familiar dishes with a healthy slant. Pre-theatre dinner served Mon-Fri, 6-7.30. ***Seats*** *54.*

Private Room 20. L 12-3 D 6-11. Closed L Sat, all Sun, Bank Holidays. Set L from £7.50 Set D from £12.50. AMERICAN EXPRESS *Access, Diners, Visa.*

W8 Al Basha

£70

Tel 071-938 1794

R

Troy Court 222 Kensington High Street W8 5RG

Map 19 A4

Lebanese restaurant with the accent on comfort and good service. Plenty of tables outside in summer. Late licence Fri & Sat with music in the lower ground dining room. ***Seats** 100. Private Room 60. Meals noon-midnight. Set L £12.50 Set D £20.* AMERICAN EXPRESS *Access, Diners, Visa.*

SW1 Al Bustan

£60

Tel 071-235 8277

R

27 Motcomb Street SW1X 8JU

Map 19 C4

One of the prettiest and best of London's Lebanese restaurants. A generous plateful of salad items is as crisp and fresh as the summery decor. A robust selection of hot and cold hors d'oeuvre accounts for more than half the menu: moutabal, kibbeh, spicy mini-sausages, grilled quails and Lebanese-style pizza with thyme and olive oil are among 30 choices. Main-course grills include boneless chicken with garlic sauce. Good choice of honey-rich sweets. ***Seats** 65. Meals noon-11pm (Sun to 10pm). Closed 25 & 26 Dec.* AMERICAN EXPRESS *Access, Diners, Visa.*

W1 Al Hamra

£50

Tel 071-493 1954

R

31 Shepherd Market W1Y 7RJ

Map 18 C3

One of London's best-known and most popular Lebanese restaurants, with close-set tables and outside eating in fine weather. Munch on crunchy salad, olives and bread while awaiting your meal – typically a selection of hot and cold hors d'oeuvre, something from the charcoal grill and, if you're still not replete, a honey-sticky sweet or two. ***Seats** 60. Meals 12-12. Closed 25 Dec-1 Jan.* AMERICAN EXPRESS *Access, Diners, Visa.*

W2 Al San Vincenzo ★

£70

Tel 071-262 9623

R

30 Connaught Street W2 2AS

Map 18 B2

Red and orange candy-striped loose-covered chairs provide almost the only decorative colour in this tiny seven-table restaurant close to Marble Arch. The stark modesty of the decor is mostly counterbalanced by the friendly warmth of Elaine Borgonzolo's service assisted by daughter, Angela. Vincenzo, in the meantime, works almost singlehanded in the downstairs kitchen. Originally from Naples, he nevertheless cooks dishes gleaned throughout Italy. Traditional bourgeois dishes have been subtly modernised using ingredients of irreproachably good quality. Now comfortably settled in after his move here from Cheam he has in the last few years developed his own distinctive style. It's not a restaurant that follows the latest fads and trends, neither will you find the likes of minestrone soup, spaghetti alla carbonara and steak pizzaiola. Instead the genuinely home-made pastas will include orechiette with black olives, pesto, capers, chili and Parmesan or stunningly good gargonelli (akin to penne) with a wonderful creamy asparagus sauce subtly flavoured with tarragon and accompanied by a generous amount of freshly grated Parmesan. Pan-fried fillets of red mullet are spread with a thin layer of smooth basil pesto and are surrounded by pine kernels cooked in olive oil with the carefully pounded livers – a brilliant touch, the resulting flavours outstandingly good even if the fish is sometimes a trifle overcooked. Other main courses include a generous very plump double breast of guinea fowl lightly glazed with honey and vin Santo and roasted with quartered fennel bulbs and potatoes. Even the accompanying side plate of vegetables has been transformed.

See over

Broad beans are flavoured with ground pancetta and the carrots delicately flavoured with cumin. His innovative and original touch extends to the desserts which include his unmissably delicious panettone bread pudding – slices of panettone dribbled with Cinzano bianco, before being baked with a sauce of mascarpone, eggs, vin Santo, cinnamon and orange juice – the results are a rich, moist, creamy creation to die for. Cheeses are superb – Italian organic unpasteurised farmhouse. ***Seats** 22. Parties 6. L 12.30-2.15 D 7-10.30. Closed L Sat, all Sun, 2 weeks Christmas. Access, Visa.*

W1 Alastair Little ★★ £85

Tel 071-734 5183 **R**

49 Frith Street W1V 5TE **Map 21 A2**

Only the modern artwork (for sale) on the walls changes the decor of Alastair Little's eponymous Soho restaurant. The stark monochrome decor is showing signs of age – the black tables and chairs and the cream walls are no longer pristine in appearance which is what this type of minimalist decor requires to be effective. Paper napkins, even in the evening, are a sign of the sheer informality and lack of pretension of the whole place. The food too has an intrinsic simplicity but is nevertheless brilliant and exciting in both concept and execution whether it's the retiring Little in the kitchen or one of sous chefs headed by the ebullient Jeremy Lee. None of the usual two-star pleasantries like canapés, amuse-gueule or petits fours here, just a basket of superb Neal's Yard breads including excellent poppy, sesame and linseed bread left on the table. As well as the à la carte there's a no-choice 3-course upstairs and a 2-course £10 menu in the bar downstairs. Changing daily, the dishes range from a seasonal Caesar salad or pasta and beans with olive oil and Parmesan to a plate of eight Pacific oysters with a shallot relish and a side dish of spicy sausages. These sausages are truly sensational: Thai-inspired balls of lightly pan-fried pork, chili, lemon grass, ginger, garlic, lime leaves and fish sauce. Asparagus risotto arrives, the rice cooked to the right creamy consistency with chopped asparagus, a little chive and a generous grating of fresh Parmesan. This rivals his other risottos in that, yet again, he perfectly balances the flavours and textures of the rice with that of the main added ingredient. Sea bass roasted till its skin is crisp and yet the flesh remains moist and succulent is served on a flat-leaf parsley salad with a riot of Mediterranean ingredients and flavours: sun-dried tomatoes, black olives and extra-fine capers with Parmesan, parsley and olive crumbs. Other choices are fillet of lamb with haricot beans and rosemary sauce, roast Bresse pigeon with girolles, calf's liver 'en persillade' with sarladaise potatoes or roast marinated chicken with new garlic and lemon. To finish, either Spanish or British cheeses or simple classics such as crème brulée, cherry and almond tart with crème fraiche or chocolate brownie with fudge sauce and ice cream. Service is casual but friendly complementing the rest of the restaurant perfectly. The wine list is short but well chosen, accurately matching the eclectic influences of the extraordinary cooking. ***Seats** 35. Parties 15. L 12-3 D 6-11.30. Closed L Sat & Christmas/New Year, all Sun, Bank Holidays. Set L £18.* AMERICAN EXPRESS *Access, Visa.*

EC1 Alba £60

Tel 071-588 1798 **R**

107 Whitecross Street EC1Y 8JD **Map 16 D3**

A friendly Italian restaurant very close to the Barbican Centre. Cooking puts the emphasis on good honest flavours throughout a menu which mixes familiar favourites such as minestrone, *risi e bisi* and calf's liver with sage with some much more unusual offerings, notably thinly sliced raw veal with Parmesan, rocket and truffle olive oil, and bresaola of deer. ***Seats** 50. L 12-3 D 7-11. Closed Sat & Sun, Bank Holidays, 2 weeks Christmas.* AMERICAN EXPRESS *Access, Visa.*

is our symbol for an outstanding wine list.

SW3 Albero & Grana ↑ NEW £70

Tel 071-225 1048 Fax 071-581 3259 **R**

Chelsea Cloisters 89 Sloane Avenue SW3 3DW **Map 19 B5**

Previous restaurants (and there have been many) on this spacious corner site all suffered from an excess of style with food playing an ancillary role. Here, at last, is a restaurant that gives equal footing to both bringing to this country, for the first time, and long overdue, a modern interpretation of Spanish food. A loud and busy bar at the front serves traditional tapas lunchtime and evening, the noise and background music encroaching on the dining area – an otherwise splendid room, designed by Jose Antonio Garcia. An undulating back wall has the Seville sand colour of the bullring, another wall is of glass bricks and the ceiling is tented with striped cotton ticking. A short menu lists the likes of melon stuffed with fish tartare, a warm tartlet which turns out to be a croquette of a well-combined mixture of crab and cauliflower topped with a tender scallop and decorative crab leg. Mains include hake with a saffron sauce, breast of duck with apples and almond paste and delicious lamb fillet with a garlic confit and fried artichoke hearts. Exquisite but simple sweets include a rice cream with brulée crust and a crisp puff pastry layer topped with sliced pears under a caramelised sugar topping surrounded by a custard cream. ***Seats** 50. Parties 14. Private Room 25. D only 7.30-midnight. Closed Sun and Bank Holidays.* AMERICAN EXPRESS *Access, Diners, Visa.*

SW7 Alexander Hotel 64% £116

Tel 071-581 1591 Fax 071-581 0824 **H**

9 Sumner Place SW7 3EE **Map 19 B5**

Well located in the centre of South Kensington, the Alexander offers quiet accommodation behind an elegant town house facade. A large patio makes an attractive, cool retreat in summer days. Some bedrooms and bathrooms need refurbishment. Bar and breakfast room are in the basement. No restaurant. ***Rooms** 37.* AMERICAN EXPRESS *Access, Diners, Visa.*

W1 alistair Greig's Grill £90

Tel 071-629 5613 **R**

26 Bruton Place London W1X 7AA **Map 18 C3**

Prime Scotch steaks have been the speciality here for 30 years, simply grilled with traditional accompaniment of grilled tomato and button mushrooms. Behind the red door there's red plush and old-fashioned civility. ***Seats** 65. Parties 20. L 12.30-2.30 D 6.30-11. Closed L Sat, all Sun, 25, 26 Dec, 1 Jan and L over Bank Holidays. Set L £19.50.* AMERICAN EXPRESS *Access, Diners, Visa.*

W11 L'Altro £60

Tel 071-792 1066 **R**

210 Kensington Park Road W11 **Map 17 B4**

A glass front encloses a stylish recreation of a very Italianate courtyard complete with authentic wall lamps and trompe l'oeil stone walls and classical statues. A sister to *Cibo* (qv), *L'Altro* specialises in seafood prepared simply in the modern Italian manner. The cooking is uncomplicated allowing the flavours of the fish and shellfish to dominate. This simplicity is exemplified in the likes of tiny baby cuttlefish and squid lightly deep-fried and served on a bed or rocket or carpaccio of marinated swordfish, tuna and scallops with a lemon and thyme dressing. Pasta dishes include excellent pappardelle (wide noodles) with rocket in a sauce of lobster and red mullet. Main dishes include a fish stew for two people which involves sea bream, sea bass, rascasse, monkfish and shellfish or grilled sea bass with balsamic vinegar and grilled radicchio and endives. There are a couple of meat dishes too, such as baked rack of lamb in a rocket and artichoke sauce. ***Seats** 43. Parties 20. L 12-2.30 (Sat till 3) D 7-11 (Fri & Sat to 11.30). Closed D Sun, Bank Holidays, Christmas, Easter. Set L £10. Access, Visa.*

N1 Anna's Place £44

Tel 071-249 9379 **R**

90 Mildmay Park Newington Green N1 4PR **Map 16 D2**

Anna Hegarty's eponymous restaurant continues to draw in the crowds so booking is essential. Decorated with Swedish posters and colourful vinyl tablecloths, it has a friendly, informal atmosphere. The food is also uncomplicated and approachable, featuring a good smattering of Swedish specialities. Marinated herrings, gravad lax (delicious with a glass of ice-cold schnapps), and roast turbot with grated fresh horseradish are typical fishy choices, while hearty meat hot pots are a popular winter order. Among the desserts the Swedish waffles with blueberry compote and cream should not be missed. ***Seats** 45. Parties 30. L 12.15-2.15 D 7.15-10.45. Closed Sun, Mon, 2 weeks Christmas, 2 weeks Easter, Aug. No credit cards.*

W8 Apollo Hotel £64

Tel 071-835 1133 Fax 071-370 4853 **H**

18-22 Lexham Gardens W8 5JE **Map 19 A5**

Long-established bed and breakfast hotel off Cromwell Road, offering value-for-money accommodation with few frills. Most rooms have private facilities, all have TVs and dial-out phones. One child up to 12 can stay free in parents' room. Manager Maurice Monina has been in charge since 1960. ***Rooms** 59. Closed Christmas/New Year.* AMERICAN EXPRESS *Access, Diners, Visa.*

SW3 The Argyll £60

Tel 071-352 0025 **R**

316 Kings Road SW3 **Map 19 B6**

A warm welcoming restaurant with a simple decor mixing well-established Chelsea money with a younger trendy crowd. Cooking by Anand Sastry is a personal mix of influences and dishes like pig's trotter stuffed with wild mushrooms and caramelised onions can be seen as a wink to Pierre Koffmann. Ravioli of foie gras with Sauternes sauce and turban of navarin of lamb with aubergine and thyme sauce are regulars on the often-changing menus. Results can bring mixed feelings, possibly brilliant like a roasted celeriac parcel of snails and mushrooms or simply dull, like a bland terrine of baby leeks, lobster and langoustine. Desserts can be an interesting research on the harmony of tastes, like lemon tart with celery and vodka sorbet or terrine of rhubarb with raspberry tea sorbet. The £10 lunch menu contrasts with the pricy à la carte bill. Wines are reasonably priced with many under £20. In the basement, Po-Na-Na Souk Bar, fitted out like a Bedouin tent, serves starters from the Argyll menu. ***Seats** 50. L 12-2.30 D 7-11. Closed L Mon, all Sun, Bank Holidays. Set L £8.50/£10.* AMERICAN EXPRESS *Access, Diners, Visa.*

W1 Arirang Korean Restaurant £50

Tel 071-437 6633 **R**

31 Poland Street W1V 3DB **Map 18 D2**

Pleasant service accompanies the fiery flavours of Korean cuisine on the fringes of Soho. Bulgogi – thinly sliced marinated beef – is the national dish, while among the more intriguing items are bracken stalks, a pizza made of ground green peas and wings of skate in a hot chili sauce. ***Seats** 100. Private Room 30. L 12-3 D 6-11. Closed L Bank Holidays, all Sun, 25 Dec, 1 Jan. Set meals from £19.50.* AMERICAN EXPRESS *Access, Diners, Visa.*

We endeavour to be as up-to-the-minute as possible, but inevitably some changes to key personnel may occur at restaurants and hotels after the Guide goes to press.

W1 Arisugawa **£60**

Tel 071-636 8913 **R**

27 Percy Street W1P 9FF **Map 18 D2**

The first choice of many Japanese diners, this smart modern restaurant in a basement has a menu of more than usual interest. The à la carte selection contains many unfamiliar dishes, while the set menus are a better bet for the less adventurous. Teppan cuisine is offered in the ground-floor room, traditional Japanese in the basement. ***Seats** 100. Private Room 20. L 12.30-2.30 D 6-10. Closed L Sat, all Sun, Bank Holidays, Christmas/New Year. Set L from £4.50 Set D from £20.* AMERICAN EXPRESS *Access, Diners, Visa.*

W8 The Ark **£45**

Tel 071-229 4024 **R**

122 Palace Gardens Terrace Notting Hill Gate London W8 4RT **Map 18 A3**

Wood-built neighbourhood restaurant at Notting Hill Gate. The menu stays true to its early-70s origins, with classics like steak and kidney pie and fish pie answering the demand of the many regulars. Other favourites from the repertoire run from crab pancakes and assorted charcuterie to chicken Kiev and pepper steak. Chocolate pot tops the popularity stakes among the desserts. Go early in the evening, or book. ***Seats** 70. Parties 14. Private Room 25. L 12-3 D 6.30-11.15 Closed L Sun & Bank Holidays, 3 days Christmas.* AMERICAN EXPRESS *Access, Diners, Visa.*

WC2 Arts Theatre Café **£46**

Tel 071-497 8014 **R**

6 Great Newport Street WC2 **Map 21 B2**

Tucked away in the basement of the theatre, the café has an unassuming, utilitarian decor belying Italian cooking that's considerably above average. The menu changes every day: typical choices run from crostini with chicken liver paté and home-pickled vegetables to chump chop with green beans and zucchini via pasta, fish and vegetarian specials. Exclusively Italian, sensibly-priced wine list to match. ***Seats** 30. Meals 12-10. Closed Sun, Bank Holidays, Easter, 1 week Christmas/New Year. Set D from £11.50. No credit cards.*

SW7 Aster House **£91**

Tel 071-581 5888 Fax 071-584 4925 **H**

3 Sumner Place SW7 3EE **Map 19 B5**

A charming home-from-home at the end of an early-Victorian terrace, run since 1982 by Mr and Mrs Carapiet. Bed and breakfast is offered with rooms ranging from small singles to a four-poster studio suite, all with private bath/shower, TVs, dial-out phones, fridges and mini-safes. A health-conscious buffet breakfast is served in a sunny first-floor conservatory. No smoking. Unlicensed. No children under 12 except babies in cots. No dogs. Minimum booking for two nights. ***Rooms** 12. Access, Diners, Visa.*

NW1 Asuka **£70**

Tel 071-486 5026 **R**

209a Baker Street NW1 6AD **Map 18 C2**

In an arcade at the northern end of Baker Street, Asuka is also the name of a traditional ten-course feast of soup, seven dishes and fruit. That's at the top of the price range, but there's plenty more to choose from, including some items daintily prepared at the table (wheat noodles with seafood, meat and vegetables in thick broth) by waitresses in kimonos. ***Seats** 34. L 12-3 D 6-11. Closed L Sat, all Sun, Bank Holidays. Set L from £12.50 Set D from £25.* AMERICAN EXPRESS *Access, Diners, Visa.*

W1 The Athenaeum 78% £230

Tel 071-499 3464 Fax 071-493 1860 **HR**

116 Piccadilly W1V 0BJ **Map 18 C3**

New owners have instigated a major programme of renovation since taking over from Rank Hotels in September 1992; by April 1994 everything from refurbished designer bedrooms to a new kitchen should have been completed. It's a peaceful and luxurious hotel near Hyde Park Corner, overlooking Green Park. Public rooms are limited for the size and location of the hotel but are homely and cosy, if lacking in daylight; the Windsor Lounge is an attractive room – a quiet retreat for afternoon tea; the clubby cocktail bar has a choice of 56 single malt whiskies. Bedrooms and bathrooms are already exceptionally well appointed and likely to improve; bedrooms overlooking an inside courtyard can be rather dark; Executive doubles overlooking the park are most agreeable and benefit from efficient double-glazing; a full valet service is offered. A choice of four meeting rooms caters for gatherings of up to 44 people. Valet car parking. 34 recently renovated apartments are in town houses next door to the hotel in Down Street. The new Health and Leisure Club with gymnasium, sauna, steam room and health and beauty treatment rooms was due to open in the basement as we went to press. ***Rooms 144.*** AMERICAN EXPRESS *Access, Diners, Visa.*

Restaurant £80

Masculine and clubby the bar may be, but the restaurant dining room is feminine and muffled, done out in pink tones and low lights – a perfect place for a romantic evening. Executive chef David Marshall's menu caters for many tastes, from a mousseline of scallops and scampi with basil-flavoured gnocchi served on a bed of chives with a cream sauce to a more traditional braised oxtail with mashed potato and vegetables glazed in butter. The cooking focuses on the best-quality products, but traditional dishes win over the more modern. Exclusively British and Irish farmhouse cheese selection and tempting desserts. Good-value menu served at both lunchtime and in the evening. ***Seats 60.*** *Private Room 40. L 12.30-2 (Sun 11.30-1.30) D 6-10. Closed L Sat. Set meals £16.50/£19.50.*

W8 Atlas Hotel £64

Tel 071-835 1155 Fax 071-370 4853 **H**

24-30 Lexham Gardens W8 5JE **Map 19 A5**

Neighbour of the Apollo Hotel (see above), in the same ownership, with the same long-serving manager and offering the same services. ***Rooms 66.*** *Closed Christmas/New Year.* AMERICAN EXPRESS *Access, Diners, Visa.*

W1 Au Jardin des Gourmets £75

Tel 071-437 1816 Fax 071-437 0043 **R**

5 Greek Street W1V 5LA **Map 21 A2**

All change at the Jardin – downstairs is now a brasserie/salle à manger divided into two rooms, one with Chinese-style decor; upstairs is smarter, cleverly redesigned in sections and still incorporating a private room. The food in the brasserie can arrive with indecent haste – fine if you're in a hurry – and is generally acceptable; ask to see the restaurant wine list if you want a serious bottle. Three *plats du jour* complement the three-course fixed-price menu (dishes are also individually priced) which has half a dozen or so choices at each course: perhaps fettuccine with tuna, tomato and olive sauce, French sausage with green haricot beans, sea bream with a tomato and basil coulis, confit of duck with a mountain of lentils. Bread-and-butter pudding and crèpe Suzette among the desserts. Upstairs extends to include the likes of pan-fried foie gras in a sweet and sour sauce, Dover sole, grilled Scotch rib of beef with béarnaise sauce, and steak tartare. Unobtrusive service, less formal downstairs than upstairs. There's only a smattering of non-French wines on the fabulous and fairly-priced restaurant wine list, which is easy to use and has many old and mature classics. 15% service charge is added to the bill. ***Seats*** *85. Parties 55. Private Rooms 12, 18 & 55. L 12.15-2.30 D 6.15-11.15. Closed L Sat, all Sun, Bank Holidays. Set meals £10.75/£13.50 & £15/£19.50.* AMERICAN EXPRESS *Access, Diners, Visa.*

NW8 L'Aventure £65

Tel 071-624 6232 **R**

3 Blenheim Terrace NW8 0EH **Map 16 B3**

Owner Catherine Parisot's personality is stamped all over this delightful little French restaurant with a terrace for summer eating. In a friendly, intimate atmosphere a short, appealing menu offers the likes of *crème Dubarry, coquilles St Jacques florentine, cote de veau rotie aux herbes* (for 2) and *pavé de porc poelé aux morilles.* ***Seats*** *40. L 12.30-2.30 D 7.30-11 (Sun to 10). Closed L Sat, 1 week Christmas, 4 days Easter. Set L £17.50 Set D £25.* AMERICAN EXPRESS *Access, Diners, Visa.*

W1 Bahn Thai £60

Tel 071-437 8504 **R**

21a Frith Street W1V 5TS **Map 21 A2**

Kensington was the original (1981) location of Bahn Thai, and in its Soho premises the aim is unchanged – to prepare and present authentic Thai cooking. The menu covers an unusually wide range, from familiar satay and tom yum soup to more recondite choices such as stewed pig's trotters or sea perch poached at the table over a charcoal brazier. It also offers guidance notes on ordering and eating Thai food, plus various health and heat warnings. The ground floor has recently been refurbished and a 'Thai Tapas Bar' opened. ***Seats*** *80. Private Room 20. L 12-2.45 (Sun 12.30-2.30) D 6-11.15 (Sun 6.30-10.30). Closed all Bank Holidays.* AMERICAN EXPRESS *Access, Visa.*

W12 Balzac Bistro Restaurant £50

Tel 081-743 5370 **R**

4 Wood Lane W12 7DT **Map 17 A4**

For many years a favourite with BBC staff, Balzac continues to please the crowds with its menus of old-fashioned bistro dishes soundly prepared and fairly priced. Onion soup, seafood pancake or asparagus hollandaise might precede chicken grilled with herbs, veal escalope with mushrooms and cream, rabbit with a mustard sauce or grilled Dover sole. ***Seats*** *80. Private Room 20. L 12-2.30 D 7-11. Closed L Sat, all Sun, Bank Holidays, 2 weeks Christmas. Set D £13.90 & £15.90.* AMERICAN EXPRESS *Access, Visa.*

SW7 Bangkok £36

Tel 071-584 8529 Fax 071-823 7883 **R**

9 Bute Street SW7 3EY **Map 19 B5**

One of the area's first Thai restaurants, the sparsely appointed Bangkok has been run by the same family since its opening in 1967. The short menu includes beef and pork satay, minced beef omelette, fried prawns, spare ribs, beef and chicken curry and Thai rice-noodles. ***Seats*** *60. Private Room 24. L 12.15-2.15 D 7-11.15. Closed Sun, Bank Holidays. Set L from £12.50. Access, Visa.*

We welcome bona fide complaints and recommendations on the tear-out pages at the back of the book for readers' comments. They are followed up by our professional team.

SE3 Bardon Lodge 56% £84

Tel 081-853 4051 Fax 081-858 7387 **H**

15 Stratheden Road SE3 7TH **Map 17 D5**

Close to Blackheath and Greenwich, Bardon Lodge comprises two Victorian houses. Most bedrooms are fairly modest in size, with modern furniture and compact carpeted bathrooms. The hotel is in new hands. *Rooms 37. Garden.* AMERICAN EXPRESS *Access, Visa.*

SW3 Basil Street Hotel 71% £178

Tel 071-581 3311 Fax 071-581 3693 **H**

Basil Street SW3 1AH **Map 19 C4**

An Edwardian English atmosphere pervades a privately-owned hotel just 191 steps (according to their publicity) from Harrods. Public areas have a country house feel, from the antique-lined corridor leading to the dining room to the spacious lounge in sunny yellow with rug-covered polished parquet floor. Well-kept bedrooms are of a good size, usually with a sitting area, traditionally furnished and decorated with understated good taste. Most have equally roomy private bathrooms. Old-fashioned standards of courteous and obliging service include shoe cleaning, servicing of rooms in the evenings and 24hr room service. Children under 16 stay free in parents' room. ***Rooms** 92.* AMERICAN EXPRESS *Access, Diners, Visa.*

SW3 Beauchamp Place NEW £60

Tel 071-589 4252 Fax 071-584 9350 **R**

15 Beauchamp Place SW3 1NQ **Map 19 C4**

A comparison with its illustrious predecessor *'Ménage à Trois'* is inevitable; indeed, former manager Eddie Khoo is now a partner here along with chef David Wilby. Extending to three storeys the restaurant is bright and modern with dramatic splashes of colour from multihued mosaics streaking across the rough plaster walls. The cooking is Anglo-European with robust, direct flavours and a stress on fresh seasonal produce. Breads to begin come with spiced virgin olive oil and a fruit or nut butter as well as celeriac tapénade. Wind-dried beef with marinated artichokes, chicken, pancetta and foie gras terrine with sweet onion chutney and toasted brioche or warm crab and cucumber tart are typical of the monthly-changing starters while main dishes could include mixed seafood fritters with chunky chips and garlic mayonnaise, grilled breast of chicken with a spaghetti of vegetables and coriander salsa or a sausage of pigs' trotters, calf's sweetbreads and leeks on creamed potatoes. Excellent sweets too, such as an apricot and almond gratin with Kirsch or a triple chocolate terrine. Otherwise there are some unusual cheeses for example Haives Wensleydale served with good crisp oatmeal biscuits. ***Seats** 74. Parties 25. Private Room 22. L 12-3.15 (Sat till 3.30, Sun till 4) D 7-12 (Sun till 10.30). Closed 25 & 26 Dec.* AMERICAN EXPRESS *Access, Diners, Visa.*

SW3 The Beaufort £135

Tel 071-584 5252 Fax 071-589 2834 **PH**

33 Beaufort Gardens SW3 1PP **Map 19 C4**

In a quiet, tree-lined cul-de-sac 100 yards from Harrods, the Beaufort offers personal service and almost rural peace. Guests are given front door keys and terms include VAT, service, all drinks from the 24hr drawing room bar, Continental breakfast (served in the room only), room service snacks and membership of a local health club. Air-conditioned, pastel-decorated bedrooms – full of extras large and small – range from a single with shower/WC only to a junior suite. A wonderful collection of over 400 English floral watercolours graces the walls. No children under ten except babes in arms. No dogs. ***Rooms** 28. Closed 23-28 Dec.* AMERICAN EXPRESS *Access, Diners, Visa.*

Consult page 16 for a full list of starred restaurants

NW1 **Belgo** **£40**

Tel 071-267 0718 **R**

72 Chalk Farm Road NW1 8AN **Map 16 C3**

A remarkable example of post-modern design, with a flat concrete frontage, a high-tech wheel and pulley design for the stairs, a bar made of latex rubber, an environment-friendly, heating and air system using huge chrome pipes, and a restaurant area conceived as a brewery eating hall. Its walls are also concrete, with a frieze inlaid with Rabelais-inspired names of obscure fish. Tables are refectory-style (for four), topped with ash, chairs are minimalist, with wooden axe handle seats which deliver more comfort and support than looks likely. Waiters are dressed in monk's habits, a practical garb for serving the hefty portions of mussels that are the most popular order. These and other marginally more refined Belgian dishes – mash with wild boar sausage, witloof au gratin, rabbit à la flamande – are washed down with Belgian beer, some of it monastery-brewed, some fruit-fermented, one sour and lemony, one as strong as wine! A real one-off and a big hit from the moment it opened, Belgo is a place for tucking into simple, sustaining food, for drinking beer and talking – but definitely not in a whisper. Bookings can now be made before the day of your visit. Open all day at weekends. ***Seats** 110. Parties 25. Closed 25 Dec, 1 Jan. L 12-3 D 6-11.30 (Sat & Sun 12-11.30). Set menu £8.95.* AMERICAN EXPRESS *Access, Visa.*

NW3 **Benihana** **£75**

Tel 071-586 9508 **R**

100 Avenue Road NW3 3HF **Map 16 B3**

American-style Japanese teppanyaki griddle cooking in large and often lively basement surroundings, next to the Hampstead Theatre. Surf 'n' turf is served with showbiz flair by knife-flailing chefs at hibachi tables. Great value week-day lunches and children's menu (with entertainment on Sundays). Specialities include vegetable ginza (stuffed green pepper with textured soy, asparagus, baby corn, spinach, shiitake mushrooms, carrots, lotus roots and potato). Branches around the world, from Beverly Hills to Bangkok. ***Seats** 120. L 12.30-3 D 6.30-12. Closed L Mon, 25 Dec. Set L from £8.45.* AMERICAN EXPRESS *Access, Diners, Visa.*

W1 **Bentinck House Hotel** **NEW** **£76**

Tel 071-935 9141 Fax 071-224 5903 **H**

20 Bentinck Street W1M 5RL **Map 18 C2**

Large comfortable bedrooms (three family rooms, 9 rooms not en suite) in a small hotel behind Oxford Street. ***Rooms** 20.* AMERICAN EXPRESS *Access, Diners, Visa.*

W1 **Bentley's** **£80**

Tel 071-287 5025 **R**

11 Swallow Street W1R 7HD **Map 18 D3**

Bottle green upholstery and polished mahogany with yellow ochre ragged walls hung with large oil paintings create a splendidly refined and civilised ambience in this elegant first-floor dining room. Very much a West End institution for fish-eaters into which Richard Corrigan has introduced an exciting new menu. The list of dishes is long, even overlong, and has some marvellous sounding combinations. The style is modern and Mediterranean but also with a nod to the specialities of his native Ireland. A salad of crubeens comes with a pigeon and port vinaigrette and poached fillets of black sole are served with lobster. On paper the menu

See over

is mouthwateringly good and well thought out – fillets of lightly smoked salmon with olive oil, potato purée and shallots, hot buttered oysters with garden herbs, fresh crab salad with fennel, orange and mayonnaise. Confit of suckling pig in a single large raviolo with a trace of foie gras and wild mushrooms is served with a rather concentrated consommé; scallops are carefully fried and served around a delicious coriander and tomato couscous. Two tiny fillets of John Dory are accompanied by two baby squid stuffed with a rather pasty lobster-flavoured risotto. There are a few meat dishes, mostly offal as in faggots of pig's head with sauté of calf's kidneys and sweetbreads. Sweets like apple tart, served dry and unglazed, can be disappointing. On the ground floor the Oyster bar offers a shorter, more traditional seafood menu. ***Seats** 100. Parties 20. Private Room 12. L 12-2.30 D 6-10.30. Closed Sun, some Bank Holidays.* AMERICAN EXPRESS *Access, Diners, Visa.*

SW1 The Berkeley 86% £252

Tel 071-235 6000 Fax 071-235 4330 **HR**

Wilton Place SW1X 7RL **Map 19 C4**

Located on the corner of Knightsbridge and Wilton Place, the hotel entrance in this elegant building could easily be missed by an inattentive eye. This image of intimacy is projected throughout the hotel and all guests are VIPs. Favourite rooms, newspapers, drinks and other customer preferences are kept on record to ensure regulars receive the best possible service. This level of attention extends to the public rooms where rugs are added for warmth in the winter, and removed to reveal cool marble floors in the summer. Two original features are the cinema and the roof-top health suite which overlooks London. Standard bedrooms are bright and homely providing comfortable seating areas scattered with cushions, satellite TV and even VCR. All bedrooms are individually decorated and the suites feel like private flats. The Wellington suite even has a conservatory and roof terrace. The decor of the bathrooms and corridors remains very 70s but renovation is planned for this year. These are minor compared to the high standards of the rest. ***Rooms** 160. Indoor swimming pool, gymnasium, sauna, solarium, beauty & hair salon, valeting, cinema, coffee shop (7am-11.30pm Mon-Sat).* AMERICAN EXPRESS *Access, Diners, Visa.*

Restaurant £82

The dining room has been given an elegant fashionable touch through the limed oak panelling and carving custom made to match Sir Edwin Lutyens' original panelling in the lounge oppoiste the entrance hall. The hotel celebrates its 21st birthday this year and chef Clement Schmidt's faithful presence since the beginning. The lack of fantasy of the highly traditional menu is quickly forgiven thanks to the quality and consistency shown over the years. *Quenelles de sole au champagne, bisque de homard, turbot poché sauce hollandaise* or *piccata de veau Joséphine* are lightly prepared with perfectly balanced sauces. Two well-priced lunch and dinner menus complement the à la carte. ***Seats** 65. Parties 12. L 12.30-2.30 (Sun to 2.15) D 6.30-10.45 (Sun 7-10). Closed Sat. Set L £19.50 Set D £21.*

W1 Berkshire Hotel 72% £185

Tel 071-629 7474 Fax 071-629 8156 **H**

350 Oxford Street W1N 0BY **Map 18 C2**

Occupying its own small triangular block on the north side of Oxford Street, almost facing the top of New Bond Street, the Berkshire possesses comfortable though not extensive public rooms, with a chintzy, panelled drawing room and the intimate Ascot Bar. Bedrooms, including 30 designated non-smoking, are attractively appointed, much use being made of rich, colourful fabrics and darkwood furniture. Executive rooms are bigger and have more accessories; suites have whirlpool baths. Owners Edwardian Hotels aim for a country-house welcome and an Edwardian feel here. ***Rooms** 147.* AMERICAN EXPRESS *Access, Diners, Visa.*

W1 Berners Park Plaza 72% £150

Tel 071-636 1629 Fax 071-580 3972 **H**

10 Berners Street W1A 3BE **Map 18 D3**

Turn-of-the-century splendour survives in the marble columns and intricate moulded ceilings of a hotel a few steps north of Oxford Street. The traditional atmosphere extends to afternoon tea and the cocktail hour. Bedrooms are of a good size, well laid-out, smartly furnished and double-glazed. Tiled bathrooms all have showers as well as tubs. Children up to 12 stay free in parents' room. Half the rooms are designated non-smoking. Conference/banqueting facilities for up to 160 delegates. ***Rooms** 229. Coffee shop (8am-10.30pm).* AMERICAN EXPRESS *Access, Diners, Visa.*

WC2 Bertorelli's £60

Tel 071-836 3969 **R**

44a Floral Street WC2E 9DA **Map 21 B2**

Modern Italian cooking by Maddalena Bonnino at a famous address by the stage door of the Royal Opera House. Deep-fried mozzarella bites with roasted peppers, capers and spring onion salsa; grilled fillets of mackerel on grilled marinated courgettes with rosemary pesto; pasta quills with French beans, hazelnuts and Parmesan; and pork involtini filled with sultanas and pine nuts served with pickled red cabbage typify an unusually interesting menu. There's an associated café/wine bar in the basement. ***Seats** 100. Parties 30. L 12-3 D 5.45-11.30. Closed Sun, 26 Dec.* AMERICAN EXPRESS *Access, Diners, Visa.*

N16 Beyoglu Ocakbasi £30

Tel 071-275 7745 **R**

4 Stoke Newington Road London N16 **Map 16 D2**

Candle-light creates a relaxed mood for enjoying some good Turkish food, which you can see the chef preparing on his ocakbasi, or charcoal grill. The grill provides most of the main courses (lamb, chicken, swordfish), while others are sautéed and served with a tomato sauce. There's a long list of starters, plus two soups – lentils and lamb. ***Seats** 40. Parties 12. Meals 11am-midnight (Fri & Sat till 5am). Closed 25 Dec, 1 Jan. No credit cards.*

WC2 Bhatti £50

Tel 071-831 0817 **R**

37 Great Queen Street London WC2B 5AA **Map 21 B2**

Popular, long-established and civilised Indian restaurant with long opening hours and a central location just off Drury Lane. A fairly familiar range of chicken, lamb and prawn dishes is joined by quail and pomfret fish – both cooked in the clay oven. Definitely a cut above average. ***Seats** 60. Parties 50. Private Room 40. L 12-2.30 D 6-11.45 (Sun 10.30). Closed 25 & 26 Dec.*

SW3 Bibendum ★↑ £130

Tel 071-581 5817 Fax 071-823 7925 **R**

81 Fulham Road SW3 6RD **Map 19 B5**

The first floor of the three-dimensional advertisement Michelin building is undeniably an extraordinary setting for a restaurant. The success of the renovation comes from a brilliant mix of original, complex design with pure geometrical structures maximising space and light. Booking is not just advisable, it is a must. Service, smoothly handled at the beginning, tends to slip throughout the meal and one should expect a long wait if the dining room is full. What two years ago was a refreshing new Mediterranean approach to cooking is now treading water. Piedmontese peppers, marinated artichokes, shrimps, black olives and basil, caponata with buffalo

See over

mozzarella, grilled squid with gremolata, chili and olive oil or grilled pigeon, herb crust and balsamico lack inspiration and can be disappointing. More so is the weakness shown in the more traditional repertoire during a recent visit, with a watery *soupe de poissons,* undercooked kidneys, sauces overpowered by herbs or overcooked vegetables. Let's hope success hasn't spoiled Simon Hopkinson's talent. "Nunc est bibendum", and drinking is more than an invitation thanks to the impressive wine list. ***Seats** 70. Parties 8. L 12.30-2.30 (Sat & Sun to 3) D 7-11.30 (Sun to 10.30). Closed 4 days Christmas, Easter Monday. Set L from £25.* AMERICAN EXPRESS *Access, Visa.*

SW3 — Bibendum Oyster Bar — £60

Tel 071-589 1480 Fax 071-823 7925 — R

Michelin House 81 Fulham Road SW3 6RD — Map 19 B5

At the front of the superbly restored Michelin building, the Oyster Bar serves a day-long menu based largely on high-quality seafood. Nine varieties of oysters head the list, which also includes lobster, langoustine and crab mayonnaise, clams and *crevettes grises*, smoked salmon and grilled squid with spicy noodles. Mainly cold dishes. ***Seats** 50. Meals Mon-Sat 12-10.30pm, Sun L 12-2 & D 7-10.30.* AMERICAN EXPRESS *Access, Visa.*

W1 — Bistrot Bruno ★ NEW — £60

Tel 071-734 4545 Fax 071-287 1027 — R

63 Frith Street W1V 5TA — Map 21 A2

In the Soho premises formerly occupied by l'Hippocampe, Pierre and Kathleen Condou in association with Bruno Loubet and chef Desmond Yare present a menu in the modern mode, with a Mediterranean influence and skilled use of spices, oils and dressings. Smoked fish cannelloni with a sharpish horseradish sauce borders on the macho, while boneless grilled quails resting on green beans and split peas with a light cardamom-flavoured jus is rather more demure. Potted oxtail on a good 'bitey' coleslaw, salmon cooked on one side on a king-size bed of dill-dressed endives and deep-fried whitebait with home-made mustard pickle are other typical items on a monthly-changing menu that's full of originality (but will still come up with the occasional old favourite such as cassoulet). Desserts more than sustain the quality, and a definite plus is awarded to sublime Pernod and honey iles flottantes. Coffee is served with marvellous frozen sorbet chocs. ***Seats** 48. Parties 10. L 12.15-2.30 D 6.15-11.30. Closed L Sat, all Sun, 4 days Christmas.* AMERICAN EXPRESS *Access, Diners, Visa.*

SW7 — Bistrot 190 ↑ — £45

Tel 071-581 5666 — R

190 Queen's Gate SW7 5EU — Map 19 B4

The lofty front room of the *Gore Hotel* (qv) is the setting for one of the capital's most successful and trendy restaurants, the brainchild of the redoubtable, once-hyphenated Antony Worrall Thompson. No bookings are taken, and it's frequently crowded by 7. The noise level is high, and you'll need to be in good shouting form to deliver all your bons mots. Good food is served at reasonable prices through long hours, starting early with breakfast, and all the wines (the supplier and therefore the list change frequently) are available by bottle or two-glass pichets. It's the sort of place where you want to return time after time to work your way through the menu, but always starting with country bread, superior French butter, tapénade, olives and olive oil. The Mediterranean influences many of the dishes – tortilla with sun-dried tomatoes and baby spinach, chargrilled tuna niçoise with Parmesan and balsamico, chicken with peperonata and pesto potatoes – while others draw their inspiration from further afield: monkfish sausages with spicy lentils and black bean vinaigrette, tuna sashimi with marinated vegetables and wasabi mayonnaise. Favourites rarely missing from the menu include AWT chargrilled pizza with sun-dried tomatoes, chargrilled vegetables and Roquefort, braised lamb shank with flageolet beans and polenta mash, and aged rump steak with frites. Supplementing the interesting carte is a new fixed-price lunch menu, available in both bistrot and bar. ***Seats** 50. Parties 12. Meals 7am-12.30am (Sun to 11.30pm). Set L £7.50/£10 (Sun £13.50/£16.50).* AMERICAN EXPRESS *Access, Diners, Visa.*

W12 Blah! Blah! Blah! NEW **£25**

Tel 081-746 1337 **R**

78 Goldhawk Road London W12 8HA **Map 17 A4**

Entertaining vegetarian restaurant close to Shepherds Bush, bringing Italian, Middle Eastern, Thai and Indian influences to roots, grains, nuts and yoghurt. Unlicensed, so bring your own bottle. ***Seats** 70. Parties 15. Private Room 30. L 12-3 D 7.30-11. Closed Sun & Bank Holidays. No credit cards.*

SW3 Blair House Hotel NEW **£85**

Tel 071-581 2323 **H**

34 Draycott Place SW3 2SA **Map 19 C5**

Well-equipped bed and breakfast hotel conveniently located near Sloane Square with quiet bedrooms at the back. ***Rooms** 17.* AMERICAN EXPRESS *Access, Diners, Visa.*

SW7 Blakes Hotel 82% **£215**

Tel 071-370 6701 Fax 071-373 0442 **HR**

33 Roland Gardens SW7 3PF **Map 19 B5**

A dark green exterior sets the scene for the drama within this most individual of hotels, created from a series of late-Victorian town houses. The small foyer/lounge area is papered black yet warmed by the browns of wood and leather seating piled high with plumped-up cushions. The overall effect is Oriental, a theme carried through to the Chinese Room that leads off the smart basement restaurant where an intimate bar is also to be found. Bedrooms vary widely in decor – from the opulence of one containing the Empress Josephine's day bed to the contrived simplicity of an all-white room with white-painted floorboards and trompe l'oeil wall paintings. The more expensive rooms are singular in design with masses of heavily swagged drapes in unusual fabrics and polished wood floors; furnished with antiques, objets d'art and a profusion of framed prints along with delicate Venetian glassware. Mostly beautiful bathrooms with marble surrounds, though standard rooms have small modern white-tiled ones. The bedrooms in the oldest part of the building have also at long last been upgraded. They suffer only in being on the small side but this has been turned to their advantage creating truly cosy, intimate rooms, many decorated in a very smart, uniform grey. The clothed walls, carpets, bedding, draped curtains, upholstery, even the woodwork are all in an absolutely identical shade of flannel grey. On the lower floors there are lighter rooms with a monochrome decor, black and white tartans against plain white backgrounds. The newest of all the bedrooms has a stunning Middle Eastern influence. An unusual and exotic hotel with friendly and helpful staff. ***Rooms** 52.* AMERICAN EXPRESS *Access, Diners, Visa.*

Blakes Restaurant ★ **£150**

A simple open staircase leads down into a basement that shares the restaurant with a dark intimate bar and small cushion-piled lounge filled with chinoiserie. The striking monochrome decor of the restaurant is broken only by glass table vases of white-flowered greenery, long green ribbons tied around the napkins and colourful wall-mounted Thai warrior costumes. Plate glass screens divide some of the tables in what is a small, discreet and very elegantly contemporary room. In this wonderful setting Peter Thornley produces food that is almost without equal. The

See over

presentation does not suffer from unnecessary flourishes yet it is very appealing to the eye. Far Eastern recipes have been re-worked, resulting in dishes that are captivatingly original. A meal here usually begins with complimentary, deliciously crisp won-ton crescents filled with a spiced chicken mixture. From the short lunchtime carte come green tea and buckwheat soba, *filetto carpaccio con parmigiano* and a piquant soup comprising a large scooped-out lime in which three tiny 'money-bag' parcels of chicken are arranged, sitting on a bed of rice noodles; into the bowl a hot consommé of chicken, lime and lemon grass with a hint of chili is added. Among the main courses could be ginger risotto, soufflé suissesse and steamed cumin scallops with fried seaweed and turmeric rice. Chicken tikka – bite-sized succulent morsels of the breast coated in a scintillating mixture of crushed, ground and chopped fresh herbs – is accompanied by chili and cucumber raitas and fluffy rice flavoured with toasted sesame seeds. Sweets include an arrestingly rich and totally satisfying iced chocolate and almond pudding. The dinner menu offers a greater choice of dishes all in the same gloriously eclectic vein. One token Australian Chardonnay appears on the otherwise short French wine list, and there's not a bottle under £20, apart from house wines. ***Seats** 32. Parties 14. Private Room 22. L 12.30-2.30 D 7.30-11.30. Set L from £28.*

E1 Bloom's

£38

Tel 071-247 6001

R

90 Whitechapel High Street E1 7RA

Map 16 D3

Morris Bloom set the ball rolling in 1920, opening a small restaurant in Brick Lane and quickly establishing a reputation for serving fine kosher food. The Whitechapel premises opened in 1952 and operate under the same strict kosher rules – a rabbi and a religious supervisor on the premises every day. Salt beef is the star of the show, best enjoyed with latkes and pickled cucumber, but chopped liver, egg and onions, bloomburgers, fried fish and roast chicken all have a strong following. Finish with lockshen pudding or halva, drink lemon tea or Israeli wine. Quick service from wise-cracking, long-serving staff. ***Seats** 150. Meals 11.30-9.30 (Fri to 3am). Closed D Fri, all Sat, Jewish Holidays, Christmas.* AMERICAN EXPRESS *Access, Diners, Visa.*

Also at:

NW11 130 Golders Green Road NW11 8HB Tel 081-455 1338 **Map 16 B1**

Closed D Fri, L Sat, Jewish Holidays.

SW6 Blue Elephant

£70

Tel 071-385 6595 Fax 071-386 7665

R

4-6 Fulham Broadway SW6 1AA

Map 19 A6

Verdant decor incorporating a waterfall, a bridge over a stream and a veritable jungle of greenery – an exotic setting in which to enjoy luxurious, MSG-free Thai cooking. If you really want to push the boat out try the 17-dish Royal Thai banquet menu (from £25). Hot dishes are indicated by little red elephants (up to three) on the menu. Separate vegetarian list. Buffet lunch available Mon-Fri (£19.50), Sunday brunch £14.50 with special price for children. ***Seats** 250. Private Room 100. L 12-2.30 D 7-12.30 (Sun to 10.30). Closed L Sat, 24-27 Dec, 1 Jan.* AMERICAN EXPRESS *Access, Diners, Visa.*

SE1 Blue Print Café

£60

Tel 071-378 7031

R

Design Museum Shad Thames Butlers Wharf SE1 2YD

Map 20 D3

A stylish Sir Terence Conran-owned restaurant on the first floor of the Design Museum with views overlooking the Thames; chef Lucy Crabb cooks an archetypal modern menu that changes daily. The Med might be represented by grilled goat's cheese with roquette and roasted peppers or avocado with anchovy salad; spinach and ricotta gnocchi; rare-grilled una with tomato salsa and guacamole or chicken breast with lentils, ancetta and garlic. From elsewhere come Caesar salad, steamed John Dory vith leeks and oyster mushrooms, and oxtail faggots with celeriac purée. ummer eating on the outside balcony tables has the added benefit f wonderful views of Tower Bridge. 15% service charge is added to menu rices. Wine list includes many New World and South African bottles. *eats 85. L 12-3 D 7-11. Closed D Sun. Set L & D £15/£20.* AMERICAN EXPRESS *Access, Diners, Visa.*

SW7 Bombay Brasserie ★ £70

Tel 071-370 4040 R

Courtfield Close Courtfield Road SW7 4UH Map 19 B5

The most glamorous Indian restaurant in town. The handsome room, with ts Raj pictures and paddle fans, is from a time past, evoking a grand hotel f a century ago. Entrance is to a roomy bar area where mango Bellini s a popular cocktail. One part of the restaurant proper is a large and lowery conservatory which despite its lack of views manages to convey garden feel. Staff are smart, polite, well-informed and abundant. The itchen garners its recipes from all parts of the sub-continent: potato cakes nd colourful puri from Bombay, Moghlai chicken biryani, Goan fish urry with chilis and coconut, tandoori preparations from the North-West rontier, a pungent lamb curry from Hyderabad. House specialities include obster peri peri (hot with chilis) and lamb korma. Buffet at lunchtime. Owned by Taj International Hotels. ***Seats** 200. Private Room 100. L 12.30-3 D 7.30-12 (Sun to 11.30). Closed 26 & 27 Dec. Set L from £13.95. Access, Diners, Visa.*

SW2 Bon Ton Roulet £40

Tel 081-678 0880 R

43 Tulse Hill SW2 Map 17 D6

The good times have rolled further down the road. Little else has changed - the same friendly relaxed and informal atmosphere is still there and the ood, a good-value selection of mostly familiar favourites – paté maison, aked stuffed mushrooms, garlic mussels, roast loin of pork with apples and ider – continues to please. Fully licensed but also bring your own. ***Seats** 30. Private Room 25. L Sun only 12.30-2.30 D 7-10.30 (Sat to 11). Closed D Sun, Bank Holidays, 1 week Christmas. No credit cards.*

WC1 Bonnington Hotel 61% £108

Tel 071-242 2828 Fax 071-831 9170 H

92 Southampton Row WC1B 4BH Map 16 C3

n the same family ownership for 80 years, the Bonnington is just south f Russell Square – close to the British Museum and within easy walking listance of the Oxford Street shops. Extensive public areas include a lounge ar, breakfast room and many meeting/function rooms for up to 250 lelegates. Bedrooms with all the usual accessories include 56 (and ncreasing) designated non-smoking. Rooms on Southampton Row are louble-glazed. ***Rooms** 215.* AMERICAN EXPRESS *Diners, Visa.*

SW7 La Bouchée NEW £35

Tel 071-589 1929 R

56 Old Brompton Road South Kensington SW7 3DY Map 19 B5

Unusual to find this tiny restaurant anything other than packed and ustling. The simple bistro-style fare served in simple bistro-style urroundings varies from average to good but always offers decent value or money. ***Seats** 85. Parties 10. Private Room 60. Meals 9am-11pm. Set meal from £4.95. Closed 25 & 26 Dec, 1 Jan. Access, Visa.*

WC2 Boulestin

£100

Tel 071-836 7061 Fax 071-836 1283

R

Garden Entrance 1a Henrietta Street WC2E 8PS

Map 21 B:

The traditional decor has a timeless elegance. The well-proportioned basement dining room is done in ochre tones with soft lights. The menu offers well-executed classic dishes from the French repertoire with the unexpected addition of fashionable dishes like *friture japonaise de légumes au coriandre* or *filet de selle d'agneau à l'embeurrée de choux et son jus au balsamique*. Recession-beater menus were introduced to boost what was once the bastion of French cuisine. The cooking is light and unpretentious: *foie gras de canard en terrine avec sa brioche aux raisins, turban de coquilles St Jacques au coulis de crabe, caneton de Gressingham à la normande*. Coffee and after-dinner drinks can be served in the comfortable Lounge bar. Plenty of half bottles on a generally pricy wine list that features many classic clarets and burgundies as well as a decent offering from the New World. ***Seats** 75. Private Room 30. L 12-2.30 D 7.30-11.15. Closed L Sat, all Sun, Bank Holidays, 1 week Christmas, 3 weeks Aug. Set L £14/£16.50. Set D £21.75/£25.75.* AMERICAN EXPRESS *Access, Diners, Visa.*

W8 Boyd's

£70

Tel 071-727 5452

R

135 Kensington Church Street W8 7LP

Map 18 A:

Boyd Gilmour's base is a pleasant conservatory restaurant with a varnished wooden floor, rattan chairs, green-stained table tops, plenty of greenery, ceiling fans and blinds on the glass dome. It's a bright, pretty setting, and pretty also is the presentation of his carefully prepared dishes. Chinese noodles with roasted aubergine come topped with sesame seeds and dressed with sesame oil and tamari; game terrine has a slight blandness lifted by a good fruity cranberry sauce; chargrilled turbot (there are always a couple of daily fish specials) is accompanied by a basil beurre blanc; pan-fried calf's liver and sweetbreads are served on potato and celeriac pancakes with a foie gras sauce. The food sparkles rather than stuns, but this is certainly a very decent neighbourhood restaurant and the two-course lunch menu provides excellent value for money. ***Seats** 35. Parties 20. L 12.30-2.30 D 7-11. Closed Sun, 2 weeks Christmas. Set L £14.* AMERICAN EXPRESS *Access, Visa.*

W6 The Brackenbury

£30

Tel 081-748 0107

R

129-131 Brackenbury Road W6

Map 17 A

Sensible, realistic pricing is one of the strongest points at the Robinsons' hugely popular restaurant, along with straightforward cooking that can look deceptively simple. The place used to be a wine bar, and a bar area still remains; the eating areas are utilitarian yet welcoming, with salmon pink and green paintwork and some pew seating. Adam Robinson cooks a short menu that changes at each session and manages to encompass much of what is best in London's voguish simple, modern cooking style; always an interesting soup (Andalucian garlic), often a signature dish of potato pancake with salmon caviar and crème fraiche and an Italian-inspired vegetarian dish like mushroom risotto. Main dishes might range from fish stew with rouille and saffron potatoes to grilled chump of lamb with a warm haricot bean salad or pork with buckwheat noodles and black bean dressing; vegetables are always an integral component of each dish. The interesting plate of mixed savouries (sufficient for four diners) that starts the menu is a clever way of charging for amuse-gueule, but customers are unlikely to complain. Cheeses are always immaculately kept (the emphasis is firmly on quality not quantity). Puddings might include iced praline terrine or steamed marmalade pudding with custard. Over twenty wines are offered by the glass from a wine list that is broadly based and concisely described. ***Seats** 55. Parties 12. L 12.30-3 D 5.30-11. Closed L Mon & Sat, D Sun, Christmas, Easter.* AMERICAN EXPRESS *Access, Visa.*

SW14 Le Braconnier **£60**

Tel 081-878 2853 **R**

467 Upper Richmond Road West SW14 7PU **Map 17 A5**

The menu of French regional dishes is always of interest in this splendid little restaurant. *Menu de la Loire,* for example, with fresh rabbit and mushroom soup, quenelles de poissons and pan-fried rump steak with shallots and red wine sauce supplements regular favourites like seafood terrine, rack of lamb or Toulouse cassoulet. ***Seats** 30. D 7-11. Closed Sun & Mon, Bank Holidays, 5 days Christmas. Set D £13.95/£15.95.* AMERICAN EXPRESS *Access, Visa.*

SW3 La Brasserie **£55**

Tel 071-581 3089 **R**

272 Brompton Road SW3 **Map 19 B5**

Authentic French brasserie almost opposite the Michelin building. Breakfast with the papers expands to baguette and toasted sandwiches and, from lunchtime, the full menu of brasserie classics. ***Seats** 140. Parties 14. Meals 8am-midnight (Sun 10am-11.30pm). Closed 25 & 26 Dec. Set L £12.50.* AMERICAN EXPRESS *Access, Diners, Visa.*

W10 Brasserie du Marché aux Puces **£48**

Tel 081-968 5828 **R**

349 Portobello Road W10 5SA **Map 16 B3**

A bright, informal brasserie with large windows, plain wooden tables and a mahogany bar with a wire fruit basket, a plateau of cheeses and a huge flower display on the counter. The shortish menu, which changes every few weeks, presents the occasional old-fashioned items such as kidneys Turbigo or grilled steak with deep-fried onion rings among generally modern and eclectic choices: leek and cheese terrine with poppy seeds and saffron vinaigrette, natural smoked haddock with rocket and frisée, smoked wild boar with marrow chutney, roast breast of goose with green tomato and walnuts. Steamed ginger and syrup pudding with custard is a dessert guaranteed to fill any gaps. ***Seats** 40. Parties 16. Private Room 36. Meals noon-11pm (Sun 11-4). Closed D Sun, Bank Holidays. No credit cards.*

SW8 Brasserie Faubourg **£55**

Tel 071-622 6245 **R**

28 Queenstown Road SW8 3RX **Map 17 C5**

A sunny little spot over Chelsea Bridge, just south of the river. The menu (French with translation) is typified by fish soup, salmon in lemon sauce, breast of duck with raspberry sauce and Scotch ribeye with shallots and red wine. ***Seats** 28. L 12-2.30 D 7-11. Closed L Mon & Sat, all Sun, Bank Holidays, 10 days Aug. Set L £9.50. Access, Visa.*

Many hotels offer reduced rates for weekend or out-of-season bookings.
Always ask about special deals.

W1 Britannia Inter-Continental Hotel 77% £210

Tel 071-629 9400 Fax 071-629 7736 **H**

Grosvenor Square W1A 3AN **Map 18 C3**

Behind the grand, colonnaded frontage of three Georgian houses overlooking the Mayfair square is an appropriately elegant interior. The luxurious, chandeliered lobby sets the civilised tone, which the cocktail lounge and bar follow. The latter has live piano music every evening. The Waterloo Despatch bar is in pub style serving traditional ales and snacks. Air-conditioned bedrooms range from standards (decent size, with reproduction furniture) to de luxe, with desks, seating areas and bars, and the top-of-the-range suites, which offer many extras and luxury touches. Conference/banqueting facilities for 100/80, supported by 24hr business services. Car parking below the hotel. Children under 14 stay free in parents' room. No dogs. See entry under *Shogun* for details of their Japanese restaurant. ***Rooms** 317. Valeting, shopping arcade (inc news kiosk & hairdressing), cocktail lounge (7am-11pm).* AMERICAN EXPRESS *Access, Diners, Visa.*

E14 Britannia International Hotel 68% £113

Tel 071-712 0100 Fax 071-712 0102 **H**

Marsh Wall E14 9SJ **Map 20 D3**

Blending in with the surrounding modern architecture the tall International stands just off West Ferry Road almost in the shadow of the Canary Wharf Tower which faces it across part of the former West India and Millwall Docks. Public rooms make full and good use of the waterside location and the views become panoramic from the bedrooms. The first floor features a range of conference suites while on the ground floor there's a pizzeria with an adjacent disco which is approached through a waterfall. The hotel is colourfully decorated throughout and features numerous large Chinese artefacts. There's limited underground parking. ***Rooms** 442. Indoor swimming pool, gymnasium, sauna, spa bath, steam room, beauty & hair salon.* AMERICAN EXPRESS *Access, Diners, Visa.*

W1 Brown's Hotel 74% £239

Tel 071-493 6020 Fax 071-493 9381 **H**

Albermarle Street W1A 4SW **Map 18 D3**

James Brown, a retired gentleman's gentleman, opened a hotel in fashionable Mayfair in 1837, the year Queen Victoria came to the throne. Now a Forte flagship and long favoured as a rendezvous for afternoon tea (jackets and ties required), it retains great period style and elegance in fine furnishing, richly panelled woods and original moulded ceilings. Individually decorated bedrooms offer guests a complementary mixture of the traditional and modern, with high-quality fabrics, bright patterns and bold designs. Room numbers are down on last year, as a result of several rooms being enlarged. No dogs. ***Rooms** 120.* AMERICAN EXPRESS *Access, Diners, Visa.*

W1 Bryanston Court 61% £102

Tel 071-262 3141 Fax 071-262 7248 **H**

56 Great Cumberland Place W1H 7FD **Map 18 C2**

One minute away from Marble Arch and Oxford Street, the family-run Bryanston Court is well situated for shopping and sightseeing. Day rooms and bedrooms offer home-from-home comfort. Improvements have recently been made in the bathrooms, most of which have shower/WC only. ***Rooms** 54.* AMERICAN EXPRESS *Access, Diners, Visa.*

We publish annually, so make sure you use the current edition.
It's worth it!

EC1 **Bubb's** **£75**

Tel 071-236 2435 **R**

329 Central Markets EC1A 9NB **Map 20 A1**

A stone's throw from Smithfield yet offering superb fresh fish dishes as well as the expected prime meats, Bubb's is decorated in true French style with wine-coloured gloss-painted wood-strip walls hung with numerous framed French prints and posters. Lace curtains at the window, discreet French music and charming French staff together with well-prepared familiar bourgeois cooking all add up to a memorable and enjoyable experience. Evenings with candle-light are quieter and with several interconnected small rooms a degree of intimacy can easily be achieved. Booking is essential lunchtimes. ***Seats** 70. Parties 16. Private Room 25. L 12-2 D 6.30-9.30. Closed Sat, Sun & all Bank Holidays.* AMERICAN EXPRESS *Access, Diners, Visa.*

SW11 **Buchan's** **£45**

Tel 071-228 0888 **R**

62 Battersea Bridge Road SW11 3AG **Map 19 B6**

The style is French/Scottish, and business at this well-liked local restaurant just south of Battersea Bridge is divided between the wine bar and the restaurant. The two cuisines merge in such dishes as *bouillabaisse écossaise*, beef casserole basquaise and Toulouse sausage with mashed tatties. Elsewhere on the main menu you might find pan-fried pork with chestnuts, salmon fish cakes and vegetarian curry with rice. Sunday lunch is particularly popular. ***Seats** 70. Parties 25. Private Room 55. L 12.15-2.45 D 6-10.45 (Sun 7-10.30). Closed 25 & 26 Dec. Set L (Sun) £9.50/£11.50.* AMERICAN EXPRESS *Access, Diners, Visa.*

SW15 **Buzkash** **£45**

Tel 081-788 0599 **R**

4 Chelverton Road SW15 1RH **Map 17 B5**

A friendly Afghan restaurant off Putney High Street with the same menus and prices as *Caravan Serai*. Specialities include the national dish *ashak* (pasta filled with freshly chopped leek served with minced fillet of lamb and seasoned yoghurt), *poorshuda* (delicately spiced stuffed poussin) and *lugary* (pan-fried king prawns). Courtyard tables in summer. ***Seats** 70. Private Room 20. L 12-3 D 6-11 Closed Sun, 24-26 Dec, Muslim Holidays. Set L from £9.95.* AMERICAN EXPRESS *Access, Diners, Visa.*

W8 **Byblos** **NEW** **£50**

Tel 071-603 4422 **R**

262 Kensington High Street W8 **Map 19 A4**

A dark, intimate restaurant filled with Middle Eastern artefacts. The Lebanese food is simple yet authentic. Good deals for two or more. Very quiet at lunchtime. ***Seats** 45. Meals 12-12. Closed 25 & 26 Dec. Set L & D £9.85.* AMERICAN EXPRESS *Access, Diners, Visa.*

SW1 **Cadogan Hotel** **74%** **£170**

Tel 071-235 7141 Fax 071-245 0994 **H**

75 Sloane Street SW1X 9SG **Map 19 C4**

Acquired in 1990 by Historic House Hotels, the Cadogan was actress Lillie Langtry's home for many years. Oscar Wilde was a regular guest. The panelled drawing room and elegant restaurant are part of its traditional old-fashioned charm. Management pay great attention to offer a personal welcome and service. Guests are automatically upgraded to a better bedroom according to hotel availability. Double bedrooms are large and attractively arranged. Most have sofas. Amenities include colour TV, *See over* trouser press, mini-bar, hairdryer and safe. Double glazing doesn't completely shut out noise from the occasional night-time lorry. Bathrooms are beautifully done out with blue Portuguese tiles. Enquire about the hotel's special rates during the summer, on weekends and during major London shows. ***Rooms** 71.* AMERICAN EXPRESS *Access, Diners, Visa.*

NW1 Café Delancey

£36

Tel 071-387 1985 Fax 071-383 5314

R

3 Delancey Street NW1 7NN

Map 16 C3

Every item on the menu is available throughout opening hours at this popular Continental-style café just off Camden High Street. This could be anything from a croissant with coffee to croque monsieur, an omelette, rack of lamb or superior sausages served with fried onions and rösti. Tables outside in summer. Customers who don't want to eat can enjoy a drink during pub hours (11-11 Mon-Sat, 12-3 & 7-10.30 Sun). ***Seats** 160. Parties 20. Meals 8am-midnight. Closed 25 & 26 Dec, 1 Jan. Access, Visa.*

EC1 Café du Marché

£40

Tel 071-608 1609

R

22 Charterhouse Square Charterhouse Mews EC1M 6AH

Map 16 D3

Tucked away in a mews between Smithfield Market and the Barbican, this former meat warehouse has the feel of a converted country barn. The appealing set menus offer French regional cooking made with fresh products and commendable care to detail. The cheaper set meal (perhaps egg mayonnaise, *boudin noir aux pruneaux* with red wine sauce and cheese or dessert) offers no choice for the first two courses, while the carte (also at a fixed, 3-courses price) extends from fish soup and *terrine de canard et foie gras en brioche* to cassoulet, *cote de boeuf*, a fresh fish dish, *tarte aux fruits* and cheeses. Upstairs, *Le Grenier du Café* is open only for lunch and specialises in grills. Both floors are extremely popular – booking is advisable at lunchtime. ***Seats** 65. Parties 10. Private Room 55. L 12-2.30 D 6-10. Closed L Sat, all Sun, Bank Holidays, Christmas/New Year. Set meals £11 & £19.50. Access, Visa.*

SW1 Café Fish

£55

Tel 071-930 3999

R

39 Panton Street SW1Y 4EA

Map 25 A3

Informal café-restaurant just off Haymarket with a French atmopshere. The menu is more or less all fish from oysters, mussels and squid to bouillabaisse, roast monkfish, fish cakes and Chinese-style sautéed scallops. There's also a small section of vegetarian dishes. Downstairs is a wine bar open from 11.30 to 11 Mon-Sat and serving a simpler selection plus steak and club sandwiches. Convenient for Haymarket theatres and Leicester Square. ***Seats** 90. Parties 30. L 12-3 D 5.45-11.30. Closed L Sat, all Sun, 25 & 26 Dec, 1 Jan.* AMERICAN EXPRESS *Access, Diners, Visa.*

SW7 Café Lazeez NEW

£40

Tel 071-581 9993

R

93 Old Brompton Road SW7 3LD

Map 19 B5

A stark, minimalist-style café next to Christie's South Kensington auction rooms is the unlikely setting from some refined Indian cooking. The menu ranges from traditional dishes like lamb korma, bhindi gosht and chicken tikka via Raj-inspired creations – Indian Welsh rarebit, frontier burger – to self-styled 'Evolved Main Dishes' such as tuna steak (prepared with chilis, cinnamon sticks and ginger), officers' chops (lamb chops marinated in honey and soya) and baked trout (marinated in freshly ground spices and served with a mushroom and Dijon mustard sauce). The main à la carte menu is available from noon-3 and 7-12.30am but a shorter café menu

(11am-7pm) of similar dishes bridges the gap between lunch and dinner. Sunday brings a fixed-price buffet menu. ***Seats** 130. Private Room 60. Meals 11am-12.30am (Sun 10.30am-10.30pm). Closed 25 Dec.* AMERICAN EXPRESS *Access, Diners, Visa.*

WC2 Café Pelican

£55

Tel 071-379 0309 Fax 071-379 0782

R

45 St Martin's Lane WC2N 4EJ

Map 21 B3

Parisian-style bar-brasserie with a wiggly wooden counter and tables on the thronging pavement outside. The bar is open all day for good strong coffee with baguettes, tartines and pastries, salads, platters of meat, steaks with excellent little chips, cheese, pastries and desserts. Also a more elaborate menu served in the large restaurant to the rear, where live music keeps diners happy into the wee small hours (salmon mousseline with crayfish and cognac sauce, grilled lamb steak, calf's liver with red onion compote). French staff cope amiably with the crowds at this really useful pre-and post-theatre spot. ***Seats** 125. Meals 12-12 (Sun to 11). Closed 24-26 Dec. Set D £16.95. Promotional menu £17.50 Pre-theatre menu £9.95/£10.95.* AMERICAN EXPRESS *Access, Visa.*

W1 Café Royal Grill Room ★

£110

Tel 071-439 6320

R

68 Regent Street W1R 6EL

Map 18 D3

Under new management, the Café Royal is starting a new life. Amid the rococo decor, lightly refurbished and more luminous, new hands have many projects and improvements. Chef Herbert Berger, in charge of the menu, skilfully mingles traditional dishes like *escalope de foie gras* with ravioli of celeriac in truffle sauce or tournedos of Scottish beef with shallot confit in a rich claret sauce and a potato and wild mushroom galette, with spanking concoctions like pressed terrine of braised calf's sweetbreads with a spicy coulis of broad beans or breast of free-range chicken and morels and Chablis sweetcorn wafers. More restrained desserts include caramel mousseline with mango compote and lime or caramelised pastry leaves with bitter chocolate, poached pears and Williamine sauce. ***Seats** 55. Parties 30. L 12.30-3 D 6-10.30. Closed L Sat, all Sun, Bank Holidays. Set L from £19.50.* AMERICAN EXPRESS *Access, Diners, Visa.*

NW1 Camden Brasserie

£53

Tel 071-482 2114

R

216 Camden High Street NW1 8QR

Map 16 C3

Busy brasserie with a short menu based around charcoal-grilled meats (all served with terrific little chips) and fresh pasta. Spicy chicken wings and gravad lax with dill mustard sauce are among the starters and there are some excellent salads (spinach and goat's cheese, eel with chorizo and aged vinegar). From the grill come corn-fed chicken, calf's liver, salmon, Toulouse sausages, fillets of lamb and steaks. At 214 (Tel 071-482 0010) is the sister restaurant *The Underground Café* open for dinner Mon-Sat. ***Seats** 110. Parties 20. L 12-3 (Sun 12.30-3.30) D 6-11.30 (Sun 5-10.30). Closed 24-26 & 31 Dec. Access, Visa.*

W10 Canal Brasserie

£50

Tel 081-960 2732

R

Canalot Studios 222 Kensal Road W10 5BN

Map 20 C3

Open only for lunch Monday to Friday and serving a thriving local business community. The canal-side location is an attractive bonus. Large modern artwork reflects a short and simple contemporary menu. ***Seats** 67. L only 12.30-3.30. Closed Sat, Sun & Bank Holidays. Access, Visa.*

SW19 Cannizaro House 76% £138

Tel 081-879 1464 Fax 081-879 7338 H

West Side Wimbledon Common SW19 4UF Map 17 B6

On the edge of Wimbledon Common, a Georgian mansion where the tone is set by stately lawned gardens and the bay-windowed drawing room, which boasts giant flower arrangements, antique furniture, oil paintings and sumptuous seating. Similar elegance is to be found in the restaurant and Queen Elizabeth room, with cream, pale green and pink colour scheme, crystal chandelier, draped curtains and ornate gilt mirror. The bedrooms, each with its own character, are superbly appointed, with top-quality reproduction furniture and bathrooms featuring marble fittings, radio/TV speakers, phones and bathrobes. New-wing rooms are smaller, their views inferior. Reduced rates at weekends; higher rates during the All England Lawn Tennis Championships at the end of June. No children under 8 but 8-16s stay free in parents' room. No dogs. A Thistle Country House Hotel. ***Rooms** 46. Garden.* AMERICAN EXPRESS *Access, Diners, Visa.*

SW10 The Canteen ★ NEW £60

Tel 071-351 7330 R

Harbour Yard Chelsea Harbour SW10 Map 19 B6

Marco Pierre White's undeniable flair has spilled over from *Harveys* to create a stimulating and entertaining restaurant in Chelsea Harbour at agreeably accessible prices. In a light and airy atmosphere, with the bonus of marina views from conservatory window tables and plenty of interior interest as well as a good buzz, the scene is set for chef Stephen Terry to produce an innovative and amusing meal. Drinks are taken in the foyer/bar area where there are just a few tables and seats at the high bar counter; the distinctive playing card decor links this area with the main restaurant. In the large, L-shaped dining rooms on two levels, begin, perhaps, with that breakfast you missed earlier (salade frisée with poached egg, crispy bacon and croutons) or smart baked scallops, cooked and served in the sealed shell to release a wonderful aroma of cinnamon and lemon when opened. And, to follow, how about a cheeky little grilled lobster with garlic butter and chips? Other dishes on the seasonally-changing menus might range from escabèche of red mullet and saffron, bang bang chicken salad, vichyssoise, risottos and spaghetti with pesto or langoustines to guinea fowl with creamed cabbage and pommes Anna, daube of beef with parsnip purée, or cod viennoise with noodles. The choice is diverse, the same menu (changed seasonally) offered for lunch and dinner, desserts delightful (lemon or chocolate tart, tarte tatin of pears, sablé of red fruits, champagne jelly with fresh fruits) and service sometimes decidedly less amusing. A single cheese is plated and served with fine chutney. Wines are sensibly priced with 30 bottles under £20. ***Seats** 150. Parties 12. L 12-3 (12.30-3.30 Sun) D 6.30-12 (7-11 Sun). Access, Visa.*

SE1 Cantina del Ponte NEW £60

Tel 071-403 5403 Fax 071-403 0267 R

Butlers Wharf Building 36C Shad Thames SE1 2YE Map 20 D3

The opportunity for fine weather al fresco dining on a terrace overlooking the Thames is a major plus in this restaurant's favour. Inside rough terracotta tiled floors, simple square maple tables and rush seated chairs create a sunny Mediterranean ambience. The food too follows in being simple, rustic and fashionable. One or two dishes have somewhat mismatched ingredients but overall the concept is a successful one, the smiling staff assisting greatly in this. The Cantina is next to Pont de la Tour. ***Seats** 90. Parties 6. L 12-3 D 6-11. Closed D Sun, 3 days Christmas.* AMERICAN EXPRESS *Access, Diners, Visa.*

SW3 The Capital 81% £235

Tel 071-589 5171 Fax 071-225 0011 **HR**

22-24 Basil Street SW3 1AT **Map 23 D2**

A privately-owned hotel which recently celebrated its 21st anniversary as a self-styled grand hotel in miniature, where elegance and charm make up for the small size of the public rooms. Professional, attentive service is impeccably orchestrated by David Levin. Part of the hotel has been stylishly redecorated by Nina Campbell, although some bedrooms still retain the original homely, traditional feel. Double bedrooms are carefully decorated with fine prints, highly polished furniture and soft lighting. All have a mini-bar and satellite TV. De luxe doubles are better equipped with a safe, trouser press and a guest umbrella. Beds have top-notch Egyptian cotton sheets. Newly redecorated bathrooms are particularly stylish and well appointed. The Eaton and Cadogan rooms on the first floor provide elegant dining/meeting rooms for up to 20/24 guests. Between Sloane Street and Harrods. ***Rooms** 48.* AMERICAN EXPRESS *Access, Diners, Visa.*

Capital Restaurant ★↑ £120

Elegantly refurbished by Nina Campbell, the dining room's intimate proportions feel more like a private dining room than a hotel restaurant. Heavy chintz striped curtains, discreet patterns and peachy tones create a peaceful, muffled atmosphere. Chef Philip Britten serenely supervises his kitchen, visible through lightly tinted glass, while at the front of house service is impeccably handled with discretion and courtesy. Dining is centred on a three-course fixed-price menu with the addition of an extensive selection of dishes, all of which feature supplements to the basic dining price. A spring menu offered tempting sole and tomato soufflé onion soubise, beetroot and chicken liver salad with endive and mushroom oil or duck confit with glazed apples and a Calvados sauce, with typical supplementary offerings of assiette of foie gras, lobster pasta, and baked sea bass with basil and a mousseline of red pimento: a modern French repertoire which highlights freshness and delicate combinations. Everything is not always perfect, but a recent visit was a crescendo meal, commencing poorly but ending with superb lemon cream pudding in a lavender honey sauce with orange and first-rate assorted petits fours. The well-selected wine list is extensive with an interesting choice of half bottles. ***Seats** 35. Parties 24. Private Room. L 12-2.30 D 7-11. Set L £20 & £23 Set D £25 & £37.50.*

SW1 Le Caprice ↑ £70

Tel 071-629 2239 Fax 071-493 9040 **R**

Arlington House Arlington Street SW1A 1RT **Map 18 D3**

A cool, fashionable restaurant in black and white, with David Bailey's classic photographs on the walls. Dishes are sometimes as trendy as the clientele: tomato and basil galette, baked antipasto of vegetables, risotto of butternut squash. Others are nostalgic, like deep-fried cod or eggs Benedict. Sunday brunch pitches off with pitchers of Bucks Fizz or Bloody Mary and swaggers onwards with foie gras, fried egg and wild mushrooms. Booking essential. ***Seats** 80. Parties 8. L 12-3 (Sun to 3.30) D 6-12. Closed D 24 Dec-2 Jan (open L 2 Jan).* AMERICAN EXPRESS *Access, Diners, Visa.*

W1 Caravan Serai £45

Tel 071-935 1208 **R**

50 Paddington Street W1M 3RQ **Map 18 C2**

A sister restaurant to *Buzkash* in Putney, with the same menu and prices. Caravan Serai is a cheerful, relaxed place with authentic Afghan cooking that puts the emphasis more on subtle spices than fiery chili. Among the house recommendations is the national dish *ashak* – pasta filled with leeks served with minced lamb and yoghurt. Note also *istaliffee* – veal on the

See over

bone, fresh tomatoes; *poorshuda* – stuffed poussin; and *lugary* – king prawns dipped in a delicate sauce and pan-fried. ***Seats** 55. Private Room 20. L 12-3 D 6-11 (Sun to 10.30). Closed 24-26 Dec. Set L £9.95.* AMERICAN EXPRESS *Access, Diners, Visa.*

W5 Carnarvon Hotel 58% NEW £125

Tel 081-992 5399 Fax 081-992 7082 **H**

Ealing Common W5 3HN **Map 17 A4**

Motel-style amenities in a functional hotel on the North Circular between Chiswick roundabout and Hangar Lane on Ealing Common. Bedrooms have compact bathrooms en-suite. ***Rooms** 145.* AMERICAN EXPRESS *Access, Diners, Visa.*

SW1 Carriages £45

Tel 071-834 8871 **R**

43 Buckingham Palace Road SW1W 0PP **Map 19 D4**

Pleasant wine bar-bistro, close to Victoria Station, with a smart, well-prepared menu. Specials might include a refreshing tartare of salmon trout, ballotine of chicken with a sage mousse and a vegetarian pepper and mozzarella pancake with cream cheese and basil sauce. ***Seats** 100. Private Room 100. Meals 8am-10.30pm. Closed Sat, Sun, Bank Holidays. Set L & D £9.50.* AMERICAN EXPRESS *Access, Diners, Visa.*

SE6 Casa Cominetti £50

Tel 081-697 2314 **R**

129 Rushey Green SE6 4AA **Map 17 D6**

Italian restaurant with exceptional staying power (it dates back to 1916!). The menu rarely departs from standard dishes, but cooking is consistently enjoyable. ***Seats** 50. L 12-2.30 D 6.30-11. Closed L Sat, all Sun, 25 & 26 Dec.* AMERICAN EXPRESS *Access, Diners, Visa.*

N1 Casale Franco £58

Tel 071-226 8994 **R**

134 Upper Street N1 1PQ **Map 20 C2**

The illuminated chevron sign of a Citroën garage locates the alleyway on Upper Street which opens out into a courtyard with outside tables. The restaurant has a truly authentic rustic decor with rough redbrick walls and a concrete floor. The fact that it looks like an outbuilding is part of its charm. No bookings are taken in the evening so it's best to arrive before 8pm if queues outside are to be avoided, such is the continuing popularity of the place. The food is fairly classic Italian, the staple being pasta with grilled meats, fish and pizzas. The latter are not available lunchtimes or as a single course meal after 8pm. Cooking and presentation can be a little off-hand but flavours are true and the food is, on the whole, enjoyable. ***Seats** 100. Parties 50. Private Room 50. L 12.30-2.30 D 6.30-11.30. Closed L Tue-Thu, all Mon, Bank Holidays, 2 weeks Aug, 1 week Dec. Access, Visa.*

SW16 Caterino's £45

Tel 081-764 6022 **R**

1540 London Road SW16 4EU **Map 17 C6**

Very much a Caterino family affair, with a daughter and Maurizio, the manager, helping Giovanni at front of house and Maria-Grazia in the kitchen of this smart Italian restaurant on the A23 Brighton road, near Norbury BR station. The menu is extensive, with seafood and shellfish (skate, halibut, trout, prawns, Dover sole) a particular speciality on the carte. Daily specials such as chicken wings in a hottish sauce or venison with cherry sauce extend the range and there are simpler but equally well-executed dishes on a choice of economical fixed-price menus. Ample parking space at the rear. Uno Plus is an integral wine bar next door serving a wide selection of simpler fare – from Mediterranean tapas to pasta, pizzas and burgers. ***Seats** 70. L 12-3 D 6-11.30. Closed L Sat & Bank Holidays, all Sun. Set meals £10.50 & £12.50.* AMERICAN EXPRESS *Access, Diners, Visa.*

SW10 Chapter 11 **£50**

Tel 071-351 1683 **R**

47 Hollywood Road SW10 **Map 19 B5**

An informal, busy brasserie off Fulham Road (opposite the new Chelsea & Westminster Hospital) serving a menu that mixes traditional and modern elements: smoked haddock fish cake, melted goat's cheese on chargrilled aubergine, Thai chicken curry, fillet steak béarnaise. In summer tables are set out in the back garden. ***Seats** 60. Private Room 38. D only 6.45-12. Closed Sun, some Bank Holidays, 3 days Christmas.* AMERICAN EXPRESS *Access, Visa.*

NW3 Charles Bernard Hotel 60% **£65**

Tel 071-794 0101 Fax 071-794 0100 **H**

5 Frognal Hampstead NW3 6AL **Map 16 B2**

Just off Finchley Road and well connected by public transport to the West End, this is a 70s' hotel with open-plan day rooms and practical overnight accommodation. Children up to 12 stay free in parents' room. No dogs. ***Rooms** 57.* AMERICAN EXPRESS *Access, Diners, Visa.*

W5 Charlotte's Place **£50**

Tel 081-567 7541 **R**

16 St Matthew's Road W5 3JT **Map 17 A4**

Intimate pink and green restaurant on the edge of Ealing Common (easy parking) serving unpretentious, mainly English fare from haddock smokie pie and salmon hollandaise to Stilton-stuffed breast of chicken in puff pastry and lamb cutlets with redcurrant jelly. ***Seats** 40. Private Room 35. L 12.30-2 D 7.30-10. Closed L Sat, all Sun, Bank Holidays, 1 week Christmas/New Year. Set L £12.50/£14.50.* AMERICAN EXPRESS *Access, Visa.*

SW1 Chelsea Hotel 63% **£155**

Tel 071-235 4377 Fax 071-235 3705 **H**

17-25 Sloane Street SW1X 9NU **Map 19 C4**

A modern Sarova Group hotel close to Knightsbridge underground station, Harrods and many fashion shops. Chief feature of the public areas is a glass-roofed atrium with a polished steel spiral staircase; this runs up to a restaurant and bar whose dominant black decor gives a rather stark look. Food and drink are available at all hours in the lounge. Bedrooms are generally not very roomy, but the expected modern accessories are provided and there's 24hr room service and porterage. One floor of rooms is designated non-smoking. Children up to 14 stay free in parents' room. No dogs. ***Rooms** 225. Hairdressing, coffee shop (7am-2am).* AMERICAN EXPRESS *Access, Diners, Visa.*

NW1 Cheng-Du **£60**

Tel 071-485 8058 **R**

9 Parkway Camden Town NW1 7PG **Map 16 C3**

Friendly Szechuan restaurant next to the Jazz Café at the lower end of Parkway. Among the specialities are braised duck in plum sauce, hot and sour pork and shredded veal with bamboo shoots, carrots and peppers. ***Seats** 70. L 12-2.30 D 6.30-11.30. Set D £17.80. Closed Bank Holidays.* AMERICAN EXPRESS *Access, Visa.*

W1 Chesterfield Hotel 70% £190

Tel 071-491 2622 Fax 071-491 4793 **H**

35 Charles Street W1X 8LX **Map 18 C3**

Courteous staff go out of their way to help you at this very English, very charming hotel close to Berkeley Square. The site is that of the grand Palladian mansion which the third Earl of Chesterfield built in the 18th century. A splendid old chandelier, a huge leather chesterfield and leather buttonback chairs set the tone in the foyer and a pianist enlivens the evenings in the dark-coloured, English club-style bar. By contrast, the Terrace is a light, cheerful, modern room full of plants where you can take a late breakfast, a snack or a full meal. The bedrooms are comfortably appointed with sturdy good taste, using bold fabrics and darkwood furniture; Executive Club members get extra service such as shoe cleaning, secretarial facilities and complimentary newspaper; there are also several suites. No dogs. ***Rooms 110.*** AMERICAN EXPRESS *Access, Diners, Visa.*

N4 Chez Liline £45

Tel 071-263 6550 **R**

101 Stroud Green Road Finsbury Park N4 3PX **Map 16 C2**

Sister to *La Gaulette*, this Mauritian restaurant offers a long, exclusively fishy menu that could include parrot fish, red snapper, bourgeois (served meunière with mango and orange, or in a creamy peppercorn sauce) and vacoa with aïoli or tamarind. Assiette Créole is a selection of tropical fish with tomatoes, herbs and chili. Lobsters and prawns are other specialities. ***Seats 50.*** *Set D from £12.75. L 12.30-3 D 6.30-11. Closed Bank Holidays.* AMERICAN EXPRESS *Access, Visa.*

W11 Chez Moi £70

Tel 071-603 8267 **R**

1 Addison Avenue Holland Park W11 4QS **Map 17 B4**

Plush, quiet and discreet, Chez Moi has stood the test of time. The menu, once more or less confined to the French classics, now ventures further afield, especially on the short set lunch menu (where you might find Thai-style chicken salad or chakchuka – a Tunisian vegetable stew). Traditionalists might opt for *sole meunière, carré d'agneau* or *tournedos béarnaise*. Chocolate truffle cake made with brandy and Benedictine is among the wicked desserts. Fine value three-course lunches, with a small choice. Decent wine list at a fair price with plenty of half bottles. ***Seats 45.*** *Parties 15. L 12.30-2 D 7-11. Closed L Sat, all Sun, Bank Holidays, 1 week Christmas. Set L £14.* AMERICAN EXPRESS *Access, Diners, Visa.*

> Never leave money, credit cards or valuables lying around in your hotel room. Use the hotel safe or the mini-safe in your room.

W1 Chez Nico at Ninety Park Lane ★★★↑ £135

Tel 071-409 1290 Fax 071-355 4877 **R**

90 Park Lane London W1A 3AA **Map 18 C3**

It is over a year since Nico Ladenis and his team of chefs headed by Paul Flynn moved into *Grosvenor House* at 90 Park Lane and the full tables show that the venture has been an unqualified success. Jean-Luc Giguel orchestrates the exemplary standards of service in an elegantly appointed, opulent dining room with honey-coloured panelling brightened by mirrors and discreet lighting. There are those who believe Nico reached the zenith of his personal, highly individual style of creativity during his all too brief sojourn at Shinfield. Since that time he as continued to evolve, albeit not at the same pace. More recently there has been a reworking of the earlier creations simplifying but also subtly redefining and refining them. There has also been a marked and stated return to the classic repertoire. His sensational signature dishes remain as in a salad of foie gras on toasted brioche with caramelised orange – a dish of unsurpassable eminence, 'boudin blanc' with caramelised apples – a moist veal, pork, chicken and foie gras sausage, and shin of veal on the bone braised in Madeira. In addition a few very much simpler dishes have been incorporated including, "for the lighter eater", plain melon and grilled Dover sole on the bone with tartare sauce, and even plain grilled steak. Dishes from the classic repertoire include terrine of foie gras flavoured with Sauternes and green peppercorns and tournedos of Scotch beef Rossini – a true and accurate interpretation – the thick slice of fillet sitting on a brioche croute and topped with pan-fried medallions of foie gras with slices of truffle and a superb demi-glace. Not that invention has taken a back seat with such new dishes, generally following lighter, healthier disciplines, as a Japanese-influenced dish of crispy salmon fingers 'Teriyaki' with plum sauce, an escalope of brill studded with tiny croutons on a bed of sweet shallots or breast of guinea fowl stuffed with its own liver and served with grapes and little herb ravioli. A magnificent climax to a truly unforgettable meal is the grand plate of assorted mini-desserts – a tasting of many of the desserts including a slice of chocolate tart with orange-flavoured custard, honey ice cream with gratinated grapefruit, lemon tart with lemon sorbet and raspberry sauce and iced nougat with caramelised nuts. Cutting corners is not in Nico's repertoire – all sauces, for example, are based on veal stock, ensuring quality and consistency. Nico is a man dedicated to a quest for perfection and a meal here amply demonstrates that he is achieving his goal. ***Seats** 60. Private Room 20. L 12-2 D 7-11. Closed L Sat, all Sun, 10 days Christmas/New Year. Set L £25 Set D £42 (2 courses).*

W3 **Chi Mai** **£35**

Tel 081-992 3160 **R**

2 The Broadway Gunnersbury Lane W3 **Map 17 A4**

Szechuan and Peking cooking in a cool, tall-ceilinged restaurant next to Acton Town underground station. Specialities include salt-baked baby squid, wun tun, venison village style and several ways with tofu. ***Seats** 100. L 12-2.30 D 6-12. Set L from £9.50 Set D from £13.* AMERICAN EXPRESS *Access, Diners, Visa.*

W1 **Chiang Mai** **£40**

Tel 071-437 7444 **R**

48 Frith Street W1V 5TE **Map 21 A2**

Vatcharin Bhumichitr, author of *The Taste of Thailand* and *Thai Vegetarian Cooking*, runs this Thai restaurant next door to Alastair Little's eponymous restaurant and Ronnie Scott's jazz club. The menu runs from satay, tempura and soups to hot and sour salads flavoured with lemon and chili and good-value, one-dish rice and noodle dishes. Vegetarians are well catered for. ***Seats** 56. Private Room 25. L 12-3 D 6-11. Closed L Sun and Bank Holidays. Set meals from £18.* AMERICAN EXPRESS *Access, Visa.*

NW1 **China Jazz** **£70**

Tel 071-482 3940 **R**

29-31 Parkway NW1 7PN **Map 16 C3**

Drumsticks meet chopsticks in a cool, contemporary setting on busy Parkway. Jazz (live every evening, late at weekends) accompanies fairly expensive Chinese food cooked without additives, preservatives, artificial colouring or much finesse. Valet parking. ***Seats** 90. Parties 90. L 12.30-3 (Sun 1-5) D 6.30-12 (Fri & Sat 7.30-2am Sun 7.30-11). Closed L Sat.* AMERICAN EXPRESS *Access, Visa.*

W14 Chinon ↑

£100

Tel 071-602 5968

R

25 Richmond Way Shepherds Bush W14 0AS

Map 17 B4

The move (just one door along) and the addition of a wine bar (open Monday to Saturday for lunch and dinner) have widened the scope of this fine little restaurant tucked behind Shepherds Bush. The basement dining room is quite simple in its appointments, its walls hung with motley paintings (some for sale) and its windows opening on to a paved garden. Jonathan Hayes' style does not, from an early visit, seem to have changed much, nor his menus – a short but sufficient choice of dishes that use raw materials of impeccable quality and freshness. 'Diver-caught scallops' sound as precious as pearls and are priced more or less accordingly. They're also handled very carefully, beautifully and lightly cooked, with a suitably delicate leek sauce. A small starting portion was pushed to the periphery of the plate by a large, squat cushion of cabbage filled with chopped leeks, an accessory which was neither necessary nor apt, and which virtually relegated the scallops from a starring to a support role. More cabbage and kindred greens made appearances: a single stalk (an odd touch this) lying athwart a bowl of fresh clams in a thickish mushroom sauce; as a wrapper for halibut – the fish carefully cooked but accompanied by a slightly too powerful (pesto) sauce; and as another cushion, this one a container for mashed potato, one of the 'plated accompaniments' of a fine dish of squab and foie gras in a rich, well-constructed sauce (the other was a Savoy cabbage parcel containing chopped greenery and bacon). Crab ravioli – in fact just one, and draped insouciantly on the plate like an unmade bed of lasagne sheets – was decorated with a couple of clams in their shells and some wisps of dried mushrooms; the sauce with this dish, a deliciously rich saffron butter, was much more in harmony. The signature dessert is a plate of eight or more assorted sorbets, ices, creams, tarts and fruits – an appealing palette that provides a cool and colourful finale. ***Seats** 36. Restaurant D only 7-11. Closed Mon, most Bank Holidays, last week Aug.* American Express *Access, Visa.*

W4 Christian's

£55

Tel 081-995 0382

R

Station Parade Burlington Lane W4 3HD

Map 17 A5

The attractive decor of light blue striped wallpaper covered with carefully selected prints, the green plants, the sparkling clean tiled kitchen visible from the dining room and the overwhelming welcome all contribute to the charm of Christian Gustin's homely restaurant. A limited selection on the menu ensures freshness. King prawn chowder, Cheddar and tomato soufflé, steamed salmon with aubergine and peppers, poached corn-fed chicken with a tarragon cream sauce are unpretentious, precisely executed dishes. Desserts might include an airy chocolate mousse cake. ***Seats** 42. Parties 18. L Sun 12.30-2.30 otherwise by arrangement D 7.30-10.30. Closed D Sun, all Mon, Bank Holidays, 25 & 26 Dec. Set D £15.50. Access, Visa.*

WC2 Christopher's

£80

Tel 071-240 4222

R

18 Wellington Street Covent Garden WC2E 7DD

Map 17 C4

A grand Victorian building which in 1863 became the first licensed casino in London. Today, a sweeping stone staircase leads past reception (reservations are a must) up to a lofty, tall-windowed dining room resplendent in its stylishly ultra-modern interpretation of neo-classical decor. Criticisms voiced in last year's guide have now been dispelled, the menu offering a very successful and enjoyable blend of modern American and Mediterranean cooking. Goat's cheese mousseline – hot, light and fluffy – comes with a balsamic vinegar and virgin olive oil dressing, citrus-cured gravad lax is served with griddled corn cake and sour cream; a fat salmon fish cake has fiery harissa and a cooling watercress salad; carpetbag steak – a good thick piece of tender fillet – has fresh rock oysters at its heart; grilled swordfish with red pepper and rosemary mayonnaise, a 3lb Maine lobster (for 2), New York strip steak and even a hamburger are also typical and all are available with separately priced vegetables. Sweets too have an American slant with the likes of Key lime pie, New York cheesecake and pecan pie. Pre-theatre menu and now open for Sunday brunch. ***Seats** 100. Parties 32. Private Room 32. L 12-3 (Sun brunch 11.30-2.30) D 6-11.30. Closed L Sat, all Sun, Bank Holidays.* AMERICAN EXPRESS *Access, Diners, Visa.*

W1 Chuen Cheng Ku

£35

Tel 071-734 3281

R

17 Wardour Street W1V 3HD

Map 21 A2

Vast Chinese restaurant on several floors serving a long selection of Cantonese dishes. The popular daytime choice is dim sum, served from little wagons which ply between the kitchen and the tables. ***Seats** 400. Private Room 50. Meals 11.30am-11.45pm. Closed 24 & 25 Dec. Set meals from £18 for 2.* AMERICAN EXPRESS *Access, Diners, Visa.*

W1 Churchill Inter-Continental

£242

Tel 071-486 5800 Fax 071-486 1255

HR

30 Seymour Street Portman Square W1A 4ZX

Map 18 C2

The Churchill is now part of Inter-Continental hotels, and as we went to press wasundergoing complete refurbishment. Bedrooms and bathrooms will have a new decorative style though their comfort and accessories will stay at their traditionally high levels: air-conditioning, multi channel-TV, mini-bars and 24h room service. One complete floor of rooms is designated non-smoking. No changes are envisaged to the look of the restaurant (now called Clementines), where Idris Caldora, newly appointed executive chef, introduced his Mediterranean menu in the autumn of 1993. The hotel was graded at 80% in our 1993 Guide. ***Rooms** 414. Portman Square garden, business centre (9am-6pm Mon-Fri), beauty & hair salon, coffee shop (7am-1am), news kiosk, theatre desk, children's play area, garage.* AMERICAN EXPRESS *Access, Diners, Visa.*

SW10 Chutney Mary ↑

£60

Tel 071-351 3113 Fax 071-351 7694

R

535 Kings Road SW10 0SZ

Map 19 B6

Almost on the corner of Kings Road and Lots Road, Chutney Mary describes itself as the world's first Anglo-Indian restaurant. Behind a nondescript modern facade, it's a roomy, attractive place with Raj pictures on pale walls, mirrored alcoves and a jungly glazed conservatory. The menu is like no other, with dishes based on recipes of the Memsahibs: curried mango and yoghurt soup, lamb's liver in a sauce of pepper, cumin and onions served on toast, Bangalore bangers and mash, grilled bream Madras-style. There are also "Unabashedly Indian" dishes such as chicken Korma and roghan josh, plus vegetarian main dishes. Everything is home-made, and the food is miles away from standard Indian and a great deal more interesting. Desserts include a spicy 'Hill Station' version of bread-and-butter pudding with pistachio and cashew nuts, spices and Madeira. Sunday sees a grand buffet for both lunch and dinner. The colonial-style Verandah Bar at street level serves drinks, snacks and light meals, plus the restaurant menu in the evening. ***Seats** 115. Parties 12. L 12.30-2.30 (Sun to 3) D 7-11.30 (Sun to 10). Closed Sun for bar food. Set L from £10.25.* AMERICAN EXPRESS *Access, Diners, Visa.*

Set menu prices may not always include service or wine.

W14 Cibo £65

Tel 071-371 6271 **R**

3 Russell Gardens W14 8EZ **Map 17 B4**

Cibo means food in Italian, and here it's served on huge, colourful plates which match the paintings for exuberance. Italian regional cuisine finds a contemporary expression in dishes like sautéed chicken and duck livers with onions and balsamic vinegar, wide noodles pressed with rocket in scallop and red mullet sauce, and grilled sole with lemon-flavoured spinach. ***Seats*** *55. Parties 12. Private Room 16. L 12-2.30 D 7-11. Closed 24-26 Dec, 1 Jan. Set L £10.* AMERICAN EXPRESS *Access, Diners, Visa.*

W1 Claridge's 88% £304

Tel 071-629 8860 Fax 071-499 2210 **HR**

Brook Street W1A 2JQ **Map 18 C3**

"We strive for excellence" is Claridge's motto, a heraldic escutcheon surmounted by a crown is the emblem of this, one of the world's great hotels, and one that is much favoured by foreign royalty and heads of states. Established almost 100 years ago the hotel is synonymous with classic elegance, grace and dignity which characterise every aspect. From the imposing front entrance to its numerous magnificent suites, to the lilting strains of a Hungarian quartet that plays in the foyer at lunchtime and in the evening, to the very handsomely liveried, discreet and attentive staff, Claridge's marries the calm and tranquillity of the past with modern comforts. The Front Hall with a wide, sweeping staircase and black and white marble floor, cleaved to a literally mirror-like shine, has been refurbished to its original art deco splendour. There is no bar proper but footmen in scarlet breeches, white hose and gold-braided tail coats are constantly on hand. The Reading Room, a softly-lit lounge, is dominated by a portrait of Mrs William Claridge, the hotel's founder. It is here that sedate afternoon teas are served. A significant part of the hotel was added in 1932 to include the ballroom and many of the bedrooms. These are all furnished and decorated in a distinctive art deco style, each retaining irreplaceable original furnishings and fittings. The remaining bedrooms contrast in being more traditional in character and ambience featuring fine plaster mouldings and beautiful period furniture. Modern influences include satellite TVs but thankfully little else has changed over the years. Bathrooms, throughout are magnificent, marble clad and boasting probably the best showers in London with sunflower-size shower heads, many also with additional shoulder showers. Standards of service are exemplary with room buttons to summon maid, valet or floor waiter. For room service breakfast there is no menu but a waiter will discuss and comply with all individual requirements. Gentlemen have the use of the Bath and Racquets Club adjoining the hotel while ladies can visit the Berkeley Hotel's Health Club roof-top swimming pool and gymnasium. ***Rooms*** *190. Valeting, hair salon.* AMERICAN EXPRESS *Access, Diners, Visa.*

Restaurant £130

The opulent and magnificent art deco room was originally designed by Basil Ionides in 1926 and now features a new and fabulous mirrored mural by Christopher Ironside as well as a new terrace off which is the Orangery. The latter accommodates up to 14 guests privately. In such elegant and very formal surroundings *maitre chef des cuisines* Marjan Lesnik offers a suitably classical French menu now with an emphasis on more modern interpretation and presentation. The three-course set menus represent good value as, though simpler in concept still use luxury ingredients as in mousseline of smoked salmon with pink champagne and roast quail with goose liver and truffle. From the à la carte come starters such as lobster salad with mango and lime, potted wild salmon sausage with aromatic jelly or small lobster and crab fritters encasing a quail's egg, accompanied by a simple dressed salad and herby mayonnaise. Scallops with pastry, herbs and spinach with mild garlic; lobster fricassee with cardamom and couscous;

wild salmon medallions with leeks and asparagus and seared sea bass with fried vegetables and aromatic vinaigrette feature as innovative but expensive fish dishes. Meat offerings include pot-roasted guinea fowl with black pudding ballotine, fillet of new season lamb with minted vegetables and celery sauce or tournedos of beef with a mushroom sauce and sun-dried tomatoes. Vegetables are straightforward and simple. Sweets, from a beautifully presented trolley, are enjoyable. Indeed, the cooking, as a whole, can most aptly be described as enjoyable. Service runs as smoothly as the trolley. Dinner dances are now held on Friday and Saturday nights. ***Seats** 120. Parties 14. Private Room 14. L 12.30-3 D 7-11. Closed L Sat. Set L & D from £24.*

The Causerie £85

The fixed-price lunchtime smörgåsbord is still the main attraction here. Simple pre-and post-theatre suppers are served from 5.30-7.30pm and 10.15-11pm. A la carte dinner is offered throughout the evening, ranging from spinach salad with warm chicken livers or glazed quail eggs in creamed smoked haddock to seared sea bass with fennel and Tuscan puréed potatoes, straightforward grills and lamb cutlets Reform. ***Seats** 40. Parties 8. L 12-3 D 5.30-11 (Sun from 7). Closed Sat. Set meals from £16.*

W8 Clarke's ★ £88

Tel 071-221 9225 Fax 071-229 4564 **R**

124 Kensington Church Street W8 4BH **Map 18 A3**

Sally Clarke and Elizabeth Payne's praiseworthy cooking is invariably interesting and inventive, but, although constantly changing, intentionally limited on a day-to-day basis, thus keeping her standards consistently high. The chargrill is still the most important aspect of the kitchen, where the mix of influences ranges from the Mediterranean to California, off to the Far East and back, producing wonderful dishes – perhaps potted crab with wild salmon, baby spinach and toasts followed by grilled breast of corn-fed chciken with cracked-wheat salad, rocket and basil-roasted aubergine and peppers, finishing with apricot and bitter almond wafer tartlet with vanilla ice cream. Both menus and dishes are always carefully thought out, perfectly presented and rarely, if ever, repeated. Lunchtime sees a two- or three-course menu with a choice of three dishes per course, while a no-choice, four-course affair is offered in the evening. Cheeses are served in prime condition with home-made oatmeal biscuits and grapes, fennel or celery. Puddings, typically, might be strawberry and tayberry floating island or baked purple fig in red wine with chilled zabaglione. Dinner menus change daily but are advertised by the week; however, Clarke's' popularity makes it essential to book and almost impossible to choose a fancied menu with only a few days' notice. The ground-floor dining room is more formal, while downstairs (where the kitchen is open to view) is more vibrant, particularly when full; an open, airy feel belies the fact that it is a basement room. Vegetarians should advise in advance. *& Clarke's*, next door, provides all the superb baking. A no-nonsense wine list, naturally strong in Californian wines, has something for everyone; good choice of wines by the glass. Menu prices include service, coffee and truffle. ***Seats** 90. Parties 10. L 12.30-2 D 7-10. Closed Sat & Sun, Bank Holidays, 2 weeks Aug, 1 weekXmas, 4 days Easter. Set L £22/£26 Set D £37. Access, Visa.*

W1 The Clifton-Ford 73% £196

Tel 071-486 6600 Fax 071-486 7492 **H**

47 Welbeck Street W1M 8DN **Map 18 C2**

60s-built hotel with conference facilities (max 120) and a handy location for the shops of Oxford Street. Day rooms are particularly good, especially the lounge, which has almost a country house atmosphere. The bar feels more masculine and clubby. Bedrooms, each floor with its own colour scheme, include some roomy studio suites. The hotel's refurbishment was completed with the new restaurant, Doyles. ***Rooms** 212.* AMERICAN EXPRESS *Access, Diners, Visa.*

NW3 Clive Hotel 64% **£64**

Tel 071-586 2233 Fax 071-586 1659 **H**

Primrose Hill Road NW3 3NA **Map 16 C3**

Modern Hilton-owned hotel on the fringes of Hampstead, between Swiss Cottage and Chalk Farm. Children up to 12 free in parents' room. Free car park. Versatile conference facilities for up to 350. ***Rooms** 96.*
AMERICAN EXPRESS *Access, Diners, Visa.*

W2 Coburg Resort 60% **£122**

Tel 071-221 2217 Fax 071-229 0557 **H**

129 Bayswater Road W2 4RJ **Map 18 A3**

Recently acquired by Resort Hotels, the Coburg is going through major refurbishment. Lobby and bar have an attractive Regency feel. Bedrooms are irregular in size but offer adequate comfort. Bathrooms are small but elegant. The top-floor suite has a magnificent view of London. ***Rooms** 132.*
AMERICAN EXPRESS *Access, Diners, Visa.*

SW1 Collin House **£54**

Tel 071-730 8031 **H**

104 Ebury Street SW1W 9QD **Map 19 C5**

Privately-owned bed and breakfast hotel in a mid-Victorian town house just minutes from Victoria railway and coach stations. Most rooms have their own shower and WC. Good cooked breakfasts. No dogs. ***Rooms** 13.*
Closed 2 weeks Christmas. No credit cards.

W9 Colonnade Hotel 60% **£80**

Tel 071-286 1052 Fax 071-286 1057 **H**

2 Warrington Crescent W9 1ER **Map 18 A2**

Close to Warwick Avenue underground station in residential Little Venice, the Victorian grade-two listed building offers a friendly welcome and comfortable accommodation. Best of the bedrooms are the suites and four-poster rooms, all recently refurbished; some bathrooms have been done in marble, some have spa baths. Unrenovated rooms need attention too, though they are quite big and comfortable. Family owned and run; guests are well taken care of and the management is happy to deal with children.
***Rooms** 49.* AMERICAN EXPRESS *Access, Visa.*

W2 Columbia Hotel **£55**

Tel 071-402 0021 Fax 071-706 4691 **H**

95 Lancaster Gate W2 3NS **Map 18 B3**

Returning guests provide much of the business at a privately-owned hotel facing Hyde Park 400 yards west of Lancaster Gate underground station. Reasonably priced bedrooms (many with park views), roomy lounge and cocktail bar. Several function rooms, maximum capacity 120 for banquets, 200 for theatre-style conferences. ***Rooms** 102.* AMERICAN EXPRESS *Access, Visa.*

SW5 Concord Hotel **£60**

Tel 071-370 4151 **H**

155 Cromwell Road SW5 0TQ **Map 19 A5**

Bed and breakfast hotel with some family-size bedrooms. Situated on the main road west to the airport, handy for Earls Court, Olympia and the South Kensington museums. Unlicensed. ***Rooms** 40.* AMERICAN EXPRESS *Access, Visa.*

W1 Concorde Hotel NEW **£84**

Tel 071-402 6169 Fax 071-724 1184 **H**

50 Great Cumberland Place W1H 7FD **Map 18 C2**

Next door to the *Bryanston Court Hotel* and under the same ownership, it offers cheaper accommodation with colour TV tea/coffee facilities, hair dryer, brand new bathrooms and a friendly welcome. ***Rooms*** *27.* *Closed 1 week Christmas.* AMERICAN EXPRESS *Access, Diners, Visa.*

W1 The Connaught 91% **£278**

Tel 071-499 7070 Fax 071-495 3262 **HR**

Carlos Place W1Y 6AL **Map 18 C2**

Built in 1897, the Connaught was opened as a London home for the landed gentry; today's guests may be more cosmopolitan but the gentlemanly atmosphere remains. You will never be asked for an imprint of your credit card on arrival, for example, or to sign for anything – a less risky policy than it may sound as 85% of guests at any one time will have stayed here before and most will be known by name to the long-serving staff. It's just one of the things that makes this a very special hotel. Day rooms, from which business meetings are banned in the interests of tranquillity, are grand in style but not in scale, with a clubby, oak-panelled, leather-seated bar and elegant lounges. Traditionally furnished bedrooms, some with antiques, are individually decorated in an English country style with a variety of fine fabrics from floral chintzes to restrained damasks. Rooms are not cluttered with such things as fax machines or mini-bars (although each of the 24 suites' sitting rooms has an antique chinoiserie cocktail cabinet), but these, and anything else within reason, are available on request and the next time you stay here you will find that they will have remembered such requirements and any other personal preferences. A guest who is known to have failing eyesight, for example, may not be consciously aware that the light bulbs have been changed for brighter ones. Only 30 or so rooms have air-conditioning and consommé is the only hot food on the overnight room service menu; but major pluses are the luxurious bathrobes, fine linen bedding and exemplary service throughout. Own charged parking. No printed brochure or tariff is produced, but prices are, almost unbelievably, competitive. A fine, grand hotel with commendable old-fashioned values. ***Rooms*** *90.* AMERICAN EXPRESS *Access, Diners, Visa.*

Restaurant & Grill Room ★★ £160

Not one restaurant, but two, sharing an identical à la carte menu. Highly polished panelling features in the formal restaurant, while the sage-green Grill Room is warmer and more intimate. That a large portrait of Auguste Escoffier hangs in the kitchen is the clue to the classical French carte, printed in French without translations; there are a few exceptions (Irish stew and braised gammon California) including regular daily-changing luncheon dishes like boiled silverside (Thurs) or *coulibiac de saumon* and oxtail (both Fri). Specialities, to ordered in advance, include *zéphirs de sole "tout Paris", noisettes d'agneau Edward VII* and *filet d'Angus farci en croute strasbourgeoise.* The genius of chef Michel Bourdin is the way in which he interprets the dishes with lighter, more refined sauces without changing their essential, unashamedly old-fashioned character. Finish with traditional British savouries such as Scotch woodcock (or 'champignons sur toast'), or head for the list of mixed classical French (*peche Escoffier, soufflé aux liqueurs*) and homely (sherry trifle, bread-and-butter pudding) desserts. Fixed-price meals offer tremendous value, given the surroundings (and the à la carte prices). Service is very traditional with a myriad of waiters organised in an elaborate hierarchy but tempered by an innate and entirely appropriate friendliness. The way fresh tablecloths are put on the tables after the main course, without causing so much as a ripple in the conversation around the table, is a minor miracle, performed nightly. This is *ancien régime* par excellence, an experience not to be missed. Only France

See over

(many classic names), Germany and Italy are represented on the wine list, and for such a grand establishment prices are not too outrageous. No smoking. Not suitable for any children under 6 years of age. ***Seats*** *Restaurant 75. Grill Room 35. Parties 10. Private Room 22. L 12.30-2 D 6.30 (Grill from 6)-10.30. Set L £25 (£30 Sun) Set D (Grill only) £35. Grill Room closed weekends & Public Holidays.*

SW10 Hotel Conrad 85% £225

Tel 071-823 3000 Fax 071-351 6525 **H**

Chelsea Harbour SW10 0XG **Map 19 B6**

The design of this purpose-built, curving building puts one in mind of a great ocean liner of the 1930s, especially with its long deck-like terrace (where an outdoor barbecue is set up in summer) overlooking the boats and distinctive apartment block of Chelsea Harbour Marina. Free from traffic noise, the suites (there are no ordinary rooms here) all have a lobby insulating them from the corridor and this makes them even more peaceful than one might expect. Designed by David Hicks, with limed-oak furniture and soft colour schemes, the air-conditioned suite rooms offer every modern comfort: twin wardrobes; three telephones with two lines; multi-channel TVs with videos; a mini-bar and many little extras – from fresh fruit and flowers to magazines, books, suit-carriers, bathrobes and even an umbrella. Marble bathrooms are particularly luxurious with shower cubicles in addition to deep tubs, twin washbasins, bidets and separate loos. Many suites also have a guest loo off the lobby and many boast a terrace with table and chairs (the best have views of the marina). Marble-floored public areas have a cool, spacious feel and numerous smartly-dressed staff offer a high standard of service throughout, including excellent room service. Modern function facilities for up to 200. ***Rooms** 160. Indoor swimming pool, sauna, solarium, steam room, gymnasium.* AMERICAN EXPRESS *Access, Diners, Visa.*

W8 The Copthorne Tara 69% £114

Tel 071-937 7211 Fax 071-937 7100 **H**

Scarsdale Place Kensington W8 5SR **Map 19 A4**

Extensive renovations have maintained standards throughout this modern 12-storey hotel, well-sited in a fairly quiet cul de sac conveniently close to Kensington High Street. Thoughtfully furnished rooms, ranging from 'Classic' singles to suites, include non-smoking rooms and facilities for disabled guests, all with efficient air-conditioning and electronic controls on lighting and other facilities. Improvements to the extensive banqueting/conference areas (for up to 500 guests) will complete the refurbishment programme. ***Rooms** 825. Café.* AMERICAN EXPRESS *Access, Diners, Visa.*

EC2 Corney & Barrow £80

Tel 071-638 9308 **R**

109 Old Broad Street EC2N 1AP **Map 20 C1**

Two identical doorways from the street – on the right leading into a long, narrow wine bar, on the left into a tiny vestibule and a dark staircase descending into a small, rectangular room whose walls are clothed in bottle-green fabric. High-back armchairs also in bottle green, bottle-green carpet and mahogany woodwork all create a distinctive club-like ambience. The walls are hung with 7 large cartoons of City worthies who are regular customers. The location, a stone's throw from the Stock Exchange, has all the hushed formality of a directors' dining room. Prices too, tend to be geared to top earners' pockets. Chef Lorcan Cribbin offers a menu of high calibre dishes with modern influences present as a subtle understatement. There's a careful blending of textures and flavours with light saucing – nothing to detract too greatly from the business probably being conducted here or later in the afternoon. Quiet efficient service from young waitresses. Jackets and ties are required. ***Seats** 28. Parties 8. L only 11.30-3.30. Closed Sat & Sun, Bank Holidays. Set L from £19.95.* AMERICAN EXPRESS *Access, Diners, Visa.*

EC4 Corney & Barrow £60

Tel 071-248 1700 **R**

44 Cannon Street EC4N 6JJ **Map 20 C2**

Fairly modern premises with a lively bar on the ground floor and an alcoved restaurant in the basement. A TV monitor keeps the largely City clientele in touch with the latest FT Index. An uninspired choice of either 2 or 3 courses ranges from the likes of avocado mousse with dressed prawns to crab fish cakes and fillets of lamb with mint béarnaise. Fast, efficient and friendly service. ***Seats** 55. Parties 12. L only 11.30-3. Closed Sat, Sun & Bank Holidays. Set L £16.95/£21.95.* AMERICAN EXPRESS *Access, Diners, Visa.*

W8 Costa's Grill £25

Tel 071-229 3794 **R**

12-14 Hillgate Street W8 7SR **Map 18 A3**

Attic food at basement prices. Moussaka, stifado and kleftiko typify the robust Greek fare that has kept Costa's Grill so popular since 1951, but charcoal-grilled fish also has a large following. A few outside tables on a rear patio in summer. Almost next door is Costa's fish and chip shop. ***Seats** 70. Private Room 25. L 12.30-2.30 D 5-10.30. Closed Sun, Bank Holidays, 4 weeks Aug/Sep. No credit cards.*

W2 Craven Gardens Hotel £66

Tel 071-262 3167 Fax 071-262 2083 **H**

16 Leinster Terrace W2 3ES **Map 18 B3**

Comfortable, well-kept bed and breakfast hotel just off Bayswater Road, handy for Hyde Park, British Rail Paddington, London Underground stations and the cosmopolitan appeal of Queensway. No dogs. ***Rooms** 43.* AMERICAN EXPRESS *Access, Diners, Visa.*

SW10 La Croisette ↑ £80

Tel 071-373 3694 **R**

168 Ifield Road SW10 9AF **Map 19 A6**

Once you have negotiated the tricky spiral staircase down to the dining room you can soak in the evocative South of France decor. Consistency is the watchword here, with little changing over the years. The fixed-price menu still represents unusually good value for money, providing a glass of kir, nibbles, two fish courses, Stilton and salad, plus dessert and coffee. Highlights of the carte remain the seafood platter – a cornucopia of crab, oysters, mussels, clams, langoustines and winkles – and fish served plain-grilled or with classic sauces. A handful of lamb and contrefilet dishes complete the picture. No longer open at lunchtime. ***Seats** 55. D only 7-11.30. Closed Sun, Mon. Set menu £18/£30.* AMERICAN EXPRESS *Access, Diners, Visa.*

See the Conference and Banqueting section for lists of hotels arranged by county.

SW14 Crowthers £65

Tel 081-876 6372 R

481 Upper Richmond Road West SW14 7PU Map 17 A5

A small neighbourhood restaurant where the traditional Bordeaux decor and darkwood furniture will never be in or out of fashion. Like the decor, the cooking is safe. A well-priced set menu might offer shiitake mushroom parcels with wild mushroom sauce, grilled aubergine with tomato, feta and pesto, confit of duck with flageolets, bacon and garlic, halibut with yoghurt, lime and ginger. Some dishes might be more satisfying than others, but the overall impression is of good value for money. ***Seats** 32. L 12-2 D 7-10.45. Closed L Mon & Sat, all Sun, Bank Holidays. Set L £12.50/£15.50 Set D £14.50/£19. Access, Visa.*

W1 Cumberland Hotel 69% £140

Tel 071-262 1234 Fax 071-724 4621 H

Marble Arch W1A 4RF Map 18 C3

London's second largest hotel is at the Marble Arch end of Oxford Street, overlooking Speakers' Corner. An impressive octagonal central lobby has bright red columns, white marble and a large floral display as its focal point, from where four restaurants (including a carvery – where children under 5 eat free – and *Mon* Japanese restaurant) and three bars lead. Bedrooms are spacious, well maintained and attractive with pleasant matching fabrics and good darkwood furniture. A variety of conference and banqueting suites cater for 475/560. Children under 16 free in their parents' room. No dogs. Forte. ***Rooms** 890. News kiosk, coffee shop (6.30am-midnight).* AMERICAN EXPRESS *Access, Diners, Visa.*

SW15 Dan Dan NEW £50

Tel 081-780 1953 R

333 Putney Bridge Road SW15 Map 17 B5

Just off the bridge end of Putney High Street, an unpretentious Japanese restaurant offering good-value lunches based around one main dish (plus miso soup, appetiser and fresh fruit) and a wider choice of Japanese classics in the evening. Good fresh sushi and kaiseki dinners with hors d'oeuvre chosen from a trolley. ***Seats** 70. Parties 20. Private Room 20. L 12-2.30 D 6.30-10. Closed L Sun, all Mon, 25 & 26 Dec, 1 Jan. Set L from £6.50 Set D from £18. Access, Visa.*

SW3 Dan's £60

Tel 071-352 2718 R

119 Sydney Street SW3 6NR Map 19 B5

A bright, informal restaurant with a large garden that's a boon in summer. Dishes are generally straightforward, with some modern touches: vegetable terrine with creamed shallots, warm salad of lamb's sweetbreads with deep-fried celeriac, roast pigeon with pigeon liver stuffing on toast. Others are firmly traditional, including entrecote steak, plain or with béarnaise, and French fries. ***Seats** 52. Private Room 35. L 12.30-2.30 D 7.30-10.45 (Sat to 10.30). Closed L Sat, all Sun, Bank Holidays, 1 week Christmas. Set L £10/312.50 Set D £14/£16.50.* AMERICAN EXPRESS *Access, Diners, Visa.*

NW1 Daphne £45

Tel 071-267 7322 R

83 Bayham Street NW1 Map 16 C3

In a part of town where Greek restaurants abound, Daphne has the edge over most of them. Its menu of traditional favourites is given a boost by numerous daily specials with an emphasis on fish: charcoal-grilled bream, cod croquettes, even a fish meze. Choice is also generous for meat-eaters and vegetarians. The restaurant extends over two floors, with a roof garden for summer use. ***Seats*** *85. Parties 30. Private Room 30. L 12-2.30 D 6-11.30. Closed Sun & Bank Holidays. Meze (min 2) £8.25. Access, Visa.*

SW3 Daphne's — £75

Tel 071-589 4257 Fax 071-581 2232 — **R**

112 Draycott Avenue SW3 3AE — **Map 19 B5**

Daphne's has started a new life with a new decor, new owner Mogens Tholstrup and chef Eddie Baines who worked at the *River Café, Bibendum* and *Est.* Reminiscent of a Tuscan courtyard, it can be refreshingly cool in the summer with a open-roof rear conservatory and comfortingly warm in the winter with a large open fire. Cooking is modern and healthy, of northern Italian influences. Emphasis is on quality ingredients prepared simply. Bruschetta with mussels and saffron, foie gras with wild asparagus, risotto milanese, sea bass with herb and balsamic salsa, rack of lamb with a crust of fresh herbs are examples of safe, reliable dishes. The lunch menu has lighter dishes including a memorable panzanella salad, a refreshing mix of pugliese bread soaked in fresh tomato juice, onions, olives, capers and basil. Desserts include a perfect almond and plum tart with amaretto cream. Brunch on Sundays mixes egg Benedict and risotto with smoked haddock with Lincolnshire sausage and mash. Booking recommended. ***Seats*** *120. Parties 50. Private Room 50. L 12-3 (Sun 11-4) D 7-11.30. Closed Bank Holidays.* AMERICAN EXPRESS *Access, Diners, Visa.*

SW6 De Cecco NEW — £40

Tel 071-736 1145 — **R**

189 New Kings Road Parsons Green London SW6 4SW — **Map 17 B5**

Booking is advisable at this bright, bubbly place, which has quickly established a loyal following. The range of pizza and pasta includes several surprises (pizza with smoked salmon and pineapple, fettuccine with lamb's kidneys and spinach), and main courses are typified by osso buco, squid with garlic, lemon, white wine and tomato, and beef in a Calvados and wine sauce served on a bed of pappardelle. ***Seats*** *60. Parties 12. L 12.30-2.30 D 6.45-11.15. Closed Sun & Bank Holidays. Access, Visa.*

W1 Defune — £80

Tel 071-935 8311 Fax 071-487 3762 — **R**

61 Blandford Street W1H 3AJ — **Map 18 C2**

Book to be sure of a table, as this is a popular (and very small) Japanese restaurant. Otherwise you can sit at the counter and see your sushi and sashimi being prepared. The à la carte spans a fairly familiar Japanese range, from soups and noodle dishes to barbecued beef, pork and fish, and specialities such as *shabu-shabu* and *yosenabe.* ***Seats*** *30. Parties 15. L 12-2.30 D 6-10.30. Closed Sun, Bank Holidays, 1 week Christmas. Set L from £12.* AMERICAN EXPRESS *Access, Diners, Visa.*

SW15 Del Buongustaio ↑ NEW — £50

Tel 081-780 9361 — **R**

283 Putney Bridge Road London SW15 2PT — **Map 17 B5**

Simple but imaginative decor in soft shades of sand and terracotta with colourful Faenza ceramics sets the tone for a relaxing meal in this cheerful country Italian restaurant. The emphasis is on a slightly updated version of classic Northern Italian cooking, and its authenticity is almost unrivalled in this country. Irresistible black olives with orange zest are soon followed by a basket of home-made breads, while the meal proper could start with rustic *zuppa di fagioli alla trevisana* (hearty dried bean soup, garnished with grilled radicchio). From a wide choice of main courses, try spicy Calabrian meatballs served on soft polenta or stuffed calamari with a basil sauce and finish with baked fresh figs and zabaglione or a sinful dark chocolate

See over

semifreddo with a vanilla cream. ***Seats** 45. Parties 8. L 12-3 D 6.30-11.30. Closed Sun, Bank Holidays, 2 wks Christmas, 4 days Easter. Set D £19.50.* AMERICAN EXPRESS *Access, Visa.*

W1 **dell'Ugo** ↑ **£40**

Tel 071-734 8300 Fax 071-734 8784 **R**

56 Frith Street Soho W1V 5TA **Map 21 A2**

Antony Worrall Thompson is the inspiration behind one of London's most popular and trendy restaurants. In the heart of Soho, dell'Ugo provides something for everyone on a menu which, after the AWT style, is full of good ideas. The Mediterranean influence is strong – bruschetta of plum and sun-dried tomato with basil, salade niçoise, chargrilled squid and Mediterranean vegetable salad with tapénade crostini. Other dishes are homespun favourites with comtemporary tuning: sausages and mash with white bean casserole and caramelised onions, Barnsley chop with chili chutney, roast pepper and aubergine tart. Most of the list is essentially fairly simple in concept and preparation, with an emphasis on strong, fresh flavours, typified by crostini of chicken liver, goat's cheese and spinach, pan-fried sardines with wilted greens and lemon vinaigrette, or crunchy chicken with slow-cooked courgettes and peppers with garlic potatoes. Lamb shank with flageolet beans, rosemary, garlic and mash is a standing dish at Bistrot 190 and will be equally popular here. Pasta and rice plates, like many others, are available as either starters or mains, and puddings include banana cream pie with passion fruit sauce and chocolate and nut fudge cake with caramelised oranges and crème fraiche. A sensible wine list with affordable quality, available either by the pichet or the bottle. The ground-floor café/bar, one of the busiest places in town, is open all day, the two floors above for lunch and dinner. ***Seats** 170. Parties 65. Private Room 16. L 1st & 2nd floor: 12.30-3, D 1st floor: 7-11.45, 2nd floor: 5.30-11, Ground floor café: 11am-12.30am. Closed L Sat on 1st and 2nd floors only & all Sun.* AMERICAN EXPRESS *Access, Visa.*

NW8 **Don Pepe** **£50**

Tel 071-262 3834 **R**

99 Frampton Street St John's Wood NW8 8NA **Map 18 B2**

London's first tapas bar when it opened 20 years ago, Don Pepe has survived and thrived. Besides the tapas there's a full restaurant menu including Spanish classics such as gazpacho, Asturian-style bean stew, zarzuela and paella. ***Seats** 50. Private Room 20. L 12-3 D 7-1. Closed D Sun, 24 & 25 Dec. Set L from £10.50 Set D from £12.95.* AMERICAN EXPRESS *Access, Diners, Visa.*

W1 **The Dorchester** **91%** **£278**

Tel 071-629 8888 Fax 071-409 0114 **HR**

Park Lane W1A 2HJ **Map 18 C3**

For 60 years the Dorchester has been among the world's top hotels, renowned for its enviable standards of service, comfort and food. The grand oval foyer, with its rug-strewn black-and-white marble floor, bustles with the comings and goings of smartly attired porters, page boys and guests. The splendid, long Promenade, complete with enormous floral display at one end and rows of faux-marble columns with ornate gilt capitals, is very much the heart of the hotel and a wonderful place to take traditional English afternoon tea. Bedrooms have an essentially English style with fine fabrics varying from striking floral prints and delicate damasks to heavy tapestries; the bed linen is, of course, real linen. All rooms are now triple-glazed and have white Italian marble bathrooms with bidets and hand showers in addition to powerful showers over the bathtubs; many even have separate shower cubicles and twin washbasins, while most have natural light (a real luxury in a hotel bathroom). Four superb roof garden suites, all now restored to their original splendour, put the icing on the cake. Standards of service throughout the public areas are superlative and are matched on the bedroom floors following the implementation of the call button system for valet, maid and waiter room service. Breakfasts, as one can expect from a hotel with such an outstanding culinary history, are first rate, covering English (a superior fry-up, poached haddock, grilled kippers, coddled egg with smoked salmon or chives), Continental (excellent baking includes croissants and apple scones) or low-fat and low-cholesterol options; served from 7am (7.30am Sun) in the Grill Room. Among the many elegant public rooms, opulent banqueting and conference facilities (for up to 550) feature over 1,500 square metres of gold leaf gilding and are among London's finest. The Dorchester Spa offers thermal therapy as well as the more usual relaxations. ***Rooms** 197. Gymnasium, sauna, spa bath, steam room, solarium, beauty & hair salon, shopping gallery.* AMERICAN EXPRESS® *Access, Diners, Visa.*

Terrace Restaurant ★★ £120

There are not many locations in London where you can dine well in wonderful surroundings and dance, but you can here, and what a joyous occasion it is. You can experience everything you could possibly want under the cornice ceiling – opulent decor with chinoiserie, draped windows, a romantic central gazebo with four tables that offers a little privacy, table candle lamps, a pianist (joined later in the evening by a crooner and guitarist), playing until 1am, and a menu that really excites, showing chef de cuisine Willi Elsener's talents to the full. Trained in the classical manner, his cooking, over the years, has evolved into a more modern, lighter approach with several ingredients from the Orient, ably demonstrated by a delicate amuse-bouche of salmon set in a jellied fish stock with crème fraiche and dill. There is a choice of menus – the à la carte, which changes four times a year, a three-course *trouvailles du marché*, a daily-changing affair based on the best fresh produce available from the markets that morning (note the suggested wines by the glass to accompany this menu), and a *menu léger* which is nutritionally and healthily balanced. On our most recent visit in late June, three of the eight starters on the à la carte menu were terrines, but since they all appeared thoroughly enticing, it was perhaps less noticeable than it might have been. One of the said dishes, a terrine of seasonal vegetables on thin slivers of beef (carpaccio) brushed with truffle oil and lemon juice with horseradish sauce was quite perfect, as was a warm gratin of crayfish tails and thin green asparagus with chives. So too was a baked escalope of sea bass filled with herbs and zest of limes, served with onions and strips of bacon (one forgets how well bacon complements fish) and Chinese greens. Equally sublime was a main course of grilled breast of chicken marinated in soya and honey served with batons of polenta, leeks and carrots with a lemon grass sauce. This is cooking of a very high standard, beautifully presented, and matched by faultless service from maitre d'hotel Peter Buderath and his enthusiastic team. You can choose your dessert from either the menu or the daily-changing platter which is presented visually first, so that you have something to see before making up your mind – a crème brulée surrounded by a brunoise of fruit soaked in Sauternes, an almond basket with an exotic fruit salad and pink champagne sorbet, or a chocolate mousse with caramelised banana, in a dark and white chocolate case, served with a coffee sauce – all creatively indulgent! Alternatively, there's a trolley of Continental and British cheeses in tip-top condition. Before coffee and delectable petits fours, you are offered a small dish of fresh fruit which might include grapes, a fig, dates, a peach, and an exotic ramboutan. The very fine wine list seems less expensive than of old, with plenty of good drinking under £25, and includes good Italian and New World sections. ***Seats** 80. Parties 14. D only 7-11. Closed Sun & Mon, Bank Holidays. Set D £25 & £30.*

Grill Room £130

Largely unchanged since the hotel first opened in 1931 the grand Spanish-style decor of the Grill Room belies the comprehensive Britishness of the menu. Tables are widely spread, which is just as well given the numerous

See over

trolleys that bring not just the traditional roast rib of beef and Yorkshire pudding and the side of smoked salmon – to be sliced at the table – but also the dish of the day (steak and kidney pudding on Wednesdays, boiled lamb with caper sauce on Thursday etc), the wide range of breads, 'bespoke' salads, good desserts and the notably wide selection of British cheeses. The à la carte extends to just about every corner of the British Isles from Jersey potatoes (that accompany salmon with watercress salad, horseradish in elderberry vinaigrette), dressed crab from Cornwall, Morecambe Bay potted shrimps, Dublin Bay prawns (with cardamom, herb and pepper butter), air-dried Cumberland ham, black pudding (in a pastry case with sweet chicory and rocket salad) and there's Dover sole amongst the grills. The £20 set lunch is particularly good value. A special pre-theatre supper (£20 for two courses, £25 for three) is served between 6-7pm. ***Seats** 81. Parties 12. L 12.30-2.30 D 6-11 (Sun 7-10.30). Set L £27 Set D £28.*

Oriental Room ↑ £120

London's most exclusive Chinese restaurant and almost certainly the most expensive, too. Some dishes work better than others on a menu that runs from steamed scallops and cold sesame jelly fish through a classic lemon chicken to luxurious shark's fin, abalone and lobster. Staff smart, charming and knowledgable under a suave and accomplished manager. Lovely private rooms. ***Seats** 77. Parties 30. Private Room 14. L 12-2.30 D 7-11. Closed L Sat, all Sun. Set L £20 Set D £28.*

W4 La Dordogne £50

Tel 081-747 1836 **R**

5 Devonshire Road W4 2EU **Map 17 A4**

"A corner of France in west London" whose menu mixes traditional and more contemporary dishes: foie gras (a glass of sweet Jurançon wine is recommended to accompany this), moules marinière, terrine of vegetables with tomato coulis, chicken with tarragon sauce, fillet of beef with a potato pancake and either a green peppercorn or a Quercy wine sauce. Also oysters and lobsters. Classic desserts include chocolate marquise and crepes Suzette (*assiette gourmande* is a little taste of several). ***Seats** 80. Private Room 50. L 12-2.30 D 7-11. Closed L Sat & Sun, Bank Holidays.* AMERICAN EXPRESS *Access, Visa.*

NW1 Dorset Square Hotel 74% £142

Tel 071-723 7874 Fax 071-724 3328 **H**

39 Dorset Square NW1 6QN **Map 18 C2**

A charming, elegant house almost unnoticed in the white Georgian facade of Dorset Square buildings. An attractive combination of hand-painted woodwork, gilt-framed paintings, tapestry cushions and antique furniture gives a warm, refined atmosphere to the public rooms on the ground floor. The guest lounge is furnished with colourful armchairs, a 19th-century rolltop desk and an antique cabinet which holds an honesty bar. Each bedroom has its own personality, artistically blending patterns and materials. Most rooms are air-conditioned, and all have satellite TV, books and magazines. Marble and mahogany bathrooms enjoy natural daylight. Careful thinking has gone into every detail, making one feel a guest in a friend's home. A chauffeur-driven Bentley Continental is available by prior arrangement. As our research closed the restaurant was due to undergo a change of name and style. ***Rooms** 37.* AMERICAN EXPRESS *Access, Visa.*

SW7 Downstairs at 190 £60

Tel 071-581 5666 **R**

190 Queen's Gate SW7 5EU **Map 19 B4**

Busy brasserie-style basement restaurant (beneath *Bistrot 190*) whose seafood menu is a medley of many fashionable ingredients and lots of good ideas. The fish and chips section spans cod, halibut, lobster and scallops and these single dishes are often a better bet than some of the more elaborate offerings. The successful Bistrot 190 concept of seasonally-changing wine suppliers now applies downstairs, too, along with a list for connoisseurs. ***Seats** 70. Private Room 35. D only 7-12. Closed Sun, Bank Holidays, 24-26 Dec.* AMERICAN EXPRESS *Access, Diners, Visa.*

W1 Dragon Inn **£30**

Tel 071-494 0870 **R**

12 Gerrard Street W1 **Map 21 A2**

Set on three floors, an unsophisticated Cantonese restaurant with a staggeringly long menu covering everything from chicken with cashew nuts to spiced belly pork with yam served in a clay pot. Daytime dim sum are always popular. ***Seats** 100. Parties 12. Meals 12-11.45 (dim sum 12-4.45). Closed 25-26 Dec & from 8pm 24 Dec. Set meals from £8.50.* AMERICAN EXPRESS *Access, Visa.*

W1 Dragon's Nest **£45**

Tel 071-437 3119 **R**

58 Shaftesbury Avenue W1V 7DE **Map 21 A2**

Smarter-than-average Chinese restaurant offering a range of dishes both familiar and unusual. ***Seats** 120. Parties 40. Private Room 60. L 12-3 D 5-11.30 Closed 25 & 26 Dec. Set meals from £10.50.* AMERICAN EXPRESS *Access, Diners, Visa.*

SW3 The Draycott **£235**

Tel 071-730 6466 Fax 071-730 0236 **PH**

24-26 Cadogan Gardens SW3 2RP **Map 19 C5**

Formed from a pair of redbrick Victorian town houses, the Draycott is announced by a discreet little brass plate. One is admitted to a yellow drag-painted entrance hall beyond which is an appealing drawing room where Victorian paintings, objets d'art, fresh flowers and a mix of sofas and armchairs creates a certain old-fashioned elegance enhanced by views of (and access to) Cadogan Gardens, one of London's most peaceful garden squares. Bedrooms vary considerably in size and all are individually decorated in a non-hotel town-house style with antiques, porcelain ornaments and paintings of rural scenes as well as satellite TVs, video players and mini-bars. Good bathrooms with Penhaligon toiletries. The Draycott offers a charming and romantic alternative to more conventional hotels. 24hr room service makes up for the lack of a restaurant and there are concierge, fax, limousine and nanny services available. Children stay free in parents' room. Guests have free use of the nearby Synergy Centre Health Centre and the Vanderbilt tennis club. ***Rooms** 25.* AMERICAN EXPRESS *Access, Diners, Visa.*

SW1 Dukes Hotel 79% **£238**

Tel 071-491 4840 Fax 071-493 1264 **HR**

35 St James's Place SW1A 1NY **Map 18 D3**

In a quiet cul-de-sac off St James's Street, a charming and secluded hotel in a tranquil setting neighbouring Green Park. The elegant Edwardian building is conservatively and tastefully furnished in a club-like fashion, with a cosy sitting room and splendid cocktail bar; public rooms reflect the traditional qualities aimed for by the management and the smartly uniformed staff. Bedrooms have fine antiques and period furniture complemented by chintzy floral fabrics. While there is no air-conditioning, there are ceiling fans for sultry days. Bathrooms are not large but have smart marble tiling and a range of luxurious toiletries. 26 of the rooms are suites with homely sitting rooms; some have small kitchens. No children under seven. No dogs. Part of the Cunard Group. ***Rooms** 64.* AMERICAN EXPRESS *Access, Diners, Visa.*

See over

Restaurant £95

An intimate, elegant restaurant offering a mix of classical and modern, but mainly French-inspired dishes, all competently prepared. Seasonal game, daily roasts served from a trolley and desserts that include traditional favourites. ***Seats** 30. Parties 12. L 12.30-2 D 6-10 (Sun from 7). Closed L Sat. Set L £17.75 Set D £28.50.*

SW1 Durley House 74% £275

Tel 071-235 5537 Fax 071-259 6977 **H**

115 Sloane Street SW1X 9PJ **Map 19 C4**

A finely furnished residence comprising eleven self-contained one-and two-bedroom suites, Durley House commends itself to clients seeking the quiet life in central London, a civilised antidote to the bustle of a large hotel. Indeed, its Sloane Street location is handy as a pied-à-terre for Knightsbridge stores, yet guests can step literally across the road for a game of tennis in Cadogan Park. Each of its spacious apartments is individually designed and furnished with antiques and original oil paintings. Some fine architectural features, carved wooden mantels and curved panelling are embellished with flamboyant drapes; king-size beds have crown canopies and matching covers in bold colours. The lounges include polished mahogany dining tables and, in some cases, grand pianos. There's a level of service to match: a full 24hr room service includes breakfast, which arrives by way of a traditional service lift. Under the same ownership as *Dorset Square* and *Pelham* hotels. ***Rooms** 11.* AMERICAN EXPRESS *Access, Visa.*

W1 Durrants Hotel 65% £112

Tel 071-935 8131 Fax 071-487 3510 **H**

George Street W1H 6BJ **Map 18 C2**

A stone's throw from Oxford Street, just off Manchester Square opposite the Wallace collection, Durrants comprises four creeper-clad Georgian houses. Its appeal is traditional and club-like with wood panelling in the foyer, a clubby bar, authentic smoking room and cosy, but not large, bedrooms. Old-fashioned hospitality is dispensed by the Miller family, here since the 1920s. Marble bathrooms have quality fittings. Seven rooms are not en suite. ***Rooms** 96.* AMERICAN EXPRESS *Access, Visa.*

EC1 The Eagle £40

Tel 071-837 1353 **R**

159 Farringdon Road EC1R 3AL **Map 16 C3**

If the atmosphere is unmistakably one of a pub, the food is far from any pub grub. Hearty Mediterranean dishes are produced behind the bar, in the open-plan kitchen. No bookings here and getting a table might be a struggle. Sharing tables and shouting to be heard are well worth a try for the daily changing menu which might offer Castilian garlic soup, linguine with roasted aubergine, garlic and pine nuts, roasted duck with cannellini beans and frisée or citrus and olive oil cake. Twelve different wines are available by the glass. ***Seats** 45. L 12.30-2.30 D 6.30-10.30. Closed Sat & Sun, Bank Holidays, 3 weeks Christmas. No credit cards.*

SW6 Earls Court Park Inn International 69% £109

Tel 071-385 1255 Fax 071-381 4450 **H**

47 Lillie Road SW6 1UQ **Map 19 A5**

Tour parties are big business, so too conferences, with up to 1750 delegates accommodated theatre-style in the huge Thames Suite. Just by the side entrance to Earls Court Exhibition Centre. Children up to 16 free in parents' room. No dogs. ***Rooms** 501. Business centre, coffee shop (11am-midnight).* AMERICAN EXPRESS *Access, Diners, Visa.*

SW1 Ebury Wine Bar — £40

Tel 071-730 5447 — **R**

139 Ebury Street Victoria SW1 — **Map 19 C5**

Long-established Victoria watering hole on the corner of Ebury Street and Elizabeth Street. Lunchtime and evening menus combine modern and traditional elements, from warm pigeon salad with artichoke bottoms to grilled lamb cutlets. Bar open all day. ***Seats** 80. Parties 16. L 12-2.45 D 6-10.30. Closed 25, 26 Dec, 1 Jan & Easter Sun. Set L (Sun) £10.50.* AMERICAN EXPRESS *Access, Diners, Visa.*

W1 Efes Kebab House — £40

Tel 071-636 1953 — **R**

80 Great Titchfield Street W1N 5FD — **Map 18 D3**

Brothers Khazim and Ibrahim opened their Turkish restaurant in 1974 and it's remained popular ever since. Lamb and chicken kebabs are the principal attraction, preceded by a wide selection of hors d'oeuvre including stuffed vine leaves, deep-fried lamb's liver, cream cheese salad and green peppers filled with nuts, raisins and rice. ***Seats** 160. Parties 80. Meals 12-12. Closed Sun, Christmas, 1 Jan, Good Friday. Set meals from £15.* AMERICAN EXPRESS *Access, Diners, Visa.*

SW3 Egerton House — £185

Tel 071-589 2412 Fax 071-584 6540 — **PH**

17-19 Egerton Terrace SW3 2BX — **Map 19 B4**

In a quiet location off Brompton Road, close to Harrods, this handsome Victorian redbrick town house opened as a privately owned hotel in September 1990. Bedrooms (on four floors, all served by a lift) are individually decorated with traditional fabrics, antiques and oil paintings and there's a luxurious look and feel to the marble bathrooms. Some rooms have four-posters, the majority overlook gardens and all are air-conditioned. Excellent breakfasts are served in the rooms or in the bright, basement breakfast room. Extensive room service, concierge, valet. No children under eight. No dogs. ***Rooms** 30.* AMERICAN EXPRESS *Access, Diners, Visa.*

SW6 El Metro — £45

Tel 071-384 1264 — **R**

10-12 Effie Road Fulham Broadway SW6 — **Map 19 A6**

Tapas bar and café-brasserie in a side street opposite Fulham Broadway underground station. Breakfasts, burgers, sandwiches, pasta, steaks, tapas, paella. ***Seats** 42. Parties 30. Meals 8am-midnight (Sun till 11pm). Closed 3 days after Christmas. Set L & D £15.* AMERICAN EXPRESS *Access, Diners, Visa.*

SW1 Elizabeth Hotel — £70

Tel 071-828 6812 — **H**

37 Eccleston Square SW1V 1PB — **Map 19 D5**

Friendly privately-owned bed and breakfast hotel in a garden square near Victoria station. Bedrooms range from singles to family-size; en-suite facilities are being extended to more rooms. No dogs. ***Rooms** 40. No credit cards.*

We publish annually, so make sure you use the current edition. It's worth it!

SW7 Embassy House Hotel 59% £106

Tel 071-584 7222 Fax 071-589 8193 **H**

31 Queen's Gate SW7 5JA **Map 19 B4**

Modern comfort in a late-Victorian building near Hyde Park, the Royal Albert Hall and the Kensington Museums. Children under 16 can stay free in their parents' room; in their own room they pay 50% of the adult rate. 15 bedrooms are reserved for non-smokers. Jarvis. ***Rooms** 69.* American Express *Access, Diners, Visa.*

SW3 English Garden £65

Tel 071-584 7272 Fax 071-581 2848 **R**

10 Lincoln Street off Draycott Avenue SW3 2TS **Map 19 C5**

English cooking in a stylishly converted Chelsea terrace house. The menu changes with the seasons: typical spring options on the carte include sole, scallop and saffron terrine, baked field mushrooms glazed with goat's cheese and green peppercorns, steamed salmon roulade with crab and ginger, pot-roast saddle of hare with roasted vegetables and juniper gravy, finishing with apple syllabub with cinnamon shortbread, hot chocolate tart topped with meringue or a salad of red fruits. Three dishes at each stage on the fixed-price lunch menu. The room has an attractive conservatory to the rear. ***Seats** 50. Private Room 30. L 12.30-2.30 (Sun to 2) D 7.30-11.30 (Sun to 10). Closed 25 & 26 Dec. Set L £14.75.* American Express *Access, Diners, Visa.*

SW3 English House £85

Tel 071-584 3002 Fax 071-581 2848 **R**

3 Milner Street Chelsea SW3 2QA **Map 19 C5**

English cooking in a homely Victorian setting just off Kings Road. From a winter carte come pigeon breast and wild mushroom salad, galantine of duck with fig preserve, boned baby chicken with lemon and coriander, collops of venison with game forcemeat and Cumberland sauce, braised beef, stout and oyster pie; vegetarians might enjoy curried parsnip and potato cakes baked with spring onions and ginger. Fixed-price menus including 'Sunday supper' offer a good choice with four dishes at each stage. ***Seats** 33. Parties 25. Private Room 20. L 12.30-2.30 D 7.30-11.30 (Sun to 10). Closed D 25 Dec, all 26 Dec. Set L £14.75 Set D £19.75 (Sun only).* American Express *Access, Diners, Visa.*

SW15 Enoteca £45

Tel 081-785 4449 **R**

28 Putney High Street SW15 1SQ **Map 17 B5**

On a corner site just south of Putney Bridge, Enoteca offers modern Italian cooking at very reasonable prices in a friendly, relaxed atmosphere. The menu is strong on pasta (spaghetti with mussels, penne with Tuscan sausage and mushrooms) and main courses could include chicken baked with lemon and capers or lamb cutlets with a Lambrusco sauce. Also a weekly-changing set menu. Suitable wines are helpfully noted against each dish. ***Seats** 35. Private Room 45. L 12.30-3 D 7-11.30. Closed L Sat, all Sun, Bank Holidays, 1 week Christmas.* American Express *Access, Visa.*

SW3 The Enterprise NEW £55

Tel 071-584 3148 **R**

35 Walton Street SW3 **Map 19 C4**

A charming pub, tastefully refurbished, with a restaurant and American bar. It's a pleasant retreat for lunch, dinner or a drink. The modern menu offers the likes of quesadillas with sour cream, apple chutney and salsa, mussels and Jerusalem artichoke salad or corn-fed chicken with roasted peppers and garlic. Cooking is unpretentious and plates are put together with care. ***Seats*** *34. L 12.30-2.30 D 7.30-10.30. Closed D Sun, Christmas Day. Set L £13.50/£16.50 (Sun only).* AMERICAN EXPRESS *Access, Visa.*

If we recommend meals in a hotel or inn a separate entry is made for its restaurant.

W1 L'Escargot

£70

Tel 071-437 6828 Fax 071-437 0790

R

48 Greek Street W1V 5LR

Map 21 A2

Part of the Soho scene since 1927, L'Escargot has undergone a major change of style and decor under new owner Jimmy Lahoud, already an established local restaurateur. Abstract art on cream-coloured walls features both in the smaller first-floor restaurant and the main ground-floor brasserie with its red banquettes, parquet floor and chairs in yellow, green and blue check. Upstairs, a short menu might offer gaspacho, carpaccio of beef or baked scallops with lemon (served in the shell), followed by risotto milanaise with fried squid, baked sea bass and fennel with shallots and garlic or chateaubriand with pommes Anna; warm cherry tart, rhubarb crumble or chocolate marquise might complete a meal. Downstairs, in the more popular brasserie, the largely French menu contains plenty of familiar dishes: *soupe au pistou*, Provençal fish soup with a very spicy rouille, *assiette of charcuterie* (sliced at the table from a trolley – a nice touch)), *terrine en croute, pot au feu, cassoulet toulousain, tarte tatin* with cinnamon ice cream, *Paris-Brest* gateau, along with the likes fillet of smoked whiting with bubble and squeak, Caesar salad and 'fromage Fran-Glais'. Everything is well within the skills of the kitchen and cooking is generally of a high standard but there can be the occasional hiccup – unsuccessful cassoulet, a salad of lamb and deep-fried vegetables arrived without the latter and an excellent terrine of foie gras with shallots and lentils looked rather lost in the middle of a large white plate without the garnish (some toasted brioche to accompany it had to be requested). Main courses in the restaurant will be served without vegetables unless you ask – no mention is made on the menu. Service is willing (an unexpected child diner was warmly welcomed on a Saturday night), but two months after opening was still far from smooth. ***Seats*** *Restaurant 45 Brasserie 40. Private Room 45. L 12-2.30 D 6-11.30 (from 7pm in the restaurant). Closed L Sat, (Restaurant all Sun), 25 & 26 Dec, 1 Jan.* AMERICAN EXPRESS *Access, Diners, Visa.*

W8 L'Escargot Doré

£70

Tel 071-937 8508

R

2 Thackeray Street W8 5ET

Map 19 A4

A basement restaurant which offers a cool retreat on hot summer days or intimate candle-lit dinners. Simpler dishes on the menu like *escargots de Bourgogne farcis* or *demi canard roti Aylesbury* (both specialities) are more accomplished than other associations. The two-and three-course menus are availabe in the small bar-brasserie upstairs or in the basement dining room. ***Seats*** *50. Parties 30. Private Room 17. L 12-2.30 D 6.30-11.30 (Sat from 7). Closed L Sat, all Sun, Bank Holidays, 2 weeks Aug. Set L & D £9.90/£14.90.* AMERICAN EXPRESS *Access, Diners, Visa.*

Our inspectors *never* book in the name of Egon Ronay's Guides. They disclose their identity only if they are considering an establishment for inclusion in the next edition of the Guide.

W1 **Est** **£40**

Tel 071-437 0666 **R**

54 Frith Street W1V 5TE **Map 21 A2**

A Soho media restaurant with large windows looking on to Frith Street. The menu is very much in the modern Mediterranean mode, with simple, straightforward dishes often using the chargrill: polenta with salsa, asparagus with Parmesan shavings and garlic butter, chicken with artichoke trifolate and zucchini fritters, spring lamb with mustard pesto, mixed leaves and baked potato. ***Seats** 40. Parties 26. L 12-3 D 6-11 (Fri & Sat to 11.30). Closed L Sat, all Sun, Bank Holidays. AMERICAN EXPRESS Access, Visa.*

WC2 **L'Estaminet** **£60**

Tel 071-379 1432 **R**

14 Garrick Street WC2 **Map 21 B2**

On the former site of *Inigo Jones*, an attractive French brasserie on the fringe of Covent Garden (off Floral Street) The short menu runs from fish soup and Burgundy snails to omelettes, cod baked with meat juice, coq au vin and speciality steaks (plain or with pepper, béarnaise or shallot sauce). ***Seats** 60. Private Room 20. L 12-2.30 D 6.30-11.30. Closed Sun, Bank Holidays. AMERICAN EXPRESS Access, Visa.*

W1 **L'Etoile** **£80**

Tel 071-636 7189 **R**

30 Charlotte Street W1P 1HJ **Map 18 D2**

One of the bastions of traditional French cooking, L'Etoile has been in business for almost 90 years. Salade niçoise, frogs' legs, fish or onion soup, goujons of sole, veal escalope Zingara, duck à l'orange and tournedos béarnaise show the style. ***Seats** 60. Private Room 30. L 12-2.30 D 6-11. Closed L Sat, all Sun, Bank Holidays. Set L & D £17.50. AMERICAN EXPRESS Access, Diners, Visa.*

WC1 **Euston Plaza Hotel** **67%** **£129**

Tel 071-383 4105 Fax 071-383 4106 **H**

17 Upper Woburn Place WC1H 0HT **Map 19 D5**

Formerly the Scandic Crown Euston, it is now independently owned but the decor remains Scandinavian. Two original conservatories at the back of the building offer an unusual refuge as a light snack restaurant and as a health club. Bedrooms are well equipped, with mini-bar, trouser press, satellite TV and hairdryer, orthopaedic beds and fibre-filled duvets. A pity the double-glazing is not more efficient in the front part of the building. Children under 14 can stay free in parents' room. South of Euston Road, opposite Euston Station. ***Rooms** 150. Coffee bar (10.30am-11pm). AMERICAN EXPRESS Access, Diners, Visa.*

NW1 **Fanari** **£30**

Tel 071-586 1969 **R**

40 Chalcot Road NW1 **Map 16 C3**

Off Regents Park Road, Fanari is a very friendly and unpretentious Greek restaurant where a meal is like a family supper. Portions are generous, flavours robust, prices very reasonable. Dinner ends with a plateful of fresh fruit. ***Seats** 95. Private Room 40. D only 6-12. Closed Sun. Access, Visa.*

Changes in data sometimes occur in establishments after the Guide goes to press. Prices should be taken as indications rather than firm quotes.

E8 Faulkners £22

Tel 071-254 6152 **R**

424 Kingsland Road E8 4AA **Map 16 D2**

Busy fish'n'chip restaurant with an even busier takeaway section. Groundnut oil is used to fry generous portions of fish purchased daily from Billingsgate, from cockney favourites like cod and rock salmon to more patrician halibut and Dover sole. Special value children's menu (£2.95). ***Seats** 60. L 12-2 D 5-10 (Sat 11.30-10, Sun 12-9). Closed Sun, Bank Holidays, 10 days Christmas. No credit cards.*

SW3 The Fenja £156

Tel 071-589 7333 Fax 071-581 4958 **PH**

69 Cadogan Gardens SW3 2RB **Map 19 C5**

A handsome private residence turned into a home-from-home hotel of town house character with bedrooms each named after a notable writer or painter who lived nearby. Antiques, fresh flowers and English prints and paintings of the 18th and 19th centuries are a feature, and both towels and bedding are of high quality. Breakfast (served until 2pm for late risers!) and light meals from room service (no restaurant); drinks on a tray in the room or in the cosy drawing room with an open fire. Guests have access to Cadogan Gardens. No dogs. ***Rooms** 13. Garden.* AMERICAN EXPRESS *Access, Visa.*

SW1 Fifth Floor at Harvey Nichols NEW £80

Tel 071-235 5250 Fax 071-235 5020 **R**

Knightsbridge SW1 **Map 19 C4**

An express lift whisks you smoothly from street level to fifth floor into a fully refurbished area divided into food store and bar/restaurant with a glass wall separating the two. The restaurant has a modern pale grey hangar-like appearance, the bar being more discreetly lit but very busy. With a menu that encompasses the gamut of currently fashionable foods the place has quickly established itself with the Sloane set who crowd into its relaxed, informal ambience. Starters such as crab salad with coriander and lime vie with wild mushroom risotto or rock oysters with miniature merguez. Main dishes range from lobster with coriander, ginger and noodles through roast rabbit and garlic with lentil vinaigrette to Bury black pudding with onion gravy and mash. There's a long list of exotic sweets like turtle sundae, plum fool and lemon macarronade. Skilful cooking but somehow some ingredients lose their influence. Exemplary service. ***Seats** 115. Parties 8. L 12-3 (Sat & Sun to 3.30) D 6.30-11.30. Closed D Sun, 25 & 26 Dec. Set L £15.50/£18.50.* AMERICAN EXPRESS *Access, Diners, Visa.*

N8 Florians £50

Tel 081-348 8348 **R**

4 Topsfield Parade Middle Lane Crouch End N8 8RP **Map 16 C1**

Busy and loud premises with a wine bar at the front. Simple, unfussy Italian food is prepared in the modern, lighter manner. ***Seats** 67. Parties 12. Private Room 24. L 12-3 D 7-11 (Sun to 10.30). Closed Mon, 25 & 26 Dec, 1 Jan, Bank Holidays. Access, Visa.*

SW10 Formula Veneta NEW £50

Tel 071-352 7612 **R**

14 Hollywood Road SW10 **Map 19 B6**

Garden restaurant, one of several in a road running north from Fulham Road. The menu is modern Italian plus some classics. Risotto is a speciality, and other choices could include cold scampi topped with roasted pepper

See over

purée, fillets of sole with lime sauce, breast of duck with aubergine and charcoal-grilled marinated lamb. ***Seats** 55. Parties 30. Private Room 35. L 12.30-2.45 D 7-11.15. Set L £9.95. Closed D Sun, Bank Holidays, Easter.* AMERICAN EXPRESS® *Access, Visa.*

WC1 Forte Crest Bloomsbury 65% £120

Tel 071-837 1200 Fax 071-833 2290 **H**

Coram Street WC1N 1HT **Map 18 D1**

Bedroom refurbishment continues in this large hotel with conference/banqueting facilities for 550/700. No dogs. ***Rooms** 284. Brasserie (7.30am-11pm).* AMERICAN EXPRESS® *Access, Diners, Visa.*

W1 Forte Crest Regent's Park 64% £121

Tel 071-388 2300 Fax 071-387 2806 **H**

Carburton Street W1P 8EE **Map 18 D2**

Several categories of accommodation are available in this large hotel just off Euston Road. It's a popular base for overseas visitors and also has extensive conference facilities. No dogs. ***Rooms** 320. Coffee shop (6.30am-11pm, from 7am Sun)* AMERICAN EXPRESS® *Access, Diners, Visa.*

SW1 Forte Crest St James's 68% £119

Tel 071-930 2111 Fax 071-839 2125 **H**

81 Jermyn Street SW1Y 6JF **Map 18 D3**

The former Cavendish, built in 1966, stands directly behind Fortnum & Mason, just a short walk from Piccadilly Circus and Green Park. Marble floors and modern wood panelling set the tone in the foyer and there's a clubby bar. Bedrooms are to the usual Crest standard and all have recently been refurbished. The Executive 15th floor rooms have a lounge area and jacuzzi baths. 80-space basement car park. 24hr room and valet services. ***Rooms** 256. Business centre.* AMERICAN EXPRESS® *Access, Diners, Visa.*

NW3 Forte Posthouse 65% £68

Tel 071-794 8121 Fax 071-435 5586 **H**

215 Haverstock Hill NW3 4RB **Map 16 B2**

Close to Belsize Park underground station and a short walk from Hampstead. Top-floor bedrooms offer splendid views; 30 recently converted Executive rooms are equipped with various extras, including mini-bars and stereo in the bathrooms. Ample free parking. Brasserie with outdoor seating. ***Rooms** 140.* AMERICAN EXPRESS® *Access, Diners, Visa.*

W1 47 Park Street 86% £326

Tel 071-491 7282 Fax 071-491 7281 **H**

47 Park Street W1Y 4EB **Map 22 C2**

In the heart of Mayfair, a block away from the American Embassy in Grosvenor Square and close to Hyde Park, this gracious Edwardian town house offers sumptuous accommodation in its luxuriously appointed and air-conditioned suites, designed by Monique Roux (the wife of Albert Roux who oversees his son Michel's cooking in the kitchens at the celebrated *Le Gavroche* downstairs). The suites comprise one or two bedrooms, an elegant and spacious lounge/dining area and exquisite bathrooms, are tastefully furnished with antiques, comfortable sofas and armchairs, beautiful fabrics, many objets d'art and paintings. All have triple glazing, air-conditioning and fully equipped kitchens, though these are rarely needed since an extensive 24hr room service is provided, including Continental and English breakfast. Other services are exemplary, too, from your arrival at the impressive entrance and oak-panelled lounge to the concierge, business centre (9am-5pm) and housekeeping: linen sheets and duvets, nightly bed turn-down and daily changing of fresh flowers. Guests are welcomed with champagne and bowls of fresh fruit; the triple-glazed rooms have personal safes, private baths and satellite TV (videos can be installed on request). Bathrooms provide all the extras that one might expect, including power showers (some have separate shower rooms) and bathrobes. There are good leisure club facilities (gymnasium, sauna, swimming pool, solarium) a short walk from Park Street; entrance to *Tramp* nightclub for guests. The third-floor private dining or meeting room (from 8 to 20 people) has a separate lounge; no room charge is made when used as a dining room. Charged parking. ***Rooms 52.*** *Hotel limousine, valeting (8am-5pm), baby-sitting, hairdressing, shopping service.* AMERICAN EXPRESS *Access, Diners, Visa.*

SW7 Forum Hotel 62% £144

Tel 071-370 5757 Fax 071-373 1448 **H**

97 Cromwell Road London SW7 4DN **Map 19 A5**

One of the largest hotels in London, the Forum is ideally located for those coming in from Heathrow with easy connections to the Airbus and tube. This Inter-Continental hotel doesn't offer the same standards as its sister hotels in London but certainly provides the basics. Bedrooms are small and contain all the expected amenities, including satellite TV and a mini-bar; only 30 rooms are non-smoking. Public rooms provide appropriate entertaining with two restaurants, a cocktail lounge and a traditional pub. ***Rooms 910.*** AMERICAN EXPRESS *Access, Diners, Visa.*

W2 Four Seasons £50

Tel 071-229 4320 **R**

84 Queensway W2 3RL **Map 18 A3**

In an area thronged with Chinese restaurants, this is one of the most up-market in terms of both decor and price. Service is friendly and attentive, and the predominantly Cantonese menu runs the gamut of familiar dishes. Chef's specialities include shredded beef with crispy rice noodles, stuffed bean curd in a hotpot and fried prawn cake with vegetables. Sizzling dishes are also popular. ***Seats 60.*** *Parties 12. Meals 12-11.15. Closed 25 & 26 Dec. Set D from £10.50. Access, Visa.*

W1 Four Seasons Hotel 89% £315

Tel 071-499 0888 Fax 071-493 1895 **HR**

Hamilton Place Park Lane W1A 1AZ **Map 19 C4**

The bland modernity of a purpose-built high-rise block belies the elegant, individual interior of this luxurious hotel (formerly the Inn On The Park). This is grandness on a modern scale: marble floors, lush plants and flower displays set the tone in the spacious foyer and the chandeliered lounge and panelled cocktail bars live up to expectations. The superb bedrooms are large and decorated in the same quiet good taste as the public areas. All have numerous telephones with two lines, sofas, huge beds, video players, room safe, teletext and Reuters; robes and thick towels in the bathrooms. Conservatory rooms are the best, offering marble-floored, plant-filled sitting areas off the bedrooms; the 26 suites are quite outstanding and even include humidifiers and stereo sytems. Children up to 12 stay free in parents' room; baby-listening and baby-sitting service available; half-price menu in Lanes for children. Two bedrooms have been specially adapted for disabled guests. Afternoon tea is served in the ground-floor lobby lounge to the strains of piano or harp music; light meals are also available here throughout the day. Banqueting facilities for up to 400, theatre-style conferences of up to 500 delegates. The Pine Room, featuring original carved panels from the 18th-century town house that once stood on the site, is a magnificent setting for private dining. Valet parking, twice-daily maid service, same-day dry cleaning and laundry, one-hour pressing round the clock plus no-smoking bedroom floors and Japanese breakfasts are all examples of the attention to detail that puts the Four Seasons in the top echelon of London hotels. ***Rooms 227.*** *Garden, valeting, coffee shop (9am-1am).* AMERICAN EXPRESS *Access, Diners, Visa.*

See over

Four Seasons Restaurant £120

As we went to press the reports were that chef de cuisine Bruno Loubet was about to depart this glorious, grand hotel dining room after six years in situ. Tall windows overlook the hotel's private garden, a theme reflected within by stone urns on pedestals containing potted palms and plants, and the mix of well-spaced tables and curved banquette booth seating gives a spacious air, on which the discreet service almost floats. It is to be hoped that Loubet's distinctive *cuisine du terroir* style continues and that any new chef is also unencumbered by the banqueting duties that many chefs at other major London hotels have to oversee. Many of the best wine-makers appear on the excellent wine list, reappraised from last year, that now offers better value; plenty of half bottles and good wines by the glass. ***Seats** 60. L 12.30-3 D 7-11 (lounge: 9am-2am, Sun 9am-1am). Set L £25 (Sun £28) Set D £40.*

Lanes Restaurant £80

One of London's most stylish late-night restaurants, with last orders at midnight Mon-Sat – ideal for post-theatre dining; it's also open early enough for a pre-theatre bite to eat (from 6pm). The windowless room has a light and contemporary decor and features a central buffet with wonderful displays throughout the day. The choice of fixed-price three-course lunch menus all include wine. Executive chef Eric Deblonde offers special dishes for breakfast, lunch and dinner that are lower in calories, cholesterol, sodium and fat – from scrambled egg whites with asparagus and tomato for breakfast to an East and West platter of risotto with stir-fried vegetables, Japanese soba noodles and cep mushroom cake. Trenchermen can stick to daily specials like roast loin of veal with sorrel sauce, the help-yourself buffet or traditional grills. The nicely presented wine list perfectly matches the food; good house suggestions, aslo served by the glass. One half of the restaurant is reserved for non-smokers. ***Seats** 75. Parties 10. L 12-3 D 6-12 (6.30-11.30 Sun). Set L £24.75-£29.50.*

SW3 Foxtrot Oscar £50

Tel 071-352 7179 R

79 Royal Hospital Road SW3 4HN **Map 19 C5**

Long-fashionable neighbourhood Chelsea restaurant serving a large variety of straightforward fare including potted shrimps, salmon fishcakes, burgers, duck breast and lamb cutlets. Lengthy list of cocktails. A fun place – be sure to book. ***Seats** 50. Parties 35. L 12.30-2.30 (Sat & Sun to 3.30) D 7.30-10.30. Closed some Bank Holidays, 24 Dec-1 Jan, Easter.*

AMERICAN EXPRESS *Access, Visa.*

N1 Frederick's £65

Tel 071-359 2888 Fax 071-359 5173 R

Camden Passage Islington N1 8EG **Map 16 D3**

Smart conservatory restaurant, established in 1969, offering mostly safe, classical French food on a fortnightly-changing menu. Note early evening opening times for pre-theatre dinner. The garden patio opens for outdoor eating in summer. Some keen prices on the decent wine list. Non-smoking area. ***Seats** 140. Private Room 26. L 12-2.30 D 6-11.30. Closed Sun, Bank Holidays. Set L £16.95 Set D £12.95 (up to 6.45)/£16.95.* AMERICAN EXPRESS *Access, Diners, Visa.*

W1 French House Dining Room NEW £45

Tel 071-437 2477 R

49 Dean Street London W1V 5HL **Map 21 A2**

On the first floor of an old-fashioned Soho pub, the dining room offers an interesting menu of essentially English dishes typified by chick pea and tomato soup, smoked haddock pie, roast pork belly with cabbage and gingerbread pudding. Good British cheeses and Welsh rarebit. ***Seats** 30. Parties 8. L 12.30-3 D 6.30-11.30 Closed Sun, 25 & 26 Dec.* AMERICAN EXPRESS *Access, Diners, Visa.*

W1 **Fuji** **£70**

Tel 071-734 0957 **R**

36 Brewer Street W1R 3HD **Map 22 C3**

Well-prepared selection of Japanese standards (yakitori, sushi, sashimi and tempura) served by charming waitresses. Prices on the menu include service charge but not VAT. Japanese tea is served free with all meals. ***Seats** 55. Parties 24. L 12-2.30 D 6-10.45. Closed L Sun, Bank Holidays, Christmas/New Year. Set L from £7 Set D from £14.* AMERICAN EXPRESS *Access, Diners, Visa.*

WC2 **Fung Shing** ★ **£52**

Tel 071-437 1539 **R**

15 Lisle Street Soho WC2 **Map 21 A2**

In the very top flight of London's Chinese restaurants, Fung Shing presents a relatively well-scrubbed face in a distinctly unkempt Soho street, between Gerrard Street and Leicester Square. Dishes on the long Cantonese-themed menu read fairly similarly to their Chinatown neighbours, but what arrives on the plate is, quite simply, better – probably because the chef has been here since 1985 when it opened. Deep-fried oysters in batter, soft-shell crab with chili and salt, soup of winter melon with dried scallops, roast duck stuffed with yam, spiced brisket of beef in a pot, and many other dishes using crab, eel, abalone, carp, prawns – even veal and venison (and crispy fried intestine for that matter). If you want to be adventurous, here's the place to do it (how about spicy jelly fish with chicken and pickles?); equally, it's a place to enjoy tried and tested dishes that you might be more familiar with – you'll still find satay, hot and sour soup, chicken with cashew nuts and sizzling dishes on the long menu. Booking is almost essential. ***Seats** 85. Private Room 30. Meals 12-11.30. Closed 24-26 Dec. Set meals from £11.* AMERICAN EXPRESS *Access, Diners, Visa.*

W1 **La Gaulette** **£70**

Tel 071-580 7608 **R**

53 Cleveland Street W1P 5PQ **Map 18 D2**

The refreshing decor in blue tones, with a tiled floor, soft lights and Mauritian background music, set the mood for an exclusively fish menu with vegetarian dishes on request. *Soupe de poissons* and half a lobster with garlic and brandy mingle with moules mauricienne or red snapper à la creole (unfortunately the same sauce). The unusual selection of fish includes merou, vacqua and parrot fish. The downstairs bistro has the same opening hours and offers a fixed-price menu (£13.25). ***Seats** 30. Parties 12. L 12.30-2.30 D 6.30-11. Closed Bank Holidays, 25 & 26 Dec. Set meals £13.95.* AMERICAN EXPRESS *Diners, Visa.*

W1 **Le Gavroche** ★★★ **£160**

Tel 071-408 0881 Fax 071-409 0939 **R**

43 Upper Brook Street W1Y 1PF **Map 18 C3**

Chef Michel Roux Jr, son of Albert and nephew of Michel Sr (see *Waterside Inn*, Bray), writes on the menu "we have no specialities as such in our menu as we have created the great majority of our dishes" to which, of course, there can be no argument. He adds "the few classical dishes which figure in our menu also have the hallmark of our interpretation" – again, without dispute, indeed Albert used to write the very same words. And yet, many of the dishes that appear on the menu today have done so for several years, and therefore are Roux classics: *papillote de saumon fumé Claudine, soufflé Suissesse, mousseline de homard au champagne, oeuf froid*

See over

à la Tzarine, flan de poireaux aux coquilles St Jacques, bar au fenouil en papillote, bavarois de piments doux, l'assiette du boucher and signature desserts such as *soufflé framboise* and *l'assiette du chef.* This is no criticism, on the contrary, it is one of the restaurant's great strengths – why change a winning combination? On the other hand, while other top-class restaurants have perhaps adapted more to new ideas and styles of cooking and moved forward, it seems that things have remained almost static here, and a restaurant that has always been at the forefront of cooking in this country is in danger of being left behind. Two schools of thought maybe, but an independent comment. However, make no mistake, this is a very fine restaurant with arguably the best and most professional service in town, for which restaurant manager Silvano Giraldin must be given the credit. The really hungry and adventurous can order the *menu exceptionnel* (for a minimum of two diners) which comprises six courses and, in the context of what you pay here, is really good value at £59, as is the set lunch, which now includes some well-chosen wines to complement the dishes. At dinner, note there is a minimum charge of £50 per person. The accoutrements that accompany restaurants of this class are all there – excellent and imaginative canapés, super bread, mouth-watering petits fours, and splendid coffee. As you would expect, the wine list is both extensive and expensive, though there are several regional wines at fair prices; the number of classics is quite staggering; plenty of half bottles too. ***Seats*** *60. Parties 10. Private Room 20. L 12-2 D 7-11. Closed Sat & Sun, Bank Holidays, 23 Dec-2 Jan. Set L £36 Set D £59.* AMERICAN EXPRESS *Access, Diners, Visa.*

SW1 Gavver's £55

Tel 071-730 5983 **R**

61 Lower Sloane Street SW1W 8DH **Map 19 C5**

Chef Bruno Valette, here since 1992, offers à la carte selections as well as the established all-in menu at this civilised Roux restaurant just south of Sloane Square. His dishes are interesting but not over-elaborate, and both preparation and presentation receive full attention. White bean soup garnished with pesto croutons; quenelles of brandade with a tomato sauce, *fondant* leeks and leek vinaigrette; fillet of John Dory with saffron risotto; and an artistic, richly sauced *assiette* of duckleg, breast and confit show his style. Crème brulée with armagnac-steeped prunes provides a smoothly sumptuous finale. ***Seats*** *60. Parties 35. L 12-2.30 D 6.30-11. Closed L Sat, all Sun, Bank Holidays, 1 week Christmas, Easter Sat. Set L £12.50/£14.75 Set D £19.75. Access, Diners, Visa.*

W1 Gay Hussar £60

Tel 071-437 0973 **R**

2 Greek Street W1V 6NB **Map 21 A1**

A Soho institution offering hearty portions of traditional Hungarian food. Try the chilled wild cherry soup, veal goulash, chicken paprikash or Transylvanian stuffed cabbage. Desserts include sweet cheese pancakes, poppy-seed strudel and a rum, cream and walnut delicacy. ***Seats*** *70. Parties 20. Private Room 12. L 12.30-2.30 D 5.30-11. Closed Sun, Bank Holidays. Set L £15.50.* AMERICAN EXPRESS *Access, Diners, Visa.*

W8 Geale's £30

Tel 071-727 7969 **R**

2 Farmer Street W8 7SN **Map 18 A3**

Behind the Gate cinema stands one of London's oldest and best-loved fish restaurants. For well over 50 years they've been serving traditional fish and chips, the fish cooked in beef dripping, the chips in vegetable fat. English favourites – from cod to halibut – are joined by more unusual offerings like deep-fried clams and parrot fish. Nearly always busy, and no bookings, but you can wait upstairs with a drink for a table. Pavement tables in summer.

Seats 100. Private Room 25. L 12-3 D 6-11. Closed Sun & Mon, Tues after Bank Hol Mons, 2 weeks Christmas, 3 days Easter, 2 weeks Aug. Access, Visa.

WC1 George Hotel £50

Tel 071-387 8777 Fax 071-383 5044 **H**

58 Cartwright Gardens WC1H 9EL **Map 18 D1**

In a crescent near the British Museum, the George and its neighbour the Euro offer very reasonably priced accommodation, with children up to 13 staying free in parents' room at weekends and at reduced rates at other times. Unlicensed. No dogs. ***Rooms*** *75. Access, Visa.*

SW7 Gilbert's £55

Tel 071-589 8947 **R**

2 Exhibition Road SW7 2HF **Map 19 B5**

A warm red ochre decor and formally set tables set the mood for a quiet meal. Ann Wregg warmly welcome her customers while her partner Julia Chalkey prepares unpretentious dishes with care. The *prix fixe* menu changes every two weeks with additional dishes for a small supplement. Carrot soup with fresh coriander, green bean and hazelnut salad or vegetarian stuffed cabbage are examples of simple, healthy preparations. Desserts include Mrs. Beeton's delicate lemon tart, chocolate tipsy cake and home-made ice cream. Interesting selection of unpasteurised cheeses from Neal's Yard. Terrific and fairly priced wine list with a good selection of half bottles, and wines under £15, as well as helpful notes. London Regional Cellar of the Year winner (see earlier pages). ***Seats*** *32. Parties 40. L 12.30-2 D 7-10.15. Closed L Sat, all Sun, 1 week Christmas/New Year, Bank Holidays. Set L £11.50/£16 Set D £13.50/£18.* American Express *Access, Diners, Visa.*

EC1 Ginnan NEW £50

Tel 071-278 0008 **R**

1/2 Rosebery Court Rosebery Avenue EC1R 5HP **Map 16 C3**

Opened in 1992, Ginnan is a welcome venue in this neighbourhood of mainly office buildings. Decor is modern and kept simple. Tables are separated by mid-height partitions, giving some privacy. The menu is extensive. Oxtail boiled with garlic, grated white radish with baby sardine, and cucumber and seaweed seasoned with savoury rice vinegar are unusual choices for starters. A large selection of set lunches of very good value offer the likes of sashimi, tempura, tonkatsu, ramen gyoza (egg noodles in soup with various toppings) and kushiyaki (delicious skewers of grilled meat with sauce). A restaurant where the freshness of produce and the customers' satisfaction are major concerns. ***Seats*** *72. Parties 14. L 12-2.30 D 6-10.30. Closed L Sat, all Sun, Bank Holidays, 11 days at Christmas/New Year, 1 week Aug.* American Express *Access, Diners, Visa.*

WC2 Giovanni's £65

Tel 071-240 2877 **R**

10 Goodwin's Court St Martin's Lane WC2A 4LL **Map 21 B2**

Theatregoers and business people are among those attracted to Giovanni Colla's long-established Italian restaurant off St Martin's Lane. The menu is familiar Italian, with variations on pasta, meat, poultry and fish dishes. ***Seats*** *38. Parties 10. L 12-3, D 6-11.30. Closed L Sat, all Sun, Bank Holidays.* American Express *Access, Visa.*

Our inspectors are full-time employees; they are professionally trained by us.

SW10 Glaister's Garden Bistro £40

Tel 071-352 0352 **R**

4 Hollywood Road SW10 9HW **Map 19 B6**

Restaurant, café-bar and garden in a road opposite the new Chelsea & Westminster Hospital. The bistro-style menu offers dishes like grilled vegetable bruschetta with melted mozzarella, Caesar salad, eggs Benedict, salmon fish cakes, spaghetti with pesto and steak, Guinness and mushroom pie with prunes. Traditional roast sirloin of beef is served on Sundays, when children can be looked after in a registered crèche next door. ***Seats*** *80. Private Room 40. L 12.30-3 (Sun to 4) D 7-11.30 (Sun to 10.30). Closed Bank Holidays, 2 weeks Christmas. Set L & D £6.95.* AMERICAN EXPRESS *Access, Diners, Visa.*

SW7 The Gloucester 74% £160

Tel 071-373 6030 Fax 071-373 0409 **H**

4 Harrington Gardens SW7 4LH **Map 19 B5**

High standards of housekeeping, pleasant staff and good accommodation are among the strengths of this tall modern hotel close to Gloucester Road underground station. A lot of money has been spent on 95 Club-floor bedrooms, with their own lift service, check-in facilities and private lounge area. As we went to press, the lobby and restaurants were next in line for refurbishment. Even the standard rooms are of a decent size, light, double-glazed and air-conditioned with all the expected accessories; all rooms have small dressing areas and there is good desk space, plus plenty of shelf space in the tiled bathrooms. Children up to 12 stay free in parents' room. There is an up-to-the-minute business centre and banqueting/conference space for 600. The main restaurant is open evenings only. ***Rooms*** *548. News kiosk, coffee shop (6.30am-11.30pm).* AMERICAN EXPRESS *Access, Diners, Visa.*

WC1 Gonbei £45

Tel 071-278 0619 **R**

151 Kings Cross Road WC1X 9BN **Map 16 C3**

A mixture of imitation wood, metallic chairs, Japanese lamps and rush-covered benches provides a simple setting for an introduction to Japanese culinary art. Sashimi is beautifully fresh, tempura is coated in the lightest, crispest batter. A choice of four speciality dishes based on beef, chicken and fish is prepared at the table. ***Seats*** *26. Private Room 20. D only 6-10.30. Closed Sun, Bank Holidays. Set D from £15. Access, Visa.*

SW3 Good Earth £55

Tel 071-584 3658 **R**

233 Brompton Road SW3 2EP **Map 19 B4**

Comfortable, elegant, smartly staffed, with consistently capable cooking: the usual attributes of a superior non-Soho Chinese restaurant. This one (and its stablemates in Mill Hill and Esher) has two floors of main dining space, plus a large bar with stools. The menu, while not of epic Chinatown proportions, nonetheless offers a more-than-generous variety of dishes from the general repertoire of Chinese favourites. The kitchen is very reliable, and notable in recent visits were crispy spring rolls, lettuce-wrapped meats and prawns, deep-fried squid with peppercorns and spiced salt, and a sizzling, fuming platter of lamb with spring onions. There's a particularly good choice for vegetarians. ***Seats*** *140. Private Room 32. Meals 12-11.15. Closed 23-27 Dec. Set L from £12 Set D from £17.50.*
AMERICAN EXPRESS *Access, Diners, Visa.*

Also at:

NW7 143 The Broadway Mill Hill NW7 Tel 081-959 7011. **Map 16 A1**

Seats *90. Private Room 30.Open 12-2.30 (Sun to 3) & 6-11.15.*

W1 Gopal's of Soho £40

Tel 071-434 0840 **R**

12 Bateman Street W1V 5TD **Map 21 A2**

Head chef and co-owner N P Pittal, known to his friends as Gopal, runs one of the capital's best Indian restaurants. Little is likely to disappoint on a menu which includes some out-of-the-ordinary specialities: king prawns with spring onions, chicken steamed in a sealed pot with Hyderabadi herbs and spices, mutton xacutti (a Goan dish of lamb with coconut, vinegar and rare spices). Note too lentil-stuffed potato patties, Mangalorean crab and minced lamb cooked in a colocassia leaf. ***Seats** 45. Parties 25. L 12-3 D 6-11.30 (Sun to 11). Closed 25 & 26 Dec. Set meals from £9.75.* AMERICAN EXPRESS *Access, Diners, Visa.*

SW7 The Gore 65% £145

Tel 071-584 6601 Fax 071-589 8127 **H**

189 Queen's Gate SW7 5EX **Map 19 B4**

Near the Royal Albert Hall and Hyde Park, the Gore is a hotel of pleasantly mellow character. The striking bar-lounge has dark green walls and comfortably arranged sofas. Best bedrooms are elegant and well appointed, with small sitting areas; among them is the fine Tudor room, dark and atmospheric. The hotel houses the successful *Bistrot 190* and *Downstairs at 190. **Rooms** 54.* AMERICAN EXPRESS *Access, Diners, Visa.*

SW1 The Goring 79% £192

Tel 071-396 9000 Fax 071-834 4393 **HR**

17 Beeston Place Grosvenor Gardens SW1W 0JW **Map 19 D4**

Close to Victoria Station and directly behind Buckingham Palace, a very English hotel in the old style, "loved and nurtured" by the Goring family since it was built in 1910. George Goring, the owner for more than 30 years, believes the place has a soul, and he could just be right! Behind the splendid Edwardian facade is a high level of service and elegant, busy day rooms that make a good first impression with polished marble, paintings and leather sofas. Bedrooms are individually decorated, but with the unanimously traditional feel of solid furnishings using various woods and comfortable settees. Brass bedsteads often feature and bathrooms are particularly good, mostly fitted out in marble; 24hr room and evening maid turn-down services are offered. Many rooms are air-conditioned and the best have balconies that overlook the manicured Goring garden (which, sadly, has no access for guests); similarly, the Garden lounge and Garden bar have delightful outlooks. Private dining rooms cater for up to 70. Children up to 14 stay free in parents' room. ***Rooms** 82. Valeting.* AMERICAN EXPRESS *Access, Diners, Visa.*

Restaurant £90

A traditionally elegant dining room (with service to match), where chef John Elliott prepares a good choice of dishes on both the table d'hote and à la carte menus, ranging from the classics – lobster bisque, eggs Benedict, lamb cutlets, liver and bacon – to those representing the more modern school, such as warm goat's cheese with sun-dried tomatoes, or brochette of monkfish with Parma ham. A splendid carefully-chosen wine list offers many bottles at quite reasonable prices. Note the mature classics and succinct comments from the pen of George Goring himself! ***Seats** 75. Parties 20. Private Room 55. L 12.30-2.30 D 6-10. Closed L Sat. Set L £16.50/£19.50 Set D £26.*

Any person using our name to obtain free hospitality is a fraud.
Proprietors, please inform the police and us.

SW4 Grafton Français £65

Tel 071-627 1048 **R**

45 Old Town Clapham Common SW4 0JL **Map 17 C5**

Traditional French cooking in Clapham's oldest building, dating from the 17th century. Some typical dishes: cream of mussel soup with saffron, mousse of smoked fish, salmon with a muscatel sauce, roast fillet of pork with sage and apple, chicken stuffed with mushrooms, beef bordelaise. Grand Marnier soufflé is a speciality dessert. ***Seats** 72. Parties 28. Private Room 26. L 12.30-3 D 7.30-11.30. Closed L Sat, all Sun, Bank Holidays, 3 weeks Aug, 1 week Christmas. Set L £8/£12.50 Set D £14.95.* AMERICAN EXPRESS *Access, Diners, Visa.*

W1 Grafton Hotel 63% £160

Tel 071-388 4131 Fax 071-387 7394 **H**

130 Tottenham Court Road W1P 9HP **Map 18 D1**

Edwardian Hotels own the Grafton, whose own Edwardian origins are still in evidence (but bedrooms are modern). Children under 12 stay free in parents' room. The hotel's location at the northern end of Tottenham Court Road makes it convenient for the British Museum and Regent's Park. ***Rooms** 324.* AMERICAN EXPRESS *Access, Diners, Visa.*

W1 Grahame's Seafare £40

Tel 071-437 3788 **R**

38 Poland Street W1V 3DA **Map 18 D2**

Kosher fish, deep-fried, grilled or steamed in simple spick and span premises near Oxford Circus underground station. ***Seats** 86. L 12-2.45 D 5.30-9 (Fri & Sat to 8). Closed Sun, Bank Holidays, Jewish New Year.* AMERICAN EXPRESS *Access, Visa.*

N1 Granita NEW £50

Tel 071-226 3222 **R**

127 Upper Street N1 **Map 16 C3**

The connections of La Bougie in Camden Town have opened up in new premises just north of the King's Head in Upper Street. The decor is mainly the inspiration of co-owner Vikky Leffman, whose partner is the chef. Granita is set in concrete outside, à la *Belgo*; inside is light, bright and airy, with noisy wooden floors, the simplest of tables and chairs, a zinc bar and very little in the way of decor. The chef has a fairly easy time, one supposes, with a menu of four starters, a pasta and four mains, one cheese and five desserts. The style is new Med with a nod to California: lots of salads, beans, olive oil, healthy vegetables and no sauces. Lunch is of two or three courses with a choice of borlotti bean soup, salad of wilted spinach, red cabbage, garlic, olives and feta cheese or chargrilled egg plant with garlic mayonnaise to begin followed by fillet of chargrilled organic salmon potato cakes and grilled courgettes or marinated corn-fed chicken with broccoli and roasted red pepper. Neals Yard dairy cheese, bittersweet chocolate torte and vanilla chocolate whisky ice cream complete a meal that satisfies the taste buds but portions – a dozen or so French fries with a dish of chargrilled squid – could be regarded by some as somewhat niggardly, particularly when they are among the best fries in town, competing with Nico Central and Camden Brasserie. Paxarran – a Basque liqueur made from bilberries and anise – is an unusual and quite delicious after-dinner tipple. ***Seats** 62. L 12.30-2.30 (Wed-Sun) D 6.30-10.30 (Tue-Sun). Closed L Tue, all Mon, Bank Holidays, 10 days Christmas, 1 week Easter, 10 days August. Access, Visa.*

NW1 Great Nepalese **£30**

Tel 071-388 6737 **R**

48 Eversholt Street NW1 **Map 18 D1**

Pork and duck are added to a large variety of more familiar Indian dishes in a durable restaurant near Euston station. Other out-of-the ordinary dishes include black lentils, chicken liver bhutuwa with mushrooms and a Tibetan dry vegetable curry. ***Seats** 50. Parties 35. L 12-2.45 D 6-11.45. Closed 25 & 26 Dec. Set meals £9.95.* AMERICAN EXPRESS *Access, Diners, Visa.*

N1 Great Northern Hotel 60% **£83**

Tel 071-837 5454 Fax 071-278 5270 **H**

King's Cross N1 9AN **Map 18 D1**

The Great Northern Hotel, opened in 1854 as London's first purpose-built hotel, is a convenient pausing point for travellers and meeting point for businessmen; it's right next door to St Pancras British Rail Station, one minute from King's Cross and five from Euston. Accommodation is comfortable rather than stylish and includes family rooms, all but ten with en-suite facilities. Function facilities for 100+. No dogs. ***Rooms** 89. Closed 25-27 Dec.* AMERICAN EXPRESS *Access, Diners, Visa.*

NW8 Greek Valley **£40**

Tel 071-624 3217 **R**

130 Boundary Road NW8 0RH **Map 16 B3**

Effie Bosnic creates something of a party atmosphere in her popular Greek-Cypriot restaurant, while husband Peter satisfies the inner man with some very good cooking. Familiar dishes like taramasalata, kleftiko and moussaka share the menu with some less universal choices such as grilled mushrooms, stuffed cabbage (seasonal and delicious) or prawns baked in tomato sauce with feta cheese. Glyko is an unusual sweet of preserved fruit or vegetables. ***Seats** 62. Parties 16. Private Room 30. L 12-2.30 D 6-midnight. Closed L Sat, all Sun, 26 Dec. Access, Visa.*

NW3 Green Cottage **£40**

Tel 071-722 5305 **R**

9 New College Parade Finchley Road NW3 5EP **Map 16 B2**

A Cantonese restaurant that is seemingly the most popular Chinese restaurant of the half dozen in the area. Old favourites like roasted duck and pork, barbecued spare ribs, baked crab with chili and black bean sauce, steamed fish and stir-fried everything are all on offer. Crispy fragrant duck, dry shredded beef with chili, stuffed green peppers in gravy and fried beancurd with mushrooms are also better than average. The adventurous should try soyed mixed meats (liver, gizzard, squid and duck wings). Unusual vegetarian Zhai duckling is formed from deep-fried soy bean sheets. ***Seats** 90. Meals 12-11.15. Closed 25-26 Dec. Set D from £11.50 (min 2).* AMERICAN EXPRESS *Access, Visa.*

W1 Green Park Hotel 70% **£163**

Tel 071-629 7522 Fax 071-491 8971 **H**

Half Moon Street W1Y 8BP **Map 18 C3**

Off Piccadilly in the heart of Mayfair, this Sarova hotel created from a terrace of Georgian town houses tries hard to combine old-fashioned values and modern amenities. There are several meeting rooms (capacity 100), a conservatory and a cocktail bar (the Half Moon) with intimate alcoves. Grey-wood fitted units furnish the bedrooms, their marble-floored bathrooms traditionally resplendent with white suites, some including bidets and spa baths. Children up to 12 stay free in parents' room. ***Rooms** 161.* AMERICAN EXPRESS *Access, Diners, Visa.*

SW11 The Green Room £50

Tel 071-223 4618 **R**

62 Lavender Hill SW11 5RQ **Map 17 C5**

At the Queenstown Road end of Lavender Hill, an organically and ecologically sound restaurant that's comfortable and unpretentious. Spinach and lentil soup, asparagus and soft cheese pancakes and Cantonese stir-fried vegetables typify the vegetarian section of the menu, while among the fish/meat items are crab strudel, pepper-crusted monkfish, turkey provençale and charcoal-grilled steak. ***Seats** 40. L 12-4 (Sun 1-4.30) D 7-11.45.* AMERICAN EXPRESS *Access, Diners, Visa.*

SW1 Green's Restaurant & Oyster Bar £75

Tel 071-930 4566 Fax 071-930 1383 **R**

36 Duke Street St James's SW1Y 6DF **Map 18 D3**

A pillar of St James which hasn't changed in style or quality. Booking is advisable to get a table in one of the small dining rooms but there are seats around the bar behind which salads are freshly prepared: crab cocktail, smoked eel platters or cold poached wild Scotch salmon.Renowned for the quality of the seafood, they also offer well-executed traditional dishes such as boiled beef, carrots and dumplings, shepherd's pie or grilled wild boar sausage with braised red cabbage and herb mash or roast Scotch beef for Sunday lunch. Perfect banana and toffee pie and tempting cheese platter from Paxton & Whitfield to end a satisfying meal. ***Seats** 75. Parties 24. Private Room 26. L 11.30-3 (Sun 12-2.30) D 5.30-11. Closed D Sun, 25 Dec.* AMERICAN EXPRESS *Access, Diners, Visa.*

W1 Greenhouse ↑ £80

Tel 071-499 3331 **R**

27a Hays Mews W1X 7RJ **Map 18 C3**

One of the most attractive approaches to a London restaurant – a quiet, wide mews in pukka Mayfair, a leafy paved courtyard, a trelissed canopy leading to the entrance. Inside, there's certainly *something* of a greenhouse look, with windows running along both sides, plants fresh and dried, and handsome horticultural prints. The customers tend to be fashionably old-fashioned, and that's true of much of Gary Rhodes' menu. Chicken liver paté, smoked haddock with Welsh rarebit, braised oxtail and faggots in rich gravy are satisfyingly nostalgic, so too bread-and-butter pudding, apple fritters and Spotted Dick with custard. First-time fashionable are smoked eel kedgeree with a poached egg, spinach and ricotta gnocchi and mackerel croquettes with a lemon butter sauce – will these one day come to be regarded as old friends? The Sunday lunch set menu always includes a traditional roast, and the Greenhouse now caters for the Sunday evening set – back from the country? up too late for lunch? needing a treat to face the week? – with a special menu of light or lightish dishes, all reassuringly familiar and British by either birth or adoption: watercress soup, salmon fish cakes, fish and potato bake, home-made baked beans, cold meats and pickles, beef stroganoff and the latest English breakfast in town. With it comes a short selection of wines, plus jugs of beer, Buck's Fizz and Pimms. Overall, the cooking here is good but not startlingly good – it's sometimes easy to imagine a production line and ladles behind the ever-swinging kitchen door. But the appeal of the Greenhouse lies at least partly in its very lack of surprises, and the absolute need to book shows that it clearly fits the bill. Management is on the ball, and service is grown-up, with an appealing dash of big-sisterliness. ***Seats** 100. Parties 16. L 12-2.30 (Sun to 3) D 7-11 (Sun 6-10). Closed L Sat, all Bank Holidays.* AMERICAN EXPRESS *Access, Visa.*

W1 Greig's Grill: see under alistair Greig's Grill p. 53.

SW1 The Grenadier

£65

Tel 071-235 3074

R

18 Wilton Row SW1 7NR

Map 19 C4

Secreted down a quiet mews near Belgrave Square, a small, but striking and very typical London pub whose dark, candlelit restaurant offers good traditional fare: Stilton puffs, seafood pie, beef Wellington and roast duck show the style. ***Seats** 21. Parties 8. L 12-2.30 D 6-10.* AMERICAN EXPRESS *Access, Diners, Visa.*

SW3 Grill St Quentin

£55

Tel 071-581 8377 Fax 071-584 6064

R

2 Yeoman's Row SW3 2AL

Map 19 E4

Steps lead down from a neon-lit entrance just off Brompton Road to a large and handsome restaurant in Paris brasserie style with bright yet subtle lighting, pretty shows of flowers and effective use of light wood and brass. French staff of youth and charm provide semi-formal service, and the whole place invites relaxation over a leisurely meal. Charcoal-grilled steaks, cutlets and fish served with splendid little chips are the mainstay of the menu, supported by *plats cuisinés* such as *brandade de morue*, devilled poussin and sausages with lentils. Also plenty of salads, moules marinière, fish soup, langoustines, oysters and excellent patisserie from Spécialités St. Quentin. *Seats 150. Parties 60. L 12-3 D 6.30-11.30 (Sun to 10.30). Set L £10/£13.50.* AMERICAN EXPRESS *Access, Diners, Visa.*

W1 Grosvenor House 83%

£256

Tel 071-499 6363 Fax 071-493 3341

HR

90 Park Lane W1A 3AA

Map 18 C3

Some of the most spacious day rooms in London are to be found at Grosvenor House, which was built in 1929 with a facade designed by Sir Edwin Lutyens. Pride of place must go to the splendid banqueting hall (originally an ice rink) with a capacity of 1500. The ballroom can hold 500+ and there are various private dining and conference suites. There's a vast lounge, an intimate Japanese-themed bar and three restaurants (*Chez Nico* – see separate entry, the *Pavilion* and the Italian *Pasta Vino*). All bedrooms have a lobby and even single rooms have double beds. Solid furniture and soft colours please the eye and the bathrooms are splendid, with marble floors and excellent toiletries. The fifth floor is the Crown Club, with separate Executive check-in and a small lounge and boardroom for executive guests only; rates include breakfast, mini-bar, room service lunch and valet pressing. No dogs. Forte Exclusive. ***Rooms** 454. Indoor swimming pool, gymnasium, sauna, spa bath, solarium, beauty & hair salon, valeting, coffee shop (6.30am-10pm).* AMERICAN EXPRESS *Access, Diners, Visa.*

Pavilion Restaurant

£60

An almost colonial-style setting on a split level with parquet floors, cherrywood mouldings and brightish art. Competent cooking (note the open-face kitchen) is contemporary with an English bias – marinated smoked haddock with lime and rum dressing, boneless braised oxtail with green lentils, bangers and mash, roast pike and walnuts, and treacle tart of bread and butter pudding. Mediterranean dishes, such as tomato tarte tatin, and ricotta and spinach ravioli were less successful. Regrettably, vegetables at £2 per portion are charged extra, and willing service sometimes misses a beat. Super selection of fairly-priced wines by the glass – other restaurants and hotels please follow! ***Seats** 150. Parties 24. L 12.30-2.30 D 6-10. Set L £13.50.*

SW1 Grosvenor Thistle Hotel 64% £138

Tel 071-834 9494 Fax 071-630 1978 **H**

101 Buckingham Palace Road SW1W 0SJ **Map 19 D4**

Built in the 1850s, the Grosvenor Thistle still boasts some handsome Victorian touches, notably in the splendid foyer with pillars and fine tile work. The stylish Harvard Bar has mahogany panelling, mottled green walls and brown leather sofas. Bedrooms are spacious, with a sitting area and desk space, and bathrooms, too, are more than adequate in size. Banqueting/conference facilities for 150/200. Direct access from Victoria railway station. Children up to 12 stay free in parents' room. No dogs. 24hr lounge service. ***Rooms** 366.* AMERICAN EXPRESS *Access, Diners, Visa.*

NW6 Gung-Ho NEW £50

Tel 071-794 1444 **R**

330-332 West End Lane NW6 1LN **Map 16 B2**

Stylish Chinese restaurant located on the northern extremity of West End Lane. The decor is a fashionable mix of ochre red and dark blue with direct spotlights on the table centre to highlight the food. The menu, less stylish, offers the usual Szechuan dishes like bang bang chicken, braised fish in hot bean sauce and crispy aromatic duck. Specialities include crispy Mongolian lamb with iceberg lettuce. ***Seats** 70. L 12-2.30 D 6.30-11.30. Closed 25 & 26 Dec. Set meals from £17.20. Access, Visa.*

W11 The Halcyon 79% £261

Tel 071-727 7288 Fax 071-229 8516 **HR**

81 Holland Park W11 3RZ **Map 17 B4**

The conversion of two Victorian town houses on the corner of Holland Park Avenue and Holland Park has been done most sympathetically, leaving not only lovely architectural features like ornate plaster cornices and fireplaces, but also the original proportions. Needless to say, the preserved period charm is enhanced by quality antiques. The accommodation varies from quite opulent suites (the best has its own conservatory) to single bedrooms that are modest but attractive. Marble bathrooms, whirlpool baths, bidets and night safes are added luxuries. Residents have temporary membership of the exclusive, and expensive, Vanderbilt tennis club close by. An elegant, homely hotel with panache. ***Rooms** 43.* AMERICAN EXPRESS *Access, Diners, Visa.*

The Room at the Halcyon £75

The restaurant opens on to an ornamental garden and patio (smart parasols offer shade to outside diners) through large French windows. Laid-back style, modern cooking: tomato and rosemary soup, saffron risotto with chargrilled vegetables, strips of salmon in sorrel sauce, grilled breast of chicken with basil and grapes. OK desserts such as creamy lemon tart or crème caramel with savarin and ice cream. Sunday brunch menu from 12-4. Very concise wine list, quite fairly-priced. ***Seats** 80. Private Room 16. Set L £14.95. L 12-2.30 D 7-11.*

W2 Halepi £50

Tel 071-262 1070 **R**

18 Leinster Terrace W2 3ET **Map 18 B3**

Greek favourites, including dips, salads, charcoal grills, afelia and moussaka, are served throughout the day in one of London's most cheerful and bustling tavernas. More upmarket dishes, too, like milk-fed baby lamb or sea bass. Meze at £15 a head is a popular choice that should satisfy the hungriest customer. ***Seats** 68. Meals noon-1am. Closed 25 & 26 Dec.* AMERICAN EXPRESS *Access, Diners, Visa.*

SW1 Halkin Hotel 86% £239

Tel 071-333 1000 Fax 071-333 1100 **HR**

5 Halkin Street SW1X 7DJ **Map 19 C4**

Set in a peaceful side street, between the rear of Buckingham Palace and Belgrave Square, the neo-Georgian facade of this modern, five-storey purpose-built luxury hotel blends happily with surrounding Belgravia, in contrast with the interior, which is strikingly contemporary Italian in style. The marble terrazzo and mosaic floor of the lobby takes its design from Michelangelo's Campidoglio piazza in Rome and smart staff uniforms were designed by Giorgio Armani. In curved bedroom corridors doors merge imperceptibly into black-ribbed panelling and, while the bedrooms all share a similar style, each floor has a subtly different colour scheme based on the Elements: earth, fire and water. Beautiful wood-veneer panelling blends with glass and marble surfaces and clever use is made of mirrors, adding a feeling of spaciousness. The occasional antique-style Korean chest or small Oriental statuette only serves to point up the essentially modernist style. Bathrooms, in coloured marble to match the room colour scheme, are particularly stunning and luxurious. With the business person very much in mind, the state-of-the-art technology not only includes touch-activated panels to control lights and air-conditioning but two telephone lines with three phones (all with speaker and conference-call facilities) and a direct-line fax machine in each room. Push-button butler service, room safes, mini-bars and video recorders are all provided in every room. A strikingly different hotel concept, bearing all the hallmarks of the very best in contemporary Italian design from Laboratorio Associati in Milan. Only the lack of any real public rooms holds our grading back from being one of the highest in London. Private meeting room for up to 30. ***Rooms** 41.* AMERICAN EXPRESS *Access, Diners, Visa.*

Restaurant ★ £100

As of July 31st 1993 Gualtiero Marchesi's part-time association with the Halkin ended leaving Stefano Cavallini, after a summer stint in Japan, in full control. Well deserving of his star and upward arrow in last year's Guide his return at the beginning of September heralded new menus of a similar style and content to those he offered previously.
Lunch is of two-courses at £19.50 with desserts £5.50 extra. There is a choice of four dishes for each course. They change every four or five weeks. Evenings feature an à la carte menu with six choices per course. ***Seats** 50. Private Room 26. L 12.30-2.30 D 7.30-10.30. Closed L Sat & Sun. Set L £18/£24.50 Set D £24.50.*

WC2 Hampshire Hotel 78% £220

Tel 071-839 9399 Fax 071-930 8122 **HR**

31 Leicester Square WC2 7LH **Map 21 A3**

Work is now completed in Leicester Square and the hotel residents can fully enjoy its central location. Low-ceilinged public rooms have an elaborate decor with a strong Oriental theme through hand-woven Thai carpets and Chinese furnishings. Although not to scale with the 124 bedrooms, the small lounge with cosy sofas and fireplace, the wood-panelled bar and elegant restaurant have the comforting feel of a private club. Bedrooms vary in size, the most agreeable ones being the suites with large tinted picture windows overlooking Leicester Square. Decor is rather busy with chintzy flowery fabrics done in shades of pink or blue. Bathrooms, all in Italian marble and mahogany finish, are well appointed. The Penthouse suite, which can accommodate up to 80, has a beautiful view over Trafalgar Square and Westminster. ***Rooms** 124. Business centre, Oscars wine bar.* AMERICAN EXPRESS *Access, Diners, Visa.*

Restaurant £75

Intimate dining room with comfortable seating and an elaborate elegant decor. Cooking is of international influence and variable quality: polenta,

See over

green salad and Parma ham, crab spring roll with Oriental vegetables or braised scrag of lamb with couscous, cumin and lemon balm. Good-value luncheon menu, and less formal eating in Oscar's Wine bar. ***Seats** 55. Parties 50. Open 7-10pm L 12-3 D 6-10.45. Set L £15/£19.50 Set D £27.50.*

W1 Harbour City NEW £40

Tel 071-439 7859 **R**

46 Gerrard Street W1 **Map 21 A2**

From the profusion of Chinese restaurants on Gerrard Street here is one that stands out. Set on three floors, the restaurant is extremely busy with an almost exclusively Chinese clientele. Unlike most of its competitors in the street, staff take good care of their customers, advising on the menu or recommending dishes. Dim sum (served until 5pm) are selected from an extensive menu (of nearly 90 items) rather than from a trolley and are among the best in London, most being prepared to order. Other menus include a standard Chinese list and a chef's specials of mainly fish dishes such as steamed bean curd stuffed with fresh scallop in a black bean sauce, sautéed jellyfish with seafood in light wine sauce. Other tempting dishes include Cantonese hot pot and sizzling platters. Ingredients are fresh and of excellent quality. ***Seats** 160. Private Room 60. Meals noon-11.30. Closed 24 & 25 Dec. Set meals from £10.50.* AMERICAN EXPRESS *Access, Diners, Visa.*

W1 Hardy's £45

Tel 071-935 5929 **R**

53 Dorset Street off Baker Street W1 **Map 18 C2**

Lively bistro with tables on the pavement in fine weather. The menu changes every day, combining British classics like fish and chips or sausage and mash with vegetarian dishes, pasta and modern ideas like baked snapper with salsa verde and fried leeks. ***Seats** 80. Parties 20. Private Room 20. L 12.30-3.30 D 5.30-10.30. Closed Sat, Sun & Bank Holidays.* AMERICAN EXPRESS *Access, Visa.*

SW7 Harrington Hall 72% NEW £117

Tel 071-396 9696 Fax 071-396 9090 **H**

5-25 Harrington Gardens SW7 4JW **Map 19 B5**

Opened in April 1993, the impressive, newly refurbished building on Harrington Gardens is privately owned. The open-plan public rooms are airy and comfortable. Meals and afternoon teas are served to the sound of a mechanical baby grand piano. Large bedrooms offer extensive amenities: discreet door bells, spy-eyes, message telephone as well as the usual mini-bar, trouser press and tea/coffee facilities. Bathrooms are basic. There is a small fitness centre and sauna. Stylish conference facilities and a business centre. ***Rooms** 200. Gymnasium, sauna.* AMERICAN EXPRESS *Access, Diners, Visa.*

SW17 Harveys

Tel 081-672 0114 **R**

2 Bellevue Road SW17 7EG **Map 17 C6**

Information as we went to press was that Harveys was about to change its identity completely, with Marco Pierre White himself moving to the *Hyde Park Hotel* and *Harveys*, after a period of closure, reopening as a bistro, still under his auspices.

SW10 Harveys Café £30

Tel 071-352 0625 **R**

The Black Bull 358 Fulham Road SW10 9UU **Map 19 A6**

A bright restaurant above the the *Black Bull* pub with huge modern paintings on the walls and simple decor in Mediterranean blue and pine. Owner/chef Harvey Sambrook prepares a regularly changing menu of modern dishes with Mediterranean and Californian influences: chilled tomato and ginger soup, roasted peppers with feta cheese, pizza with marinated artichoke and sun-dried tomatoes, spiced chicken with salad and raita. Harvey's Bar, at street level, offers light snacks taken from the restaurant menu, and many wines by the glass. ***Seats** 60. Parties 35. L 12-3 D 7.30-11. Closed D Sun, L Mon, May & Aug Bank Holidays, last 2 weeks Aug, 1 week Christmas. Set L £5 Tue-Fri. No credit cards.*

Any person using our name to obtain free hospitality is a fraud.
Proprietors, please inform the police and us.

NW1 Hellas £30

Tel 071-267 8110 **R**

158 Royal College Street NW1 0TA **Map 16 C3**

Good Greek food at very reasonable prices, with a larger-than-usual menu. Chef's specialities include kioftedes (minced lamb grilled or skewered) and chicken grill. ***Seats** 60. L 12-3 D 6-12. Closed L Sat, all Sun, Bank Holidays.* AMERICAN EXPRESS *Access, Diners, Visa.*

NW4 Hendon Hall 63% £105

Tel 081-203 3341 Fax 081-203 9709 **H**

Ashley Lane NW4 1HE **Map 16 B1**

Once the home of actor/manager David Garrick, this Georgian building with a handsome portico is now a comfortably modernised hotel catering for private guests, banquets and conferences up to 330. The Pavilion Bar is open from 11am to 10pm. Children up to 15 stay free in parents' room. Near A1 and M1, but the setting is peaceful. No dogs. Mount Charlotte Thistle. ***Rooms** 52. Garden.* AMERICAN EXPRESS *Access, Diners, Visa.*

SW7 Hilaire ★↑ £85

Tel 071-584 8993 **R**

68 Old Brompton Road SW7 3LQ **Map 23 E1**

Unpretentious yet stylish little restaurant which has a peaceful decor in greenish shades of grey, black and white prints and discreet green plants behind its high windows. Chef Bryan Webb, of Welsh origin, skilfully executes its new menu of many influences. His cooking, free of gimmicks, is true to flavours and freshness. Dishes like oyster au gratin with laverbread and Stilton has the precision and balance of a metronome. More elaborate is the baked lemon sole with a herb crust served on a broad bean purée surrounded by grilled scallops and fresh broad beans in an olive oil vinaigrette, a delicate sonata of flavours. Other refreshingly simple dishes include brill in dill and mustard sauce, and roast rump of veal with Piedmontese pepper. Desserts are unpretentious with the likes of prune and almond tart with crème fraiche or pears poached in wine with cinnamon ice cream. An easy-to-use and manageable wine list at fair prices includes lots of half bottles and helpful notes. ***Seats** 40. Private Room 35. L 12.30-2.30 D 7-11.30. Closed L Sat, all Sun, Bank Holidays, 4 days Christmas, 4 days Easter. Set L £10.95-£14.45 Set D £25.* AMERICAN EXPRESS *Access, Diners, Visa.*

W11 Hilton International Kensington 67% £150

Tel 071-603 3355 Fax 071-602 9397 **HR**

179 Holland Park Avenue W11 4UL **Map 17 B4**

Large, busy, modern hotel next to Shepherds Bush roundabout. The Executive Floor has superior bedrooms and business facilities. The coffee shop is open 24 hours every day of the week. Banqueting and conference amenities for up to 250. ***Rooms*** *603. Hair & beauty salon, car hire desk, news kiosk.* AMERICAN EXPRESS® *Access, Diners, Visa.*

Hiroko Restaurant £80

High standards of cooking and service in a Japanese restaurant reached either from the street or through the hotel. The menu spans a wide range, including all the familiar dishes plus specialities such as sankaiyaki (beef, pork, chicken, prawns, scallops, oysters and vegetables cooked at the table and served with a soy-flavour sauce) or queen roll, with prawns, cucumber and mayonnaise. ***Seats*** *72. Parties 30. L 12-2.15 D 6-10.15. Closed Mon. Set L £15/£18 Set D £30/£32.*

NW8 Hilton International Regent's Park 73% £148

Tel 071-722 7722 Fax 071-483 2408 **HR**

18 Lodge Road St John's Wood NW8 7JT **Map 18 B1**

Close to London Zoo and Lord's cricket ground, this Hilton International numbers free parking and 24hr room service among its facilities. There are three restaurants (one Japanese, one modelled on a New York deli), a lounge bar, a well-equipped business centre and several conference suites catering for up to 150 delegates. Bedrooms, some with balconies, include Executive rooms and three-bedded rooms for family occupation. High-pressure showers are a good feature. No dogs. ***Rooms*** *377. Coffee shop (8.30am-11.45pm).* AMERICAN EXPRESS® *Access, Diners, Visa.*

Kashi Noki Restaurant £70

Sister restaurant to *Hiroko* (at the *Hilton International Kensington*), offering classic Japanese food, from a long sushi list (cuttlefish, sea urchin, sea eel, surf and giant clams, mackerel, tuna, salmon roe...) to beef teriyaki and shabu shabu. Unusual red bean or green tea ice creams. Choice of à la carte and interesting set menus. ***Seats*** *42. Parties 10. L 12-2 D 6-10. Closed Mon, 25 & 26 Dec, 1-3 Jan. Set L from £11 Set D from £30.*

N1 Hodja Nasreddin £25

Tel 071-226 7757 **R**

53 Newington Green Road N1 **Map 16 D2**

Turkish eating in friendly, homely surroundings. Highlights include houmus, mixed meze (5 dishes, minimum 2 people), spicy sausages and succulent kebabs. ***Seats*** *48. Parties 20. Private Room 35. Meals noon-3am. Closed 25 Dec.* AMERICAN EXPRESS® *Access, Visa.*

SW5 Hogarth Hotel 62% £85

Tel 071-370 6831 Fax 071-373 6179 **H**

Hogarth Road SW5 0QQ **Map 19 A5**

Modern hotel located in the quiet part of Hogarth Road (off Earls Court Road) and convenient for Earls Court exhibitions. Recently renovated bedrooms have an attractive emerald green decor. Amenities include satellite TV, trouser press, hairdryer, tea and coffee facilities and a small safe. Most bathrooms still need renovation. Children under 12 stay free in their parents' room. Secure underground parking (£10 per night). Marston Hotels. Limited 24hr room service is available. ***Rooms*** *85.* AMERICAN EXPRESS® *Access, Diners, Visa.*

SW7 Holiday Inn Kensington 68% £185

Tel 071-373 2222 Fax 071-373 0559 **H**

100 Cromwell Road SW7 4ER **Map 19 B5**

Right on Cromwell Road, opposite Gloucester Road underground station, a stylishly modern hotel behind an Edwardian facade with double or triple glazing for all bedrooms. There's one floor each of Executive and non-smoking rooms, plus 19 Duplex suites; some rooms are adapted for disabled guests. ***Rooms** 162. Keep-fit equipment, sauna, spa bath, steam room, café.* AMERICAN EXPRESS *Access, Diners, Visa.*

WC1 Holiday Inn Kings Cross/Bloomsbury 69% £135

Tel 071-833 3900 Fax 071-917 6163 **H**

1 Kings Cross Road WC1X 9HX **Map 16 C3**

Opened in April 1992, the capital's newest Holiday Inn is just a few minutes from Kings Cross station. A large floral display takes pride of place in the cool, marble-floored lobby and the lounge, decorated in autumnal shades, is roomy and restful. Bedrooms have all the Holiday Inn hallmarks: large beds (even single rooms get double beds), open clothes-hanging space and powerful showers over short tubs in the bathrooms. Extensive room service can run to a choice of hot dishes around the clock. Conference-room facilities for up to 250. Children under 19 stay free in parents' room. The whole hotel is air-conditioned. Very limited parking. ***Rooms** 405. Indoor swimming pool, gymnasium, squash, sauna, spa bath, steam room, solarium, beauty & hair salon.* AMERICAN EXPRESS *Access, Diners, Visa.*

W1 Holiday Inn Mayfair 72% £207

Tel 071-493 8282 Fax 071-629 2827 **H**

3 Berkeley Street W1X 6NE **Map 18 D3**

A splendid central location just a few steps from Bond Street, Green Park and the Royal Academy. The bar, lounge and restaurant merge one into the other and gain an elegant air from the moulded ceiling and glittering chandeliers. Good-size bedrooms (24hr room service) offer luxuriously large beds and all the expected accessories including air-conditioning and mini-bars. Executive rooms are even more generously proportioned and have fax machines, spa baths and bathrobes. Children stay free in parents' room. ***Rooms** 185. Coffee lounge (11am-11pm).* AMERICAN EXPRESS *Access, Diners, Visa.*

WC2 Hong Kong £40

Tel 071-287 0324 **R**

6 Lisle Street WC2 **Map 21 A2**

A cavernous setting serving a daytime selection of dim sum popular with snackers and a Cantonese menu of proverbial favourites like sculptured squid and prawn balls, fried noodles with roast pork, sizzling platters and hotpots (including exceptional braised lamb with dried bean curd). The more adventurous might choose crispy pig's intestines, fried fillet of eel, fried oyster with scrambled egg or even stir-fried carp with superior soup. ***Seats** 180. Parties 150. Meals 12-11.15. Closed 25 & 26 Dec. Set L from £10 Set D from £11.* AMERICAN EXPRESS *Access, Visa.*

EC1 The Hope & Sirloin £40

Tel 071-253 8525 **R**

94 Cowcross Street Smithfield EC1 **Map 16 D3**

Some of the biggest and best breakfasts in town are served in the dining room above a traditional Smithfield pub. Egg, bacon, sausage, black pudding, kidneys, livers, baked beans, tomatoes, mushrooms, toast and tea or coffee will set you back £7.50 and up for the day. Meat also features *See over* strongly at lunchtime with rack of lamb, steaks and a giant mixed grill. *Seats 32. Parties 16. Private Room 20. Meals 7.15am-10am & 12-2. Closed Sat, Sun & Bank Holidays.* AMERICAN EXPRESS *Access, Diners, Visa.*

W2 Hospitality Inn Bayswater 60% £102

Tel 071-262 4461 Fax 071-706 4560 **H**

104 Bayswater Road W2 3HL **Map 18 A3**

Practical and modern, with plenty of free parking in their own underground car park. Immediately opposite Hyde Park (Kensington Gardens) and a short walk from Notting Hill Gate. Children up to 16 stay free in parents' room. 66 rooms are designated non-smoking. ***Rooms** 175.* AMERICAN EXPRESS *Access, Diners, Visa.*

W1 Hospitality Inn Piccadilly 64% £149

Tel 071-930 4033 Fax 071-925 2586 **H**

39 Coventry Street W1V 8EL **Map 21 A3**

If you think that Piccadilly Circus is the hub of the universe, then hotels don't come more central than this Mount Charlotte Thistle establishment. Peace and comfort wait behind the grand Victorian facade. ***Rooms** 92.* AMERICAN EXPRESS *Access, Diners, Visa.*

SW3 L'Hotel £133

Tel 071-589 6286 Fax 071-225 0011 **HR**

28 Basil Street SW3 1AT **Map 19 C4**

Just yards from Harrods, accommodation at this *pension* (under the same ownership as *The Capital* hotel next door) comprises 11 individually designed twin-bedded rooms and one suite decorated in French country style. Continental breakfast is served in *Le Metro.* No dogs. ***Rooms** 12.* AMERICAN EXPRESS *Access, Diners, Visa.*

Le Metro £40

A bistro-cum-wine bar in the basement of the building serving coffee and breakfast from 8 till 11 in the morning and the full menu from noon onwards. A short, French-inspired menu ranges from salade niçoise or croque monsieur to boeuf bourguignon and navarin of lamb, although bangers and mash and seafood fettuccine also get a look in. Chocolate mousse cake and apple tart to finish, plus good coffee. A Cruover machine allows fine wines to be served by the glass; bottles are also fairly priced. ***Seats** 50. Parties 8. Meals Noon-10.30. Closed Sun, 25 & 26 Dec.*

WC2 The Howard 81% £254

Tel 071-836 3555 Fax 071-379 4547 **HR**

Temple Place Strand WC2R 2PR **Map 20 A2**

Handily sited off the Strand, "where the City of London meets the West End", the Howard is a hotel in the grand tradition. Reception staff and porterage are first-rate, well able to handle the demands of visitors. Public areas are dominated by the fine decorations, Adam-style friezes and Italian marble columns of the foyer-lounge, which typifies the ornate tone throughout. The Temple Bar has views over the tiered garden and leads through into the Quai d'Or restaurant; both are pretty in pink with ruched window drapes, plush green chairs and intricate ceilings. Bedrooms are mainly twin-bedded and classically furnished with French marquetry pieces and have modern comforts such as air-conditioning, individual heating control and multiple phones, plus superb marbled bathrooms. Best rooms have small terraces with panoramic views over the river Thames – from St Paul's to Westminster. A special Japanese breakfast (among others) with Japanese omelette, seaweed, soya bean soup, pickles, rice and Japanese tea is served either in the restaurant or in your room. Function rooms cater for up to 120. No dogs. ***Rooms** 137. 24hr lobby service, valeting.* AMERICAN EXPRESS *Access, Diners, Visa.*

Le Quai d'Or £100

The traditional classic carte befits the rose-pink rococo surroundings of a classic hotel restaurant. The cooking proved acceptable on a recent visit – a fish mousse arrived light and fluffy, accompanied by a decent watercress sauce. Beef Wellington to follow was tender, pink and baked in pastry that remained crisp until the waiter poured the Madeira sauce all over it. Good selection of not overcooked vegetables. Diplomat pudding to finish – one of a selection from the trolley – was a classic rendition, complete with a delicious red fruit sauce. Several inexpensive wines on a list which unusually includes Swiss and Austrian bins. ***Seats** 95. Parties 25. L 12.30-3 D 6.30-11 (Sun till 10.30). Set L £25*

W2 Hsing £50

Tel 071-402 0904 **R**

451 Edgware Road W2 1TH **Map 18 B1**

Metal, wood, water, fire and earth: Hsing represents the five elements on which the restaurant decor and philosophy are based. The interesting menu puts an emphasis on fish: special crispy fish with vegetables or sweet and sour sauce or Hsing special feast of braised shark fin or abalone. Meat dishes include a delicious, crispy, fragrant and aromatic lamb and vegetarians are not forgotten. ***Seats** 60. Parties 12. L 12-3 D 6-11.30. Closed Sun, 3 days Christmas.* AMERICAN EXPRESS *Access, Diners, Visa.*

SW1 Hunan £50

Tel 071-730 5712 **R**

51 Pimlico Road Belgravia SW1W 8NE **Map 19 C5**

Small Chinese restaurant where the chef-owner prepares Hunan specialities. The atmosphere is quiet and homely with classical music in the background and very attentive service. The menu is limited and offers interesting dishes like crispy green beans in peppery chili, camphor wood-and tea-smoked duck or lamb in Hunan hot and spicy sauce. A special leave-it-to-us feast is prepared for a minimum of two from £19.30. ***Seats** 45. Parties 35. L 12.30-3 D 6.30-11.30 (Sun 7-11). Closed L Sun, 4 days Christmas, 2 days Easter.* AMERICAN EXPRESS *Access, Visa.*

SW1 Hyatt Carlton Tower 88% £240

Tel 071-235 5411 Fax 071-245 6570 **HR**

2 Cadogan Place SW1X 9PY **Map 19 C4**

Fashionable shopping in Knightsbridge and Sloane Street is close at hand to this first-class hotel where great emphasis is placed on personal service and highly professional staff maintain an excellent reputation. From standard rooms through to the spacious de luxe suites the level of decor is exemplary; the Presidential suite on the 18th floor has a full-time butler and maid and is furnished in truly sumptuous style. Beds are extravagantly large and furnishings lavish and luxurious. The gracious Chinoiserie lounge still holds its place as one of *the* London venues for exchanging smart gossip; a harpist plays during afternoon tea. The 9th-floor Peak health club is another notable feature, with rooftop views and a club room restaurant and bar. Banqueting/conference facilities for 300/260. One child can stay free in parents' room. No dogs. ***Rooms** 224. Garden, gymnasium, sauna, steam bath, solarium, beauty and hair salon, tennis, valeting, Chinoiserie (7am-11pm).* AMERICAN EXPRESS *Access, Diners, Visa.*

Chelsea Room ↑ £112

The conservatory dining room, which overlooks Cadogan Gardens, is a sumptuous setting. It gives a bright and open feel to the rest of the dining room, elegantly decorated with pickled wood panelling. In the evening, soft lights and piano music complete the picture. Following the Mediterranean craze, long-serving chef Bernard Gaume's menu offers *soupe*

See over

au pistou with Dublin Bay prawns and lobster, *sole au four catalane, tian d'agneau niçois* along with *saumon en papillote beurre au caviar* or *mignon de canard aux agrumes et poivre vert.* It's difficult to be disappointed by the high standard of cooking and the constant quailty practised over the years. *Assiette de desserts Robert Mey*, a sample of six light desserts, is a refreshing way to end the meal. The second restaurant is the club-like *Rib Room*, renowned for traditional roasts and English fare. The wine list is quite pricy and mostly French, though the short New World section is carefully chosen. ***Seats** 60. Parties 30. Private Room 48. L 12.30-2.45 D 7-10.45 (Sun to 10). Set L £21.50 Set D £29.50.*

SW1 Hyde Park Hotel 82% £244

Tel 071-235 2000 Fax 071-235 4552 **H**

66 Knightsbridge SW1Y 7LA **Map 19 C4**

Commanding an unrivalled position in Knightsbridge, opposite Harvey Nichols department store, with a suitably imposing Edwardian frontage and interior to match. The reception foyer and central lobby are particularly impressive, with marble walls and floors of eight different colours, pilasters with Corinthian capitals picked out in gold, ornate ceilings and glittering chandeliers. The Park Room, is elegantly comfortable, and next to it the Ferrari Lounge serves as residents' lounge and cocktail bar. Bedrooms are individually and charmingly decorated, with quality matching fabrics, traditional polished wood furniture and good armchairs and settees; bathrooms have loudspeaker extensions, telephones and bidets. Service is good, with numerous smart and attentive staff. 19 elegant suites are decorated with antiques and overlook the Serpentine in Hyde Park. Valet parking. Up to 250 delegates can be accommodated theatre-style. The food at the Hyde Park has not always matched the grand surroundings, but news as we went to press was that Marco Pierre White was about to move here from *Harveys*, where he first caused a sensation on the gastronomic scene. Forte Exclusive. ***Rooms** 185. Gymnasium, valeting.* AMERICAN EXPRESS *Access, Diners, Visa.*

W1 Ikeda £100

Tel 071-629 2730 **R**

30 Brook Street W1Y 1AG **Map 18 C3**

Traditional Japanese cooking by Mr Ikeda in a popular little West End restaurant. A place at the bar gets you a ringside seat to the sushi show, while the tables are all close enough to the kitchen to make you feel part of the action. The daily-changing chef's specials are the choice of many, or you can venture round an à la carte selection. Lunchtime bills are generally much lower than those for dinner. ***Seats** 30. Parties 8. L 12.30-2.30 D 6.30-10.30 (Sat 6-10). Closed L Sat, all Sun, Bank Holidays. Set L from £12 Set D from £30.* AMERICAN EXPRESS *Access, Diners, Visa.*

W1 Ikkyu £50

Tel 071-636 9280 **R**

67a Tottenham Court Road W1 **Map 18 D2**

Busy basement Japanese restaurant by Goodge Street underground station offering fine home-style cooking (robatayaki) on a long and varied menu. Good-value lunchtime menus include grilled fish set, sushi set and ramen noodles. Finish off with fresh fruit. ***Seats** 65. Parties 30. L 12.30-2.30 D 6-10.30. Closed L Sun, all Sat, 10 days Christmas.* AMERICAN EXPRESS *Access, Diners, Visa.*

Changes in data sometimes occur in establishments after the Guide goes to press. Prices should be taken as indications rather than firm quotes.

EC3 Imperial City NEW £55

Tel 071-626 3437 Fax 071-338 0125 **R**

Royal Exchange Cornhill EC3V 3LL **Map 20 C3**

In the brick-lined vaults beneath the Royal Exchange, Imperial City is a welcome, and from initial visits, a busy and popular newcomer to the square mile. Decor is bright and colourful, the menu, compiled with the help of Ken Hom short and succinct featuring a mix of Northern Chinese dishes and other regional specialities. The food is very much geared to City palates, spicing, even of Szechuan dishes, being fairly conservative. Service is friendly and quick if required. ***Seats*** *175. Private Room 100. Meals 11.30am-8.30pm. Closed Sat, Sun & Bank Holidays. Set L from £13.50.* AMERICAN EXPRESS® *Access, Diners, Visa.*

SW1 L'Incontro £100

Tel 071-730 3663 Fax 071-730 5062 **R**

87 Pimlico Road SW1 8PH **Map 19 C5**

A stylishly modern, up-market Italian restaurant in the same stable as *Santini*. Lunchtime now sees a new 2- and 3-course menu with a small choice; cover charges and the automatic addition of 12% service manage to push up the bill. Specialities on the carte include Venetian-style bean and pasta soup, warm salad of scampi, king prawns, cannellini beans and rucola, roast lamb cutlets in sweet and sour sauce (*agnello in agrodolce*) and grilled sardines. Italian wines dominate the wine list which has a handful of luxury clarets and champagnes for those with expense accounts or just expensive tastes. ***Seats*** *65. Parties 50. Private Room 30. L 12.30-2.30 D 7-11.30 (Sun to 10.30). Closed L Sat & Sun, Bank Holidays. Set L £13.50/£16.80.* AMERICAN EXPRESS® *Access, Diners, Visa.*

W1 Inter-Continental Hotel 84% £307

Tel 071-409 3131 Fax 071-409 7460 **HR**

1 Hamilton Place Hyde Park Corner W1V 1QY **Map 19 C4**

Exciting new changes have taken place on Hyde Park Corner with the creation of a modern new-look entrance, the transformation of the Grand Ballroom (now with natural daylight), and a business centre on the ground floor. Always popular with Americans both on business and on holiday, the hotel has a vast, elegant foyer leading to a stylish lounge well provided with supremely comfortable seating. Bedrooms are sleek and airy with seating areas, air-conditioning, double-glazing and mini-bars; bathrooms provide quality towelling and good toiletries. Two brand new 7th-floor meeting rooms, which can be joined together, have superb views of the London skyline; there are conference and banqueting facilities for 1000/750. The hotel offers a luxury airport service – the chauffeur will telephone ahead to advise reception of your arrival ensuring minimum delay when checking-in. ***Rooms*** *467. Plunge pool, gymnasium, sauna, spa bath, solarium, beauty salon, coffee shop (7am-11pm, Sat till 11.30).* AMERICAN EXPRESS® *Access, Diners, Visa.*

Le Soufflé® Restaurant ★★↑ £150

Subtle improvements to the decor have been made, the restaurant retaining its elegantly modern and ultra-stylish decor of cool cream and pale turquoise. Lighting is very kind, being softly diffused. A white baby grand now occupies the centre of the room, a pianist playing soothing renditions of light classics and popular music. This fine setting is the perfect backdrop to Peter Kromberg's extraordinary talents. Now in his 18th year here he continues as a leader, nurturing and encouraging new talents as in his current team of excellent sous chefs headed by Richard Thompson. Together they produce menus of superbly constructed complexity, the individual dishes creating genuine frissons of delight. Each day sees a new stunning eight-course gourmet menu, the different dishes all perfectly balanced and complementing one another. Portions too, are carefully judged to leave one very pleasantly content but not satiated. There is an underlying classicism to the cooking though combinations are such that the dishes are far removed from traditional concepts. The results are ethereal as in a salad of grilled green asparagus spears flavoured with a citrus fruit vinaigrette with a light crème fraiche, a smooth fluffy smoked salmon bavarois and slices of the softest, most delicate smoked salmon creating a dish of pure enchantment. Soufflés, sadly missing from the gourmet menus, are the signature dishes of the restaurant with a choice of both savoury and sweet. For instance a steamed spinach soufflé is served in an artichoke bottom with roasted pine kernels, braised anglerfish cheeks in tomatoes and a herb-flavoured balsamic vinegar and olive oil vinaigrette dressing. Main courses are exemplified by a pan-fried supreme of Lunesdale duck, the skin replaced by crisply cooked potato scales and served with a Cabernet Sauvignon vinegar sauce, apples cooked in cider and cream, artichokes, fresh broad beans and a dice of beetroot – a wealth of mouthwatering flavours and textures. There are no less than four different soufflés on the dessert menu including a marbled bitter chocolate and orange soufflé flavoured with Grand Marnier. This is cooking of the highest order, the restaurant well deserving its award of Restaurant of the Year (see earlier pages). Note the inexpensive sommelier's suggestions on the mostly French wine list, which is disappointingly thin in the New World. ***Seats** 70. Parties 12. L 12.30-3 D 7-10.30. Closed Sun, Mon, 26 Dec, Good Friday. Set L £25.50 Set D £43*

> We welcome bona fide complaints and recommendations on the tear-out pages at the back of the book for readers' comments. They are followed up by our professional team.

SW1 Isohama £55

Tel 071-834 2145 **R**

312 Vauxhall Bridge Road SW1V 1AA **Map 19 D4**

Whitewashed walls, bare darkwood tables and purple velvet chairs add up to a simply decorated little restaurant just a few steps from Victoria station. Japanese dishes both familiar and less so make up an interesting menu which staff will happily explain to you. Good cooking, unfussy presentation, and it's open early enough for a meal before *Starlight Express*. Lunchtime sees simpler fare, but using equally good-quality ingredients. The special lunch at £6.50 gets you deep-fried chicken, garlic rice, mixed vegetable salad, soya bean soup, pickles and fruit. ***Seats** 30. L 12-2.30 D 6-10.30. Closed L Sat, all Sun, Bank Holidays. Set L from £6.50 Set D from £25.* AMERICAN EXPRESS *Access, Diners, Visa.*

N16 Istanbul Iskembecisi £30

Tel 071-254 7291 Fax 071-881 3741 **R**

9 Stoke Newington Road N16 8BH **Map 16 D2**

The smartest Turkish restaurant in the area. Pale pink walls, chandeliers and ornate gilt framed pictures contrast with the taped Turkish music playing in the background. The menu of authentic, simple fare includes tripe soup, boiled sheep's head soup and whole roast lamb's head as popular dishes with a clientele of largely Turkish émigrés. The rest of the menu features more familiar kebabs and quite competently prepared dishes like kleftiko. Instead of the usual thin pitta bread here you'll find their version: thick, bubbly, doughy and quite delicious. Staff are helpful and friendly. ***Seats** 80. Parties 40. Meals 5pm-5am (Sun from noon).* AMERICAN EXPRESS *Access, Visa.*

WC2 The Ivy ★ £70

Tel 071-836 4751 Fax 071-497 3644 **R**

1 West Street WC2H 9NE **Map 21 B2**

The design-conscious Ivy has mirrored wood panelling, stained-glass diamond lattice windows and art all around. Following along the lines of its glamorous heyday in the 30s, the customers are still the theatrical and theatre-going crowd who come for the company, the atmosphere and the thoroughly reliable, easy-to-enjoy cooking. Many dishes are from the traditional English and international repertoire – potted shrimps with toast, Caesar salad, terrine of foie gras, eggs Benedict, salmon fish cakes with sorrel sauce, liver and bacon, rack of lamb – while others have a more modern or exotic ring, including roasted artichokes and leeks with treviso and truffle oil, crostini of lamb's brains and sweetbreads, and seared wild salmon with endive and wild garlic. Desserts are equally diverse and there are a couple of savouries. Good choice of coffees and teas, and plenty of good drinking around £20 on a shortish, no-nonsense wine list. No longer a Sunday brunch menu, but instead a well-priced set lunch (Sat & Sun) supplementing the carte. ***Seats** 100. Parties 8. Private Room 60. L 12-3 D 5.30-12. Closed 25 & 26 Dec, 1 Jan. Set L (Sat & Sun) £12.50.* AMERICAN EXPRESS *Access, Diners, Visa.*

W1 Jade Garden £35

Tel 071-437 5065 **R**

15 Wardour Street W1V 3HA **Map 21 A2**

The dim sum are among the best in town and they serve them until 5pm – Sunday lunchtime is particularly popular. Elsewhere on the long menu are sections for prawns, eel, oysters, abalone, a dozen ways with pork, sizzling dishes and noodles (fried or in soup). The cooking is mainly Cantonese, but one of the set menus features Peking cuisine. ***Seats** 150. Private Room 70. Meals 12-11.45 (Sat from 11.30, Sun 11.30-10.45). Closed 25 & 26 Dec. Set meals from £9.50.* AMERICAN EXPRESS *Access, Visa.*

SW10 Jake's NEW £45

Tel 071-352 8692 **R**

2 Hollywood Road SW10 9HY **Map 19 B6**

On the corner premises previously occupied by *Vin Santo*, Jake's is a bright, summery restaurant (with a little open courtyard at the back) serving a straightforward menu of English and international dishes. Duck liver paté, chicken and ham pie and bread-and-butter-pudding are popular choices, also Caesar salad, spaghetti carbonara, sole Walewska. ***Seats** 56. Parties 12. Private Room 35. L 12.30-2.45 D 7.30-11.45. Closed D Sun, 1 week after Christmas. Set L £6.95.* AMERICAN EXPRESS *Access, Visa.*

WC2 Joe Allen £40

Tel 071-836 0651 Fax 071-497 2148 **R**

13 Exeter Street WC2E 7DT **Map 17 C4**

A brash, resiliently American basement restaurant with a menu that runs from roast fennel and tomato soup to chopped chicken liver, warm goat's cheese on rocket with sweet chili jelly, and barbecue ribs with spinach, black-eyed peas and corn muffins. Also main-course salads and some Mexican-influenced dishes. Two sittings in the evening, the second post-theatre from 10pm. ***Seats** 150. Parties 8. Meals noon-1am (Sun to 11.45). Closed 24 & 25 Dec. No credit cards.*

Consult page 16 for a full list of starred restaurants

SW3 Joe's Cafe £70

Tel 071-225 2217 **R**

126 Draycott Avenue SW3 3AH **Map 19 B5**

Stylish split-level brasserie-restaurant with an oyster and black decor offering a simple, fashionable menu. Dishes reflect a wide range of cuisines, from croustade of wild mushrooms with goat's cheese, marinated breast of chicken orientale and Porkinson's bangers and mash. ***Seats** 80. L 12-3.30 (Sun 10-3.30) D 6.30-11.15 (Sat at 7.30). Closed D Sun, 25 & 26 Dec.* AMERICAN EXPRESS *Access, Diners, Visa.*

WC2 Joy King Lau £50

Tel 071-437 1132 **R**

Leicester Street WC2 **Map 21 A2**

The decor is modern, done in claret and blue tones with an intimate atmosphere. The menu offers well-executed familiar dishes like Peking duck or beef in black bean sauce, along with more unusual duck webs with sea cucumber, fried pig intestine and braised fish lips. There is a large selection of fish and shellfish on the extensive menu. Dim sum served until 5pm are among the best in London. ***Seats** 240. Parties 12. Private Room 60. Meals 11am-11.30pm. Closed 25 & 26 Dec.* AMERICAN EXPRESS *Access, Diners, Visa.*

> Many establishments are currently on the market, so ownership could change after we go to press.

W11 Julie's £70

Tel 071-229 8331 **R**

135 Portland Road Holland Park W11 4LW **Map 17 A4**

A Holland Park institution, popular for its wine bar and Sunday lunches. The succession of dining rooms each has a unique atmosphere, from the flowery champagne bar to a fairy pink room or even a smart white theme conservatory. Cooking emphasises English cuisine, big on sweet and sour associations, some more successful than others: duck and chicken liver paté with gooseberry and mango chutney or English rack of lamb with honey garlic crust. Puddings are rich and scrumptious: butterscotch, banana and allspice crepes or apple, fig and cardamom strudel. A good selection of English cheeses, including Innes goat's cheeses, can be enjoyed with a glass or port. The wine list is well priced and includes organic Cotes du Rhone and Italian white. ***Seats** 100. Parties 40. Private Room 26. L 12-2.45 (Sun 12.30-3) D 7.30-11 (Sun to 10). Closed 4 days Easter, 1 week Christmas. Set L £14.95 (Sun £15.£18) Set D £19.95.* AMERICAN EXPRESS *Access, Diners, Visa.*

WC2 Kagura NEW £50

Tel 071-240 0634 Fax 071-240 3342 **R**

13-15 West Street Cambridge Circus WC2H 9BL **Map 21 A2**

Part of an entertainment complex including a basement karaoke and top-floor nightclub, the restaurant, done in a stylish black and grey decor, has a sushi bar and teppanyaki counter. Along with the expected sushi, sashimi, tempura and sukiyaki, the menu offers unusual specialities like tuna with yam potatoes, vinegared seafood and grilled aubergine topped with white and dark miso plus noodle dishes and rice with Japanese tea. Dishes are beautifully executed with some palate-puzzling flavour contrasts. Each dish is served on a different colour plate and pickled vegetables are beautifully carved. ***Seats** 20. L 12-2.30 D 6-11. Closed L Sat, Sun. Set D from £25.* AMERICAN EXPRESS *Access, Diners, Visa.*

W2 Kalamaras £40

Tel 071-727 9122 **R**

76-78 Inverness Mews W2 3JQ **Map 18 A3**

On of the best loved, busiest and liveliest of London's Greek restaurants, largely because it's also one of the best. It's genuinely Greek, as opposed to the usual Cypriot, and its menu extends far beyond familiar dishes like *taramasalata, dolmades* and *moussaka.* Try *fassolia plaki* (baked haricot beans with tomatoes, onions and parsley), fillets of hake and salmon baked in filo pastry, young lamb baked with garlic and lemon juice and any of the daily fish specials. The speciality sweet is *bouyatsa* (a sweetmeat with eggs, semolina and cinnamon, served hot). There's a list of 20 Greek wines. The restaurant is located at the end of a mews running parallel to Queensway. *Kalamaras Micro,* an unlicensed sibling, is at no. 66 (Tel 071-727 5082). ***Seats*** *92. Parties 12. Private Room 28. D only 6.30-12. Closed Sun, Bank Holidays. Set D from £15.50.* AMERICAN EXPRESS *Access, Diners, Visa.*

W1 Kaspia NEW £70

Tel 071-493 2612 Fax 071-408 1627 **R**

18/18a Bruton Place W1X 7AH **Map 18 C3**

The London offshoot of the renowned Paris caviar shop and restaurant is tucked away discreetly off Berkeley Square. It's a comfortable, well-appointed place, with lightwood panelling, sea-blue tablecloths, Russian pictures and plates on display and Russian bassi profundi gently exercising their tonsils on the sound system. If the order is for caviar all round the bill here will naturally be hefty, but elsewhere on the menu prices are reasonable, particularly for the splendid smoked fish salad – a very generous plateful of smoked salmon, trout, eel, sturgeon and cod roe. There's now a short list of daily specials, often including fish soup, fish cakes with sorrel sauce, and beef stroganoff. ***Seats*** *40. Private Room 16. L 12-3 D 7-11.30. Closed Sun.* AMERICAN EXPRESS *Access, Diners, Visa.*

W1 Kaya £70

Tel 071-437 6630 **R**

22 Dean Street Soho W1V 5AL **Map 21 A2**

Korean food, not as varied as Chinese nor as "pretty" as Japanese, finds a friendly home in Soho. Some items, including squid, pork fillet, venison and marinated steak for the national dish *bulgogi,* are prepared at the table. 15% service is added to your bill. ***Seats*** *70. Private Room 40. L 12-3 D 6-11.30. Closed L Sun, also Christmas/New Year. Set D £38.* AMERICAN EXPRESS *Access, Diners, Visa.*

SW1 Ken Lo's Memories of China £75

Tel 071-730 7734 Fax 071-730 2992 **R**

67 Ebury Street SW1W 0NZ **Map 19 C5**

London's serious Chinese eating is largely concentrated in Soho, but Ken Lo's long-established restaurant is outside that area, just moments from Victoria coach and railway stations. It's much more comfortable and sophisticated (and, it must be said, rather more expensive) than its Soho counterparts, and chef Kam-Po But continues to produce fine dishes such as siu mai (steamed dumplings), pomegranate prawn balls, iron-plate sizzling dishes and Mongolian barbecued lamb in lettuce puffs. 'Old family favourites and specialities' include Szechuan double-cooked pork and Peking mu shu rou (quick-fried sliced pork with eggs and tree-ear mushrooms). Cheaper eating is available at the Chelsea branch (qv). ***Seats*** *100. Parties 40. Private Room 20. L 12-2.45 D 7-11.30. Closed L Sun, Bank Holidays, few days at Christmas. Set meals from £16.* AMERICAN EXPRESS *Access, Diners, Visa.*

SW10 Ken Lo's Memories of China £60

Tel 071-352 4953 Fax 071-351 2096 **R**

Harbour Yard Chelsea Harbour SW10 **Map 19 B6**

The Chelsea Harbour branch of Ken Lo's Ebury Street original caters for all pockets and purses by offering various à la carte and set menus. Best value is undoubtedly provided by the bar snack menu (12-2.30 Mon-Fri) with main courses priced under £3. The favourite way to start is with a selection of excellent crispy dim sum. The main menu ranges far and wide, with Cantonese lobster and steamed sea bass at the luxury end. ***Seats** 175. Private Room 70. L 12-2.30 D 7-10.45 (Sun 12.30-10). Closed 25 & 26 Dec, 1 Jan. Set L from £8 Set D from £24.* AMERICAN EXPRESS *Access, Diners, Visa.*

WC1 Kenilworth Hotel 63% £172

Tel 071-637 3477 Fax 071-631 3133 **H**

97 Great Russell Street WC1B 3LB **Map 21 B1**

A handsome redbrick building near the British Museum. The foyer gives a good impression, decorated in warm colours, with plenty of seating. All public areas, including the restaurant, have recently been refurbished. There are seven conference rooms, the larger with a capacity of 100. Bedrooms are quite pretty in floral pinks and green, and some top-floor rooms have four-posters. All are double-glazed, with two armchairs and a desk. In the bedrooms are plenty of shelves and good towels and toiletries. No dogs. Edwardian Hotels. ***Rooms** 192.* AMERICAN EXPRESS *Access, Diners, Visa.*

NW1 Kennedy Hotel 63% £102

Tel 071-387 4400 Fax 071-387 5122 **H**

Cardington Street NW1 2LP **Map 18 D1**

Conveniently situated near to the west side of Euston station, a modern hotel with simply decorated rooms. Close to Drummond Street where there's a fine choice of Indian restaurants. Conference facilities for up to 100, banqueting to 85. Mount Charlotte Thistle. ***Rooms** 360. Business centre.* AMERICAN EXPRESS *Access, Diners, Visa.*

W8 Kensington Close 59% £99

Tel 071-937 8170 Fax 071-937 8289 **H**

Wrights Lane W8 5SP **Map 19 A4**

Excellent leisure facilities and a convenient location are the main attractions in this large hotel. Rooms are on the small side, but the majority have been recently refurbished and good planning, plus availability of leisure facilities, goes a long way to compensate for lack of space. Frequent special promotions can be very good value, but remember to ask for a refurbished room. Breakfasts, in The Original Carvery, are excellent. ***Rooms** 530. Indoor swimming pool, gymnasium, squash, sauna, solarium, beauty salon, pool table.* AMERICAN EXPRESS *Access, Diners, Visa.*

SW5 Kensington Court Hotel £59

Tel 071-370 5151 Fax 071-370 3499 **H**

33 Nevern Place SW5 9NP **Map 19 A5**

Six-storey modern block in a Victorian terrace. Decent-size bedrooms, bar, basement restaurant. Car parking facility for 10 cars. ***Rooms** 35.* AMERICAN EXPRESS *Access, Diners, Visa.*

SW7 Kensington Manor £94

Tel 071-370 7516 Fax 071-373 3163 **H**

8 Emperor's Gate South Kensington SW7 4HH **Map 19 A4**

Small bed and breakfast hotel just moments from Gloucester Road underground station (cross Cromwell Road into Grenville Place which leads to Emperor's Gate) and handy for the South Kensington museums. 24hr private bar. Extensive buffet breakfast. Children up to 12 share parents' room free of charge. ***Rooms** 15.* AMERICAN EXPRESS *Access, Diners, Visa.*

W8 Kensington Palace Thistle 67% £131

Tel 071-937 8121 Fax 071-937 2816 **H**

De Vere Gardens W8 5AF **Map 23 D1**

Well-equipped bedrooms, two bars, conference rooms (for up to 250) and an all-day restaurant serving dishes from around the world. It's just across the road from Kensington Gardens and close to the Albert Hall and high-street shops. ***Rooms** 298. News kiosk, coffee shop (7am-11pm).* AMERICAN EXPRESS *Access, Diners, Visa.*

W8 Kensington Park Thistle Hotel 67% £166

Tel 071-937 8080 Fax 071-937 7616 **H**

16-32 De Vere Gardens W8 5AG **Map 19 A4**

Quiet, comfortable and fairly roomy hotel opposite Kensington Gardens. Though lacking the facilities of many big hotels, it has two reasonable restaurants in the Cairngorm Grill and Monique's Brasserie, the latter open 7am-10.30pm. ***Rooms** 332.* AMERICAN EXPRESS *Access, Diners, Visa.*

W8 Kensington Place ★ £60

Tel 071-727 3184 **R**

205 Kensington Church Street W8 7LX **Map 18 A3**

One of the capital's culinary hot spots, busy from the day it opened in 1987, and always full at peak times in spite of the addition of 40 covers a couple of years ago. It's also one of the noisier restaurants in town, abuzz with lively conversation, with no great concessions to comfort or ornamentation. At one end is a glitzy bar, at the other a vast mural depicting an alfresco eating scene in gay pastel shades. Rowley Leigh's modern style of cooking is as frill-free as the table settings, relying on simple techniques and fresh, honest flavours. Chicken and goat's cheese mousse, *omelette fines herbes* and griddled foie gras with sweetcorn pancake are more or less permanent choices among the dozen or so starters, while main course are typified by herb-crusted baked cod, breast of duck with griottines and rib-eye steak with shallots and red wine sauce. There's an interesting selection of worldwide wines, including several dessert wines by the glass to accompany tarte tatin or caramel mousse. ***Seats** 130. L 12-3 (Sat & Sun to 3.45) D 6.30-11.45 (Sun to 10.15). Closed 3 days Christmas, 3 days Aug. Set L £13.50. Access, Visa.*

SW7 Khan's of Kensington £50

Tel 071-584 4114 Fax 071-581 5980 **R**

3 Harrington Road SW7 3ES **Map 19 B5**

Just a few steps from South Kensington Station. Light green is the main colour of the stylish modern decor, and the greens and pinks of the chairs are taken up in the waiters' waistcoats. Tiny lights are hung from tramline wires, and a silk banana plant stands in one corner. Downstairs is a colonial-style lounge bar. The menu includes familiar items from the lexicon of Indian cuisine and some less usual choices such as *gujrati patra* (lotus leaves rolled with herbs and sesame seeds), fried pomfret, tandoori salmon

See over

(marinated in yoghurt, dill and spices) and *simla mirchi* – capsicum stuffed with cheese and fresh herbs. Besides the à la carte there are meat and vegetarian set menus for one, a set lunch (Mon-Fri) and a Sunday lunchtime buffet (£8.95). ***Seats** 60. Private Room 30. L 12-2.30 (Sun 1-3.30) D 5.30-11.30 (Sun from 6.30). Closed 25 & 26 Dec. Set L from £7.50 Set D from £14.50.* AMERICAN EXPRESS *Access, Diners, Visa.*

SW3 Khun Akorn £65

Tel 071-225 2688 Fax 071-225 2680 **R**

136 Brompton Road Knightsbridge SW3 1HY **Map 19 B4**

Owned by the Imperial Hotel in Bangkok, with a sister branch in Paris, this is an up-market Thai restaurant, where particular attention has been put into the decor, reminiscent of colonial days. The menu lists well-known Thai specialities and doesn't venture much into originality. Cooking is reliable and prices substantial, except for a bargain lunch menu. ***Seats** 60. Parties 30. L 12-3 D 6.30-11. Closed 25 & 26 Dec, 1 Jan. Set L £12.50 Set D £17.50.* AMERICAN EXPRESS *Access, Diners, Visa.*

SW7 Khyber Pass £30

Tel 071-589 7311 **R**

21 Bute Street SW7 3EY **Map 19 B5**

Popular little Indian restaurant established well over 20 years ago and still attracting a loyal local following with its reliable run-of-the-mill cooking. Curries climb all the way up to the blistering Bangalore phal. ***Seats** 36. L 12-2.45 D 6-11.30. Closed 25 & 26 Dec.* AMERICAN EXPRESS *Access, Diners, Visa.*

SW10 Kingdom NEW £50

Tel 071-352 0206 **R**

457 Fulham Road SW10 9UZ **Map 19 B6**

A quiet, civilised restaurant with very polite and obliging staff. Greenery running up to a skylight is a central feature of the back room, whose walls are lined with prints of Chinese emperors. The menu is pan-Chinese, interesting without being outré, and cooking is of a good standard. Best dishes include prawn-stuffed squid with Szechuan peppercorn salt, grilled chicken with garlic and sizzling dishes in which you choose your own sauce from five offered. ***Seats** 80. Private Room 30. L 12-2.30 D 6-11.30. Closed Bank Holidays. Set L £5.50 Set D from £12.50 (min 2).* AMERICAN EXPRESS *Access, Diners, Visa.*

SW1 Knightsbridge Green Hotel £117

Tel 071-584 6274 Fax 071-225 1635 **PH**

159 Knightsbridge SW1X 7PD **Map 19 C4**

A family-run private hotel in the heart of Knightsbridge offering comfortable, spotlessly-kept accommodation with double-glazing and the usual conveniences – except, that is, for a restaurant or bar as the hotel is unlicensed; however, this is hardly an inconvenience given the location. Breakfast (English or Continental) is served in the bedrooms and tea/coffee and cakes are available all day long in the Club Room. No dogs. ***Rooms** 24. Closed 4 days Christmas.* AMERICAN EXPRESS *Access, Visa.*

SW5 Krungtap NEW £25

Tel 071-259 2314 **R**

227 Old Brompton Road Earls Court SW5 **Map 19 A5**

Acceptable cooking at more than acceptable prices in a friendly little Thai restaurant at the busy junction of Old Brompton Road and Earls Court Road. Best are soups, salads, one-plate noodle and rice dishes, and specials which range from fish cakes, mussels and herring roes to frogs' legs, rabbit and venison. ***Seats** 30. D only 6-10.30.* AMERICAN EXPRESS *Access, Diners, Visa.*

SW1 Kundan **£55**

Tel 071-834 3434 **R**

3 Horseferry Road SW1P 2AN **Map 18 D5**

Politician-spotting comes as a free side order with a meal in this comfortable and roomy basement restaurant on the division bell circuit. All parties are agreed on the quality of the Mogul-inspired Indian cooking. Yakhni (chicken consommé), mulligatawny or shami kebab ('a favourite of Nawabs') could precede dishes which are both rich and fragrant: chicken or lamb jalfrezi, chicken makhani, boiled eggs coated with marinated minced meat. Note also dishes from the tandoor, the day's dal and very good vegetable patties. ***Seats** 130. L 12-3 D 7-11.30. Closed Sun, Bank Holidays. Set L £15 Set D £15.50.* AMERICAN EXPRESS *Access, Diners, Visa.*

W1 Lal Qila **£40**

Tel 071-387 4570 **R**

117 Tottenham Court Road W1P 9HN **Map 22 B3**

A serious, elegant restaurant in a busy location near the BT Tower. The comparatively short North Indian menu covers mainstream tandoori offerings and lamb and chicken curries, plus specials that include lamb brain masala, tandoori trout, fish curry and thalis. Fresh mangoes to finish when in season. ***Seats** 78. L 12-3 D 6-11.30. Closed 25 & 26 Dec. Set L from £10 Set D from £15.* AMERICAN EXPRESS *Access, Diners, Visa.*

SW1 The Lanesborough 89% **£290**

Tel 071-259 5599 Fax 071-259 5606 **H**

1 Lanesborough Place Hyde Park Corner SW1X 7TA **Map 22 D3**

Originally Lanesborough House, a private residence demolished in the 1820s and replaced by St George's Hospital which in turn was gutted in 1987 but with most of the original Regency facade kept intact. Now transformed into one of London's grandest hotels and a sister to Caroline Rose Hunt's *Mansion on Turtle Creek* in Dallas, the Lanesborough enjoys a fine central location overlooking Hyde Park Corner. Great care has been taken to faithfully restore some of the original Regency-era designs and furnishings. Enormous and exotic flower arrangements abound complementing the polished marble floors and the colourful and stylish neo-Georgian furniture and furnishings. The hotel's bar – The Library – has rich mahogany panelling inset with bookshelves which, along with leather-upholstered seating, creates a deeply civilised effect. Next door is The Withdrawing Room, a sumptuously elegant room with a striking old-gold colour scheme. Public rooms have many quiet corners and a general level of intimacy is to be found here that one might more usually associate with country house hotels in rural England. Very effective triple soundproofed glazing throughout the hotel ensures that outside noises appear as no more than a distant murmur. On arrival, guests are issued with their own personalised stationery, while each of the 95 bedrooms (which include 46 suites) has two direct access telephone lines as well as a fax line (their system allows for 1000 numbers with 200 reserved permanently for repeat guests). Security, too, is given a very high priority with 35 surveillance cameras, window sensors and alarms that include a sophisticated door-key system; briefcase-sized safes are also provided. Upon being shown to their rooms, guests are introduced to a butler who, in terms of service and information, is their only point of contact; all the butlers have been trained in the traditional manner and will unpack, pack, iron, and even run baths as required. Bedrooms are equipped to a high-tech standard as well as having exquisite decor, with comfort being paramount. Each has a VCR, CD and tape decks – all fully remote and secreted in attractive pieces of furniture, together with the TVs. Bathrooms are

See over

lined with white marble and have every conceivable amenity including, in most, steam showers and spa baths. Valet parking for the basement car park. ***Rooms*** *95. Car hire desk, coffee shop (7am-midnight).* American Express *Access, Diners, Visa.*

The Dining Room ★ £110

The grand dining room decor, done in pure Regency style, is a trip into the past. The bull's blood walls and columns, rather gaudy in daylight, get a strange reflection from the evening lights, giving a surrealist atmosphere to the room's pink and gold tones. In the evenings light guitar music echoes softly. Service, sometimes clumsily stiff and ceremonious, doesn't blend into the magical surroundings. In this grand dining room chef Paul Gayler offers skilled, elaborate cooking with a tempting menu where vegetables play an important part; a set vegetarian menu is offered and precise associations with meat and fish are created: tart of sweetbread and white chicory, steamed salmon with asparagus, cucumber and watercress or fillet of hare with beetroot and clove chutney. On a recent visit some dishes like roast rack of lamb cooked in hay with garden herbs, a spectacular sight when brought to the table in a sculpted bread basket, rather surprisingly lacked flavour and interest; overly salted mashed potato and olive oil and floury fresh peas were also disappointing. But these mistakes were quickly forgiven thanks to the perfection found in desserts like nougatine parfait with orange sorbet and orange sabayon or a soufflé with prunes and Armagnac served with caramel ice cream. For a change of scenery, coffee and sweetmeats can be served in the sumptuous withdrawing room. Roast sirloin of beef is served daily from a trolley at lunchtimes. ***Seats*** *66. L 12.30-2.30 D 7-10.30. Closed all Sat & Sun. Set L from £19.50 Set D from £29.50.*

The Conservatory £80

The decor is Chinese-inspired under a high glass cupola housing giant potted palms; however, by late evening candle-light and the sound of splashing fountains and tinkling piano keys turn the mood into pure New Orleans. The menus are international, with forceful flavourings and presentation in the modern idiom; the choice is wide – from Thai mussels with minted peanut sauce or bresaola to fillet of beef with celery, walnuts and Stilton sauce, cappuccino brulée and lemon tart with sour cherry syrup – and the results mixed. Fixed-price menus offer only alternatives at each course. Breakfast (if you want huevos rancheros with chorizo sausage and guacamole and spicy red salsa you can have it) and afternoon tea (3-6pm) are also served in the Conservatory. Dinner dances Fri & Sat. ***Seats*** *106. Parties 20. L 12.30-2.30 (Sun brunch 11-3) D 7-12. Set L £24.50 (Sun brunch £21 children under 12 £15) Set D £26.50.*

W1 Langan's Bistro £65

Tel 071-935 4531 **R**

26 Devonshire Street W1N 1RJ **Map 18 C2**

A popular bistro next to its big brother *Odin's* just off Marylebone High Street. The short menu is mostly mainstream, with dishes like spinach, bacon and crouton salad, baked snails with wine and garlic, grilled fillets of lemon sole, pan-fried kidneys with creamed onion sauce and grilled sirloin steak with a tarragon sauce. ***Seats*** *30. Parties 12. L 12.30-2.30 D 7-11.30. Closed L Sat, all Sun, Bank Holidays.* American Express *Access, Diners, Visa.*

W1 Langan's Brasserie ↑ £85

Tel 071-491 8822 **R**

Stratton Street W1X 5FD **Map 18 D3**

An enormous brasserie on two floors, its walls are covered in modern art. Downstairs is the place to see and be seen, but the Venetian room above has its own quieter charm and a speciality – roast beef from the trolley. The long menu includes many well-loved standards (pea and ham soup,

Burgundy snails, cod and chips, veal Cordon Bleu) and some dishes that hit a more modern note, typified by grilled swordfish with lime butter sauce or cauliflower and celeriac mousse with a red pepper sauce. Almost 30 desserts, from strawberries and clotted cream to *kougelhopf glacé au Gewurztraminer.* ***Seats*** *275. Parties 12. L 12.30-3 D 7-11.45 (Sat 8-12.45). Closed L Sat, all Sun, Bank Holidays.* AMERICAN EXPRESS *Access, Diners, Visa.*

W1 The Langham 75% £222

Tel 071-636 1000 Fax 071-323 2340 **HR**

Portland Place W1N 3AA **Map 18 C2**

Built in 1865 and lavishly restored to pristine splendour, the Langham Hilton stands across the road from a temple of the 30s – the BBC's Broadcasting House. Smart doormen in Tsarist uniforms set the tone for the stylish interior which has been transformed into a sophisticated modern hotel retaining many of the original features. The Grand Entrance Hall with polished marble, oriental rug-strewn floors and thick Portland stone pillars leads to a light yet fairly intimate Palm Court, where afternoon tea is served (to the accompaniment of a pianist) and food is available all day and all night. Heavy burgundy velvet drapes divide this from Tsar's – a vodka, champagne and caviar bar. The Chukkha Bar is very much in the gentleman's club tradition with polo memorabilia decorating the walls. Bedrooms, furnished in solid, traditional style have all the expected extras but the suites, of which there are 50, also have video recorders and hi-fi units. Bathrooms throughout are in white marble and, while all have good showers, only some have bidets. A health club opened last year. Conference facilities for up to 320, banqueting to 280. Recent visits found the King's Room restaurant on better form than the larger Memories of the Empire. ***Rooms*** *411. Gymnasium,steam room, sauna.* AMERICAN EXPRESS *Access, Diners, Visa.*

The King's Room £100

With just 20 seats, the King's Room has the proportions and atmosphere of a private dining room. Light stencilled walls, a ceiling trompe l'oeil of the sky surrounded by tropical plants and a burgundy decor recall an elegant colonial atmosphere. Executive chef Anthony Marshall proposes a short menu of light dishes. Some combinations are unnecessarily complicated but dishes are generally pleasant and always beautifully presented: snow peas, asparagus, vacherin and tomatoes served with an orange dressing, smoked corn-fed chicken with a millefeuille of pancakes and wild mushrooms served on a truffle dressing. Orange and lemon tart with a lime-flavoured syrup sauce is an interestuing and successful dessert. Well thought-out wine list with a good choice from the New World. ***Seats*** *20. L 12.30-3 D 6.30-10.30. Closed Sun.*

W8 Launceston Place £65

Tel 071-937 6912 Fax 071-938 2412 **R**

1a Launceston Place W8 5RL **Map 19 A4**

Nick Smallwood and Simon Slater may have made more waves at their fashionable Kensington Place, but this quieter, more comfortable amd more elegant restaurant off the tourist track has also proved a considerable success. British cooking appeals to the traditional palates of loyal locals as well as to the slightly more adventurous on a menu that could include Jerusalem artichoke soup with hazelnuts, herb and Parmesan risotto, roast monkfish with thyme, vegetable couscous and lamb chump with basil and tomato. Supplementing an interesting wine list are a few suggestions to accompany dessert: perhaps a late harvest New Zealand Gewurztraminer or Somerset cider brandy. ***Seats*** *70. Private Room 16. L 12.30-2.30 (Sun to 3) D 7-11.30. Closed L Sat, D Sun, Bank Holidays. Set L £12.50/£15.50.* AMERICAN EXPRESS *Access, Visa.*

NW2 Laurent £28

Tel 071-794 3603 **R**

428 Finchley Road NW2 2HY **Map 16 B2**

In surroundings as simple as the menu Laurent Farrugia has run his couscous restaurant for ten years. This excellent North African dish of steamed semolina grain comes in three forms: *vegetarian* with basic vegetables, *complet* with added lamb and merguez, and *royal* boosted to festive proportions by lamb chop and brochette (chicken and fish versions are available on request, and a take-away service is offered). The only starter is *brique à l'oeuf,* a deep-fried thin pastry parcel with a soft egg inside – fun but tricky to eat. Algerian or Moroccan wine stands up well to the hearty food. ***Seats** 36. L 12-2 D 6-11. Closed Sun, Bank Holidays, 3 weeks Aug. Access, Visa.*

W11 Leith's £104

Tel 071-229 4481 **R**

92 Kensington Park Road W11 2PN **Map 18 A3**

1994 is the 25th anniversary of Prue Leith's renowned restaurant located between Notting Hill and Ladbroke Grove. Decor has remained the same for many years, namely, white-framed mirror windows arranged on oatmeal coloured walls and a spotlight starred ceiling. Many of the staff too, are long-serving and possess that quality of discreet charm that matches the modern bourgeois cooking of Alex Floyd. This is one of the few serious restaurants to offer a full vegetarian menu (priced identically to the full menu). One change that has occurred is that sweets are now à la carte and no longer served from a trolley. The hors d'oeuvre still come on a trolley and make a splendid beginning to a meal that features careful cooking with due thought shown in the flavour combinations which all mix well with one another. From the trolley to begin come the likes of artichoke and olive pie, crab quenelles in orange sauce as well as the more familiar: game terrine, quail's eggs and chargrilled Mediterranean vegetables. Pan-fried sea bream with saffron noodles in a delicate butter sauce garnished with tomato and basil is one of a choice of some nine main dishes from a seasonally changing menu. Other choices include a rich and tender casserole of ox cheeks with celery accompanied by creamy mashed potato or lamb cutlets topped with olive and parsley mousse and surrounded by a red wine sauce. Well worth the 15 minute wait is a light fluffy soufflé such as pineapple with rum which comes with a side dish of delicious coconut ice cream. Excellent house selections and monthly recommendations alongside a super list of very well-chosen wines. ***Seats** 80. Parties 38. Private Room 40. D only 7.30-11.30. Closed 2 days Aug Bank Holiday, 4 days Christmas. Set D £30-£40.* AMERICAN EXPRESS *Access, Diners, Visa.*

NW1 Lemonia £30

Tel 071-586 7454 Fax 071-483 2630 **R**

89 Regent's Park Road NW1 8UY **Map 16 C3**

Roomy though this splendid Greek restaurant certainly is, it's still full to bursting at peak evening times. Outside and in there's a Mediterranean air, with lots of light and masses of hanging flower baskets. Table settings are very simple, so too the main menu, but Lemonia scores through reliability and the lovely relaxed atmosphere. The speciality is the meze selection at £8.95 (plus extra for pitta bread), which should satisfy even the biggest appetite. Look, too, for the daily specials that supplement the regular menu. ***Seats** 135. Parties 24. Private Room 40. L 12-3 D 6-11.30. Closed L Sat, D Sun. Access, Visa.*

Set menu prices may not always include service or wine.

SW11 **Lena's** **£40**

Tel 071-228 3735 **R**

196 Lavender Hill SW11 1JA **Map 17 C5**

Good Thai cooking on a menu with a particularly good choice of seafood. ***Seats** 50. L 12.30-2.30 D 6.30-11 (Sun from 7). Closed Christmas, Easter, 1 Jan. Set L £12 Set D £15/20.* AMERICAN EXPRESS *Access, Diners, Visa.*

W8 **Hotel Lexham** **£63**

Tel 071-373 6471 Fax 071-244 7827 **H**

32 Lexham Gardens W8 5JU **Map 19 A4**

In a surprisingly peaceful garden square within walking distance of Kensington's shops and museums, the Lexham has been in the same family ownership since 1956 and provides good-value bed and breakfast accommodation. Cheapest rooms (from £45 twins) are without private facilities. No dogs. ***Rooms 66. Garden.*** AMERICAN EXPRESS *Access, Visa.*

W1 **The Lexington** **NEW** **£60**

Tel 071-434 3401 **R**

45 Lexington Street W1R 3LG **Map 18 D3**

Once upon a time there was Sutherlands, a restaurant of some style and distinction which offered elaborate dishes. It's now a much simpler but still smartly contemporary restaurant with high-back navy-blue leather-look banquettes and small beech tables, and the food has also undergone a dramatic change. The relatively limited choice follows current trends although execution does falter at times. Red onion soup, salad of goat's cheese and roast pepper, baked tilapia fillets with herb crust and garlic roasted rack of pork with braised cabbage are typical. ***Seats** 50. Parties 24. Private Room 20. L 12-3 D 6-11.30. Closed Sun, Easter & Christmas Bank Holidays. Set D £10.* AMERICAN EXPRESS *Access, Diners, Visa.*

W1 **Lido** **£40**

Tel 071-437 4431 **R**

41 Gerrard Street W1V 7LP **Map 21 A2**

A maze of sparsely decorated rooms behind darkened glass in the middle of Chinatown's main street. Night owls flock here to eat from a wide-ranging menu that's particularly strong on seafood, with sections for crab and lobster, scallops and squid, prawns, eel and abalone. ***Seats** 140. Parties 50. Meals 11.30am-4.30am. Closed 25 Dec. Set D £10.50.* AMERICAN EXPRESS *Access, Diners, Visa.*

W1 **Lindsay House** **£80**

Tel 071-439 0450 Fax 071-581 2848 **R**

21 Romilly Street Soho W1V 5TG **Map 21 A2**

Ring the bell to gain admittance through the heavy front door of the 17th-century Lindsay House. A comfortable lounge has sofas and armchairs for drinks, while upstairs the dining room is in country-house style. 2-course lunches (guaranteed served within 45 minutes) might offer potted shrimps and mussels or a warm salad of chicken livers and artichoke followed by puff pastry-topped steak and mushroom pie or steamed salmon with a fennel and saffron sauce; those with a little more time on their hands might stay and enjoy the home-made ice creams or Stilton or delve into the à la carte to find pan-fried scallops with cullen skink, rack of lamb with rosemary jus, wild mushroom ravioli or rice pudding served with fresh fruit and spiced custard. Conveniently situated (and open early enough) for the Shaftesbury Avenue theatres. Mostly French wines at reasonable prices. ***Seats** 40. Private Room 20. L 12.30-2.30 (Sun to 2) D 6-12 (Sun 7-10). Closed 25 & 26 Dec. Set L £10/£14.75.* AMERICAN EXPRESS *Access, Diners, Visa.*

is our symbol for an outstanding wine list.

W1 **Little Akropolis** **£30**

Tel 071-636 8198 **R**

10 Charlotte Street W1P 1HE **Map 18 D2**

Long-established Greek restaurant in a street of restaurants. Meze for variety, klefticon, moussaka, kebabs and the other Greek classics. ***Seats** 30. L 12-2.30 D 6-10.30. Closed L Sat, all Sun, Bank Holidays, 2 weeks Aug.* AMERICAN EXPRESS *Access, Diners, Visa.*

W1 **Lok Ho Fook** **£35**

Tel 071-437 2001 **R**

4 Gerrard Street W1 **Map 21 A2**

The menu at this simply appointed Chinatown restaurant covers Cantonese, Peking and Szechuan dishes – from a choice of 16 soups to sea-spice braised egg plant, fried squid cake with minced meat, belly pork and yam hot pot, to braised carp with ginger and spring onion, and all the usual favourites. There's also a pictorially descriptive dim sum menu for daytime eaters (noon until 6pm). ***Seats** 100. Private Room 40. Meals 12-11.45 (dim sum 12-6). Closed 25 & 26 Dec. Set L from £6.60.* AMERICAN EXPRESS *Access, Diners, Visa.*

W2 **London Embassy** **68%** **£132**

Tel 071-229 1212 Fax 071-229 2623 **H**

150 Bayswater Road W2 4RT **Map 18 A3**

Modern accommodation overlooking Kensington Gardens, appealing to both business and tourist visitors. Children up to 16 stay free in parents' room. 30 of the rooms are designated non-smoking. ***Rooms** 193.* AMERICAN EXPRESS *Access, Diners, Visa.*

W1 **London Hilton on Park Lane** **75%** **£212**

Tel 071-493 8000 Fax 071-493 4957 **H**

22 Park Lane W1A 2HH **Map 18 C3**

Towering above Park Lane, rooms on the higher floors of London's first skyscraper hotel enjoy panoramic views across the capital. A few easy chairs and settees on a carpeted island, amidst a sea of marble, in the spacious lobby are the only lounge seating although the Victorian-themed St George's Bar offers comfortable leather tub chairs. Other public areas include an all-day brasserie, Trader Vic's Polynesian-styled restaurant in the basement and the Windows of the World restaurant (with good lunchtime cold buffet) and cocktail bar on the 28th floor. Standardised bedrooms are of a reasonable size, without feeling spacious, and have polished mahogany furniture, which neatly hides the multi-channel TV, and the convenience of telephones at both desk and bedside in addition to an extension in the marble bathroom. De luxe and Executive rooms are the same size as the others, though bathrooms are larger, but have newer lightwood furniture and more stylish soft furnishings. The latter also enjoy the privilege of a special Club Lounge with complimentary Continental breakfast, drinks, use of small meeting room, free local phone calls (from the lounge) and separate check-in and out. There are over 50 full suites, some luxurious, others in similar style to the standard rooms. Beds are turned down on request and there is an extensive 24hr room service menu. ***Rooms** 448. Sauna, beauty & hair salon, brasserie (7am-12.45am Fri & Sat to 1.45am).* AMERICAN EXPRESS *Access, Diners, Visa.*

W1 London Marriott 77% £280

Tel 071-493 1232 Fax 071-491 3201 **H**

Grosvenor Square W1A 4AW **Map 18 C3**

A redbrick Georgian facade heralds the prime Mayfair location of this modern hotel (entrance in Duke Street). Public areas include a small foyer with sofas set in mirrored alcoves, a comfortable lounge and a panelled bar. Bedrooms are big and well designed, with large double beds, armchairs and plenty of modern desk furniture. Greens and pinks predominate among the fairly sober soft furnishings. Each bedroom has its own air-conditioning. Superior Executive rooms and suites enjoy their own lounge and complimentary happy hour cocktails and Continental breakfast. Bathrooms are on the small side, but are comprehensively kitted out. No dogs. Conference/banqueting facilities for 800/550. ***Rooms*** *223. Valeting, flower shop, coffee shop (10.30am-1am).* AMERICAN EXPRESS *Access, Diners, Visa.*

W2 London Metropole Hotel 69% £182

Tel 071-402 4141 Fax 071-724 8866 **H**

Edgware Road W2 1JU **Map 18 B2**

The new £50 million addition, an interesting sight of modern architecture on Edgware Road, now hosts impressive conference facilities, an open-plan marble lobby and lounge, a well-fitted leisure centre, two restaurants and more up-to-date bedrooms. Despite the new business image, the majority of the bedrooms (572) remain ordinary in comfort and decor, more suited for groups than executives. However the newly-built Crown bedrooms and suites are attractively shaped and furnished. Seating areas, mini-bars and complimentary newspapers are features, and most bathrooms have separate showers. Conference facilities are the highlight of the new building, from the Palace suites which can accommodate 1,000 delegates to the 20 syndicate rooms. Children up to 16 stay free in parents' room. ***Rooms*** 747. *Indoor swimming pool, keep-fit equipment, sauna, spa bath, solarium, kiosk, coffee shop (7am-11pm).* AMERICAN EXPRESS *Access, Diners, Visa.*

W1 London Mews Hilton on Park Lane 67% £139

Tel 071-493 7222 Fax 071-629 9423 **H**

2 Stanhope Row Park Lane W1Y 7HE **Map 18 C3**

Close to Park Lane, tucked away behind the London Hilton this is a small (for the area) hotel with the look of a club or town house. ***Rooms*** 72. AMERICAN EXPRESS *Access, Diners, Visa.*

W14 London Olympia Hilton 66% £149

Tel 071-603 3333 Fax 071-603 4846 **H**

380 Kensington High Street W14 8NL **Map 17 B4**

The closest hotel to the Olympia exhibition halls, a busy conference and tour group hotel with a choice of standard or superior Plaza rooms. State-of-the-art TVs and video systems. ***Rooms*** *406. Coffee shop (7am-10.30pm).* AMERICAN EXPRESS *Access, Diners, Visa.*

W6 Los Molinos NEW £35

Tel 071-603 2229 **R**

127 Shepherds Bush Road W6 **Map 17 B4**

Tapas come in two sizes at this popular pine-furnished restaurant next to Brook Green. Served in pretty earthenware dishes, they number about 60, including crisp-battered squid, aubergine croquettes, potato and chorizo stew and monkfish skewered with peppers and onion. ***Seats*** *80. Parties 10. Private Room 40. L 12-3 D 6-12 (Sat from 7). Closed L Sat, all Sun & Bank Holidays.* AMERICAN EXPRESS *Access, Diners, Visa.*

SW5 Lou Pescadou £50

Tel 071-370 1057 **R**

241 Old Brompton Road Earls Court SW5 9HP **Map 19 A5**

The nautical decor points to the main attraction, which runs from oysters, mussels (marinière and stuffed) or fish soup to daily specials such as red mullet, skate or an excellent *brandade de morue*. Also good are omelettes, pasta, pizza and pissaladière; steaks for the red-blooded. It's quiet at lunchtime, but in the evening it fills up, so arrive early or expect a wait, as they don't take bookings. Lou Pescadou is just by the junction with Earls Court Road. ***Seats** 60. Private Room 40. L 12-3 D 7-12. Closed 25 & 26 Dec.* AMERICAN EXPRESS *Access, Diners, Visa.*

SW1 The Lowndes Hyatt Hotel 76% £233

Tel 071-823 1234 Fax 071-235 1154 **H**

Lowndes Street Belgravia SW1X 9ES **Map 19 C4**

The Lowndes Hyatt is the smaller, more intimate sister hotel to the nearby *Hyatt Carlton Tower* (where guests may use the Peak Health Club and charge restaurant meals to their room here). Public rooms are limited to a small limed-oak panelled lounge area partly open to the lobby and an all-day brasserie (doubling up as the bar) with pavement tables in summer. Bedrooms are appealing with good-quality darkwood furniture, chintzy floral curtains and more masculine check-patterned bedcovers over duvets. All are air-conditioned, but controllably so (and the windows open), and have smart, marble bathrooms with good towelling. There are five splendidly-appointed suites. Beds are turned down in the evening, but room service ends at midnight. 32 of the rooms are designated non-smoking. The new wood-panelled Library meeting room overlooks a garden/terrace and holds up to 25 people in theatre-style. No dogs. ***Rooms** 78. Brasserie (7am-11.15pm), tennis.* AMERICAN EXPRESS *Access, Diners, Visa.*

EC3 Luc's Restaurant & Brasserie £50

Tel 071-621 0666 **R**

17-22 Leadenhall Market EC3V 1LR **Map 20 C2**

Well located in the very centre of Leadenhall Market, this busy French brasserie is open Monday to Friday for lunch (dinner by arrangement for large parties only). Food is well prepared and deftly served, from fish soup, duck terrine and vegetable pancakes to brochettes of coquilles St Jacques and speciality steaks with béarnaise sauce. Classic desserts include profiteroles and crepes Suzette. ***Seats** 150. L only 11.30-3. Closed Sat, Sun, Bank Holidays, 5 days Christmas.* AMERICAN EXPRESS *Access, Visa.*

SE19 Luigi's £65

Tel 081-670 1843 **R**

129 Gipsy Hill SE19 1QS **Map 17 D6**

The standard of cooking here remains reliable and consistent. The long-standing menu offers daily specials to supplement the choice of Italian classics. There are fairly few pasta dishes (linguine with clams and home-made cannelloni are favourites available as either starter or main course) but a good choice of antipasti, fish, meat and poultry in generally familiar preparations. ***Seats** 65. Private Room 25. L 12-2.30 D 6-11. Closed L Sat, all Sun, Bank Holidays.* AMERICAN EXPRESS *Access, Diners, Visa.*

SW7 Majlis £35

Tel 071-584 3476 **R**

32 Gloucester Road SW7 4RB **Map 19 B4**

Same ownership as *Memories of India* a few doors away, with a similar menu based around lamb, chicken and prawns (plus a fair vegetarian choice). A la carte, or set menus for one upwards. ***Seats** 36. L 12-2.30 D 6-12. Closed 25 & 26 Dec. Set meals from £14.95.* AMERICAN EXPRESS *Access, Diners, Visa.*

W8 Malabar £40

Tel 071-727 8800 **R**

27 Uxbridge Street Notting Hill W8 7TQ **Map 18 A3**

Indian restaurant behind the Coronet cinema, with a look and style all its own. The look is Mediterranean (an Italian restaurant was on the site previously) but the home-style cooking features unusual dishes like charcoal-grilled chicken livers, chili bhutta (sweetcorn, chili, green peppers), chicken cooked with cloves and ginger, and skewered king prawns in lemon sauce. Accompaniments include preparations of banana and pumpkin. More everyday items, too, plus a vegetarian thali, a set menu for two and a good-value Sunday buffet lunch. ***Seats** 56. Parties 15. Private Room 20. L 12-3 (Sun from 12.30) D 6-11.15. Closed 4 days Xmas, last week Aug. Set meals from £11.75. Access, Visa.*

SW6 Mamta NEW £30

Tel 071-736 5914 **R**

692 Fulham Road London SW6 5SA **Map 17 B5**

A partnership of ex-*Mandeer* chefs has recently opened at the Parsons Green end of Fulham Road. The restaurant has something of a spartan air with quarry-tiled floor and mushroom-coloured walls hung with earthy coloured Indian art. The food has an ethereal quality – the cooking of vegetables and exotic spices creating a myriad of stunning flavours and textures completely obviating the need for meat. The selection of dishes is long and, considering only vegetables are used, surprisingly varied. Traditional Indian set meals represent excellent value. All the food is served on and eaten off polished stainless-steel platters with helpful and amiable service making the experience a highly enjoyable one. ***Seats** 42. Parties 25. L 12.30-3 D 6-10.30 (Fri-Sun till 11.30). Closed 25, 26 Dec & 1 Jan. Set L £4.95 (Mon-Sat).* AMERICAN EXPRESS *Access, Diners, Visa.*

W2 Mandarin Kitchen £32

Tel 071-727 9012 **R**

14 Queensway W2 3RX **Map 18 A3**

A spacious restaurant with twin arched Artex ceilings, plastic plants and quaint 70s' mauve vinyl seating. The speciality is seafood – fresh lobsters, crabs, carp and eel are all available as well as some delicious sea bass and king prawn dishes. The menu additionally runs through the gamut of familiar Peking and Cantonese dishes, everything being competently and very enjoyably prepared with good use of fresh spicing. Quiet at lunchtimes but booking advisable in the evenings, when it's at its best. ***Seats** 110. Parties 30. Meals 12-11.30. Closed 24 & 25 Dec. Set meals from £8.90.* AMERICAN EXPRESS *Access, Diners, Visa.*

We endeavour to be as up-to-the-minute as possible, but inevitably some changes to key personnel may occur at restaurants and hotels after the Guide goes to press.

W1 Mandeville Hotel 62% £130

Tel 071-935 5599 Fax 071-935 9588 **H**

Mandeville Place W1M 6BE **Map 18 C2**

Sprawling, purely functional hotel behind Wigmore Street with an all-day coffee house, two bars and a late night bar lounge. Close to Oxford Street shops. ***Rooms** 165.* AMERICAN EXPRESS *Access, Diners, Visa.*

W11 Manzara NEW £25

Tel 071-727 3062 **R**

24 Pembridge Road Notting Hill Gate London W11 3HG **Map 18 A3**

In the window is a mouthwatering array of home-baked pastries, beyond it a smart modern restaurant serving Turkish specialities. Main courses – cooked in foil, casseroled or charcoal grilled – are served with pommes noisettes or Basmati rice. ***Seats** 40. Parties 40. Meals 8am-midnight (Sun from 10).* AMERICAN EXPRESS *Access, Diners, Visa.*

WC2 Manzi's £70

Tel 071-734 0224 Fax 071-437 4864 **R**

1 Leicester Street WC2H 7BL **Map 21 A2**

London's oldest seafood restaurant offers a largely unchanging menu of fish and shellfish, usually at its best when prepared in the simplest ways: fried whitebait, potted shrimps, grilled sardines, skate with black butter, battered squid, skewers of scallops and bacon. Strawberry tart is the favourite sweet. Choose the street level room for buzz and banter, upstairs for a more sedate ambience. The restaurant has sixteen basic letting bedrooms. ***Seats** 200. Parties 20. L 12.30-3 D 5.30-11.30 Closed Sun, Christmas.* AMERICAN EXPRESS *Access, Diners, Visa.*

E14 Manzi's £50

Tel 071-538 9615 **R**

Turnberry Quay Pepper Street E14 9TS **Map 16 D3**

Lost in the middle of the Isle of Dogs, a glass-fronted room overlooking Millwall Dock, busy at lunchtime but less so in the evening. Simple decor with red check tablecloths; fish, such as simply grilled sardines and skate au beurre noir, is the main strength on a mixed Italian and French menu. Wine bar upstairs, outside eating on the waterfront. No children under 5. Sister to *Manzi's* in Leicester Street, WC2. ***Seats** 80. Parties 14. L 12-3 D 6-11. Closed Sat & Sun, Bank Holidays.* AMERICAN EXPRESS *Access, Diners, Visa.*

W1 Marble Arch Marriott 68% £177

Tel 071-723 1277 Fax 071-402 0666 **H**

134 George Street W1H 6DN **Map 18 C2**

Formerly a *Holiday Inn*, the hotel has completed its refurbishment, favouring the public rooms and two floors of Executive bedrooms. Darkwood clubby decor gives an elegant feel throughout. The Executive bedrooms are the most comfortable, with three telephones, including one in the bathroom, mini-bar and quality tea/coffee facilities. The Executive lounge provides free soft drinks and complimentary Continental breakfast. Rooms in general are of a good size. Unrefurbished standard ones have basic amenities; twins and double beds are ideal for families. Free parking for guests. ***Rooms** 239. Indoor swimming pool, keep-fit equipment, sauna, spa bath, solarium, whirlpool bath, beauty salon, gift shop.* AMERICAN EXPRESS *Access, Diners, Visa.*

WC1 The Marlborough 69% £190

Tel 071-636 5601 Fax 071-636 0532 **H**

9-14 Bloomsbury Street WC1B 3QD **Map 21 B1**

In the heart of Bloomsbury, just off New Oxford Street and close to the British Museum, the restored Edwardian-style facade gives a good impression of the mix of modern amenity and old-fashioned comfort within. Liveried porters, fresh flowers and green leather settees greet guests in the lobby, beyond which there is a mix of both quiet and busy public rooms. Porcelain and polished brass lamps add a touch of elegance to the bedrooms, where children up to 12 stay free with parents. 50 of the rooms are designated non-smoking. Conference/banqueting facilities for 200. Edwardian Hotels. ***Rooms 169.*** AMERICAN EXPRESS *Access, Diners, Visa.*

W2 Maroush £60

Tel 071-723 0773 **R**

21 Edgware Road W2 **Map 18 C3**

Probably London's most luxurious Lebanese restaurant, serving a standard range of above-average hot and cold starters and mainly charcoal-grilled main courses of lamb and chicken. Cover charge £1.50 lunchtime, £3 in the evening. Minimum charge £38 after 10pm. No cheques. ***Seats 95.*** *Parties 95. Meals 12 noon-2am.* AMERICAN EXPRESS *Access, Diners, Visa.*

Also at:

Maroush II 38 Beauchamp Place SW3. Tel 071-581 5434. Open till 5am. **Map 18 C3**

Maroush III 62 Seymour Street W1. Tel 071-724 5024. Open till 1am. **Map 19 C4**

W1 Masako £100

Tel 071-935 1579 **R**

6 St Christopher's Place W1M 5HB **Map 18 C2**

Delightful Japanese restaurant with friendly, attentive staff and traditional decor of black lacquered tables, open screens and red plush chairs. A fine selection of set meals provides good value, using quality ingredients and showing delicacy in preparation. Soft-shell crab, deep-fried oysters, fish bouillon soup and teriyaki fillet steak sit happily alongside the sushi, sashimi, sukiyaki and kaiseki dinners. ***Seats 80.*** *Parties 18. Private Room 35. L 12-2 D 6-10. Closed Sun, Bank Holidays. Set L from £20 Set D from £35.* AMERICAN EXPRESS *Access, Diners, Visa.*

Our inspectors *never* book in the name of Egon Ronay's Guides. They disclose their identity only if they are considering an establishment for inclusion in the next edition of the Guide.

W1 May Fair Inter-Continental 79% £270

Tel 071-629 7777 Fax 071-629 1459 **HR**

Stratton Street W1A 2AN **Map 18 C3**

For a hotel with so many rooms the public areas have a surprisingly intimate feel; the small lounge area opposite the reception desk is a little exposed, perhaps, but a tranquil atmosphere is created by the harpist who plays there each afternoon. The bars have red leather seating, the smaller Chateau cocktail bar (open to 2am with live piano music) sporting photos of many showbiz personalities who have stayed at the hotel. Spacious

See over

bedrooms featuring silk moiré walls come in two different styles, English or French; the former with green leather armchairs and traditional darkwood furniture, the latter with velvet soft furnishings and French-style furniture. Under the direction of general manager Dagmar Woodward, levels of service are high, right from the uniformed doorman to extensive room service providing hot meals at all hours. There's a luxurious health club, a new business centre, and the theatre can accommodate around 290 for conferences. The Crystal Ballroom seats 300. Children up to 14 stay free in parents' room. No dogs. Reduced tariff from June to early Sept. ***Rooms** 287. Indoor swimming pool, sauna, solarium, keep-fit equipment, beauty salon, news kiosk, valeting.* AMERICAN EXPRESS *Access, Diners, Visa.*

Le Chateau Restaurant — £75

The setting is stylish and relaxed for consistent and imaginative cooking by executive chef Michael Coaker, backed up by fine service from Richard Griggs and his team. The style is contemporary classic (on both à la carte and fixed-price menus), demonstrated by dishes like fillet of red mullet with fried salad leaves and a black olive dressing, baked haddock with herbs and tomato mash, roast rack of lamb with herb crust and tarragon gravy, and supreme of chicken with avocado fritters and stir-fried vegetables. The well-balanced, fixed-price dinner menu extends to five courses, although no choice is offered. Jazz brunch on Sundays with buffet-style first-course. Easy-to-use wine list with plenty under £20, and some fine clarets served by the glass. ***Seats** 65. L 12.30-2.30 D 7-11. Closed L Sat. Set L £22 (£19.50 Sun) Set D £26.50.*

SW7 Memories of India — £40

Tel 071-589 6450 — **R**

18 Gloucester Road SW7 4RB — **Map 19 B4**

Sticking to familiar variations on lamb, chicken and prawns, the glossy menu at this dimly-lit, flock-free, neighbourhood Indian restaurant is helpfully pictorial. Sister restaurant to *Majlis*, a few doors away. Set meals for one upwards. ***Seats** 70. Private Room 30. L 12-2.30 D 5.30-11.30. Closed 25 & 26 Dec. Set L from £6.95 Set D £14.50.* AMERICAN EXPRESS *Access, Diners, Visa.*

W1 Le Meridien 84% — £271

Tel 071-734 8000 Fax 071-437 3574 — **HR**

Piccadilly W1V 0BH — **Map 18 D3**

In the heart of town, hard by Piccadilly Circus, a haven of peaceful elegance and comfort. A harpist plays under the chandeliers in the grand Lounge during afternoon tea, while a pianist tinkles away in the Burlington bar (open to 1am except Sundays) which evokes the aura of a gentleman's club with its baize-green decor. Bedroom decor is tasteful, with style and quality in equal evidence: pink and turquoise are dominant colours, with flowery quilted bedspreads and reproduction pieces featuring; the marbled bathrooms are nothing short of immaculate; bathrobes are, of course, provided. 4th-floor rooms are reserved for non-smokers. Under-12s stay free in parents' room. Afternoon tea is served in the elegant Tea Lounge (3-6pm). Impeccable service. Membership of Champneys health-club downstairs is free to guests – the fun-dungeon is a real plus point. Conference & banqueting facilities for 250. ***Rooms** 263. Indoor swimming pool, plunge pools, Turkish baths & sauna, spa bath, solarium, gymnasium & dance studio, squash, snooker, beauty & hair salons, news kiosk & gift shop, coffee shop (7am-11.30pm).* AMERICAN EXPRESS *Access, Diners, Visa.*

Oak Room Restaurant ★↑ — £135

An opulent dining room with chandeliers hanging from high ceilings, limed oak panelling and gilt abounding. Deep-pile carpets, floral displays, shining glassware and crisp linen help create a luxurious setting for executive chef David Chambers' modern French cooking. Michel Lorain from *La Cote Saint Jacques* in Joigny is his consultant chef and together they produce involved dishes such as a 'marbre' of goose liver on a cushion of wild mushrooms with 'pourpier' salad; sautéed red mullet with artichoke and a brunoise provençale of olives and peppers; roast fillet of turbot spiced with pink and white pepper and served with baby vegetables in a lemon grass-flavoured nage; gaspacho with warm langoustines and quenelles of courgette and breast of Gressingham duck with sautéed endive and a sauce infused with Arabica coffee. The styles of Lorain and Chambers become inextricably intermixed on the 7-course *menu gourmand* with dishes ranging from cold crab 'lasagne', scallops on forest mushrooms and foie gras with wild berries to roast wild duck with carrot mousse and confit of Brussels sprouts, fine cheeses, and warm pancakes with grapefruit and sorbet, to leaves of bitter chocolate with praline cream and caramel sauce – a gastronomic marathon! Lunchtimes offer lighter dishes on a very short carte and a 3-course table d'hote: perhaps clear oxtail consommé with baby vegetables, followed by braised leg of chicken stuffed with crawfish and sweetbreads, plus cheeses or desserts from a trolley. Service is attentive yet suitably discreet. California apart, the New World is poorly represented on an expensive wine list that is mostly French. ***Seats** 40. Parties 10. L 12-2.30 D 7-10. Closed L Sat, all Sun, Bank Holidays. Set L £24.50 Set D £46/£49.*

Terrace Garden Restaurant — £65

Two floors up, overlooking busy Piccadilly, is the lovely, leafy, two-floor-high, conservatory-style restaurant, the front, lower section of which is reserved for non-smokers. Served from breakfast until dinner, dishes range from carpaccio of beef or club sandwich to gumbo and panaché of shellfish and seafood with noodles on a table d'hote. Grills, fish, soups and salads complete the picture. The setting is unusual, the food not so. Fine wines by the glass from a Cruvinet machine. ***Seats** 130. Parties 30. Meals 7am-11.30pm (Sun 11.30am-2.30pm). Set meals from £18.50. Closed Bank Holidays.*

W1 Merryfield House — £48

Tel 071-935 8326 — H

42 York Street W1H 1FN — **Map 18 C2**

Run by the same family since 1958 and ideally located for the West End, just off Gloucester Place and five minutes walk from Baker Street underground station. Full English breakfast is served in the small but comfortable and clean bedrooms, all of which have smart bathrooms en suite. Unlicensed. ***Rooms** 8. No credit cards.*

EC1 Le Mesurier — £65

Tel 071-251 8117 Fax 071-608 3504 — R

113 Old Street EC1V 9JR — **Map 16 D3**

Competent cooking in a small, intimate and individualistic restaurant. Lunchtime brings three choices per course, typified by twice-baked cheese soufflé, sea bass with ratatouille, noisettes of venison with cranberry sauce, tagliatelle and bacon, and pancakes stuffed with candied fruit. Short, uninspiring wine list. ***Seats** 20. L only 12-3 (Open in the evening by arrangement for parties of 15+). Closed Sat & Sun, Bank Holidays, 10 days Christmas.* AMERICAN EXPRESS *Access, Diners, Visa.*

SW6 Le Midi — £50

Tel 071-386 0657 — R

488 Fulham Road SW6 — **Map 19 A6**

Fish or pistou soup, grilled goat's cheese salad, duck confit casserole, chargrilled Mediterranean fish, Toulouse sausages, minute steak. Competent cooking and generous portions in an easy-going little place at Fulham Broadway. ***Seats** 38. Private Room 14. L 12-2.30 (Sun to 3) D 7-10.30. Closed L Sat, L Bank Holidays also L Sun Jul & Aug.* AMERICAN EXPRESS *Access, Visa.*

SW1 Mijanou ↑ £95

Tel 071-730 4099 Fax 071-823 6402 **R**

143 Ebury Street SW1W 9QN **Map 19 C5**

"This menu is not original, it merely re-arranges the natural ingredients which have always existed. Each 'Cuisinier' brings a 'Nouvelle Cuisine' – I hope that you will enjoy mine." So writes Sonia Blech on the menu at the intimate little restaurant owned since 1980 by Sonia and her husband Neville. The style is classically based and French-inspired, but Sonia's dishes (described in both French and English) are very much her own: terrine of sole, leeks and lobster served with a seafood sauce; puff pastry filled with asparagus tips served with goat's cheese and an orange sauce; grilled veal escalope with oregano and a port and pecan nut sauce; fillet of beef stuffed with a wild mushroom mousse and served with a mushroom sauce. Good French cheeses and desserts both simple (sorbets with or without tropical and seasonal fruits) and more elaborate (Swiss roll cassata made with white chocolate, Tia Maria, pecan nuts and coffee ice cream). Separate vegetarian menu. Neville's side is the service and the wine, and the menu suggests wines from the list appropriate to each dish. It's not just a wine list, but a wine company too – if you like what you drink, take home a case! Plenty of choice at good value, with additional helpful notes. The ground-floor room is non-smoking. ***Seats** 35. Private Room 24. L 12.15-2 D 7.15-11. Closed Sat & Sun, Bank Holidays, 3 weeks Aug, 2 weeks Christmas, 1 week Easter. Set L £12/£15 Set D £36. Access, Visa.*

W8 The Milestone 78% £237

Tel 071-917 1000 Fax 071-917 1010 **H**

1-2 Kensington Court W8 5DL **Map 19 A4**

Conveniently located on Kensington High Street, on the south side of Kensington Gardens, it is an important addition to the London hotel scene. Total refurbishment of this Victorian mansion has been completed under close surveillance by English Heritage. Original fireplaces, ornate windows and carved wood panelling have been carefully restored, including the original oratory, now a private dining room. Bedrooms, individually decorated to high standards, most with antiques and four-poster beds, offer modern comforts of air conditioning, two telephone lines, private fax machines, satellite TV and VCR. Although all are elegantly furnished, some lack warmth and personality. Suites have been cleverly designed, creating mezzanine levels in the 24-foot-high rooms which overlook the Park. 24hr room service offers a creative menu for breakfast. Nothing here is left to random, from the complimentary basket of fruit on arrival to valet parking or the house doctor. ***Rooms** 56. Gymnasium, sauna, spa bath, solarium.* AMERICAN EXPRESS *Access, Diners, Visa.*

SW1 Mimmo d'Ischia £90

Tel 071-730 5406 **R**

61 Elizabeth Street Eaton Square SW1 **Map 19 C5**

Sound, straightforward Italian cooking – but at a serious price –in a durable and fashionable restaurant whose walls are adorned with signed photographs of celebrity visitors. Spare ribs a speciality! ***Seats** 90. Private Room 20. L 12.30-2.15 D 7.30-11.15. Closed Sun, Bank Holidays.* AMERICAN EXPRESS *Access, Diners, Visa.*

Set menu prices may not always include service or wine.

W1 Ming ★ £55

Tel 071-734 2721 **R**

35 Greek Street W1V 5LN **Map 21 A2**

On the corner of Greek Street and Old Compton Street, Ming is thus slightly adrift from the throb of Chinatown. Its menus are particularly interesting, and the fish and seafood (much of it kept live on the premises) are highly commendable. 'Ming Specials' include sizzling prawns in hot or garlic sauce, hot fish mousse and crab on a bed of soft noodles. Lamb is also prepared expertly, as in Ta Tsai Mi (an 18th-century Imperial recipe) or Tibetan garlic lamb. Monthly specials add further to the choice (tofu in spiced salt and fried squid with sweet and sour sauce – both excellent, or try the tree mushroom cake blended with seafood) and there are various good-value set menus ranging upwards from the two-course set lunch and the Ming Bowl menu of one-plate meals (including some with mantou Chinese bread – a Northern Chinese speciality, and others with long E Fu noodles that symbolise long life in China) to vegetarian meals and full banquets. Friendly staff are another plus at one of London's best Chinese restaurants. Ten tables are set on the pavement in very good weather. A carefully chosen wine list includes a good choice of champagnes and New World wines recommended for certain dishes. ***Seats** 75. Meals 12-11.45 (Bank Holidays from 5.30pm) Closed Sun (open Chinese New Year), 25 & 26 Dec. Set L from £7.50 Set D from £12.* AMERICAN EXPRESS *Access, Diners, Visa.*

W1 Mirabelle ★★ £110

Tel 071-499 4636 Fax 071-499 5449 **R**

56 Curzon Street W1 **Map 18 C3**

Re-opened in 1992 under Japanese ownership, setting high standards of cooking, the Mirabelle has fulfilled and exceeded our expectations this year. The basement setting is unusual, uniting traditional English (dressed Cornish crab, grills), French and Japanese dining under the same roof (there's even a Japanese tea room). As you walk towards the dining room, crossing the bar down the long carpeted corridors, you catch the appetising whiffs from the two separate teppanyaki rooms. Surprisingly, it is not the basement dining room that one expects when descending the staircase from the Curzon Street entrance; it opens on to a terrace and is bathed with light from the glass-panelled roof. Dinners are not served outside, just drinks. The classic decor of warm pink tones, velvet bergères and subdued evening lighting sets the mood for French haute cuisine. The starting point is a traditional menu from which chef Michael Croft works up a perfect mix of flavours and textures. The delicate balance of soft and crisp takes an important place in his cooking with dishes like *galette de pommes de terre et foie gras aux champignons sauvages et échalotes, chausson de céléri-rave aux morilles et truffes fraiches.* Most impressive is his fantastic technique of poaching, cooking salmon to perfection (keeping the centre raw and warm, an amazing combination of tastes with its cooked envelope) or giving a new dimension to a fillet of beef by poaching it in a delectable mushroom broth. Skills extend to simple garnishes like potatoes served as light crispy galettes, encased in pastry with hints of basil; or slowly *confites* in goose fat. Superior quality of ingredients is of course one of the secrets here and dishes like *minestrone de langoustines aux pates fraiches* confirm that these are some of the best fish dishes to be found in London. Desserts which include *soufflé chaud au chocolat, feuillantine à la citronelle* or *apple croustade* are pleasant endings, perhaps not as delightful as the rest or the wonderful petits fours! Interesting list of vegetarian dishes. The fixed-price *menu du jour* offers three or so dishes at each course and include half a bottle of wine per person; *menu surprise* offers a six-course, daily-changing menu for whole table parties. Only a handful of non-French wines on a good, but mostly expensive list, though we note some reductions from last year! ***Seats** 100. Parties 70. Private Room 32. L 12-2 D 6.30-10.30. Closed L Sat, all Sun, Bank Holidays, 31 Jul-21 Aug, 1 week Christmas. Set L £19/£25 Set D £28.* AMERICAN EXPRESS *Access, Diners, Visa.*

NW3 Mr Ke £42

Tel 071-722 8474 **R**

7 New College Parade Finchley Road NW3 5EP **Map 16 B3**

Mr Zhu-Qi Ke was born in a 'land of fish and rice', the Jiangnan region south of the great Yangtse river. He served his apprenticeship in a leading hotel in Peking, where he learned to make fine roast duck and dumplings. Even now, many years later in Finchley Road, amid fierce competition, cooking of these specialities is nothing short of exceptional: the dumplings are poached, or fried on one side then steamed with a crispy base and soft top, known as kuo tish (pot stickers); then they are served with either red chili and garlic oil (Szechuan style) or ginger and vinegar dip sauce (Jiangnan and Peking style). Over 100 items on the menu, including a good range of seafood. ***Seats** 55. Parties 10. L 12-2.30 D 6-11.30. Closed L Mon-Thur, 25 & 26 Dec. Set meals from £14 (minimum two).* AMERICAN EXPRESS *Access, Diners, Visa.*

W6 Mr Wong Wonderful House £40

Tel 081-748 6887 **R**

313 King Street Hammersmith W6 **Map 17 A4**

One of the friendliest Chinese restaurants in London, decorated in gentle eau-de-nil with Mr Wong leading a team of helpful staff. The food, based on Peking and Singapore cuisine, includes a good selection of day time dim sum (note, no cheung fun on Mondays). ***Seats** 200. Parties 12. Private Room 80. L 12-3 D 6-midnight (Sat & Sun noon-midnight). Closed 25 & 26 Dec. Set L from £14.50.* AMERICAN EXPRESS *Access, Diners, Visa.*

SW1 Mitsukoshi £100

Tel 071-839 6714 **R**

Dorland House 14-20 Regent Street SW1 4PH **Map 18 D3**

In the basement of a Japanese department store, this is a roomy, comfortable restaurant making stylish use of frosted glass panelling. You can choose from the à la carte selection or plump for one of the many set meals. These range from a fairly simple *hana* – appetiser, tempura, grilled fish, rice, miso soup and pickles – to all sorts of sushi and the *Kaiseki* ten-course feasts. 15% service charge is added to all bills. ***Seats** 140. Parties 22. Private Room 24. L 12-2.30 D 6-10.30. Closed Sun, Bank Holidays. Set L from £20 Set D from £30.* AMERICAN EXPRESS *Access, Diners, Visa.*

W1 Miyako NEW £50

Tel 071-287 3713 **R**

10 Greek Street Soho W1 **Map 21 A2**

Right in the middle of Soho and behind a discreet front is a small, quality Japanese restaurant. There is an 8-seat sushi bar in front with the main restaurant secluded at the back. The menu emphasises sushi and sashimi with the addition of a few grilled fish, teriyaki and tempura dishes. Sashimi, prepared on round blue plates, are works of art. Tempura are lightly coated and healthily fried. The decor is stylishly black and white, service very helpful. ***Seats** 24. Parties 20. Private Room 22. L 12-2.30 D 6-10.30. Closed L Sun, all Sat. Set L £15 Set D £22.50.* AMERICAN EXPRESS *Access, Visa.*

EC4 Miyama £80

Tel 071-489 1937 Fax 071-329 4225 **R**

17 Godliman Street EC4V 5BD **Map 20 B2**

A stylish operation offering immaculately produced Japanese food in crisp business-like surroundings: a sushi bar upstairs and tables downstairs. As is often the case, the most interesting dishes are on the part of the menu written in Japanese script (partially translated into English); it's often worth selecting a few at random, perhaps turning up chopped natto with grated yam, or soft-shell crabs. The main menu holds few surprises (sushi, sashimi, shabushabu, sukiyaki, tempura, teppanyaki) but all dishes are prepared with a high degree of competence and beautifully presented. 15% service is automatically added to all bills. The entrance is in Knightrider Street. ***Seats** 85. L 12-2.30 (Sat from 11.30) D 6-10. Closed L Sat, all Sun, Bank Holidays. Set L from £16 Set D from £15.* AMERICAN EXPRESS *Access, Diners, Visa.*

W1 Miyama £75

Tel 071-499 2443 R

38 Clarges Street W1Y 7PJ **Map 18 C3**

The West End version of the City branch, stylish and modern, with opaque screens for privacy. Cooking is of a high standard, flavours delicate and refined. Set lunches offer the best value (raw fish, grilled fish, tempura, beef or chicken teriyaki, pork ginger or pork deep-fried). The rest of the menu spans the expected range, from *zen-sai* (hors d'oeuvre) to rice and noodle dishes and *nabemono* specialities prepared at the table. Excellent service (for which 15% is added). ***Seats** 65. Private Room 20. L 12.30-2.30 D 6.30-10.30. Closed L Sat & Sun, all Bank Holidays, Christmas/New Year. Set L from £16 Set D from £30.* AMERICAN EXPRESS *Access, Diners, Visa.*

WC2 Moat House 65% £148

Tel 071-836 6666 Fax 071-831 1548 H

10 Drury Lane WC2B 5RE **Map 21 B1**

High-rise hotel handy for Covent Garden and many West End theatres. Children up to 16 stay free in parents' room. Conference and banqueting facilities for 100 delegates. ***Rooms** 153.* AMERICAN EXPRESS *Access, Diners, Visa.*

W5 Momo £50

Tel 081-997 0206 R

14 Queens Parade W5 3HU **Map 17 A4**

Cosy Japanese restaurant behind a smoked-glass frontage just off Hanger Lane (by North Ealing underground). One-dish lunches served with rice, miso soup, pickles and a piece of fresh fruit offer particularly good value, as does a fine *shokado bento* box with tempura and sashimi; the extensive menu in the evenings includes the likes of grilled eel, soft-shell crab and pork grilled with ginger sauce. ***Seats** 24. L 12-2.30 D 6-10. Closed Mon, Bank Holidays, 1 week Christmas. Set L from £6.50. Set D from £23.* AMERICAN EXPRESS *Access, Diners, Visa.*

WC2 Mon Plaisir £50

Tel 071-836 7243 Fax 071-379 0121 R

21 Monmouth Street WC2H 9DD **Map 21 B2**

Popular and long-established theatreland restaurant with cooking in classic French bistro style. Go for traditional favourites like onion soup, garlic snails, wild mushroom brioche, sole meunière, coq au vin and daube de boeuf. A la carte, plus set menus at lunch and pre-theatre times (6-7.15pm). ***Seats** 90. Parties 30. Private Room 20. L 12-2.15 D 6-11.15. Closed L Sat, all Sun, Bank Holidays. Set L and early D £13.95.* AMERICAN EXPRESS *Access, Diners, Visa.*

Changes in data sometimes occur in establishments after the Guide goes to press. Prices should be taken as indications rather than firm quotes.

SW3 Monkeys £70

Tel 071-352 4711 **R**

1 Cale Street SW3 3QT **Map 19 B5**

In season, an extensive selection of mostly feathered game is a feature of a charming local restaurant whose pine-panelled walls are hung with a fine selection of Victorian monkey prints and paintings. Good-value, simple classic favourites appear throughout the year. ***Seats 36.*** *L 12.30-2.30 D 7.30-11. Closed Sat & Sun, Bank Holidays, 2 weeks Easter, 3 weeks Aug. Set L £12.50 Set D £22.50. Access, Visa.*

WC1 Montague Park Hotel 64% NEW £149

Tel 071-637 1001 **H**

12-20 Montague Street Bloomsbury WC1B 5BJ **Map 18 D2**

A Georgian-fronted hotel located next to the British Museum. Public rooms are spacious and comfortable. The bar has a small terrace looking out on to private gardens and the basement breakfast room has a bright conservatory roof. Bedrooms are small but well equipped with satellite TV, trouser press, hairdryer and tea/coffee facilities. Sparkling clean bathrooms are well appointed. There are four conference suites. Children up to 15 stay free in parents' room. ***Rooms 109.*** AMERICAN EXPRESS *Access, Diners, Visa.*

W1 Montcalm Hotel 74% £230

Tel 071-402 4288 Fax 071-724 9180 **H**

Great Cumberland Place W1A 2LF **Map 18 C2**

There's some justification to the Montcalm's claim to be "the best-kept secret in London": behind a listed Georgian frontage, the hotel stands in a tree-lined crescent, surprisingly quiet considering it's only two minutes walk from Marble Arch and Oxford Street. The staff – from management to maid service – are among the friendliest in London. The atmosphere in the day rooms is redolent of a very English, very private club: discreet reception desks, leather armchairs and low coffee tables set the tone. The Marquis de Montcalm suite can accommodate up to 80 for meetings. Splendidly appointed bedrooms include 12 duplex apartments and two penthouse suites. Air-conditioning is first-class, and bathrooms contain bidets and bathrobes. Children up to 12 stay free in parents' room. 24hr room service. No dogs. ***Rooms 116.*** *Valeting.* AMERICAN EXPRESS *Access, Diners, Visa.*

W2 Mornington Hotel 63% £96

Tel 071-262 7361 Fax 071-706 1028 **H**

12 Lancaster Gate W2 3LG **Map 18 B3**

In a residential area just north of Hyde Park, the Swedish-owned Mornington (spot the Swedish flag over the entrance) scores on housekeeping and efficiency. There's a fresh, bright look to the place, both in the day rooms (panelled foyer-lounge, library bar) and in the bedrooms. Rates include a Swedish buffet breakfast – full English is available at extra cost. Children up to 12 stay free in parents' room. ***Rooms 68.*** *Sauna. Closed 23 Dec-3 Jan.* AMERICAN EXPRESS *Access, Diners, Visa.*

W1 Mostyn Hotel 62% £124

Tel 071-935 2361 Fax 071-487 2759 **H**

Bryanston Street W1H 0DE **Map 18 C2**

Tucked away quietly behind Marble Arch, the 18th-century building was originally the home of Lady Black, a lady-in-waiting to the Court of George II. Inside, period detail blends with up-to-date amenities, but the most impressive features – a Georgian staircase, Adam carved ceilings and fire surrounds – are in the conference areas. Public rooms include the colonial-style Tea Planter restaurant (where breakfast is served) with its own street entrance. Bedrooms come in various sizes. ***Rooms** 122. Coffee shop (7am-11pm).* AMERICAN EXPRESS® *Access, Diners, Visa.*

SW1 Motcomb's **£60**

Tel 071-235 9170 **R**

26 Motcomb Street SW1X 8JU **Map 19 C4**

Old-established basement restaurant beneath a wine bar. Typical items on a wide-ranging menu include mussel and Chablis soup, scallops with black-eyed bean cake, seasonal game, grilled baby chicken with yoghurt dressing and fillet steak béarnaise. ***Seats** 70. Private Room 22. L 12-3 D 7-11. Closed L Sat, all Sun, Bank Holidays. Set L from £11.95.* AMERICAN EXPRESS® *Access, Diners, Visa.*

WC2 Mountbatten Hotel 70% **£193**

Tel 071-836 4300 Fax 071-240 3540 **H**

20 Monmouth Street WC2H 9HD **Map 21 B2**

By Seven Dials in Covent Garden, the hotel is themed around the late Lord Louis, with a glass case of memorabilia in the lobby and photographs and cartoons in both the smart, wood-panelled Broadlands drawing room (named after his family home in Hampshire) and the small Polo Bar. The marble-floored reception is elegant, as is the tip-top Lord Mountbatten suite (one of seven). Larry's Bar is open noon till 11 for food and drink. Decent bedrooms (children up to 14 stay free with parents) have darkwood furniture, mini-bars and remote-control TVs; bathrooms are marble-tiled and luxuriously large bathrobes are provided. Edwardian Hotels. ***Rooms** 127.* AMERICAN EXPRESS® *Access, Diners, Visa.*

W1 Mulligans of Mayfair **£65**

Tel 071-409 1370 **R**

13-14 Cork Street W1X 1PF **Map 18 D3**

In the basement of a busy pub and oyster bar, the restaurant is quieter, with a traditional feel assisted by half-panelled walls and portraits of notable Irishmen. Irish rock oysters are of course on the menu, along with traditional dishes like home-made white pudding with fried apple and grain mustard sauce, baked ham and colcannon or Irish stew. ***Seats** 60. Parties 20. L 12-2 D 6.15-11. Closed L Sat, all Sun, Bank Holidays.* AMERICAN EXPRESS® *Access, Diners, Visa.*

W1 Le Muscadet **£60**

Tel 071-935 2883 **R**

25 Paddington Street W1M 3RF **Map 18 C2**

Classic French bistro dishes are listed on the handwritten menu at this popular little spot. Paté maison, asparagus with hollandaise sauce, sole dugléré, chicken breast with thyme and pepper steak show the range. ***Seats** 40. L 12.30-2.30 D 7.30-10.45 (Sat to 10). Closed L Sat, all Sun, Bank Holidays, 3 weeks Aug. Access, Visa.*

WC1 Museum Street Café ★ **£55**

Tel 071-405 3211 **R**

47 Museum Street Bloomsbury WC1A 1LY **Map 21 B1**

In a side street between the British Museum and New Oxford Street, the Museum Street Café goes from strength to strength. Food will always be number one here and since space is very limited it's always best to book well in advance. Decor is unfussily spartan in the single, small room, with naive artwork on the walls. Don't expect any airs and graces (it's not the kind of place of for a special night out, unless you wish to match a fine

See over

bottle of wine with fine, straightforward food) – the ambience is informal, almost laid-back: there are no side plates for the superb home-baked breads and glasses for wine (bring your own – no corkage) are in school dining room tumbler style. Gail Koerber and Mark Nathan show a commendable degree of commitment, working in a tiny kitchen to produce delightfully simple dishes that show Italian and Californian influences and more than a nod to Sally Clarke's sunny style. The choice is always short and always interesting: a menu from last spring offered just rocket salad with sliced fennel, sliced mushrooms, pine nuts and Parmesan shavings or chick pea and rosemary soup with red pepper purée and basil oil to start, followed by salmon and gurnard on a skewer with herb mayonnaise or pigeon breast with apple compote and Madeira sauce (both cooked on the chargrill and served with roast new potatoes, sugarsnap peas and green beans). Dark chocolate tart or chilled zabaglione with prunes cooked in red wine for dessert (or a tip-top cheese from Neal's Yard). At lunchtime, main courses are accompanied by generous salads, reflected in the price. No smoking. ***Seats** 22. L 12.30-2.30 D 7.30-9.15. Closed Sat & Sun, Bank Holidays, 1 week summer. Set L £11/£14 Set D £19.50. No credit cards.*

SE1 Mutiara £25

Tel 071-277 0425 **R**

14 Walworth Road Elephant & Castle London SE1 1HY **Map 17 D4**

Indonesian/Malaysian restaurant whose decor is highlighted by large paintings and an enormous vase of exotic leaves. Try classics like satay, prawn fritters, sesame chicken and beef slices with five spices, served by charming, helpful staff. ***Seats** 70. Parties 30. L 12-2.30 D 6-11. Closed L Sat, all Sun & Bank Holidays. Access, Visa.*

W1 Nakamura £50

Tel 071-935 2931 **R**

31 Marylebone Lane W1M 5FH **Map 18 C2**

A sushi bar is at street level, and a narrow stairway spirals down to the sparsely appointed main restaurant. Food takes centre stage: prettily presented sushi and sashimi, tempura, deep-fried bean curd, yakitori, soups, composite rice and noodle dishes, chicken or beef teriyaki. ***Seats** 35. Parties 25. Private Room 8. L 12-2.30 D 6-10.30. Closed L Sun, all Sat, 1 week Christmas. Set L from £6 Set D from £24.80* AMERICAN EXPRESS *Access, Diners, Visa.*

SW1 Nakano £75

Tel 071-581 3837 **R**

11 Beauchamp Place SW1 **Map 19 C4**

A steep flight of stairs leads down from Beauchamp Place to a very simply furnished room with white walls and red-tiled floor. Sweet-mannered waitresses will guide you through a Japanese menu that's longer and more varied than most. Chef's specials change every month: in April you might find yellowtail sashimi, baby squid marinated with its own gut, grilled chicken wing with salt, pickled bracken and crabmeat salad. ***Seats** 30. L 12.30-3 D 6.30-11 (Sun from 7). Closed L Sun, all Mon, Bank Holidays, 1 week Aug, Christmas/New Year. Set L from £11 Set D from £26.50.* AMERICAN EXPRESS *Access, Diners, Visa.*

E1 Namaste £35

Tel 071-488 9242 **R**

30 Alie Street London E1 8DA **Map 20 D2**

Behind a bare front, in a neat, simple decor of green walls with framed Indian prints, interesting Goan specialities are listed on a special menu which changes every week. The chef, who comes from Goa, prepares fiery dishes using some unexpected ingredients such as snails, rabbit, baby squid, bamboo shoots and mustard cress. ***Seats*** *70. Parties 10. Private Room 30. L 12-3 D 6-11.30 (Sat 7-11). Closed L Sat, all Sun, Bank Holidays.* AMERICAN EXPRESS *Access, Diners, Visa.*

W6 Nanking £60

Tel 081-748 7604 **R**

332 King Street W6 **Map 17 A4**

In a street bursting with ethnic restaurants Nanking is the best of the Chinese. Decor is cool, staff admirably helpful and friendly. The menu is strong on Szechuan dishes and a warning fire symbol is much in evidence. "Special selections" include crispy chili squid with onions and peppers, double-sautéed string beans with pork mince and a particularly good sizzle-grilled sesame steak with teriyaki sauce. In the same group and with a similar menu are *Cheng-Du* (Parkway NW1) and *Mao Tai* (King's Road SW6). ***Seats*** *60. Private Room 60. L 12-2.30 D 6.30-11.30. Set meals from £17.80.* AMERICAN EXPRESS *Access, Visa.*

WC2 Neal Street Restaurant ★ £95

Tel 071-836 8368 **R**

26 Neal Street WC2H 9PH **Map 21 B2**

The decor has changed little over the years – brick walls hung with abstract artwork – but essentially this is a modern Italian restaurant in terms of both appearance and what the menu offers. Two things you come to expect on arrival are the fatherly figure of Antonio Carluccio beaming a welcome, and a magnificent display of all manner of mushrooms. The selection of mushrooms changes almost daily – chanterelles, wild and cultivated horse mushrooms, puffballs the size of rugby balls – and there's often a separate menu for them. A dish that must not be missed (but is not always available) is carpaccio with truffle cheese – a stunningly simple combination of paper-thin beef fillet, scrapings of a cheese made with white truffles, and a liberal dribble of extra virgin olive oil. Tagliolini with a truffle sauce uses the black truffles, the deliciously earthy aroma and flavour making a truly memorable dish. Breads, of which there is a wide selection, include some excellent focaccia – an onion one and a peppery one sprinkled with rosemary – the dough soft and moist with its high olive oil content. Wild garlic soup with dumplings, open seafood ravioli, nettle gnocchi with dolcelatte, seafood casserole livornese, Roman-style fresh eel, liver veneziana and home-made Luganega sausage with leeks and lentils with just a few of the delights on an early summer menu, along with the occasional non-Italian guests such as schmalz herring with aquavit or Dover sole meunière. Vin Santo with cantuccini is an excellent way to round off a meal with many high points. Leave room for the special Amaretti served with the coffee, moist in the centre and much more almondy that the ordinary ones. 15% service is added to your bill. ***Seats*** *60. Parties 12. Private Room 24. L 12.30-2.30 D 7.30-11. Closed Sun, Bank Holidays, 1 week Christmas/New Year.* AMERICAN EXPRESS *Access, Diners, Visa.*

N1 Neshiko £90

Tel 071-359 9977 **R**

265 Upper Street Islington N1 2UQ **Map 16 D3**

Named after a southern Japanese fishing village, Neshiko is a bright modern restaurant on two floors (the ground floor has a sushi counter that's also used for lone diners). The varied and interesting menu is clearly laid out in sections, by style of dish: deep-steamed, rice, simmered, deep-fried, grilled and raw. Chef's specials of the week (steamed crabmeat dumpling, crispy-fried mackerel, asparagus salad) add further choice. ***Seats*** *55. Parties 25. L 12-2.30 D 6.30-11. Closed L Sat, all Sun, Bank Holidays. Set L from £12 Set D from £35.* AMERICAN EXPRESS *Access, Diners, Visa.*

EC1 New Barbican Hotel 51% £101

Tel 071-251 1565 Fax 071-253 1005 **H**

Central Street Clerkenwell EC1V 8DS **Map 16 D3**

Large Mount Charlotte hotel close to the City and ten minutes from the Barbican Exhibition Centre. Popular with tour groups and conferences. ***Rooms*** *470. AMERICAN EXPRESS Access, Diners, Visa.*

W1 New Fook Lam Moon £40

Tel 071-734 7615 **R**

10 Gerrard Street W1 **Map 21 A2**

A simply furnished restaurant in Soho's Chinatown where meats hang invitingly in the window. Fast service from a long list of sound Cantonese cooking. Good choice of one-pot, porridge and noodles in soup dishes – stewed spare ribs with pig's liver, duck with yam and Mandarin minced meat with noodles are typical. Order barbecue suckling pig in advance. ***Seats*** *80. Meals 12-11.30 (Sun to 10.30). Closed 25 & 26 Dec. Set meals from £9.40. AMERICAN EXPRESS Access, Diners, Visa.*

W2 New Kam Tong £35

Tel 071-229 6065 **R**

59 Queensway W2 4QH **Map 18 A3**

Long-established Chinese restaurant in Queensway (almost next door to Bayswater underground station). The menu is predominantly Cantonese, with a huge choice, from deep-fried stuffed crab claws and 17 soups to dozens of ways with chicken, beef, prawns and pork, plus oodles of noodles and braised, roast or aromatic crispy duck. Daytime dim sum. ***Seats*** *120. Meals 12-11.15. Set meals from £9.80. AMERICAN EXPRESS.*

W1 New World £35

Tel 071-434 2508 **R**

1 Gerrard Place W1V 7LL **Map 21 A2**

Join several hundred others and enjoy a meal in one of Soho's most typical and traditional Chinese restaurants. The menu is suitably vast, starting from daytime dim sum and ranging through seafood and vegetarian specials, popular provincial dishes and chef's specialities. ***Seats*** *600. Private Room 250. Meals 11am-11.45pm (Fri & Sat to 12.15am, Sun 11-11). Closed 25 & 26 Dec. Set L £6.60 Set D from £10.50. AMERICAN EXPRESS Access, Diners, Visa.*

SW4 Newtons £45

Tel 081-673 0977 **R**

73 Abbeville Road SW4 9LA **Map 21 E2**

Bistro-like in both physical appearance and menu style, the latter showing strong Oriental and Mediterranean influences. Children get a good deal on Saturdays with a clown, balloons and little gifts. ***Seats 82.*** *Parties 25. L 12.30-2.30 D 7-11.30 Meals Sat & Sun 12.30-11.30. Closed 25 & 26 Dec, Easter Sun. Set L £9.95 Set D £11.95. Access, Visa.*

W1 Nico Central ★↑ £70

Tel 071-436 8846 Fax 071-436 0134 **R**

35 Great Portland Street W1N 5DD **Map 18 D2**

One of Nico Ladenis' three starred restaurants, this is a smart, brightly-lit, up-market brasserie with beautiful modern artwork by Juan Gris and Picasso on walls which have a mirrored dado strip. In the ceiling a central stained-glass art deco illuminated skylight is reflected in a large mirror with ornately engraved edges while the bar counter alongside has a polished granite top and two-toned mirrored front. The art of Nico is to take the familiar and rework it by returning to its classical origins and embellishing it with a subtle but telling touch of inspiration. Thus a seemingly simple chicken soup – a velouté of voluptuous delicacy – is given an added edge by the use of a sprinkle of coarsely chopped rocket leaves and an extra element of soft texture from a softly-poached egg. A leg of duck is 'confited' to an incredibly tender, melting crispness then served on a bed of plump, juicy yet firm borlotti beans dressed in olive oil, the whole surrounded by a mayonnaise tinged with grain mustard. A main course fillet of lamb is roasted pink then sliced on to a bed of cabbage with gentle creamy carrot and garlic sauce. Vegetables are uncomplicated – served as a plated mixture, potatoes include wonderful crisp chips or are puréed with olive oil, equally irresistible. Classic sweets such as crème caramel, tarte tatin, sherry trifle and even Bakewell tart are all perfect examples of their type. Profiteroles are the lightest choux pastry accompanied by a richly dark hot chocolate sauce. There are plans to keep the present style of menu but restricting it to lunchtime while for dinner a slightly more elaborate menu will come into operation. ***Seats** 60. Private Room 10. L 12-2.15 D 7-11. Closed L Sat and Bank Holidays, all Sun, L Bank Holidays, 10 days Christmas.* AMERICAN EXPRESS *Access, Diners, Visa.*

SW10 Nikita's £70

Tel 071-352 6326 Fax 081-993 3680 **R**

65 Ifield Road SW10 9AU **Map 19 A6**

For more than 20 years diners have come to this snug red-and-gold basement restaurant to dive into the fast-flowing waters of the River Vodka and tuck into hearty Russian food. ***Seats** 60. Parties 35. Private Room 12. L by arrangement for 20 or more only D 7.30-11.30. Closed Sun, Bank Holidays, 2 weeks Aug. Set D from £25.50.* AMERICAN EXPRESS *Access, Visa.*

W1 Ninjin £60

Tel 071-388 4657 **R**

244 Great Portland St W1N 5HF **Map 18 C2**

A modestly appointed Japanese restaurant beneath its own food shop, Ninjin is in the same group as *Masako, Hiroko* and *Kashi-Noki.* Set lunches (£10-£14) include appetiser, miso soup, rice, pickles and fresh fruit plus one of a dozen main dishes, from bean curd to oysters, fish (cooked or raw), pork and beef. Also sukiyaki, shabu shabu and bento lunches. Dinner brings more elaborate set meals plus an à la carte menu featuring kushiyaki (skewered dishes) as a speciality. ***Seats** 64. Parties 20. L 12-2.30 D 6-10.30. Closed Sun, Bank Holidays. Set L £8.50-£20 Set D £26-£32.* AMERICAN EXPRESS *Access, Diners, Visa.*

> We do not accept free meals or hospitality – our inspectors pay their own bills.

NW1 Nontas £25

Tel 071-387 4579 **R**

14 Camden High Street London NW1 0JH **Map 16 C3**

A bustling, neighbourhood Greek Cypriot restaurant which also offers overnight accommodation. The menu covers a familiar range, including the ever-popular meze for two or more. The separate Ouzerie area serves snacks, teas and coffee from 8.30am-11.30pm. ***Seats** 50. Parties 24. L 12-2.45 D 6-11.30. Closed Sun, Bank Holidays. Set meals from £8.75.* AMERICAN EXPRESS *Access, Diners, Visa.*

SW5 Noor Jahan **£40**

Tel 071-373 6522 **R**

2a Bina Gardens off Old Brompton Road SW5 **Map 19 B5**

Popular and durable Indian restaurant with a straight-down-the-line menu: various styles and heat levels of lamb, chicken and prawn dishes. Swift, friendly service. ***Seats** 60. Parties 30. L 12-2.45 D 6-11.45. Closed 25 & 26 Dec.* AMERICAN EXPRESS *Access, Diners, Visa.*

SW7 Norfolk Hotel 69% **£125**

Tel 071-589 8191 Fax 071-581 1874 **H**

2 Harrington Road South Kensington SW7 3ER **Map 19 B5**

Close to major museums and the 'French quarter' of South Kensington. Built in 1888, the Norfolk retains a certain Victorian air, although the amenities are up to date. Standard rooms are in soft pastel shades, with attractive limed wood furniture. Children up to 16 stay free in parents' room. Day rooms include a brasserie, a basement wine bar (11am-11pm) and a traditionally-styled English pub. Queens Moat Houses. ***Rooms** 96. Keep-fit equipment, sauna, solarium.* AMERICAN EXPRESS *Access, Diners, Visa.*

W6 Novotel 65% **£97**

Tel 081-741 1555 Fax 081-741 2120 **H**

1 Shortlands W6 8DR **Map 17 B4**

Very large modern hotel alongside (but not accessible from) Hammersmith flyover. It's popular for banquets and conferences (up to 900 delegates). The restaurant is open from 6am to midnight. ***Rooms** 640.* AMERICAN EXPRESS *Access, Diners, Visa.*

WC2 Now & Zen **£75**

Tel 071-497 0376 **R**

Orion House 48 Upper St Martin's Lane WC2 **Map 21 B2**

High on interior design (by Rick Mather) and handy for theatreland, Lawrence Leung's stylish, ultra-modern restaurant is on three levels with minimalist decor behind a sleek glass frontage. The menu is a mix of modern and classic Chinese cooking – from dim sum to coriander and cuttlefish cakes, shin of beef with coconut in a clay pot and tofu almond jelly with fresh fruit. ***Seats** 200. Private Room 40. L 12-3 D 6-11.30 (Sun to 11). Closed 25 & 26 Dec.* AMERICAN EXPRESS *Access, Diners, Visa.*

SW7 Number Sixteen **£135**

Tel 071-589 5232 Fax 071-584 8615 **PH**

16 Sumner Place SW7 3EG **Map 19 B5**

In a terrace of white-painted early-Victorian houses, Number Sixteen offers style, elegance and seclusion. There's a comfortable informality about the drawing room, and the conservatory opens on to a walled garden. Bedrooms are smartly furnished with a combination of antiques and traditional pieces. A tea and coffee service is available throughout the day. Room rate includes Continental breakfast. No children under 12. No dogs. ***Rooms** 36.* AMERICAN EXPRESS *Access, Diners, Visa.*

W1 Nusa Dua **£35**

Tel 071-437 3559 **R**

11-12 Dean Street W1V 5AH **Map 18 D2**

Indonesian food is a delightful mixture of tastes and aromas involving sweet, pungent, hot and spicy. Otto, the manager, who dispenses charm and information in equal measure, comes from Java, where they like their food sweet, but his menu spans the whole range. Set meals provide good value, or you can explore the carte. Chicken, beef, prawn and beancurd satays, whole fish cooked in banana leaves, lamb chops with chili and sweet soya sauce, and mixed vegetables cooked in tamarind soup are just a few of the 70+ dishes on offer. The restaurant is on two levels, lighter at street level, more intimate below. Set meals provide good value, ranging from low-priced lunches to a rijsstafel (rice table) banquet. ***Seats** 50. Parties 40. Private Room 12. L 12-2.30 D 6-11.30. Closed L Sat & Bank Holidays, all Sun. Set L from £4.95 Set D £35 for 2. Access, Visa.*

W1 O'Keefe's NEW £44

Tel 071-495 0878 Fax 071-629 7082 **R**

19 Dering Street W1R 9AA **Map 18 C2**

Sophisticated deli-restaurant serving well-prepared Mediterranean-inspired dishes like grilled baby chorizo with butter beans and salsa verde or home-made focaccia with Parma ham, artichokes, rocket and cherry tomatoes. Open daily for free-range breakfast and on Thursday candle-light dinners. Good selection of cheeses from Neals Yard. ***Seats** 37. Parties 12. Breakfast 8-12 L 12-3 D Thur only 7.30-10.30. Closed Sun, Bank Holidays, 25 & 26 Dec, 4 days Easter, 2 weeks August. Set D £13.50. No credit cards.*

NW1 Odette's £65

Tel 071-586 5486 **R**

130 Regent's Park Road NW1 8XL **Map 16 C3**

Close to Primrose Hill, the restaurant is located in the centre of Regent's Park Road activity. The main dining room is attractively decorated in green with gilded mirrors of all sizes covering the walls. At the back, a charming balcony room overlooks a conservatory. The menu, which changes daily, offers voguish Mediterranean dishes of uneven quality: skate, scallop and oyster terrine with cucumber, corinader and lime relish; grilled sea bass, peas, rocket and salsa verde; polenta-fried calf's liver with turnip mash and sage. Strong attention is paid to wines with a list laid out by wine style, and a basement wine bar. ***Seats** 55. Parties 30. Private Room 8. L 12.30-2.30 (Sun 12-3) D 7-11. Closed L Sat, D Sun, Bank Holidays, 1 week Christmas.* AMERICAN EXPRESS *Access, Diners, Visa.*

W1 Odin's Restaurant £85

Tel 071-935 7296 **R**

27 Devonshire Street W1N 1RJ **Map 18 C2**

Just off Marylebone High Street, and no doubt popular with the surrounding medical profession, the restaurant is endearingly old-fashioned and almost club-like, with the walls covered with art, mostly oil paintings and line drawings of the restaurant's founder, the late Peter Langan (the bistro is next door). The menu's tried and tested formula works well – after good appetisers, including baby spicy sausages and a savoury tartlet, perhaps a starter of haddock soufflé with dill sauce or leek pie with a subtle mustard sauce, and main courses might include grilled darne of tasty wild salmon with a perfect hollandaise or tender roast best end of English lamb. A traditional pudding (date and ginger with butterscotch sauce or Mrs Langan's chocolate) will not disappoint. Attentive service, concise list of well-chosen wines, though entry price for champagne is a bit steep! ***Seats** 60. Parties 10. L 12.30-2.30 D 7-11.30. Closed L Sat, all Sun, Bank Holidays.* AMERICAN EXPRESS *Access, Diners, Visa.*

SW7 Ognisko Polskie £55

Tel 071-589 4635 **R**

55 Exhibition Road SW7 2PG **Map 19 B4**

Gold is the dominant colour in the slightly faded grandeur of a hotel-style dining room in the Polish Hearth Club. Staff and most of the guests are Polish, and the walls are hung with portraits of notable Poles past and

See over

present. The menu is Polish plus Continental, portions more than robust, flavours bold but certainly not without subtlety. Beetroot soup – a sparkling, brilliantly fresh-tasting consommé, comes with a herby veal sausage roll; buckwheat blinis are topped with smoked salmon, cream and sevruga caviar; ham knuckle, falling off the bone and beautifully succulent, is teamed with a splendid mustard sauce; cheesecake is a traditional baked version with sultanas. The main-course set lunch and dinner menu offers remarkable value. ***Seats** 70. Private Room 150. L 12.30-3 D 6.30-11. Closed 2/3 days Easter, 4 days Christmas. Set L & D from £7.50.* AMERICAN EXPRESS *Access, Diners, Visa.*

SW17 Oh'Boy £40

Tel 081-947 9760 **R**

843 Garratt Lane Tooting SW17 0PG **Map 17 B6**

A garish purple neon sign announces a neighbourhood Thai restaurant whose menu delivers authentic tastes and good-value Royal Thai set meals. Try the interestingly sweet Thai beer called Singha or green tea served in Royal Doulton china! *Also at:* 18 South End, Croydon, Surrey (081-760 0278). ***Seats** 45. Parties 25. Private Room. L 12-2.30 (Croydon branch only) D 7-11. Closed Sun. Set D £10/£15.50.* AMERICAN EXPRESS *Access, Diners, Visa.*

W14 Oliver's £35

Tel 071-603 7645 **R**

10 Russell Gardens W14 8EZ **Map 17 B4**

A friendly little restaurant between Kensington and Shepherds Bush. From a choice of twenty starters and even more main courses, you might choose crab soup, salmon mayonnaise or chicken livers and toast to start, then braised wood pigeon, osso buco, garlic king prawns or one of the popular steaks to follow. Main-course salads also available, and a traditional roast Sunday lunch. ***Seats** 75. Meals noon-11.30. Closed 25 & 26 Dec. Set L £9. Access, Visa.*

SW1 Olivo £55

Tel 071-730 2505 **R**

21 Eccleston Street SW1W 9LX **Map 19 C5**

A busy and cheerfully casual Italian restaurant with rough plaster walls in blue and mustard yellow, and stained-wood floorboards. The menu has a contemporary ring with several chargrilled dishes: yellow pepper salad, fillet of grey mullet with plum tomatoes, swordfish with herbs, veal escalope with spinach. Amaretto-flavoured crème caramel is a popular dessert. ***Seats** 45. Parties 6. L 12-2.30 D 7-11. Closed L Sat, all Sun, Bank Holidays, 3 weeks Aug/Sep. Set L £13/£15.* AMERICAN EXPRESS *Access, Visa.*

W11 192 £60

Tel 071-229 0482 **R**

192 Kensington Park Road W11 2JF **Map 16 B3**

A splendid, informal restaurant run efficiently by a team of young, casually attired staff. The premises have been revamped following expansion which took over a former wine merchant's next door. This has created a much enlarged bar on the ground floor while downstairs the kitchen has been increased in size together with restaurant. Apart from the quality of the food one of the highlights is the extensive selection of wines offered by the glass, both regular and large size. An eclectic, weekly changing menu that is full of interest features some carefully cooked dishes with good clear flavours. Typical of a mix of starters and main courses which have no set delineation between them are: Japanese shellfish consommé, a salad of avocado, fresh beans, toasted almonds, cherry tomatoes and herbs; rigatoni provençale; smoked haddock, sole and salmon fishcakes with a herb crust and wilted sorrel; Toulouse sausages with mash and red onions or roast red-leg partridge served with polenta, bubble and squeak and a truffle sauce. Enjoyable sweets to finish such as date and ginger cake with hot toffee sauce and amaretti ice cream with Italian biscuits or else cheese such as Caerphilly and Cashel Blue with salad and chutney. ***Seats** 130. Parties 12. Private Room 30. L 12.30-3 (Sun 1-3.30) D 7.30-12 (Sun to 11.30). Closed Bank Holidays except Good Friday.* AMERICAN EXPRESS *Access, Visa.*

SW5 Hotel 167

£77

Tel 071-373 0672 Fax 071-373 3360

H

167 Old Brompton Road SW5 0AN

Map 19 B5

Frank Cheevers has transformed a Victorian private house into a most delightful little hotel. Each room has its own character, with inspiration ranging from pine to art deco. Central heating and double-glazing keep things warm and peaceful. Breakfast is served in the bedrooms or in a pleasant reception room. Light evening meals also available. Unlicensed. No dogs. The hotel is located on the corner of Cresswell Gardens. ***Rooms** 19.* AMERICAN EXPRESS *Access, Diners, Visa.*

WC2 Orso

£65

Tel 071-240 5269 Fax 071-497 2148

R

27 Wellington Street WC2E 7DA

Map 17 C4

A basement restaurant in Covent Garden whose walls are hung with arty black and white photographs. Wonderful small pizzas come with a variety of toppings: spinach and pancetta, goat's cheese with roasted garlic cloves, anchovies with onions, mozzarella and black olives. Elsewhere on the menu (printed in both Italian and English) you might find pasta with rabbit and porcini, vitello tonnato, grilled swordfish and venison steaks with green peppercorns and polenta. Chocolate cake with coffee zabaglione tempts among the desserts. Waiters serve and pose with style. Easy-to-use list of good Italian wines. ***Seats** 100. Parties 8. Meals 12-12. Closed 24 & 25 Dec. No credit cards.*

SW11 Osteria Antica Bologna

£40

Tel 071-978 4771

R

23 Northcote Road SW11 1NG

Map 17 C6

Italian cooking at kind prices in friendly, unpretentious surroundings. That's the Osteria formula, and it works well. The food, which takes its inspiration from all parts of Italy, is not what you'll find in the usual high-street Italian restaurant. *Assaggi dell'Osteria* (Bolognese tasting portions) are a fun way to start a meal, or can make up into an excellent light meal. These run from olives to mozzarella rice balls, marinated sardines and baked aubergine rolls stuffed with provolone and pancetta. Other sections on the menu cover salads, soft polenta dishes, pasta, meat and fish courses (young goat cooked with rice almond and tomato pasta is a speciality) and traditional puddings. The Italian wine list has several interesting selections at fair prices – ask for advice. ***Seats** 70. Parties 25. Meals noon-11pm (Sun 12.30-10.30 Mon 6-11pm). Closed Bank Holidays, 2 weeks Christmas.* AMERICAN EXPRESS *Access, Visa.*

SW18 Le P'tit Normand

£48

Tel 081-871 0233

R

185 Merton Road Southfields SW18 5EF

Map 17 A6

Cheerful *restaurant du quartier* with mock-rustic decor and good honest cooking. The printed carte reflects owner Philippe Herrard's Normandy origins with dishes like *boudin noir aux pommes* and *magret de canard Vallée d'Auge* while the blackboard menu might include boeuf bourguignon and rabbit with mustard sauce. Standard puds like tarte tatin and crème brulée

See over

and a good French cheese tray. For the first week of each month there is a special two-course fixed-price lunch on offer at just £5 per head. ***Seats** 30. Private Room 26. L 12-1.30 D 7-10.30. Closed L Sat. Set L from £9.75.* AMERICAN EXPRESS *Access, Diners, Visa.*

W8 La Paesana **£40**

Tel 071-229 4332 **R**

30 Uxbridge Street Notting Hill W8 7TR **Map 18 A3**

Standard Italian fare in a lively Notting Hill restaurant behind the Coronet cinema. All the antipasti and pastas are available as either starters or main courses. ***Seats** 90. Private Room 30. L 12-2.45 D 6.30-11.45. Closed Sun, Bank Holidays. Set L £9.95.* AMERICAN EXPRESS *Access, Diners, Visa.*

WC2 Le Palais du Jardin NEW **£50**

Tel 071-379 5353 **R**

136 Long Acre London WC2E 9AD **Map 21 B2**

Covent Garden is the setting for a stylish Parisian-style brasserie offering superior cooking at very reasonable prices. The café is open from 10 for a civilised breakfast, while from noon onwards you can enjoy a grill, a salad, delicious moules parmentier, duck à l'orange or anything else from the mainly traditional French menu. ***Seats** 150. Parties 40. Private Room 20. Meals 12-12 (Sun to 10.50).* AMERICAN EXPRESS *Access, Diners, Visa.*

W1 Panda Si Chuen ★ **£45**

Tel 071-437 2069 **R**

56 Old Compton Street W1V 5PA **Map 21 A2**

One of London's very best Chinese restaurants, and perhaps the most authentic of the Szechuan specialists. The chef of many years' standing is a real expert in his field, and staff will cheerfully give you any help needed in ordering. Among many interesting dishes on a menu of almost 100 choices are smoked and spiced fish; special herb-marinated beef; pelmeni (won ton) in consommé, hot-sour soup or red chili oil and soya sauce; tea-smoked duck; stewed croaker fish; grilled chicken with egg and garlic; sizzling oysters in fish-flavour sauce; bean thread with minced meat and dry shrimp. ***Seats** 60. Parties 40. Private Room 14. Meals 12-11.30. Closed Sun, 25 & 26 Dec. Set meals from £9.50.* AMERICAN EXPRESS *Access, Diners, Visa.*

W1 The Park Lane Hotel 77% **£195**

Tel 071-499 6321 Fax 071-499 1965 **HR**

Piccadilly W1Y 8EB **Map 18 C3**

Built in 1927, the hotel retains some of its distinctive art deco features, although the feel throughout the public rooms and bedrooms is very traditional. The Palm Court lounge, where afternoon teas are served, is brightened by a magnificent vaulted ceiling with arched art deco stained glass. Bracewells Bar and the Brasserie on the Park (specialising in pre-and post-theatre suppers) are more modern in style. Standard bedrooms are well sized but tend to look out on the dark inside courtyard. All rooms have double-glazing, multi-channel TV, mini-bars and bathrobes. The best rooms are the suites, more than 30 in number: all air-conditioned, they look out on to the central court or Green Park and benefit from private sitting rooms and more luxurious bathrooms. Large-scale banqueting suites (including an art deco ballroom) for up to 600; conference facilities for up to 500. Private parking for 180 cars is provided in a covered garage opposite the main entrance. ***Rooms** 320. Keep-fit equipment, solarium, beauty & hair salons, brasserie noon-11.30pm, business centre, garage.* AMERICAN EXPRESS *Access, Diners, Visa.*

Bracewells

£70

The restaurant atmosphere is traditional. The decor is of dark carved wood, light flowery panels, mirrors and silver trolleys; jacket and tie are a must. Jon Tindall plays comfortably with English and French classics adding his own individual touches: salmon and sole sausage topped with fresh crab meat on an avocado sauce, spinach and walnut soufflé, classic sole meunière, plain grills, pot-roasted chicken served on a potato cake with braised vegetables. Pancakes Belmonte, flamed at the table, are the speciality dessert. The wine list is well constructed and the three-course luncheon menu offers good value. ***Seats** 90. Parties 20. Private Room 20. L 12.30-2.30 D 7-10.30 Set L £17 Set D £24.*

W2 Parkwood Hotel

£65

Tel 071-402 2241 Fax 071-402 1574

H

4 Stanhope Place W2 2HB

Map 18 C3

Bed and breakfast town house hotel close to Marble Arch and Oxford Street shops. Special rates for children under 13. Unlicensed. No dogs. ***Rooms** 18. Access, Visa.*

SW1 Pearl of Knightsbridge

£75

Tel 071-225 3888

R

22 Brompton Road Knightsbridge Green SW1

Map 19 C4

A stylish Cantonese restaurant overlooking Knightsbridge Green (the 'green' now comprising one grown-up tree and a sapling). Prices are on the high side on menus that range from weekend dim sum through many familiar favourites and up to luxury items like shark's fin consommé (a voracious £50 for 2), braised abalone and whole suckling pig. Judged on our 1993 visits, the dim sum are the most accomplished, with some of the main-menu dishes being either too oily or too salty. ***Seats** 80. Private Room 16. L 12-3 D 6-11.30 (Sat 12-11.30 Sun 12-11). Closed 25 & 26 Dec. Set L from £12.50 Set D from £25.* AMERICAN EXPRESS *Access, Diners, Visa.*

SW7 Pelham Hotel 74%

£160

Tel 071-589 8288 Fax 071-584 8444

H

15 Cromwell Place SW7 2LA

Map 19 B5

Friendly, helpful staff and owners Kit and Tim Kemp's flair combine to create a charmingly intimate hotel in the heart of South Kensington. A certain country-house style has been created in a part of town that's just a few minutes walk from Harrods and the major museums. Day rooms, like the bar with 18th-century pine panelling and the cosy Victorian snuggery, are most appealing with deeply comfortable armchairs and profusion of fresh flowers. Paintings and antique furniture have been carefully chosen by the owners. Bedrooms vary from small and cosy to grand and high-ceilinged (on the first floor) but all feature fine fabrics varying from traditional floral prints to bold black and white stripes. Practicalities are not forgotten, either, with all rooms having a useful second telephone by the desk and full air-conditioning. Excellent bathrooms. Under the same ownership as *Durley House* and *Dorset Square* hotels. Valet service and 24hr room service. Guests have free use of the garden and outdoor swimming pool of the hotel's administrative building opposite. ***Rooms** 37.* AMERICAN EXPRESS *Access, Visa.*

W2 Pembridge Court Hotel 65%

£140

Tel 071-229 9977 Fax 071-727 4982

H

34 Pembridge Gardens W2 4DX

Map 18 A3

Very close to Portobello Road antiques market, Pembridge Court has personality, warmth and charm thanks to a delightful, long-serving

See over

manager (Valerie Gilliat) and well-motivated staff. There's an inviting feeling to the town house as soon as you cross the threshold into the lobby with its exposed brickwork, a style continued in the downstairs bar and Caps restaurant. Most of the bedrooms are luxurious with stylishly co-ordinated fabrics and furnishings and Victorian prints on the wall. Many of the bathrooms have chic Italian tiles. Rooms are generally of a good size with three very spacious top-floor rooms but there are also some small singles. Children up to 10 stay free in parents' room. Good breakfasts. ***Rooms** 21.* AMERICAN EXPRESS *Access, Diners, Visa.*

SW7 The Periquito Queen's Gate £81

Tel 071-370 6111 Fax 071-370 0932 **H**

68-69 Queen's Gate SW7 5JT **Map 19 B5**

New owners plan major changes at the former *Eden Plaza*, with full refurbishment due to have been completed by the time we went to press. The hotel is very close to the South Kensington museums. ***Rooms** 63.* AMERICAN EXPRESS *Access, Diners, Visa.*

NW6 Peter's £55

Tel 071-624 5804 **R**

65 Fairfax Road NW6 4EE **Map 16 B3**

20s' French decor provides a suitable backdrop for chef-partner Jean Charles' fairly traditional style of cooking. The chef is keen on pastry (puff for asparagus, filo for snails and wild mushrooms) and on salmon, which on the same evening could appear as gravad lax, smoked encasing avocado mousse, with halibut wrapped in cabbage leaves served with Pernod sauce and as one of several fish in a panaché grilled or poached. Best end of lamb and rib of beef are specialities for two. Daily specials such as spicy boned sardines or grilled calf's liver and sweetbreads extend the choice. Menus are either set price or à la carte (dishes in each course priced the same). Live piano music (but the pianist didn't turn up on our latest visit!). ***Seats** 60. L 12-3 D 6.30-11.30. Closed L Sat, D Sun, 26 Dec, 1 Jan. Set L £11.95 Set D £13.95 (not Sat).* AMERICAN EXPRESS *Access, Diners, Visa.*

NW5 Le Petit Prince £30

Tel 071-267 0752 **R**

5 Holmes Road NW5 3AA **Map 16 C2**

Decor is inspired by St Exupéry's Petit Prince and the atmosphere is often fittingly exuberant. Couscous is the main offering, along with salady starters, spicy fried plantain and a few daily specials. Chocolate mousse is the speciality dessert. Drink Algerian red wine or Normandy cider. ***Seats** 54. Private Room 20. L 12-3 D 7-11.30 (Sat to 11.45, Sun to 11.15). Closed L Sat-Mon, 1 week Christmas, 1 week Aug. No credit cards.*

W8 Phoenicia £50

Tel 071-937 0120 Fax 071-937 7668 **R**

11-13 Abingdon Road W8 6AH **Map 19 A4**

A relaxed and civilised, family-run Lebanese restaurant just off Kensington High Street. Hot and cold hors d'oeuvre, from aubergine, stuffed vine leaves and home-made cream cheese to grilled quails and spicy sausage, precede charcoal-grilled main courses, with delicious sweets to finish. Besides the à la carte there are several set menus, including vegetarian options, and a good-value lunchtime buffet (30 dishes, eat as much as you like). Six tables are in a conservatory. ***Seats** 100. Private Room 50. Meals 12-11.45. Closed 24 & 25 Dec. Set L £9.95 Set D £15.30.* AMERICAN EXPRESS *Access, Diners, Visa.*

W1 Pied à Terre ★ £100

Tel 071-636 1178 **R**

34 Charlotte Street W1P 1HJ **Map 21 A1**

Brightened by the clever use of floor-length peach and apricot tablecloths with Warhol and Richard Hamilton artwork adding a bigger splash of colour to the otherwise plain white-painted rough plaster walls, the restaurant is undergoing a transition. At the time of publication the entrance and bar area should have been altered to create more ergonomic use of the available space. The plaster legs, the Warhol tomato soup can carrier bag remain in their illuminated glass case at the rear. Appealing place settings feature large, delightfully rustic hand-painted plates. The hard-working partnership of Richard Neat and David Moore, both with a pedigree including the Manoir aux Quat'Saisons, brings a seriously high level of skill and sophistication to this street. An amuse-gueule of a deep-fried scallop coated in very fine crisp breadcrumbs with a sliver of salmon in the centre comes topped with tiny courgette batons on pimento with a parsley sauce. Breads offered at the same time include warm freshly baked olive, walnut and raisin – quite irresistible. With a complex and involved menu that changes twice daily Richard Neat's talents are put fully to the test. However, all is not as successful as should be expected: for instance a bouillon of langoustines with sliced roasted artichokes and a hint of ginger used so much truffle oil that the resulting flavour was marred by a pungent unctuousness and a passion fruit soufflé innovatively cooked in a paper-thin crisp pastry was undercooked in the centre (though to mitigate this the fruit's sorbet and sauce provided a delicious contrast of consistency and sweetness). Neat's well-known dedication to offal continues with the likes of a confit of duck's neck – stuffed with the heart, gizzard and livers chopped and slow-cooked in duck fat, then sliced on to a bed of wonderful creamy purée of white haricot beans. ***Seats*** *40. Parties 8. Private Room 12. L 12.15-2 D 7.15-10. Closed L Sat, all Sun, Bank Holidays. Set L £19.50 Set D £36.* AMERICAN EXPRESS *Access, Diners, Visa.*

NW1 Pinocchio's £60

Tel 071-388 7482 **R**

160 Eversholt Street NW1 1BL **Map 18 D1**

A smart, modern interior somehow belies the location (by the side of Euston station) of what is a good local restaurant. The short carte features capably prepared modern and more traditional Italian dishes. ***Seats*** *45. L 12-3 D 6.30-11. Closed L Sat, all Sun, Bank Holidays, 24-31 Dec.* AMERICAN EXPRESS *Access, Diners, Visa.*

SW3 Poissonnerie de l'Avenue £80

Tel 071-589 2457 **R**

82 Sloane Avenue SW3 3DZ **Map 19 B5**

Darkwood panelling and marine artefacts give this old-fashioned fish restaurant and oyster bar (opposite Sir Terence Conran's eponymous shop) a relaxed and comfortable atmosphere. Cooking is careful and classic, service solicitous. Vegetables, charged separately, and 15% automatic service bump up the final bill beyond expectation. A larger kitchen has put more pasta and meat dishes on the menu. ***Seats*** *70. Parties 12. Private Room 22. L 12-3 D 7-11.45. Closed Sun, Bank Holidays, 23 Dec-3 Jan, 4 days Easter.* AMERICAN EXPRESS *Access, Diners, Visa.*

SW1 Pomegranates £80

Tel 071-828 6560 **R**

94 Grosvenor Road SW1V 3LE **Map 19 D5**

"Variety is the spice of life" could be the motto of this durable basement restaurant, where Patrick Gwynn-Jones takes his customers on a gastronomic tour of the world. Danish pickled herrings, burek with Sudanese pepper sauce, Caribbean spicy-fried 'goatfish', Cantonese roast duck and Creole-Cajun jambalaya are typical exotic items on a menu that also offers rather more domestic game pie or boiled chicken with parsley sauce. ***Seats** 50. Private Room 12. L 12.30-2.15 D 7.30-11.15. Closed L Sat, all Sun, 25 & 26 Dec. Set L from £9.95 Set D from £17.75.* AMERICAN EXPRESS *Access, Diners, Visa.*

SE1 Le Pont de la Tour £80

Tel 071-403 8403 **R**

Butlers Wharf Building 36D Shad Thames Butlers Wharf SE1 **Map 20 D3**

Sir Terence Conran's Gastrodrome in a spectacular Thamesside wharf conversion is an Aladdin's cave for foodies; besides the restaurants (see also entry under *Cantina del Ponte*) and all-day bar and grill there's a food store, bakery, smoked fish and crustacea shop and wine merchant. The setting must be the envy of other restaurants – right alongside the river at the south-east end of Tower Bridge, and the 30 tables on the terrace provide the best alfresco eating in town. Parking is at the bottom end of Curlew Street. Chef David Burke presents a prix-fixe lunch menu of few words and instant appeal: Bayonne ham, celeriac rémoulade; spring onion, garlic and parsley soup; deep-fried plaice and chips with tartare sauce; black pudding with apples and Calvados; roast leg of lamb with mint. The evening à la carte is more extensive but equally laconic, typified by crab cakes with lentils and coriander, ricotta and bresaola with rocket and truffle oil, sautéed scallops with fennel purée and lemon olive oil, calf's liver and onion and braised lamb shank with rosemary mash. There are no vegetarian main dishes. A pre-and post-theatre menu (£19.50) is available 6-6.45 and 10.30-midnight. The restaurant is approached via the *Bar & Grill*, a separate eating area next to the Crustacea Bar just inside the door, where a menu similar to the *Bibendum Oyster Bar* is offered: simple starters like egg mayonnaise, Piedmontese peppers, chicken liver paté and scallops ceviche, followed by plateau de fruits de mer (£35 for two minimum), oysters, salads (foie gras and French bean), crustacea and grills (calf's liver, entrecote with béarnaise sauce, Dover sole). The imaginative wine list, last year's London Cellar of the Year, contines to evolve; there's marvellous depth throughout – note the house selections. "15% service charge will be added" to all bills. ***Seats** 109. Parties 9. Private Room 22. L 12-3 D 6-12 (Sun to 11) Bar & Grill 12-12 daily (Sun to 11). Closed 3 days Christmas. Set L £25. Access, Visa.*

We endeavour to be as up-to-the-minute as possible, but inevitably some changes to key personnel may occur at restaurants and hotels after the Guide goes to press.

W2 Poons £55

Tel 071-792 2884 **R**

Unit 205 Whiteleys Queensway W2 4YN **Map 18 A3**

Located in the food court on the third floor. Cool, black and white decor; varying standards of service. A large range of dim sum, including steamed buns, pot rice and soft rice pasta sheets, is served between noon and 4pm. There's a long and varied main menu. ***Seats** 120. Meals 12-11.*

Closed 25 & 26 Dec. Set meals from £12. AMERICAN EXPRESS *Access, Diners, Visa.*

WC1 Poons **£50**

Tel 071-580 1188 **R**

50 Woburn Place WC1 **Map 22 A4**

Another outlet in this Chinese chain, but with more than a few out-of-the-ordinary dishes: quail's eggs and minced prawns on toast, dumplings in red pepper sauce, deep-fried cod fillets in crab and asparagus sauce, chicken with dried tiger lilies and fungi, lamb curry enriched with coconut milk. Specialities include fresh crab and lobster, prepared with either ginger and sping onion or green pepper and black beans. ***Seats*** *100. Parties 50. L 12-3 D 5.30-11.30. Closed Bank Holidays, 4 days Christmas. Set meals from £9.* AMERICAN EXPRESS *Access, Diners, Visa.*

WC2 Poons **£70**

Tel 071-240 1743 **R**

41 King Street WC2E 8JS **Map 21 B2**

Just a few moments from the Covent Garden piazza, the smartest and most expensive of the Poons restaurant, to where William Poon expanded after opening his original, small café in Lisle Street (see entry) more than 20 years ago. The unusual greenhouse-style kitchen forms the centrepiece of the interior decor and was designed in the mid-70s to deter customers from believing horror stories about Chinese restaurant kitchens. Nowadays, customers are more certain about what actually goes into an authentic Cantonese menu and choose the house wind-dried specialities such as sausages, duck and bacon. Hot pots and dishes cooked in the style of Mr Poon's home town (typically deep-fried stuffed bean curd and stir-fried beef) are also specialities of the house, along with a three-course duck feast. A la carte, or various set menus, including a pre-theatre meal. ***Seats*** *100. Meals 12-12. Closed Sun Jan-Jun, 24-27 Dec. Set L from £6.80 Set D from £23.50 (pre-theatre from £7.50).* AMERICAN EXPRESS *Access, Diners, Visa.*

WC2 Poons **£30**

Tel 071-437 1528 **R**

4 Leicester Street WC2H 7BL **Map 21 A2**

Unsophisticated, yet wholesome, mainly Cantonese food served swiftly in simple surroundings; better value than its Covent Garden sister. Wind-dried meats and steamed chicken with Chinese sausage are specialities here. Original rice hot pot and noodle soup dishes make for inexpensive eating out. They no longer accept credit cards. ***Seats*** *100. Parties 55. Meals 12-11.30. Closed 3 days Christmas. Set meals from £6.50.*

WC2 Poons **£20**

Tel 071-437 4549 **R**

27 Lisle Street WC2 **Map 21 A2**

William Poon's original Cantonese café is little changed, though when we went to press a licence had been applied for. The decor plays third fiddle to the food and the rock-bottom prices. Barbecued and wind-dried food is the speciality, covering duck, pork, sausages and bacon, and there's a big choice of composite rice and noodle dishes. ***Seats*** *40. Parties 20. Private Room 20. Meals 12-11.30. Closed 25 & 26 Dec. No credit cards.*

Our inspectors are full-time employees; they are professionally trained by us.

EC3 Poons in the City NEW £50

Tel 071-626 0126 **R**

Minster Pavement Minster Court Mincing Lane EC3R 7PP **Map 20 D2**

Located below the architecturally stunning Minster Court, Poons is one of the few Chinese restaurants in the City. In a semi-basement setting the Poon family have created a spacious and elegant dining room replete with traditionally carved teak-like furniture, subtle lighting and smartly attired staff. Cooking by Mr Poon is classic Cantonese with a good variety of dim sum available, along with the rest of the menu, throughout the day. The selection also includes starters of the likes of lap yuk soom – wind-dried bacon with bamboo shoots and water chestnuts which you wrap in lettuce leaves – and crispy soft-shell crabs. Main courses range from stir-fried shredded lamb with ginger and spring onions to crab baked with black beans and peppers and three-course kam ling style duck. ***Seats** 150. Parties 10. Private Room 50. Meals 11.45am-10.15pm. Closed Sat, Sun and all Bank Holidays. Set L £15.99 Set D £25.* AMERICAN EXPRESS *Access, Diners, Visa.*

W11 Portobello Hotel 60% £120

Tel 071-727 2777 Fax 071-792 9641 **H**

22 Stanley Gardens W11 2NG **Map 18 A3**

Two six-floor houses in an 1850 terrace near Portobello antiques market converted into a unique hotel decorated in an eclectic mix of styles. There are singles, doubles, twins and suites, plus some compact cabins. The 24hr bar/restaurant in the basement caters admirably for those guests with nocturnal life styles. Guests have free membership of a nearby health club. ***Rooms** 25. Closed 2 weeks Christmas.* AMERICAN EXPRESS *Access, Diners, Visa.*

SW1 La Poule au Pot £55

Tel 071-730 7760 **R**

231 Ebury Street SW1W 8UT **Map 19 C5**

Khaki walls, bare stripped floorboards, lacy tablecloths with cream paper covers, heaps of straw and wicker baskets filled with dried flowers and twigs and huge red clay garden pots with luxuriant weeping figs all combine to create a suitably rustic ambience for simple homely cuisine grandmère. The choice is recited and includes perennial favourites like fish mousse, terrine du chef, egg mayonnaise and hot tomato soup for starters then *gigot d'agneau, steak béarnaise, boeuf à la bourguignonne, raie au beurre noir* and *poulet à l'éstragon* for mains. To finish, *crème brulée, mousse au chocolat* or *tarte tatin.* While the food is variable the young French waiters provide consistently campy, friendly service. ***Seats** 72. Parties 12. L 12.30-2.30 D 7-11.15. Closed 24-28 Dec. Set L £12.75.* AMERICAN EXPRESS *Access, Diners, Visa.*

WC1 President Hotel £64

Tel 071-837 8844 Fax 071-837 4653 **H**

Russell Square WC1N 1DB **Map 18 D2**

Large bed and breakfast hotel next door to the Imperial, on the corner of Guilford Street and Russell Square, catering mainly for tour parties and exhibition delegates from surrounding sister hotels. Rooms are currently being renovated. Close to the British Museum. ***Rooms** 447. Coffee shop (10.30am-2am).* AMERICAN EXPRESS *Access, Diners, Visa.*

is our symbol for an outstanding wine list.

SW7 Prince Hotel £71

Tel 071-589 6488 Fax 071-581 0824 **H**

6 Sumner Place SW7 3AB **Map 19 B5**

A bed and breakfast hotel conveniently located near South Kensington tube. Bedrooms are well decorated but offer very basic bathrooms, most of them built into the room. Now under Resort hotel management, the two Victorian terrace houses could use some refurbishment. Conservatory and patio garden are pleasant features. Breakfasts are served at the nearby Alexander hotel. One family room sleeps four. ***Rooms*** *37. Garden.* AMERICAN EXPRESS *Access, Diners, Visa.*

SW7 Pun £50

Tel 071-225 1609 **R**

53 Old Brompton Road SW7 3JS **Map 19 B5**

More comfortable, more Westernised and more expensive than its Soho compatriots, Pun is also a much friendlier place than some of those. The food's pretty good, too, and from a reasonably wide-ranging menu you could choose minced meat, shrimps and vegetables in a rich brown sauce, served with iceberg lettuce for wrapping; braised tofu with mixed vegetables; and sizzling fish fillet with ginger and onions. ***Seats*** *70. Parties 40. L 12-2.30 D 6-11.30 Meals Sat 12-11.30 Sun 12-11. Closed 25 Dec. Set D £13.80/£18.* AMERICAN EXPRESS *Access, Diners, Visa.*

NW3 Qinggis £45

Tel 071-586 4251 **R**

30 Englands Lane NW3 **Map 16 B2**

Squashed between the shops of Englands Lane, this open-plan restaurant serves Chinese dishes and some decidely un-Chinese desserts (*cassata Siciliana*!). Good cooking through a menu that's strong on seafood, with whole sections for sole and sea bass. ***Seats*** *75. L 12-2.30 D 6-11. Closed 24-27 Dec. Set meals from £17.* AMERICAN EXPRESS *Access, Visa.*

SW1 Quaglino's NEW £70

Tel 071-930 6767 Fax 071-836 2866 **R**

16 Bury Street St James's SW1Y 6AL **Map 18 D3**

Since the restaurant's highly publicised and much-hyped opening last February, we have carefully monitored its progress, and at least on our last visit we enjoyed our dishes, though service was painfully slow and the staff seriously lacking in charisma, in complete contrast to the restaurant itself, which is cavernously stylish as one would expect from a Sir Terence Conran design. Descending the staircase to the gallery level, there's an informal anitpasti bar area (no bookings) serving snacks all day, and a private room, overlooking the dining area with its individually-commissioned painted columns. At its head is the mirrored crustacean altar, above, a computer-programmed skylight, the length of the restaurant, imitating natural skies. Half the fun of the place is its noise and bustle, but the quality of the food is commendable, given the restaurant's size and number of covers it turns over daily. Try the warm pan-fried foie gras served with baby spinach leaves coated in a pleasant light balsamic dressing, or steamed mussels with pesto, and move on to oxtail in red wine, char-grilled calf's liver with bacon (shame about the accompanying limp corn cake), or roast cod with warm artichoke salad. End with a crème brulée which has the right velvety voluptuousness of consistency or a crisp *tarte fine aux pommes*. There's a good choice of wines on a sensible list, decent bread rolls and unsalted butter, and coffee (when it eventually arrives) is pleasingly strong. Remember that a hefty 15% service charge is automatically added to the final bill. Late-night dining with live music Fri, Sat. ***Seats*** *300. Parties 12. Private Room 40. L 12-3 D 5.30-12 (Fri, Sat till 1.45am, Sun till 11). Set L & D £35.* AMERICAN EXPRESS *Access, Diners, Visa.*

W8 Le Quai St Pierre ↑ **£70**

Tel 071-937 6388 **R**

7 Stratford Road W8 3JS **Map 19 A4**

Decor, menu and staff all evoke the south of France in this well-liked seafood restaurant between upper Earls Court Road and Marloes Road. Lobster, kept live in a tank, heads the list, with langoustines, coquilles St Jacques, clams and mussels available in various preparations. White fish specials change with the market, and other popular choices include feuilletés, salads and steaks. Plats du jour and the wine list have recently been expanded and some of the food prices reduced. A reliable local with a real flavour of the sea, and a good place for blowing the cobwebs off your French. ***Seats** 58. L 12.30-2.30 D 7-11.30. Closed L Mon, all Sun.*
AMERICAN EXPRESS *Access, Diners, Visa.*

EC1 Quality Chop House **£40**

Tel 071-837 5093 **R**

94 Farringdon Road EC1R 3EA **Map 16 C3**

Chef-proprietor Charles Fontaine reopened a Victorian chop house in 1990 with the aim of providing straightforward, no-nonsense food in friendly, informal surroundings. Much of the original atmosphere survives, and period features include the high-backed mahogany booths and the embossed wallpaper. Value for money is a watchword throughout the menu, which combines traditional English café food with the occasional French or exotic element. In the former category come corned beef hash, lamb chops and rhubarb crumble, in the latter confit of duck, bang bang chicken and grilled swordfish steak with lime hollandaise. Salmon fishcakes and liver and bacon are almost permanent favourites and the chips are among the best in town. A number of dishes are available as starter or main course. ***Seats** 46. Parties 6. L 12-3 (Sun 12-4) D 6.30-12 (Sun 7-11.30). Closed L Sat, L Bank Holidays, Christmas. No credit cards.*

NW2 Quincy's **£60**

Tel 071-794 8499 **R**

675 Finchley Road NW2 2JP **Map 16 B2**

The best sort of local restaurant – friendly front-of-house, good quality fresh food, reasonable prices. The menu, of British, French and Mediterranean inspiration, is short but varied (it changes monthly) with dishes such as chicken mousseline in field mushrooms with tarragon, assorted crostini, breast of duck with cider and apples, and venison rosettes with sauce poivrade, polenta and cranberries. The fish dish depends on what's good in the market. Desserts could be traditional – bread-and-butter pudding, treacle tart – or more modern like gratin of satsumas with fruit ices in brandy snap. ***Seats** 30. Private Room 16. D only 7-11. Closed Sun & Mon, 2 weeks Sep, 1 week Christmas. Set D £22.*
AMERICAN EXPRESS *Access, Visa.*

SE1 RSJ **£63**

Tel 071-928 4554 **R**

13a Coin Street SE1 8YQ **Map 20 A3**

Within easy reach of the South Bank complex, thus a handy spot for pre- and post-theatre dinners. Modern British cooking with French influences in a very friendly and relaxing restaurant (upstairs) and brasserie (downstairs). Fixed-price 2- or 3-course menus might offer goat's cheese in puff pastry or tartare of smoked haddock followed by roast guinea fowl with braised savoy cabbage and bacon in a rich game sauce, or fillet of halibut on a langoustine cream. Ratatouille terrine, stuffed saddle of rabbit and ginger and glacé fruit parfait typify the more adventurous carte. The sensational Loire wine list deserves careful scrutiny. Not only is it fairly priced, but the interesting notes make fascinating reading. The odd burgundy, claret and Australian get a mention. ***Seats** 90. Private Room 24. L 12-2 D 6-11. Closed L Sat, all Sun, Bank Holidays. Set meals from £13.95.* AMERICAN EXPRESS *Access, Visa.*

W1 Ragam **£25**

Tel 071-636 9098 **R**

57 Cleveland Street W1P 5PQ **Map 18 D2**

Popular little South Indian restaurant specialising in vegetarian cooking making good use of rice and lentil flour, green chilis, semolina, yoghurt, coconut, curry leaves and tamarind juice. It's not exclusively vegetarian by any means, and prawn, beef, lamb and chicken appear in biryani, dopiaza, korma, vindaloo and Madras styles. Under joint management with *Sree Krishna* (qv). ***Seats** 36. Parties 20. L 12-3 D 6-11.15 (Fri to 11.45 Sun to 10.45). Closed 25 & 26 Dec.* AMERICAN EXPRESS *Access, Diners, Visa.*

W12 Rajput **£25**

Tel 081-740 9036 **R**

144 Goldhawk Road W12 8HH **Map 17 A4**

North Indian restaurant with helpful staff, near Goldhawk Road underground station. Dishes on a straightforward menu include curries ranging from mild (korma, Malaya) to mind-blowing (Bangalore phal). Sunday buffet. Some prices have gone down since last year. ***Seats** 48. Parties 20. L 12-2.30 D 6-12. Closed 25 & 26 Dec.* AMERICAN EXPRESS *Access, Visa.*

N3 Rani **£40**

Tel 081-349 4386 **R**

7 Long Lane Finchley Central N3 2PR **Map 16 B1**

Five minutes walk from Finchley Central station, Rani may well be the queen of London's Gujerati restaurants – a clean and sparkling family-run diner with a wide frontage and a fine repertoire of vegetarian-only food. Full use is made of grain flours and various dal combined with fresh, exotic vegetables and delicate spicing. Start perhaps with a choice of spiced lentil soups or bhajia, bhel poori, bean papri chat (spicy beans and chopped onions served on crispy pooris with tamarind and yoghurt sauce), or a daily special (perhaps rani tiffin, kachori or stuffed green chili). Similarly, a special curry changes daily (spinach and sweetcorn, gram flour and fenugreek balls or stuffed okra). Chutneys are made on the premises and desserts should not be missed. The children's set menu (£5) serves tomato ketchup with potato bhajia followed by poppadum, bean curry, dosa (potatoes in a rice pancake) and bhatoora (deep-fried bread) – showing that this is no ordinary Indian restaurant! Two high-chairs are provided for junior diners with a taste for the spicy, but no children under 6 after 7pm. Prices are extremely reasonable and service is by professional, young and motivated staff who operate a 'no tipping' policy. Equally good-value set meals only all lunchtimes and Monday dinner. All no-smoking on Saturdays. ***Seats** 90. L 12.15-2 D 6-10.30. Closed L Mon & Sat, 25 Dec. Set meals £6-£19. Access, Visa.*

SW11 Ransome's Dock NEW **£50**

Tel 071-223 1611 **R**

35 Parkgate Road Battersea SW11 4NP **Map 19 B6**

Near the south bank of the Thames midway between Albert and Battersea Bridges, Ransome's Dock occupies part of a modern dockside development with the potential for al fresco dining in the summer. The cooking by Martin Lam, long-time head chef at L'Escargot in Soho, is executed with flair. On offer is a short, modern and somewhat eclectic brasserie-style

See over

menu: mussels with saffron, duck terrine with home-spiced quinces, chargrilled quails with couscous and lemon sauce. Good puddings. ***Seats** 60. Parties 50. Meals Mon-Fri 11-11 Sat 12-12 Sun 12.30-3.30pm. Closed D Sun, 2 weeks summer, 1 week Christmas. Set L £10.50.* AMERICAN EXPRESS *Access, Diners, Visa.*

W9 Raoul's **£65**

Tel 071-286 2266 **R**

30 Clifton Road London W9 **Map 18 B1**

Wrought-iron chairs and walls the colour of sun-bleached stucco give a suitably Roman feel to a smart, new-wave Italian restaurant in Maida Vale. Starters like fresh vegetables grilled with aromatic olive oil, gnocchi al pesto and ravioli stuffed with spinach and ricotta in walnut sauce are followed by main dishes such as breast of duck on a bed of lentils, scampi in Italian mustard sauce and veal cutlet with brandy and fresh basil. ***Seats** 50. Parties 20. Private Room 22. L 12-2.30 D 7-10.30. Closed D Sun Oct-April, 25, 26 Dec, 1 Jan, Good Friday & Easter Mon. Set L £12.50. Access, Visa.*

W2 Rasa Sayang **£40**

Tel 071-229 8417 **R**

38 Queensway W2 **Map 18 A3**

Malaysian and South-East Asian food (prepared without using MSG) served in congenial surroundings. Set meals provide a good introduction to an interesting cuisine that includes traditional dishes like orange chicken, special rice dishes and rendang (cutlets of beef in coconut gravy). ***Seats** 62. Meals noon-11.15pm. Closed 25 Dec. Set meals from £19.* AMERICAN EXPRESS *Access, Diners, Visa.*

W1 Rathbone Hotel 69% **£161**

Tel 071-636 2001 Fax 071-636 3882 **H**

30 Rathbone Street W1P 1AJ **Map 18 D2**

An intimate hotel notable for its location (minutes from Oxford Street) and personal air. Crystal chandeliers, Italian marble and objets d'art adorn the limited public areas. The stylishness is matched in carefully modelled bedrooms (all now fully air-conditioned), where smoked-glass mirrors add depth and boldly patterned curtains enrich the colour. Brightly lit, marbled bathrooms all have powerful showers. Executive and single-bedroomed suites feature whirlpool baths. Plush, perhaps, but not de luxe; no leisure facilities. ***Rooms** 72.* AMERICAN EXPRESS *Access, Diners, Visa.*

NW1 Ravi Shankar **£25**

Tel 071-388 6458 **R**

133-135 Drummond Street NW1 2HL **Map 18 D1**

South Indian vegetarian cooking at basement prices in friendly, informal surroundings. The house speciality is Shankar Thali, a complete set meal. ***Seats** 58. Private Room 25. Meals 12-11. Set meals from £3.50. Access, Visa.*
Also at:
422 St John Street EC1 Tel 071-833 5849 **Map 20 C1**
L 12-2.30 D 6-11 (Fri & Sat till 11.30).

W1 La Reash **£35**

Tel 071-439 1063 **R**

23 Greek Street W1V 5LG **Map 21 A2**

In the heart of Soho, at the junction of Old Compton Street and Greek Street, La Reash specialises in Lebanese and Moroccan cuisine. Mazah (a selection of hot and cold starters) represents the former, couscous and tagines the latter. There's a tapas bar beneath the main restaurant.

***Seats** 70. Meals 12-12. Closed 25 Dec. Set L from £6.50.* AMERICAN EXPRESS *Access, Diners, Visa.*

W1 Red Fort **£50**

Tel 071-437 2525 **R**

77 Dean Street W1V 5HA **Map 21 A2**

Opened in 1983 by Amin Ali, the stylish Red Fort takes its name from the red sandstone fort built by Emperor Shah Jahan on the banks of the river Jamuna in Delhi. Tandoori food is a popular choice and other specialities include jumbo prawns pickled in mustard and fenugreek seeds, dry ginger, yoghurt and lemon; Goan-style pomfret; and chicken with spinach, mint and coriander leaves. The restaurant is on two floors: street-level fronted by a bar area with seats, and a more intimate, low-lit basement. ***Seats** 150. Private Room 75. L 12-3 D 6-11.30. Buffet L £12.50.* AMERICAN EXPRESS *Access, Diners, Visa.*

SW7 Regency Hotel 68% **£133**

Tel 071-370 4595 Fax 071-370 5555 **H**

100 Queen's Gate SW7 5AG **Map 19 B5**

Privately owned hotel at the junction with Old Brompton Road, near the South Kensington museums and Knightsbridge shopping. Beyond the marble foyer the Terrace (more marble, and natural light) is a pleasant spot for afternoon tea, and there's a cocktail bar, a health spa and several conference rooms (maximum capacity 100). Children up to the age of 7 stay free in parents' room. Full 24hr room service (including a night chef) and an on-site health spa are among the bonuses. No dogs. ***Rooms** 210. Keep-fit equipment, sauna, spa bath, steam room, solarium, beauty salon.* AMERICAN EXPRESS *Access, Diners, Visa.*

NW1 The Regent London 83% NEW **£238**

Tel 071-631 8000 Fax 071-631 8080 **HR**

222 Marylebone Road NW1 6JQ **Map 18 C2**

This important new addition to the London hotel scene opened in February 1993 in what used to be the Great Central (originally opened in 1899 as one of the last grand railway hotels, the original brainchild of Sir Edward Watkins who envisaged a channel tunnel terminating at Marylebone Station behind the hotel), now claiming "history and tradition meet luxury and convenience". Three and a half years of renovation have returned this impressive piece of Grade II-listed Victorian Gothic architecture to its former glory, creating a luxurious hotel with a relaxed and informal atmosphere. From the oak-panelled entrance hall, a majestic staircase leads to the Winter Garden, an eight-storey glass-covered atrium of breathtaking proportions. Gigantic palm trees, mezzanine-level Gazebo sitting area and fashionable furniture contribute to a light modern interpretation of its Victorian ancestry. Bedrooms are among the largest in London; even the Executive bedrooms conceived for single businessmen are unusually large. Decor is identical in all rooms, an elegant mix of smoky green and bronze, with large custom-made cabinet hiding mini-bar and satellite TV, relaxing sitting areas with elephant-theme cushions, large desks and comfortable beds. Rooms overlooking the Winter garden tend to be darker; two floors of rooms are non-smoking. Top of the range are the sixth-floor Penthouse suite and the fifth-floor Presidential suite, the latter featuring two bedrooms, a private dining room and even a grand piano. Marble bathrooms, equipped with quality towels, bathrobes, Crabtree & Evelyn toiletries and telephone extension by the bath, are also spacious, most with separate showers and all with twin washbasins. Well equipped for families, the hotel provides an endless list of baby accessories which even includes electric socket guards, playpen and thermometers; children up to 14 may share their parents' room at no charge and there are 100 interconnecting rooms. The

See over

basement health club, with a 15m swimming pool, is open from 6am offering a complimentary healthy breakfast buffet. Breakfast, also available in the dining room, extends to frittata, carrot bran muffins and banana pancakes and is one of the best to be found in London. Light meals and afternoon tea (3-6pm) are served all day in the Winter Garden. Lunches and evening snacks are also available in the Cellars, an elegant, wood-panelled pubby wine bar with its own entrance (closed all Sun and Bank Holidays). Service handled by young, enthusiastic staff is one of the hotel's biggest assets – from 24hr room service, picnic baskets in summer and 4-hour rush dry cleaning service to an evening turn-down and overnight shoe shine. A shop and hairdressing salon were due to open on the mezzanine floor as we went to press. Impressive function rooms hold up to 350; the Tower Suite on the fifth floor is next to the Penthouse suite and has a lovely double-storey-high glass ceiling plus facilities for up to 20 boardroom-style. Limited underground car parking. Business centre with Reuters information. Regent International Hotels/Four Seasons Hotels. ***Rooms** 309. Indoor swimming pool, spa bath, gymnasium, sauna, massage, news kiosk, hair salon, coffee shop (9am-11pm).* AMERICAN EXPRESS *Access, Diners, Visa.*

Dining Room — £90

A magnificent room, built on the grand scale with three huge glittering chandeliers suspended from the ornate plaster ceiling. Contrasting this classicism is a menu of mostly modish Italian food which is enjoyably prepared and attractively presented, under Executive Chef Ralph Kutzner and Paolo Simioni. Only the desserts from the trolley manage not to always live up to expectations. Cosmopolitan but pricy wine list with an accent on Italian wines, though France and the New World are also well represented. ***Seats** 100. Parties 12. L 12-3 (Sun from 12.30) D 7-11. Set L £19.50.*

NW3 Regent's Park Marriott 73% £192

Tel 071-722 7711 Fax 071-586 5822 **H**

128 King Henry's Road Swiss Cottage NW3 3ST **Map 16 B3**

A modern hotel with a lot to offer: good-sized rooms with large beds, desks, breakfast tables and easy chairs; 120 free car spaces; facilities for up to 400 conference delegates; a well-equipped health and leisure centre. The foyer features marble flooring, pale-wood panelling (also in the bar lounge) and an enormous vase of flowers. Two children (max age 18) can stay free in parents' room. Two minutes walk from Swiss Cottage underground. ***Rooms** 303. Garden, indoor swimming pool, sauna, solarium, beauty and hair salon, gift shop.* AMERICAN EXPRESS *Access, Diners, Visa.*

SW7 Rembrandt Hotel 67% £144

Tel 071-589 8100 Fax 071-225 3363 **H**

11 Thurloe Place SW7 2RS **Map 19 B4**

The Aquilla health and fitness centre, designed along the lines of an ancient Roman Spa, is a notable feature of a well-kept Sarova Group hotel opposite the Victoria and Albert Museum. Best of the stylish day rooms is a marble-pillared bar-lounge with a glass-roofed annexe where a pianist plays. Many of the bedrooms are designated Executive, with jacuzzis. Conference facilities for up to 250. ***Rooms** 195. Indoor swimming pool, gymnasium, sauna, spa bath, solarium, beauty salon.* AMERICAN EXPRESS *Access, Diners, Visa.*

SW6 La Réserve 62% £90

Tel 071-385 8561 Fax 071-385 7662 **H**

422 Fulham Road SW6 1DU **Map 19 A6**

Contemporary small hotel favoured by overseas visitors and people in the television and music business. Bar and lounge have comfortable modern leather sofas. Bedrooms (some small road-facing singles; rear rooms look on to Chelsea football ground) feature modern art and modern technology. Room service and light snacks available 24 hours. ***Rooms** 40.* AMERICAN EXPRESS *Access, Diners, Visa.*

W1 The Ritz 86% **£249**

Tel 071-493 8181 Fax 071-493 2687 **HR**

150 Piccadilly W1V 9DG **Map 18 D3**

When César Ritz opened this hotel in 1906 it was his intention to create "the most fashionable hotel in the most fashionable city in the world". Today's management endeavours to keep at least the first part true, and standards of service, comfort and housekeeping are enviably high. Tea at the Ritz is part of our heritage and the Palm Court is one of London's most elegant teatime settings. The rest of the hotel is equally grand: the Long Gallery, the sumptuously beautiful restaurant, the private salons and the bedrooms, with delicate pastels and gold leaf, marble fireplaces, Louis XVI furnishings and lavishly equipped marble bathrooms. Children up to 14 stay free in parents' room. This is the flagship of the Cunard group, owners also of Dukes and Stafford hotels. Own, charged parking. No dogs. ***Rooms** 129. Garden, valeting, dinner dance (Fri & Sat).*

AMERICAN EXPRESS *Access, Diners, Visa.*

Restaurant ↑ **£120**

A grandiose dining room of perfect proportions, elegantly furnished in pink, harmoniously matching the marble decor. A giant trompe l'oeil ceiling from which hangs a carousel of gilded chandeliers highlights the room. The Italian garden and terrace for alfresco dining are as sumptuous. Never too stiff, the service is helpful and attentive, giving tempting descriptions of chef David Nicholls' menu. His refreshing approach to cooking is given life through interesting associations like pan-fried foie gras with Calvados, grape and onion compote; hot, glazed oysters with cucumber and caviar in champagne sabayon and a light interpretation of classic dishes like supreme of free-range guinea fowl with Alsace bacon and sweet red cabbage; roast venison lightly peppered with creamed celeriac and blackcurrants. Results are sometimes too timid. A multitude of well-conceived menus caters for lunch, dinner, theatre (6-6.45 & 10.30-11.15) and even Friday and Saturday dinner-dances (in the Palm Court from 10.30pm). ***Seats** 100. Parties 40. Private Room 60. L 12.30-2.30 D 6.30-11.15. Set L from £26 Set D from £39.50.*

SW13 Riva **£60**

Tel 081-748 0434 **R**

169 Church Road Barnes SW13 9HR **Map 17 A5**

In the forefront of Italian cooking of the post-spaghetti bolognese and veal escalope era, Riva keeps its appeal to both meals and a wider-ranging clientele. A trip to Barnes and Andrea Riva's sparsely decorated modern restaurant is rewarded by food notable for honest, robust flavours, and many of chef Franco Zanchetta's regularly changing dishes are seldom seen elsewhere: white cabbage and onions with sauguinaccio (black pudding) and luganega sausage; focaccia with smoked salmon, horseradish and watercress; sliced baked potatoes topped with mushroom caps stuffed with snails and fennel fronds; ravioli filled with lobster and prawns, leeks and aromatic herbs; rabbit roasted with mushrooms and carrots and served with spätzlie. The menu, then, is nothing if not interesting, and the Italian wine list is equally appealing (though hardly any half bottles) and there's a splendid selection of grappa plus good strong espresso. ***Seats** 50. L 12-2.30 D 7-11. Closed L Sat, Bank Holidays, last 2 weeks Aug. Access, Visa.*

Consult page 16 for a full list of starred restaurants

W6 River Café £80

Tel 071-381 8824 Fax 071-381 6217 **R**

Thames Wharf Studios Rainville Road Hammersmith W6 9HA **Map 17 B5**

Rose Gray and Ruth Rogers set the pace when they opened their new-wave Italian venture in 1987. They have managed to create a mix of earthy and high-style dishes born from a genuine love of regional Italian cooking making good use of simple, fresh ingredients, marinades and the chargrill. Prices are highish and apparently willingly paid by the equally stylish clientele who book some way ahead; 12½% service charge is automatically added to all bills and sometimes seems inappropriate when diners are rushed or service is lacklustre. The setting is trendily stark and canteen-like with no tablecloths and simple glassware; the menu is short, offering dishes abounding with Mediterranean flavours – witness a dish of calf's brains baked in a bag with sage butter and lemon and served with a salad of dandelion, chicory and green bean salad plus sour-dough bruschetta (*cervelle di vitello in cartoccio*), or grilled marinated leg of lamb with borlotti beans, sage, plum tomatoes, grilled leeks and salsa verde (*coscia d'agnello*). Classic dishes often take on enticing new angles – spring minestrone with peas, asparagus, green beans, celery, chicken stock and pesto or prosciutto served with broad beans marinated with mint; chargrilled scallops with artichoke hearts and black olives; spaghettini with Cornish crab; spinach and ricotta gnocchi with Parmesan and sage butter. The execution is not always as clever as the ideas, but their success cannot be doubted. Leave room for polenta and lemon cake with vin santo, pear and almond tart, chocolate nemesis, or Italian cheeses. An excellent all-Italian wine list, with the addition of two champagnes. Very close to the Thames, but not so close as to offer views of the river, even from the eight tables set outside in good weather. Local restrictions insist that diners must leave the premises by 11pm sharp. ***Seats** 75. Parties 15. Private Room 12. L 12.30-3 D 7.30-9.45. Closed D Sun, 10 days Christmas, 4 days Easter, Bank Holidays. Access, Visa.*

W4 Robbie's Restaurant NEW £35

Tel 081-742 3620 **R**

Burlington Lane W4 3HB **Map 17 A4**

An unusual and tiny restaurant located at the entrance to Chiswick British Rail station. Booking is essential to taste the elaborate weekly menu of Robbie Simon, executed in his little open-plan kitchen. A choice of five starters and main courses is followed by a small savoury course and dessert. Typical dishes are prune and cognac sausages on a confit of red cabbage, julienne of celeriac soup, black-feathered chicken with a selection of wild mushrooms and red fish fillet with lobster sauce. Alfresco eating in the summer. Bring your own wine to match the cuisine! Also open for afternoon teas. ***Seats** 24. L 12-3 (bookings only) D 6-11.30. Closed L Sat, D Sun, Bank Holidays, 24-26 Dec. Set L £14.50 Set D £16.50. No credit cards.*

W2 Romantica Taverna £40

Tel 071-727 7112 **R**

10 Moscow Road W2 4BT **Map 18 A3**

Enjoyable, straightforward Greek fare in a long-established restaurant just off Queensway. Meze for two is the speciality of the house, along with classic dolmades, afelia, kleftiko and moussaka. ***Seats** 74. Private Room 70. L 12-3 D 5.30-12. Closed L Sat, 3 days Christmas.* AMERICAN EXPRESS *Access, Diners, Visa.*

W12 The Rotisserie £40

Tel 081-743 3028 **R**

56 Uxbridge Road W12 8LP **Map 17 B4**

Friendly and informal eating place next to Shepherds Bush underground station. Pride of place in the large, airy room goes to the charcoal grill/rotisserie, where the main courses are prepared: corn-fed chicken, paper-wrapped salmon, Toulouse sausages, Barbary duck, calf's liver, rack of lamb, and the very popular Aberdeen Angus steaks. It's in the same ownership as the *Camden Brasserie*, and the little chips are just as good. ***Seats** 90. Private Room 40. L 12-3 D 7-11. Closed L Sat & Sun. Access, Visa.*

W2 Royal China £50

Tel 071-221 2535 **R**

13 Queensway W2 **Map 19 A3**

Striking decor of black lacquered walls, with gold and silver inlaid murals, spotlights and smartly uniformed staff. This is a very serious Chinese restaurant serving many dishes that get out of the rut: steamed curried squid, marinated chicken feet and chilled mango pudding in the long and excellent dim sum selection (served noon-5pm); pan-fried minced pork with salted fish and beef steamed with preserved vegetables among the "chef's favourites." Also of note are hot and spicy veal, six ways with lobster, Szechuan whole fish and the sizzling dishes. Sunday lunchtime brings queues from about 12.30, so arrive early as they don't take bookings. ***Seats** 100. Private Room 15. Meals 12-11.30. Set D from £20.*
AMERICAN EXPRESS *Access, Diners, Visa.*

SW1 Royal Court Hotel 68% £145

Tel 071-730 9191 Fax 071-824 8381 **H**

Sloane Square SW1W 8EG **Map 19 C5**

The reception area, with its panelling and chandeliers, sets an elegant tone for the Royal Court, which stands on a prime site immediately next to Sloane Square tube station. The Tavern is a traditional English pub serving meals at lunchtime, while Courts is an intimate wine bar. Bedrooms feature limed oak period-style furniture and soft pastel colour schemes. Children up to 15 stay free in parents' room. Queens Moat Houses. ***Rooms** 102.* AMERICAN EXPRESS *Access, Diners, Visa.*

W8 Royal Garden Hotel 82% £191

Tel 071-937 8000 Fax 071-938 4532 **HR**

Kensington High Street W8 4PT **Map 19 A4**

Ideally located on the edge of Kensington Garden and right on Kensington High Street, the hotel has a policy geared towards service and care. Standard bedrooms, on Kensington High Street, are spacious but have a homely feel. All superior bedrooms overlook Hyde Park, with large picture windows and balconies. Bedrooms have satellite TV, in-house movies, well-stocked mini-bar and hairdryer. The Reserve, on the 10th floor, offers superior accommodation and a butler service. Suites are well conceived and contain safe, jacuzzi bath and bathrobes. The Garden café and bar both overlook the park. The Lobby bar on the lobby mezzanine has a more clubby feel. Flexible conference facilities include an impressive Palace suite for up to 900 delegates theatre sytle. ***Rooms** 398. Valeting, car park, news kiosk, Garden Café (7am-11pm).* AMERICAN EXPRESS *Access, Diners, Visa.*

Royal Roof Restaurant £124

Not only the most striking view in London but a clever layout which enables all tables to enjoy it in the comfortably sized dining room. Gunther

See over

Schlender is now in charge of a menu full of attractive ideas under the sign of lightness like *artichauts farcis aux petits legumes à la grecque avec lentilles à l'orange, filet de rouget à la nage de coquilles St Jacques aux truffes, magret de canard et confit-cuisse aux pommes roties et gingembre.* Precise skills do not always fulfil their aspiration but certainly produce a high level of quality. Service is particularly attentive under the professional and dedicated eye of Mario Martinelli. Dancing is still a ritual on Thursday, Friday and Saturday nights. ***Seats** 70. Parties 18. L 12.30-2.30 D 7.30-10.30 (Fri & Sat to 11). Closed Sun & Bank Holidays. Set L £18.95 Set D £33.*

SW1 Royal Horseguards Thistle 71% £110

Tel 071-839 3400 Fax 071-925 2263 **H**

2 Whitehall Court SW1A 2EJ **Map 18 D3**

A spacious foyer with beautiful Wedgwood-style, moulded ceilings sets the tone of elegant public rooms in a comfortable hotel close to the Thames Embankment. A charming lounge area in cool, pastel lemon shades boasts chandeliers, oil paintings and a country-house style of furniture. The main restaurant is in the style of a gentlemen's club, and the Terrace Coffee Shop is open all day for snacks and light meals. Bedrooms range widely from a single overlooking Whitehall Court to the Tower Suite on two floors with a panoramic view of the City. The best are grand, spacious rooms with attractive limed oak furniture, elegant mirrors and colourful chintzy fabrics. Superb marble bathrooms are a stunning feature of some rooms. Children up to the age of 12 are accommodated free in parents' room. ***Rooms** 376. Coffee shop (7am-11.15pm).* AMERICAN EXPRESS *Access, Diners, Visa.*

W2 Royal Lancaster Hotel 75% £179

Tel 071-262 6737 Fax 071-724 3191 **H**

Lancaster Terrace W2 2TY **Map 18 B3**

Directly above Lancaster Gate tube station (Central Line), this fine modern hotel enjoys splendid views of Hyde Park from its upper floors. Day rooms show style and quality: the long-hours Pavement Café (6.45am-11pm), the elegant lounge – a favourite spot for afternoon tea, La Rosette restaurant, and several suites with technical facilities for meetings and conferences (up to 1400 delegates). Best of the high-class accommodation is on the Reserve Club floors (15th to 18th) with five luxurious suites and a reserved drawing room, bar and boardroom. No dogs. ***Rooms** 418. Hairdressing, news kiosk, car hire desk, garage.* AMERICAN EXPRESS *Access, Diners, Visa.*

WC2 Royal Trafalgar Thistle 65% £135

Tel 071-930 4477 Fax 071-925 2149 **H**

Whitcomb Street WC2 7HG **Map 21 A3**

Modern hotel behind the National Gallery, close to Leicester and Trafalgar Squares. Best rooms are on the top floor. Recent improvements include refurbishment of some bedrooms, refurbishing the foyer and changing the concept of the restaurant to more informal. Children up to the age of 12 are accommodated free in parents' room. ***Rooms** 108. Hamiltons Brasserie (7am-11.30pm).* AMERICAN EXPRESS *Access, Diners, Visa.*

SW1 Royal Westminster Thistle 71% £146

Tel 071-834 1821 Fax 071-828 8933 **H**

Buckingham Palace Road SW1W 0QT **Map 19 D4**

Polished marble and carved wood grace the foyer, where smartly turned-out staff provide a warm and efficient welcome. The Royal Lounge is a stylish venue for afternoon tea, while the Parisian-style Café Saint-Germain provides a relaxed, casual ambience for a drink or snack. Individually air-conditioned bedrooms are of a generally good size and have pickled-pine furnishings and a wide range of accessories. Children up to the age of 16 are accommodated free in parents' room. The hotel is handily placed for Victoria Station and Buckingham Palace. ***Rooms** 134. Café (10am-11pm).* AMERICAN EXPRESS® *Access, Diners, Visa.*

SW1 Rubens Hotel 66% £141

Tel 071-834 6600 Fax 071-828 5401 H

Buckingham Palace Road SW1W 0PS Map 19 D4

Opened at the turn of the century, the Rubens stands in a prime position facing the Royal Mews behind Buckingham Palace; it's also conveniently close to Victoria Station and Westminster. Comfortable day rooms in country house style include a library lounge and a cocktail bar with resident pianist. Well-appointed bedrooms (just one suite) offer the usual extras. Children up to 12 stay free in parents' room. Five conference suites cater for up to 75 delegates. No dogs. Sarova Hotels. ***Rooms** 189.* AMERICAN EXPRESS® *Access, Diners, Visa.*

WC2 Rules £60

Tel 071-836 5314 Fax 071-497 1080 R

35 Maiden Lane WC2E 7LB Map 21 B2

Tradition rules in one of London's oldest eating places (but your order gets keyed into pocket computers). Oysters, game, pies and puddings are the specialities. ***Seats** 135. Parties 9. Private Room 48. Meals 12-11.30 (Sun 12-10.30). Closed 3/4 days Christmas.* AMERICAN EXPRESS® *Access, Visa.*

WC1 Hotel Russell 68% £141

Tel 071-837 6470 Fax 071-837 2857 H

Russell Square WC1B 5BE Map 18 D1

An imposing late-Victorian hotel, handy for both the City and the West End, with a hugely impressive marble foyer complete with grand staircase, crystal chandeliers and ornate plasterwork; public areas include a clubby panelled bar. Bedrooms are up-to-date, with a variety of attractive fabrics and well-maintained bathrooms. The Executive floor of 24 rooms has its own lounge where guests can take breakfast. Banqueting facilities for 350, conferences for up to 450. No dogs. Forte Grand. ***Rooms** 328. Brasserie 11am-11pm (from 5pm Sat, Sun, Mon).* AMERICAN EXPRESS® *Access, Diners, Visa.*

SW3 S & P Thai NEW £40

Tel 071-351 5692 R

181 Fulham Road SW3 Map 19 B3

S and P are the two sisters who own this restaurant on the corner of Sydney Street and Fulham Road. The short menu includes a delicious crispy basket of noodles topped with prawns and stir-fried roast duck in a not-too-fiery red curry sauce. ***Seats** 58. Parties 16. Private Room 20. L 12-3 D 6.30-11. Set L £7.95. Closed L Sun, 25 & 26 Dec, 1 Jan.* AMERICAN EXPRESS® *Access, Diners, Visa.*

W1 SAS Portman Hotel 77% £193

Tel 071-486 5844 Fax 071-935 0537 H

22 Portman Square W1H 9FL Map 18 C2

Now under the management of Scandinavian Air Services, the 70s-built Portman is one block from Marble Arch and caters very well for the businessman in a hurry with an in-room check-out via the TV, SAS flight check-in for full-fare passengers, a 3-hour express laundry service and a complimentary buffet for early birds. The traditional hotel comfort and atmosphere remains the same, however, with uniformed, efficient reception staff in the spacious lobby (where afternoon tea is served and there's a news kiosk and gift shop). Bedrooms, planned for refurbishment commencing at the end of 1993, offer quiet, controllable air-conditioned accommodation with stereo remote-controlled TV and mini-bar; a telephone extension

See over

is provided in the marble bathrooms; Superior double bedrooms with sofa beds are ideal for families; Royal Club rooms include further extras like a trouser press, safe, bathrobes, slippers and a wider range of toiletries. Check-out time is set late at 3pm, even later (8pm) on Sundays. Among the day rooms are the buffet-style Bakery coffee shop (which also serves a Sunday brunch) and the Pub, open throughout the day for informal meals and pub lunches; a terrace is popular in summer. First-floor function facilities cater for up to 400 in a variety of suites. Service throughout is on the ball, and the promised facelift for the bedrooms will be welcome. Charged parking in the NCP car park beneath the hotel. ***Rooms** 272. Coffee shop (11am-11pm).* AMERICAN EXPRESS *Access, Diners, Visa.*

NW10 Sabras

£25

Tel 081-459 0340

R

263 High Road NW10 2RX

Map 16 A2

Opened in 1973, Sabras maintains its reputation for excellent vegetarian cooking from Bombay, Gujarat and South India. Many of the ingredients are not seen in many London establishments – violet Indian yam, cluster beans, split pigeon peas, unripe bananas. Value for money is exceptional, with some curries (with bread) costing as little as £1. ***Seats** 32. L 12.30-3 D 6-10. Closed L Sat & Sun, all Mon. Set L (Thali) from £2.95. Access, Visa.*

W1 Saga

£85

Tel 071-408 2236

R

43 South Molton Street W1Y 1HB

Map 18 C3

The sushi bar is now on the ground floor, and the teppanyaki bar has been turned into a private dining room. It's now open on Sundays, but one thing that hasn't changed is the quality of the Japanese cuisine, especially the first-rate sushi. ***Seats** 100. Parties 25. Private Room 12. L 12.30-2.30 D 6.30-10. Closed Sun. Set L from £6.50 Set D from £35.* AMERICAN EXPRESS *Access, Diners, Visa.*

W1 St George's Hotel 65%

£147

Tel 071-580 0111 Fax 071-436 7997

H

Langham Place W1N 8QS

Map 18 D2

Modern accommodation on the site of the old Queen's Hall. Good views of London's rooftop lights; dinner dances Fri & Sat. ***Rooms** 86. Coffee shop (7am-11pm).* AMERICAN EXPRESS *Access, Diners, Visa.*

WC1 St Giles Hotel

£108

Tel 071-636 8616 Fax 071-631 1031

H

Bedford Avenue WC1B 3AS

Map 21 A1

Angular tower block offering neat, practical accommodation among the bright lights of the West End. In the basement are excellent leisure facilities, plus car parking. No dogs. ***Rooms** 600. Indoor swimming pool, gymnasium, squash, sauna, solarium, beauty salon, badminton.* AMERICAN EXPRESS *Access, Diners, Visa.*

SW1 St James Court 73%

£179

Tel 071-834 6655 Fax 071-630 7587

HR

41 Buckingham Gate SW1E 6AF

Map 19 D4

Within walking distance of the magnificent Queen Elizabeth II conference centre opposite Westminster Abbey, and also very close to Buckingham Palace. A grand-scale Edwardian redbrick building converted into an almost palatial hotel, at the heart of which is a self-contained business centre offering an extensive range of rooms and services for up to 250 delegates. At the heart of the hotel stands a fine open-air courtyard with ornamental trees and a period fountain – an ideal setting for alfresco receptions. Bedrooms are furnished and equipped to a high standard, with smart reproduction furniture and luxurious bathrooms. 75 apartments and 19 suites are also available. Children under 12 may share their parents' room. The Olympian health club includes a health bar and an aerobic dance studio. The choice of restaurants includes the French, Szechuan-orientated Chinese and the all-day Café Mediterranée serving brasserie-style meals. Daytime valet parking (free after 6.30pm Friday). No dogs. European flagship of Taj International Hotels. ***Rooms** 390. Gymnasium, sauna, steam room, spa bath, solarium, squash, beauty therapist, business centre, brasserie (7am-11pm).* AMERICAN EXPRESS *Access, Diners, Visa.*

Auberge de Provence £86

The restaurant is closely linked to *L'Oustau de Baumanière*, in the beautiful village of Les Beaux de Provence. Their chef Jean-André Charial is strongly involved in the design of the Auberge's menu, making sure that each member of staff first trains at *L'Oustau* before coming to London. Chef Bernard Brique is in charge of the kitchen over here, offering a fixed-price lunch (with a good choice) and two interesting evening menus: a three-course *menu provençal* with a substantial selection, and a *menu surprise*, conceived according to individual tastes. Provençal inspiration is more obvious in the main courses with *rose de saumon aux olives de Baud et ses nouillettes, noisette d'agneau à l'anchoïade* or *blanc de volaille mariné au basilic, sauce aïoli*. The achievement is one of quality, but too often involved in heavy, elaborate preparation and not truthful enough to the "parfums de Provence". Desserts include a notable *soufflé renversé à la rhubarbe* with *sauce au miel de Provence*. The well-designed wine list includes a selection from Baumanière. Service is irreproachable. Reservations on 071-821 1899. ***Seats** 65. L 12.30-2.30 D 7.30-11. Set L £22.50 Set D £30. Closed 2 weeks August, 26-30 Dec, 1-7 Jan.*

W1 St Moritz £40

Tel 071-734 3324 **R**

161 Wardour Street W1 **Map 18 D2**

A small, charming Swiss establishment on two floors whose extensive menu offers meat and cheese fondues as well as other Swiss specialities including air-cured beef, rösti potatoes, spatzle noodles and veal zurichoise, plus game and wild mushrooms in season. ***Seats** 45. L 12-3 D 6-11.30. Closed L Sat, all Sun, Bank Holidays.* AMERICAN EXPRESS *Access, Diners, Visa.*

SW3 St Quentin £55

Tel 071-581 5131 Fax 071-584 6064 **R**

243 Brompton Road SW3 2EP **Map 19 B4**

Right on Brompton Road, but effectively soundproofed by two doors. It still has the elegance of Brompton Grill days, a belle epoque-inspired decor with mirrors and pillars, wall chandeliers, brass, banquettes and flower arrangements. A bar runs down one side, propped up by smartly attired diners awaiting their tables. French staff are kitted out in formal black and white and perform their tasks with youthful gravity and reasonable efficiency. The menu is basically from a generation ago, but that's clearly what the folks want as the place is very well patronised: *paté de campagne, terrine de canard et venaison* with redcurrant compote, goat's cheese salad, tomato or French onion soup, fresh foie gras, cassoulet, Dover sole, *feuilleté de St Jacques et crevettes au safran, magret de canard aux navets*, chicken fricassee with wild mushrooms, gigot of lamb, a puff-pastry-topped 'marmite' of scallops, salmon, prawn and mussels. Parfaits, ices and tarts round off a well-cooked meal properly served in civilised surroundings. ***Seats** 70. Private Room 25. L 12-3 (Sat & Sun to 4) D 7-11.30 (Sat from 6.30). Set L £13.50 Set D £15.25.* AMERICAN EXPRESS *Access, Diners, Visa.*

W5 Sala Thai — £30

Tel 081-560 7407 — R

182 South Ealing Road W5 4RJ — **Map 17 A4**

Choosing from the 100 plus dishes on the menu of this friendly Thai restaurant is a pleasant task with which the staff will gladly assist. Thai dim sum, fried bean curd skin with crab meat and minced pork, chicken or pork in a pepper and garlic mixture, dried sweet beef with coriander seeds, king prawns in oyster sauce with broccoli, deep-fried mackerel with red curry sauce, squid in half a dozen ways, Thai curry with mixed vegetables and prawns or cod show the flavour of what's on offer. ***Seats** 60. L 12-2.30 D 6-11.30. Closed L Sat, all Sun, 24 Dec-2 Jan.* AMERICAN EXPRESS *Access, Diners, Visa.*

SW1 Sale e Pepe — £70

Tel 071-235 0098 — R

13 Pavilion Road SW1 — **Map 19 C4**

The complete Italian job, with singing waiters, a permanent party atmosphere and a menu of well-prepared dishes from the standard repertoire. ***Seats** 75. Parties 12. L 12-2.30 D 7-11.30. Closed Sun, Bank Holidays.* AMERICAN EXPRESS *Access, Diners, Visa.*

SW1 Salloos — £70

Tel 071-235 4444 — R

62-64 Kinnerton Street SW1X 8ER — **Map 19 C4**

Established in Lahore in 1966, Salloos has been in London since 1977. Tandoori grills – fat-free, long marinated and with no added colour – have a great reputation here, especially the little lamb chops, and other special dishes include gosht khara masala (braised lamb, onions, ginger, garlic), chicken in cheese (baked in a soufflé mixture of eggs, cheese and milk), haleem akbari (shredded lamb, wheatgerm, lentils, spices – a soft, pappy dish, almost a thick sauce) and vegetable kebabs (spicy mixed vegetables coated with mashed potato and fried like cutlets). ***Seats** 70. L 12-2.30 D 7-11.15. Closed Sun, Bank Holidays. Set L from £18.40 Set D from £28.75.* AMERICAN EXPRESS *Access, Diners, Visa.*

SW3 Sambuca — £70

Tel 071-730 6571 — R

6 Symons Street SW3 — **Map 19 C5**

Straightforward Italian cooking in a popular, bustling restaurant by Sloane Square (opposite the rear door of *Peter Jones*). The menu sticks mainly to established favourites, with oven-braised lamb a speciality for two. Long list of Italian wines. ***Seats** 70. Parties 30. L 12.30-2.30 D 7-11.30. Closed Sun, Bank Holidays.* AMERICAN EXPRESS *Access, Diners, Visa.*

SW3 San Frediano — £50

Tel 071-584 8375 Fax 071-589 8860 — R

62 Fulham Road SW3 6HH — **Map 19 B5**

Buzzing with atmosphere and old-fashioned Italian charm, San Fred is one of the real survivors among London's trattorias. Honest cooking, decent wine, ungreedy prices and slick service have provided a quarter of a century of customer satisfaction and a long list of daily specials always adds interest to the menu: marinated herrings with beans, crab salad, guinea fowl with wine and grapes, chicken escalopes with cheese and asparagus tips. ***Seats** 110. Private Room 50. L 12-2.45 D 7-11.30. Closed Sun, Bank Holidays.* AMERICAN EXPRESS *Access, Diners, Visa.*

SW3 San Lorenzo £100

Tel 071-584 1074 **R**

22 Beauchamp Place SW3 1NL **Map 19 C4**

High prices are no deterrent to the smart set who keep this Beauchamp Place hot spot permanently hot. Cooking is capable throughout a fairly standard Italian menu. Almost a club, not always easy to get a booking, and a huge success down the years. ***Seats** 120. Parties 12. L 12.30-3 D 7.30-11.30. Closed Sun, Bank Holidays. No credit cards.*

SW3 San Martino £60

Tel 071-589 3833 **R**

103 Walton Street SW3 2HP **Map 19 B5**

One of London's busiest and friendliest Italian restaurants, where Costanzo Martinucci and his family are completely involved. The owner himself grows herbs, vegetables and ingredients for the splendid made-to-order salads and plays a major role in the kitchen. The ever-changing menu provides great variety and three of the most renowned dishes are fish soup, tagliatelle with hazelnuts, tarragon and wild mushroom sauce, and spaghetti cooked with seafood in a paper bag. Seasonal game plus chef's recommendations such as wild boar sausages or carpaccio of swordfish add to the choice. ***Seats** 165. Private Room 35. L 12-3 D 6.30-11.30. Closed 10 days Christmas, 4 days Easter. Set L from £9.50.* AMERICAN EXPRESS *Access, Diners, Visa.*

SW3 Sandrini £65

Tel 071-584 1724 **R**

260 Brompton Road SW3 2AS **Map 19 B5**

High marks for comfort and smart modern decor. Above-average marks for Italian cooking throughout a menu which mixes the traditional and the modern (*mozzarella in carrozza, penne arrabbiate,* wind-dried venison, Barbary duck with cinnamon, balsamic vinegar and cranberries). *Libaio ruffino* is a very drinkable white wine that goes with most of the dishes. Tables outside in appropriate weather. ***Seats** 75. L 12-3 D 7-11.30.* AMERICAN EXPRESS *Access, Diners, Visa.*

SW1 Santini £100

Tel 071-730 4094 Fax 071-730 0544 **R**

29 Ebury Street Victoria SW1W 0NZ **Map 19 C4**

Business people at lunchtime (when there's a short, 2-course, fixed-price lunch) and theatre-goers in the evening keep things busy at Santini's close-set tables; a profusion of waiters provide rapid service. House specialities include stuffed courgette flowers, four types of pasta each with a separate sauce, grilled swordfish with tomato sauce, Ventian-style squid with polenta and spicy Italian sausages with cannellini beans. The main carte covers more familiar ground – at a price. Desserts, Italian cheeses and fresh fruit served from a trolley. Just a few minutes walk from Victoria Station. Sister to *L'Incontro* in Pimlico Road. ***Seats** 60. Parties 14. L 12.30-2.30 D 7-11.30 (Sun to 11). Closed L Sat & Sun, all Bank Holidays. Set L £16.50.* AMERICAN EXPRESS *Access, Diners, Visa.*

N1 Satay Hut £30

Tel 071-359 4090 Fax 071-482 4513 **R**

287 Upper Street N1 2TZ **Map 16 D3**

The surroundings belie the name, as this is a roomy, comfortable restaurant with air-conditioning. Satay of lamb, beef, chicken or prawns (plus vegetarian) tops the menu, with four sticks as a starter portion, six for a main course. Otherwise the menu runs through the cuisines of Singapore,

See over

Malaysia, Indonesia and Thailand. MSG is not used. ***Seats** 100. L 12.30-3 D 6-12 (Sat & Sun 12-12). Closed 25 & 26 Dec.*
Set meals from £9.50. AMERICAN EXPRESS® *Access, Diners, Visa.*

W1 Les Saveurs ★★★ £120

Tel 071-491 8919 **R**

37a Curzon Street W1Y 8EY **Map 18 C3**

An elegant and formal basement restaurant approached down a grand and wide staircase from a spacious reception area decorated sumptuously with fresh flowers and an impressive display cabinet of fine crystal. The overall soft creamy tones of the decor come into their own downstairs where lighting is soft and walls, panelled with bird's eye maple, have antiqued mirrors, modern flower paintings and fresh flower arrangements. Miniature glass spirit lamps, more flowers and gleaming place settings additionally help to create the luxurious and sophisticated ambience. The reputation and renown of the restaurant is spreading with Joël Antunès at last receiving due acclaim for what is the most exciting cooking currently being offered in this country. He has garnered supplies from carefully vetted producers and stockists to ensure the optimum quality of what emanates from the kitchen. His experience in France, with the likes of Troisgros, Duquesnoy and Paul Bocuse as well as a successful three-year stint as head chef of the Oriental, Bangkok has culminated in a style of cooking that emphasises a profound knowledge of classic principles with well-thought-out and carefully judged innovative touches. His food combines great visual appeal with stunning creativity, dishes being suffused with an unparalleled magical and delicate complexity. Even for the Financial Times £5 lunches in recessionary January 1993, standards were never compromised, making it the very best for value. For example a cream of chestnut soup laced with truffle oil perfectly encapsulated the delicate essence of sweet chestnut and to follow tender, pink sliced duck breast was presented with a fruity orange sauce and 'confited' turnips. Set menus at £29.50 for dinner are still excellent value with an appetiser followed by four light and well-balanced courses plus a very fine selection of prime French cheeses. A terrine of duck foie gras from a set menu is layered with slices of 'confited' aubergines and is preceded by an appetiser such as a little pot of pea mousse served on a duck liver parfait. From the à la carte paper-thin slices of duck carpaccio are colourfully accompanied by a salad, a finely diced ratatouille, a light pistou dressing and thin, crunchy artichoke crisps which contrast the softness of the duck perfectly. Scallops lightly smoked à la minute come with a refreshingly acidulated cream with dill and finely diced cucumber. In the centre is a tiny sautéed hollowed new potato filled with caviar. A risotto made with basmati rice instead of the usual arborio for its more nutty flavour is topped with plump Dublin Bay prawns with truffle oil adding a complementary earthiness. Breast of pigeon topped with fresh duck liver and steamed in a savoy cabbage leaf is served pink and meltingly tender surrounded by a field of tiny wild mushrooms. Desserts (London winner of Dessert of the Year) are as involved and stunning as the rest, for instance, three small warm freshly baked chocolate madeleines filled with soft chocolate and accompanied by small quenelles of almond cream are delicious as is a hot lime soufflé with a light acacia honey ice cream or rhubarb millefeuille with saffron cream. The fabulous coffee tart with whisky cream made a very welcome return with the new menu which came into operation at the end of September. Pre-desserts such as a white and yellow peach salad are accompanied by their own platter of petits fours. Another quite different platter arrives with coffee. An expensive wine list, French for the most part, has several grand wines, but little of note under £20. Service under Emmanuel Menjuzan is faultlessly professional and extremely pleasant and in Yves Sauboua they have one of London's top sommeliers. ***Seats** 50. Parties 35. Private Room 10. L 12-2.30 D 7-10.30. Closed all Sat & Sun, 10 days Christmas/New Year, 2 weeks Aug. Set L £18 Set D £29.* AMERICAN EXPRESS® *Access, Diners, Visa.*

WC2 The Savoy 91% £260

Tel 071-836 1533 Fax 071-379 5421 **HR**

1 Savoy Hill WC2R 0BP **Map 21 B2**

On top of the rebuilt and reopened Savoy Theatre, the hotel has also constructed a fine and beautifully designed leisure centre, benefiting from natural daylight and fresh air. Called The Fitness Gallery (complimentary for guests) it has a rooftop swimming pool (the pool atrium), his and hers saunas and steam rooms, warm up and workout rooms, and a massage room. This enhances the hotel's very own and special atmosphere and long-standing reputation as one of the world's finest hotels with tip-top standards of service, under the direction of General Manager Herbert Striessnig. There's an international feel to the public areas – contrast the genteel Englishness of the peaceful drawing room with the brashness of the American Bar, or the grandeur of the ornate and marble-pillared Thames Foyer (afternoon tea and light snacks) with the 'Upstairs' (see below). Bedrooms, many in the original art deco style, include the much sought-after river suites, and boast such luxuries as real linen bedding, huge cosseting bath sheets, a nightly turn-down of beds and personal maid, valet and waiter bell service. There are banqueting and conference facilities for up to 500, with a variety of stylish private rooms to choose from. Guests have temporary membership of the Wentworth Club, the renowned golf and country club a short drive from London, which has tennis courts and an outdoor pool in addition to several golf courses. Proof of handicap required. No dogs. ***Rooms 202.*** *Leisure club, beauty & hair salon, news kiosk, flower shop, valeting.* AMERICAN EXPRESS *Access, Diners, Visa*

River Restaurant ★ £130

Opinions differ as to whether it's better to come here for lunch or dinner. It's probably busier and more animated at lunchtime, when the kitchen seems to be at its best and the atmosphere is completely unlike that in the evening (dancing to a live band playing old chestnuts, and twinkling lights across the river). Naturally, the best tables are located by the picture windows with the Thames in the background, but it's such a grand room (except for the ceiling) that you are well placed wherever you're seated. Service is charming and smooth – maitre d'hotel Luigi Zambon has now been in situ for eleven years, arriving at the same time as maitre chef des cuisines Anton Edelmann – with staff gliding around almost unnoticeably, whether in charge of the smoked salmon and dessert trolleys, or the silver-domed 'roast of the day' chariot. The new daily-changing seasonal dinner menu (five courses, £45) includes wines selected by sommelier Werner Wissmann to complement each course – a typical menu might start with marinated fish with chicory salad and an orange dressing, crab mousseline with sweetcorn, peppers and spicy sauce, breast of pigeon filled with black pudding on a bed of home-made pasta, goat's cheese on a garlic-flavoured crouton, finishing with a raspberry soufflé. Alongside this menu are à la carte dishes and a less expensive *diner au choix*, which is similar to the lunchtime *déjeuner au choix* – on our most recent lunchtime visit we had a marvellous dish of thinly sliced marinated langoustines with caviar, perfect roast saddle and best end of lamb off the trolley, ending with a delightful warm cherry tart. The wine list has greatly improved, features wines from around the world, and even has the odd bargain! ***Seats 150.*** *Parties 60. Private Rooms. L 12.30-2.30 D 7.30-11.30 (Sun to 10.30). Set L £25.75 Set D £31.25 & £45.*

Grill Room ★ £120

The quality of the service under maitre d'hotel Angelo Maresca shines as brightly as the beautiful polished yew panelling of this mellow-toned, very grand hotel dining room. This is an institution with a number

See over

of regular patrons each assigned a favourite table, though other diners are treated with the same high level of deference and civility. The cooking, still under David Sharland's direction, perhaps lacks the consistency and traditional quality of previous years, and the classic favourites remain the best bet – dressed crab, or omelette Arnold Bennett to precede daily-changing specials from the carving trolley, a pot-roasted loin of veal with basil and Adgestone wine (Monday dinner) or roast Norfolk duck cooked with almond and apples (Friday dinner). Steak and kidney pie as well as braised lamb shank with rosemary and tomato appear Tuesday lunchtime, while on Thursday you could have a jarret of ham with horseradish or roast rib of beef and Yorkshire pudding. Sweets from the trolley presented, as is the rest, with style and panache, include the likes of summer pudding, crème brulée and an unusual chocolate pecan pie. The evening theatre menu allows you to have your first and main courses before the show, returning for coffee and pastries in the Thames Foyer afterwards. ***Seats** 85. Parties 12. L 12.30-2.30 D 6-11.15. Closed L Sat, all Sun, Bank Holidays (open 25 Dec), Aug. Set D (6-7.30pm) £26.75/£29.75*

Upstairs at the Savoy — £50

An ideal venue for an informal meal, overlooking the comings and goings and hustle and bustle of The Savoy Courtyard – it's a champagne, Chablis and oyster bar specialising in seafood dishes (salmon kedgeree, fricassee of monkfish with wild rice, grilled cod with a white bean stew) and fine wines by the glass from a 'Cruvinet' machine. Mainly tables for two, and seats at the counter. ***Seats** 28. 12.30-midnight (Sat 5-midnight) Closed Sun.*

SW3 Scalini — £70

Tel 071-225 2301 — R

1 Walton Street SW3 2JD — **Map 19 C4**

An attractive restaurant which benefits from a bright conservatory at the back. A traditional Italian menu is well prepared and served in a jolly, smart atmosphere: *bresaola* and *ricotta, tortellini "fatta in casa" Gorgonzola* and *scaloppa di vitello tirolese* (with egg, anchovy and capers). ***Seats** 45. Parties 20. L 12.30-3 D 7-12. Closed 3 days Christmas & 2 days Easter.* AMERICAN EXPRESS *Access, Diners, Visa.*

SE16 Scandic Crown Nelson Dock 69% — £119

Tel 071-231 1001 Fax 071-231 0599 — H

265 Rotherhithe Street SE16 1EJ — **Map 17 D4**

Impressive modern hotel which brings some life to the new development project of Nelson Docks. The stylish building offers two restaurants, a bar, a pub, a small leisure centre and comprehensive conference facilities. Efficiency is the symbol here as in all Scandic Crown – managed hotels. Rooms are spacious but some tend to be darker than others. They are all well equipped with desk, seating area, mini-bar, trouser press, tea and coffee facilities, satellite TV and in-house movies. Club bedrooms are larger with a view of the Thames, fax point and bathrobes. ***Rooms** 390. River terrace, indoor swimming pool, gymnasium, sauna, spa bath, solarium, tennis, games room, snooker.* AMERICAN EXPRESS *Access, Diners, Visa.*

SW1 Scandic Crown Victoria 66% — £154

Tel 071-834 8123 Fax 071-828 1099 — H

2 Bridge Place SW1V 1QA — **Map 19 D5**

A centrally located hotel which combines Scandinavian practicality and efficiency with agreeably redecorated surroundings. Air-conditioned bedrooms are comfortable, with sturdy Scandinavian furniture, duvets and even Scandinavian beers in the mini-bar. The Scandic hotel club membership, reserved for frequent customers, offers priority check-in, guaranteed rooms and discount on food and drinks. Children free up to the age of 14 in parents' room. ***Rooms** 210. Indoor swimming pool, gymnasium, sauna, spa bath, solarium, coffee shop (11am-10.30pm).* AMERICAN EXPRESS *Access, Diners, Visa.*

W1 The Selfridge 75% £181

Tel 071-408 2080 Fax 071-629 8849 **H**

Orchard Street W1H 0JS **Map 18 C2**

A covered porte-cochère with brass lanterns and greenery makes a good first impression at this modern hotel adjacent to the famous department store. Warm cedar panelling lends a traditional English feel to the reception foyer and a smart first-floor lounge with leather wing armchairs. In complete contrast, Stoves Bar is olde-worlde rustic with wheelback chairs and genuine old beams and timbers recovered from a medieval barn. Bedrooms (96 designated non-smoking) vary in size and are more comfortable than luxurious, with darkwood units and TV remote controls wired to the bedside; all have air-conditioning and telephones by the bed, at the desk and in the modestly-sized bathrooms that also offer good towelling and marble vanitory units. Children up to 14 stay free in parents' room. Valet parking. Conferences up to 300. ***Rooms** 296.* AMERICAN EXPRESS *Access, Diners, Visa.*

SE22 Sema £35

Tel 081-693 3213 **R**

57 Lordship Lane SE22 **Map 17 D6**

A small, informal Thai restaurant with gentle and helpful service. Start with 'Golden Sema' – a selection of fried dumplings and spring rolls, follow with green curry or stir-fried beef with chili and onions. The special Thai noodles (*pud thai*) are a must. ***Seats** 70. Private Room 15. L 12-3 D 6-11.30. Closed L Mon-Fri, 25 Dec, 1 Jan. Set meals from £15.* AMERICAN EXPRESS *Access, Diners, Visa.*

W1 La Sémillante ↑ £80

Tel 071-499 2121 **R**

3 Mill Street W1R 9TF **Map 18 D3**

In theatrically elegant basement premises just north of Conduit Street, Mayfair, Patrick Woodside produces meals of extraordinary novelty and originality. La Sémillante is old-fashioned French for libertine, one of whom nakedly adorns the cover of the menu. Underneath that cover the dish descriptions only hint at what will turn up on the plate: "quail eggs and escargot in garlic and fine herbs, sautéed foie gras, a light hollandaise" sounds a little out of the ordinary but turns out to be totally off the wall: barrels of courgettes each containing either a snail or a raw quail egg yolk; little slices of foie gras sautéed beyond the usual wobbly stage; a rather fossilised looking garnish of slivers of dried turnips and other vegetables/salads; a dribble of yolk running right round the plate. "Salad of duck in Thai spices with roasted apple and celeriac" suggested more piquancy than the dish actually possessed – if there were any Thai spices they were overpowered by a sweet fruit purée. These starters prepared us for more surprises among the main courses, but by now the shock was wearing off so that sea bass stuffed with sweetbreads served with wild mushrooms and "supreme of turbot laced in a light beer, roasted and dressed with a caressing touch of fried onions" seemed no more than mildly eccentric. Desserts are given only a word or two of description on the menu ("honeysuckle", "chocolate royale", "a butterfly display"), so if you want some idea of what you're ordering (you order desserts at the same time as the other dishes) you'll need help from one of the serious, formally attired staff. Explanations are usually given over drinks in the ground-floor reception/bar area. These desserts are a presentational tour de force, some of them arriving almost hidden under an Ascot hat of spun sugar. This, then, is the Woodside style – elaborate, imaginative and intriguing, and based of course on classic cooking skills. His is not a restaurant for traditionalists, and we're still not sure whether London has enough

CLOSED-NEW

See over

adventurous spirits to keep it full. Prices are reasonable, particularly on the concise, cosmopolitan wine list, and he certainly deserves to succeed. ***Seats** 40. L 12.25-2.15 D 7.15-10.45. Closed L Sat, all Sun, 2 weeks Aug, 2 weeks Dec. Set L £16 Set D £28. Access, Visa.*

W1 Shampers £48

Tel 071-437 1692 **R**

4 Kingly Street W1R 5LF **Map 18 D3**

Between Regent Street and Carnaby Street, this is one of the West End's most popular drinking spots and has a thriving food side, too. The wine bar menu runs from oysters, charcuterie and salads to chicken casserole, steak sandwich, raised ham and cheese pie and evening specials such as grilled lamb's kidneys or pan-fried tiger prawns with noodles, garlic and ginger. Lunchtime in the small restaurant downstairs always offers soup, fish and vegetarian dishes of the day. A fun but serious wine list offers quality at ridiculously low prices – probably the best in town. An espresso machine has recently been installed. ***Seats** 70. Private Room 50. Restaurant Mon-Fri 12-3, Wine bar 11-11 (Sat 11-3). Closed D Sat, all Sun, Easter, Christmas.* AMERICAN EXPRESS *Access, Diners, Visa.*

W8 Shanghai £60

Tel 071-938 2501 **R**

38c Kensington Church Street W8 4BX **Map 19 A4**

On the bend on Kensington Church Street, Shanghai looks smart with its modern paintings and chrome feature pillar at street level and a comfortable main basement section where a pianist plays in the evening. The menu of Shanghai, Peking and Szechuan cuisine does not stray far from the safe (unless you count eels – here they appear deep-fried and delicious in a salt and pepper crust, sizzling with black bean sauce and Shanghai-style braised with vegetables). Dumplings are a speciality, along with Peking and Szechuan duck. Try also fish soup (for 2), Tibetan garlic lamb and fried bean curd Shanghai family style. Smooth, urbane service. ***Seats** 90. Parties 25. Private Room 70. L 12-2.30 D 6.30-11.30. Closed Sun, Bank Holidays. Set D £16.50.* AMERICAN EXPRESS *Access, Diners, Visa.*

WC2 Sheekey's £65

Tel 071-240 2565 Fax 071-491 2477 **R**

28-32 St Martins Court Leicester Square WC2N 4AL **Map 21 B2**

Old-style fish restaurant (established 1896) with menus covering a wide choice, from oysters, jellied eels, fish soup and potted crab to fish pie, plaice meunière, flambéed scallops and lobster Thermidor. Well-priced lunch and pre-theatre menus. ***Seats** 110. Private Room 36. L 12.30-3 D 6-11.15. Closed L Sat, all Sun, Bank Holidays, 24 Dec-2 Jan. Set L & pre-theatre dinner £9.90/£13.50.* AMERICAN EXPRESS *Access, Diners, Visa.*

SW1 Shepherd's NEW £55

Tel 071-834 9552 **R**

Marsham Court Marsham Street SW1 **Map 19 D4**

The successful formula of Langan's Brasserie (Richard Shepherd and Michael Caine) is well known, and now Westminster can enjoy something similar. There is no Mediterranean influence here, but good old British favourites like Stilton and spinach turnover with apple and celery salad, roast duck with sage and onion stuffing and apple sauce or salmon and prawn fish cakes. The setting is also traditional with dark wood mid-height partitions and almond green velvet wall seats. For those in a hurry, a selection of cold dishes is available in the bar area. ***Seats** 60. Parties 30. L 12.30-3 D 6.30-11.30 (Bar 5.30-8). Set L £15.95. Closed Sat, Sun, Bank Holidays.* AMERICAN EXPRESS *Access, Diners, Visa.*

SW1 Sheraton Belgravia 75% **£250**

Tel 071-235 6040 Fax 071-259 6243 **HR**

20 Chesham Place SW1X 8HQ **Map 19 C4**

Personal service is high on the list of priorities at this luxurious modern hotel and its relatively small size allows it to be achieved. Day rooms, including the lobby, split-level lounge and library bar, offer abundant comfort, and bedrooms sport freestanding yew furniture. All the rooms are air-conditioned. Children up to 12 stay free in parents' room. ***Rooms*** *89.* AMERICAN EXPRESS *Access, Diners, Visa.*

Chesham's **£70**

An attractive restaurant designed in sections – one of them with a palm tree, glass-domed roof and wall mirrors. The back section is designated non-smoking. Cooking mixes updated classical French with traditional English cream of asparagus soup, grilled Dover sole, sirloin steak served plain or flambéed with black peppercorn sauce, steamed chicken breast with morels and a sherry sauce. ***Seats*** *54. Private Room 22. L 12.30-2.30 D 6.30-10.30. Closed L Sat & Sun. Set L £19.95.*

SW1 Sheraton Park Tower 79% **£270**

Tel 071-235 8050 Fax 071-235 8231 **HR**

101 Knightsbridge SW1X 7RN **Map 19 C4**

A distinctive, circular high-rise tower within a stone's throw of Harrods and with splendid city views from the upper floors. Bedrooms, apart from the 31 luxury suites, are identical in size and feature rather pleasing burr walnut-veneered furniture. Thick quilted bedcovers, turned down at night, match the curtains; TVs and mini-bars are discreetly hidden away. There are telephones by the bed, on the desk and in the bathrooms, which have marble-tiled walls, good shelf space, towels and toiletries. A new messaging system has recently been installed. Extra services on Executive floors include valet unpacking, two-hour laundering, a special check-out service and extra toiletries. 60 rooms are designated non-smoking. Meeting facilities can handle up to 80 people theatre style. Children up to 17 stay free in parents' room. ***Rooms*** *295. Beauty & hair salon.* AMERICAN EXPRESS *Access, Diners, Visa.*

Restaurant 101 **£50**

As we went to press the restaurant was in the process of being renovated and a new-style modern English menu introduced. ***Seats*** *80. Parties 25. Private Room 150. L 12-3 D 6.30-11.*

W1 Sherlock Holmes Hotel 61% **£132**

Tel 071-486 6161 Fax 071-486 0884 **H**

108 Baker Street W1M 1LB **Map 18 C2**

Conveniently located close to Marylebone Road, a Hilton-owned hotel with average size but well-equipped bedrooms. Given its name, where else could it be but Baker Street? Public rooms include Dr Watson's Bar and Mrs Hudson's Teashop. ***Rooms*** *125.* AMERICAN EXPRESS *Access, Diners, Visa.*

SW7 Shezan NEW **£70**

Tel 071-584 9316 **R**

16-22 Cheval Place Knightsbridge SW7 1ES **Map 19 B4**

Reopened early in 1993 after a major refit, Shezan is one of London's most stylish and comfortable Indian restaurants. A stairway runs down from street level to a bar area and a room of quiet elegance. There's nothing much to get excited about on the menu, but cooking is competent throughout a familiar range, and there are plenty of friendly, attentive staff. ***Seats*** *100. L 12-3 D 7-11.30. Closed 25 Dec.* AMERICAN EXPRESS *Access, Diners, Visa.*

W1 Shogun £80

Tel 071-493 1877 **R**

Britannia Hotel Adams Row W1 **Map 18 C3**

Kimono-clad waitresses serve good-quality Japanese food in an atmospheric vaulted basement restaurant behind the Britannia Inter-Continental Hotel. Suits of samurai armour add an interesting touch to the decor. The clearly set-out menu includes a Japanese-scripted section which the staff are happy to explain and a range of set menus provides a good introduction to the uninitiated – tempura, sashimi, salmon, chicken, duck or beef. Some further choice is provided à la carte, including half-a-dozen soups, steamed belly pork, pork fried with ginger and deep-fried calamari. ***Seats*** *55. Parties 12. D only 6-11. Closed Mon, Bank Holidays, 1 week Christmas. Set D from £30.* AMERICAN EXPRESS *Access, Diners Visa.*

SW18 Siam Oriental Restaurant NEW £45

Tel 081-877 0032 **R**

145 Wandsworth High Street SW18 4JB **Map 17 B6**

This modestly appointed restaurant earns our seal of approval with cooking way above the average high-street Thai. Lime, chili, garlic, coriander and coconut milk figure prominently through a menu of dishes which are at once down-to-earth and subtle – none more than the splendid hot and sour soups, the peppy salads and the one-plate rice and noodle dishes. Smiling service is another plus. ***Seats*** *30. L 12-2.30 D 6-11.30. Set L £5.95. Closed L Sat, all Sun.* AMERICAN EXPRESS *Access, Diners, Visa.*

W13 Sigiri £30

Tel 081-579 8000 **R**

161 Northfield Avenue Ealing London W13 9QT **Map 17 A4**

Sri Lankan restaurant decorated with drawings inspired by those found on the rocks around the ancient island fortress from which Sigiri takes its name. Among the Sinhalese offerings are unusual rice-flour hoppers, deep-fried green banana slices, coconut-based curries and sizzling dishes (yoghurt-marinated chicken with cashew nuts). Help-yourself buffet Tues-Thur and all day Sunday. ***Seats*** *62. Parties 24. Meals D 6.30-11 (Sun noon-11). Closed L Tues-Sat, all Mon, 25, 26 Dec & Bank Holidays. Access, Visa.*

SW1 Signor Sassi £60

Tel 071-584 2277 **R**

14 Knightsbridge Green SW1X 7QL **Map 19 C4**

Simple Italian close to Harrods. Straightforward menu of classic dishes – bresaola with mango and rucola salad, chicken broth with tortellini, calf's liver with butter and sage, ham-stuffed veal escalope and the like. ***Seats*** *70. Parties 40. L 12-2.30 D 7-11.30. Closed Sun, 24-26 Dec.* AMERICAN EXPRESS *Access, Diners, Visa.*

SE5 Silver Lake £40

Tel 071-701 9961 Fax 071-708 5718 **R**

59 Camberwell Church Street SE5 8TR **Map 17 D5**

A busy and homely Chinese restaurant offering a mix of Peking, Cantonese and Szechuan cooking. 130 dishes cover the range from prawn, beef or chicken satay sticks and crab meat and seaweed soup to monkfish in black bean sauce, sizzling dishes and red-braised duck. ***Seats*** *40. L 12-2 D 5.30-12 (Fri & Sat to 12.30, Sun & Bank Holidays from 6). Set L from £4 Set D from £12.* AMERICAN EXPRESS *Access, Diners, Visa.*

SW1 Simply Nico ★ £75

Tel 071-630 8061 **R**

48a Rochester Row SW1P 1JU **Map 19 D5**

Three-course lunch and dinner menus (the price includes 10% service charge) display a simple, straightforward approach, eschewing undue elaboration and fussy garnishes. Typical dishes run from pork sausage with an onion compote or smoked haddock risotto among the starters to roast baby chicken with tomato sauce, sautéed lamb's kidneys with sage blinis, pan-fried fillet of brill with a sharp sherry sauce and (£4 supplement) charcoal-grilled cote de boeuf béarnaise. The house aperitif is Cardinal – a 'Kir' made with Gamay and blackberry liqueur. The restaurant's yellow rag-rolled walls are hung with framed cartoons; chairs are bentwood and wicker. ***Seats** 48. L 12-2 D 7-11. Closed L Sat, all Sun & Bank Holidays, 10 days Christmas, Easter. Set L £23 Set D £25.* AMERICAN EXPRESS *Access, Diners, Visa.*

WC2 Simpson's-in-the-Strand £75

Tel 071-836 9112 **R**

100 The Strand WC2R 0EW **Map 17 C4**

One of the most venerable and best known of all London restaurants, not greatly changed in concept for almost 150 years. It was under the direction of John Simpson that joints of meat were first wheeled around on silver carving trolleys, and that's what still happens today in the handsome panelled dining room and in the larger upstairs room overlooking the Strand. The same farm in the north of Scotland has supplied the beef for 70 years, and Simpson's gets through an average of 25 sirloins per day (80% of customers order it). Saddle of lamb, roast Aylesbury duck, seasonal game and steak, kidney and mushroom pie are other stalwarts on the menu, which remains staunchly traditional. The Chandelier Room now serves a fish and vegetarian menu at lunchtime. London Regional British Cheeseboard winner (see earlier pages) Staff provide a nice balance of formality, efficiency and good humour. ***Seats** 300. Parties 80. Private Room 150. L 12-2.30 D 6-10.45. Closed Bank Holidays. Set L & D £10.* AMERICAN EXPRESS *Access, Diners, Visa.*

W4 Singapore £35

Tel 081-995 7991 **R**

94 Chiswick High Road W4 2EF **Map 17 A4**

Neat, cool and smart little restaurant whose specialities include sautéed green beans with minced pork, lettuce-wrapped seafood and sliced braised duck in cranberry sauce. The cuisine is Singaporean and Malaysian, and the popular curries feature a creamy, spicy coconut sauce. ***Seats** 60. Private Room 16. L 12-2.30 D 6-11.30. Closed 25 & 26 Dec. Set L from £6.80 Set D from £17.50.* AMERICAN EXPRESS *Access, Diners, Visa.*

NW6 Singapore Garden £45

Tel 071-328 5314 **R**

83 Fairfax Road NW6 4DY **Map 16 B3**

A long Singaporean, Malaysian and Chinese menu with fresh seasonal choices such as soya bean fish, soft-shell crab and lobster with ginger, chili or black pepper and butter. Sizzling dishes are good, so too beef rendang and the other curries. Steamboat (£28 per head) is a traditional Chinese fondue. ***Seats** 96. Private Room 60. L 12-2.45 D 6-10.45 (Fri & Sat to 11.15). Closed 1 week Christmas. Set D from £14.85.* AMERICAN EXPRESS *Access, Diners, Visa.*

Also at:

154 Gloucester Place NW1 6DT Tel 071-723 8233 **Map 18 C2**

W6 Snows on the Green £60

Tel 071-603 2142 **R**

166 Shepherds Bush Road W6 7PB **Map 17 B4**

Well reviewed last year as a new interesting opening in West London, Snows has not fulfilled our expectations this year. Sebastian Snow's modern Mediterranean menu offers inventive dishes with risky, unconvincing combinations like pan-fried mackerel, foie gras, rösti potatoes and apples. The quality of ingredients and the consistency in cooking are questionable. Let's hope things will improve again. Typical dishes include foie gras with fried egg and balsamic vinegar; chargrilled polenta with snails, field mushrooms and gruyère; and chump of lamb with mozzarella and aubergine gratin. Simple desserts like rhubarb and apple charlotte or crème caramel. Concise wine list with most bottles under £20. ***Seats** 70. Parties 12. Private Room 22. L 12-3 D 7-11. Closed L Sat, D Sun, Bank Holidays. Set L £10.50/£12.50. Access, Visa.*

W1 Soho Soho £70

Tel 071-494 3491 **R**

11-13 Frith Street W1 **Map 21 A2**

Part of Groupe Chez Gérard restaurants. At street level is a lively café/bar spilling out on to the pavement and serving rôtisserie food – hors d'oeuvre, salads, egg and pasta dishes, grills and daily specials. Upstairs there's a more formal restaurant with a menu that leans towards The Med with dishes such as *soupe de poissons à la marseillaise, pissaladière* (caramelised onion tart with thyme, anchovies, black olives and sliced tomatoes), and *lotte rotie* (roasted monkfish served with caponata and garlic oil). Several *plats du jour*, tasty desserts and good coffee, though it's not that cheap, with a cover charge and separately charged vegetables bumping up the price. ***Seats** 70. Parties 12. Private Room 60. L 12-3 D 6-12. Closed L Sat, all Sun, Bank Holidays.* American Express *Access, Diners, Visa.*

N16 Le Soir £35

Tel 071-275 8781 **R**

226 Stoke Newington High Street London N16 7HU **Map 16 D2**

Popular neighbourhood restaurant run by a husband-and-wife team. A varied menu could include filo parcels of cheese and herbs, chicken satay, garlicky lamb steak and duck en croute. Also fish of the day, salads, a vegetarian menu and simple desserts like chocolate mousse. ***Seats** 46. Parties 20. D only 6-midnight (Sun till 11pm). Closed 25-28 Dec. Access, Visa.*

N1 Sonargaon £42

Tel 071-226 6499 **R**

46 Upper Street Islington N1 **Map 16 C3**

Decent Indian cooking, crisp table settings, sharp service and cheaper than the West End. Chef's recommendations include ginger chicken, hash and bash (duck with spices and bamboo shoots) and a festive whole leg of lamb for four. ***Seats** 50. L 12-3 D 6-12. Closed 25 Dec.* American Express *Access, Diners, Visa.*

SW13 Sonny's £55

Tel 081-748 0393 **R**

94 Church Road SW13 0DQ **Map 17 A5**

New chef in June 1993, Alec Howard, has brought his own touches to the menu at Rebecca Mascarenhas' already successful Sonny's. More Pan-European than Modern British, his cooking has a sure touch and gives more than a mere nod to the trends of other chefs in the capital (he came from the Bath Spa Hotel). New dishes he has introduced are chicken liver parfait with fig relish and toasted brioche, a salad of smoked haddock and poached egg, griddled scallops with mashed potato, roast chump of lamb with macaroni cheese. Old favourites on the pudding menu such as crème brulée or vanilla ice with chocolate sauce jostle alongside a fruit brochette with coconut rice pudding – a potentially powerful mixture of exotic flavours (pineapple, mango, papaya and kiwi – and a passion fruit coulis) but cleverly combined. A reasonably priced wine list helps ensure a regular and happy clientele. ***Seats** 90. Parties 20. L 12.30-3 D 7.30-11. Closed D Sun, 25 & 26 Dec, 1 Jan, Good Fri & Easter Mon. Set L & D £12.50 (2-course), Sun L £14.50 (3-course).* AMERICAN EXPRESS *Access, Visa.*

N16 Spices £26

Tel 071-254 0528 **R**

30 Stoke Newington Church Street London N16 0LU **Map 16 D2**

Friendly South Indian vegetarian restaurant with a varied menu that includes one special each day. One of the most popular dishes is Bombay tiffin, an assortment of Gujerati snacks comprising samosas, pakoras, vegetable cutlets and aubergines topped with sour cream and spices. ***Seats** 65. Parties 30. L 12-2.30 D 6-midnight. Closed 25 & 26 Dec.* AMERICAN EXPRESS *Access, Diners, Visa.*

SW1 The Square ★ £80

Tel 071-839 8787 **R**

32 King Street St James's SW1 6RJ **Map 18 D3**

Large brass helical mobiles adorn the shop-like frontage of this otherwise minimally decorated modern restaurant just off St James's Square. Deep blue, orange and ochre fabrics are used in the seat upholstery to add a useful splash of colour to an otherwise creamy, well-lit room. Philip Howard's daily changing menus show a genuine flair for very well-judged combinations and a keen eye for detail – the results on the plate can be wonderful. Dishes are light and uncomplicated yet may comprise an amazingly wide variety of ingredients – all assembled to complement one another, utilising every flavour and texture to the fullest. A mixed sea food hors d'oeuvre could include a ceviche of queenie scallops set on a crab and tomato salsa served in a scallop shell, miniature smoked salmon cornets filled with cream cheese, smoked eel fillet on a bed of boulangère potatoes and a wedge of raw tuna, one side seared and coarsely peppered, topped with marinated chopped scallions and arranged on a bed of cold spinach salad. A warm salad of duck comprises the tenderest, pinkest, thinly sliced duck in a salad of mixed green leaves, cut Kenya beans and black lentils, dressed in a sauce of warm port and raisins. The dish is further garnished with tiny, thin potato crisps and equally crisp strips of deep-fried ginger – a dish of marvellously contrasting flavours and textures. Fillet of sea bass, with olive oil mash and red wine sauce is good but not exciting. The rectangular fillet of baked sea bass comes on a bed of mashed potatoes surrounded by a well-made red wine sauce and a garnish of two chargrilled courgettes: a dish without faults but lacking the sparkle and innovation of other dishes. Passion fruit soufflé is served with a crème anglaise, which is poured into the centre of the beautifully risen soufflé. Wines are somewhat confusingly listed by country, region and grape variety, but the list is a fine one nevertheless. Professional and very attentive service. ***Seats** 75. Parties 8. Private Room 30. L 12-2 D 6-11.45. Closed L Sat, most Bank Holidays. Access, Visa.*

Our inspectors *never* book in the name of Egon Ronay's Guides. They disclose their identity only if they are considering an establishment for inclusion in the next edition of the Guide.

SW17 Sree Krishna £25

Tel 081-672 4250 **R**

192-194 Tooting High Street SW17 **Map 17 C6**

Good-value Indian restaurant specialising in dishes from Kerala in the south. These are mostly vegetarian but the usual range of meat and prawns is also available. ***Seats*** *170. Parties 50. Private Room 70. L 12-3 D 6-11 (Fri & Sat to midnight). Closed 25 & 26 Dec.*

W1 Sri Siam £55

Tel 071-434 3544 **R**

14 Old Compton Street W1V 5PE **Map 21 A2**

Traditional Thai food cooked to order in a lively Soho atmosphere. Good range of dishes on à la carte and set menus, and a separate vegetarian list. Regular favourites include fried noodles (topped with beef, pork or chicken), satay, fish/prawn cakes and classic tom yum soup. ***Seats*** *80. L 12-3 D 6-11.15 (Sun to 10.30). Closed L Sun, 25 & 26 Dec, 1 Jan. Set L from £9 Set D from £14.95.* AMERICAN EXPRESS *Access, Diners, Visa.*

EC2 Sri Siam City £55

Tel 071-628 5772 **R**

85 London Wall EC2 **Map 20 C1**

Stylish Thai basement restaurant and bar that's a good alternative to City wine bars. The main menu, supplemented by various set meals, includes classics like tom yum soup and rarer items such as *pla pao numpla wan* – fresh marinated fish grilled in a banana leaf and served with two sauces – one chili-based, the other with tamarind and palm sugar. ***Seats*** *120. Meals 11.30am-8pm. Closed Sat, Sun, 24-26 Dec, Bank Holidays. Set meals from £13.50.* AMERICAN EXPRESS *Access, Diners, Visa.*

SW1 The Stafford 74% £240

Tel 071-493 0111 Fax 071-493 7121 **H**

16 St James's Place SW1A 1NJ **Map 18 D3**

In keeping with its clubland address the Stafford exudes civilised discretion, an impression enhanced by long-serving staff looking after long-serving clients. Paintings line the foyer walls and leather chesterfields create a scene of cultured calm. Deeper in, a drawing room is made elegant by antiques and fresh with cut flowers; the American Bar features a collection of American club and university ties, caps and badges. Accommodation ranges from singles with queen-size beds through doubles and junior suites in the Carriage House to the Terrace Garden suite complete with terrace and fountain. Decor is individual, with fabrics and furniture of a high standard. Part of the Cunard group. No dogs. ***Rooms*** *74.* AMERICAN EXPRESS *Access, Diners, Visa.*

SW1 Stakis St Ermin's 71% £159

Tel 071-222 7888 Fax 071-222 6914 **H**

Caxton Street SW1H OQW **Map 19 D4**

Ideally situated, with Westminster Abbey, the Houses of Parliament and Buckingham Palace only a neighbourly distance away, the Stakis St Ermins offers a perfect base for tourists. Extensive conference facilities (for up to 200 delegates theatre-style) also make it a primary choice for functions and banquets. Behind an opulent Edwardian facade day rooms are equally sumptuous: luxurious furnishings follow a green theme and the elegant furniture, much of it antique, finds an ideal setting among marble and ornate plasterwork. A splendid Baroque staircase leads to the five floors of bedrooms which offer every modern comfort and are well appointed and furnished with taste. 53 rooms are designated non-smoking. Children up to 16 stay free in parents' room. ***Rooms*** *290.* AMERICAN EXPRESS *Access, Diners, Visa.*

W1 Stephen Bull £80

Tel 071-486 9696 **R**

5-7 Blandford Street W1H 3AA **Map 18 C2**

Stephen Bull's eponymous restaurant has all the trappings, or rather lack of them, of an ultra-modern restaurant. The stark minimalism of the monochromatic decor is emphasised by the wall-to-wall, floor-to-ceiling plate glass frontage. Menus, which change daily, are appealingly innovative and imaginative. There's an inherent lightness to the cooking which relies on the uncomplicated use of seasonings and flavourings. Much is Mediterranean in origin and the use of good-quality raw materials is very apparent. But some of the component flavours can be overpowering, resulting in an unbalanced dish. A lighter touch would make for truly exquisite eating. A twice-cooked goat's cheese soufflé (simply preprepared and then reheated before serving) is so popular it has virtually become a menu standard. It is also one of the simplest dishes. It arrives beautifully risen, moist and with fine flavour. An escalope of salmon with preserved lemons, pistachios and Sauternes can suffer from a surfeit of lemon as well as sweetness, the salmon itself, though, being of a wonderfully melting texture. Dishes such as ravioli of leeks and walnuts with an apple butter sauce, a tartlet of veal kidneys with salsify, red wine and gherkins or smoked rump of beef, black beans, chili and corinader are typical of his adventurous style. The desserts include two luxurious composites – a grand selection and variation on a theme of chocolate. Laid-back, informal ambience and service. ***Seats*** *60. Parties 14. L 12.15-2.30 D 6.30-10.30. Closed L Sat, all Sun, Bank Holidays, 10 days Christmas/New Year. Access, Visa.*

W6 Sumos £35

Tel 081-741 7916 **R**

169 King Street W6 9JT **Map 17 A4**

An unassuming Japanese snack restaurant on Hammersmith's main shopping street. Besides sushi and sashimi there's tempura (evenings), miso soup, griddle-fried dumplings, beef with ginger, chicken yakitori and sushi. ***Seats*** *40. Parties 10. L 12-3 D 6-11. Closed L Sat, all Sun, Bank Holidays. Set L from £4.90 Set D from £9.80. No credit cards.*

SW1 Suntory £110

Tel 071-409 0201 **R**

72 St James's Street SW1A 1PH **Map 18 D3**

One of London's longest-established Japanese restaurants, with more of a Western style than Oriental; the cooking is of a high standard and staff have an exemplary attitude towards politeness, patience and understanding. The main dining area is on the ground floor, but there are several teppanyaki tables on the lower ground. The complete teppanyaki experience (appetisers, dobin-mushi soup, sashimi, foie gras, mixed seafood, fillet steak, mixed salad, rice, miso soup, pickled vegetables, dessert and coffee or green tea) is £64, but alternatives include turbot, lobster, salmon and chateaubriand with prawns. The traditional side of the menu is also long in choice and ranges from sushi and tempura to one-pot dishes such as shabu-shabu and yose-nabe cooked at your table. Prices at lunchtime are considerably less than in the evening. Suitably stylish for expense-account dining. ***Seats*** *120. Parties 21. Private Room 14. L 12-2 D 7-10. Closed Sun, Bank Holidays. Set L from £15 Set D from £48.* AMERICAN EXPRESS *Access, Diners, Visa.*

W9 Supan £35

Tel 081-969 9387 **R**

4 Fernhead Road W9 3ET **Map 16 B3**

Just around the corner from Harrow Road, Supan is a really delightful Thai restaurant with charming staff and well-prepared food. Stuffed chicken wings, Thai beef salad, tod mun (fish cakes) and crabmeat-and-cream-cheese pastry parcels to start, then a soup with or without coconut milk and on to a main-course curry or a stir-fry. ***Seats** 30. Parties 15. L 12-2.30 D 6.30-11.30. Closed L Sat, all Sun, Bank Holidays, Notting Hill Carnival. Access, Visa.*

SW3 Le Suquet ★ £70

Tel 071-581 1785 **R**

104 Draycott Avenue SW3 3AE **Map 19 B5**

In surroundings inspired by the seafront at Cannes, fresh fish and shellfish get traditional treatment on a menu whose only changing element is the *plats du jour*. These often include sea bass (sold by weight), sole grilled or meunière, seafood pot au feu and salmon feuilleté. Otherwise it's shellfish almost all the way, with crab, langoustines, mussels, clams and oysters. For a major treat the mighty *plateau de fruits de mer* is a must. Steaks and confit de canard for meat-eaters. ***Seats** 70. Parties 16. Private Room 16. L 12.30-3 D 7-11.30.* AMERICAN EXPRESS *Access, Diners, Visa.*

N1 Suruchi £30

Tel 071-241 5213 **R**

82 Mildmay Park Newington Green London N1 4TR **Map 16 D2**

Classical music and pastel prints provide the background to Indian cooking notable for judicious use of fresh herbs and spices. Nearly half the menu is vegetarian. Thalis (set meals) provide particularly good value for money. ***Seats** 30. Parties 15. L 12-2.30 D 6-11.30. Closed 25 & 26 Dec. Access, Visa.*

SW5 Swallow International Hotel 64% £130

Tel 071-370 4200 Fax 071-244 8194 **H**

Cromwell Road SW5 0TH **Map 19 A5**

Large hotel on busy Cromwell Road (the main route to Heathrow and points west), close to Gloucester Road underground station. Several conference rooms and suites (for up to 200), a leisure club and practical accommodation that includes 12 top-of-the-range suites. On-site car park. ***Rooms** 417. Indoor swimming pool, gymnasium, sauna, spa bath, steam room, solarium, news kiosk, coffee shop (7am-midnight).* AMERICAN EXPRESS *Access, Diners, Visa.*

NW3 Swiss Cottage Hotel 62% £140

Tel 071-722 2281 Fax 071-483 4588 **H**

4 Adamson Road NW3 3HP **Map 16 B3**

An unusally individual hotel converted from terraced houses in a quiet residential street a few minutes from Swiss Cottage underground station. The bedrooms have plenty of character, with some Victorian/Edwardian pieces of furniture, plush settees and nice old pictures. Some rooms are not all that large, and they're linked by warrens of corridors and stairs. The lounge is very appealing: ornate gold wallpaper under a moulded ceiling, sofas and button-back chairs on bright Oriental rugs, carved antique furniture and oil paintings. The hotel also has self-catered studio, one-and two-bedroom serviced apartments nearby, let by the week. Ongoing refurbishment. No dogs. ***Rooms** 81. Garden.* AMERICAN EXPRESS *Access, Diners, Visa.*

WC2 The Tageen £35

Tel 071-836 7272 Fax 071-379 0759 **R**

12 Upper St Martin's Lane WC2H 9DL **Map 21 B2**

A roomy Moroccan restaurant decorated with traditional tiles, lanterns and cushions. The rear half is now furnished as a typical Moroccan salon with brass tables and can seat 50 for private parties. Staff are dressed in Moroccan style and enjoy talking about the wonders of Moroccan cuisine, which mixes sweet, salt and sour. The menu embraces specialities such as *bastela* (crisp, light pastry revealing the savours of chicken, saffron, almonds and cinnamon), *couscous* (made with extra-fine grain imported from Morocco) and of course *tageens* – aromatic stews cooked in the pots that give them their name. ***Seats** 90. Private Room 50. L 12.30-3 D 6.30-11.30. Closed L Sat, all Sun, 1 & 2 Jan. Set L (also D till 7) £12.* AMERICAN EXPRESS *Access, Diners, Visa.*

SW6 Tandoori Lane £35

Tel 071-371 0440 **R**

131a Munster Road SW6 6DD **Map 17 B5**

East Indian and Bangladeshi cooking in a congenial local restaurant that's much longer that it is wide. House specialities include chicken tikka razala and king prawn masala. ***Seats** 44. Parties 14. L 12-2.30 D 6-11.15. Closed 25 & 26 Dec. Set meals from £9.50. Access, Visa.*

SW3 La Tante Claire ★★★ £140

Tel 071-352 6045 **R**

68 Royal Hospital Road SW3 4HP **Map 19 C5**

In the Guide's pinnacle of restaurants over the last few years, we feel that overdrive has stuck in cruise control, and while outwardly there do not seem to have been any changes except perhaps for a new picture here and there, recent expectations have disappointed, albeit only a little. The dining room is not large by any means, but the tables are decently spaced to allow a good measure of privacy; it's brightly lit, decorated in pale woods, soft pastels with grand glass screens and a matching series of modern artworks. The effect is rather akin to a saloon on a luxury liner. The menu excites with many of Pierre Koffmann's signature dishes appearing: *pied de cochon aux morilles, purée de pois cassés; assiette canardière aux deux sauces; filet de chevreuil au chocolat amer et vinaigre de framboise,* the last being tender slices of venison fillet cooked pink with a bitter chocolate and raspberry sauce with home-made noodles and wild mushrooms. Having been served an amuse-gueule of salted cod mousse on a ratatouille sauce (on our last visit the waiter had to be asked what was being eaten, likewise the variety of excellent breads was not explained) you could start perhaps with a consommé of lobster with small ravioli of the meat, served with tiny carrot and courgette balls and shelled broad beans – a snip at £18.50! – or from the good-value lunch menu, a marvellous leek terrine with foie gras, or salmon mousse and baby asparagus in a lobster sauce, followed by hake on a bed of spinach, or lamb, mash and wild mushrooms. Our pistachio soufflé (with pistachio ice cream) wasn't quite cooked through and a crème brulée had aerated, though the taste was fine, but we have absolutely no complaints over the gratin of red fruits under a warm sabayon with ice cream in a crisp tuile. Fine French cheeses, distinguished French wines, excellent coffee, dull petits fours. It we are slightly critical, remember this is still one of the top half-dozen restaurants in the country, and the odd hiccup can easily be remedied. Incidentally, there's a minimum dinner charge of £45 per person. No children under 8. ***Seats** 42. Parties 8. L 12.30-2 D 7-11. Closed Sat & Sun, Bank Holidays, 1 week Christmas. Set L £24.50. Set D £45/£55.* AMERICAN EXPRESS *Access, Diners, Visa.*

SW1 Tate Gallery Restaurant £50

Tel 071-834 6754 R

Millbank SW1P 4RG **Map 19 D5**

A basement, lunchtime-only setting with most tables designated non-smoking. Plain English dishes seem the best bet, plus almost anything from the extensive wine list that includes a good selection of half bottles. *Seats 120. Parties 30. L only 12-3. Closed Sun, most Bank Holidays. Access, Visa.*

EC2 Tatsuso ★ £80

Tel 071-638 5863 Fax 071-638 5864 R

32 Broadgate Circle EC2M 2QS **Map 24 C1**

A split-level restaurant on one of the lower levels at Broadgate Circle. Immediately next to the entrance lobby is a smart, spacious teppanyaki bar. Also from the lobby a wide staircase leads down to an elegant, formal Japanese restaurant. Ash is used to create the tables and chairs as well as the low screens that divide them, the blond wood strikingly modern, contrasting with the traditional look of kinomo-clad waitresses. An extensive à la carte offers exquisitely prepared sushi and sashimi with authentic garnishes such as imported Japanese oba leaves – these leaves also turn up deep-fried in batter in some tempura dishes adding a refreshing and delicate taste. This is a serious restaurant with no compromise made on quality. For this reason prices are high. The set dinners are of between 6 and 14 distinct courses culminating in the magnificent Momoyama at £60 a head. The finest raw materials are assembled with infinite precision. Assorted appetisers include a thin rolled slice of omelette, a tiny skewer of succulent morsels of chicken, a sprig of broccoli covered in a neatly poured soya sauce; a cherry tomato carefully filled with puréed chicken livers and a sliver of aubergine with a subtle sesame sauce. Later on a dish of grilled salmon arrives with half the fillet coated with very finely chopped egg, the other half with finely chopped seaweed. All the dishes that comprise each set dinner are balanced in perfect harmony, the small portions carefully worked out to allow the diner maximum enjoyment and nutritional benefit from the chefs' labours. ***Seats** 45. Parties 10. Private Room 8. L 11.30-2.30 D 6-9.30. Closed Sat, Sun & Bank Holidays. Set L from £20 Set D from £29.* AMERICAN EXPRESS *Access, Diners, Visa.*

SW5 Terstan Hotel £50

Tel 071-835 1900 Fax 071-373 9268 H

29 Nevern Square SW5 9PE **Map 19 A5**

Family-owned and run, the Terstan bed and breakfast hotel stands in a garden square just south of the A4 Cromwell Road (approach via Earls Court Road), a couple of minutes from Earls Court underground station and Exhibition Centre. Most bedrooms have private facilities, the exception being some budget singles. Simple accommodation at a low price. ***Rooms** 50. Closed 3 days Christmas. Access, Visa.*

W2 Thai Kitchen £50

Tel 071-221 9984 R

108 Chepstow Road W2 5QS **Map 18 A2**

The decor, kept simple, is full of refined touches like carved wood artwork set off by simply painted walls, an orchid on each table and interesting crafted crockery. The cooking, prepared with authentic Thai ingredients, emphasises freshness and true flavours. Original dishes include fried marinated chicken in pandanus leaves, spare ribs in red wine and fried shrimps with young coconut leaves. Vegetarians are well catered for. Light desserts like pumpkin or coconut custard are freshly made daily. ***Seats** 30. L 12-2.30 D 6.30-11. Closed Sun, 2 days Christmas.* AMERICAN EXPRESS *Access, Visa.*

SE14 Thailand Restaurant £35

Tel 081-691 4040 **R**

15 Lewisham Way SE14 6PP **Map 17 D6**

North-East Thailand pinpoints the cooking of Mrs Khamkhong Kambungoet in this unpretentious little place. Marinated chicken wings, hot and sour soups, plated noodle dishes and stir-fries are popular choices, and some less familiar options include crispy-fried catfish, squid stuffed with minced pork and shrimp paste with pounded chilis, garlic, fish sauce and lime juice. There's a short wine list, but more than 50 malt whiskies up to a 28-year-old Glenburgie! ***Seats** 25. D only 6-10.30. Closed Sun & Mon.* AMERICAN EXPRESS *Access, Visa.*

SW3 Thierry's £60

Tel 071-352 3365 **R**

342 King's Road SW3 5UR **Map 19 B6**

Cosy and romantic French bistro with window booths and red check tablecloths. Terrine maison, quail's eggs in puff pastry or cheese soufflé could precede roast poussin, grilled sardines or steak béarnaise wtih tarte tatin, crème brulée, chocolate or a selection of French cheeses to finish. Besides the carte there's a *menu rapide* at lunchtime, an evening party menu and – a recent introduction – an afternoon snack menu served from 3-5.30. ***Seats** 70. Parties 42. Private Room 33. L 12-2.30 (Sun to 3) D 7.30-11 (Sun 7-10.30). Closed Bank Holidays. Set L £9.90 Set D from £13.50.* AMERICAN EXPRESS *Access, Diners, Visa.*

SE22 Thistells £45

Tel 081-299 1921 **R**

65 Lordship Lane SE22 **Map 17 D6**

Sami Youssef has firmly established himself as owner and chef at his ornately tiled former grocer's shop. It's an unusual and atmospheric place serving good food at reasonable prices. Sami is Egyptian and many of his dishes are Middle Eastern: mixed pulse salad with mint and lemon, three-bean soup with coriander and country bread, falafel with tahini sauce. Others are soundly prepared renditions of French classics like best end of lamb with paloise sauce, coq au vin and breast of duck with cassis. Home-made ices are a speciality dessert. ***Seats 30.** L Sun only 12-3 D 7-10.30. Closed L Mon & Sat, D Sun. Set L from £5 Set D from £10. Access, Visa.*

W1 Tiberio £75

Tel 071-629 3561 Fax 071-409 3397 **R**

22 Queen Street W1 **Map 18 C3**

New customers and old are welcomed warmly at this long-established basement Italian restaurant in Mayfair. Good cooking through a fairly traditional menu. Dancing to live music till 2am. ***Seats** 65. Parties 40. L 12-2.30 D 7-11.30. Closed L Sat & all Sun, Christmas, all Bank Holidays.* AMERICAN EXPRESS *Access, Diners, Visa.*

SW6 Tien Phat £30

Tel 071-385 7147 **R**

1 The Arcade Fulham Broadway Station London SW6 **Map 19 A6**

Vietnamese and Chinese food in café surroundings. Choose à la carte or house special set dinners (minimum two people). ***Seats** 40. L 12-3 D 5.30-11.30. Closed 25 Dec.* AMERICAN EXPRESS *Access, Visa.*

NW11 Tiger under the Table £40

Tel 081-458 9273 **R**

643 Finchley Road Golders Green NW11 7RR **Map 16 B1**

Singapore specialities are a good choice at this stylish, shiny restaurant at Golders Green. Dishes are sometimes fiery, sometimes subtle: crispy squid, peppered crab, baked chicken in fragrant spices, cloud mushroom and scallop soup. The Sunday buffet is very popular with both adults and children. ***Seats** 70. Parties 17. L 12-3 D 6-11.15. Closed 25 & 26 Dec. Set L £5.90 Set D from £13.90.* AMERICAN EXPRESS *Access, Diners, Visa.*

SW5 Tom Yum NEW £40

Tel 071-244 6060 **R**

233b Earls Court Road SW5 9AH **Map 19 A5**

Friendly basement Thai restaurant at the very bottom of Earls Court Road. Cooking is to order, so everything arrives fresh and hot, served on lovely chinaware specially imported from Thailand. Tom Yum takes its name from the classic Thai soup, which appears here in prawn, chicken and mixed seafood varieties. Other dishes not to be missed are prawn cakes, stuffed chicken wings and vegetable-stuffed pancakes; spicy Thai salads; green or red curries featuring coconut milk; and main courses enhanced variously by fresh chili, ginger, garlic and basil leaves. ***Seats** 44. D 6-11.30. Closed 25 Dec, 1 Jan. Set D £15.95.* AMERICAN EXPRESS *Access, Diners, Visa.*

SW1 Tophams Ebury Court 60% £100

Tel 071-730 8147 Fax 071-823 5966 **HR**

28 Ebury Street Victoria SW1W 0LU **Map 19 C4**

In the same family ownership for more than half a century, Tophams Ebury Court offers old-fashioned courtesy and charm in a central location three minutes walk from Victoria station (300yds down Lower Belgrave Street). Accommodation ranges from singles without en-suite facilities to luxury four-poster/triple rooms with bath. All are equipped with hair-dryers and satellite TVs. ***Rooms** 40. Closed Christmas/New Year.* AMERICAN EXPRESS *Access, Diners, Visa.*

Tophams £50

Three elegantly appointed rooms, their walls adorned with paintings by the owners' ancestors, are the setting for meals that combine traditional and modern elements. Chicken liver paté, grilled Dover sole and roast leg of pork with apple sauce represent the school of old favourites, which are joined by a few more contemporary offerings. Good value for both food and wine. ***Seats** 45. Parties 14. Private Room 18. L 12-2.30 D 7-9.30. Closed L Sat, D Sun.*

W1 Topkapi £35

Tel 071-486 1872 **R**

25 Marylebone High Street W1M 3PE **Map 18 C2**

Turkish cuisine in an all-day restaurant named after the ancient Ottoman palace in Istanbul. Hot and cold hors d'oeuvre (stuffed vine leaves, meat balls, aubergines, yoghurt, peppers); main-course kebab grills. Quick lunches, relaxed dinners. ***Seats** 50. Meals 12-12. Closed 25 & 26 Dec. Set meals from £12.50.* AMERICAN EXPRESS *Access, Diners, Visa.*

> Never leave money, credit cards or valuables lying around in your hotel room. Use the hotel safe or the mini-safe in your room.

E1 Tower Thistle 66% £176

Tel 071-481 2575 Fax 071-488 4106 **H**

St Katharine's Way Tower Bridge E1 9LD **Map 20 D3**

The enormous Tower Thistle hotel enjoys one of the finest settings in the capital, next to Tower Bridge and the Tower of London, with views of the Thames and St Katharine's Dock. Behind a strikingly original modern shell there's style inside, too, notably in the airy, high-ceilinged marbled foyer. The Which Way West café has views overlooking the bridge and turns into a video night club Tuesday to Saturday evenings. The Tower Suite can accommodate up to 250 function delegates theatre-style. All bedrooms are air-conditioned and there are three floors of Executive rooms with many extra accessories and a dedicated check-out desk; four floors of the rooms have been recently refurbished. A secure, charged car park for guests' use adjoins the hotel. Children up to 14 stay free in parents' room. Function facilities for around 200. No dogs. ***Rooms 808.*** *News kiosk, coffee shop (7.30am-10pm), covered garage.* AMERICAN EXPRESS *Access, Diners, Visa.*

NW1 Trattoria Lucca £45

Tel 071-485 6864 **R**

63 Parkway Camden Town NW1 7PP **Map 16 C3**

Halfway along Parkway, and just moments from Camden Town station, this is a popular Italian restaurant whose standard trattoria menu is supplemented by daily specials which usually include some very good stuffed vegetables. Steak dishes are a speciality. ***Seats 65.*** *Parties 40. Private Room 40. L 12-3 D 6-10.45. Closed Sun, Bank Holidays. Set L & D £8/£10.50.* AMERICAN EXPRESS *Access, Diners, Visa.*

SW3 Travellers NEW £40

Tel 071-351 0775 **R**

338 Kings Road London SW3 **Map 19 B6**

CLOSED

A smart, comfortable restaurant with large, colourful paintings on rough plaster walls. In summer the whole front opens out on to the pavement. Johnny Johnson's cooking is an imaginative mix of European and Eastern, shown in creations like a warm timbale of artichoke with langoustine tails and a cardamom sauce, or stir-fried beef with mixed peppers and crispy noodles. ***Seats 48.*** *Parties 12. L 12.30-2.30 D 7-11. Closed Sun, Mon, 25, 26 Dec & 1 Jan. Set L £7.95/£9.95 Set D £15/£17.50. Access, Visa.*

SW7 Tui £42

Tel 071-584 8359 **R**

19 Exhibition Road SW7 2HE **Map 19 B5**

Tom yum, a traditional clear spicy soup scented with lemon grass, lime leaves and fresh chilis and served in a fire pot, is an almost essential element in a meal at this civilised Thai restaurant in South Kensington. Pork and water chestnut dumplings with garlic sauce, satay, spare ribs, galangal and coconut-flavoured soup (*tomkha gai*) all feature among the starters; red (both chicken and duck) and green curries, crab claws, marinated beef with chilis and basil, deep-fried pomfret, Thai-style sweet and sour prawns are among the main dishes. *Mee Grorb* is typical of the unusual, yet classic Thai tastes on offer – a dish of crisply-fried rice noodles tossed in a tamarind-based sauce of pork and shrimps; ***Seats 60.*** *Private Room 40. L 12-2.30 (Sun 12.30 to 3) D 6.30-11 (Sun 7-10.30). Closed Bank Holidays.* AMERICAN EXPRESS *Access, Diners, Visa..*

Set menu prices may not always include service or wine.

N1 Tuk Tuk

£30

Tel 071-226 0837

R

330 Upper Street N1 2XQ

Map 16 D3

Small, stylish and informal restaurant, taking its name from the rickshaw-style taxis that ply the streets of Bangkok. Satay, chicken wings or fish patties could precede hot and sour soup with prawns and rice, a mild or chili-hot curry, garlicky fried beef or noodles with mixed seafood. ***Seats 80.*** *Private Room 50. L 12-3 D 6-11.15. Closed L Sat, all Sun, Bank Holidays.* AMERICAN EXPRESS *Access, Visa.*

SW3 Turner's ★

£95

Tel 071-584 6711

R

87-89 Walton Street SW3 2HP

Map 19 B5

The set lunch here must be one of the best bargains in town, especially when you consider that the prices (£9.95 for two courses, £13.50 for three) include delectable amuse-gueule, splendid petits fours and service. Only the coffee is charged extra. The surroundings are restful and comfortable, the service keen, and the food tastes as good as it looks. Fish dishes are plentiful, and sometimes appear with unusual accompaniments – sea bream with a red wine sauce, mushrooms and roast parsnips, or salmon and braised lentils with a herb sauce. But don't ignore the meat dishes – try a prime rib of grilled beeef with a bone marrow and garlic sauce. Brian Turner is a Yorkshireman after all, in fact Sunday lunch is the real McCoy … with style. Leave space for some marvellous desserts; the only complaint about the steamed pudding is that there isn't enough! A carefully selected and wholly French wine list has many champagnes and Chablis. ***Seats 50.*** *L 12.30-2.30 D 7.30-11 (Sun to 10). Closed L Sat, Bank Holidays, 1 week Christmas. Set L £9.95/££13.50 Set D £23.50/£26.50.* AMERICAN EXPRESS *Access, Diners, Visa.*

SW9 Twenty Trinity Gardens

£50

Tel 071-733 8838

R

20 Trinity Gardens SW9 8DP

Map 17 C5

A stone's throw off Acre Lane but by car it can only be approached via Brighton Terrace and only from the northbound side of Brixton Road. With a bright, plant-filled conservatory at the front, there's plenty of light during the day while candles burn at night. A honey-coloured pine dado runs round the white-painted walls, which are hung with colourful and modern artwork. Menus offer a modern mix of dishes, a few Caribbean among a short classical and Mediterranean selection. Marinated ricotta cheese on a bed of garlic croutons and salad, spicy fish soup or three soft-boiled quail's eggs mashed in hollandaise in a mushroom duxelle placed on a slice of puff pastry make delicious starters. Main dishes could be Cajun lamb with hash browns and yoghurt sauce, grilled magret of goose with apples and calvados, pepper steak with red onion butter or a delicious dish of hot and spicy curried goat with rice 'n' peas (red kidney beans) and fried plantain. A few vegetarian options too. A meringue basket, wonderfully chewy and topped with banana batons, whipped cream and a liberal dribble of rum, makes a very good finale. Other equally tempting desserts are treacle tart with ginger and cream, or iced nougat glacé with chocolate sauce. Talented cooking with charming informal service. ***Seats 60.*** *Parties 33. Private Room 20. L 12.30-2.30 (Sun 11.30-4) D 7-10.30. Closed 25 Dec & 1 Jan. Set L from £8.50 Set D £17.50.* AMERICAN EXPRESS *Access, Visa.*

Changes in data sometimes occur in establishments after the Guide goes to press. Prices should be taken as indications rather than firm quotes.

SW1 22 Jermyn Street **£200**

Tel 071-734 2353 Fax 071-734 0750 **PH**

22 Jermyn Street SW1Y 6HL **Map 18 D3**

50 yards from Piccadilly, 22 Jermyn Street was established as 'residential chambers' by Anthony Glyka in 1915. The fine Edwardian property has been converted with panache by his grandson, Henry Togna, to a small and luxurious private hotel. 13 self-contained suites and 5 studios retain their period furniture and objets d'art and are brightened daily with fresh flowers. Business facilities include fax points and a 'speed-dial' phone directory; housekeeping, 24hr room services (including medical and dental support) and Continental breakfast are similarly comprehensive and guests can avail themselves of a personal shopping service. King-size beds, make-up mirrors, bespoke toiletries and monogrammed bathsheets and robes set the tone. ***Rooms** 18.* AMERICAN EXPRESS *Access, Diners, Visa..*

SW7 The Vanderbilt 62% **£139**

Tel 071-589 2424 Fax 071-225 2293 **H**

68 Cromwell Road London SW7 5BT **Map 19 B5**

The Edwardian Hotel group's first acquisition (1977) is a Grade II listed building comprising ten linked Regency town houses on busy Cromwell Road. Matching floral drapes and bedspreads brighten stereotyped bedrooms, a high proportion of which are smallish singles. No dogs. ***Rooms** 223.* AMERICAN EXPRESS *Access, Diners, Visa.*

W2 Veronica's **£65**

Tel 071-229 5079 **R**

3 Hereford Road W2 4AB **Map 18 A3**

Overlooking Bayswater's Leinster Square and close to Whiteley's shopping centre, indefatigable Veronica Shaw's restaurant has monthly-changing, well-researched culinary themes; English based, and including recipes dating back many centuries. There's always a good selection of British farmhouse cheeses (from Mendip Hill Goat to Cornish Yarg). Low-fat, high-fibre and vegan dishes are always indicated on the wordy menus. Outdoor tables in good weather. ***Seats** 80. Private Room 40. L 12-3 D 7-12. Closed L Sat, all Sun, Bank Holidays.* AMERICAN EXPRESS *Access, Diners, Visa.*

NW6 Vijay **£25**

Tel 071-328 1087 **R**

49 Willesden Lane NW6 7RF **Map 16 B3**

Popular preparations of lamb, chicken and prawns supplement South Indian vegetarian specialities at this unpretentious restaurant. Adai is a pancake made from rice and three varieties of lentils; iddly is a steamed cake made of rice and garam flour; avial mixes several vegetables cooked with ground coconut, yoghurt, butter and curry leaves. ***Seats** 78. Parties 25. L 12-2.45 D 6-10.45 (Fri & Sat till 11.45). Closed 25 & 26 Dec.* AMERICAN EXPRESS *Access, Diners, Visa.*

W1 Villandry Dining Room **£45**

Tel 071-224 3799 **R**

89 Marylebone High Street W1M 3DE **Map 18 C2**

By day, an upmarket delicatessen with a small restaurant at the rear offering superior snacks both sweet and savoury plus a few more substantial dishes. However one evening, once a month the whole place transforms into a restaurant. Bookings have to be made well in advance and confirmed a few days beforehand. For this you sit at small bare wood tables surrounded by shelves stacked with the likes of fine olive oils, teas and mustards. Occasionally dinner is combined with a musical evening. The

See over

menu is short, varied and very imaginative. The execution is skilled, presentation simple and the results extremely enjoyable – there's a wonderful lack of pretension to the whole proceedings. Starters could include a lemon grass, ginger and sweetcorn soup left in a large tureen on the table along with excellent breads. Other starters are a warm pigeon salad or a delicate fish and vegetable terrine with tomato vinaigrette. Main dishes range from a vegetarian potato and goat's cheese tatin with rich red wine sauce to best end of lamb with baby hachis parmentier. Cheeses are superb – mostly French, all in prime condition. Sweets include strawberry and chocolate tart, sticky toffee pudding or a quite irresistible moist chocolate cake with white and dark chocolate ice cream. No smoking. ***Seats** 48. L 12.30-2.30 (D once a month). Closed Sun, Bank Holidays, 10 days Christmas. Access, Visa*

WC1 Wagamama NEW £25

Tel 071-323 9223 **R**

4 Streatham Street off Bloomsbury Street WC1 1JB **Map 21 B1**

'Positive eating, positive living' is the philosophy at this fast-food, Japanese-style noodle bar. The large and spartan basement room fills up soon after opening time with a young crowd who appreciate the quick service, the value for money and the simple, healthy food served at communal tables. No bookings. ***Seats** 104. L 12-2.30 (Sat 1-3.30) D 6-11. Closed Sun, 25 & 26 Dec, 1 Jan & Easter Mon. No credit cards.*

NW3 Wakaba £70

Tel 071-586 7960 **R**

122a Finchley Road NW3 5HT **Map 16 B2**

Behind curved glass frosted from busy Finchley Road the decor is designer-zero, canteen-style, basically plain white. The menu provides an interesting span of Japanese dishes, and novitiates in this acquired, pretty cuisine would do well to opt for one of the set meals, which offer various choices. Some dishes, including sukiyaki, shabushabu and yosenabe (Japanese-style bouillabaisse) are prepared at the table. ***Seats** 55. D 6.30-11. Closed Sun, 24-27 Dec, Good Friday, Easter Monday, 1 week Aug. Set L from £9.50 Set D from £23.60.* AMERICAN EXPRESS *Access, Diners, Visa.*

WC2 The Waldorf 83% £206

Tel 071-836 2400 Fax 071-836 7244 **HR**

Aldwych WC2B 4DD **Map 17 C4**

Opened in 1908 (and in 1958 the first hotel to be acquired by Charles Forte – the company now has over 800) the Waldorf has celebrated its 85th anniversary with a multi-million pound refit. Regular guests will be relieved to find the public areas, though refurbished, otherwise unchanged – the Club Bar with polished wood panelling, leather chesterfields and marble fireplaces; pubby Footlights Bar; traditional Aldwych Brasserie and, at the heart of the hotel, the truly grand Palm Court where Saturday and Sunday tea dances are a veritable institution with their origins in the Waldorf's famous Tango Teas of the 1920s and 30s. Most of the £16 million has been spent on the bedrooms, which have been totally transformed. The smallest rooms have gone and all now have air-conditioning, secondary sockets for fax or modems and even 110-volt outlets for the convenience of transatlantic guests. Every bedroom has its own entrance lobby, new traditionally-styled darkwood, polished furniture, brand new beds and one of nine bold decorative schemes. Elaborately draped curtains and chandeliers hark back to the opulence of the hotel's Edwardian origins as do the period-style washstands in marble-trimmed bathrooms that all have both fixed and hand-held showers over the tubs; bathrobes, speaker extensions and good toiletries. Well turned out staff provide a proper turn-down service in the evenings and valet parking but overnight room service is limited to sandwiches and snacks. ***Rooms** 292.* AMERICAN EXPRESS *Access, Diners, Visa.*

Restaurant £88

A grand, high-ceilinged room with Corinthian columns and French doors opening on to the Palm Court. The menu is strong on grills and fairly traditional dishes: cock-a-leekie soup, escalope of veal Holstein, steak Diane, crepes Suzette. The sweet trolley holds no surprises. Cooking is workmanlike rather than inspired. An oddity of the formal service is the practice of serving and pouring the coffee while you still eating dessert. ***Seats*** *70. Parties 10. Private Room 30. L 12.30-2.30 D 6-11 (Sun 7-10). Set L & D £21/£25. Closed L Sat & Sun.*

W1 Walsh's NEW £55

Tel 071-637 0222 **R**

5 Charlotte Street W1P 1HD **Map 18 D2**

A smart glittering oyster bar with tall bar stools occupies the front while elsewhere highly-polished wood tables are arranged in a series of brightly-lit dining rooms. The likes of lobster ravioli with a Chablis and garlic sauce, mackerel tart with tomato and basil and pan-fried scallops on a bed of lettuce with hazelnut dressing are a few innovations on what is a very traditional seafood menu. Dover sole prepared in twelve ways, lobster in six feature alongside other classics – grilled turbot with béarnaise sauce, scampi provençale and scallops florentine. Christopher German cooks with skill producing dishes that are very enjoyable and satisfying whether classic or modern. Caring, well-trained staff. ***Seats*** *70. Parties 25. Private Room 25. L 12-2.30 D 6-11. Closed L Sat, all Sun.* AMERICAN EXPRESS *Access, Diners, Visa.*

SW3 Walton's £100

Tel 071-584 0204 Fax 071-581 2848 **R**

121 Walton Street South Kensington SW3 2PH **Map 19 B5**

Polished service matches the luxuriously comfortable surroundings and in the kitchen Paul Hodgson shows his considerable skills in some highly enjoyable dishes. The à la carte menu mixes the traditionally English with the modern and international: prime fillet of Scottish beef, steamed Scottish salmon and rack of Southdown lamb sit happily alongside seafood sausage (scallop and lobster), terrine of truffled foie gras with Sauternes jelly and toasted brioche, oven-baked guinea fowl in sesame seed pastry with a lime and white wine sauce. Sticky toffee pudding with butterscotch sauce, lemon tart with vanilla and Grand Marnier custard and a fine Stilton add the finishing touch. Traditional 3-course Sunday lunch usually includes roast sirloin of beef served with Yorkshire pudding and horseradish sauce; 2-course after-theatre supper offers a small choice from the carte; "Simply Walton's" lunch is very good value; and there's an à la carte menu. ***Seats*** *65. Parties 20. L 12.30-2.30 (Sun to 2) D 7.30-11.30 (Sun 7-10). Closed 26 Dec. Set L £10/£14.75 (£16.50 Sun) Set D £21.* AMERICAN EXPRESS *Access, Diners, Visa.*

W1 Washington Hotel 70% £199

Tel 071-499 7000 Fax 071-495 6172 **H**

5 Curzon Street W1Y 8DT **Map 18 C3**

Between Berkeley Square and Park Lane, in the heart of Mayfair, a smart hotel with elegant public areas – from the marble-floored reception to Madison's lounge-bar with Oriental carpets, comfortable seating, elaborately-draped curtains and bird's-eye maple panelling. Bedrooms vary in size and shape but have a distinctive 30s' feel, with striking burred oak furniture in Art Deco style matched by agreeable abstract-patterned fabrics. There's a floor of non-smoking rooms. Bathrooms have particularly good shower heads over the tubs, plus convenient phone and loudspeaker extensions. Long beds and a breakfast table, room safes and a computer-coded locking system are standard throughout. Over 30 rooms are state rooms or suites. Bright, modern meeting rooms for up to 80. No dogs. Sarova Hotels. ***Rooms*** *173.* AMERICAN EXPRESS *Access, Diners, Visa.*

W1 The Westbury 75% £203

Tel 071-629 7755 Fax 071-495 1163 **H**

Conduit Street W1A 4UH **Map 18 D3**

Opened in 1955 as sister hotel to the *Westbury* in New York, the London version is just off New Bond Street. Sparkling chandeliers and smartly liveried porters create a formal impression on first entering the marble-floored lobby. The pine-panelled Polo Lounge (open 24 hours for refreshments) and dark green Polo Bar boast polo murals and memorabilia, inspired by original owners who had a passion for the sport. Bedrooms vary in size from smallish singles through mini-suites to 13 full suites and a penthouse; all share the same traditional-style darkwood furniture with pleasing floral fabrics and many extras like mini-bars. 20 of the rooms are suitable for families, with cots, funpacks and babysitting available. Conference facilities for up to 120, but no leisure amenities (residents have complimentary use of a nearby private health and fitness club). Forte Grand. ***Rooms** 244.* AMERICAN EXPRESS *Access, Diners, Visa.*

NW1 White House 71% £136

Tel 071-387 1200 Fax 071-388 0091 **H**

Albany Street NW1 3UP **Map 18 D1**

Just off Euston Road, close to Regent's Park and opposite Great Portland Street underground station. Built as a block of flats in the 1930s, hence the numerous pillars to be found in the public rooms. There is no separate lounge in the smart marble-floored reception/foyer, but it does offer some seating and the sophisticated bar has plenty of lounge-style armchairs. There's a cocktail lounge, a restaurant, a long-hours garden café and the Wine Press wine bar. Bedrooms vary in size from compact to suites; most have decent lightwood units, soft colour schemes and matching fabrics. All have double-glazed windows and American electric sockets as well as British ones plus mini-bars, security chains and spyholes. Well used by coachloads of international travellers stopping over briefly in London. One floor, called the Reserve Floor, has separate check-in and lounge plus lots of extras. No dogs. Conference and banqueting facilities for 120/100. Rank Hotels. ***Rooms** 576. Keep-fit equipment, sauna, coffee shop (7am-10.30pm), news kiosk & gift shop.* AMERICAN EXPRESS *Access, Diners, Visa.*

W1 White Tower £70

Tel 071-636 8141 **R**

1 Percy Street W1P 0ET **Map 18 D2**

The good times seem to be back after a management buy-out at this comfortable, old-fashioned restaurant facing the south end of Charlotte Street. The walls are lined with pictures and painting of Asian Minors and Greek and Middle-Eastern dishes form the bulk of a wordy menu. One of the most famous dishes is Aylesbury Duckling Farci à la Cypriote – weighty chaps stuffed with bourgourie, chopped almonds and livers, and roasted to a crisp dark brown. Each provides a festal dish for two (though a single helping may be ordered). Start with mixed patés or mezedes, finish with fresh fruit salad. Some of the staff have seen more than 40 years service in this most traditional of addresses. ***Seats** 70. Private Room 16. L 12.30-2.15 D 6.45-10.15. Closed Sat & Sun, Bank Holidays, 3 weeks Aug, 1 week Christmas.* AMERICAN EXPRESS *Access, Diners, Visa.*

> Never leave money, credit cards or valuables lying around in your hotel room. Use the hotel safe or the mini-safe in your room.

W2 **Whites Hotel** 77% £198

Tel 071-262 2711 Fax 071-262 2147 H

90 Lancaster Gate W2 3NR Map 18 B3

Originally part of a terrace of private houses, it was built in 1866 in the style then known as French renaissance. A cobbled forecourt leads through glass-topped canopies into a Victorian mansion with a colonnaded facade. There's a feeling of quiet opulence in day rooms like the graceful reception with a marble fireplace and a rug-covered marble floor, a bar with tub chairs and a partly-panelled writing room. Bedrooms have panel-effect walls, good-quality limed furniture, easy chairs, swagged silk drapes and luxurious Italian marble bathrooms. There are two suites, one in Louis XV style, the other with an Oriental inspiration. No dogs. ***Rooms** 54.* AMERICAN EXPRESS *Access, Diners, Visa.*

EC4 **Whittington's** £70

Tel 071-248 5855 R

21 College Hill EC4 2RP Map 20 C2

Dick Whittington once owned these 14th-century wine cellars, whose short menu (changing every three weeks or so) is supplemented by a daily specials board. The choice runs from filo parcel of sweet and sour pork and spring vegetable terrine among the starters to salmon fish cakes, monkfish couscous, chargrilled brochette of turkey breast with a mild mustard sauce and fillet of beef served on celeriac purée. ***Seats** 53. Private Room 80. L only 11.45-2.15. Closed Sat & Sun, Bank Holidays.* AMERICAN EXPRESS *Access, Diners, Visa.*

SW1 **Wilbraham Hotel** 55% £86

Tel 071-730 8296 Fax 071-730 6815 H

Wilbraham Place Sloane Street SW1X 9AE Map 19 C5

Modest Belgravia hotel formed from three Victorian town houses. Bedrooms and bathrooms are generally quite small and spartan, though there are two large suites on the ground floor. The bar is closed Sundays and Bank Holidays. ***Rooms** 52. No credit cards.*

SW10 **The Wilds** £55

Tel 071-376 5553 R

356 Fulham Road SW10 Map 19 A6

A change of chef there may have been but the food remains as innovative and as well prepared as ever. The dinner menu offers dishes like roast corn and asparagus soup, smoked salmon with rösti and crème fraiche, or saffron rice, lentils and cold lamb salad with cumin, yoghurt and coriander relish. Main dishes range from linguine with crispy aubergine and pesto to home-made farm sausages with mash and salsa verde to breast of chicken with shallots, lemon and oregano. The desserts too are unmissable with the likes of sticky toffee pudding, poached nectarine with a caramel and pine nut sauce or chocolate brownies with crème fraiche. On Friday lunchtime there's a short fixed-price menu of simpler items from the dinner carte – equally well treated and highly enjoyable. ***Seats** 60. Parties 14. Private Room 35. L 12.30-2.30 (Sun till 4) D 7-11.30. Closed L Mon-Thur, D Sun, 24 Dec-5 Jan and all Bank Holidays. Set Sun L £9.95. Access, Visa.*

SW1 **Willett Hotel** £97

Tel 071-824 8415 Fax 071-730 4830 H

32 Sloane Gardens SW1X 8DT Map 19 C5

Victorian townhouse in the heart of Chelsea converted into a peaceful hotel offering bed and breakfast accommodation, but limited public rooms. Three bedrooms are not en suite. Friendly staff. ***Rooms** 18.* AMERICAN EXPRESS *Access, Diners, Visa.*

W14 Wilson's £45

Tel 071-603 7267 **R**

236 Blythe Road W14 0HJ **Map 17 B4**

Robert Wilson and his chef present an eclectic menu with some Scottish influences in this agreeable little bare-boarded restaurant on the corner of Shepherds Bush Road. Finnan haddock pudding with spinach and bacon salad, haggis with neeps and escalope of calf's liver with mustard and ginger sauce are typical dishes, the first two being available as either starter or main course. On the pudding list could be Athol Brose, lemon tart with a blackcurrant sauce and summer pudding accompanied by almond ice cream. ***Seats** 40. Parties 30. L 12.30-2.30 (Sun to 3) D 7.30-10. Closed L Sat, D Sun, Bank Holidays, 2 weeks Christmas, 2 weeks Aug.* AMERICAN EXPRESS *Access, Visa.*

SW1 Wilton's £110

Tel 071-629 9955 Fax 071-495 6233 **R**

55 Jermyn Street SW1Y 6LX **Map 18 D3**

Oysters, fish and game are the specialities in one of London's best-known restaurants, which has been in business for 250 years. The classic à la carte menu offers a mainstream menu that includes smoked, marinated, grilled and poached salmon, whitebait, omelettes, sole and lobster and grilled meats. Service is of the old school, in keeping with and contributing to the atmosphere. ***Seats** 90. Parties 25. Private Room 16. L 12.30-2.30 D 6.30-10.30. Closed L Sat, all Sun, Bank Holidays.* AMERICAN EXPRESS *Access, Diners, Visa.*

W5 Wine & Mousaka £30

Tel 081-998 4373 **R**

30 & 33 Haven Green W5 2NX **Map 17 A4**

A popularly-priced restaurant on two sides of a corner site offering most of the traditional Greek favourites, including meat or vegetarian mou(s)saka, souvla, winy sausages, *tava* (oven-cooked lamb on the bone) and *triada* (courgette, green pepper and vine leaves stuffed with pork mince, rice and herbs). See also entry under Richmond. ***Seats** 100. Parties 50. L 12-2.30 D 6-11.30. Closed Sun, Bank Holidays. Set L from £4.95 Set D from £6.95.* AMERICAN EXPRESS *Access, Diners, Visa.*

Also at:

12 Kew Green Kew Surrey TW9 3BH Tel 081-940 5696 L 12-2.30 D 6-11 **Map 15 E2**

W8 Wodka £45

Tel 071-937 6513 **R**

12 St Alban's Grove Kensington W8 5PN **Map 19 A4**

The classic green-and-white tiles have partly survived the summer 1993 extension at this popular drinking and eating spot away from the general Kensington bustle. The menu is Polish by main inspiration, with favourite dishes including veal and wild mushrooms pierogi, blinis with toppings of herring, smoked salmon, aubergine mousse or caviar, excellent chunky fishcakes with dill sauce, veal goulash, pork shank roasted in beer. A dozen vodkas are available by glass or carafe – try lemon, honey … and maybe a few others. ***Seats** 60. Private Room 30. L 12.30-2.30 D 7-11. Closed L Sat, Bank Holidays.* AMERICAN EXPRESS *Access, Diners, Visa.*

See the Conference and Banqueting section for lists of hotels arranged by county.

SE9 Yardley Court £52

Tel 081-850 1850 **H**

18 Court Yard SE9 5PZ **Map 17 D5**

A neat Victorian house surrounded by attractive gardens. Bed and breakfast accommodation. Children up to the age of 5 free in parents' room. ***Rooms*** *9. Access, Visa.*

W5 Young's Rendezvous £40

Tel 081-840 3060 **R**

13 Bond Street Ealing W5 **Map 17 A4**

Small, smart Chinese restaurant one street down from the Broadway centre, with smooth service from waiters and waitresses in tunics. Good sizzling dishes, sea food and Szechuan dishes; particularly fine lobster feast set menu. Try the chef's specials, and to finish the banana, red bean paste or ko-lei pancake or beancurd in jade with crème de menthe. Short list of dim sum served every day from 12.15 to 2.45pm; choice of business lunches. ***Seats*** *100. Private Room 80. L 12.15-2.45 D 6.15-11.45 (Fri & Sat to 12). Closed 25 & 26 Dec. Set L £7.50 & £9.50 Set D from £13.80.* AMERICAN EXPRESS *Access, Diners, Visa.*

N16 Yum Yum NEW £45

Tel 071-254 6751 Fax 071-241 3857 **R**

26 Stoke Newington Church Street N16 0LU **Map 16 D2**

Immediately next door to and co-owned by *Spices* (qv) this colourful restaurant run by Moi, Atique Choudary's Thai wife, has a menu of equally colourful, spicy foods, much of it cooked in a wok to retain as much natural colour and goodness as possible. There is excellent use of fresh herbs. Vegetarians have their own special section on the menu with some 25 dishes to choose from. ***Seats*** *38. Parties 20. D only 6-12. Closed 2 weeks Christmas, 2 weeks Easter.* AMERICAN EXPRESS *Access, Diners, Visa.*

W1 Yumi £80

Tel 071-935 8320 **R**

110 George Street W1H 6DJ **Map 18 C2**

Decor is simplicity itself, and the menu is scarcely more complicated; set meals (particularly good value for money) and à la carte choices run the gamut of familiar Japanese dishes prepared with skill, from steamed abalone and crab dumplings to fillet of Scoth beef grilled and flavoured with soy sauce. Owner Yumi Fujii is always on hand with a smile, a bow and advice. Upstairs and in the private rooms you sit cross-legged at very low tables, and it's only downstairs or in the bar that you can adopt a more conventionally Occidental seat. No children under 10. ***Seats*** *76. Parties 30. Private Room 14. L 12.30-2.30 D 5.30-10.30. Closed L Sat, all Sun, 1 week Christmas. Set L from £5.90 Set D from £26.* AMERICAN EXPRESS *Access, Diners, Visa.*

SW3 Zen £80

Tel 071-589 1781 Fax 071-437 0641 **R**

Chelsea Cloisters Sloane Avenue SW3 **Map 19 B5**

Chelsea Cloisters is the first of the chain. The decor is restrained and slightly outdated compared to the other branches: pink atmosphere with low ceilings, Chinese zodiac on the windows and a small waterfall near the entrance. The extensive menu is tempting. "A Feast on its own" offers specialities for two like braised fluffy supreme shark's fin in spicy sauce, roasted Peking duck in two courses, or crispy aromatic leg of lamb. Better still are dishes from the separate menu of regional Chinese specialities.

See over

Quality has been uneven over the years, but when dishes are good they are excellent. ***Seats** 120. Parties 20. Private Room 22. L 12-3 D 6-11.30 (Sun to 11). Closed 25 & 26 Dec.* AMERICAN EXPRESS *Access, Diners, Visa.*
Also at:
Zen Central 20 Queen Street Mayfair W1 071-629 8103 **Map 18 C3**
Zen NW3 83 Hampstead High Street NW3 071-794 7863 **Map 16 B2**
See also entry for *Now & Zen.*

SW3 Ziani £65

Tel 071-352 2698 **R**

45/47 Radnor Walk SW3 4BT **Map 19 C5**

A brightly decorated Italian restaurant named after an ancient Venetian family. Seafood is quite a strength, and assorted grilled fish is a popular choice, along with trout with almonds, deep-fried scampi and boneless sardines with garlic, capers and breadcrumbs. Daily specials are always worth a try. Decent Italian wine list. ***Seats** 60. Parties 22. L 12.30-2.45 (Sun to 3.15) D 7-11.30 (Sun to 10.30). Closed Bank Holidays.* AMERICAN EXPRESS *Access, Diners, Visa.*

W1 Zoe NEW £55

Tel 071-224 1122 **R**

St Christopher's Place W1M 5HH **Map 18 C2**

Modern basement brasserie with a café at street level, both done in bright and fashionable colours. The atmosphere is hectic and loud. Two menus, one Country, the other City, mix Mediterranean ideas with Latin-American ingredients without neglecting fish and chips and sausage and mash. If the menu if different and spirited, the cooking is of a good, reliable standard, though without any real sparkle. ***Seats** 80. Parties 20. L 12.30-3 D 6.30-11.30. Closed D Sun, 24-26 Dec.* AMERICAN EXPRESS *Access, Diners, Visa.*

Consult page 16 for a full list of starred restaurants

Serviced Apartments in London

Serviced apartments have developed into a thriving industry, and are certainly a preferred alternative for longer visits. More and more company and leisure travellers are experiencing the benefits that this type of accommodation can offer, not only in terms of cost but also the extra privacy, security, and freedom that an apartment can provide. If you're tired of hotels, an apartment offers many advantages, not least its own kitchen, as well as being equally comfortable and luxurious, with facilities and standards of service to match. Those linked with a hotel have access to all its amenities. Undoubtedly, apartments have more space, and there's probably little or no extra cost for family or additional guests.

They can range from studio rooms to penthouse suites, from prestige addresses to leafy cul-de-sacs, and accommodation can vary considerably within the same building in respect of price and other aspects. Daily maid service is usually provided and most apartments have a dishwasher and wash/dryer in the well-equipped kitchens. Telephone charges are noticeably cheaper than in hotels, and often the only extras you need pay for. In the main weekly prices are quoted, but these are normally not so hard and fast as those at hotels (themselves negotiable), and may be influenced by the length of stay.

Over the last two years this Guide has recommended and graded apartments in line with our percentage ratings of hotels, ranging from de luxe (80%+), to superior (70–80%), and standard (60–70%). We list below two examples that have met our minimum high standards—further details of these and others can be obtained from The Apartment Service (see over).

SW3 Draycott House 80%

13 apartments immaculately kept and well run by Linda Coulthard and her team, in a quiet tree-lined street, the majority with their own balconies, and one a roof terrace. Typically, the living areas feature period furniture, custom-made sofas, pictures, objets d'art, books, magazines and flowers while the bedrooms have co-ordinating fabrics and cosseting extras such as pot-pourri and pomanders. Bathrooms sparkle and modern fitted kitchens are well stocked with provisions on arrival, and milk is delivered daily. Answerphones and fax machines can be installed on request and the remote-control TVs (with VCR) have fastext. *Nearest tube: Sloane Square. Parking: own garage. Maid service: Mon-Fri. Telephone charge: 12p per unit. Amenities: video entryphone, lift, courtyard garden, business services, laundry room, baby-sitting, cots, highchairs. Credit cards: none.*

W1 23 Greengarden House 73%

Situated in a smart pedestrian street between Oxford and Wigmore Streets, the apartments are perhaps on the small side, but splendidly furnished in a warm and individual style, some with period pieces, others more modern. Sofa coverings and fabrics are of particularly high quality, and the compact kitchens expensively fitted out with good equipment, including microwave and wash/dryer. Excellent housekeeping is evident throughout these 24 apartments, which are well run, typified by the attractive window boxes outside each. *Nearest tube: Bond Street. Parking: difficult. Maid service: Mon-Fri. Telephone charge: 16p per unit. Amenities: entryphone, lift, boardroom and business services, laundry service, cable TV, baby-sitting, cots. Credit cards: all.*

Places of interest

London Tourist Information

Transport Tel 071-222 1234.
Tourist Board Tel 071-730 3488.
Railway Termini
Euston & St Pancras 071-387 7070
Kings Cross 071-278 2477
Paddington & Marylebone 071-262 6767
Victoria, Waterloo, Charing Cross & Liverpool Street 071-928 5100
Riverboat Information Tel 071-730 4812.

London Theatres

Adelphi Strand WC2 Tel 071-836 7611.
Albery St. Martins's Lane WC2 Tel 071-867 1115.
Aldwych Aldwych WC2 Tel 071-836 6404.
Ambassadors West Street, Cambridge Circus WC2 Tel 071-836 6111.
Apollo Shaftesbury Avenue W1 Tel 071-437 2663.
Apollo Victoria Wilton Road SW1 Tel 071-630 6262.
Arts 6-7 Gt Newport Street WC2 Tel 071-836 2132.
Astoria Charing Cross Road WC2 Tel 071-434 0403.
Bloomsbury Gordon Street WC1 Tel 071-387 9629.
Comedy Panton Street, Haymarket SW1 Tel 071-867 1045.
Criterion Piccadilly Circus W1 Tel 071-839 4488.
Drury Lane Theatre Royal WC2 Tel 071-836 8108.
Duchess Catherine Street WC2 Tel 071-836 8243.
Duke of York's St. Martin's Lane WC2 Tel 071-836 5122.
Fortune Russell Street WC2 Tel 071-836 2238.
Garrick Charing Cross Road WC2 Tel 071-379 6107.
Globe Shaftesbury Avenue W1 Tel 071-437 3667.
Greenwich Theatre Crooms Hill SE10 Tel 081-858 7755.
Haymarket Theatre Royal SW1 Tel 071-930 9832.
Her Majesty's Haymarket SW1 Tel 071-839 2244.
Lyric King Steeet, Hammersmith W6 Tel 081-741 2311.
Lyric Shaftesbury Avenue W1 Tel 071-437 3686.
Mayfair Stratton Street W1 Tel 071-629 3036.
Mermaid Puddle Dock Blackfriars EC4 Tel 071-410 0000.
National Upper Ground South Bank SE1 Tel 071-928 2252.
New London Parker Street WC2 Tel 071-405 0072.
Old Vic Waterloo Road SE1 Tel 071-928 7616.
Palace Shaftesbury Avenue W1 Tel 071-434 0909.
Palladium Argyll Street W1 Tel 071-437 7373.
Phoenix Charing Cross Road WC2 Tel 071-867 1044.
Piccadilly Denman Street W1 Tel 071-867 1118.
Players Theatre Villiers Street WC2 Tel 071-839 1134.
Prince Edward Old Compton Street W1 Tel 071-734 8951.
Prince of Wales Coventry Street W1 Tel 071-839 5972.
Queens Shaftesbury Avenue W1 Tel 071-494 5040.
Regents Park (Open Air) Regent's Park NW1 Tel 071-486 2431.
Royal Court Sloane Square SW1 Tel 071-730 1745.
St. Martins West Street WC2 Tel 071-836 1443.
Savoy Strand WC2 Tel 071-836 8888.
Shaftesbury Shaftesbury Avenue WC2 Tel 071-379 5399.
Shaw Euston Road NW1 Tel 071-388 1394.
Strand Aldwych WC2 Tel 071-240 0300.
Vaudeville Strand WC2 Tel 071-836 9987.
Victoria Palace Victoria Street SW1 Tel 071-834 1317.
Westminster Palace Street SW1 Tel 071-834 0283.
Whitehall Whitehall SW1 Tel 071-867 1119.
Wyndham's Charing Cross Road WC2 Tel 071-836 3028.
Young Vic 66 The Cut Waterloo SE1 Tel 071-928 6363.

London Fringe Theatres

Almeida Almeida Street N1 Tel 071-359 4404.
Hackney Empire Mare Street E8 Tel 081-985 2424.

Hampstead Avenue Road NW3 Tel 071-722 9301.
King's Head Upper Street N1 Tel 071-226 1916.
Old Bull Arts Centre High Street, Barnet Tel 081-449 0048.
Riverside Studios Crisp Road W6 Tel 081-748 3354.

London Concert Halls

Royal Opera House Covent Garden WC2 Tel 071-240 1066/240 1911.
English National Opera – The London Coliseum St Martin's Lane WC2 Tel 071-836 3161.
Barbican Centre Silk Street EC2 Tel 071-638 4141.
Purcell Room South Bank SE1 Tel 071-928 3002.
Queen Elizabeth Hall South Bank SE1 Tel 071-928 8800.
Royal Albert Hall Kensington Gore SW7 Tel 071-589 8212.
Royal Festival Hall South Bank SE1 Tel 071-928 8800.
St. John's Smith Square Smith Square SW1 Tel 071-222 1061.
Sadlers Wells Rosebery Avenue EC1 Tel 071-278 8916.
Wigmore Hall Wigmore Street W1 Tel 071-935 2141.

London London Night Life

Hippodrome Charing Cross Road WC2 Tel 071-437 4311.
Limelight Shaftesbury Avenue WC2 Tel 071-434 0572.
Madame Jo-Jo's Brewer Street W1 Tel 071-734 2473.
Ronnie Scott's Frith Street W1 Tel 071-439 0747.
Stringfellows Upper St. Martin's Lane WC2 Tel 071-240 5534.
Stork Club Swallow Street W1 Tel 071-734 3686.
Xenon Piccadilly W1 Tel 071-734 9344.

London Historic Houses, Castles and Gardens

Wellington Museum Apsley House, Hyde Park Corner W1 Tel 071-499 5676.
Banqueting House Whitehall SW1 Tel 081-930 4179.
Chelsea Physic Garden Royal Hospital Road SW3 Tel 071-352 5646.
Chiswick House Burlington Lane W4 Tel 081-995 0508.
Ham House (NT) Ham, Richmond Tel 081-940 1950.
Hampton Court Palace East Molesey Tel 081-977 8441.
Hogarth's House Chiswick Tel 081-994 6757.
Keats House Wentworth Place, Keats Grove, Hampstead Tel 071-435 2062.
Kensington Palace W8 Tel 071-937 9561.
Kenwood House Hampstead Tel 081-348 1286.
Marble Hill House Richmond Road, Twickenham Tel 081-892 5115.
Osterley Park (NT) Isleworth, Middlesex TW7 4RB Tel 081-560 3918.
The Queen's House Greenwich SE10 Tel 081-858 4422.
Royal Botanic Gardens (Kew Gardens) Kew Tel 081-940 3321.
Syon House and Park Gardens Brentford Tel 081-560 0881/3.
Tower of London Tower Hill EC3 Tel 071-709 0765.

London Museums and Art Galleries

Barbican Art Gallery Level 8, Barbican Centre EC2 Tel 071-638 4141 Ext 306.
Bethnal Green Museum of Childhood Cambridge Heath Road E2 Tel 081-980 3204.
Boxing Museum Thomas à Becket Pub, Old Kent Road SE1 Tel 071-703 2644.
British Museum & British Library Great Russell Street WC1 Tel 071-636 1555.
Buckingham Palace The Queen's Gallery, Buckingham Palace Road SW1 Tel 071-799 2331.
Cabinet War Rooms Clive Steps, King Charles Street SW1 Tel 071-930 6961.
Cutty Sark Clipper Ship King William Walk, Greenwich SE10 Tel 081-858 3445.
The Design Museum at Butlers Wharf Shad Thames SE1 Tel 071-403 6933.
Anthony d'Offay Gallery 9/21 & 23 Dering Street, off New Bond Street W1 Tel 071-499 4100.
Dickens House Museum Doughty Street WC1 Tel 071-405 2127.

Dulwich Picture Gallery College Road SE21 Tel 081-693 5254.
Florence Nightingale Museum Lambeth Palace Road SE1 Tel 071-620 0374.
Freud Museum 20 Maresfield Gardens, Hampstead NW3.
Geffrye Museum Kingsland Road E2 Tel 071-739 8368.
Guinness World of Records The Trocadero, Coventry Street W1 Tel 071-439 7331.
Hayward Gallery South Bank Centre Belvedere Rd SE1 Tel 071-928 3144 *Recorded information 071-261 0127.*
HMS Belfast Morgan's Lane, Tooley Street SE1 Tel 071-407 6434
Horniman Museum London Road, Forest Hill SE23 Tel 081-699 1872/2339/4911.
ICA Carlton House Terrace, The Mall SW1 Tel 071-930 0493 *Recorded Information on 071-930 6393.*
Imperial War Museum Lambeth Road SE1 Tel 071-735 8922.
Keats House (Wentworth Place) Keats Grove, Hampstead NW3 Tel 071-435 2062.
Kenwood House (EH) Hampstead Lane NW3 Tel 081-348 1286/1287.
Leighton House Museum Holland Park W11 Tel 071-602 3316.
London Dungeon Tooley Street SE1 Tel 071-403 0606.
London Planetarium Baker Street NW1 Tel 071-486 1121.
London Transport Museum Covent Garden WC2 Tel 071-379 6344.
Madame Tussaud's Waxworks Museum Baker Street W1 Tel 071-935 6861.
Mall Galleries Carlton House Terrace, The Mall SW1 Tel 071-930 6844.
Museum of Garden History (The Tradescant Trust) St Mary-at-Lambeth, Lambeth Palace Road SE1 Tel 071-261 1891.
Museum of London London Wall EC2 Tel 071-600 3699.
Museum of Mankind Burlington Gardens W1 Tel 071-636 1555.
Museum of the Moving Image (MOMI) South Bank, Waterloo SE1 Tel 071-401 2636.
National Army Museum Royal Hospital Road SW3 Tel 071-730 0717.
The National Gallery Trafalgar Square WC2 Tel 071-839 3321 *Recorded information on 071-839 3526.*
National Maritime Museum Romney Road, Greenwich SE10 Tel 081-858 4422.
National Portrait Gallery St. Martin's Place, Trafalgar Square WC2 Tel 071-306 0055.
Natural History Museum Cromwell Road, South Kensington SW7 Tel 071-938 9123.
Operating Theatre Museum and Herb Garret St. Thomas Street SE1 Tel 071-955 4791.
R.A.F. Museum Hendon NW9 Tel 081-205 2266.
Royal Academy of Arts Piccadilly W1 Tel 071-439 7438.
Science Museum Exhibition Road, South Kensington SW7 Tel 071-938 8000.
Serpentine Gallery Kensington Gardens W2 Tel 071-402 6075.
Sir John Soane's Museum Lincoln's Inn Fields WC2 Tel 071-430 0175.
Tate Gallery Millbank SW1 Tel 071- 821 1313 *Recorded information on 071-821 7128.*
Thames Barrier Visitors' Centre Unity Way, Woolwich SE18 Tel 081-854 1373.
Tower Bridge SE1 Tel 071-403 3761.
Tower of London Tower Hill EC3 Tel 071-709 0765.
Victoria and Albert Museum Cromwell Road, South Kensington SW7 Tel 071-938 8500.
Wallace Collection Hertford House, Manchester Square W1 Tel 071-935 0687.
Whitechapel Art Gallery Whitechapel High Street E1 Tel 071-377 0107.

London Exhibition Halls

Wembley Arena, Conference and Exhibition Centre Tel 081-900 1234.
Olympia Kensington W14 Tel 071-603 3344.
Earl's Court Warwick Road SW5 Tel 071-385 1200.
Business Design Centre Upper Street N1 Tel 071-359 3535.

London Cathedrals

St. George's R.C. Cathedral Lambeth Road SE1 Tel 071-928 5256.

St. Paul's Cathedral EC4 Tel 071-248 4619.
Southwark Cathedral Borough High Street SE1 Tel 071-407 2939.
Westminster Abbey Broad Sanctuary SW1 Tel 071-222 5152.
Westminster R.C. Cathedral Ashley Place SW1 Tel 071-834 7452.

London Swimming Pools and Sports Centres

Chelsea Sports Centre Manor Street, Chelsea Tel 071-352 6985.
Crystal Palace Sports Centre Ledrington Road, Norwood Tel 081-778 0131.
Dolphin Sports Centre Pimlico. Tel 071-798 8686.
Finsbury Leisure Complex 1-11 Ironmongers Row, Finsbury Tel 071-253 4011.
Ken Barrington Centre Fosters Oval, Kennington SE11 Tel 071-582 9495.
Kensington Sports Centre Tel 071- 727 9747.
Marshall Street Leisure Centre Tel 071-798 2007.
Porchester Baths Queensway Tel 071-229 9950.
Queen Mother Sports Centre Vauxhall Bridge Road Tel 071-798 2125.
Richmond Baths Old Deer Park, Richmond Tel 081-940 8461.
Seymour Leisure Centre Bryanston Place, Marylebone Tel 071-298 1421.
White City Pool Bloemfontein Road, White City Tel 081-734 3401.

London Cricket & Tennis Grounds

Lords St. John's Wood NW8 Tel 071-289 1300
Lords Gestetner Tour Tel 071-266 3825.
The Oval Kennington SE11 Tel 071-582 6660.
Queen's Club W14 Tel 071-385 3421.
Wimbledon (All England Lawn Tennis & Croquet Club) SW19 Tel 081-946 2244.

London Football and Rugby Grounds

Arsenal Highbury N5 Tel 071-226 0304.
Charlton Athletic Upton Park E13 Tel 081-293 4567.
Chelsea Stamford Bridge, Fulham SW5 Tel 071-385 5545.
Crystal Palace Selhurst Park SE25 Tel 081-771 8841.
Millwall The Den, Bermondsey SE16 Tel 071-232 1222.
Queens Park Rangers South Africa Road W12 Tel 081-743 0262.
Rugby Football Union Twickenham General Enquiries Tel 081-892 8161.
Tottenham Hotspur High Road, Tottenham N17 Tel 081-808 8080.
Wembley Stadium Tel 081-900 1234.
West Ham United Upton Park E13 Tel 081-472 2740.
Wimbledon Selhurst Park SE25 Tel 081-771 8841.

London Ice Rinks

Alexandra Palace Wood Green N22 Tel 081-365 2121.
Broadgate Arena Broadgate EC2 Tel 071-588 6565.
Lee Valley Leyton E10 Tel 081-533 3156.
Queens Bayswater W2 Tel 071-229 0172.
Streatham Streatham High Road SW16 Tel 081-769 7771.

London Dry Ski Slopes

Alexandra Palace Ski Slope Tel 081-888 2284.
Beckton Alps Alpine Way E6 Tel 081-511 0351.
Crystal Palace National Sports Centre Tel 081-778 0131.
Hillingdon Sports Centre Uxbridge Tel 0895 55181.
Woolwich Ski Slope Repository Road SE18 Tel 081-317 1726.

London Zoos and Wildlife Parks

London Zoo Regent's Park Tel 071-722 3333.
Brent Lodge Park Animal Centre Uxbridge Road Tel 081-579 2424.
Battersea Park Children's Zoo SW11 Tel 081-7530.

London Other attractions

Battersea Dog's Home Battersea Park Road SW8 Tel 071-622 3626.
Pirate Ships Tobacco Dock E1 Tel 071-702 9681.
Highgate Cemetery Swain's Lane N6 Tel 081-340 1834.

Quick Reference Lists: London

Hotels under £80 for 2

Apollo Hotel **W8**
Atlas Hotel **W8**
Bentinck House Hotel **W1**
Charles Bernard Hotel **NW3**
Clive Hotel **NW3**
Collin House **SW1**
Colonnade Hotel **W9**
Columbia Hotel **W2**
Concord Hotel **SW5**
Craven Gardens Hotel **W2**
Elizabeth Hotel **SW1**
Forte Posthouse **NW3**
George Hotel **WC1**
Kensington Court Hotel **SW5**
Hotel Lexham **W8**
Merryfield House **W1**
Hotel 167 **SW5**
Parkwood Hotel **W2**
President Hotel **WC1**
Prince Hotel **SW7**
Terstan Hotel **SW5**
Yardley Court **SE9**

Town House Hotels (see p. 927)

Alexander Hotel **SW7**
Dorset Square Hotel **NW1**
Green Park Hotel **W1**
Pelham Hotel **SW7**
Pembridge Court **W2**
Portobello Hotel **W11**

Private House Hotels (see p. 928)

Abbey Court **W2**
The Beaufort **SW3**
The Draycott **SW3**
Egerton House **SW3**
The Fenja **SW3**
Knightsbridge Green Hotel **SW1**
Number Sixteen **SW7**
22 Jermyn Street **SW1**

Hotels with Sporting Facilities

Tennis Courts

Cadogan Hotel **SW1**
Churchill Hotel **W1**
The Halcyon **W11**
Hyatt Carlton Tower **SW1**
St Giles Hotel **WC1**
SAS Portman **W1**
Scandic Crown Nelson Dock **SE16**

Indoor Swimming

The Berkeley **SW1**
Britannia International **E14**
Hotel Conrad **SW10**
The Dorchester **W1**
Grosvenor House **W1**
Holiday Inn Kings Cross/Bloomsbury **WC1**
London Metropole **W2**
Marble Arch Marriott **W1**
May Fair Inter-Continental **W1**
Le Meridien **W1**
The Regent London **NW1**
Regent's Park Marriott **NW3**
Rembrandt Hotel **SW7**
The Savoy WC2
Scandic Crown Nelson Dock **SE16**
Scandic Crown Victoria **SW1**

Leisure Centres

Britannia International **E14**
Hotel Conrad **SW10**
The Dorchester **W1**
Grosvenor House **W1**
Holiday Inn Kings Cross/Bloomsbury **WC1**
London Metropole **W2**
May Fair Inter-Continental **W1**
Le Meridien **W1**
Regent's Park Marriott **NW3**
The Regent London **NW1**
Rembrandt Hotel **SW7**
St Giles Hotel **WC1**
The Savoy **WC2**
Scandic Crown Nelson Dock **SE16**
Scandic Crown Victoria **SW1**
Swallow International **SW5**

Hotels with Wheelchair Facilities

Compiled in association with the Holiday Care Service: Tel 0293 774535
Reservations Helpline: Tel 0891 515494 (Premium Rate Call charges)

Copthorne Tara **W8**
Cumberland Hotel **W1**
Knightsbridge Green Hotel **SW1**
The Marlborough **WC1**
Le Meridien **W1**
Sheraton Park Tower **SW1**
White House **NW1**

Restaurants under £40 for 2

Adam's Café **W12**
Bangkok **SW7**
Belgo **NW1**
Beyoglu Ocakbasi **N16**
Bhatti **WC2**
Blah! Blah! Blah! **W12**
Bloom's **NW11**
Bloom's **E1**
Bon Ton Roulet **SE24**
La Bouchée **SW7**
The Brackenbury **W6**
Café Delancey **NW1**
Café Lazeez **SW7**
Café du Marché **EC1**
Chez Gérard **W1**
Chi Mai **W3**
Chiang Mai **W1**
Chuen Cheng Ku **W1**
Costa's Grill **W8**
De Cecco **SW6**
Dragon's Nest **W1**
Dragon Inn **W1**
The Eagle **EC1**
Ebury Wine Bar **SW1**
Efes Kebab House **W1**
L'Escargot Doré **W8**
Est **W1**
Fanari **NW1**
Faulkners **E8**
Geales **W8**
Giovanni's **WC2**
Glaister's Garden Bistro **SW10**
Gopal's of Soho **W1**
Grahame's Seafare **W1**
Great Nepalese **NW1**
Greek Valley **NW8**
Green Cottage **NW3**
Harveys Café **SW10**
Hellas **NW1**
Hodja Nasreddin **N1**
Hong Kong **WC2**
The Hope & Sirloin **EC1**
L'Hotel **SW3**
Istanbul Iskembecisi **N16**
Jade Garden **W1**
Joe Allen **WC2**
Kagura **WC2**
Kalamaras **W2**
Khyber Pass **SW7**
Krungtap **SW5**
Lal Qila **W1**
Laurent **NW2**
Lemonia **NW1**
Lena's **SW11**
Lido **W1**
Little Akropolis **W1**
Lok Ho Fook **W1**
Majlis **SW7**
Malabar **W8**
Mamta **SW6**
Mandarin Kitchen **W2**
Manzara **W11**
Memories of India **SW7**
Los Molinos **W6**
Mr Wong Wonderful House **W6**
Mutiara **SE1**
Namaste **E1**
New Fook Lam Moon **W1**
New Kam Tong **W2**
New World **W1**
Nontas **NW1**
Noor Jahan **SW5**
Nusa Dua Restoran Indonesia **W1**
Oh'Boy **SW17**
Oliver's **W14**
Osteria Antica Bologna **SW11**
La Paesana **W8**
Le Petit Prince **NW5**
Poons **WC2**
Quality Chop House **EC1**

Ragam **W1**
Rajput **W12**
Rani **N3**
Rasa Sayang **W2**
Rasa Sayang **W1**
Ravi Shankar **EC1**
Ravi Shankar **NW1**
La Reash **W1**
Robbie's Restaurant **W4**
Romantica Taverna **W2**
The Rotisserie **W12**
S & P Thai **SW3**
Sabras **NW10**
St Moritz **W1**
Sala Thai **W5**
Satay Hut **N1**
Sigiri **W13**
Silver Lake **SE5**
Singapore **W4**
Le Soir **N16**
Spices **N16**
Sree Krishna **SW17**
Sumos **W6**
Supan **W9**
Suruchi **N1**
Tandoori Lane **SW6**
Thailand Restaurant **SE14**
Tien Phat **SW6**
Tiger under the Table **NW11**
Tom Yum **SW5**
Topkapi **W1**
Travellers **SW3**
Tuk Tuk **N1**
Vijay **NW6**
Wagamama **WC1**
Wine & Mousaka **W5**
Young's Rendezvous **W5**
Yum Yum **N16**

London Restaurants with Private Rooms

Adam's Café **W12** (24)
Ajimura **WC2** (20)
Al Basha **W8** (60)
Alastair Little **W1** (20)
Albero & Grana **SW3** (25)
Arirang Korean Restaurant **W1** (30)
Arisugawa **W1** (20)
The Ark **W8** (25)
Asuka **NW1** (12)
The Athenaeum **W1** (40)
Au Jardin des Gourmets **W1** (55)
Bahn Thai **W1** (20)
Balzac **W12** (20)
Bangkok **SW7** (24)
Beauchamp Place **SW3** (22)
Bentley's **W1** (12)
The Berkeley **SW1** (34)
Bhatti **WC2** (40)
Bistrot 190 **SW7** (22)
Blah! Blah! Blah! **W12** (30)
Blakes Hotel **SW7** (22)
Blue Elephant **SW6** (100)
Bombay Brasserie **SW7** (100)
Bon Ton Roulet **SE24** (25)
La Bouchée **SW7** (60)
Boulestin **WC2** (40)
Brasserie du Marche aux Puces **W10** (36)
Bubb's **EC1** (25)
Buchan's **SW11** (55)
Buzkash **SW15** (20)
Café du Marche **EC1** (55)
Café Fish **SW1** (30)
Café Lazeez **SW7** (60)
The Capital **SW3** (24)
Caravan Serai **W1** (20)
Carriages **SW1** (100)
Casa Cominetti **SE6** (30)
Casale Franco **N1** (50)
Chapter 11 **SW10** (38)
Charlotte's Place **W5** (35)
Chez Gérard **W1** (28)
Chez Nico at Ninety Park Lane **W1**
Chi Mai **W3** (60)
Chiang Mai **W1** (25)
Christopher's **WC2** (32)
Chuen Cheng Ku **W1** (50)
Cibo **W14** (16)
The Connaught **W1** (22)
Costa's Grill **W8** (25)
Dan Dan **SW15** (20)
Dan's **SW3** (35)
Daphne **NW1** (30)
Daphne's **SW3** (50)
Defune **W1** (15)
dell'Ugo **W1** (16)
Don Pepe **NW8** (20)
The Dorchester Oriental Room **W1** (20)
The Dorchester Terrace Restaurant **W1** (14)
La Dordogne **W4** (50)
Downstairs at 190 **SW7** (35)
Dragon's Nest **W1** (60)
Dukes Hotel **SW1** (120)
English Garden **SW3** (30)
English House **SW3** (20)
Enoteca **SW15** (45)
L'Escargot **W1** (45)
L'Estaminet **WC2** (20)
L'Etoile **W1** (30)
Fanari **NW1** (40)
Florians **N8** (24)
Formula Veneta **SW10** (35)
Frederick's **N1** (26)
Fung Shing **WC2** (30)
La Gaulette **W1** (40)
Le Gavroche **W1** (20)
Gay Hussar **W1** (12)
Glaister's Garden Bistro **SW10** (40)
Gonbei **WC1** (15)
Good Earth **NW7** (30)
Good Earth **SW3** (32)
The Goring **SW1** (55)

Grafton Français **SW4** (28)
Greek Valley **NW8** (30)
Green's Restaurant & Oyster Bar **SW1** (26)
The Halcyon **W11** (24)
Halkin Hotel **SW1** (26)
Harbour City **W1** (60)
Hardy's **W1** (20)
Hilaire **SW7** (35)
Hodja Nasreddin **N1** (35)
Hong Kong **WC2** (80)
The Hope & Sirloin **EC1** (20)
Hyatt Carlton Tower **SW1** (40)
L'Incontro **SW1** (30)
The Ivy **WC2** (60)
Jade Garden **W1** (60)
Jake's **SW10** (35)
Joy King Lau **WC2** (60)
Julie's **W11** (26)
Kalamaras **W2** (28)
Kaspia **W1** (12)
Kaya **W1** (40)
Ken Lo's Memories of China **SW1** (20)
Ken Lo's Memories of China **SW10** (70)
Khan's of Kensington **SW7** (25)
Kingdom **SW10** (30)
Launceston Place **W8** (16)
Leith's **W11** (40)
Lemonia **NW1** (40)
The Lexington **W1** (20)
Lindsay House **W1** (20)
Lok Ho Fook **W1** (40)
Lou Pescadou **SW5** (40)
Luigi's **SE19** (25)
Masako **W1** (35)
May Fair Inter-Continental **W1** (300)
Memories of India **SW7** (30)
Le Midi **SW6** (14)
Mijanou **SW1** (24)
Mimmo d'Ischia **SW1** (20)
Ming **W1** (16)
Mirabelle **W1** (75)
Mitsukoshi **SW1** (24)
Miyako **W1** (22)
Miyama **EC4** (10)
Miyama **W1** (20)
Los Molinos **W6** (40)
Mon Plaisir **WC2** (20)
Monkeys **SW3** (10)
Motcomb's **SW1** (22)
Mr Wong Wonderful House **W6** (80)
Nakamura **W1** (8)
Namaste **E1** (30)
Nanking **W6** (60)
Neal Street Restaurant **WC2** (24)
New World **W1** (250)
Newtons **SW4** (35)
Nico Central **W1** (10)
Nikita's **SW10** (12)
Now and Zen **WC2** (40)
Nusa Dua Restoran Indonesia **W1** (12)
Odette's **NW1** (30)
Ognisko Polskie **SW7** (150)
Oh'Boy **SW17** (16)
192 **W11** (30)
Le P'tit Normand **SW18** (26)
La Paesana **W8** (44)
Le Palais du Jardin **WC2** (20)
Panda Si Chuen **W1** (14)
The Park Lane Hotel **W1** (20)
Pearl of Knightsbridge **SW1** (20)
Le Petit Prince **NW5** (20)
Phoenicia **W8** (50)
Pied à Terre **W1** (12)
Poissonnerie de l'Avenue **SW3** (22)
Pomegranates **SW1** (14)
Poons in the City **EC3** (50)
Poons, Leicester Street **WC2** (100)
Quaglino's **SW1** (40)
Quincy's **NW2** (16)
Raoul's **W9** (22)
Rasa Sayang **W1** (60)
Ravi Shankar **NW1** (25)
Red Fort **W1** (75)
The Ritz **W1** (65)
River Café **W6** (12)
Romantica Taverna **W2** (70)
The Rotisserie **W12** (40)
Royal China **W2** (15)
Royal Garden Hotel **W8** (24)
RSJ **SE1** (20)
Rules **WC2** (48)
S & P Thai **SW3** (20)
Saga **W1** (12)
St Moritz **W1** (28)
St Quentin **SW3** (25)
San Martino **SW3** (35)
Satay Hut **N1** (70)
Les Saveurs **W1** (10)
The Savoy **WC2** (60)
Sema **SE22** (15)
La Sémillante **W1** (60)
Shampers **W1** (50)
Shepherd's **SW1** (32)
Sheekey's Restaurant **WC2** (36)
Sheraton Park Tower **SW1** (150)
Sheraton Belgravia **SW1** (22)
Simpson's-in-the-Strand **WC2** (150)
Singapore **W4** (16)
Singapore Garden **NW6** (60)
Snows on the Green **W6** (22)
Soho Soho **W1** (60)
The Square **SW1** (30)
Sree Krishna **SW17** (70)
Sumos **W6** (10)
Suntory **SW1** (14)
Le Suquet **SW3** (16)
The Tageen **WC2** (50)
Tatsuso **EC2** (8)
Thierry's **SW3** (35)
Tophams Ebury Court **SW1** (18)
Tui **SW7** (40)
Tuk Tuk **N1** (50)
Twenty Trinity Gardens **SW9** (20)
Veronica's **W2** (40)
Villandry Dining Room **W1** (45)
The Waldorf **WC2** (30)
Walton's **SW3** (20)
White Tower **W1** (16)
Whittington's **EC4** (50)
The Wilds **SW10** (35)
Wilton's **SW1** (16)
Wodka **W8** (30)
Young's Rendezvous **W5** (80)
Yumi **W1** (14)
Zen **SW3** (22)

Restaurants with a no-smoking area

Au Jardin des Gourmets **W1**
Beauchamp Place **SW3**
Bertorelli's **WC2**
Bloom's **NW11**
Bombay Brasserie **SW7**
Buzkash **SW15**
Café Fish **SW1**
Caravan Serai **W1**
Caterino's **SW16**
Chez Gérard **W1**
Churchill Hotel **W1**
Clarke's **W8**
The Connaught **W1**
Faulkners **E8**
Four Seasons Hotel Lanes Restaurant **W1**
Frederick's **N1**
Gilbert's **SW7**
Gopal's of Soho **W1**
Grafton Français **SW4**
Grosvenor House **W1**
Mamta **SW6**
Le Meridien Terrace Garden **W1**
Mijanou **SW1**
Ming **W1**
Museum Street Café **WC1**
Mutiara **SE1**
Newtons **SW4**
Pinocchio's **NW1**
Qinggis **NW3**
Rajput **W12**
Rani **N3**
Raoul's **W9**
Rasa Sayang **W1**
La Reash **W1**
Sabras **NW10**
Sala Thai **W5**
San Martino **SW3**
La Sémillante **W1**
Sheraton Park Tower **SW1**
Tate Gallery Restaurant **SW1**
Thistells **SE22**
Twenty Trinity Gardens **SW9**
Villandry Dining Room **W1**
Wagamama **WC1**
Zoe **W1**

Romantic Restaurants

L'Aventure **NW8**
Bentley's **W1**
Blakes Hotel **SW7**
Blue Elephant **SW6**
Le Caprice **SW1**
Chez Moi **W11**
Chez Nico at Ninety Park Lane **W1**
La Croisette **SW10**
Daphne's **SW3**
The Dorchester Terrace **W1**
Le Gavroche **W1**
Gay Hussar **W1**
The Halcyon **W11**
Halkin Hotel **SW1**
Hilaire **SW7**
Hyatt Carlton Tower **SW1**
Inter-Continental Hotel **W1**
The Ivy **WC2**
Julie's **W11**
Launceston Place **W8**
Mijanou **SW1**
Mirabelle **W1**
Odette's **NW1**
Odin's Restaurant **W1**
Pinocchio's **NW1**
The Ritz **W1**
San Lorenzo **SW3**
The Savoy **WC2**
Shezan **SW7**
Tophams Ebury Court **SW1**
White Tower **W1**

Open Air Eating

L'Accento Italiano **W2**
Al Basha **W8**
Al Hamra **W1**
L'Altro **W11**
Anna's Place **N1**
The Ark **W8**
L'Aventure **NW8**
Blue Print Café **SE1**
La Bouchée **SW7**
Brasserie du Marché aux Puces **W10**
La Brasserie **SW3**
Buzkash **SW15**
Café Lazeez **SW7**
Café Delancey **NW1**
Cantina del Ponte **SE1**
Casale Franco **N1**
Chapter 11 **SW10**
Cheng-Du **NW1**
Chez Gérard **W1**
Christian's **W4**
Cibo **W14**
Dan's **SW3**
Daphne **NW1**
Daphne's **SW3**

De Cecco **SW6**
Est **W1**
Formula Veneta **SW10**
Frederick's **N1**
Fuji **W1**
Glaister's Garden Bistro **SW10**
The Halcyon **W11**
Jake's **SW10**
Kalamaras **W2**
Lou Pescadou **SW5**
Luigi's **SE19**
Manzara **W11**
Manzi's **E14**
Memories of India **SW7**
El Metro **SW6**
Mijanou **SW1**
Mirabelle **W1**
Motcomb's **SW1**
Nanking **W6**
Newtons **SW4**
Nontas **NW1**
Odette's **NW1**
Poissonnerie de l'Avenue **SW3**
Le Pont de la Tour **SE1**
Ransome's Dock **SW11**
Raoul's **W9**
The Ritz **W1**
River Café **W6**
Robbie's Restaurant **W4**
San Martino **SW3**
Sandrini **SW3**
Soho Soho **W1**
The Tageen **WC2**
Thistells **SE22**
Travellers **SW3**
Veronica's **W2**

Early Evening Eating

Ajimura **WC2**
Al Basha **W8**
Al Bustan **SW1**
Al Hamra **W1**
Alastair Little **W1**
Arirang Korean Restaurant **W1**
Arisugawa **W1**
Arts Theatre Café **WC2**
Asuka **NW1**
The Athenaeum **W1**
Bahn Thai **W1**
Belgo **NW1**
Bentley's **W1**
Bertorelli's **WC2**
Beyoglu Ocakbasi **N16**
Bhatti **WC2**
Bibendum Oyster Bar **SW3**
Bistrot 190 **SW7**
Bloom's **E1**
Bloom's **NW11**
La Bouchée **SW7**
La Brasserie **SW3**
Brasserie du Marché aux Puces **W10**
Britannia Inter-Continental Hotel, Shogun **W1**
Buchan's **SW11**
Buzkash **SW15**
Byblos **W8**
Café Delancey **NW1**
Café du Marché **EC1**
Café Fish **SW1**
Café Lazeez **SW7**
Café Pelican **WC2**
Café Royal Grill Room **W1**
Camden Brasserie **NW1**
Canal Brasserie **W10**
Cantina del Ponte **SE1**
Le Caprice **SW1**
Caravan Serai **W1**
Carriages **SW1**
Caterino's **SW16**
Chez Gérard **W1**
Chi Mai **W3**
Chiang Mai **W1**
Christopher's **WC2**
Chuen Cheng Ku **W1**
Churchill Hotel **W1**
Claridge's, The Causerie **W1**
Costa's Grill **W8**
Daphne **NW1**
Defune **W1**
dell'Ugo **W1**
The Dorchester **W1**
Dragon Inn **W1**
Dragon's Nest **W1**
Dukes Hotel **SW1**
Ebury Wine Bar **SW1**
Efes Kebab House **W1**
Est **W1**
L'Etoile **W1**
Fanari **NW1**
Faulkners **E8**
Four Seasons **W2**
Four Seasons Hotel Lanes Restaurant **W1**
Frederick's **N1**
Fuji **W1**
Fung Shing **WC2**
Gay Hussar **W1**
Geales **W8**
Ginnan **EC4**
Giovanni's **WC2**
Gonbei **WC1**
Good Earth **NW7**
Good Earth **SW3**
Gopal's of Soho **W1**
The Goring **SW1**
Grahame's Seafare **W1**
Great Nepalese **NW1**
Greek Valley **NW8**
Green Cottage **NW3**
Green's Restaurant & Oyster Bar **SW1**
Grenadier **SW1**
Grosvenor House **W1**
Halepi **W2**
Hampshire Hotel **WC2**
Harbour City **W1**
Hardy's **W1**
Hellas **NW1**

Hilton International Kensington **W11**
Hilton International Regent's Park **NW8**
Hodja Nasreddin **N1**
Hong Kong **WC2**
L'Hotel **SW3**
Hsing **W2**
Ikeda **W1**
Ikkyu **W1**
Imperial City **EC3**
Isohama **SW1**
Istanbul Iskembecisi **N16**
The Ivy **WC2**
Jade Garden **W1**
Joe Allen **WC2**
Joy King Lau **WC2**
Kagura **WC2**
Kaya **W1**
Khan's of Kensington **SW7**
Khyber Pass **SW7**
Kingdom **SW10**
Krungtap **SW5**
Lal Qila **W1**
Laurent **NW2**
Lemonia **NW1**
The Lexington **W1**
Lido **W1**
Lindsay House **W1**
Little Akropolis **W1**
Lok Ho Fook **W1**
Luc's Restaurant & Brasserie **EC3**
Luigi's **SE19**
Majlis **SW7**
Malabar **W8**
Mamta **SW6**
Mandarin Kitchen **W2**
Manzara **W11**
Manzi's **E14**
Manzi's **WC2**
Maroush **W2**
Masako **W1**
Memories of India **SW7**
Le Meridien, Terrace Garden **W1**
Le Mesurier **EC1**
El Metro **SW6**
Ming **W1**
Mitsukoshi **SW1**
Miyako **W1**
Miyama **EC4**
Los Molinos **W6**
Momo **W5**
Mon Plaisir **WC2**
Mr Ke **NW3**
Mr Wong Wonderful House **W6**
Mutiara **SE1**
Nakamura **W1**
Namaste **E1**
New Fook Lam Moon **W1**
New Kam Tong **W2**
New World **W1**
Ninjin **W1**
Nontas **NW1**
Noor Jahan **SW5**
Now and Zen **WC2**
Nusa Dua Restoran Indonesia **W1**
Oliver's **W14**
Orso **WC2**
Osteria Antica Bologna **SW11**
Le Palais du Jardin **WC2**
Panda Si Chuen **W1**
Pearl of Knightsbridge **SW1**
Phoenicia **W8**
Le Pont de la Tour **SE1**
Poons **W2**
Poons **WC1**
Poons **WC2**
Poons in the City **EC3**
Pun **SW7**
Qinggis **NW3**
Quaglino's **SW1**
Ragam **W1**
Rajput **W12**
Rani **N3**
Ransome's Dock **SW11**
Rasa Sayang **W2**
Rasa Sayang **W1**
Ravi Shankar **EC1**
Ravi Shankar **NW1**
La Reash **W1**
Red Fort **W1**
Robbie's Restaurant **W4**
Romantica Taverna **W2**
Royal China **W2**
RSJ **SE1**
Rules **WC2**
S & P Thai **SW3**
Sabras **NW10**
St Moritz **W1**
Sala Thai **W5**
Satay Hut **N1**
The Savoy, Grill Room **WC2**
Sema **SE22**
Shampers **W1**
Sheekey's Restaurant **WC2**
Siam Oriental Restaurant **SW18**
Silver Lake **SE5**
Simpson's-in-the-Strand **WC2**
Singapore **W4**
Singapore Garden **NW6**
Soho Soho **W1**
Le Soir **N16**
Sonargaon **N1**
Spices **N16**
The Square **SW1**
Sree Krishna **SW17**
Sri Siam **W1**
Sri Siam City **EC2**
Sumos **W6**
Suruchi **N1**
Tandoori Lane **SW6**
Tate Gallery Restaurant **SW1**
Tatsuso **EC2**
Thailand Restaurant **SE14**
Tien Phat **SW6**
Tiger under the Table **NW11**
Tom Yum **SW5**
Topkapi **W1**
Trattoria Lucca **NW1**
Tuk Tuk **N1**
Vijay **NW6**
Wagamama **WC1**
The Waldorf **WC2**
Walsh's Seafood & Shellfish **W1**
Whittington's **EC4**
Wine & Mousaka **W5**
Yum Yum **N16**

Yumi **W1**
Zen **SW3**
Zen Central **W1**
ZeNW3 **NW3**

Late Night Eating

L'Accento Italiano **W2**
Ajimura **WC2**
Al Basha **W8**
Al Bustan **SW1**
Al Hamra **W1**
Alastair Little **W1**
Alba **EC1**
Albero & Grana **SW3**
L'Altro **W11**
The Argyll **SW3**
Arirang Korean Restaurant **W1**
The Ark **W8**
Arts Theatre Café **WC2**
Asuka **NW1**
Au Jardin des Gourmets **W1**
L'Aventure **NW8**
Bahn Thai **W1**
Balzac **W12**
Bangkok **SW7**
Beauchamp Place **SW3**
Belgo **NW1**
Benihana **NW3**
Bertorelli's **WC2**
Beyoglu Ocakbasi **N16**
Bhatti **WC2**
Bibendum **SW3**
Bistrot Bruno **W1**
Blah! Blah! Blah! **W12**
Blakes Hotel **SW7**
Blue Print Café **SE1**
Bombay Brasserie **SW7**
Bon Ton Roulet **SE24**
La Bouchée **SW7**
Boulestin **WC2**
Boyd's **W8**
Le Braconnier **SW14**
La Brasserie **SW3**
Brasserie du Marche aux Puces **W10**
Brasserie Faubourg **SW8**
Britannia Inter-Continental Hotel, Shogun **W1**
Buzkash **SW15**
Byblos **W8**
Café Delancey **NW1**
Café Pelican **WC2**
Café Fish **SW1**
Camden Brasserie **NW1**
The Canteen **SW10**
Cantina del Ponte **SE1**
The Capital **SW3**
Le Caprice **SW1**
Caravan Serai **W1**
Casa Cominetti **SE6**
Casale Franco **N1**
Caterino's **SW16**
Chapter 11 **SW10**
Cheng-Du **NW1**
Chez Gérard **W1**
Chez Liline **N4**
Chez Moi **W11**
Chez Nico at Ninety Park Lane **W1**
Chi Mai **W3**
Chiang Mai **W1**
China Jazz **NW1**
Chinon **W14**
Christopher's **WC2**
Chuen Cheng Ku **W1**
Churchill Hotel **W1**
Chutney Mary **SW10**
Cibo **W14**
Claridge's **W1**
La Croisette **SW10**
Daphne's **SW3**
Daphne **NW1**
De Cecco **SW6**
Del Buongustaio **SW15**
The Dorchester **W1**
La Dordogne **W4**
Downstairs at 190 **SW7**
Dragon Inn **W1**
Dragon's Nest **W1**
Efes Kebab House **W1**
English Garden **SW3**
English House **SW3**
Enoteca **SW15**
L'Escargot **W1**
L'Escargot Doré **W8**
Est **W1**
L'Estaminet **WC2**
L'Etoile **W1**
Fanari **NW1**
Fifth Floor at Harvey Nichols **SW1**
Florians **N8**
Formula Veneta **SW10**
Four Seasons Hotel **W1**
Four Seasons **W2**
Frederick's **N1**
French House Dining Room **W1**
Fung Shing **WC2**
La Gaulette **W1**
Le Gavroche **W1**
Gavver's **SW1**
Gay Hussar **W1**
Geales **W8**
Giovanni's **WC2**
Glaister's Garden Bistro **SW10**
Good Earth **NW7**
Good Earth **SW3**
Gopal's of Soho **W1**
Grafton Francais **SW4**
Great Nepalese **NW1**
Greek Valley **NW8**
Greenhouse **W1**
Green's Restaurant & Oyster Bar **SW1**
Green Cottage **NW3**
The Green Room **SW11**
Greig's Grill **W1**
Grill St Quentin **SW3**
Gung-Ho **NW6**
The Halcyon **W11**
Harbour City **W1**
Harveys Café **SW10**

Hellas **NW1**
Hilaire **SW7**
Hong Kong **WC2**
Howard Hotel **WC2**
Hsing **W2**
Hunan **SW1**
L'Incontro **SW1**
The Ivy **WC2**
Jade Garden **W1**
Jake's **SW10**
Joe's Cafe **SW3**
Joy King Lau **WC2**
Julie's **W11**
Kagura **WC2**
Kalamaras **W2**
Kaspia **W1**
Kaya **W1**
Ken Lo's Memories of China **SW1**
Kensington Place **W8**
Khan's of Kensington **SW7**
Khun Akorn **SW3**
Khyber Pass **SW7**
Kingdom **SW10**
Kundan **SW1**
Lal Qila **W1**
Langan's Brasserie **W1**
Langan's Bistro **W1**
Launceston Place **W8**
Laurent **NW2**
Leith's **W11**
Lemonia **NW1**
Lena's **SW11**
The Lexington **W1**
Lindsay House **W1**
Lok Ho Fook **W1**
Lou Pescadou **SW5**
Luigi's **SE19**
Majlis **SW7**
Malabar **W8**
Mamta **SW6**
Mandarin Kitchen **W2**
Manzara **W11**
Manzi's **E14**
Manzi's **WC2**
May Fair Inter-Continental **W1**
Memories of India **SW7**
Le Meridien, Terrace Garden **W1**
El Metro **SW6**
Mijanou **SW1**
Mimmo d'Ischia **SW1**
Ming **W1**
Los Molinos **W6**
Mr Ke **NW3**
Mr Wong Wonderful House **W6**
Mon Plaisir **WC2**
Monkeys **SW3**
Motcomb's **SW1**
Mulligans of Mayfair **W1**
Mutiara **SE1**
Nakano **SW1**
Namaste **E1**
Nanking **W6**
Neal Street Restaurant **WC2**
Neshiko **N1**
New Fook Lam Moon **W1**
New Kam Tong **W2**
New World **W1**
Newtons **SW4**
Nico Central **W1**
Nikita's **SW10**
Nontas **NW1**
Noor Jahan **SW5**
Now and Zen **WC2**
Nusa Dua Restoran Indonesia **W1**
O'Keefe's **W1**
Odette's **NW1**
Odin's Restaurant **W1**
Ognisko Polskie **SW7**
Oh'Boy **SW17**
Oliver's **W14**
Olivo **SW1**
192 **W11**
Orso **WC2**
Osteria Antica Bologna **SW11**
La Paesana **W8**
Le Palais du Jardin **WC2**
Panda Si Chuen **W1**
Pearl of Knightsbridge **SW1**
Peter's **NW6**
Le Petit Prince **NW5**
Phoenicia **W8**
Pinocchio's **NW1**
Poissonnerie de l'Avenue **SW3**
Pomegranates **SW1**
Le Pont de la Tour **SE1**
Poons **WC2**
Poons **WC1**
Poons **W2**
La Poule Au Pot **SW1**
Pun **SW7**
Qinggis **NW3**
Quaglino's **SW1**
Le Quai St Pierre **W8**
Quality Chop House **EC1**
Quincy's **NW2**
RSJ **SE1**
Ragam **W1**
Rajput **W12**
Ransome's Dock **SW11**
Rasa Sayang **W1**
Rasa Sayang **W2**
Ravi Shankar **EC1**
Ravi Shankar **NW1**
La Reash **W1**
Red Fort **W1**
The Regent London **NW1**
The Ritz **W1**
Riva **SW13**
Robbie's Restaurant **W4**
Romantica Taverna **W2**
The Rotisserie **W12**
Royal China **W2**
Royal Garden Hotel **W8**
Rules **WC2**
St Moritz **W1**
St James Court **SW1**
St Quentin **SW3**
Sala Thai **W5**
Sale e Pepe **SW1**
Salloos **SW1**
Sambuca **SW3**
San Frediano **SW3**
San Lorenzo **SW3**
San Martino **SW3**
Sandrini **SW3**
Santini **SW1**

Satay Hut **N1**
The Savoy **WC2**
Scalini **SW3**
Sema **SE22**
Shampers **W1**
Shanghai **W8**
Sheekey's Restaurant **WC2**
Shepherd's **SW1**
Sheraton Park Tower **SW1**
Shezan **SW7**
Siam Oriental Restaurant **SW18**
Sigiri **W13**
Signor Sassi **SW1**
Silver Lake **SE5**
Simply Nico **SW1**
Singapore Garden **NW6**
Singapore **W4**
Snows on the Green **W6**
Soho Soho **W1**
Le Soir **N16**
Sonargaon **N1**
Sonny's **SW13**
Spices **N16**
The Square **SW1**
Sree Krishna **SW17**
Sri Siam **W1**
Sumos **W6**
Supan **W9**
Le Suquet **SW3**
Suruchi **N1**
The Tageen **WC2**
Tandoori Lane **SW6**
La Tante Claire **SW3**
Thai Kitchen **W2**
Thierry's **SW3**
Tiberio **W1**
Tien Phat **SW6**
Tiger under the Table **NW11**
Tom Yum **SW5**
Topkapi **W1**
Travellers **SW3**
Tui **SW7**
Tuk Tuk **N1**
Turner's **SW3**
Veronica's **W2**
Vijay **NW6**
Wagamama **WC1**
Wakaba **NW3**
Walsh's Seafood & Shellfish **W1**
Walton's **SW3**
The Wilds **SW10**
Wine & Mousaka **W5**
Wodka **W8**
Young's Rendezvous **W5**
Zen **SW3**
Zen Central **W1**
ZeNW3 **NW3**
Ziani **SW3**
Zoe **W1**

Sunday Eating

(L) Lunch only **(D)** Dinner only
Generally open from around Noon unless specified

L'Accento Italiano **W2**
Al Basha **W8**
Al Bustan **SW1**
Al Hamra **W1**
The Ark **W8 (D)**
The Athenaeum **W1**
L'Aventure **NW8**
Bahn Thai **W1**
Beauchamp Place **SW3**
Belgo **NW1**
Benihana **NW3**
The Berkeley **SW1**
Beyoglu Ocakbasi **N16 from 11am**
Bhatti **WC2**
Bibendum **SW3**
Bibendum Oyster Bar **SW3**
Bistrot 190 **SW7 from 7am**
Blakes Hotel **SW7**
Bloom's **NW11 from 10am**
Bloom's **E1 from 10am**
Blue Print Café **SE1 (L)**
Blue Elephant **SW6**
Bombay Brasserie **SW7**
Bon Ton Roulet **SE24 (L)**
La Bouchée **SW7 from 9am**
The Brackenbury **W6 (L)**
La Brasserie **SW3 from 10am**
Brasserie du Marche aux Puces **W10 (L)**
Britannia I-C Hotel, Shogun **W1 (D)**
Buchan's **SW11**
Buzkash **SW15 (D)**
Byblos **W8**
Café Delancey **NW1 from 8am**
Café Lazeez **SW7 from 10.30am**
Café Pelican **WC2**
Camden Brasserie **NW1**
The Canteen **SW10**
Cantina del Ponte **SE1 (L)**
The Capital **SW3**
Le Caprice **SW1**
Caravan Serai **W1**
Casale Franco **N1**
Cheng-Du **NW1**
Chez Gérard **W1**
Chez Liline **N4**
Chi Mai **W3**
Chiang Mai **W1 (D)**
China Jazz **NW1**
Christian's **W4 (L)**
Christopher's **WC2 from 11:30am**
Chuen Cheng Ku **W1 from 11.30am**
Churchill Hotel **W1**
Chutney Mary **SW10**
Cibo **W14**

Claridge's, The Causerie **W1**
Claridge's **W1**
The Connaught **W1**
Dan Dan **SW15 (D)**
Daphne's **SW3 from 11am**
Don Pepe **NW8 (L)**
The Dorchester **W1**
La Dordogne **W4 (D)**
Dragon Inn **W1**
Dragon's Nest **W1**
Dukes Hotel **SW1**
Ebury Wine Bar **SW1**
English House **SW3**
English Garden **SW3**
The Enterprise **SW3 (L)**
Faulkners **E8**
Fifth Floor at Harvey Nichols **SW1 (L)**
Florians **N8**
Formula Veneta **SW10 (L)**
Four Seasons Hotel **W1**
Four Seasons **W2**
Four Seasons Hotel Lanes Restaurant **W1**
Foxtrot Oscar **SW3 (L)**
Fuji **W1 (D)**
Fung Shing **WC2**
La Gaulette **W1 (L)**
Glaister's Garden Bistro **SW10**
Good Earth **NW7**
Good Earth **SW3**
Gopal's of Soho **W1**
The Goring **SW1**
Granita **N1 (L)**
Great Nepalese **NW1**
The Green Room **SW11**
Green Cottage **NW3**
Greenhouse **W1**
Green's Restaurant & Oyster Bar **SW1 (L)**
Grenadier **SW1**
Grill St Quentin **SW3**
Gung-Ho **NW6**
The Halcyon **W11**
Halepi **W2**
Hampshire Hotel **WC2**
Harbour City **W1**
Harveys Café **SW10 (L)**
Harveys **SW17 (L)**
Hilton International Kensington **W11**
Hilton International Regent's Park **NW8**
Hodja Nasreddin **N1**
Hong Kong **WC2**
Howard Hotel **WC2**
Hunan **SW1 (D)**
Hyatt Carlton Tower **SW1**
Ikkyu **W1 (D)**
L'Incontro **SW1 (D)**
Istanbul Iskembecisi **N16 (D)**
The Ivy **WC2**
Jade Garden **W1 from 11.30am**
Jake's **SW10 (L)**
Joe Allen **WC2**
Joe's Cafe **SW3 from 9.30am**
Joy King Lau **WC2 from 11am**
Julie's **W11**
Kaya **W1 (D)**
Ken Lo's Memories of China **SW10**
Ken Lo's Memories of China **SW1 (D)** ?
Kensington Place **W8**
Khan's of Kensington **SW7**
Khun Akorn **SW3**
Khyber Pass **SW7**
Kingdom **SW10**
Krungtap **SW5 (D)**
Lal Qila **W1**
Launceston Place **W8 (L)**
Leith's **W11 (D)**
Lemonia **NW1 (L)**
Lena's **SW11**
Lido **W1 from 11.30**
Lindsay House **W1**
Lok Ho Fook **W1**
Lou Pescadou **SW5**
Majlis **SW7**
Malabar **W8**
Mamta **SW6**
Mandarin Kitchen **W2**
Manzara **W11 from 10**
Maroush **W2**
May Fair Inter-Continental **W1**
Memories of India **SW7**
Le Meridien, Terrace Garden **W1 (L)**
El Metro **SW6 from 8am**
Le Midi **SW6 (L)**
Miyako **W1 (D)**
Miyama **W1 (D)**
Momo **W5**
Mr Ke **NW3**
Mr Wong Wonderful House **W6**
Nakamura **W1 (D)**
Nakano **SW1 (D)**
Nanking **W6**
New Fook Lam Moon **W1**
New Kam Tong **W2**
New World **W1**
Newtons **SW4**
Noor Jahan **SW5**
Now and Zen **WC2**
Odette's **NW1 (L)**
Ognisko Polskie **SW7**
Oliver's **W14**
192 **W11**
Orso **WC2**
Osteria Antica Bologna **SW11**
Le P'tit Normand **SW18**
Le Palais du Jardin **WC2 from 10am**
Pearl of Knightsbridge **SW1**
Peter's **NW6 (L)**
Le Petit Prince **NW5 (D)**
Phoenicia **W8**
Le Pont de la Tour **SE1**
Poons **W2**
Poons **WC1**
Poons **WC2**
La Poule Au Pot **SW1**
Pun **SW7**
Qinggis **NW3**
Quaglino's **SW1 (L)**
Quality Chop House **EC1**
Ragam **W1**
Rajput **W12**
Rani **N3**
Ransome's Dock **SW11 (L)**
Raoul's **W9 (L)**
Rasa Sayang **W1**
Rasa Sayang **W2**
Ravi Shankar **NW1**
Ravi Shankar **EC1 (D)**

La Reash **W1**
Red Fort **W1**
The Regent London **NW1**
The Ritz **W1**
Riva **SW13**
River Café **W6 (L)**
Robbie's Restaurant **W4 (L)**
Romantica Taverna **W2**
Royal China **W2**
Rules **WC2**
Sabras **NW10 (D)**
Saga **W1**
St Quentin **SW3**
San Martino **SW3**
Sandrini **SW3**
Santini **SW1 (D)**
Satay Hut **N1**
The Savoy **WC2**
Scalini **SW3**
Sema **SE22**
Sheraton Belgravia **SW1 (D)**
Sheraton Park Tower **SW1**
Shezan **SW7**
Sigiri **W13**
Silver Lake **SE5 (D)**
Simpson's-in-the-Strand **WC2 (L)**
Singapore **W4**
Singapore Garden **NW6**
Snows on the Green **W6 (L)**
Le Soir **N16 (D)**
Sonargaon **N1**
Sonny's **SW13 (L)**
Spices **N16**
The Square **SW1**
Sree Krishna **SW17**
Sri Siam **W1 (D)**
Le Suquet **SW3**
Suruchi **N1**
Tandoori Lane **SW6**
Thierry's **SW3**
Thistells **SE22 (L)**
Tien Phat **SW6**
Tiger under the Table **NW11**
Tom Yum **SW5 (D)**
Tophams Ebury Court **SW1 (L)**
Topkapi **W1**
Travellers **SW3 (L)**
Tui **SW7**
Tuk Tuk Restaurant **N1 (D)**
Turner's **SW3**
Twenty Trinity Gardens **SW9**
Vijay **NW6**
Wagamama **WC1**
Walton's **SW3**
The Wilds **SW10 (L)**
Wilson's **W14 (L)**
Wodka **W8**
Young's Rendezvous **W5**
Zen **SW3**
Zen Central **W1**
ZeNW3 **NW3**
Ziani **SW3**
Zoe **W1 (L)**

National Cuisines

Belgian

Belgo **NW1**

British

Bentley's **W1**
Buchan's **SW11**
The Capital **SW3**
The Dorchester, Grill Room **W1**
Dukes Hotel **SW1**
English Garden **SW3**
English House **SW3**
Geales **W8**
The Goring **SW1**
Green's Restaurant & Oyster Bar **SW1**
Greenhouse **W1**
Langan's Brasserie **W1**
Launceston Place **W8**
Leith's **W11**
Lindsay House **W1**
Monkeys **SW3**
Motcomb's **SW1**
Oliver's **W14**
Quality Chop House **EC1**
The Ritz **W1**
The Savoy, Grill Room **WC2**
Shepherd's **SW1**
Simpson's-in-the-Strand **WC2**
Tophams Ebury Court **SW1**
Walton's **SW3**
Wilton's **SW1**

Chinese

Cheng-Du **NW1**
Chi Mai **W3**
China Jazz **NW1**
Chuen Cheng Ku **W1**
Dorchester, Oriental Room **W1**
Dragon Inn **W1**
Dragon's Nest **W1**
Four Seasons **W2**

Fung Shing **WC2**
Good Earth **NW7**
Good Earth **SW3**
Green Cottage **NW3**
Gung-Ho **NW6**
Harbour City **W1**
Hong Kong **WC2**
Hsing **W2**
Hunan **SW1**
Imperial City **EC3**
Jade Garden **W1**
Joy King Lau **WC2**
Ken Lo's Memories of China **SW1**
Ken Lo's Memories of China **SW10**
Kingdom **SW10**
Lido **W1**
Lok Ho Fook **W1**
Mandarin Kitchen **W2**
Ming **W1**
Mr Ke **NW3**
Mr Wong Wonderful House **W6**
Nanking **W6**
New Fook Lam Moon **W1**
New Kam Tong **W2**
New World **W1**
Now and Zen **WC2**
Panda Si Chuen **W1**
Pearl of Knightsbridge **SW1**
Poons **WC1**
Poons **WC2**
Poons in the City **EC3**
Poons **W2**
Pun **SW7**
Qinggis **NW3**
Royal China **W2**
Shanghai **W8**
Silver Lake **SE5**
Young's Rendezvous **W5**
Zen **SW3**
Zen Central **W1**
ZeNW3 **NW3**

French

Au Jardin des Gourmets **W1**
L'Aventure **NW8**
Balzac **W12**
The Berkeley **SW1**
La Bouchée **SW7**
Boulestin **WC2**
Le Braconnier **SW14**
La Brasserie **SW3**
Brasserie Faubourg **SW8**
Bubb's **EC1**
Café Pelican **WC2**
Chez Gérard **WC2**
Chez Moi **W11**
Chez Nico at Ninety Park Lane **W1**
Claridge's, The Causerie **W1**
The Connaught **W1**
La Croisette **SW10**
Dorchester, Terrace Restaurant **W1**
La Dordogne **W4**
L'Escargot Doré **W8**
L'Estaminet **WC2**
L'Etoile **W1**
Four Seasons Hotel **W1**
Le Gavroche **W1**
Gavver's **SW1**
Grafton Français **SW4**
Grill St Quentin **SW3**
Hyatt Carlton Tower **SW1**
Inter-Continental Hotel **W1**
May Fair Inter-Continental **W1**
Le Meridien **W1**
Le Mesurier **EC1**
Le Midi **SW6**
Mijanou **SW1**
Mirabelle **W1**
Mon Plaisir **WC2**
Le Muscadet **W1**
Nico Central **W1**
Le P'tit Normand **SW18**
Le Palais du Jardin **WC2**
Peter's **NW6**
Poissonnerie de l'Avenue **SW3**
La Poule Au Pot **SW1**
Le Quai St Pierre **W8**
RSJ **SE1**
St Quentin **SW3**
Les Saveurs **W1**
The Savoy **WC2**
Simply Nico **SW1**
Le Suquet **SW3**
La Tante Claire **SW3**
Thistells **SE22**

Greek

Costa's Grill **W8**
Daphne **NW1**
Fanari **NW1**
Greek Valley **NW8**
Halepi **W2**
Hellas **NW1**
Kalamaras **W2**
Lemonia **NW1**
Little Akropolis **W1**
Nontas **NW1**
Romantica Taverna **W2**
Wine & Mousaka **W5**

Hungarian

Gay Hussar **W1**

Indian

Bhatti **WC2**
Bombay Brasserie **SW7**
Café Lazeez **SW7**
Chutney Mary **SW10**
Gopal's of Soho **W1**
Great Nepalese **NW1**
Khan's of Kensington **SW7**
Khyber Pass **SW7**
Kundan **SW1**
Lal Qila **W1**
Majlis **SW7**
Malabar **W8**
Mamta **SW6**
Memories of India **SW7**
Namaste **E1**
Noor Jahan **SW5**
Ragam **W1**
Rajput **W12**
Rani **N3**
Ravi Shankar **EC1**
Ravi Shankar **NW1**
Red Fort **W1**
Sabras **NW10**
Salloos **SW1**
Shezan **SW7**
Sonargaon **N1**
Spices **N16**
Sree Krishna **SW17**
Suruchi **N1**
Tandoori Lane **SW6**
Vijay **NW6**

Italian

L'Accento Italiano **W2**
Al San Vincenzo **W2**
Alba **EC1**
L'Altro **W11**
Arts Theatre Café **WC2**
Bertorelli's **WC2**
Cantina del Ponte **SE1**
Casa Cominetti **SE6**
Casale Franco **N1**
Caterino's **SW16**
Cibo **W14**
Daphne's **SW3**
De Cecco **SW6**
Del Buongustaio **SW15**
Enoteca **SW15**
Florians **N8**
Formula Veneta **SW10**
Giovanni's **WC2**
Halkin Hotel **SW1**
L'Incontro **SW1**
Luigi's **SE19**
Mimmo d'Ischia **SW1**
Museum Street Café **WC1**
Neal Street Restaurant **WC2**
Olivo **SW1**
Orso **WC2**
Osteria Antica Bologna **SW11**
La Paesana **W8**
Pinocchio's **NW1**
Riva **SW13**
River Café **W6**
Sale e Pepe **SW1**
Sambuca **SW3**
San Frediano **SW3**
San Lorenzo **SW3**
San Martino **SW3**
Sandrini **SW3**
Santini **SW1**
Scalini **SW3**
Signor Sassi **SW1**
Tiberio **W1**
Trattoria Lucca **NW1**
Ziani **SW3**

Japanese

Ajimura **WC2**
Arisugawa **W1**
Asuka **NW1**
Benihana **NW3**
Britannia Inter-Continental Hotel, Shogun **W1**
Dan Dan **SW15**
Defune **W1**
Fuji **W1**
Ginnan **EC4**
Gonbei **WC1**
Hilton International Regent's Park **NW8**
Hilton International Kensington **W11**
Ikeda **W1**
Ikkyu **W1**
Isohama **SW1**
Kagura **WC2**
Masako **W1**
Mitsukoshi **SW1**
Miyako **W1**
Miyama **EC4**
Miyama **W1**
Momo **W5**
Nakamura **W1**
Nakano **SW1**
Neshiko **N1**
Ninjin **W1**
Saga **W1**
Sumos **W6**
Suntory **SW1**
Tatsuso **EC2**
Wagamama **WC1**
Wakaba **NW3**
Yumi **W1**

Korean

Arirang Korean Restaurant **W1**
Kaya **W1**

Lebanese

Al Basha **W8**
Al Bustan **SW1**
Al Hamra **W1**
Byblos **W8**
Maroush **W2**
Phoenicia **W8**

North African

Adam's Café **W12**
Laurent **NW2**
Le Petit Prince **NW5**
La Reash **W1**

Polish

Ognisko Polskie **SW7**
Wodka **W8**

Russian

Nikita's **SW10**

South East Asian

Mutiara **SE1**
Nusa Dua Restoran Indonesia **W1**
Rasa Sayang **W1**
Rasa Sayang **W2**
Singapore **W4**
Singapore Garden **NW6**
Tiger under the Table **NW11**

Spanish

Albero & Grana **SW3**
Don Pepe **NW8**
El Metro **SW6**
Los Molinos **W6**

Sri Lankan

Sigiri **W13**

Swedish

Anna's Place **N1**

Thai

Bahn Thai **W1**
Bangkok **SW7**
Blue Elephant **SW6**
Chiang Mai **W1**
Khun Akorn **SW3**
Krungtap **SW5**
Lena's **SW11**
Oh'Boy **SW17**
S & P Thai **SW3**
Sala Thai **W5**
Satay Hut **N1**
Sema **SE22**
Siam Oriental **SW18**
Sri Siam City **EC2**
Sri Siam **W1**
Supan **W9**
Thai Kitchen **W2**
Thailand Restaurant **SE14**
Tom Yum **SW5**
Tui **SW7**
Tuk Tuk Restaurant **N1**
Yum Yum **N16**

Turkish

Beyoglu Ocakbasi **N16**
Efes Kebab House **W1**
Hodja Nasreddin **N1**
Istanbul Iskembecisi **N16**
Manzara **W11**
Topkapi **W1**

Vietnamese

Tien Phat **SW6**

Good Seafood

L'Altro **W11**
Bentley's **W1**
Bibendum Oyster Bar **SW3**
Café Fish **SW1**
Chez Liline **N4**
La Croisette **SW10**
Faulkners **E8**
La Gaulette **W1**
Geales **W8**
Grahame's Seafare **W1**
Green's Restaurant & Oyster Bar **SW1**
Lou Pescadou **SW5**
Manzi's **E14**
Manzi's **WC2**
Poissonnerie de l'Avenue **SW3**
Le Quai St Pierre **W8**
Le Suquet **SW3**
Walsh's **W1**
Wilton's **SW1**

Outstanding Desserts

Al San Vincenzo **W2**
Alastair Little **W1**
Albero & Grana **SW3**
Bistrot Bruno **W1**
Blakes Hotel **SW7**
Boyd's **W8**
The Canteen **SW10**
The Capital **SW3**
Chez Nico at Ninety Park Lane **W1**
Chinon **W14**
Dorchester, Terrace Restaurant **W1**
Fifth Floor at Harvey Nichols **SW1**
Le Gavroche **W1**
Gilbert's **SW7**
Halkin Hotel **SW1**
Inter-Continental Hotel **W1**
The Lanesborough **SW1**
Leith's **W11**
Le Meridien **W1**
Mijanou **SW1**
Nico Central **W1**
Pomegranates **SW1**
Les Saveurs **W1**
The Savoy, River Restaurant **WC2**
La Sémillante **W1**
The Square **SW1**
La Tante Claire **SW3**
Turner's **SW3**
Villandry Dining Room **W1**

Restaurants offering a good cheeseboard

Al San Vincenzo **W2**
Alastair Little **W1**
The Athenaeum **W1**
Brasserie du Marché aux Puces **W10**
The Capital **SW3**
Chez Moi **W11**
Chez Nico at Ninety Park Lane **W1**
Claridge's **W1**
Clarke's **W8**
The Connaught **W1**
Crowthers **SW14**
Del Buongustaio **SW15**
Dorchester, Grill Room **W1**
English Garden **SW3**
Foxtrot Oscar **SW3**
French House Dining Room **W1**
Gilbert's **SW7**
The Goring **SW1**
Halkin Hotel **SW1**
Hilaire **SW7**
Inter-Continental Hotel **W1**
Julie's **W11**
The Lanesborough **SW1**
Langan's Brasserie **W1**
Launceston Place **W8**
Leith's **W11**
Luc's Restaurant & Brasserie **EC3**

Le Meridien **W1**
Mirabelle **W1**
Museum Street Café **WC1**
Nico Central **W1**
O'Keefe's **W1**
Odette's **NW1**
192 **W11**
Pied à Terre **W1**
Pomegranates **SW1**
Le Pont de la Tour **SE1**
The Regent London **NW1**
The Ritz **W1**
Royal Garden Hotel **W8**
Les Saveurs **W1**
The Savoy, River Restaurant **WC2**
The Savoy, Grill Room **WC2**
Sheraton Belgravia **SW1**
Simpson's-in-the-Strand **WC2**
Simply Nico **SW1**
Sonny's **SW13**
Stephen Bull **W1**
La Tante Claire **SW3**
Tate Gallery Restaurant **SW1**
Thistells **SE22**
Turner's **SW3**
Veronica's **W2**
Villandry Dining Room **W1**
Walton's **SW3**

Restaurants with outstanding wine lists

Au Jardin des Gourmets **W1**
Bibendum **SW3**
Boulestin **WC2**
The Capital **SW3**
Chez Nico at Ninety Park Lane **W1**
The Dorchester **W1**
Four Seasons Hotel **W1**
Le Gavroche **W1**
Gilbert's **SW7**
The Goring **SW1**
Hilaire **SW7**
Hyatt Carlton Tower **SW1**
Inter-Continental Hotel **W1**
The Langham **W1**
Leith's **W11**
Le Meridien **W1**
Mijanou **SW1**
Mirabelle **W1**
Le Pont de la Tour **SE1**
The Ritz **W1**
RSJ **SE1**
Les Saveurs **W1**
The Savoy **WC2**
Shampers **W1**
The Square **SW1**
La Tante Claire **SW3**
Turner's **SW3**

Restaurants with a good list of California wines

Alastair Little **W1**
The Athenaeum **W1**
Beauchamp Place **SW3**
Bibendum **SW3**
Bombay Brasserie **SW7**
Boulestin **WC2**
Boyd's **W8**
Café Royal Grill Room **W1**
Chapter 11 **SW10**
Chez Nico at Ninety Park Lane **W1**
Christopher's **WC2**
Claridge's **W1**
Clarke's **W8**
The Dorchester, Terrace Restaurant **W1**
Dukes Hotel **SW1**
L'Escargot **W1**
Fifth Floor at Harvey Nichols **SW1**
Four Seasons Hotel **W1**
Le Gavroche **W1**
Gilbert's **SW7**
The Goring **SW1**
Hilaire **SW7**
Hyatt Carlton Tower **SW1**
L'Incontro **SW1**
Inter-Continental Hotel **W1**
The Ivy **WC2**
Kensington Place **W8**
Joe Allen **WC2**
The Langham **W1**
Launceston Place **W8**
Leith's **W11**
The Lexington **W1**
Le Meridien, Terrace Garden **W1**
Mijanou **SW1**
Odette's **NW1**
Le Pont de la Tour **SE1**
Pomegranates **SW1**
Ransome's Dock **SW11**
The Regent London **NW1**
The Ritz **W1**
Royal Garden Hotel **W8**
The Savoy **WC2**
Shampers **W1**
Simply Nico **SW1**
The Square **SW1**
Stephen Bull **W1**

Restaurants offering a good range of wines by the glass

Alastair Little **W1**
Au Jardin des Gourmets **W1**
Beauchamp Place **SW3**
Bertorelli's **WC2**
Bibendum **SW3**
Bibendum Oyster Bar **SW3**
Bistrot 190 **SW7**
Blakes Hotel **SW7**
Blue Print Café **SE1**
Boyd's **W8**
The Brackenbury **W6**
Buchan's **SW11**
Canal Brasserie **W10**
The Canteen **SW10**
Claridge's **W1**
Clarke's **W8**
Corney & Barrow **EC2**
Corney & Barrow **EC4**
Crowthers **SW14**
dell'Ugo **W1**
The Dorchester, Terrace Restaurant **W1**
The Eagle **EC1**
Ebury Wine Bar **SW1**
English Garden **SW3**
L'Escargot **W1**
Fifth Floor at Harvey Nichols **SW1**
Four Seasons Hotel **W1**
Frederick's **N1**
Le Gavroche **W1**
Gavver's **SW1**
Gilbert's **SW7**
The Goring **SW1**
Grosvenor House **W1**
The Halcyon **W11**
Halkin Hotel **SW1**
Hilaire **SW7**
L'Hotel, Le Metro **SW3**
Julie's **W11**
Kensington Place **W8**
The Langham **W1**
Launceston Place **W8**
The Lexington **W1**
May Fair Inter-Continental **W1**
Le Meridien, Terrace Garden **W1**
Mijanou **SW1**
Newtons **SW4**
Nico Central **W1**
O'Keefe's **W1**
Odette's **NW1**
192 **W11**
The Park Lane Hotel **W1**
Pinocchio's **NW1**
Le Pont de la Tour **SE1**
Ransome's Dock **SW11**
The Ritz **W1**
River Café **W6**
RSJ **SE1**
The Savoy **WC2**
Shampers **W1**
Shepherd's **SW1**
Sonny's **SW13**
The Square **SW1**
Whittington's **EC4**
Wilton's **SW1**

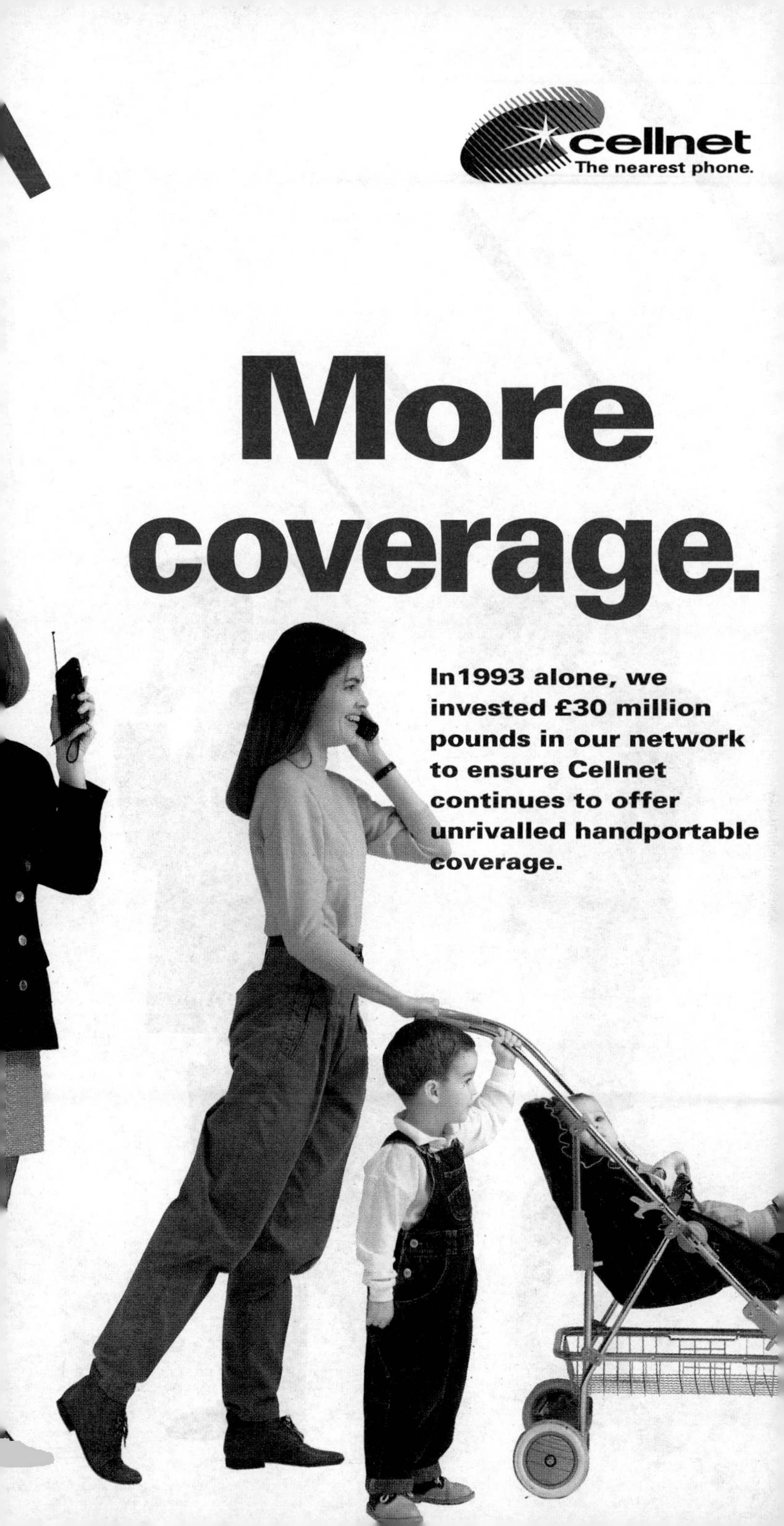

cellnet
The nearest phone.
More coverage.
In1993 alone, we invested £30 million pounds in our network to ensure Cellnet continues to offer unrivalled handportable coverage.

England

Abberley · Elms Hotel · 71% · £97

Tel 0299 896666 Fax 0299 896804 · H

Stockton Road Abberley nr Worcester Hereford & Worcester WR6 6AT · **Map 14 B1**

On the A443 between Worcester (13 miles) and Tenbury Wells (2 miles after Great Witley; do not take the turning into Abberley), the Elms Hotel is a stately country house set in ten acres of formal gardens and parkland. The Queen Anne mansion was built in 1710 by Gilbert White, a pupil of Sir Christopher Wren. The elegant foyer, with rug-covered slate floor and carved wooden fireplace, makes a splendid impression on entry, and both here and in the lounges and library fine antiques are found among good-quality reproduction pieces. Bedrooms are traditional in the main house, lighter and brighter in the converted coach house; some of the latter have balconies, and all have well-equipped bathrooms en suite. There are four studio suites. Meeting rooms (for up to 60) include the Crossthwaite Suite in the adjoining Coach House. Afternoon tea is served to non-residents. No dogs. Queens Moat Houses. ***Rooms*** *25. Garden, tennis, putting, helipad.* AMERICAN EXPRESS *Access, Diners, Visa.*

Abbot's Salford · Salford Hall · 66% · £95

Tel 0386 871300 Fax 0386 871301 · H

Abbot's Salford Evesham Hereford & Worcester WR11 5UT · **Map 14 C1**

A fascinating Tudor building with much of historical and architectural interest, once a guest residence for the monks of nearby Evesham Abbey. Dating from the late 15th century, this imposing Grade One listed mansion is a comfortable, characterful establishment, with stained-glass windows depicting coats of arms, a half-timbered, whitewashed wing and a fine walled garden. The central courtyard has been glassed in to form a pleasant conservatory, giving striking views of its gabled roofs. The lounge, once the Abbot's kitchen, displays original meat hooks suspended from oak beams. Bedrooms, split between the main house and the gate house, are mainly furnished with reproduction pieces; many have exposed timberwork and mullioned windows. Conferences for up to 50. No dogs. ***Rooms*** *33. Garden, sauna, solarium, snooker, tennis.* AMERICAN EXPRESS *Access, Diners, Visa.*

Abingdon · Abingdon Lodge · 61% · £80

Tel 0235 553456 Fax 0235 554117 · H

Marcham Road Abingdon Oxfordshire OX14 1TZ · **Map 15 D2**

Clean-lined, modern low-rise hotel at the junction of the A34 and A415. Day rooms include a distinctive octagonal bar. Several conference rooms cater for up to 180 delegates. Twenty-six bedrooms reserved for non-smokers. Children up to 14 stay free in parents' room. Ample car parking. ***Rooms*** *63.* AMERICAN EXPRESS *Access, Diners, Visa.*

Abingdon · Upper Reaches · 62% · £106

Tel 0235 522311 Fax 0235 555182 · H

Thames Street Abingdon Oxfordshire OX14 3TA · **Map 15 D2**

Six miles from Oxford, a former corn mill once operated by Benedictine monks, standing on a virtual island between the Thames and the Abbey Stream. Some bedrooms enjoy river views. The restaurant features a working water wheel and mill race. River moorings for those guests who wish to arrive by boat. Public leisure centre just across the river in the Old Gaol. Forte Heritage. ***Rooms*** *25. Terrace, fishing.* AMERICAN EXPRESS *Access, Diners, Visa.*

Consult page 16 for a full list of starred restaurants

Acle **Forte Travelodge** **£42**

Tel 0493 751970 **L**

Acle nr Norwich Norfolk NR13 3BE **Map 10 D1**

At the junction of the A47 and the Acle bypass, to the east of Acle on the main road between Norwich and Great Yarmouth. ***Rooms 40.*** AMERICAN EXPRESS *Access, Visa.*

Alcester **Arrow Mill** **£72**

Tel 0789 762419 Fax 0789 765170 **I**

Arrow Alcester Warwickshire B49 5NL **Map 14 C1**

The Arrow Mill was listed in the Domesday Book, when it was a working flour mill valued at three shillings and sixpence! The stream-driven mill wheel still turns in the restaurant, and day rooms feature heavy beams and flagstones. Bedrooms of individual character use light, attractive fabrics and pine furniture. There's parking space for 200 cars, and a heliport. Dogs in kennels only. ***Rooms** 18. Garden, fishing.* AMERICAN EXPRESS *Access, Diners, Visa.*

Alcester **Places of Interest**

Coughton Galleries Coughton Court Tel 0789 762642.
Ragley Hall Tel 0789 762090.

Aldeburgh **Brudenell Hotel** **60%** **£107**

Tel 0728 452071 Fax 0728 454082 **H**

The Parade Aldeburgh Suffolk IP15 5BU **Map 10 D3**

It's difficult to escape the North Sea at this traditional esplanade hotel, where public rooms and many of the bedrooms look out on the briny. The elegant Music Room can accommodate up to 50 people for meetings and conferences. About a third of the rooms are designated non-smoking. Forte Heritage. ***Rooms** 47.* AMERICAN EXPRESS *Access, Diners, Visa.*

Aldeburgh **Uplands** **60%** **£59**

Tel 0728 452420 **H**

Victoria Road Aldeburgh Suffolk IP15 5DX **Map 10 D3**

A Regency house, just opposite the parish church and a stone's throw from the seafront, which maintains the best aspects of a snug guest house. Public areas include a rear conservatory which opens to the landscaped gardens where there's a wing of chalets. Remaining bedrooms in the house retain some period features and have character and charm. No dogs. ***Rooms** 20. Garden.* AMERICAN EXPRESS *Access, Diners, Visa.*

Aldeburgh **Wentworth Hotel** **68%** **£80**

Tel 0728 452312 **H**

Wentworth Road Aldeburgh Suffolk IP15 5BD **Map 10 D3**

Just back from the beach opposite the fishermen's huts and boats, the Wentworth has been in the same family ownership since 1920. This continuity has built up a reputation for service and civilised comfort which brings many repeat visits, and the Pritts are always looking for ways to improve and enhance their hotel (the terrace garden, car park and bedrooms have benefited most recently). Many of the bedrooms look out to sea, and almost all have bathrooms en suite. There are two tastefully appointed lounges and a cosy bar. ***Rooms** 31. Garden. Closed 2 weeks from 27 Dec.* AMERICAN EXPRESS *Access, Diners, Visa.*

Aldeburgh — Places of Interest

Tourist Information Tel 0728 453637.
Snape Maltings Concert Hall Snape Tel 0728 452935.
Sizewell Visitor Centre Nr Leiston Tel 0728 642139.

Alderley Edge — Alderley Edge Hotel — 72% — £117

Tel 0625 583033 Fax 0625 586343 — **HR**

Macclesfield Road Alderley Edge Cheshire SK9 7BJ — **Map 7 B2**

Friendly, well-drilled staff are a big plus at this Victorian hotel on the edge of town. Fresh flowers abound in day rooms that include a comfortable conservatory lounge overlooking the garden (part of which is given over to a bird sanctuary). Soft floral schemes are favoured in the bedrooms, of which the Executive (standard) rooms are rather on the small side, with painted furniture, in contrast to spacious pine-furnished De Luxe rooms. The latter also get various extras such as decanters of sherry, mini bar, teletext TV and spa bath; four are quite cottagey with beams and some exposed stonework; all rooms include bathrobes and magazines. 24hr room service. Children under 14 stay free in parents' room. ***Rooms** 32. Garden.* AMERICAN EXPRESS *Access, Diners, Visa.*

Restaurant — £80

An 'A' for effort, with absolutely everything (including an excellent choice of Italian-style bread) being made in-house by chef Brian Joy and his team. Some over-the-top menu descriptions do not detract from the well-thought-out dishes to be found on the à la carte and table d'hote menus (the latter including a different glass of wine with each course for members of their dining club): beef and tarragon consommé with woodland mushrooms and spinach gnocchi; casserole of mussels with pesto on home-made noodles; duckling with herb and olive sauce and beetroot timbale; these are supplemented by mainly fishy *plats du marché*. An equally interesting light lunch menu is served in either the lounge or restaurant. The cheese trolley takes its pick from around the British Isles. A quite extraordinary wine list (100+ champagnes!) offers an extensive French section, but not to the exclusion of New World wines; plenty of half bottles, magnums and ports. ***Seats** 80. Private Room 22. L 12-2 D 7-10. Set L £15.50 Set D £20.50.*

Aldridge — Fairlawns — 62% — £78

Tel 0922 55122 Fax 0922 743210 — **H**

Little Aston Road Aldridge Walsall West Midlands WS9 0NU — **Map 6 C4**

A purpose-built hotel in a rural setting, catering for up to 80 conference delegates. Six of the bedrooms are suites and those in the original building are small, but pleasantly decorated. Children up to 14 stay free in parents' room. 200 yards from the junction of the A452 and A454. ***Rooms** 35. Garden, swimming pool.* AMERICAN EXPRESS *Access, Diners, Visa.*

All Stretton — Stretton Hall Hotel — 59% — £54

Tel 0694 723224 — **H**

All Stretton nr Church Stretton Shropshire SY6 6HG — **Map 6 A4**

On the A49 between Ludlow and Shrewsbury, this Victorian hotel is clean and comfortable. Beyond the main hallway, with its oak dado panelling, is a similarly panelled bar with Victorian polished wood fireplace. Bedrooms vary in size and furniture, from basic fitted units to 50s' freestanding pieces and almost-antiques. Favourite choice is the panelled four-poster room. Bathrooms, three with shower and WC only, are utilitarian. ***Rooms** 13. Garden.* AMERICAN EXPRESS *Access, Diners, Visa.*

Allendale **Bishop Field** **59%** **£76**

Tel 0434 683248 Fax 0434 683830 **H**

Whitfield Road Allendale nr Hexham Northumberland NE47 9EJ **Map 5 D2**

A mile out of Allendale on the Whitfield road, this former farmhouse was converted in 1985 by Kathy and Keith Fairless and is now run by them with their daughter Bridget, who is also the chef. There's a cheerful, relaxed atmosphere in the lounges, one of which has a cocktail bar; the other is non-smoking. Bedrooms are comfortable and rather pretty, light colour schemes contrasting well with dark-stained furniture. Children up to 10 stay free in parents' room. ***Rooms** 11. Garden, game fishing, shooting. Closed Feb & Mar. Access, Visa.*

Alnwick **White Swan** **58%** **£75**

Tel 0665 602109 Fax 0665 510400 **H**

Bondgate Within, Alnwick Northumberland NE66 1TD **Map 5 D1**

The hotel's staircase, revolving doors and some carved oak panelling all came from the *SS Olympic* (sister ship to the ill-fated *Titanic*) and fit quite happily into this town-centre coaching inn. Children under 14 stay free in parents' room. Four conference rooms (up to 150 theatre-style). ***Rooms** 43.* AMERICAN EXPRESS *Access, Visa.*

Alnwick **Places of Interest**

Tourist Information Tel 0665 510665.
Morpeth Chantry Bagpipe Museum The Chantry, Bridge Street, Morpeth Tel 0670 519466.
Historic Houses, Castles and Gardens
Alnwick Castle Tel 0665 510777.
Cragside House & Country Park (NT) Rothbury Tel 0669 20333.
Howick Hall Garden Howick Tel 0665 577285.
Wallington House, Walled Garden and Grounds (NT) Cambo, Morpeth Tel 0670 74283.

Alsager **Manor House** **65%** **£70**

Tel 0270 884000 Fax 0270 882483 **H**

Audley Road Alsager Cheshire ST7 2QQ **Map 6 B3**

A modern hotel set in its own grounds three miles from Junction 16 of the M6. The heart of the place is a 17th-century farm, and old beams preserve a traditional feel in the restaurant, bars and several meeting rooms. Bedrooms are divided between the original part and a new wing; in the latter are two rooms adapted for disabled guests and two Executive rooms with jacuzzis. Children up to 14 stay free in parents' room. Conference facilities for 250. ***Rooms** 57. Garden, indoor swimming pool, snooker.* AMERICAN EXPRESS *Access, Diners, Visa.*

Alsager **Place of Interest**

Little Moreton Hall (NT) Tel 0260 272018 *4 miles.*

Alston **Lovelady Shield** **68%** **£76**

Tel 0434 381203 Fax 0434 381515 **HR**

Nenthead Road Alston Cumbria CA9 3LF **Map 5 D3**

Set amid the wild fells of the High Pennines $2\frac{1}{2}$ miles east of Alston on the A689, Lovelady Shield is an oasis of comfort and civility. The Georgian style of the house blends in with the neat flower-bordered lawns, trees all around providing a degree of shelter and seclusion. Bordered on one side by the river Nent, the hotel bottles its own mineral water (though this is from a source higher up in the hills). Public rooms include a delightful and peaceful lounge decorated in pale cream which co-ordinates tastefully

See over

with the pale blue of the upholstery. The adjacent bar has a convivial atmosphere. Bedrooms are of good size and are attractively homely in character with some fine old pieces of furniture and carefully co-ordinated colour schemes. Useful extras include shoe-shine kits. Bathrooms, though compact, are neat and have decent shower risers. Sustaining breakfasts, for which last orders are at 9am. ***Rooms*** *12. Garden, tennis. Closed Jan-mid Feb.* AMERICAN EXPRESS *Access, Diners, Visa.*

Restaurant — £60

A charming candlelit setting for a short, four-course fixed-price dinner which is simple in both style and presentation. Changing daily, the menus begin with, say, hot baked avocado topped with prawns, cream, herbs and farmhouse Cheddar to be followed by a no-choice soup course such as cream of carrot and sweet potato. Main courses could be a white casserole of veal with root vegetables, herbs, cream and oyster mushrooms or grilled grey mullet with an anchovy and walnut butter. Desserts range from warm treacle tart to fresh fruit salad with sweetened vanilla cheese. Pleasant, informal service and a homely atmosphere make the ordinary cooking acceptable. ***Seats*** *26. D 7.30-8.30. Set D £23.50*

Alton — Forte Travelodge — £42

Tel 0420 62659 — **L**

A31 Four Marks Winchester Road Alton Hampshire GU34 5HZ — **Map 15 D3**

On the A31 northbound, 5 miles south of Alton. Close to Winchester. ***Rooms*** *31.* AMERICAN EXPRESS *Access, Visa.*

Alton — Grange Hotel — 61% — £61

Tel 0420 86565 Fax 0420 541346 — **H**

17 London Road Holybourne Alton Hampshire GU34 4EG — **Map 15 D3**

The two-acre garden, overlooked by the lounge and sun terrace, is quite a feature at the Levenes' friendly hotel. Croquet and putting are available, and the owners are involved in the mid-Hants Balloon Club which meets regularly at the hotel (they have their own hot air balloon). Individually appointed bedrooms include two honeymoon suites and the penthouse suite with a sunken bath. The conference facilities have recently been extended. ***Rooms*** *34. Garden, putting. Closed Christmas.* AMERICAN EXPRESS *Access, Diners, Visa.*

Alton — The Swan — 58% — £80

Tel 0420 83777 Fax 0420 87975 — **H**

High Street Alton Hampshire GU34 1AT — **Map 15 D3**

White-painted former coaching inn offering neat, practical accommodation alongside unfussy but comfortable public areas. Friendly staff. Banqueting and conference facilities for 120. Forte Heritage. ***Rooms*** *36. Garden.* AMERICAN EXPRESS *Access, Diners, Visa.*

Alton — Places of Interest

Oates Memorial Library and the Gilbert White Museum The Wakes, Selborne Tel 0420 50275.

Historic Houses; Castles and Gardens

Jane Austen's House Chawton Tel 0420 83262.

Jenkyn Place Garden Bentley Tel 0420 23118.

Altrincham — Bowdon Hotel — 65% — £79

Tel 061-928 7121 Fax 061-927 7560 — **H**

Langham Road Bowdon Altrincham Cheshire WA14 2HT — **Map 6 B2**

Victorian hotel with sympathetic extensions, on the B5161 and convenient for the motorway network. Neat, practical accommodation, several conference rooms and banqueting suites, a pub called *Silks* and an ample car park. Ramps have been added for visitors in wheelchairs. Children up to 14 stay free in parents' room. ***Rooms** 82. AMERICAN EXPRESS Access, Diners, Visa.*

Altrincham **Cresta Court** **61%** **£72**

Tel 061-927 7272 Fax 061-926 9194 **H**

Church Street Altrincham Cheshire WA14 4DP **Map 6 B2**

Handy for the motorway network, Manchester Airport and the North-West generally, the privately owned Cresta Court offers well-kept, up-to-date accommodation and a variety of air-conditioned conference and function rooms. ***Rooms** 139. Coffee shop (9.30am-11pm). AMERICAN EXPRESS Access, Diners, Visa.*

Altrincham **Francs** **£40**

Tel 061-941 3954 **R**

2 Goose Green Altrincham Cheshire **Map 6 B2**

Sister restaurant to Francs in Chester. A French bistro offering a wide range of food, from sandwiches to *steak frites, potage* to *poisson en croute*, plus *plats du jour* – all with a breath of French air. Sunday lunch is always busy, with children under 10 fed free. All desserts are home-made. Outdoor eating on a terrace in good weather. ***Seats** 75. Parties 40. L 12-3 D 5-11 (Sun 12-5). Set L (Sun) £7.50. Closed D Sun, all Bank Holidays. AMERICAN EXPRESS Access, Visa.*

Altrincham **George & Dragon** **60%** **£52**

Tel 061-928 9933 Fax 061-929 8060 **H**

Manchester Road Altrincham Cheshire WA14 4PH **Map 6 B2**

Smartly kept accommodation, Victorian-inspired bar-lounge. Children up to 16 stay free in parents' room. No dogs. ***Rooms** 45. Garden. AMERICAN EXPRESS Access, Diners, Visa.*

Altrincham **Places of Interest**

Dunham Massey Hall and Garden (NT) Tel 061 941 1025.
Ice Rink Devonshire Road Tel 061 926 8316.

Alveley **Mill Hotel** **66%** **£73**

Tel 0746 780437 Fax 0746 780850 **H**

Birdsgreen Alveley nr Bridgnorth Shropshire WV15 6HL **Map 6 B4**

Just off the A442, midway between Kidderminster and Bridgnorth. Ten acres of landscaped gardens surround The Mill, a 17th-century building sympathetically restored and extended to include a variety of conference facilities catering for up to 200. The mill workings can still be seen in the rustic Mill Bar, and the lounge bar is large and well furnished. Bedrooms are in a modern extension. No dogs. ***Rooms** 21. Garden, games room. AMERICAN EXPRESS Access, Diners, Visa.*

Alveston **Alveston House** **65%** **£80**

Tel 0454 415050 Fax 0454 415425 **H**

Alveston nr Bristol Avon BS12 2LJ **Map 13 F1**

Popular commercial hotel on A38 north of Bristol, with a predominance of single bedrooms. Much geared to the business trade with conference suites and syndicate rooms holding up to 100 delegates; ample parking. ***Rooms** 30. Garden, business centre. AMERICAN EXPRESS Access, Diners, Visa.*

Alveston — Forte Posthouse — 62% — £68

Tel 0454 412521 Fax 0454 413920 — **H**

Thornbury Road Alveston nr Bristol Avon BS12 2LL — Map 13 F1

11 miles north of Bristol, close to M4/M5 intersection, an extended Tudor inn with a good conference trade (facilities for up to 100). ***Rooms** 74. Outdoor swimming pool, pitch & putt, children's play area.* AMERICAN EXPRESS *Access, Diners, Visa.*

Amberley — Amberley Castle — 81% — £130

Tel 0798 831992 Fax 0798 831998 — **HR**

Amberley nr Arundel West Sussex BN18 9ND — Map 11 A6

A country hotel set within a 900-year-old castle promising serenity and tranquillity behind the stone battlements surrounding the magnificent building. Joy and Martin Cummings successfully combine modernity and antiquity in this unique setting, using carefully chosen antiques where appropriate. Bedrooms are named after local Sussex castles and have considerable charm; each has thoughtful extras like flowers, plants and video recorders (with a video library in each room); two new rooms have views of the castle gardens and ruined battlements. The day rooms are grand and peppered with suits of armour and historic weaponry as befits the castle setting. Magnificent bathrooms all have jacuzzi baths. Private dining and meeting rooms (for up to 45 delegates) include the richly panelled King Charles I room. ***Rooms** 14. Garden.* AMERICAN EXPRESS *Access, Diners, Visa.*

Queen's Room Restaurant — £100

A baronial dining room that dates back to the 13th century and boasts a historic 17th-century hunting mural, reflected in the crystal animals which add charm to the quality table settings. Chef Nigel Boschetti offers both a set menu and à la carte with a varied choice of modern dishes and traditional British favourites at lunchtime – from wild boar terrine with truffle and warm fig chutney to roast tails of monkfish with parsley purée, bacon, button onions and red wine sauce or fish and oyster pie. Good British cheeses. No smoking. ***Seats** 36. Parties 8. Private Room 48. L 12-2 D 7-9.30. Set L £13.50/£16.50 Set D £25.50.*

Amberley — Amberley Inn — 57% — £74

Tel 0453 872565 Fax 0453 872738 — **H**

Amberley nr Stroud Gloucestershire GL5 5AF — Map 14 B2

High on Minchinhampton Common, this sturdy, stone-built inn enjoys spectacular views of Woodchester Valley, particularly from the residents' lounge. Bedrooms share this aspect or overlook the garden. Four especially pleasant rooms are in the Garden House. Children up to 15 stay free in parents' room. ***Rooms** 14. Garden.* AMERICAN EXPRESS *Access, Diners, Visa.*

Ambleside — Kirkstone Foot — 65% — £99*

Tel 053 94 32232 Fax 053 94 31110 — **H**

Kirkstone Pass Road Ambleside Cumbria LA22 9EH — Map 4 C3

The original 17th-century manor house and its extensions and outbuildings offer hotel accommodation plus self-catering cottages and apartments (dogs welcome in the latter only). Many guests return year after year and the place has a homely feel, especially in the lounge and bar areas which look out on fine gardens and over Ambleside's rooftops. Bedrooms mainly have floral fabrics, colour co-ordinated schemes and smart modern furniture. They come in various sizes, among which front-facing rooms are decidedly superior. *Half-board terms only. ***Rooms** 16. Garden. Closed Jan.* AMERICAN EXPRESS *Access, Diners, Visa.*

Ambleside Nanny Brow 62% £90

Tel 053 94 32036 Fax 053 94 32450 **H**

Clappersgate Ambleside Cumbria LA22 9NF Map 4 C3

An interesting Edwardian building, built in Tudor style a mile and a half from Ambleside on the A593 Coniston/Langdale road. Nanny Brow has fine, stepped gardens and views over the Brathay valley. Lounge and bar retain a cosy feel with open log fires. Chintz decor predominates in the main-house bedrooms; those in the wing are generally larger, with good views. The hotel has its own ski boat, and fishing is available on a private stretch of the River Brathay. ***Rooms** 19. Garden, spa bath, solarium, tennis, fishing. Closed 3 weeks Jan.* AMERICAN EXPRESS *Access, Visa.*

Ambleside Rothay Manor 71% £104

Tel 053 94 33605 Fax 053 94 33607 **HR**

Rothay Bridge Ambleside Cumbria LA22 0EH Map 4 C3

A balconied Regency frontage is echoed by an elegant, restful interior of cool decor, deep-cushioned seating and garden views which are shared by the best, front-facing bedrooms. Of the three garden suites two are well suited to family use (children up to 10 stay free in parents' room) and the third is equipped for disabled guests. A convenient location on the Coniston road ($\frac{1}{4}$ mile out of Ambleside) is handy for the bustle of Ambleside yet well protected from it in secluded grounds. The Nixons have been here since 1976 and personal touches are evident throughout; service is very friendly and attentive. Guests have free use of a nearby leisure club (swimming pool, sauna, steam room, spa bath) and permits may be obtained for trout fishing. Traditional afternoon tea is served every day between 3.30 and 5.30pm. No dogs. ***Rooms** 18. Garden. Closed early Jan-mid Feb.* AMERICAN EXPRESS *Access, Diners, Visa.*

Restaurant £70

Three to five-course nightly menus make the most of local produce, with wine suggestions appended to each course. Dishes typically run from Stilton, port and herb paté served with home-made oat biscuits to wood pigeon with smoked bacon braised in red wine, and coffee and walnut gateau. Vegetarians are particularly well catered for. Lunch is a buffet Mon-Sat, with a traditional roast on Sunday (booking advisable). The setting of polished mahogany tables and soft candle-light accompanies an unfailingly traditional style of cooking and service. Prices are fair on a good all-round wine list; admirable half-bottle policy of opening a full bottle and charging three-fifths of the full price. No smoking. ***Seats** 60. Parties 30. L 12.30-2 (buffet only Mon-Sat) (Sun 12.30-1.30) D 8-9. Set L £14.50 (Sun) Set D £19/£22.*

Ambleside Wateredge Hotel 63% £118

Tel & Fax 053 94 32332 **HR**

Waterhead Bay Ambleside Cumbria LA22 0EP Map 4 C3

A lakeside hotel of inherent charm, originally a row of 17th-century cottages, with added attractions of water-edge garden, jetty and rowing boat – hence no children under seven. Modern extensions have added garden rooms with private balcony or patio and two spacious ground-floor suites. A cosy bar, bright airy lounge and Windermere views provide the unifying theme; the Cowap family and cheerful staff provide the welcome. Guests have free membership of a nearby leisure club. ***Rooms** 23. Garden, boating, coarse fishing. Closed mid-Dec & all Jan.* AMERICAN EXPRESS *Access, Visa.*

Restaurant £63

Nightly six-course dinners are taken at leisure in adjoining candle-lit rooms. Cooking is careful and the choice sensibly limited, with typical dishes like crab soufflé fritters, carrot and lentil soup, halibut hollandaise, roast loin of venison on a caramel orange sauce, and shortbread with chocolate

See over

bavarois. All bread, pastries and preserves are home-made. Friendly service is again a plus, as is a non-smoking policy. Lighter lunches – served out on the patio in warm weather. ***Seats** 50. L 12-2 D 7-8.30.*

Amesbury — Forte Travelodge — £42

Tel 0980 624966 — **L**

A303 Amesbury Wiltshire SP4 7AS — **Map 14 C3**

At the junction of the A345 and the A303 eastbound, 8 miles north of Salisbury on the major route for the West Country. ***Rooms** 32.* AMERICAN EXPRESS *Access, Visa.*

Ampfield — Potters Heron Hotel — 60% — £87

Tel 0703 266611 Fax 0703 251359 — **H**

Ampfield nr Romsey Hampshire SO51 9ZF — **Map 15 D3**

White-painted thatched building on the A31 with conference facilities for up to 140 and all-day informal eating in Potters Pub. Lansbury. ***Rooms** 54. Keep-fit equipment, sauna, pool table.* AMERICAN EXPRESS *Access, Diners, Visa.*

Andover — White Hart Inn — £82

Tel 0264 352266 Fax 0264 323767 — **I**

Bridge Street Andover Hampshire SP10 1BH — **Map 14 C3**

Former coaching inn in the centre of town. Period character (c. 1900) created by pictures, posters and bric-a-brac in the day rooms. New eat-anywhere catering operation with blackboard menus. Forte Heritage. ***Rooms** 20.* AMERICAN EXPRESS *Access, Diners, Visa.*

Andover — Places of Interest

Cricklade Theatre Tel 0264 365698.
Hawk Conservancy Park Weyhill Tel 0264 772252.
Thruxton Motor Racing Circuit Tel 0264 772696.
Finkley Down Farm Park Tel 0264 352195

Ansty — Ansty Hall — 71% — £108

Tel 0203 612222 Fax 0203 602155 — **H**

Ansty nr Coventry Warwickshire CV7 9HZ — **Map 7 D4**

Many of the bedrooms date back to the hall's founding in the late 17th century while others are in a modern conversion. Both types overlook the lawns that provide a peaceful setting (yet it's only two minutes from Junction 2 of the M6). Smart reproduction furniture is used throughout, and the day rooms have a quiet, traditional elegance. No longer closed over Christmas. ***Rooms** 31. Garden.* AMERICAN EXPRESS *Access, Diners, Visa.*

Appleby-in-Westmorland — Appleby Manor Hotel 66% — £98

Tel 076 83 51571 Fax 076 83 52888 — **HR**

Roman Road Appleby-in-Westmorland Cumbria CA16 6JD — **Map 5 D3**

A relaxing and friendly family-owned hotel overlooking Appleby Castle and the Eden valley. Most of the original (1870s) architectural features remain, including the main fireplace and old hooks that used to carry rods to hang tapestries and pictures. Bright and cheerful bedrooms, whether in the main house, modern wing or coach house annexe, provide everything you need, from powerful hairdryers to in-house video films. ***Rooms** 30. Garden, indoor swimming pool, spa bath, sauna, steam room, sunbed, mini-gym, snooker. Closed 3 days Xmas.* AMERICAN EXPRESS *Access, Diners, Visa.*

Oak Room Restaurant — £40

A panelled room with a hand-painted tiled fireplace. 'Speciality' menu dishes are almost gratingly twee in description, but the no-nonsense food is served in decent portions with plenty of well-cooked vegetables. Dishes such as duck and beetroot bortsch, chargrilled noisettes of lamb glazed with orange curaçao and 'trout of the times' will doubtless satisfy, and there's a commendable attitude to wine pricing – apart from four value-for-money fine wines, there's a fixed £4.50 mark-up on the purchase price of every bottle, and only £6 on champagnes. Sweets from a trolley. Youngsters' menu served in the restaurant from 5-7.30pm. ***Seats** 70. Parties 30. L 12-1.45 D 7-9. Closed 3 days Xmas. Set L & D from £17.*

Appleby-in-Westmorland — Tufton Arms 66% — £75

Tel 076 83 51593 Fax 076 83 52761 — **H**

Market Square Appleby-in-Westmorland Cumbria CA16 6XA — **Map 5 D3**

An unusual and rather evocative conversion of a once run-down Victorian pub, now restored with authentic pieces, period prints and atmospheric appeal. Clubby townspeople's bar and more restful conservatory dining. More Victorian features and carefully updated bathrooms in the original bedrooms; a more modest modern wing is fitted out with the businessman in mind. In the centre of Appleby, by the A66. ***Rooms** 19. Fishing, children's playground.* AMERICAN EXPRESS *Access, Diners, Visa.*

Applethwaite — Underscar Manor 74% — £150*

Tel 076 87 75000 Fax 076 87 74904 — **HR**

Applethwaite Keswick Cumbria CA12 4PH — **Map 14 C3**

One mile from the Keswick roundabout on the A66, a distinctive Italianate house, built in the Victorian era, commanding spectacular views over Derwentwater. Set in 40 acres of gardens and woodland, like so many places in the Lake District, this can be described as the perfect spot. Much of the original architecture has been retained – ornate fireplaces and mouldings, bay windows and plasterwork ceilings, supplemented by many antiques, fine fabrics and carpets, elegant furniture and lovely flower arrangements. Luxurious bedrooms have been carefully refurbished to a high standard, as have the bathrooms, and service under the direction of Pauline and Derek Harrison (who also own *Moss Nook* restaurant near Manchester Airport – see entry) is discreet and caring. No children under 12 in either hotel or restaurant. Conference room for 16, boardroom-style. Full afternoon tea is served to non-residents. *Half-board terms. ***Rooms** 11. Garden.* AMERICAN EXPRESS *Access, Visa.*

Restaurant — £65

Two elegant rooms (both non-smoking), one domed conservatory-style, are the setting for Robert Thornton and Steve Yare's sound cooking. Particular attention is paid to the artistic presentation of dishes, although this is in itself no fault when the ingredients and flavours succeed. Typical examples from the wordy menus might be 'a light chicken and morel mousse baked inside crisp puff pastry garnished with celeriac purée and a Madeira and chervil sauce', followed by 'medallion of venison roasted with juniper berries and garnished with baby pears and a gratin of macaroni with its own sauce scented with cepes'. Sweets can be equally involved: 'Packham pears poached in red wine and kirsch served with cinnamon shortbread and a baby chocolate mousse'. A 6-course *menu surprise* with no 'controversial ingredients' is offered to complete table parties. Lighter lunches offer a small choice of more straightforward dishes. There are no notes on the wine list, so you are encouraged to ask for advice. Commendable and unobtrusive service. Six tables on the lawn in good weather. ***Seats** 60. Parties 40. Private Room 20. L 12-1.30 D 7-8.30. Set L £18.50 Set D £25.*

Many hotels offer reduced rates for weekend or out-of-season bookings.
Always ask about special deals.

Arundel Norfolk Arms 60% £70

Tel 0903 882101 Fax 0903 884275 **H**

22 High Street Arundel West Sussex BN18 9AD **Map 11 A6**

A Georgian coaching inn without the benefit of modernisation in the public rooms. By contrast, the bedrooms are bright, with pale floral patterns, and families of yellow ducks enliven the modern bathrooms. Newer rooms are in a detached wing to the rear. Children up to 14 stay free in parents' room. Functions and conferences for up to 100. Arundel Castle is an easy walk away. ***Rooms** 34.* AMERICAN EXPRESS *Access, Diners, Visa.*

Arundel Places of Interest

Arundel Castle Tel 0903 883136.
Denmans Garden Fontwell Tel 0243 542808.
Arundel Wildfowl and Wetlands Trust Tel 0903 883355.
Fontwell Park Racecourse 0243 543335.

Ascot Berystede Hotel 67% £129

Tel 0344 23311 Fax 0344 872301 **H**

Bagshot Road Sunninghill Ascot Berkshire SL5 9JH **Map 15 E2**

Just to the south of Ascot, this Forte Grand hotel is based on a large Victorian house standing in its own 6 acres of wooded grounds. As popular with racegoers as business people, the public rooms and the best of the bedrooms are in the original house and share its period feel. The majority of the bedrooms, however, are in a modern extension. The hotel has its own conference centre, catering for up to 120 delegates. ***Rooms** 91. Garden, outdoor swimming pool, putting, games room.* AMERICAN EXPRESS *Access, Diners, Visa.*

Ascot Hyn's £50

Tel 0344 872583 **R**

4 Brockenhurst Road Ascot Berkshire **Map 15 E2**

Peking, Szechuan and Cantonese all have their place on the menu (neatly and clearly printed, and no numbers!). Most of the dishes will be familiar to habitués of this most varied of cuisines, but slightly out of the ordinary are chicken liver with chili and garlic salt, Szechuan beef soup and steamed Dover sole with ginger and spring onions. There's also a small choice of Thai dishes. ***Seats** 90. Parties 10. L 12-2.30 D 6-11. Closed 25 & 26 Dec. Set meals from £14.50.* AMERICAN EXPRESS *Access, Diners, Visa.*

Ascot Royal Berkshire 76% £168

Tel 0344 23322 Fax 0344 874240 **HR**

London Road Sunninghill Ascot Berkshire SL5 0PP **Map 15 E2**

Previous occupants of this Queen Anne mansion, located between Ascot race course and the Polo Club, have included the Churchill family and a certain Colonel Horlicks (of malted drink fame) who developed the 15 acres of superb gardens and woodlands. It's operated by Hilton International. The public areas retain an air of elegance with restful colour schemes and quality furnishings. Bedrooms in the original house are spacious and stylish with freestanding furniture and plenty of extras; those in the extensions are a little simpler. The largest of the nine conference rooms can accommodate up to 70 delegates theatre-style. ***Rooms** 63. Garden, indoor swimming pool, sauna, whirlpool bath, tennis, squash, putting, helipad.* AMERICAN EXPRESS *Access, Diners, Visa.*

State Room Restaurant £90

An elegant dining room overlooking manicured lawns makes an appropriate setting for Andy Richardon's refined and inventive cooking. Both à la carte and fixed-price menus are sensibly limited in extent enabling Andy to concentrate his considerable skills on such dishes as pan-fried foie gras with plum and raisin chutney and warm brioche loaf, breast of chicken with morel cream and stewed peppers, loin of venison with peppered noodles and mulled pear, and ginger and praline mousse with a candied orange marmalade. Plain dishes are available on request. ***Seats** 35. L 12.30-2 D 7.30-9.30. Set L £19.95 Set D £28.*

Ascot — Places of Interest

Racecourse Tel 0344 22211.
Ascot Park Polo Club Wood Hall Tel 0344 20399.

Ashbourne — Ashbourne Lodge Hotel — 66% — £69

Tel 0335 46666 Fax 0335 46549 — **H**

Derby Road Ashbourne Derbyshire DE6 1XH — **Map 6 C3**

On the A52 from Derby to Leek, this modern redbrick hotel (previously the Ashbourne Oaks) is lent some old-world style by rustic-designed public areas. Bedrooms are neat and light but not over-large. Banqueting/conference facilities for 170/250. There's an all-day brasserie (The Black Sheep) with a children's menu. No dogs. ***Rooms** 50. Garden.* American Express *Access, Visa.*

Ashbourne — Callow Hall — 69% — £90

Tel 0335 343403 Fax 0335 343624 — **H**

Mappleton Road Ashbourne Derbyshire DE6 2AA — **Map 6 C3**

Five minutes' drive from the centre of Ashbourne, the Spencers' family home is an ideal retreat. Approached by a tree-lined drive through 44 acres of woodland, it enjoys a mile of private fishing on the nearby Bentley Brook. Quality antiques and family memorabilia are the main features of the drawing room and homely little bar. Bedrooms with tasteful design and elegant furnishings of the highest standard provide plenty of extras – from books and magazines to fresh fruit and mineral water; one spacious ground-floor room faces the house and is equipped for disabled guests. Sumptuous tiled bathrooms boast bathrobes and locally made toiletries. Private meetings for up to 40, banquets maximum 30. 'All young childen' stay free in their parents' room. No dogs. ***Rooms** 13. Garden, game fishing. Closed 25 & 26 Dec.* American Express *Access, Diners, Visa.*

Ashford — Ashford International — 71% — £107

Tel 0233 611444 Fax 0233 627708 — **H**

Simone Weil Avenue Ashford Kent TN24 8UX — **Map 11 C5**

A long, glass-roofed boulevard contains the spacious lobby at this smart hotel by Junction 9 of the M20. Various shops are down one side – an art gallery, golf shop and Avis car hire among others – and a lively bar, restaurant with smart cocktail bar plus a brasserie with tables spilling out on to the tiled concourse, down the other. A fountain and a large, four-face hanging clock complete the rather pleasing Continental air. Spacious bedrooms are well laid out with a couple of easy chairs, breakfast tables and good desk space, but are unremarkably decorated with muted colour schemes and floral fabrics. 24hr room service. Queens Moat Houses. ***Rooms** 200. Indoor swimming pool, sauna, solarium, whirlpool bath, beautician, gymnasium, brasserie (7am-11pm).* American Express *Access, Diners, Visa.*

Ashford — Eastwell Manor — 82% — £110

Tel 0233 635751 Fax 0233 635530 — **HR**

Eastwell Park Boughton Aluph Ashford Kent TN25 4HR — **Map 11 C5**

Set in 62 acres of grounds, a splendid Jacobean-style mansion built in the 1920s. An open courtyard leads through to public rooms that are every bit as impressive as the grand exterior. Real fires burn in the large fireplaces

See over

of the stone-flagged entrance hall and the mellow, oak-panelled day rooms, some of which boast ceilings with fine, detailed plasterwork and leather button-back armchairs. Spacious bedrooms vary considerably but are traditionally furnished (usually including an antique or two) and luxuriously appointed with large floral print fabrics and many extras like magazines, fruit and mineral water. The large bathrooms have bidets, bathrobes and quality toiletries. Queens Moat Houses. ***Rooms** 23. Garden, tennis, snooker, helipad.* AMERICAN EXPRESS *Access, Diners, Visa.*

Restaurant — £102

A coffered ceiling, stone-mullioned windows and armed dining chairs all contribute to a baronial feel here. Chef Mark Clayton is skilfully producing varied and imaginative dishes for his menus that encompass simpler lunches (grilled mackerel with tomato and onion compote, sautéed calf's liver with pearl barley and mustard sauce, banoffi pie) and involved dinners, table d'hote dinner and full à la carte. Grilled black pudding with lamb's kidneys, fillet of salmon with spinach on a mussel and mushroom cream sauce, and pancakes with an orange sauce give the style of the evening table d'hote, while the carte extends to more involved dishes such as warm chicken mousseline flavoured with sweetbreads and sweetcorn and finished with sage, roast monkfish tail wrapped in Bayonne ham set on a warm pulse and lentil dressing, and a chilled chocolate soufflé flavoured with oranges and Grand Marnier. Vegetarian options. The good wine list has tasting notes for each wine. Simpler 'country house' lunches served in the lounge.
***Seats** 80. Private Room 90. L 12.30-2 D 7.30-9.30 (Fri/Sat to 10). Set L £14 Set D £25.*

Ashford — Forte Posthouse — 66% — £68

Tel 0233 625790 Fax 0233 643176 — H

Canterbury Road Ashford Kent TN24 8QQ — **Map 11 C5**

Half a mile out of Ashford on the A28 to Canterbury and one mile from junction 9 of the M20. A modern hotel based around a 17th-century barn, now the restaurant. Conferences for up to 120 delegates. ***Rooms** 60. Garden.* AMERICAN EXPRESS *Access, Diners, Visa.*

Ashford — Holiday Inn Garden Court — 65% — £70

Tel 0233 713333 Fax 0233 712082 — H

Maidstone Road Hothfield Ashford Kent TN26 1AR — **Map 11 C5**

A no-frills Holiday Inn offering only limited services and public areas, but spacious bedrooms with big beds and lightwood furniture. Good value, with free accommodation for children in parents' room and greatly reduced rates at weekends. ***Rooms** 104. Keep-fit equipment.* AMERICAN EXPRESS *Access, Diners, Visa.*

Ashford — Travel Inn — £43

Tel 0223 712571 Fax 0223 713945 — L

Maidstone Road (A20) Hothfield Common Ashford Kent TN26 1AP — **Map 11 C5**

***Rooms** 40.* AMERICAN EXPRESS *Access, Diners, Visa.*

Ashford — Places of Interest

Tourist Information Tel 0233 629165.
Godinton Park Tel 0233 620773.

Ashford-in-the-Water — Riverside Hotel — 65% — £85

Tel 0629 814275 Fax 0629 812873 — H

Fennel Street Ashford-in-the-Water Derbyshire DE4 1QF — **Map 6 C2**

Sue and Roger Taylor, here since 1981, provide a home from home in their Georgian house, which stands in the centre of the village in mature gardens by the river Wye. There are two comfortable sitting rooms, one making the most of the views, the other smaller and convivial, with oak panelling and an inglenook fireplace. Individually decorated bedrooms, furnished with either four-posters or half testers, feature elegant soft furnishings (the work of Sue). All are designated non-smoking. Luxury rooms (added in 1991) carry a small supplement. A cottage on the river bank is let on a self-catering basis. Meals are served all day in the Terrace Room coffee shop/brasserie. ***Rooms** 15. Garden.* AMERICAN EXPRESS *Access, Visa.*

Ashford-in-the-Water Places of Interest

Buxton Tourist Information Tel 0298 25106.
Buxton Opera House Water Street Tel 0298 71382.
Buxton Museum and Art Gallery Terrace Road Tel 0298 24658.

Ashington Mill House Hotel

£74

Tel 0903 892426 Fax 0903 892855

I

Mill Lane Ashington West Sussex RH20 3BZ

Map 11 A6

Comfortable, friendly and homely, this 300-year-old cottagey hotel is clearly signposted on the northbound carriage of the A24 (it's less easy to find from the London side). Low ceilings and uneven floors characterise day rooms and bedrooms, the latter quite well equipped but simply decorated and generally on the small side. Children up to 11 are accommodated free in parents' room (breakfast only charged). There are two four-poster rooms. ***Rooms** 10. Garden.* AMERICAN EXPRESS *Access, Diners, Visa.*

Ashington The Willows

£55

Tel 0903 892575

R

London Road Ashington West Sussex RH20 3JR

Map 11 A6

Set back from the A24, this 15th-century farmhouse retains an inglenook fireplace and old black beams. Chef/patron Carl Illes offers three-course, fixed-price lunch and dinner menus plus a long à la carte. Dishes range from the simple (home-made cream of leek and potato soup) to the involved (salmon mousse and white crabmeat-filled ravioli flambéed in brandy, served with a tomato coulis and lemon butter sauce), from the ordinary (fanned avocado with prawns and Mary Rose sauce) to the unusual (pan-fried chicken breast with curried lemon lentils); portions are invariably generous. Chocaholics should be well satisfied by Willows truffle torte, baked white chocolate cheesecake or chocolate and rum mousse – well-executed desserts that remain on the menu. Ice cream lovers should seek out the Willows' speciality of vanilla, caramel and dark chocolate ice creams laced with Amaretto, Strega and Galliano, finished with whipped cream and frosted nuts. Vegetarians should notify their requirements in advance. ***Seats** 26. L 12-2 D 7-10. Closed L Sat, D Sun, all Mon. Set L £12.50/£15.50 (Sun £15) Set D £17.65.* AMERICAN EXPRESS *Access, Visa.*

Aspley Guise Moore Place 70%

£75

Tel 0908 282000 Fax 0908 281888

H

The Square Aspley Guise nr Woburn Bedfordshire MK17 8DW

Map 15 E1

Junction 13 of the M1 is just one-and-a-half miles away, but this finely restored Georgian country house, built in 1786, stands in a peaceful village square. Day rooms echo the image of a squire's residence in a rural idyll and are decorated in handsome period style with some original features remaining. Extensions include a sympathetically designed bedroom courtyard block, joined to the original house by a spacious glassed-in area where the reception and bar/lounge are located. Bedrooms are of a generous size, bright and airy, with lightwood furnishings and a good range of up-to-date accessories. ***Rooms** 54. Garden, games room.* AMERICAN EXPRESS *Access, Diners, Visa.*

Aston Clinton — Bell Inn 78% — £176

Tel 0296 630252 Fax 0296 631250 — **HR**

London Road Aston Clinton Buckinghamshire HP22 5HP — **Map 5 E2**

Family owners generate a unique blend of homely charm and serious professionalism in their 17th-century coaching inn on the A41. An appealing mix of log-burning fire, fresh flowers and pine panelling sets the scene in the public rooms, where the mark of time and history is firmly stamped. The flagstoned smoking room with its brass ornaments and sporting pictures, and the elegant dining room are particularly notable. Bedrooms in the main house and those around a cobbled courtyard with a fountain are individually decorated with co-ordinated fabrics and antique pieces; some open directly on to the garden. Useful extras range from fluffy towelling robes and toiletries to a mini-bar. Enjoyable breakfasts. Large conference (up to 250) and banqueting (up to 300) facilities. *Rooms 21. Garden.* AMERICAN EXPRESS *Access, Visa.*

Restaurant — £120

A new chef this year, as last, but continuity is provided by owner Michael Harris who takes a close and knowledgeable day-to-day interest in both restaurant and kitchen. The main menu with the likes of foie gras terrine with muscat jelly, aubergine parfait on tomato and basil, panaché of seafood 'pot au feu', and corn-fed chicken with woodland mushroom sauce, comes at £35 for two courses; for value go for the daily-changing three-course table d'hote menu (lunch £18.50, dinner £22.50) that offers three choices at each stage. The traditional Bell Inn Menu at £36 comprising Bell Inn smokies followed by locally-reared Aylesbury duck (carved at the table), a cheese soufflé and desserts is also a good bet. New this year is a Bistro menu of single dishes served in the bar – Ceasar salad, duck confit, fish soup, beef bourguignon, Italian salad. Service, on a recent visit, failed to live up to the Bell's normal high standards. ***Seats 120. Parties 18.*** *Private Room 20. L 12.30-2 D 7.30-9.45 (Sun to 8.45). Set meals from £17.35.*

Aston Clinton — Place of Interest

Zoological Museum, British Museum (Natural History) Akeman Street, Tring Tel 044 282 4181 *3 miles.*

Axbridge — Oak House — £51

Tel 0934 732444 Fax 0934 733112 — **I**

The Square Axbridge Somerset BS26 2AP — **Map 13 F1**

Less atmosphere than one would expect of an inn dating back to 1342 but there's a nice old inglenook with real fire in the lounge area. Inexpensively furnished bedrooms are well kept and offer the usual amenities. Bathrooms, three with shower and WC only, come with unwrapped soap and no extras. ***Rooms 10.*** AMERICAN EXPRESS *Access, Visa.*

Axbridge — Places of Interest

Tourist Information Tel 0934 744071.
Cheddar Showcaves Museum and Exhibition Tel 0934 742343.
Millfield School Polo Club Gunthorpe Farm, Chapel Allerton Tel 0458 42291.

Aylesbury — Hartwell House 86% — £157

Tel 0296 747444 Fax 0296 747450 — **HR**

Oxford Road Aylesbury Buckinghamshire HP17 8NL — **Map 15 D2**

80 acres of parkland surround this magnificent country house, once the home in exile of Louis XVIII of France. Dating back to the 16th century, it's notable for having two facades, one Jacobean and the other Georgian. Beautifully restored to its former glory by Historic House Hotels, it is the

epitome of luxury. Day rooms have many notable features like rococo ceilings, choice antiques, oil paintings and chandeliers. Wonderful plump-cushioned seating spreads through the grandly proportioned reception rooms. Bedrooms show high standards of luxury and comfort; sumptuously appointed in impressive fashion, they employ antiques, rich fabrics and a host of pampering extras, plus huge beds. Bright, neatly fitted bathrooms. Motivated staff provide high levels of service. 100 yards from the main house is the Hartwell Spa, modelled on an orangery inspired by Sir John Soane and incorporating fine leisure facilities – the grand 50-foot swimming pool is surrounded by an arched arcade and overlooked by a gallery where you will find the Spa Bar and Buttery. The new Hartwell function Rooms are situated in a restored 18th-century coach house and can accommodate up to 100 delegates; the rooms are named after distinguished architects who have contributed to the evolution of Hartwell House – James Gibbs, James Wyatt, Henry Keene and Eric Throssell. There are also interesting rooms in the main house for private dining. In addition to the leisure and meeting facilities Hartwell Court houses the 16 most recent bedrooms and suites. No children under 8. Dogs are not allowed in the grounds, but good kennels are nearby. ***Rooms*** *47. Garden, indoor swimming pool, spa bath, steam room, sauna, gymnasium, beauty salon, solarium, Spa Buttery (7.30am-9pm, Sun 9am-9pm), fishing.* AMERICAN EXPRESS *Access, Diners, Visa.*

Restaurant

£100

New chef Alan Maw offers 2- or 3-course luncheons (perhaps confit of duck, fillets of John Dory with a brioche crust, Trinity College burnt cream) and an extensive à la carte. The latter covers a wide range, perhaps starting with Scotch broth, salad of langoustines or pheasant paté, followed by grilled Dover sole, Highgrove lamb with a risotto of lamb's kidneys, canon of venison with a fruit pudding, roasted apple and a game sauce, or simpler dishes on request. The long wine list has obviously been chosen with care and includes a good choice of half bottles and house wines at reasonable prices, plus a couple of rare Vouvrays and Australian liqueur muscat dessert wines (sold by the glass). No smoking. ***Seats*** *70. Parties 8. Private Room 30. L 12.30-2 D 7.30-9.45. Set L £16.50/£22.40 Set D £38.*

Never leave money, credit cards or valuables lying around in your hotel room. Use the hotel safe or the mini-safe in your room.

Aylesbury — Post House — 69% — £68

Tel 0296 393388 Fax 0296 392211 — H

Aston Clinton Road Aylesbury Buckinghamshire HP22 5AA — **Map 15 D2**

A purpose-built modern hotel constructed around a central courtyard, alongside the A41 three miles east of the town centre. Public areas are open-plan and very smart. The tile-floored foyer leads to spacious lounges, furnished in contemporary fashion and making good use of attractive, colourful fabrics. Bedrooms are of a fair size and decorated in restful shades, with solid furniture and fully tiled bathrooms. Banqueting facilitites for 80, conferences up to 100. Formerly the Forte Crest. ***Rooms*** *94. Indoor swimming pool, gymnasium, sauna.* AMERICAN EXPRESS *Access, Diners, Visa.*

Aylesbury — Places of Interest

Tourist Information Tel 0296 382308.
Limelight Theatre Queen's Park Centre, Queen's Park. Tel 0296 431272.
Buckinghamshire County Museum Tel 0296 88849.
Weedon Park Showground Tel 0296 83734.
Historic Houses, Castles and Gardens
Claydon House Nr Winslow Tel 0296 730349.
Waddesdon Manor (NT) Waddesdon Tel 0296 651211/651282.

Bagshot — Pennyhill Park — 75% — £134

Tel 0276 471774 Fax 0276 475570 — H

London Road Bagshot Surrey GU19 5ET — **Map 15 E3**

A driveway leads from the A30 to this well-equipped hotel and country club, where professional tuition is available in a number of sporting activities. Notable architectural features of the 19th-century house include the baronial-style foyer-lounge with stained-glass windows, exposed stone walls and slate floor, and the lounge, on two levels, with a beamed gallery upstairs and panelling downstairs. Bedrooms in the main building are spacious and charming, and those around the redeveloped courtyard vary from cosy and intimate to elegant mini-suites; all are named after flowers or shrubs, except for the luxurious Hayward suite. Children up to ten stay free in parents' room. Exclusive Hotels. ***Rooms** 76. Garden, outdoor swimming pool, sauna, solarium, tennis, 9-hole golf course, riding, stabling, fishing.* AMERICAN EXPRESS *Access, Diners, Visa.*

We welcome bona fide complaints and recommendations on the tear-out pages at the back of the book for readers' comments. They are followed up by our professional team.

Bainbridge — Rose & Crown Inn — £64

Tel 0969 50225 Fax 0969 50735 — I

Bainbridge Wensleydale North Yorkshire DL8 3EE — **Map 5 D4**

Overlooking the green in an attractive Wensleydale village, the Rose & Crown has a history going back to the 15th century. The famous Forest Horn, once used to guide lost travellers and still blown on winter evenings, hangs in the panelled hall. Elsewhere, old-world character is most notable in the low-beamed bar. Floral fabrics give the bedrooms a cottagey look; several rooms have four-poster beds. Ample free parking. TVs, tea-makers and hairdryers in all rooms. ***Rooms** 12. Garden. Access, Visa.*

Bakewell — Hassop Hall — 74% — £93

Tel 0629 640488 Fax 0629 640577 — H

Hassop nr Bakewell Derbyshire DE45 1NS — **Map 6 C2**

The ancient seat of the Eyre family stands among trees and parkland at the heart of the Peak District National Park. Owned and run by Thomas Chapman since 1975, it provides space, comfort and more than a little style: beyond the marbled hallway with its antiques and oil paintings is a chandeliered lounge in Regency style, a drawing room, a room for non-smokers and a relaxing oak-panelled bar. The large, luxurious bedrooms are individually decorated and furnished, with embroidered bed linen and splendidly appointed bathrooms. From Bakewell take the Sheffield road. Turn left on to the B6001 to Hassop. No dogs. ***Rooms** 13. Garden, tennis, helipad. Closed 3 days Christmas.* AMERICAN EXPRESS *Access, Diners, Visa.*

Bakewell — Places of Interest

Tourist Information Tel 0629 813227.
Chatsworth House Tel 0246 582204.
Haddon Hall Tel 0629 812855.

Baldock — Forte Travelodge — £42

Tel 0462 835329 — **L**

Great North Road Hinxworth nr Baldock Hertfordshire SG7 5EX — **Map 15 E1**

Southbound on the A1, north of Baldock. ***Rooms** 40.* AMERICAN EXPRESS *Access, Visa.*

Bamburgh — Lord Crewe Arms — 58% — £62

Tel 066 84 243 — **H**

Front Street Bamburgh Northumberland NE69 7BL — **Map 5 D1**

Virtually in the shadow of Bamburgh Castle, the Lord Crewe has been owned and run by the Holland family since 1968. This is splendid walking country so the choice of bars and lounges (one reserved for non-smokers) is most welcome for casual callers; the Toby Jug bistro is open from 10am to 10pm. Well-kept bedrooms offer modest comfort; they mostly have laminate-topped fitted furniture and TVs, but there are no radios or phones. Five rooms do not have en-suite facilities. No children under 5. ***Rooms** 25. Closed Nov-Mar. Access, Visa.*

Bamburgh — Places of Interest

Bamburgh Castle Tel 06684 208.
Grace Darling Museum Tel 0665 720037.
Bamburgh Beach.

Banbury — Moat House — 62% — £79

Tel 0295 259361 Fax 0295 270954 — **H**

27-29 Oxford Road Banbury Oxfordshire OX16 9AH — **Map 15 D1**

A handsome Georgian house offering all the modern comforts. Star of the accommodation is the Blenheim Suite with a four-poster bed and whirlpool bath. Children up to 12 stay free in parents' room. Functions (up to 70) and conferences (to 80) are a speciality. Access to the car park is from Lucky Lane. ***Rooms** 48. Closed 26-29 Dec.* AMERICAN EXPRESS *Access, Diners, Visa.*

Banbury — Whately Hall — 65% — £105

Tel 0295 263451 Fax 0295 271736 — **H**

Banbury Cross Banbury Oxfordshire OX16 0AN — **Map 15 D1**

Dating from 1632, Whately Hall stands in gardens opposite Banbury Cross of nursery rhyme fame. Fine panelling, mullion windows and antiques give character to the day rooms. Bedrooms, some in a modern wing, all have well-lit, tiled bathrooms. Children up to 16 stay free in parents' room. Forte. ***Rooms** 74. Garden, coffee shop (8.30am-5pm).* AMERICAN EXPRESS *Access, Diners, Visa.*

Banbury — Places of Interest

Banbury Museum Tel 0295 259855.
Open Air Pool Tel 0295 62742.
Broughton Castle Tel 0295 262624.
Farnborough Hall Tel 0295 89202.
Upton House (NT) Edgehill Tel 0295 87266.

Barford — Glebe Hotel — 68% — £105

Tel 0926 624218 Fax 0926 624625 — **H**

Church Street Barford Warwickshire CV35 8BS — **Map 14 C1**

The rectory to the Church of St Peter was converted for hotel use in 1948. Today, though less than a mile from the M40/A46 junction, it claims to be Warwickshire's best-kept secret. Several extensions have been added *See over*

over the last few years, including the spacious conservatory restaurant (which serves an excellent-value Sunday lunch), the Glades leisure club and conference facilities for up to 150. The latest addition of five bedrooms includes the Shakespeare suite, which, though it overlooks the car park, does have a jacuzzi corner bath. The other bedrooms, individually decorated in soft pastel shades, feature four-poster or crown canopy beds, and the bathrooms are finished in gold plate with Italian marble floors. Children up to 12 stay free in parents' room. Good service throughout. ***Rooms** 41. Garden, indoor swimming pool, keep-fit equipment, spa bath, sauna, steam room.* AMERICAN EXPRESS *Access, Diners, Visa.*

Barnard Castle — Jersey Farm Hotel — 59% — £50

Tel 0833 38223 Fax 0833 31988 — H

Darlington Road Barnard Castle Co Durham DL12 8TA — **Map 5 D3**

A working farm surrounds this informal and friendly little hotel, which current owners the Watsons started as a bed and breakfast place in 1965. Public areas are homely and unfussy and the bedrooms, in the old farmhouse and in extensions, are modest but comfortable, with freestanding furniture and carpeted bathrooms. Superior rooms are larger, with more extras, and there are six suites. The conference centre can cater for banquets up to 150 and conferences up to 200. The hotel stands a mile east of town on the A67. ***Rooms** 22. Garden. Access, Visa.*

Barnard Castle — Places of Interest

Historic Houses, Castles and Gardens

Barnard Castle Tel 0833 38212.
Bowes Museum Gardens Tel 0833 690606.
Raby Castle Staindrop Tel 0833 38212.

Barnby Moor — Ye Olde Bell — 60% — £80

Tel 0777 705121 Fax 0777 860424 — H

Barnby Moor nr Retford Nottinghamshire DN22 8QS — **Map 7 D2**

On the edge of Sherwood Forest, just a mile from the A1, Ye Olde Bell has been offering hospitality to travellers for hundreds of years. Old oak panelling, open fireplaces and diamond-pane leaded lights retain the character of the public rooms while bedrooms offer modern comforts like direct-dial phones and hairdryers. Conferences for up to 250 delegates. Principal Hotels. ***Rooms** 55. Garden.* AMERICAN EXPRESS *Access, Diners, Visa.*

Barnham Broom — Barnham Broom Hotel — 62% — £82

Tel 060 545 393 Fax 060 545 8224 — H

Honingham Road Barnham Broom nr Norwich Norfolk NR9 3DD — **Map 10 C1**

A large modern complex comprising hotel, golf and country club and conference centre (up to 200 delegates). All the bedrooms have writing desks and other extras include radios in the bathrooms. ***Rooms** 52. Indoor swimming pool, squash, sauna, spa bath, steam room, solarium, beauty salon, hairdressing, tennis, two championship golf courses, snooker, coffee shop (9.30am-11.30pm).* AMERICAN EXPRESS *Access, Diners, Visa.*

Barnsley — Ardsley Moat House — 65% — £60

Tel 0226 289401 Fax 0226 205374 — H

Doncaster Road Ardsley Barnsley South Yorkshire S71 5EH — **Map 6 C2**

Mellow stone, late 18th-century mansion with modern extensions, housing a good variety of conference and function rooms holding 14 to 300. 30 bedrooms are designated non-smoking. ***Rooms** 73. Garden.* AMERICAN EXPRESS *Access, Diners, Visa.*

Barnsley — Armstrongs — £50

Tel 0226 240113 — R

6 Shambles Street Barnsley South Yorkshire S70 2SQ — **Map 6 C2**

Opposite the town hall, Armstrongs is a cheerful, informal restaurant/café-bar whose menu incorporates influences from home and overseas. A recent dinner choice included potato, chervil and watercress soup, pesto-filled beetroot pasta, sea bass poached with spring onions and ginger, marinaded breast of chicken with papaya, avocado, chili and lime salsa, and braised shin of venison with cumin, coriander and a celeriac relish. ***Seats** 60. L 12-2 D 7-10. Closed L Sat, all Sun & Mon, Bank Holidays. Set D £12.95.* AMERICAN EXPRESS *Access, Visa.*

Barnsley — Forte Travelodge — £42

Tel 0226 298799 — L

Stairfoot Roundabout Barnsley South Yorkshire — **Map 6 C2**

At the roundabout of A633 and A635, close to the centre of Barnsley. ***Rooms** 32.* AMERICAN EXPRESS *Access, Visa.*

Barnsley — Restaurant Peano — £60

Tel 0226 244990 — R

102 Dodworth Road Barnsley South Yorkshire S70 6HL — **Map 6 C2**

Michael and Tracey Peano's sturdy Victorian house, one mile from junction 37 of the M1, is home to some good, down-to-earth cooking with a hint of Italy creeping through. Tuscan white bean soup, salami of pig's trotter with braised lentils and red wine sauce, onion and cider soup and venison sausage with braised red cabbage and creamed potato might appear among the five or so starters on a carte written in a refreshingly straightforward manner; main courses could include pan-fried calf's liver with braised baby onions and bacon lardons, saddle of lamb with braised couscous, pine kernels and raisins, or goose breast with roast apple and red cabbage, depending on season. There's also usually a separate list of six or seven fresh fish dishes for both first and main courses. Desserts are always interesting – poached fruits with a lemon and mint parfait, orange *sformato*, tarte tatin, lemon tart and coffee sponge pudding with a vanilla sauce. A fixed-price no-choice three-course menu offers particularly good value. Tracey Peano deftly organises the service with an informal air, while Michael works away in the kitchen; meticulous attention to detail includes a board of English farmhouse cheeses and a carefully chosen wine list with exclusively Italian and French representation. ***Seats** 45. L 12-2 D 7-9.30. Closed Mon & Sun, 2 weeks Sep. Set L & D £14.50.* AMERICAN EXPRESS *Access, Visa.*

Barnsley — Places of Interest

Cannon Hall Cawthorne Tel 0226 790270.
Wentworth Castle Stainborough Tel 0226 285426.
Oakwell Football Ground Tel 0226 295353.

Barnstaple — Imperial Hotel — 60% — £87

Tel 0271 45861 Fax 0271 24448 — H

Taw Vale Parade Barnstaple Devon EX32 8NB — **Map 13 D2**

A solid Edwardian building overlooking the river Taw. Meeting rooms for up to 80 people. Forte. ***Rooms** 56.* AMERICAN EXPRESS *Access, Diners, Visa.*

See the Conference and Banqueting section for lists of hotels arranged by county.

Barnstaple Lynwood House £61

Tel 0271 43695 Fax 0271 79340 **RR**

Bishop's Tawton Road Barnstaple Devon EX32 9DZ **Map 13 D2**

An elegant and spacious Victorian house run as a restaurant with rooms by the Roberts family since 1969. Ruth and her son Matthew cook in classical style; John and 'no. 3 son' Christian run the dining rooms, which have traditional decor with large windows, polished mahogany tables and discreet antique dividing screens. Seafood is the main speciality, with dishes like local mussels, quenelles of sole with a prawn sauce, chunky fish soup, Dover sole, fresh scallops pan-fried with lime juice, soy sauce and ginger, pot of seafood and goujonettes of turbot. A couple of meat options might include warm confit of duck or pheasant served off the bone with a rich pear sauce. Good choice of desserts. Light 2- and 3-course business lunches are served Monday to Friday; there is also a long menu of lighter dishes. No smoking in dining room. ***Seats** 40. **Private Room** 20. L 12-2 D 7-10. Closed Sun. Set L £10.95/£12.95.* AMERICAN EXPRESS *Access, Visa.*

Rooms £60

Overnight guests are accommodated in five Executive bedrooms, all with armchairs and plenty of creature comforts. Two rooms for non-smokers. Separate breakfast room; fresh Scottish kippers. No dogs.

Barnstaple Places of Interest

Tourist Information Tel 0271 47177.
Arlington Court (NT) Tel 0271 850296.
Marwood Hill Marwood Tel 0271 42528.
Museum of North Devon incorporating Royal Devon Yeomanry Museum Tel 0271 46747.
Exmoor Bird Gardens South Stowford Tel 05983 352/412.

Barton Mills Forte Travelodge £42

Tel 0638 717675 **L**

Barton Mills Mildenhall Suffolk IP28 6AE **Map 10 B2**

On the A11, at the 5 ways roundabout, 8 miles north-east of Newmarket. ***Rooms** 32.* AMERICAN EXPRESS *Access, Visa.*

Barton Stacey Forte Travelodge £42

Tel 0264 72260 **L**

Barton Stacey nr Andover Hampshire SO21 3NP **Map 15 D3**

On the A303 westbound – approximately 4 miles east of Andover. ***Rooms** 20.* AMERICAN EXPRESS *Access, Visa.*

Barton-under-Needwood Forte Travelodge £42

Tel 0283 716343 **L**

Barton-under-Needwood Burton-on-Trent Staffordshire DE13 8EG **Map 6 C3**

On the A38 northbound, 4 miles south of Burton-on-Trent. ***Rooms** 20.* AMERICAN EXPRESS *Access, Visa.*

Barton-under-Needwood Forte Travelodge £42

Tel 0283 716784 **L**

Barton-under-Needwood Burton-on-Trent Staffordshire DE13 3EH **Map 6 C3**

On the A38 southbound, 3 miles to the south of Burton-on-Trent. ***Rooms** 40.* AMERICAN EXPRESS *Access, Visa.*

Basildon — Campanile Hotel — £44

Tel 0268 530810 Fax 0268 286710 — **L**

Southend Arterial Road Pipps Hill Basildon Essex SS14 3AE — **Map 11 B4**

Take Junction 29 of the M25, then Basildon exit from A127. ***Rooms** 98.* AMERICAN EXPRESS *Access, Diners, Visa.*

Basildon — Forte Posthouse — 59% — £68

Tel 0268 533955 Fax 0268 530119 — **H**

Cranes Farm Road Basildon Essex SS14 3DG — **Map 11 B4**

Modern exterior, bright and pleasant accommodation, plus lake views from the conservatory-style bar. Banqueting facilities for up to 250, conferences to 300. Formerly the *Forte Crest.* ***Rooms** 110.* AMERICAN EXPRESS *Access, Diners, Visa.*

Basildon — Travel Inn — £43

Tel 0268 522227 Fax 0268 530092 — **L**

Felmores East Mayne Basildon Essex SS13 1BW — **Map 11 B4**

Just off the M25 (J29). ***Rooms** 42.* AMERICAN EXPRESS *Access, Diners, Visa.*

Basildon — Place of Interest

Towngate Theatre Pagel Mead Tel 0268 531343.

Basingstoke — Audleys Wood — 75% — £123

Tel 0256 817555 Fax 0256 817500 — **HR**

Alton Road Basingstoke Hampshire RG25 2JT — **Map 15 D3**

Alongside the A339 Alton road, close to Junction 6 of the M3. Built in the late 1880s for Sir George Bradshaw (whose railway timetables made his fortune) and set in seven wooded acres, the overtly Victorian house had a varied history before being transformed into a hotel of some luxury (it opened in 1989). A splendid carved oak fireplace graces the panelled lounge, which also features a minstrel's gallery. Similar darkwood panelling and a handsome fireplace are to be found in the bar. The majority of the bedrooms are in sympathetically-designed extensions: roomy and tastefully appointed, with marble-tiled bathrooms; main-house bedrooms are even larger and more luxurious; 26 rooms reserved for non-smokers. Children up to 14 can share their parents' room at no charge; interconnecting rooms available. Friendly staff. Mount Charlotte Thistle. ***Rooms** 71. Garden, pétanque, putting, golf practice net, bicycles.* AMERICAN EXPRESS *Access, Diners, Visa.*

Restaurant — £66

Situated in what was the original palm house and conservatory, the striking restaurant has a most unusual vaulted wood ceiling. Terence Greenhouse, once Executive Head Chef on the *QE2*, is at the helm. An à la carte is always offered, but lunchtimes also see both 2- or 3-course fixed-price affairs and a hot 2-course business lunch served from a trolley. Both table d'hote and à la carte menus are also offered at dinner, with daily specials and a couple of interesting vegetarian dishes. Brandied crayfish bisque flavoured with thyme and garnished with vegetable pearls and 'a duet of guinea hen and pheasant breast cushioned with a woodland mushroom filling, wrapped in gammon and moistened with a port and plum sauce' show the rather grand style! Good cheeses, both French and English, served with walnut bread, chilled grapes and celery. ***Seats** 74. Parties 16. Private Room 40. L 12-1.45 (Sun to 2.15) D 7-9.45 (Fri & Sat to 10.15, Sun to 9.15). Closed L Sat, Bank Holidays. Set L £13.75 & £14.95/£17.95 Set D from £21.*

Basingstoke — Forte Posthouse — 64% — £68

Tel 0256 468181 Fax 0256 840081 — H

Grove Road Basingstoke Hampshire RG21 3EE — Map 15 D3

Leave the M3 at Junction 6 and follow signs for Alton on the A339. Accommodation includes 12 new Executive rooms. Conference and banqueting facilities for up to 180 delegates. Children's playroom and playground. ***Rooms** 84.* AMERICAN EXPRESS *Access, Diners, Visa.*

Basingstoke — Forte Travelodge — £42

Tel 0256 843566 — L

Winchester Road Basingstoke Hampshire RG22 6HN — Map 15 D3

2 miles from Junction 7 of the M3, off the A30 southbound, at the Brighton Hill roundabout. ***Rooms** 32.* AMERICAN EXPRESS *Access, Visa.*

Basingstoke — Hee's — £40

Tel 0256 464410 — R

23 Westminster House Basingstoke Hampshire RG21 1CS — Map 15 D3

Decent MSG-free Szechuan and Peking cooking on the edge of Basingstoke's huge central shopping centre. Cheerful staff provide attentive service. ***Seats** 80. L 12-2 D 6-11. Closed L Sun, 4 days Christmas. Set meals from £13.50.* AMERICAN EXPRESS *Access, Diners, Visa.*

Basingstoke — Hilton National — 66% — £87

Tel 0256 460460 Fax 0256 840441 — H

Old Common Road Black Dam Basingstoke Hampshire RG21 3PR — Map 15 D3

Bright, open-plan public areas, neat accommodation and numerous meeting rooms (conferences for up to 150) at a modern hotel a mile from junction 6 of the M3 (follow the signs for Eastrop). Formerly the *Hilton Lodge*. Children up to 16 stay free in parents' room. ***Rooms** 144. Indoor swimming pool, keep-fit equipment, sauna, assault course.* AMERICAN EXPRESS *Access, Diners, Visa.*

Basingstoke — The Ringway Hotel — 65% — £64

Tel 0256 20212 Fax 0256 842835 — H

Aldermaston Roundabout Ringway North Basingstoke Hampshire RG24 9NV — Map 15 D3

Formerly the *Hilton National* with bedrooms ranging from small singles to roomy, well-appointed suites. 26 rooms are designated non-smoking. ***Rooms** 134. Indoor swimming pool, keep-fit equipment, sauna.* AMERICAN EXPRESS *Access, Diners, Visa.*

Basingstoke — Travel Inn — £43

Tel 0256 811477 Fax 0256 819329 — L

Worting Road Basingstoke Hampshire RG22 6PG — Map 15 D3

Situated in the centre of a leisure park. ***Rooms** 49.* AMERICAN EXPRESS *Access, Diners, Visa.*

Basingstoke — Places of Interest

Tourist Information Tel 0256 817618.
Stratfield Saye Tel 0256 882882 *Home of the Duke of Wellington.*
The Vyne (NT) Sherborne St. John Tel 0256 881337.
Basing House Basing Tel 0256 467294.
Basingstoke Ice Rink Tel 0256 840219.

Baslow Cavendish Hotel 71% £117

Tel 0246 582311 Fax 0246 582312 **H**

Baslow Derbyshire DE4 1SP **Map 6 C2**

Standing on the Chatsworth Estate and commanding very fine rural views the Cavendish has a history going back several hundred years. Solidly built of local stone, it has with an exterior that is as characterful and traditional as the interior. The entrance hall is graciously inviting with fresh flower arrangements, antiques, porcelain and a roaring log fire in cooler weather. Adjoining it is a south-facing conservatory which fronts the lounge – a delightful room decorated in pale blues and yellows. The bar also has a log fire, is darker and more intimate with mahogany furniture and upholstery of striking blue and gold stripes. Bedrooms are being upgraded with the most recently completed being bright and chintzy. The Milford wing of bedrooms is decorated in more masculine tones of beige and tartan. Good beds ensure a peaceful night's sleep. Comfortable armchairs, writing desks and mini-bars with fresh milk help to make one's stay pleasurable. Bathrooms are bright with light varnished wood floors. Bathrobes and a range of toiletries are provided. ***Rooms** 24. Garden, putting, fishing.* AMERICAN EXPRESS® *Access, Diners, Visa.*

Baslow Fischer's Baslow Hall ★ £80

Tel 0246 583259 **RR**

Calver Road Baslow Derbyshire DE4 1RR **Map 6 C2**

On the A623 Manchester road just north of the village stands Baslow Hall – the home of Max and Susan Fischer – an impressive Edwardian manor house built in mellow Derbyshire stone and situated within the Peak National Park. Approached by a long, uphill, tree-lined drive, Baslow Hall dates from 1907, although it looks considerably older. A Chinese-inspired lounge and three separate dining rooms run by Susan form an appealing and elegant restaurant, wherein one can enjoy Max's consistently rewarding cooking. Though not averse to using fashionable ingredients, he sticks to what what he knows best, producing precisely cooked, strong-flavoured dishes based on traditional methods. A recent menu commenced with a warm appetiser, then a warm lobster timbale, sea bream in puff pastry with Beluga caviar or lamb's kidneys in peppercorn sauce with a parsley mousse; main courses included a saddle of venison with tortellini, lentils in mustard and tarragon sauce, tenderloin of lamb on globe artichoke in olive oil, veal steak with fresh truffles and a pair of fish dishes. The small selection of desserts is always interesting and might include apple galette with cinnamon ice cream, jasmine tea crême brulée or a rhubarb tartlet with stem ginger meringue and yoghurt sorbet. Dinner menus are hand-written in English and descriptions kept to a minimum; an element of surprise is thus very much part of the enjoyment. Lunchtime dishes are less involved: perhaps seafood salad or chicken liver parfait followed by best end of lamb or salmon with herb sauce and then white and dark chocolate terrine). Sunday lunch, when a choice of roasts is offered along with some five starters and desserts, is always popular. Simpler, but equally well-executed meals – including breakfast and afternoon tea – are served from 10am to 10pm (not Sun) in *Café Max*, a former living room off the entrance hall, and on the terrace in summer. ***Seats** 35.*
Private Room 12 & 24. L 12-2 (Sun to 2.30) D 7-9.30 (Sat to 10). Closed L Mon, D Sun (except residents), 25 & 26 Dec. Set L £18.50 Set D £34. AMERICAN EXPRESS® *Access, Visa.*

Rooms £95

Six appealing bedrooms (three large, three small) show great style amd taste with choice antique pine furniture. En-suite bathrooms are neatly up-to-date, although one has an original enamel bath and shower. Breakfast, as one might expect, is tip-top and might include smoked salmon and scrambled eggs and local honeycombs.

Bassenthwaite — Armathwaite Hall — 65% — £100

Tel 076 87 76551 Fax 076 87 76220 — **H**

Bassenthwaite Lake nr Keswick Cumbria CA12 4RE — **Map 4 C3**

In a quiet and secluded lakeside setting, lawns and parkland bordered by woodlands lead down from this historic stately house to the foreshore. Inside, the baronial feel is nurtured by oak panelling and ceilings, hunting trophies, oil paintings and pewterware. Best bedrooms in the main house have fine views and plenty of space, while rooms in the coach house/stable block are also spacious. Good views from the Lake View restaurant (where breakfast is served). The equestrian centre offers hacking and lessons among its facilities. Families are well catered for, with accommodation free for under-14s when sharing parents' room; baby-sitting by arrangement, cots and high-chairs provided; informal eating in the leisure club. A new animal farm park with a variety of farm animals and rare breeds is open between April and October. Two self-catering units are within the grounds. A choice of conference rooms caters for up to 120. ***Rooms** 42. Garden, tennis, indoor swimming pool, gymnasium, sauna, solarium, riding, spa bath, beauty salon, hairdressing, snooker, 9-hole pitch & putt, coarse and game fishing, mountain bikes, coffee shop (10am-10pm).* AMERICAN EXPRESS *Access, Diners, Visa.*

Bassenthwaite Lake — Pheasant Inn — 65% — £92

Tel 076 87 76234 Fax 076 87 76002 — **H**

Bassenthwaite Lake nr Cockermouth Cumbria CA13 9YE — **Map 4 C3**

Originally a farm, the Pheasant Inn is nevertheless an archetypal Victorian roadside inn (mercifully by-passed these days by the A66), as it was converted in 1826. It displays abundant period appeal: open fires, beams hung with brasses, old prints and antique firearms. Well-kept gardens (where afternoon tea and bar snacks can be taken) are an added summer attraction and are overlooked by tastefully furnished bedrooms in varying styles. Adequate, simply fitted bathrooms are the only obvious nod to modernity. No phones, TVs or dogs in bedrooms; no piped music or fruit machines in the public rooms – just the pervading Lakeland peace and quiet. ***Rooms** 20. Closed 25 Dec. No credit cards.*

Bath — Apsley House — 67% — £105

Tel 0225 336966 Fax 0225 425462 — **H**

141 Newbridge Hill Bath Avon BA1 3PT — **Map 13 F1**

Personally run by the Davidsons, Apsley House is a small William IV mansion on the A431 to the west of town offering a peaceful base from which to explore Bath and the surrounding area. Day rooms combine elegance with homeliness and well-kept bedrooms are spacious and comfortable. Most of the carpeted bathrooms boast bidets and separate showers in addition to the tub. Five more modest (reflected in the price), but equally immaculate rooms are in the adjacent Coach House. These share two bathrooms and conveniently divide into two family suites. Children and dogs are accommodated only in the Coach House. Room service of drinks and cold meals throughout the day and evening. Own parking. ***Rooms** 12. Garden.* AMERICAN EXPRESS *Access, Visa.*

Bath — Bath Spa Hotel — 87% — £183

Tel 0225 444424 Fax 0225 444006 — **HR**

Sydney Road Bath Avon BA2 6JF — **Map 13 F1**

Quite simply, this is a marvellous hotel deserving to be in Forte's Exclusive portfolio (which it was when first opened) rather than its present Grand status. Without doubt it is one of the company's flagship hotels with surroundings, furnishings, a splendid health and leisure spa, and service to match. Carefully restored and extended, the Georgian mansion, standing in landscaped grounds (visit the grotto at the bottom of the gardens) has panoramic views over the city, a ten-minute stroll away. Behind the elegant porticoed frontage is a good deal of style and luxury, complemented by super staff very capably directed by General Manager Robin Sheppard. A spacious entrance lobby with Oriental carpets over slate and stone diamond flooring, elaborate plasterwork ceiling, extravagant fresh flower display and antique long case clock sets the tone of public areas which include a gracious drawing room, the neo-classical Colonnade with murals and greenery, and clubby bar. At the far end of the Colonnade there is a display of mineral waters from around the world. Bedrooms (many non-smoking), including seven suites, are individually decorated in great style with a striking combination of check fabrics and floral prints. They offer a high degree of comfort, matched by particularly well-designed bathrooms in Grecian marble and mahogany, with padded towel seating, bathrobes and Penhaligon toiletries. Some fine function rooms (up to 120 theatre-style) are in keeping with the rest of the hotel. Extensive 24hr room service, ample own parking. Dogs (basket and bowls provided) welcome: their owners can be accommodated on the ground floor with easy access to the grounds at the end of the corridor. Watch out for the mice, but do not be alarmed, they are all made of pastry and are the hotel's trademark! ***Rooms** 100. Garden, indoor swimming pool, gymnasium, sauna, spa bath, solarium, beauty salon, tennis, valeting, coffee shop (7am-6pm).* AMERICAN EXPRESS *Access, Diners, Visa.*

Vellore Restaurant ↑ £90

The original ballroom makes for a fine setting in which to enjoy new chef Jonathan Fraser's excellent cooking. No stranger to the Guide (in the last ten years he has previously been in charge of three Berkshire hotel restaurants) his menus, using the best local and British produce, offer simple but quite robust dishes with style, variety and a high degree of skilful preparation, as well as pleasing presentation. A typical daily (two choices in each course) menu might consist of North Sea halibut with a pesto crust and a white burgundy sauce, loin of new season lamb with comb honey and thyme, Welsh onion cake, spinach purée and ragout of vegetables, ending with a caramelised lime tart, fresh raspberry salpicon and Old English ice cream. Exemplary amuse-gueule and petits fours, splendid coffee and caring service under the direction of maitre d'hotel David White. The comprehensive wine list has some particularly good New World wines. Lunches and informal dinners – note the wines by the glass and bottle on the good-value list – are served in the Alfresco (Colonnade), with honeyed woodstrip flooring, cane chairs and picture windows overlooking a patio garden with fountain. Seasonal dishes with an eclectic cooking style (the Far East, Mediterranean and English); you can have just a starter and dessert, or the full three courses. ***Seats** 100. Parties 8. Private Room 120. L (Sun only) 12.30-2 D 7-10; Alfresco 12.30-2 & 6.30-9.30 Set D £34.*

If we recommend meals in a hotel or inn a separate entry is made for its restaurant.

Bath Circus Restaurant £50

Tel 0225 330208 **R**

34 Brock Street Bath Avon BA1 2LN **Map 13 F1**

Lunch is now an all-day affair with about ten savoury dishes (from £2.75 to about £6) on a 'café-style' menu along with coffees and pastries etc. The format of the evening menu remains unchanged offering a varied selection of soundly cooked dishes in an informal atmosphere; grilled goat's cheese salad with roasted peppers and walnut oil dressing, rack of Wiltshire lamb with garlic and rosemary jus, tagliatelle with courgettes and mushrooms in spicy tomato sauce. Most starters have two prices and may also be taken as a main course. ***Seats** 60. Parties 40. Private Room 40. L 10-5 D 7-10 (Fri, Sat till 11). Closed D Sun, Easter Mon, 25, 26 Dec & 1 Jan. Set L £7.95/ £9.95. Access, Visa.*

Bath Clos du Roy NEW £55

Tel 0225 444450 **R**

1 Seven Dials Saw Close Bath Avon BA1 1EN **Map 13 F1**

On the first floor of the new Seven Dials development near the Theatre Royal, Philippe Roy is staging his return to town (he opened the first *Clos du Roy* in Bath in 1984 before moving out to nearby Box) in a smart setting with a musical theme. A white grand piano in the centre of the room is in use several nights a week. Through a picture window to the kitchen diners can watch the chefs preparing the likes of artichoke and mushroom cassolette with saffron sauce, hot goat's cheese with walnut salad, John Dory with onion confit, filet of widgeon with honey sauce or mango-stuffed breast of pheasant with a sauce of Noilly Prat. At night there is a choice of set menus plus an à la carte 'Theatre Special' designed for pre-or post-theatre dining but available all evening. ***Seats** 65. L 12-2.30 D 6-11.30. Closed D Sun & Mon. Set L £8.50/£11.95 Set D £17.50/ £22.50.* AMERICAN EXPRESS *Access, Diners, Visa.*

Bath Fountain House £120

Tel 0225 338622 Fax 0225 445855 **PH**

9/11 Fountain Buildings Lansdown Road Bath Avon BA1 5DV **Map 13 F1**

An 'all-suite hotel' (a familiar concept in the US but a new idea here), Fountain House comprises one, two and three bedroom suites with sitting room and smart, fully-equipped kitchen, within a Palladian mansion on the northern edge of the city centre. The idea is that one gets privacy and space with the level of service (except room service) one would expect of a conventional hotel – full maid service with fresh bed linen each day for example. Unfussy decor and good-quality furnishings are immaculately maintained. A basket of fresh bread, milk, yoghurt etc and a daily newspaper are delivered to the door each morning. Reception staff can organise most things from car hire and theatre tickets to a personal in-room fax or shooting in the owners' own 750-acre estate. Unlike in a serviced apartment there is no minimum stay and indeed many guests stay for just one night. There are no public rooms. ***Suites** 14.* AMERICAN EXPRESS *Access, Diners, Visa.*

Bath Francis Hotel 67% £125

Tel 0225 424257 Fax 0225 319715 **H**

Queen Square Bath Avon BA1 2HH **Map 13 F1**

Forte Heritage hotel set in what were Georgian town houses overlooking the gardens of Queen Square in the centre of town. Public areas have a traditional feel – sofas and chesterfields in the clubby bar, old oil portraits and lacy cloths on the coffee tables in the residents' lounge. Bedrooms in the original building generally have freestanding furniture with some having been recently refurbished in Forte's attractive new Heritage colour scheme of red and green. Rooms in a newer wing are more functional (but spacious) with older style, shelf-type furniture and somewhat dated bathrooms. Limited own parking. ***Rooms** 93.* AMERICAN EXPRESS *Access, Diners, Visa.*

Bath Garlands £60

Tel 0225 442283 **R**

7 Edgar Buildings George Street Bath Avon BA1 2EE **Map 13 F1**

Tom Bridgeman, chef, and Jo Bridgeman, front of house, own and run a relaxed little restaurant that appeals to both tourists and a regular local trade. French and English-inspired cuisine includes daily fish specials (perhaps red mullet with an orange butter sauce), and enjoyably different dishes like roast pigeon salad with pickled red cabbage and oyster mushrooms, or escalope of lamb's liver with diced tomato and avocado. Fixed-price only lunches (2-or 3-course) and à la carte dinners. Diverse wine list with interesting tasting notes. There's an informal café-bar behind the main restaurant. ***Seats** 28. Parties 14. Private room 35. L 12-2.15 D 7-10.30. Closed L Mon, 25 & 26 Dec. Set L £12.75/£14.95 Set D £15.50/£18.50.* AMERICAN EXPRESS *Access, Visa.*

Bath **Hilton National** **67%** **£120**

Tel 0225 463411 Fax 0225 464393 **H**

Walcot Street Bath Avon BA1 5BJ **Map 13 F1**

Closest to shopping and sights (a few minutes walk from the Abbey and Roman baths). Spacious public areas, business centre and leisure club; imposing new facade and accommodation that includes best-appointed Plaza rooms and a no-smoking floor. There's free parking for 30 cars in the forecourt. ***Rooms** 150. Indoor swimming pool, keep-fit facilities, sauna, spa bath, solarium.* AMERICAN EXPRESS *Access, Diners, Visa.*

Bath **Lansdown Grove** **65%** **£105**

Tel 0225 315891 Fax 0225 448092 **H**

Lansdown Grove Bath Avon BA1 5EH **Map 13 F1**

Owned by the same family for over 100 years, the Lansdown Grove, set high up above the city, has benefited from continuity of care and attention. Individually decorated bedrooms reflect the good taste of the proprietor's wife with fresh, bright colour schemes and a variety of well-chosen fabrics. Furniture varies from limed oak to more traditional freestanding pieces. Public areas are equally well kept and include a comfortable residents' lounge of grand proportions overlooking mature gardens. Good parking. ***Rooms** 45. Garden.* AMERICAN EXPRESS *Access, Diners, Visa.*

Bath **The New Moon** **NEW** **£48**

Tel 0225 444407 **R**

Seven Dials Sawclose Bath Avon BA1 1ES **Map 13 F1**

A smart, determinedly modern brasserie/restaurant in a new courtyard development near the Theatre Royal. Coffee, croissants and *pain au chocolat* start the day with chef Michel Lemoin's eclectic brasserie menu coming on stream about midday: onion tart with mustard-dressed salad, barbecued teriyaki of chicken wings, salmon with polenta and salsa. Around 6 pm the mood changes and a more formal, fixed-price dinner menu takes over. Starters like venison terrine with cranberry compote and moules marinière (the menu changes daily) might be followed by roast cod fillet with a caper and lemon sauce or steamed breast of chicken with a sweet red pepper sauce among the half-dozen or so main dishes. Despite there being a realistically priced wine list (short but varied with about a dozen available by the glass) you can also bring your own at lunchtime and again from 5.30 without any corkage charge. ***Seats** 80. Meals 9am-11pm. Closed 25 Dec. Set D £14.50/£17.50.* AMERICAN EXPRESS *Access, Visa.*

Bath **Newbridge House** **63%** **£110**

Tel 0225 446676 Fax 0225 447541 **H**

35 Kelston Road Bath Avon BA1 3QH **Map 13 F1**

A very private Georgian house in a spectacular location above Bath Marina, on the A431 a couple of miles from the city centre. Balconied, south-facing day rooms, including the Lord Kirkwood boardroom (seating 12), overlook award-winning gardens, a view shared by the best, period-style Victorian bedrooms. The smaller size of rear twins and singles, with WC/shower only, is reflected in their price. No bar. Children, pets and smokers not welcomed. ***Rooms** 12. Garden.* AMERICAN EXPRESS *Access, Diners, Visa.*

Bath Priory Hotel 79% £164

Tel 0225 331922 Fax 0225 448276 **HR**

Weston Road Bath Avon BA1 2XT **Map 13 F1**

Although less than a mile from the city centre, the Georgian-Gothic Priory with its two acres of garden is very much a country house hotel in style and atmosphere. Civilised, relaxing day rooms are matched by charming, individually-decorated bedrooms, each named after a flower, furnished with antiques and all sorts of homely touches: fresh flowers, flask of iced water, books, magazines, pot-pourri. Deluxe rooms (about half) are particularly spacious, with a separate sitting area. Bathrooms boast quality toiletries, bathrobes, telephone extensions and power showers over tubs. Just one small single room has shower and WC only. Limited room service throughout the day and evening. No dogs. ***Rooms** 21. Garden, outdoor swimming pool.* AMERICAN EXPRESS *Access, Diners, Visa.*

Restaurant £75

No flights of fancy here, just reliably sound cooking from long-serving chef Michael Collom who generally sticks to time-proven combinations: gravad lax with dill mayonnaise, rack of lamb with garlic and rosemary, saddle of venison with red cabbage and juniper sauce, and hot apple pie with Calvados sabayon give the style. A good selection of British and Continental cheeses offers an alternative to dessert for those without a sweet tooth. Choose from one of several dining rooms – the bright Garden Room, Orangery or more traditional (and slightly tired) Brown Room. Always some good value special offers and bin ends on a solid list that has something for everyone at affordable prices. No smoking. ***Seats** 70. Private Room 60. L 12-2.30 D 7-9 Set L £20 Set D £29.50.*

Bath Queensberry Hotel 75% £123

Tel 0225 447928 Fax 0225 446065 **HR**

Russel Street Bath Avon BA1 2QF **Map 13 F1**

In a quiet street just to the north of the town centre, this small Georgian terrace hotel is a haven of peace, tranquillity and luxury. Individually decorated rooms boast antique furniture, deep comfortable seating and homely touches like books, magazines, fruit and, in the spacious carpeted bathrooms, large towelling robes and quality toiletries. Day rooms include an elegant period drawing room and cosy bar overlooking secluded courtyard gardens. Full of charm and immaculately kept throughout. No dogs. ***Rooms** 22. Garden. Access, Visa.*

Olive Tree Restaurant £55

Oriental rugs over white ceramic tiles, rag-rolled walls, modernistic (though comfortable) chairs and the crispest of white linen all add up to a cool sophistication which finds its match in Stephen Ross's contemporary menu. Marinated leg of lamb grilled with an olive herb crust, puff pastry of smoked haddock with lentils and bacon, aubergine galette with tomato and mozzarella and passion fruit tart typify the carefully-cooked offerings from a sensibly short à la carte menu. The day's no-choice set lunch or dinner menu is recited at the table. Of some three dozen well-chosen wines more than half are priced under £15. ***Seats** 44. Private Room 25. L 12-2 D 7-10.30 Closed L Mon, all Sun & 2 wks Xmas/New Year. Set L £10.50 Set D £17.*

Bath Royal Crescent Hotel 84% £170

Tel 0225 319090 Fax 0225 339401 **HR**

16 Royal Crescent Bath Avon BA1 2LS **Map 13 F1**

No signs are allowed to spoil the grand sweep of John Wood's magnificent Royal Crescent so look out for the magnolia tree by a door at the centre of the terrace to find the best address in town. Day rooms, both here and in the Dower House to the rear of the enclosed garden (a delightful spot in summer), retain their 18th-century elegance along with some fine original oil paintings and a scattering of antiques. The best suites are very grand, with some fine architectural features, but even the most modest (a relative term here) have elaborate bedhead drapes or a half tester along with antique furniture and extras like mineral water, fruit and a flowery plant. Bathrooms are suitably luxurious with towelling robes and quality toiletries. Standards of service match the surroundings with full evening maid service and valet parking. No dogs. ***Rooms** 42. Garden, plunge pool.* AMERICAN EXPRESS *Access, Diners, Visa.*

Dower House Restaurant ★↑ £95

Unashamedly luxurious surroundings – elaborate gilt wall lights, marble busts and formal service – are more than matched by chef Steven Blake's sophisticated cooking. A marriage of traditional skills and a nouvelle cuisine-like emphasis on attractive presentation combine in well-conceived dishes that delight the palate as much as the eye. A novel terrine of foie gras, duck and confit with lentils might share the menu with salmon poached in an olive and pimento liquor; medallions of venison with a compote of apple, shallots, chestnuts and orange; and a simple but perfectly executed, warm chocolate tart with orange sauce. There's also an impressive selection of regional English cheeses. At lunchtime the à la carte is replaced by a menu of light dishes that may also be taken more informally in the cocktail bar. Though the wine list contains many misspellings it has improved since last year. There are well-chosen wines in most sections, lots of half bottles and a decent house selection. Prices won't please some pockets! No children under 8. Valet parking even for non-residents. ***Seats** 66. Parties 8. Private Room 80. L 12.30-2 D 7-9.30 (Sat till 10). Set L £14.50/£18.50 Set D £25.*

Bath Places of Interest

Tourist Information Tel 0225 462831.
Theatre Royal Sawclose Tel 0225 448815.
Historic Houses, Castles and Gardens
Claverton Manor Tel 0225 460503 *American Museum in Britain.*
Crowe Hall Gardens Widcombe Hill Tel 0225 310322.
Dyrham Park near Junction 18 of M4 Tel 027582 2501.
Priston Mill Nr Bath Tel 0225 23894.
Sally Lunn's House Tel 0225 61634.
Bath Racecourse Tel 0451 20517.
Museums and Art Galleries
Museum of Costume Assembly Rooms Tel 0225 461111 Ext 2785.
Roman Baths Museum Tel 0225 461111 Ext 2785.
Number One Royal Crescent (Bath Preservation Trust) Tel 0225 428126.
Victoria Art Gallery Tel 0225 461111 Ext 2772.

Battle Netherfield Place 78% £90

Tel 042 46 4455 Fax 042 46 4024 **HR**

Battle East Sussex TN33 9PP **Map 11 C6**

Owners Helen and Michael Collier personally supervise the running of their Georgian-style country retreat. Thirty acres of parkland make a very peaceful setting, and the extensive gardens provide most of the flowers that are a feature in the bright, spacious drawing room. Bedrooms are mostly of a very good size, and have sitting areas. All are beautifully furnished and there are two comfortable chairs and a writing desk in each. Carpeted bathrooms have good-quality toiletries, bathrobes and thick towels. Children under 12 stay free in their parents' room; baby-sitting by arrangement and children's high tea from 5pm. ***Rooms** 14. Garden, putting, tennis. Closed 3 weeks Christmas/New Year.* AMERICAN EXPRESS *Access, Diners, Visa.*

See over

Restaurant **£70**

The redwood-panelled dining room has garden views and is a lovely setting in which to enjoy Michael Collier's cooking. Dishes such as duet of lobster and crab ravioli, chicken boudin, loin of local venison with a fresh pear and cranberry sauce, Dutch veal cutlet with a citrus suace, and double chocolate parfait indulgence are invariably enjoyable and use first-rate ingredients. The extensive kitchen gardens provide fine fresh vegetables and herbs. Good vegetarian choices and a daily-changing table d'hote supplement the carte. Six tables in the garden in really good weather. ***Seats** 50. Private Room 40. L 12-2 D 7-9.30 (Sun to 9).*
Set L £14.50 & £15.95 Set D £22.50.

Battle Places of Interest

Tourist Information Tel 04246 3721.
Battle Abbey Tel 04246 3792.
Museums and Art Galleries
Battle Museum Langton House.
Buckleys Shop Museum Tel 04246 4269.
The Almonry Tel 04246 2727.

Bawtry The Crown 64% £88

Tel 0302 710341 Fax 0302 711798 **H**

High Street Bawtry South Yorkshire DN10 6JW **Map 7 D2**

A sturdy old coaching inn, over 300 years old, encompassing conference/function rooms for 15 to 170. Most bedrooms are in a modern wing: 50% non-smoking, one four-poster room, another equipped for disabled guests. Forte Heritage. ***Rooms** 57. Garden.* AMERICAN EXPRESS *Access, Diners, Visa.*

Beaconsfield Bellhouse Hotel 67% £115

Tel 0753 887211 Fax 0753 888231 **H**

Oxford Road Beaconsfield Buckinghamshire HP9 2XE **Map 15 E2**

De Vere hotel on the A40, close to junction 2 of the M40, with an impressive Spanish-style frontage. Six separate conference suites accommodate up to 450 delegates. Popular leisure club includes beauty therapy. Children up to 14 stay free in parents' room. ***Rooms** 136. Indoor swimming pool, gymnasium, squash, sauna, spa bath, solarium, beauty salon, snooker.* AMERICAN EXPRESS *Access, Diners, Visa.*

Beaconsfield Places of Interest

Bekonscot Model Village Tel 0494 672919.
Chiltern Open Air Museum Newland Park Tel 02407 71117 *5 miles.*
Milton's Cottage Tel 02407 2313.

Beanacre Beechfield House 70% £80

Tel 0225 703700 Fax 0225 790118 **H**

Beanacre nr Melksham Wiltshire SN12 7PU **Map 14 B2**

An ornate Victorian mansion surrounded by eight acres of mature gardens containing many specimen trees, after which individual bedrooms are named. A white marble fireplace in the reception area houses a real log fire to welcome guests in winter. The two main day rooms are appropriately furnished with reproduction period-style easy chairs plus an incongruously modern, low-backed settee. A new addition is the bar counter in the larger room. Bedrooms vary in size but all have pretty, matching fabrics and most an antique or two plus fruit, flowers and mineral water. Good carpeted bathrooms no longer offer bathrobes. ***Rooms** 24. Garden, outdoor swimming pool.* AMERICAN EXPRESS *Access, Diners, Visa.*

Bearsted Tudor Park Golf & Country Club 67% £109

Tel 0622 34334 Fax 0622 735360 **H**

Ashford Road Bearsted nr Maidstone Kent ME14 4NQ **Map 11 C5**

Modern hotel near Junction 8 of the M20 and just two miles from Leeds Castle. Extensive leisure facilities that include a spectacular 18-hole golf course and covered practice ground are the main attraction. The public rooms are interestingly laid out and include an intimate piano bar, the garden restaurant overlooking the golf course and plum-coloured cocktail bar. Bedrooms are of a good size and feature large, comfortable beds. Attractive, curved swimming pool. Banqueting/conference facilities for 216/275. Country Club Hotels. ***Rooms** 120. Indoor swimming pool, spa bath, sauna, steam room, solarium, gymnasium, snooker, squash, tennis, car hire, coffee shop (10am-10pm), beautician, children's play area, table tennis, golf (18), helipad.* AMERICAN EXPRESS *Access, Diners, Visa.*

Our inspectors are full-time employees; they are professionally trained by us.

Beaulieu Montagu Arms 68% £96

Tel 0590 612324 Fax 0590 612188 **H**

Beaulieu New Forest Hampshire SO42 7ZL **Map 14 C4**

Situated in the centre of a charming village, the 13th-century Montagu Arms is near the Abbey and the motor museum. The comfortable, relaxed feel is greatly enhanced by the welcoming log fires that warm the foyer and lounge in cooler months. There's also a library bar and conservatory. Individually furnished bedrooms (some with four-posters or brass bedsteads) have modern bathrooms. Some rooms have separate sitting rooms. ***Rooms** 24. Garden.* AMERICAN EXPRESS *Access, Diners, Visa.*

Beaulieu Places of Interest

Tourist Information Tel 0590 612345 ext 278.
Beaulieu Abbey and National Motor Museum Tel 0590 612123.

Bebington Forte Travelodge £42

Tel 051-327 2489 **L**

Bebington New Chester Road Eastham Wirral Merseyside L62 9AQ **Map 6 A2**

On the A41 northbound, off Junction 5 of the M53. ***Rooms** 31.* AMERICAN EXPRESS *Access, Visa.*

Beccles Waveney House 59% £60

Tel 0502 712270 Fax 0502 712660 **H**

Puddingmoor Beccles Suffolk NR34 9PL **Map 10 D2**

Boating people appreciate the riverside position of 16th-century Waveney House, and there's a certain amount of nautical chat in the bar and residents' lounge. Even bedrooms have a shipboard feel with creaking floorboards, uneven walls and beams beneath which to duck. ***Rooms** 13. Garden, fishing, mooring.* AMERICAN EXPRESS *Access, Diners, Visa.*

Beccles Places of Interest

Marina Theatre Lowestoft Tel 0502 573318.
Somerleyton Hall Nr Lowestoft Tel 0502 730224/730308.
Kessingland Beach *4 miles south of Lowestoft.*
Lowestoft Beach.
Pleasurewood Hill American Theme Park Corton Tel 0493 441611.

Beckingham Black Swan £50

Tel 0636 626474 **R**

Hillside Beckingham Lincolnshire LN5 0RF **Map 7 E3**

A converted village pub with a country atmosphere and a charming riverside garden where light summer lunches are served. The à la carte and fixed-price menus provide an interesting selection of dishes, some classic, others with original touches: quail and oyster mushroom soup served with sherry, duck breast served with glazed rhubarb on a candied ginger sauce, vegetable and cashew nut filo parcels on a tomato vinaigrette. Desserts often include a tempting dark chocolate terrine with chocolate ice cream on a white chocolate sauce. No smoking. ***Seats** 30. L 12-2 D 7-10. Closed D Sun, all Mon. Set L Sun £12.50 Set D £14.75. Access, Visa.*

Bedford Moat House 65% £70

Tel 0234 355131 Fax 0234 340447 **H**

2 St Mary's Street Bedford Bedfordshire MK42 0AR **Map 15 E1**

Modern tower block in a prime riverside position in the town centre. Banqueting and conference facilities for 300+. ***Rooms** 100. Keep-fit equipment, sauna.* AMERICAN EXPRESS *Access, Diners, Visa.*

Bedford Woodlands Manor 70% £97

Tel 0234 363281 Fax 0234 272390 **H**

Green Lane Clapham Bedford Bedfordshire MK41 6EP **Map 15 E1**

Now under new ownership, a honey-coloured turn-of-the-century manor house in its own grounds off the A6 2 miles north of Bedford. Best of the bedrooms, housed in a sympathetic extension, are spacious and stylishly furnished, with sofas and breakfast tables. Bathrooms are impressive, with Italian marble tiling. No children under seven. No dogs. ***Rooms** 25. Garden, helipad.* AMERICAN EXPRESS *Access, Visa.*

Bedford Places of Interest

Tourist Information Tel 0234 215226.
Bowen West Community Theatre Tel 0234 2193331.
The Swiss Garden Old Warden, Biggleswade Tel 0234 228330.
Wrest Park House and Gardens Silsoe, Nr Ampthill Tel 0525 60718.
Stagsden Bird Gardens Tel 02302 2745.

Museums and Art Galleries

Bromham Mill Bromham Tel 0234 228330.
Cecil Higgins Art Gallery and Museum Tel 0234 211222.
Bedford Museum Tel 0234 53323.
The Shuttleworth Collection (Aviation History) Old Warden, Biggleswade Tel 076 727 288.

Belford Blue Bell Hotel 63% £66

Tel 0668 213543 Fax 0668 213787 **H**

Market Square Belford Northumberland NE70 7NE **Map 5 D1**

A creeper-clad, family-run hotel in the centre of the village. Much period charm has been retained, with two bedrooms in the old coach house opposite. Children up to 14 stay free in their parents' room. A public bar is across a courtyard, leaving the cocktail bar free for residents. Nearby, Cheviot House is under the same ownership and offers guest house accommodation. ***Rooms** 17. Garden.* AMERICAN EXPRESS *Access, Visa.*

Belton — Belton Woods Hotel — 72% — £115

Tel 0476 593200 Fax 0476 74547 — **H**

Belton nr Grantham Lincolnshire NG32 2LN — **Map 7 E3**

Just off the A607, north of Grantham, a modern complex standing in 475 acres of grounds, with outstanding sports facilities that are matched by equally impressive accommodation. A spacious, high-ceilinged lounge leading off the main foyer is filled with parlour plants and hanging baskets, and overlooks one of three golf courses (two 18-hole and one 9-hole). The cocktail bar on the first floor is more club-like, with easy chairs and rich decor. Spacious bedrooms have good seating and working areas; plain painted walls lighten up the use of contemporary fabrics. Ambassador rooms feature extras like a mini-bar and settee. Excellent facilities for children include a children's playground and swimming pool, cots and baby-sitting. Now under the group ownership of De Vere Hotels who, as we went to press, had plans for 40 further bedrooms and even larger leisure facility areas. ***Rooms** 96. Garden, indoor swimming pool, spa bath, sauna, steam room, solarium, beauty salon, hairdressing, gymnasium, games room, snooker, golf courses (9 & 18 hole), golf driving range, fishing, tennis, coffee shop (7am-10.30pm).* AMERICAN EXPRESS *Access, Diners, Visa.*

Belton — Place of Interest

Tourist Information Tel 0476 66444.
Historic Houses, Castles and Gardens
Belton House (NT) Tel 0476 66116.
Fulbeck Hall Tel 0400 72205.
Woolsthorpe Manor (NT) Tel 0476 860338 *Birthplace of Sir Isaac Newton.*
Belvoir Castle Tel 0476 870262.

Berwick-upon-Tweed — Funnywayt'mekalivin — £45

Tel 0289 308827 — **R**

41 Bridge Street Berwick-upon-Tweed Northumberland TD15 1ES — **Map 3 D6**

Elizabeth Middlemiss runs a more roomy and relaxed restaurant than in her previous premises and now also opens for lunch; the unusual name belies the serious atmosphere and intentions within. Lunchtime sees a choice of six or so good-value, straightforward dishes, and dinner extends to four or five courses. The latter may be a set menu commencing with canapés and a complimentary glass of pineau de Charente, tomato and mint soup with crusty bread and then crab and avocado salad; roast sirloin of Scottish beef served with a Madeira sauce, glazed beetroot, spring cabbage with garlic and juniper and home-made horseradish sauce might feature as the main course, followed by chocolate marquise with two sauces (raspberry and strawberry coulis and white chocolate). Local farmhouse cheeses are offered as an alternative to dessert or as an additional course. The wine list is simple and sensibly priced. Vegetarians should notify in advance of evening reservations. ***Seats** 32. Private Room 24. L 11.30-2.30 D 7-8.30. Closed D Mon & Tues, L Sat, all Sun, 25 & 26 Dec, 1 Jan. Set D £18.50. Access, Visa.*

Berwick-upon-Tweed — Kings Arms — 59% — £75

Tel 0289 307454 Fax 0289 308867 — **H**

Hide Hill Berwick-upon-Tweed Northumberland TD15 1EJ — **Map 3 D6**

Dating from the 18th century, this town-centre hotel offers agreeable overnight accommodation that includes three rooms with four-posters. Solid oakwood furnishings give a reassuringly traditional feel, and there's plenty of room to relax in the chandelier-hung lounge and the cocktail bar. The Royal Suite is a popular venue for banquets and conferences. ***Rooms** 36. Coffee shop (9.30-6).* AMERICAN EXPRESS *Access, Diners, Visa.*

Berwick-upon-Tweed Places of Interest

Tourist Information Tel 0289 330733.
Lindisfarne Castle Holy Island Tel 0289 89244 *Causeway flooded at high tide.*
Berwick Borough Museum & Art Gallery (EH) Tel 0289 330933.
Manderston Duns Tel 0361 83450 *15 miles.*
Paxton House Tel 0289 86291.

Beverley Beverley Arms 62% £90

Tel 0482 869241 Fax 0482 870907 **H**

North Bar Within Beverley Humberside HU17 8DD **Map 7 E1**

300-year-old coaching inn that retains a certain period interest. Bedrooms are mostly in a modern block. Conferences facilities for up to 80. Forte. ***Rooms** 57. Courtyard/patio, news kiosk, coffee shop (9.30am-6.30pm).*
AMERICAN EXPRESS *Access, Diners, Visa.*

Beverley Places of Interest

Art Gallery and Museum Tel 0482 882255.
Beverley Minster Tel 0482 868540.
Racecourse Tel 0482 867488.

Bexley Forte Posthouse 56% NEW £68

Tel 0322 526900 Fax 0322 526113 **H**

Black Prince Interchange Southwold Road Bexley Kent DA5 1ND **Map 11 B5**

Beside the A2 this much extended former public house provides simple, no-frills accommodation in a purpose-built bedroom block. Self-contained business centre has up-to-date features. ***Rooms** 102. Terrace, games room.*
AMERICAN EXPRESS *Access, Diners, Visa.*

Bexleyheath Swallow Hotel 71% NEW £94

Tel 081-298 1000 Fax 081-298 1234 **H**

1 Broadway Bexleyheath Kent DA6 7JZ **Map 11 B5**

An Italianate-style brick exterior to this newly constructed hotel a short drive from the A2 conceals a modern and contemporary interior design within. Public areas range from a stylish and slightly more traditional foyer-lounge with gas effect fireplace to an American 50s-inspired cocktail bar. The Copper Restaurant is mainly an all-day operation with buffet service, while the Galleria Restaurant is a more formal room with painted ceiling and modern furnishings. The basement area has a well equipped and thoughtfully constructed leisure club (they even have good facilities for disabled guests, wheelchair and pool lift and separate changing rooms). Bedrooms of generous size have modern pastel-coloured designer fabrics and soft furnishings; thoughtful touches here include irons and ironing boards and cartons of fresh milk in mini-bars for tea and coffee. Bathrooms have marble tiled floor, decent-sized towels, good shower baths and phone extension. Meeting and banqueting facilities are extensive including six boardroom-style rooms equipped with all the latest technology. Very stylish and pleasing artwork and pictures throughout the hotel. ***Rooms** 142. Terrace, indoor swimming pool, gymnasium, spa bath, steam room, solarium.*
AMERICAN EXPRESS *Access, Diners, Visa.*

Bibury The Swan 78% £128

Tel 0285 740695 Fax 0285 740473 **HR**

Bibury Gloucestershire GL7 5NW **Map 14 C2**

Just a pretty little creeper-clad village hotel with a garden across the road alongside the river Coln – that's the impression, at least until one enters this remarkable hotel that has been virtually recreated by Alex Furtek and Liz

Hayles over the last couple of years. The reception area, with automatic grand piano that plays in the evenings, and, more particularly, the twin lounges (one for non-smokers) have a strong 1940s feel with high plate shelves and an excess of overstuffed settees. Explore further through and one finds a splendid long bar with pale oak panelling, leather tub chairs on flagstone floor, log fire and one wall covered with a mural depicting various folk involved in the hotel's transformation. Press on and the mood changes yet again in a stylish all-day brasserie (an unexpected find in a sleepy Cotswold village) complete with Italian wrought-iron furniture; a useful alternative to the hotel's rather grand dining room and the place where late-risers will find breakfast. There are all sorts of fine decorative fabrics throughout the hotel including a collection of Charles Rennie Mackintosh chairs. Upstairs even the standard bedrooms have great appeal with antique furniture and individual decor, the best might have a four-poster bed, crystal chandelier, spa bath or luxuriously large, old-fashioned freestanding tub. Fine toiletries and bathrobes are standard. Quality of service from friendly, well-motivated staff is high, with nice touches like the linen mat placed by the side of the bed when rooms are serviced in the evenings. No dogs. ***Rooms** 18. Garden, fishing, brasserie (10am-10pm). Closed 24 Dec-8 Jan. Access, Visa.*

Restaurant ↑ — £98

Coming to the Cotswolds and eating here, you may be surprised, but not disappointed, by the Gallic flair that accompanies the cooking, due entirely to new chef Alain Pochciol. His evening menu includes a glass of carefully selected wine to complement each of the five courses, so in effect you're drinking the value of a bottle in the "ridiculously low price of £27.50". He applies a French interpretation to dishes such as green pea soup with minted dumplings, braised lettuce and lardons, marinated Scotch salmon with garlic chips and candied vegetables, ballotine of roasted guinea fowl served with a wild mushroom risotto, or a pavé of cod cooked with fennel marmalade and lobster ravioli. Excellent vegetables come from a newly-found and reliable local grower, the renowned Bibury trout are caught from the river literally opposite, and fine local cheeses are supplemented by a Stilton and a mature Scottish Cheddar. Hot and cold puddings – try an old-fashioned chocolate cream with a warm honey madeleine or a terrine of yellow peach in a Sangria jelly surrounded by a caramelised orange sauce. A well-presented wine list has a good choice under £20. The surprisingly large dining room is quite impressive with chandeliers and heavy, elaborately draped damask curtains. Jacket and tie required. No smoking. ***Seats** 60. Private Room 12. L Sun 12.30-2 other days by arrangement D 7.30-9.30 (Fri & Sat till 10) Set L £21.50 Set D £27.50/£35.*

Bigbury-on-Sea — Burgh Island Hotel — 66% — £168*

Tel 0548 810514 Fax 0548 810243 — H

Burgh Island Bigbury-on-Sea Devon TQ7 4AU — **Map 13 D3**

A 26-acre private island with a unique Art Deco hotel restored by current owners Beatrice and Tony Porter to the glory of its opening day in 1929. That splendour includes the Palm Court with its Peacock Dome and cocktail bar, a glass sun lounge, jet-black glass and pink mirrors on the staircase, and a magnificent ballroom. Period furniture abounds in day rooms and in the bedrooms, all of which are suites. A lift serves all three floors. Banqueting/conference facilities for 100 delegates. You should telephone for the best time to arrive, which depends largely on the tide (a giant sea tractor makes the short trip from the mainland to the island, which was once a notorious smugglers' haunt). *Half-board terms only, therefore one is obliged to eat in the hotel. No dogs. ***Rooms** 14. Garden, sauna, solarium, tennis, keep-fit equipment, games room, snooker, sea fishing. Closed mid-week during Jan & Feb.* AMERICAN EXPRESS *Access, Visa.*

Bilbrough Bilbrough Manor 75% £105

Tel 0937 834002 Fax 0937 834724 **HR**

Bilbrough nr York North Yorkshire YO2 3PH **Map 7 D1**

An attractive manor house among fine Georgian gardens in a quiet village off the A64, six miles from York. Though the present house "only" dates from 1901, there's been an abode here for some 700 years, and it's probably best known as the family home of Thomas Fairfax, Cromwell's right-hand man. The Manor was restored by Colin and Sue Bell and opened as a country house hotel in 1987. Day rooms include a foyer-bar and a splendid lounge with lightwood panelling and comfortable sofas. Prettily decorated bedrooms are light and airy with carefully matched colour schemes and soft furnishings, but rather plain modern furniture. Compact, carpeted bathrooms. No children under 10. ***Rooms** 12. Garden. Closed 25-29 Dec.* AMERICAN EXPRESS *Access, Diners, Visa.*

Restaurant £65

Andrew Pressley's menus are classically based with many innovative touches (the innovation occasionally getting the better of the cooking techniques): tortellini of smoked cheese and sun-dried tomato with a light dill cream sauce; steamed purse of sea bass filled with a purée of nettles and salad rocket set on a crab sauce; grilled Dover sole with quenelles of tomato ragout; calf's liver coated in brioche crumbs pan-fried and set on a sweet pepper coulis; a speciality dessert of thin, crisp leaves of nougatine layered with raspberries, strawberries and Chantilly cream. Vegetarian menu available. ***Seats** 70. Parties 45. Private Room 20. L 12-2 D 7-9.30 (Sun to 9). Set L £10.50/£14.50 Set D £20/£25.*

Billingshurst Forte Travelodge £42

Tel 0403 782711 **L**

Staines Street Five Oaks Billingshurst West Sussex RH14 9AE **Map 11 A6**

On the A29 northbound, 8 miles south-west of Horsham. ***Rooms** 26.* AMERICAN EXPRESS *Access, Visa.*

Bingley Bankfield Hotel 61% £105

Tel 0274 567123 Fax 0274 551331 **H**

Bradford Road Bingley West Yorkshire BD16 1TU **Map 6 C1**

On the A650 Bradford/Skipton road, a castellated Gothic frontage that "wouldn't look out of place on a Hollywood film set". Inside, handsome Victorian day rooms and mainly modern, decent-sized bedrooms, 29 of which have been recently refurbished. Conference facilities and winter dinner dances. Jarvis Hotels. ***Rooms** 103. Garden.* AMERICAN EXPRESS *Access, Diners, Visa.*

Birdlip Kingshead House £55

Tel 0452 862299 **RR**

Birdlip nr Gloucester Gloucestershire GL4 8JH **Map 14 B2**

Judy and Warren Knock run a relaxed, informal and welcoming country restaurant with serious intentions in the kitchen. Judy offers fixed-price-only dinner menus that vary weekly plus lighter, value-conscious lunch options available in the bar as well as restaurant. A typical dinner menu offers a handful of choices at each stage, perhaps starting with green pepper and fennel soup, then trout stuffed with spinach and pine nuts, roast topside of veal with anchovies and Parmesan and finishing with prune and Armagnac ice cream. Traditional Sunday lunches. Popular culinary evenings have recently covered 17th-century and Catalonian themes. Lots of half bottles on a concise and informative wine list with friendly prices. ***Seats** 32. L 12.30-2.15 (Sun to 2) D 7.30-10. Closed L Sat, D Sun, all Mon, 25 & 26 Dec, 1 Jan. Set Sun L £15.50 Set D £22.50/£24.50.* AMERICAN EXPRESS *Access, Diners, Visa.*

Room **£55**

The one and only en-suite double bedroom is a delightful place to stop over for a night. Birdlip lies on the lovely Cotswold Way and is equidistant (8 miles) from Gloucester and Cheltenham. Accommodation closed over Christmas holidays.

Birkenhead — Bowler Hat Hotel 65% — £70

Tel 051-652 4931 Fax 051-653 8127 — **H**

2 Talbot Road Oxton Birkenhead Merseyside L43 2HH — **Map 6 A2**

One mile off the M53, junction 3, a large Victorian house with the majority of rooms in a redbrick extension to the rear. Two new function rooms have brought the conference capacity up to 240. Children up to 12 stay free in parents' room. ***Rooms** 32. Garden.* AMERICAN EXPRESS *Access, Diners, Visa.*

Birkenhead — Places of Interest

Tourist Information Woodside Visitors Centre Tel 051 647 6780.
Birkenhead Park Tel 051 647 2366.
Williamson Art Gallery and Museum Tel 051 652 4177.
Lady Lever Art Gallery Port Sunlight Village Tel 051 645 3623.
Oval Sports Centre Bebington Tel 051 645 0551.

Birmingham — Adil Tandoori — £25

Tel 021-449 0335 — **R**

148-150 Stoney Lane Sparkbrook Birmingham West Midlands B11 8AJ — **Map 6 C4**

Basic balti house with a spreading reputation. Unlicensed, and the splendid nan bread does the work of knives and forks. ***Seats** 100. Parties 40. Private Room 25. Meals 12-12. Closed 25 Dec.* AMERICAN EXPRESS *Access, Diners, Visa.*

Any person using our name to obtain free hospitality is a fraud.
Proprietors, please inform the police and us.

Birmingham — Birmingham Metropole 72% — £190

Tel 021-780 4242 Fax 021-780 3923 — **H**

National Exhibition Centre Birmingham West Midlands B40 1PP — **Map 6 C4**

A huge, modern hotel at the heart of the National Exhibition Centre site with over 800 hundred rooms in three wings – Crown, Executive and Standard; it caters mainly for conference delegates and business folk. Decor is light and up-to-date, and the matching fabrics are contemporary in style; all rooms have smart, solid furniture and modern tiled bathrooms with good mirrors and showers. Twenty-six pairs of rooms interconnect, making them ideal for family or small business use. Public areas include a striking foyer, a bar-lounge with mirrored columns and contemporary seating and decor plus three restaurants. 700 car parking spaces are available free to residents. The magnificent conference and banqueting facilities cater for up to 2000 delegates. ***Rooms** 802. Closed Christmas/New Year.* AMERICAN EXPRESS *Access, Diners, Visa.*

Birmingham — Campanile Hotel — £44

Tel 021-622 4925 Fax 021-622 4195 — **L**

Irving Street Lee Bank Birmingham West Midlands B1 1DH — **Map 6 C4**

City-centre site, off Bristol street, near Queensway. ***Rooms** 50.* AMERICAN EXPRESS *Access, Diners, Visa.*

Birmingham — Chung Ying — £37

Tel 021-622 5669 — **R**

16 Wrottesley Street Birmingham West Midlands B5 6RT — **Map 6 C4**

The Chinese flock to this well-established, traditionally appointed restaurant for its long Cantonese menu. The choice extends to well over 300 dishes, including more than 40 dim sum items and a 'special dishes' section that covers fried prawn balls with ginger and spring onion; steamed pork pie with salted egg, diced squid or fresh squid; and stuffed peppers with black bean sauce. ***Seats** 220. Meals 11.30-12. Closed 25 Dec.* AMERICAN EXPRESS *Access, Diners, Visa.*

Birmingham — Chung Ying Garden — £37

Tel 021-622 5669 — **R**

17 Thorp Street Birmingham West Midlands B5 4AT — **Map 6 C4**

Sister and near neighbour of the original *Chung Ying*, this has more modern decor, with pillars, plants and murals. The menu is no less extensive and the chef's specialities include king prawn casserole with spicy cream sauce, paper-wrapped fillet of beef and quick-fried dry squid and shredded jellyfish with celery. The menu also lists 40 dim sum dishes, half of them not available after 5. ***Seats** 300. Meals 12-11.30 (Sun till 10.30). Closed 25 Dec.* AMERICAN EXPRESS *Access, Diners, Visa.*

Birmingham — Copthorne Hotel — 70% — £127

Tel 021-200 2727 Fax 021-200 1197 — **H**

Paradise Circus Birmingham West Midlands B3 3HJ — **Map 6 C4**

Close to the International Convention Centre, and overlooking Centenary Square, the hotel has a striking black glass exterior to complement the sleek and contemporary public areas which include a marble-floored foyer and raised bar-lounge. The ongoing refurbishment programme has introduced a number of Connoisseur bedrooms which offer guests extras to the standard rooms, though all enjoy excellent bathrooms with large mirrors and plenty of shelf space. Children up to 16 stay free in parents' room. At a hotel of this class one can reasonably expect coffee at breakfast to be served in a pot and not just in a cup, especially since everything else is self-service. Comprehensive conference, banqueting and fitness facilities, as well as a business centre. Own limited free parking, and nearby multi-storey car park. ***Rooms** 212. Indoor swimming pool, gymnasium, sauna, spa bath, steam room, solarium, news kiosk.* AMERICAN EXPRESS *Access, Diners, Visa.*

Birmingham — Days of the Raj — £35

Tel 021-236 0445 — **R**

51 Dale End Birmingham West Midlands B4 7LS — **Map 6 C4**

Northern Indian food served in relaxing surroundings. Specialities include mixed meat biryani, lamb chops masala and makhan chicken. Lunchtime and weekday evening buffet. ***Seats** 80. Parties 30. Private Room 15. L 12-2.30 D 7-11.30 (Fri & Sat 6-12). Closed L Sat & Sun.* AMERICAN EXPRESS *Access, Diners, Visa.*

Birmingham — Forte Crest — 68% — £97

Tel 021-643 8171 Fax 021-631 2528 — **H**

Smallbrook Queensway Birmingham West Midlands B5 4EW — **Map 6 C4**

By the inner ring road, a concrete tower hotel with adjacent multi-storey car park. There's a business centre supporting conferences of up to 630 delegates. The former Albany is in good condition after refurbishment. More than half the bedrooms are designated non-smoking. ***Rooms** 253. Indoor swimming pool, keep-fit equipment, squash, sauna, solarium.* AMERICAN EXPRESS *Access, Diners, Visa.*

Birmingham — Forte Posthouse — 60% — £68

Tel 021-357 7444 Fax 021-357 7503 — **H**

Chapel Lane Great Barr Birmingham West Midlands B43 7BG — **Map 6 C4**

Practical, modern hotel on the A34, near Junction 7 of the M6. Conference and banqueting facilities for 150. ***Rooms** 192. Garden, indoor & outdoor swimming pool, sauna, spa bath, children's playroom and playground.* AMERICAN EXPRESS *Access, Diners, Visa.*

Birmingham — Granada Lodge — £45

Tel 021-550 3261 Fax 021-501 2880 — **L**

M5 Junction 3/4 Frankley Birmingham West Midlands B32 4AR — **Map 6 C4**

***Rooms** 60.* AMERICAN EXPRESS *Access, Diners, Visa.*

Birmingham — Henry Wong — £42

Tel 021-427 9799 — **R**

283 High Street Harborne Birmingham West Midlands B3 1RB — **Map 6 C4**

Sister restaurant to *Henry's*, a bright and airy restaurant at the top end of Harborne, two miles from the city centre. Similarly extensive Cantonese menus produce capably cooked rather than inspired results. Mixed steamed or fried dim sum, sliced duck broth, Cantonese roast pork with ginger and spring onions and yau choi green vegetables are conventional offerings, while sizzling dishes bring the menu slap bang up to date. Helpful, friendly service. ***Seats** 120. L 12-1.45 D 6-11 (Fri & Sat to 11.30). Closed Sun, Bank Holidays. Set meals from £13.* AMERICAN EXPRESS *Access, Diners, Visa.*

Birmingham — Henry's — £42

Tel 021-200 1136 — **R**

27 St Paul's Square Birmingham West Midlands B17 9QH — **Map 6 C4**

A short drive from the city centre is this a purpose-built restaurant on split levels, serviced by friendly staff. As at its sister restaurant, the Cantonese menu is extensive and dishes are competently cooked, covering a range from satay and soups to scallops, sizzling dishes, shredded beef with fruity sauce, Singapore noodles and sweet and sour vegetarian wun tun. ***Seats** 140. Private Room 40. L 12-2 D 6-11 (Fri & Sat to 11.30). Closed Sun, Bank Holidays. Set meals from £13.* AMERICAN EXPRESS *Access, Diners, Visa.*

Birmingham — Holiday Inn — 70% — £124

Tel 021-631 2000 Fax 021-643 9018 — **H**

Holliday Street Birmingham West Midlands B1 1HH — **Map 6 C4**

Located above an NCP car park in the city centre, this modern high-rise hotel with its numerous conference and meeting rooms (holding up to 160), smart public areas and choice of two bars, is a popular venue for the business community. The bedrooms all have individually controllable air-conditioning and ample work space; Executive rooms boast king-size beds and fax machines. Bathrooms are well lit, with large mirrors and decent showers. ***Rooms** 288. Indoor swimming pool, keep-fit equipment, sauna, spa bath, solarium, kiosk.* AMERICAN EXPRESS *Access, Diners, Visa.*

Birmingham — Hyatt Regency — 77% — £162

Tel 021-643 1234 Fax 021-616 2323 — **HR**

2 Bridge Street Birmingham West Midlands B1 2JZ — **Map 6 C4**

Next to the new International Convention Centre and Symphony Hall stands a striking, mirrored 25-storey feature on Birmingham's skyline. The impressive glass-roofed atrium is cool and stylishly spacious, featuring columns, plants, trees and even a fountain. A marble-floored reception boasts its own elegant lounge, while the bar, *Aston's*, is compact and subtly

See over

lit. The luxuriously appointed bedrooms include 12 suites; all are spacious and air-conditioned, featuring quality modern furniture and fashionably uncluttered decor, plus equally splendid, marble-floored bathrooms. One floor of 18 rooms is reserved for non-smokers and three floors comprise the Regency Club of superior rooms; the latter has its own Club Lounge on the 22nd floor. Floor-to-ceiling windows afford fine views over the Second City. Guests have the use of the well-equipped *Club Active* leisure centre in the basement. Young, smart and willing staff. Conference facilities for up to 240, banqueting to 170. A child up to 18 may share its parents' room free of charge. Charged, valet parking in the hotel's 24hr-manned car park nearby. ***Rooms** 319. Indoor swimming pool, gymnasium, sauna, solarium, steam room, spa bath, business centre, café (6.30am-midnight).* AMERICAN EXPRESS *Access, Diners, Visa.*

Number 282

£80

Paper place-mat menus give the day's news headlines, weather around the world, exchange rates and a local film and concert guide along with birthday greetings etc to named diners. It also finds space for a short menu with the likes of Caesar salad, prawn bisque with coriander, chicken fricassee and sirloin steak. Essentially the same menu comes for both lunch and dinner, but the good-value fixed-price lunch turns into a rather pricy à la carte style in the evening. A good bet is the list of fresh fish dishes, cooked as you choose or with a selection of suggested sauces. An additional set dinner features dishes from international Hyatt hotels. Safe cooking, vegetarian dishes and free car parking (small charge for valet parking) for diners. Further informal eating in the Californian-themed Court Café (children under 6 eat free at Sunday brunch, high-chairs provided) and Glassworks pub in the grounds overlooking a canal. ***Seats** 70. Parties 20. L 12.30-2.30 D 6.30-11. Set L £12.75. Closed L Sat, all Sun.*

Birmingham — Midland Hotel — 67%

£99

Tel 021-643 2601 Fax 021-643 5075

H

New Street Birmingham West Midlands B2 4JT

Map 6 C4

Family-owned for 200 years, the Midland is a fine old Victorian building, the closest hotel to New Street railway station. Bedrooms are now especially good with soft decor, pretty co-ordinated fabrics and matching furniture. The smart bathrooms are neatly tiled and brightly lit. There are five suites and rooms with four-posters. Spacious day rooms reflect another hotel age, with moulded ceilings and period furniture. Three bars cater for most ages and tastes and include a smoky public bar with a pub feel. Good tariff reductions at weekends; special arrangements for residents with Stocks leisure club, 5 minutes walk away. Voucher car parking after 6pm in adjacent NCP. Children up to 12 stay free in parents' room. ***Rooms** 111. Games room.* AMERICAN EXPRESS *Access, Diners, Visa.*

Birmingham — New Happy Gathering

£35

Tel 021-643 5247

R

43 Station Street Birmingham West Midlands B5 4DY

Map 6 C4

The Chan family's well-run restaurant is a short walk from Chinatown, above street level at the back of New Street Station. A tented fabric ceiling above the staircase and carved wood panels within the restaurant lend an opulent air, while traditional Chinese cuisine holds few surprises on the neatly laid out menu. Two dozen or more dim sum and a dozen soups lead to meat, fowl and seafood sections with sizzling platters and vegetarian tofu alternatives. Set meals for two or more; special banquets for eight minimum. ***Seats** 90. Private Room 100. L 12-2 D 5-11.30 (Fri till 12, Sun till 11) Sat all day 12-12. Closed 25 & 26 Dec. Set meals from £10.* AMERICAN EXPRESS *Access, Diners, Visa.*

Birmingham **Novotel** **61%** **£100**

Tel 021-643 2000 Fax 021-643 9796 **H**

70 Broad Street Birmingham West Midlands B1 2HT **Map 6 C4**

Almost next door to the International Convention Centre and the National Indoor Arena, this is a very modern Novotel with comfortable bedrooms and both leisure and business centres. Children up to 16 stay free in parents' room. Underground car park. No dogs. ***Rooms*** *148. Gymnasium, sauna.* AMERICAN EXPRESS *Access, Diners, Visa.*

Birmingham **Plough & Harrow** **59%** **£107**

Tel 021-454 4111 Fax 021-454 1868 **H**

135 Hagley Road Edgbaston Birmingham West Midlands B16 8LS **Map 6 C4**

An attractive creeper-covered 17th century building, at the city end of the long Hagley Road, to which a modern bedroom block was added in 1974. The trouble is that the rooms have not evidently been refurbished since and 20 years on the carpets, wall coverings and furniture (apart from good leather armchairs) are looking very tired indeed. In style they are very masculine and dour. On the plus side the bed linen is splendidly crisp and white and towels large and soft. Bathrooms, though dated and not in a perfect state of repair, do all have large tubs with showers above and bidets. Public areas (apart from bedroom corridors and it can be quite a trek to some rooms) are much more presentable with the main bar/lounge having plenty of good armchairs and a table spread with magazines. Another mitigating factor is the friendly staff with the receptionists being particularly charming and helpful. Cooked breakfasts come fresh from the kitchen but the cold buffet is rather limited. Ample parking surrounds the hotel but it is not supervised. ***Rooms*** *44.* AMERICAN EXPRESS *Access, Diners, Visa.*

Birmingham **Purple Rooms** **£35**

Tel 021-702 2193 **R**

1076 Stratford Road Hall Green Birmingham West Midlands B28 8AD **Map 6 C4**

Set at the city end of a shopping parade on a dual carriageway leading through the suburbs towards Shirley. Silver service, the usual hot plates, a floating candle atop the pink-clothed tables, plus fairly-priced Indian and Bangladeshi food. Sunday self-service buffet. No smoking in the middle dining room. ***Seats*** *70. Private Room 30. L 12-2.30 D 6-11.30. Closed L Mon-Thu, 25 Dec. Set meals from £6.95.* AMERICAN EXPRESS *Access, Visa.*

Birmingham **Rajdoot** **£40**

Tel 021-643 8805 **R**

12 Albert Street Birmingham West Midlands B4 7UD **Map 6 C4**

Rajdoot opened in Chelsea in 1966 and was the first to use the tandoori in Europe. In the comfortable, quietly opulent Birmingham branch (as in the other outlets in Bristol, Manchester and Dublin) the clay oven turns out not only good lamb, chicken and prawn dishes but mackerel, quail, lamb's kidneys and vegetable shashlik. Among the curries is lamb narial – an interesting preparation including coconut milk and lemon. ***Seats*** *74. Parties 40. L 12-2.15 D 6.30-11.30. Closed L Sun, Bank Holidays. Set L from £8 Set D from £13.50.* AMERICAN EXPRESS *Access, Diners, Visa.*

Birmingham **Royal Alfaisal** **£25**

Tel 021-449 5695 **R**

136-140 Stoney Lane Sparkbrook Birmingham West Midlands B11 8AQ **Map 6 C4**

It's fingers to the fore at this all-day balti house just off the Stratford road (A34) in Sparkbrook. Tables are laid, cafeteria-style, with absorbent papers in expectation of diners' dipping into Kashmiri cast-iron dishes with

See over

assorted tandoori nan. Breads, baked for five or more, are fully 18 inches across. Unlicensed. Bring your own: no corkage. ***Seats** 120. Parties 35. Private Room 50. Meals 11.30am-midnight. Closed 25 Dec.* AMERICAN EXPRESS® *Access, Diners, Visa.*

Birmingham Royal Angus Thistle 65% **£102**

Tel 021-236 4211 Fax 021-233 2195 **H**

St Chads Queensway Birmingham West Midlands B4 6HY **Map 6 C4**

Modern city-centre hotel alongside the inner ring road, with easy parking. Summery day rooms, good-size bedrooms, up-to-date accessories. ***Rooms** 133.* AMERICAN EXPRESS® *Access, Diners, Visa.*

Birmingham Sloans **£60**

Tel 021-455 6697 Fax 021-454 4335 **R**

27 Chad Square Hawthorne Road Edgbaston Birmingham West Midlands B15 3TQ **Map 6 C4**

Set in a small suburban shopping precinct, this smart, pale green, split-level restaurant is run in exemplary fashion by owner John Narbett. Serving staff are attentive and genuinely friendly while in the kitchen changes have been put under way to create more affordable all-round dining – fixed-price menus are now very competitive and the choice is broader than last year. Lunch might see smoked haddock with poached egg followed by calf's liver and smoked bacon, with warm pear tart to finish. The carte still offers a choice of ten or so dishes at each stage and extends from fish soup or goat's cheese to lobster, pot-roasted rosettes of venison and lobster and salmon mousse-filled sole with champagne sauce. Mostly French wines on a decent list, with a good regional and country selection under £20. ***Seats** 60. L 12-2 D 7-10.30. Closed L Sat, all Sun, Bank Holidays, 1 week from 25 Dec. Set L £8.50/£12 Set D £16.* AMERICAN EXPRESS® *Access, Diners, Visa.*

Birmingham Strathallan Thistle 63% **£103**

Tel 021-455 9777 Fax 021-454 9432 **H**

225 Hagley Road Edgbaston Birmingham West Midlands B16 9RY **Map 6 C4**

Circular modern building on the busy A465, very convenient for Edgbaston cricket ground. Flexible conference facilities (up to 200 theatre-style). Easy, mainly covered parking. 24hr room service. ***Rooms** 167.* AMERICAN EXPRESS® *Access, Diners, Visa.*

Birmingham Swallow Hotel 77% **£120**

Tel 021-452 1144 Fax 021-456 3442 **HR**

12 Hagley Road Five Ways Birmingham West Midlands B16 8SJ **Map 6 C4**

An imposing Edwardian building, strikingly transformed into a quality luxury hotel. The foyer features sparkling Italian marble floors, rich mahogany woodwork and crystal chandeliers; there is a refined drawing room elegantly decorated with oil paintings, a quiet, dignified library and a handsome bar with colourful floral display throughout. The air-conditioned bedrooms are stylish, well-proportioned and comfortable. Beautiful fabrics are complemented by fine inlaid furniture and bathrooms are impressive, with marble tiling and a host of extras. An interestingly designed leisure club is based around an Egyptian theme. Attentive, professional staff. ***Rooms** 98. Terrace, indoor swimming pool, gymnasium, spa bath, steam room, solarium, whirlpool bath, hair & beauty salon.* AMERICAN EXPRESS® *Access, Diners, Visa.*

Sir Edward Elgar Restaurant **£96**

A handsome Edwardian restaurant with striking hand-painted trompe l'oeil murals. Idris Caldora, who did such an excellent job as head chef, is now in charge of the kitchen at the *Churchill Hotel*, London. His successor here at the Swallow took over too late for our full appraisal. ***Seats** 55. Parties 12. Private Room 20. L 12.30-2.30 D 7.30-10.30. Closed L Sat. Set L £15.50/£19.50 Set D £18.50/£25*

Langtry's — £60

British cookery to traditional recipes produces daily lunchtime dishes of Midlands faggots with mushy peas and West Country chicken, bacon and parsley pie. Omelette Arnold Bennett, guinea fowl with bubble and squeak and steamed apple sponge extend the English offerings à la carte. ***Seats** 55. Parties 14. L 11.30-3 D 6-10. Closed Sun, Bank Holidays.*

Birmingham Airport — Forte Posthouse — 61% — £68

Tel 021-782 8141 Fax 021-782 2476 — **H**

Coventry Road Birmingham Airport Birmingham West Midlands B26 3QWQ — **Map 6 C4**

30s hotel with a modernised interior, standing on the A45, one mile from the National Exhibition Centre. Conference and banqueting facilities for up to 150. ***Rooms** 136. Children's playroom.* AMERICAN EXPRESS *Access, Diners, Visa.*

Birmingham Airport — Novotel — 65% — £92

Tel 021-782 7000 Fax 021-782 0445 — **H**

Birmingham International Airport Birmingham West Midlands B26 3QL — **Map 6 C4**

In a prime site opposite the airport's main terminals, this Novotel has sound-proofed bedrooms and stylish day rooms. Children up to 16 stay free in parents' room. ***Rooms** 195. Restaurant (7am-midnight).* AMERICAN EXPRESS *Access, Diners, Visa.*

Birmingham — Places of Interest

Convention and Visitor Bureau City Arcade Tel 021-643 2514.
Convention and Visitor Bureau National Exhibition Centre Tel 021-780 4321.
Information Desk Birmingham Airport Tel 021-767 7145/6.
Birmingham Cathedral Tel 021-236 4333.
County Cricket Ground Edgbaston Tel 021-446 4422.
Aston Villa Football Ground Villa Park Tel 021-327 6604.
Ackers Park Trust Dry Ski Slope Small Heath Tel 021-771 4448.
Drayton Manor Park Nr Tamworth Tel 0827 287979.
Birmingham Nature Centre Tel 021-472 7775.
Dudley Zoo Tel 0384 252401.

Theatres and Concert Halls

Alexandra Theatre Station Street Tel 021-643 3180.
Birmingham Hippodrome Hurst Street Tel 021-622 7286.
Birmingham Repertory Theatre Broad Street Tel 021-236 4755.
Crescent Theatre Cumberland Street Tel 021-643 5858.
Midlands Arts Centre Cannon Hill Park Tel 021-440 4221.
City of Birmingham Symphony Orchestra Symphony Hall, International Convention Centre Tel 021-782 8282.

Historic Houses, Castles and Gardens

Aston Hall Tel 021-327 0062.
Birmingham Botanical Gardens and Glasshouses Edgbaston Tel 021-454 1860.
Castle Bromwich Hall Gardens Tel 021-749 4100.
University of Birmingham Botanic Garden Tel 021-414 5613.

Museums and Art Galleries

Birmingham Museum and Art Gallery Tel 021-235 2834.
Black Country Museum Tipton Road, Dudley Tel 021-557 9643.
Museum of Science and Industry Tel 021-236 1022.
The Patrick Collection (Autoworld) Tel 021-459 9111.

Bishop's Tawton — Halmpstone Manor — 68% — £100

Tel 0271 830321 Fax 0271 830826 — **HR**

Bishop's Tawton Barnstaple Devon EX32 0EA — **Map 13 D2**

Ask directions to find the small 16th-century manor house that is at the heart of the Stanburys' working farm. One is quickly made to feel at home by Jane and Charles' easy friendliness while unwinding in front of a real fire in the spacious lounge dotted with family photos and ornaments. There is a homely feel to the shaggy-carpeted bedrooms too with all sorts of little comforts from fresh fruit and decanter of sherry to magazines and mineral water along with good armchairs and settees. Individually decorated in soft colours, rooms are furnished with a mixture of antique and reproduction pieces; two have four-poster beds. Bathrooms, two with shower and WC only, boast bathrobes and generously sized towels. Rooms are properly serviced in the evenings and next morning excellent breakfasts make a good start to the day. ***Rooms** 5. Garden. Closed end Dec-early Feb.*
AMERICAN EXPRESS *Access, Diners, Visa.*

Restaurant — £70

First-rate local produce – Jane can probably tell you from which of the neighbouring farms the lamb or beef on the menu originated – is the backbone of short but often inventive fixed-price five-course dinners: scrambled egg with rhubarb and smoked salmon; medallions of venison with poivrade sauce, apple and blackcurrants; guinea fowl with lime. Enthusiasm compensates for the occasional slip and the candle-lit, pitch-pine panelled dining room is most appealing. ***Seats** 24. Parties 18. Private Room 30. L by arrangement D 7-9.30. Set D £27.50.*

Blackburn — Moat House — 58% — £69

Tel 0254 264441 Fax 0254 682435 — **H**

Preston New Road Blackburn Lancashire BB2 7BE — **Map 6 B1**

A modern Queens Moat Houses franchise with a distinctive gabled roof and extensive conference facilities (for up to 350 theatre-style). ***Rooms** 98.*
AMERICAN EXPRESS *Access, Diners, Visa.*

Blackburn — Places of Interest

Tourist Information Tel 0254 53277.
Empire Theatre Tel 0254 698859.
Gawthorpe Hall (NT) Padiham Tel 0282 78511.
Blackburn Cathedral Tel 0254 51491.
Blackburn Rovers Football Ground Ewood Park Tel 0254 55432.
Blackburn Arena Tel 0254 668686 *Ice Rink.*
Pendle Ski Club Sabden Tel 0200 23939.
Ski Rossendale Rawtenstall Tel 0706 228844.

Museums and Art Galleries

Pendle Heritage Centre Nelson, Nr Barrowford Tel 0282 695366.
Blackburn Museum and Art Gallery Museum Street Tel 0254 667130.
Towneley Hall Art Gallery and Museums and Museums of Local Crafts and Industries Burnley Tel 0282 24213.
Museum of Childhood Church Street, Ribchester Tel 0254 878520.

Blackpool — Imperial Hotel — 64% — £114

Tel 0253 23971 Fax 0253 751784 — **H**

North Promenade Blackpool Lancashire FY1 2HB — **Map 6 A1**

A degree of Victorian grandeur survives at this Forte Grand hotel overlooking the sea on the North Promenade. Generally good-sized bedrooms offer all the usual modern conveniences. Conferences/banqueting for 500/450. ***Rooms** 183. Indoor swimming pool, keep-fit equipment, sauna, spa bath, steam room, solarium.* AMERICAN EXPRESS *Access, Diners, Visa.*

Blackpool — Pembroke Hotel — 67% — £129

Tel 0253 23434 Fax 0253 27864 — **H**

North Promenade Blackpool Lancashire FY1 5JQ — **Map 6 A1**

A modern conference hotel with facilities for up to 900 delegates (theatre-style) and up to 600 for banqueting. In the main holiday season families are well catered for, with a playroom, baby-sitting and a supervised crèche (9am-9pm) as well as a separate children's menu. A large swimming pool and Springs night club are among the leisure amenities. Metropole Hotels. ***Rooms** 274. Indoor swimming pool, sauna, solarium.* AMERICAN EXPRESS *Access, Diners, Visa.*

---

is our symbol for an outstanding wine list.

Blackpool — September Brasserie — £62

Tel 0253 23282 — **R**

15-17 Queen Street Blackpool Lancashire FY1 1PU — **Map 6 A1**

Above a hairdressers (run by Pat Wood who moves upstairs to look after front of house in the evenings) just off the promenade near North Pier this small, smart restaurant offers an adventurous menu of dishes all produced singlehandedly by Michael Golowicz – he also does the washing-up – in his tiny kitchen which is visible from the restaurant through a couple of arched openings. Cream of mooli and coconut soup; tempura of king prawns with wasabi and avocado mayonnaise; sea bass with pesto and saffron; paupiettes of pork filled with buckwheat and raisins on a redcurrant and thyme sauce and pecan pie give the general idea. A long and varied career in the kitchen enables Michael to cope confidently with the various cuisines involved. Organic produce is used wherever possible and a strictly organic wine list offers a surprisingly wide choice of some 45 bins. ***Seats** 34. L 12-2.30 D 7-9.30. Closed Sun, Mon, 26 Dec, 2 weeks summer, 2 weeks winter.* AMERICAN EXPRESS *Access, Diners, Visa.*

Blackpool — Places of Interest

Tourist Information Clifton Street Tel 0253 21623.
Tourist Information Coronation Street Tel 0253 21891.
Chingle Hall Goosnargh Tel 0772 861082.
Stanley Park Cricket Ground Tel 0253 33347.
Blackpool Icedrome Tel 0253 41707.
Blackpool Zoo Tel 0253 65027.
Theatres and Concert Halls
South Pier Theatre The Promenade Tel 0253 43096.
Winter Gardens and Opera House Church Street Tel 0253 27786.

Blakeney — Blakeney Hotel — 64% — £112

Tel 0263 740797 Fax 0263 740795 — **H**

The Quay Blakeney nr Holt Norfolk NR25 7NE — **Map 10 C1**

A family-owned hotel, run in traditional style, on the quayside overlooking the National Trust harbour. Public rooms include a first-floor sun lounge which enjoys to the full the fine views across the salt marshes towards Blakeney Point. Many front-facing bedrooms share the view; there are several mini-suites, four-poster rooms and a ground-floor room suitable for wheelchairs. Some rooms in an annexe have private patios. The Mayflower ballroom holds 200 for meetings or banquets. Children under 16 sharing with two people are charged at £5 per night. ***Rooms** 60. Garden, indoor swimming pool, keep-fit equipment, sauna, spa bath, snooker.* AMERICAN EXPRESS *Access, Diners, Visa.*

Blakeney Manor Hotel 58% £68

Tel 0263 740376 Fax 0263 741116 **H**

Blakeney nr Holt Norfolk NR25 7ND **Map 10 C1**

Privately-owned 17th-century former farmhouse on the north coast of Norfolk, right next to salt marshes and a harbour inlet – ideal for yachtsmen and bird-watchers. A flagstoned entrance hall leads into day rooms that include a spacious lounge. Spotless bedrooms with candlewick bedspreads and simple, white laminate units are arranged in single-storeyed outhouses around neat courtyards. Charming walled garden with a seating area. No children under 10. ***Rooms** 36. Garden, bowling green. Closed 3 weeks Dec or Jan. No credit cards.*

Blakeney Places of Interest

Holkham Hall Tel 0328 710227.
Walsingham Abbey Walsingham Tel 0328 820259.

Blanchland Lord Crewe Arms 63% £98

Tel 0434 675251 Fax 0434 675337 **H**

Blanchland nr Consett Co Durham DH8 9SP **Map 5 D3**

Situated in one of the most unspoilt villages in England, with a sense of history imparted by beams, flagstones and thick walls – some parts of the building date back to the 13th century. The atmospheric, stone-vaulted crypt is now a public bar. All the bedrooms are decorated in solid traditional style including some antiques. Children up to 14 stay free in parents' room. ***Rooms** 18. Garden.* AMERICAN EXPRESS *Access, Diners, Visa.*

Blandford Forum La Belle Alliance £50

Tel 0258 452842 Fax 0258 480053 **RR**

Whitecliff Mill Street Blandford Forum Dorset DT11 7BP **Map 14 B4**

Philip Davison has built up a good network of local and regional suppliers for his kitchen, and guests can enjoy the results in relaxed comfort at his and his wife Lauren's Victorian house. Dinner now sees both 'bistro' and 'gourmet' fixed-price menus; the former offers three choices per course (perhaps savoury seafood pancake, roast Nile perch with mild curry and pineapple sauce, baked syrup sponge with custard), the latter four (perhaps goat's cheese soufflé with Calvados sauce, spinach-wrapped monkfish with langoustine sauce, apple tart with butterscotch sauce). Both change roughly every four weeks. Carefully selected wine list at fair prices. No smoking in dining room. ***Seats** 30. Private Room 40. L by arrangement only D 7-10. Closed Sun (open Bank Holiday weekend Sun L), Mon, first 3 weeks Jan. Set D £13.95/£15.95 & £19.95.* AMERICAN EXPRESS *Access, Visa.*

Rooms £60

Six pretty, well-proportioned bedrooms are all en-suite and individually decorated, with canopied beds and the usual home comforts. Easy chairs, toiletries, magazines and a daily paper are provided.

Blandford Forum Places of Interest

Tourist Information Tel 0258 454770.
Royal Signal Museum Blandford Camp Tel 0258 482248.
Milton Abbey Milton Abbas Tel 0258 880484.

Blyth Forte Travelodge £42

Tel 0909 591775 **L**

Blyth Worksop Nottinghamshire **Map 7 D2**

On the A1 southbound, 10 miles south of Doncaster. ***Rooms** 32.* AMERICAN EXPRESS *Access, Visa.*

Blyth Granada Lodge £45

Tel 0909 591836 Fax 0909 591831 **L**

A1(M)/A614 Blyth Nottinghamshire S82 8HG **Map 7 D2**

Rooms 39. AMERICAN EXPRESS® *Access, Diners, Visa.*

Bodymoor Heath Marston Farm 65% £80

Tel 0827 872133 Fax 0827 875043 **H**

Dog Lane Bodymoor Heath nr Sutton Coldfield Warwickshire B76 9JD **Map 6 C4**

Ten minutes drive from Birmingham Airport and the NEC, Marston Farm is just off junction 9 of the M42: follow signs to Kingsbury and Bodymoor Heath. A 17th-century farmhouse forms the main body of the hotel, deriving both character and intimacy from oak beams and inglenook fireplaces. In a converted barn are 20 uniform bedrooms and a boardroom with conference accommodation for up to 45 and banqueting space for 95. ***Rooms** 37. Garden, tennis, fishing.* AMERICAN EXPRESS® *Access, Diners, Visa.*

Bognor Regis Royal Norfolk 60% £70

Tel 0243 826222 Fax 0243 826325 **H**

The Esplanade Bognor Regis West Sussex PO21 2LH **Map 11 A6**

The hotel dates from the 1830s and has entertained such notables as Queen Alexandra and Napoleon III. Bedrooms, in various styles, are generally bright and pleasant. Forte Heritage. ***Rooms** 51. Garden, outdoor swimming pool, tennis.* AMERICAN EXPRESS® *Access, Diners, Visa.*

Bollington Mauro's £60

Tel 0625 573898 **R**

88 Palmerston Street Bollington nr Macclesfield Cheshire SK10 5PW **Map 6 C2**

The Mauro family run an authentic north Italian restaurant with a feast of flavours in the *antipasti alla caprese*, served from a trolley. Home-made noodles and ravioli are served several ways and market-fresh fish heads a list of daily specials. Lighter dishes on a good-value, 3-course lunch menu; open for Sunday lunch (£14.25) only on the first Sunday of the month. Exclusively Italian wines, as one might expect. ***Seats** 50. L 12.15-2 (Sat to 1.30) D 7-10 (Sat to 10.30). Closed Sun & Mon, 25 & 26 Dec, 3 weeks Aug/Sep. Set L £8.75.* AMERICAN EXPRESS® *Access, Visa.*

Bolton Egerton House 63% £85

Tel 0204 307171 Fax 0204 593030 **H**

off Blackburn Road Egerton Bolton Lancashire BL7 9PL **Map 6 B2**

Rank-owned Victorian house set among trees and lawns just off the A666. Bright, comfortable lounge and bar, bedrooms graded either standard or superior. Guests have free use of the leisure facilities at the Last Drop Village Hotel, two minutes drive away. A self-contained function suite includes the Barn, catering for up to 150 delegates. Free bed and breakfast for under-5s; free bed for up-to-15s. Ample parking. ***Rooms** 32. Garden. Closed 27 Dec.* AMERICAN EXPRESS® *Access, Diners, Visa.*

Bolton Forte Posthouse 58% £68

Tel 0204 651511 Fax 0204 61064 **H**

Beaumont Road Bolton Greater Manchester BL3 4TA **Map 6 B2**

Modern hotel on the outskirts of Bolton, near Junction 5 of the M61. Two-level bedroom block. Conference/banqueting facilities for 120/90. ***Rooms** 96. Garden.* AMERICAN EXPRESS® *Access, Diners, Visa.*

Bolton — Last Drop Village Hotel — 68% — £88

Tel 0204 591131 Fax 0204 304122 — H

Hospital Road Bromley Cross Bolton Lancashire BL7 9PZ — **Map 6 B2**

A collection of 18th-century moorland farm buildings has been skilfully turned into a village with cottages, gardens, craft shops, a pub, a tea shop and, at its heart, a comfortable and well-equipped hotel. Day rooms retain some original features, while bedrooms are mainly bright and modern. Top of the range is the Lancaster Suite with traditional decor, a four-poster and a panelled lounge. Children up to 14 stay free in parents' room. There are extensive conference facilities (in a choice of rooms) for up to 200 delegates. The hotel is well signed from the A666. ***Rooms** 83. Indoor swimming pool, gymnasium, sauna, spa bath, squash, beauty salon, hairdressing, snooker, coffee shop (10am-5.30pm).* AMERICAN EXPRESS *Access, Diners, Visa.*

Bolton — Pack Horse Hotel — 62% — £60

Tel 0204 27261 Fax 0204 364352 — H

Nelson Square Bradshawgate Bolton Greater Manchester BLI 1DP — **Map 6 B2**

Redbrick building in the town centre, with up-to-date accommodation, cheerful bars and a thriving conference business (six rooms handling up to 275 delegates). Children up to 14 stay free in parents' room. De Vere. ***Rooms** 73.* AMERICAN EXPRESS *Access, Diners, Visa.*

Bolton — Places of Interest

Tourist Information Tel 0204 364333.
Little Theatre Hanover Street Tel 0204 24469.
Octagon Theatre Howell Croft, South Bolton Tel 0294 20661.

Bolton Abbey — Devonshire Arms — 73% — £110

Tel 0756 710441 Fax 0756 710564 — H

Bolton Abbey nr Skipton North Yorkshire BD23 6AJ — **Map 6 C1**

On the A59, by the edge of the Abbey estate, a much-extended 18th-century coaching inn owned since 1753 by the Dukes and Duchesses of Devonshire. Set in 12 acres of grounds in an area of outstanding natural beauty, it is furnished and appointed with much thought. Well-proportioned day rooms feature choice antiques and oil paintings from the Devonshire family home of Chatsworth in Derbyshire. The best bedrooms, in the main house, are individually themed and again show carefully chosen furnishings and fabrics; thirty rooms have recently been refurbished. Numerous little extras like a decanter of sherry, magazines and flowers are a welcoming touch. The majority of bedrooms in more recent wings are more uniform in size and style, though they are equally inviting and comfortable. Bathrooms are a little cramped. Switched-on management lead a young team. Good breakfast served in the conservatory, snack food in the bar. Children up to 12 stay free in parents' room. ***Rooms** 40. Garden, putting, fishing, helipad.* AMERICAN EXPRESS *Access, Diners, Visa.*

Bonchurch — Winterbourne Hotel — 64% — £94

Tel 0983 852535 Fax 0983 853056 — H

Bonchurch Isle of Wight PO38 1RQ — **Map 15 D4**

An enchanting garden complete with waterfalls and sea views is the outstanding feature of the hotel where Charles Dickens, in 1849, wrote most of *David Copperfield*; bedrooms are named after characters in the novel. A charming lounge with French windows opening on to the terrace and garden is the principal day room. Bedrooms range from tiny singles with basic fitted furniture to spacious and airy rooms, particularly five in the converted coach house. Bonchurch is near Ventnor, on the southern tip of the island. ***Rooms** 19. Garden, outdoor swimming pool. Closed mid Nov-early Mar.* AMERICAN EXPRESS *Access, Diners, Visa.*

Boreham Street **White Friars Hotel** **57%** **£75**

Tel 0323 832355 Fax 0323 833882 **H**

Boreham Street nr Herstmonceux East Sussex BN27 4SE **Map 11 B6**

Built in 1721, and converted to a hotel in the 1920s. Day rooms and some bedrooms have old-fashioned charm, complete with four-posters; nine rooms are in a separate cottage block. Characterful, beamed conference room for up to 30 delegates. Two acres of gardens. ***Rooms*** *20. Garden.* AMERICAN EXPRESS *Access, Diners, Visa.*

Boroughbridge **The Crown** **63%** **£50**

Tel 0423 322328 Fax 0423 324512 **H**

Horsefair Boroughbridge North Yorkshire YO5 9LB **Map 15 C6**

Once a famous coaching inn, with stabling for more than 100 horses. Comfortable, smart day rooms include a oak dado-panelled reception/lounge, a bar and several function rooms. Dinner dances are a regular feature. Children up to 12 stay free in parents' room. ***Rooms*** *42.* AMERICAN EXPRESS *Access, Diners, Visa.*

Borrowdale **Borrowdale Hotel** **60%** **£88***

Tel 076 87 77224 Fax 076 87 77338 **H**

Borrowdale Keswick-on-Derwentwater Cumbria **Map 4 C3**

A stone's throw from Derwentwater, three miles from Keswick on the B5289, stands a solid, greystone hotel whose style of hospitality resists change. Lovely enclosed garden overlooked by a bar and patio: chintz lounges with winter log fires, lake views and quiet, professional service. *Half-board terms only. ***Rooms*** *34. Garden. Access, Visa.*

Borrowdale **Stakis Lodore Swiss Hotel 71%** **£120***

Tel 076 87 77285 Fax 076 87 77343 **H**

Borrowdale Keswick Cumbria CA12 5UX **Map 4 C3**

Holiday hotel set in 40 acres by Derwentwater; good family facilities and convenient for Keswick ferry (½ mile) and town (3½ miles). Picture windows afford splendid views from day rooms and the best, front-facing bedrooms. Several splendid family rooms; resident nanny all year round. Conference/banqueting facilities for 70/55. Free golf at Keswick golf club. No dogs. *Half-board terms only. ***Rooms*** *70. Garden, indoor & outdoor swimming pools, gymnasium, squash, sauna, tennis, games room, nursery, lock-up garage.* AMERICAN EXPRESS *Access, Diners, Visa.*

Set menu prices may not always include service or wine.

Bosham **Millstream Hotel** **63%** **£99**

Tel 0243 573234 Fax 0243 573459 **H**

Bosham Lane Bosham West Sussex PO18 8HL **Map 15 D4**

Part small manor house, part malthouse, the peaceful Millstream is an attractive small hotel just a short walk from the heart of a picturesque sailing village, four miles from Chichester. A rattan-furnished bar and sunny lounge are agreeable places for a drink or a chat, as is the front lawn, past which the stream runs. Bedrooms, mostly furnished with reproduction antiques, include mini-safes and bathroom scales among their accessories; one room features a four-poster. ***Rooms*** *29. Garden.* AMERICAN EXPRESS *Access, Diners, Visa.*

Boston New England Hotel 56% £78

Tel 0205 365255 Fax 0205 310597 **H**

49 Wide Bargate Boston Lincolnshire PE21 6SH **Map 7 E3**

Former coaching inn in the town centre with decent-sized bedrooms; bathrooms are simple and compact. On the ground floor a small cocktail bar acts as a buffer between the public bar-lounge and the restaurant. Forte Heritage. ***Rooms** 25.* AMERICAN EXPRESS *Access, Diners, Visa.*

Boston Places of Interest

Tourist Information Tel 0205 356656.

Botley Cobbett's £66

Tel 0489 782068 **R**

15 The Square Botley Southampton Hampshire SO3 2EA **Map 15 D4**

In the main street (with its own car park to the rear) this centuries-old timber-framed building is a delightful and very English setting for Lucie Skipwith's cooking which is based on the cuisine of her native Bordeaux. A sauté of coquilles St Jacques with Pernod or a coarse game terrine might precede a supreme of guinea fowl with cream tarragon sauce or fillet of beef with sauce of shallots, mustard, parsley and balsamic vinegar chosen from a sensibly short à la carte (about half a dozen dishes per course) that always includes a fish dish of the day. Main dishes come with a mélange of vegetables served rather attractively in a filo pastry basket. There is no wine list as such (just six inexpensive house wines – all available by the glass) but you can 'bring your own' for a corkage charge of £2.50. ***Seats** 40. Private Room 14. L 12-2 D 7.30-10 (Sat from 7). Closed L Mon & Sat, all Sun, Bank Holidays, 2 weeks summer, 2 weeks winter. Set L £15.50. Access, Visa.*

Boughton Monchelsea Tanyard Hotel 63% £76

Tel 0622 744705 Fax 0622 741998 **H**

Wierton Hill Boughton Monchelsea nr Maidstone Kent ME17 4JT **Map 11 C5**

Jan Davies, owner for 10 years, aims for a house party atmosphere. Beautiful views over the Kentish Weald, a secluded location and 14th-century architecture make the Tanyard a house of great charm and character. A huge stone inglenook fireplace dominates the homely lounge, complemented by beams and period-style furniture. Bedrooms have uneven floors, beamed ceilings and walls and exposed stonework. No children under six. No dogs. Ask for directions from Boughton Monchelsea. ***Rooms** 6. Garden. Closed Dec-Jan.* AMERICAN EXPRESS *Access, Diners, Visa.*

Bournemouth Carlton Hotel 78% £150

Tel 0202 552011 Fax 0202 299573 **H**

East Overcliff Bournemouth Dorset BH1 3DN **Map 14 C4**

Probably Bournemouth's best, the privately-owned Carlton has a luxurious and opulent feel about it. Welcoming staff greet guests with a smile and the smart foyer sets the tone for the public areas; a walnut and mahogany-panelled library houses volumes of leather-bound books, cabinets filled with antiques and objets d'art, a bracket clock, and comfortable armchairs; a cocktail bar with leather chairs contains framed pencil sketches of the famous and antique mirrors; there's also a bright lounge which leads on to a sunny conservatory. Most of the suites and bedrooms have views of the coastline and bathrooms are designed to pamper. There's a health spa, a heated outdoor pool, and a games room with a full-size snooker table. The hotel has plenty of free parking space including an under-cover car park. Conference/banqueting for 140/120. No dogs. No children under 12.

Rooms 70. Garden, outdoor swimming pool, gymnasium, sauna, solarium, whirlpool bath, beauty & hair salon, snooker. AMERICAN EXPRESS *Access, Diners, Visa.*

Bournemouth **Chine Hotel** **65%** **£80**

Tel 0202 396234 Fax 0202 391737 **H**

Boscombe Spa Road Bournemouth Dorset BH5 1AX **Map 14 C4**

Sister establishment to the *Haven* and *Sandbanks* hotels a bit further around the bay at Poole, the 1874-built Chine has shared the same conscientious family ownership since 1945. Large bedrooms, nearly half with private balcony or patio, have all been refurbished over the last few years with light-oak units and pleasing pale-green colour scheme. Spacious public areas include a cocktail bar open-plan to the large restaurant and a cosy residents' lounge overlooking the pine-fringed outdoor swimming pool; landscaped gardens extend down one side of the Boscombe Chine Gardens to the esplanade and pier below. Business people are attracted by a number of well-equipped conference rooms (in an adjacent building) and families appreciate the playroom, games room, coin-operated laundry room and, during school holidays, a children's activities organiser. Children up to 12 are free in parents' room. No dogs. ***Rooms** 97. Garden, outdoor & indoor swimming pool, sauna, solarium, putting, games room.* AMERICAN EXPRESS *Access, Diners, Visa.*

Bournemouth **Forte Posthouse** **59%** **£68**

Tel 0202 553262 Fax 0202 557698 **H**

The Lansdowne Bournemouth Dorset BH1 2PR **Map 14 C4**

Circular hotel on three floors above a spiral car park. Practical modern bedrooms and roomy open-plan public areas. Conferences for up to 100. ***Rooms** 98.* AMERICAN EXPRESS *Access, Diners, Visa.*

Bournemouth **Langtry Manor** **62%** **£79**

Tel 0202 553887 Fax 0202 290115 **H**

26 Derby Road East Cliff Bournemouth Dorset BH1 3QB **Map 14 C4**

The house was built by Edward VII, then Prince of Wales, for Lillie Langtry. Their story is commemorated throughout the hotel and there's a glass case filled with memorabilia on the first floor. Public rooms have a period flavour; best of these is the dining hall with its minstrel's gallery. There are conference/banqueting facilities for up to 100. Bedrooms vary considerably in size and opulence; some smaller rooms have been put together to make suites, others have four-poster beds; most can best be described as romantic. ***Rooms** 27. Garden.* AMERICAN EXPRESS *Access, Diners, Visa.*

Bournemouth **Norfolk Royale** **70%** **£138**

Tel 0202 551521 Fax 0202 299729 **H**

Richmond Hill Bournemouth Dorset BH2 6EN **Map 14 C4**

Dating from Bournemouth's Edwardian heyday, the Norfolk Royale boasts a splendid two-tier cast-iron verandah as part of its listed facade and the major refurbishment of a few years back was sympathetic to the hotel's origins. Twin conservatories – one having the pool and the other part of the all-day Orangery restaurant – extend into the pretty garden to the rear and several interconnecting rooms provide plenty of lounge/bar space. Appealing bedrooms, which are properly serviced in the evening, are decorated in a variety of matching fabrics in ribbon and flower-style with limed oak furniture. Good bathrooms come with brass fittings and good-sized towels and robes. Valet parking is a big plus given the hotel's central location. Well-motivated staff. No dogs. Four function/conference suites.

See over

Fun pack, baby-sitting and high-chairs for families. ***Rooms** 95. Indoor swimming pool, sauna, spa bath, steam room.* AMERICAN EXPRESS *Access, Diners, Visa.*

Bournemouth — Ocean Palace — £45

Tel 0202 559127 Fax 0202 559130 — **R**

8 Priory Road Bournemouth Dorset BH2 5DG — **Map 14 C4**

Behind the Bournemouth International Conference Centre and not far from the seafront, this modern restaurant has a conservatory-style frontage, simple decor and plain walls hung with contemporary Chinese artwork. Hing Wong's excellent cooking skills cover Peking and Szechuan styles, with special vegetarian and good set-price seafood menus. Interesting choices from nearly 200 dishes include ginseng soup with abalone, and lamb, beef and oysters in satay sauce, plus nearly 20 sizzling dishes. ***Seats** 140. Private Room 40. L 12-2.30 D 6-11.30. Closed 3 days Christmas. Set L from £5.80 Set D from £13.* AMERICAN EXPRESS *Access, Diners, Visa.*

Bournemouth — Palace Court — 71% — £108

Tel 0202 557681 Fax 0202 554918 — **H**

Westover Road Bournemouth Dorset BH1 2BZ — **Map 14 C4**

Extensive recent refurbishment has returned this between-the-wars, high-rise hotel to its former splendour. Spacious public areas are in 1930s' style: the front lounge with leather armchairs in pale yellow and pale pink and the split-level lounge/bar on the first floor in darker, more sophisticated tones. Conservatory-style windows take advantage of views across the Solent to the Isle of Wight. A further café/lounge has rattan furniture and ceiling fans slowly swishing overhead. Decor in the bedrooms varies, but all have freestanding furniture, many with walnut veneer pieces, and smartly-tiled bathrooms. Eight de luxe rooms live up to their name with mirrored bedheads (containing cassette players as well as radios) and bathrooms with spa baths, private mini-saunas and exercise bicycles. Rooms at the front have balconies with outdoor seating. 24hr room service can provide hot meals even in the middle of the night. Function facilities for 250. Ample garage parking (minimal charge). ***Rooms** 110. Indoor swimming pool, spa baths, sauna, solarium, snooker, café-bar (10am-11pm).* AMERICAN EXPRESS *Access, Diners, Visa.*

Bournemouth — Royal Bath Hotel — 73% — £140

Tel 0202 555555 Fax 0202 554158 — **HR**

Bath Road Bournemouth Dorset BH1 2EW — **Map 14 C4**

A splendid Victorian hotel combining traditional values (courteous and helpful staff for example) and modern amenities such as the marvellous Leisure Pavilion which features a heated kidney-shaped swimming pool. The hotel stands in an immaculately-kept three-acre garden with clifftop views out to sea, enjoyed by many of the bedrooms (some with terraces) which vary in style and size but are all smartly furnished with good bathrooms that have large mirrors and decent-sized towels. Excellent housekeeping, including a turn-down service at night, is evident throughout. The vast public areas (bars and lounges), refurbished a few years ago, are comfortable and well appointed, and breakfast in the Garden Restaurant will not disappoint. Children up to the age of 14 years free in parents' room. Supervised crèche daily in high season. No dogs. De Vere Hotels. ***Rooms** 131. Garden, indoor swimming pool, gymnasium, sauna, spa bath, steam room, solarium, beauty & hair salon, putting, snooker, coffee shop (10.30am-8.15pm), children's playground, garage.* AMERICAN EXPRESS *Access, Diners, Visa.*

Restaurant — £60

In fact, there are two restaurants in the hotel. The Garden Restaurant is only open in the evenings and for Sunday lunch, serving traditional food, albeit with somewhat grand and flowery descriptions on the menu. Oscar's, a more intimate setting with Oscar Wilde memorabilia all round, offers a classical French-orientated menu though the table d'hote set-price meals have an international flavour – typical dishes being a salad of marinated brill fillets, fillet of lamb garnished with fresh pasta, and a hot and sticky toffee pudding. A safe and predictable wine list. *Garden:* ***Seats*** *220. L (Sun only) 12.45-2.15 D 7.30-9.30. Set L £14.50 Set D £24. Oscar's:* ***Seats*** *60. L 12.30-2.15 D 6.30-10 Closed Sun & Bank Holidays.*

Bournemouth — Swallow Highcliff Hotel — 70% — £120

Tel 0202 557702 Fax 0202 292734 — **H**

St Michael's Road West Cliff Bournemouth Dorset BH2 5DU — **Map 14 C4**

An imposing Victorian hotel with a splendid clifftop location giving many of the rooms fine marine views. A funicular lift carries guests from hotel to promenade. Good-sized bedrooms in the main house have dark period-style furniture, those in the converted coastguard cottages smart lightwood furniture. Numerous public rooms include a terrace bar, a lounge for non-smokers and a night club. Magnificent conference facilities can cope with up to 450 delegates. Excellent family facilities in summer include a fenced-in outdoor play area and a creche. ***Rooms*** *157. Garden, outdoor swimming pool, sauna, solarium, tennis, putting, games room, snooker, brasserie (11am-11pm), night club.* AMERICAN EXPRESS® *Access, Diners, Visa.*

Bournemouth — Places of Interest

Tourist Information Westover Road Tel 0202 789789.
Pavilion Theatre Westover Road Tel 0202 297297.
Pier Theatre Bournemouth Pier Tel 0202 20250.
Westover Ice Rink Tel 0202 293011.
Bournemouth, Christchurch (Friars Cliff), Hengistbury Beaches.

Bourton-on-the-Water — Dial House — 61% — £68

Tel 0451 22244 — **H**

The Chestnuts High Street Bourton-on-the-Water Gloucestershire GL54 2AN — **Map 14 C1**

Built as a farmhouse in 1698 and converted to a hotel in 1989, Dial House stands opposite the middle bridge across the River Windrush. Lynn and Peter Boxall have carefully enhanced the interior with family antiques and four-posters; understated decor adds to the charm of buildings and contents. Downstairs is the lounge with inglenooks, leather sofas and plentiful reading matter, upstairs bedrooms that include some with half-testers or four-posters. No children under ten. ***Rooms*** *10. Garden.* AMERICAN EXPRESS® *Access, Visa.*

Bowness-on-Windermere — Belsfield Hotel — 62% — £112

Tel 053 94 42448 Fax 053 94 46397 — **H**

Kendal Road Bowness-on-Windermere Cumbria LA23 3EL — **Map 4 C3**

Hilltop Victorian building set in six acres of gardens, overlooking Lake Windermere, Bowness landing piers and the Belle Isle beyond. Accommodation ranges from singles to suites and family rooms (some with bunk beds, others with adjoining child's room). Good leisure facilities. Forte Heritage. ***Rooms*** *65. Garden, indoor swimming pool, sauna, solarium, tennis, putting, snooker.* AMERICAN EXPRESS® *Access, Diners, Visa.*

Bowness-on-Windermere — Gilpin Lodge — 64% — £80

Tel 053 94 88818 Fax 053 94 88058 — **HR**

Crook Road Bowness-on-Windermere Cumbria LA23 3NE — **Map 4 C3**

The Cunliffes' ancestral Lakeland home (on the B5284 between Bowness and Kendal) has undergone tasteful conversion to the most relaxing of country hotels, with just the right balance of home comforts and

See over

personal service. There's a wealth of books on gardening, cookery and Lakeland walks at both fireside and bedside and an abundance of floral displays, both fresh and dried. Cane chairs, pine furnishings, close-carpeted bathrooms and corner baths contribute to a cosseted feel. Not suitable for children under nine. Guests have free membership of the nearby Parkwood Country Club. No dogs. ***Rooms** 9. Garden.* AMERICAN EXPRESS *Access, Diners, Visa.*

Restaurant — £60

Christine Cunliffe and Christopher Davies ally classical cooking skills with modern ideas. Typical dishes on the five-course dinner menu: spinach, ham and cheese strudel on a tomato and coriander bouillon; warm mousseline of sole dressed with a saffron and basil sauce; roast Barbary duck served with baked apple, ginger and sultanas on a Calvados and ginger sauce; roast rack of lamb in a garlic and herb crust on a tarragon jus. Desserts include home-made ices and hot sticky toffee pudding with *two* toffee sauces. Courteous, attentive service. Sensibly fair prices on the wine list. No smoking. Lighter lounge lunches are served Mon-Sat, while Sunday lunch choice always includes traditional roast beef and Yorkshire pudding. ***Seats** 45. Parties 14. L 12-2.30 D 7-8.45. Set L (Sun) £12.75 Set D £24.*

Bowness-on-Windermere — Linthwaite House — 72% — £118

Tel 053 94 88600 Fax 053 94 88601 — **HR**

Bowness-on-Windermere Cumbria LA23 3JA — **Map 4 C3**

Jean and Mike Bevans have a genuine desire to run a "good hotel", combining high standards of service with an amenable, unstuffy attitude. In an unsurpassed, commanding location on the B5284 overlooking Lake Windermere and views beyond to the Old Man of Coniston, Linthwaite's environment is conducive to relaxation with a unique, lived-in interior design which sees, for instance, old leather suitcases converted into practical coffee tables. Some smaller bedrooms' dimensions are similarly redeemed by Amanda Rosa's stylish interiors, with hand-made pine dressers and vanitory units providing the unifying theme; some rooms have lake views. The best bathrooms, fully carpeted and brightly lit, feature mahogany panels and strong pulse showers. Free use of nearby leisure spa with pool, spa bath, squash and gym. No dogs. ***Rooms** 18. Garden, putting, practice golf hole, fly fishing. Closed 1 week after New Year.* AMERICAN EXPRESS *Access, Diners, Visa.*

Restaurant — £68

Warming candle-light and polished mahogany tables create an intimate atmosphere in which Mike Bevans's suave supervision ensures a comfortable informality. Dinner comprises four courses and coffee with petits fours; an optional soup (courgette and cucumber) course may be preceded by warm Cheddar cheese beignets with a white onion sauce, and followed by steamed fillet of brill garnished with pan-fried scallops or sautéed medallions of pork with rosemary and wild mushrooms. Iced rosewater parfait with raspberry compote or a dark chocolate tear filled with white chocolate mousse on a pear coulis could complete a fine meal. Four tip-top British cheeses. Lighter lunches are served daily in the conservatory. No smoking. ***Seats** 40. Parties 20. Private Room 20. L 12-2 D 7.15-9. Set L (Sun only) £7.50/£9.95 Set D £16.95/£25.*

Bowness-on-Windermere — Old England Hotel — 65% — £136

Tel 053 94 42444 Fax 053 94 43432 — **H**

Church Street Bowness-on-Windermere Cumbria LA23 3DF — **Map 4 C3**

Comfortable lakeside Georgian mansion with gardens giving on to the water where there is a private jetty for the hotel's motor boat (for hire by the hour) and for guests' rowing boats. The best rooms have lake views. 24 rooms are reserved for non-smokers. Popular for conferences and banquets (100/250 people). Forte Heritage. ***Rooms*** *79. Garden, outdoor swimming pool, sauna, solarium, hairdressing, snooker, jetty.* AMERICAN EXPRESS *Access, Diners, Visa.*

Bracknell — Coppid Beech Hotel 72% NEW — £140

Tel 0344 303333 Fax 0344 301200 — **HR**

John Nike Way Bracknell Berkshire RG12 8TF — **Map 15 E2**

Of striking Swiss chalet design, the privately-owned Coppid Beech is Berkshire's newest and largest hotel. A unique feature of the interior is a triangular shaft extending to the full height of the building, lined with aquaria (the largest in Europe apparently) and mirrors creating a mesmerising, watery kaleidoscope. Extensive facilities include a lively Bierkeller with live entertainment several nights a week, plush state-of-the-art disco night club and Waves health and fitness centre. Well-thought-out bedrooms (a significant number are full or junior suites) are well equipped – there's even an account review and check-out facility available via the advanced TV system – with large, comfortable beds. 24 hr room service is extensive and beds are turned down at night. ***Rooms*** *205. Indoor swimming pool, gymnasium, spa bath, sauna, solarium, steam room, dry ski slope, ice rink, play area.* AMERICAN EXPRESS *Access, Diners, Visa.*

Rowans Restaurant — £70

A large solidly comfortable restaurant with a menu that takes its inspiration from a variety of European cuisines; bouillabaisse-style fish soup, grilled calf's liver with polenta and Swiss chard, roast partridge with celery blinis, carpaccio of beef, celeriac and goat's cheese terrine with Greek-style zucchini. Cooking has a modern, health-conscious slant and the food is attractively presented. Inventive vegetarian options. Desserts are chosen from a buffet display. ***Seats*** *128. Parties 15. Private Room 25. L 12-2.30 D 6.30-11. Set L £17.50 Set D £22.50.*

Bracknell — Hilton National 69% — £126

Tel 0344 424801 Fax 0344 487454 — **H**

Bagshot Road Bracknell Berkshire RG12 3QJ — **Map 5 E2**

In the heart of busy Bracknell, a modern hotel handy for the M3 (Junction 3) and M4 (Junction 10). Large conference and banqueting facilities for up to 300. ***Rooms*** *167. Keep-fit equipment, sauna, spa bath, plunge pool.* AMERICAN EXPRESS *Access, Diners, Visa.*

Bracknell — Places of Interest

Tourist Information Tel 0344 423149.
South Hill Park Arts Centre and Wilde Theatre Tel 0344 472272.
John Nike Leisuresport Complex Tel 0344 860033 *Ice Rink.*
Bracknell Ski Centre Tel 0344 427435 *Dry Ski Slope.*

Bradford — Bombay Brasserie — £30

Tel 0274 737564 — **R**

Simes Street Westgate Bradford West Yorkshire — **Map 6 C1**

Converted chapel turned into smart, Bombay old city style restaurant. Uniformed waiters serve a wide range of upmarket Indian dishes. ***Seats*** *130. L 12-2 D 6-12. Set L £8.95 & Sun £5.95.* AMERICAN EXPRESS *Access, Visa.*

Bradford — K2 — £20

Tel 0274 723704 — **R**

116 Lumb Lane Bradford West Yorkshire BD8 7RS — **Map 6 C1**

Clear, rich spicing comes from cook/owner Abdul Ghafoor, who comes from a northern Kashmiri (hence the name) family of cooks. He prepares a distinctive style of bhuna and balti reductions. Fine roti, outstanding

See over

balti mili juli tarkari with fresh dhaniya leaf and fresh vegetables. High-chairs and booster seats for children. ***Seats** 66. Private Room 36. Meals 11am-midnight. Diners.*

Bradford — Nawaab — £30

Tel 0274 720371 — R

32 Manor Row Bradford West Yorkshire — **Map 6 C1**

Set in a former banking house, atop Manor Row, with mushroom-coloured walls and an ornamental elephant. The extensive Pakistani menu covers tandoori specialities, balti dishes and around eight basic varieties of curry. ***Seats** 120. L 12-2 D 6-12.30 (Fri & Sat to 1.30am, Sun 12-12). Closed L Sat.* AMERICAN EXPRESS *Access, Visa.*

Bradford — Restaurant 19 ★ — £70

Tel 0274 492559 — RR

19 North Park Road Heaton Bradford West Yorkshire BD9 4NT — **Map 6 C1**

A large Victorian house, once a wool merchant's home, situated in a residential suburb of the city overlooking Lister Park and the Cartwright Hall Museum. Tables are well spaced and immaculately set in the high-ceilinged room. Stephen Smith's hand-written menus offer a four-course fixed-price menu (with coffee), the cheaper menu having been withdrawn. It's always an interesting and imaginative choice, typified by sautéed polenta with lamb's kidney, pancetta and mushrooms lightly spiced with curry, fillet of hake with spring vegetables and coriander, or rack of lamb with asparagus, broad beans, apple and mint jelly. Desserts are particularly tempting: rhubarb and ginger crème brulée with rhubarb sorbet, chocolate almond cake with hot chocolate sauce. Partner Robert Barbour runs front of house with a flair that suitably matches the eye-catching presentation of Stephen's dishes. ***Seats** 36. Parties 12. L by arrangement D 7-9.30 (Sat to 10.30). Closed Sun, 1 week Jan, 1 week May, 1 week Sep. Set D £26.* AMERICAN EXPRESS *Access, Visa.*

Rooms — £70

Four comfortable rooms, named after works of art by Sir Russell Flint, are all decorated with antiques and have smart en-suite bathrooms. No children under ten.

> We do not accept free meals or hospitality – our inspectors pay their own bills.

Bradford — Novotel 60% — £70

Tel 0274 683683 Fax 0274 651342 — H

Merrydale Road Bradford West Yorkshire BD4 6SA — **Map 6 C1**

A faceless modern exterior houses comfortable and smart accommodation. Conference/banqueting facilities for 300/250. ***Rooms** 132. Garden, outdoor swimming pool, restaurant (6am-midnight).* AMERICAN EXPRESS *Access, Diners, Visa.*

Bradford — Stakis Norfolk Gardens 65% — £106

Tel 0274 734734 Fax 0274 306146 — H

Hall Ings Bradford West Yorkshire BD1 5SH — **Map 6 C1**

In the city centre, yet only a few minutes from the M62, the Norfolk Gardens is a major conference venue with facilities for up to 700 delegates. If you feel lucky, there's a Stakis casino next door. ***Rooms** 120. Coffee shop (24 hrs).* AMERICAN EXPRESS *Access, Diners, Visa.*

Bradford Victoria Hotel 61% £77

Tel 0274 728706 Fax 0274 736358 **H**

Bridge Street Bradford West Yorkshire BD1 1JX **Map 6 C1**

Situated next to the main railway station, with public rooms on a grand scale. Clean and comfortable bedrooms. ***Rooms** 59.* AMERICAN EXPRESS *Access, Diners, Visa.*

Bradford Places of Interest

Tourist Information Tel 0274 753678.
Alhambra Theatre Morely Street Tel 0274 752000.
Bradford Cathedral Tel 0274 725958.
Museums and Art Galleries
Colour Museum Tel 0274 390955.
Cartwright Hall Art Gallery Tel 0274 493313.
National Museum of Photography, Film and Television Tel 0274 727488.
Also houses Britain's only IMAX cinema.
Mecca Leisure Ice Rink Tel 0274 729091.
Bradford Northern RLFC Tel 0274 733899

Bradford-on-Avon Woolley Grange 75% £130

Tel 0225 864705 Fax 0225 864059 **HR**

Woolley Green Bradford-on-Avon Wiltshire BA15 1TX **Map 14 B3**

It's difficult not to fall under the spell of Woolley Grange. Partly it's the charming 17th-century building with numerous comfortably lived-in day rooms full of antiques, pictures, real fires, two spaniels and a cat, but it's also to do with the unstuffy, yet not uncivilised atmosphere created by the Chapmans and their friendly young staff (whose lack of uniform is quite deliberate) who always seem to be around when you need them. Bedrooms vary considerably in size but all have great character with a beamed bathroom here (mostly with Victorian-style fittings), a rugged stone fire breast there (about half have working gas coal fires), brass bedsteads, patchwork bedcovers, antiques and fresh flowers all helping to create an appealing 'country' feel. Ideal for families, an old coach house has become 'Woolley Bear's Den' with full-time nanny and large games room. Woolley now has a collection of interesting bicycles, including a 20s' tandem, an Indian trishaw and two of the famous locally-produced Moultons. ***Rooms** 20. Garden, outdoor swimming pool, tennis, games room.* AMERICAN EXPRESS *Access, Diners, Visa.*

Restaurant £75

Colin White's uncomplicated yet sophisticated brand of cooking – salmon fish cakes with coriander butter sauce, chargrilled red mullet with griddled polenta and roasted peppers, sauté of guinea fowl with stir-fried vegetables and star anise – is entirely in keeping with the style of the hotel. A good selection of British farmhouse cheeses offers an alternative to puds like baked plums with praline mousse and almond milk. Local produce is used as much as possible and, in summer, they are pretty much self-sufficient in fruit, vegetables and herbs from a one-acre Victorian walled garden. Between noon and 10pm an informal menu – omelette Arnold Bennett, hamburger, foccacia, club sandwich – is served in the conservatory or out on the terrace. ***Seats** 52. Parties 70. Private Room 40. L 12-2.30 (Sat & Sun till 3) D 7-10. Set L £24 Set D £28.*

Bradford-on-Avon Places of Interest

Tourist Information Tel 02216 5797.
Iford Manor Gardens Tel 02216 3146/2840/2364.

Braithwaite Ivy House 66% £62

Tel 076 87 78338 **H**

Braithwaite nr Keswick Cumbria CA12 5SY **Map 4 C3**

Nick and Wendy Shill run a hotel of warmth and character in a small 17th-century house at the foot of the Lakeland fells. Guests are made welcome in the beamed lounge, where they can enjoy a drink. Fine old furniture and objets d'art are found in the neat bedrooms, which include a honeymoon suite with four-poster. The hotel is in the middle of the village just behind the Royal Oak pub. No dogs. ***Rooms** 12. Closed 1st week Jan.* AMERICAN EXPRESS *Access, Diners, Visa.*

Bramhall Moat House 63% £85

Tel 061-439 8116 Fax 061-440 8071 **H**

Bramhall Lane South Bramhall Cheshire SK7 2EB **Map 6 B2**

Built in 1972 and since expanded and refurbished four years ago, a well-kept hotel that appeals to both leisure and business visitors. Conference and banqueting facilities for 110/170. ***Rooms** 65. Keep-fit equipment, sauna, solarium.* AMERICAN EXPRESS *Access, Diners, Visa.*

Bramhope Forte Crest 66% £98

Tel 0532 842911 Fax 0532 843451 **H**

Bramhope nr Leeds West Yorkshire LS16 9JJ **Map 6 C1**

16 acres of grounds, swimming pool, keep-fit amenities and conference facilities for up to 150 in a hotel two miles from Leeds/Bradford Airport. Children free in parents' room. 83 rooms reserved for non-smokers. ***Rooms** 126. Garden, indoor swimming pool, gymnasium, sauna, solarium, weekend games room, coffee shop (12noon-10pm).* AMERICAN EXPRESS *Access, Diners, Visa.*

Bramhope Parkway Hotel 63% £122

Tel 0532 672551 Fax 0532 674410 **H**

Otley Road Bramhope nr Leeds West Yorkshire LS16 8AG **Map 6 C1**

Mock-Tudor hotel in a rural location adjoining Golden Acre Park trial gardens. Smart, up-to-date accommodation with good leisure facilities (including a health and fitness assessment centre and running track) and two acres of gardens. Conference/banqueting amenties for up to 250/300. ***Rooms** 103. Garden, indoor swimming pool, keep-fit equipment, sauna, spa bath, steam room, solarium, beauty salon, tennis, snooker.* AMERICAN EXPRESS *Access, Diners, Visa.*

Bramley Bramley Grange 64% £105

Tel 0483 893434 Fax 0483 893835 **H**

281 Horsham Road Bramley nr Guildford Surrey GU5 0BL **Map 15 E3**

Based on a mock-Tudor Victorian house, Bramley Grange now extends around three sides of a large garden (making it a popular venue for weddings) with a wooded hillside completing the square. Half the bedrooms are in the newest wing and feature limed oak furniture, plain walls and co-ordinating fabrics. Other rooms vary considerably from large with antique furniture to some small singles with shower and WC only. All but five rooms are reserved for non-smokers. ***Rooms** 46. Garden, tennis, putting.* AMERICAN EXPRESS *Access, Visa.*

Brampton **Farlam Hall** **75%** **£170***

Tel 069 77 46234 Fax 069 77 46683 **HR**

Hallbankgate Brampton Cumbria CA8 2NG **Map 4 C2**

The hotel stands on the A689 two miles from Brampton – not in Farlam village. Set in lovely grounds complete with stream and ornamental lake, the original 17th-century farmhouse was enlarged to form a manor house in Victorian times. The Quinion and Stevenson families' latter-day conversion to charming country house hotel features Victorian-design wallpapers and authentically re-upholstered original pieces. Plants and fresh flowers, books and board games enhance the lived-in feel. Individually decorated bedrooms are a model of taste; most have space for a sitting area, and bathrooms are modern and well equipped; the finest is a Victorian recreation in dark mahogany. Splendid breakfasts and the charm and courtesy of the resident hosts contribute greatly to a memorable stay. No children under five. *Half-board terms only. ***Rooms** 13. Garden. Closed 25-30 Dec.* American Express *Access, Visa.*

Restaurant **£60**

Guests are requested to arrive at 7.30 to order in the bar or front lounge. This air of formality extends to dinner. Barry Quinion's nightly fixed-price-only, 4-course menu changes daily and offers a small choice of three dishes at each course, typified by a terrine of venison, grouse and pistachio, followed by roulade of sole, salmon on a fresh dill and Noilly Prat sauce, English cheeseboard and apricot bavarois. Short, diverse, sensibly-priced wine list. ***Seats** 40. D only at 8. Set D £27.50.*

Brandon **Brandon Hall** **65%** **£107**

Tel 0203 542571 Fax 0203 544909 **H**

Brandon nr Coventry Warwickshire CV8 3FW **Map 7 D4**

An elegant mansion with a country house air, set in 17 acres of grounds. Most of the accommodation (40 rooms) is in a modern extension. Banqueting/conference facilities for up to 120. Forte Heritage. ***Rooms** 60. Garden, squash, pitch & putt, archery, games room.* American Express *Access, Diners, Visa.*

> We endeavour to be as up-to-the-minute as possible, but inevitably some changes to key personnel may occur at restaurants and hotels after the Guide goes to press.

Brands Hatch **Brands Hatch Thistle** **70%** **£97**

Tel 0474 854900 Fax 0474 853220 **H**

Brands Hatch nr Dartford Kent DA3 8PE **Map 7 D4**

A modern hotel standing on the A20, three miles from M25 and at the main entrance to Brands Hatch racing circuit. Public rooms include a spacious and quite elegant foyer with a polished granite tiled floor, pillars and deep blue leather settees; opening from this is the Bugatti Bar. Best bedrooms are those designated Executive, with remote-control teletext TVs, bidets, dressing gowns and separate shower cubicle as well as the standard hairdryers, trouser presses, room safes and individually controlled heating and ventilation. Minibars and tea-makers are also provided, and all the furniture is smartly contemporary. Conference/banqueting facilities for 300/250. Families are well catered for, and children up to 16 stay free in parents' room. ***Rooms** 137. Garden, coffee shop (9.30am-10.30pm).* American Express *Access, Diners, Visa.*

Brands Hatch **Place of Interest**

Motor Racing Circuit Fawkham Tel 0474 872331.

Branscombe **Masons Arms** **64%** **£54**

Tel 029 780 300 Fax 029 780 500 **H**

Branscombe nr Seaton Devon EX12 3DJ **Map 13 E2**

A delightful 14th-century inn half a mile from the sea, with slate floors, open fires and oak beams that were once the timbers of smugglers' boats. Guests may stay in the hotel itself, whose seven rooms are compact and quaint (two are without private bathrooms) or in the adjacent residential cottages, which have been sympathetically converted over the years. Popular with shooting parties in winter, who obviously appreciate monthly suckling pig-roasts in front of the open log fire in the bar. Children up to 10 stay free in parents' room. A new function facility, built away from the original buildings but in sympathy with them by using local stone, caters for around 95. ***Rooms** 21. Garden. Access, Visa.*

Branscombe **Place of Interest**

Seaton Beach 5 miles.

Braunton **Otters Restaurant** **£50**

Tel 0271 813633 **R**

30 Caen Street Braunton Barnstaple Devon EX33 1AA **Map 12 C2**

Carol Cowie's realistically-priced set menu offers a choice of six or more dishes per course, with supplements for some items like smoked salmon, steaks, traditional prawn cocktail, and the cheeseboard. Typical choice might include sherry-laced chestnut soup, mushroom pancake and deep-fried herb-stuffed snails to start; lemon sole paupiettes with salmon mousse and a champagne cream sauce, venison pie or pork with a honey, mint and cider glaze among the mains; and French apple tart, New Orleans-style baked banana or an ice cream platter to finish. On Wednesday nights there is a special Starters and Sweets menu (priced à la carte) in addition to the regular menu. Smoking is not allowed before 9.30pm. The restaurant stands in a little row of shops in the centre of the village, 2 miles from Saunton Sands. ***Seats** 40. D only 7-9.30. Closed Sun (& Mon in winter except Christmas), Bank Holidays, 2 weeks Nov, 2 weeks Mar. Set D £14.70/£16.95.* AMERICAN EXPRESS *Access, Visa.*

Bray-on-Thames **The Waterside Inn** ★★★ **£160**

Tel 0628 20691 Fax 0628 784710 **RR**

Ferry Road Bray-on-Thames Berkshire SL6 2AT **Map 15 E2**

On a balmy summer's day there can be no finer setting than this riverside restaurant, less than an hour's drive from London off the M4 (Junction 8/9). Prepare for your meal with a refreshing drink on the waterside terrace, or summer house, and take time in choosing from the menus. Examples of cold starters will be presented before ordering, perhaps giving you a chance to make up your mind, and though the set menu is written in French, translations are meticulously explained. Good value, certainly at lunchtime, is the three-course *menu gastronomique* at £28 which has suggested wines by the glass (additional charge) to complement the food. After a tasty *amuse-bouche*, also painstakingly explained, a typical summer menu might include *salade gourmande de canard, vinaigrette de truffes; pavé de sandre* (pike-perch) *grillé, tagliatelles de tomates, nage de céleri; soufflé tiède Tutti Frutti, sauce au miel.* There's also a *menu exceptionnel* (min two persons) which offers smaller portions of five dishes taken from the à la carte menu which includes several items that are hallmarks of the Waterside kitchens, dishes such as fresh pasta filled with a mousse of lobster and crab served with a crustacean oil flavoured with basil (incidentally, the restaurant has a fish tank for freshness), pan-fried fillet of salmon seasoned with spices, served on a bed of crunchy vegetables with a parsley nage, Challandais duck, first poached in jasmine stock, then roasted pink and served with a cinnamon-flavoured jus – this dish is served in two parts, the breast with *pommes fondantes* and *mangetout*, then the leg with a salad. A recent dish of crab meat marinated in lime juice tossed with diced green and red pepper, and avocado on a tomato mousse which tasted fine was a somewhat amateurish presentation for a restaurant of this class; similarly, and untypically, the canapés and petits fours disappointed. On the other hand, classic desserts are first-class, as you would expect from the hands of chefs trained by master *patissier* and patron Michel Roux – a warm raspberry soufflé or a slice of lemon tart and blackcurrant mousse finish off the meal with a flourish. The team, under head chef Mark Dodson and restaurant manager Diego Masciaga, has now been together for over five years – it shows in the style and professionalism of the service; the restaurant was redecorated and refurbished last year with six bedrooms added (see below). Lots of classy touches are in evidence – lovely floral decorations, a trolley of fine French cheeses, a basket of fresh strawberries offered between dessert and coffee, and a chariot that almost buckles under the sheer weight of Armagnacs, ports and digestifs. When booking, check which menus are presented and when; for instance, the £42.50 menu is not available lunchtime Saturday or on Sunday evening, nor from 1st May-30th September! Exclusively and comprehensively French wine list. *The Waterside Inn II*, an electric launch, is available for hire. No children under 12. ***Seats** 75. L 12-2 (Sun 12-3) D 7-10. Closed all Mon, L Tue, D Sun mid Oct-Easter, Bank Holidays (open L 25 Dec), 26 Dec-end Jan. Set L £28 (£34 Sat, £34/£42.50 Sun) + L & D £57. Access, Diners, Visa.*

Rooms **£105**

Six stylish and comfortable bedrooms, all en suite and some with river views, could persuade you to forget the drive home, and the fresh croissants will set you up for the day.

Brentwood Forte Posthouse 61% £68

Tel 0277 260260 Fax 0277 264264 **H**

Brook Street Brentwood Essex CM14 5NF **Map 11 B4**

Comfortable modern redbrick hotel by the M25/A12. Conference/banqueting facilities for 120. ***Rooms** 111. Garden, indoor swimming pool, gymnasium, sauna, solarium, coffee shop (10am-10.30pm).* AMERICAN EXPRESS *Access, Diners, Visa.*

Brentwood Forte Travelodge £42

Tel 0277 810819 **L**

A127 East Horndon nr Brentwood Essex CM13 3LL **Map 11 B4**

Located 5 minutes off Junction 29 of the M25 on the A127 southbound, in the grounds of Halfway House. ***Rooms** 22.* AMERICAN EXPRESS *Access, Visa.*

Brentwood Moat House 67% £118

Tel 0277 225252 Fax 0277 262809 **H**

London Road Brentwood Essex CM14 4NR **Map 11 B4**

Originally a Tudor hunting lodge and mentioned by Pepys in his diaries, the hotel has since been considerably extended but very much in keeping with the original house. Three bedrooms in the main house have antique carved beds and a period feel, while other rooms are more modern, ranged motel-style around the garden. The hotel is easy to find, standing just half a mile from junction 28 of the M25. ***Rooms** 33. Garden.* AMERICAN EXPRESS *Access, Diners, Visa.*

Brentwood Places of Interest

Southend-on-Sea Tourist Information Tel 0702 355122.
Southend-on-Sea Central Museum Tel 0702 330214.
Prittlewell Priory Museum Priory Park, Southend-on-Sea Tel 0702 342878.
South Church Park Cricket Ground Southend-on-Sea Tel 0702 610111.

Bridlington Expanse Hotel 60% £59

Tel 0262 675347 Fax 0262 604928 **H**

North Marine Drive Bridlington Humberside YO15 2LS **Map 7 E1**

Purpose-built in 1937, the Expanse is a traditional seaside hotel that has been owned by the Seymour family since 1948. Many of its guests are regulars, while others come for business meetings and conferences. Public and lounge bars are agreeable places to relax, and quite a few of the bedrooms enjoy sea views; some have balconies. Children up to 15 stay free in parents' room. No dogs. ***Rooms** 48.* AMERICAN EXPRESS *Access, Diners, Visa.*

Bridlington Places of Interest

Burton Agnes Hall Near Bridlington Tel 026289 324.
Bridlington North and South Beaches.

Bridport Riverside Restaurant £36

Tel 0308 22011 **R**

West Bay Bridport Dorset DT6 4EZ **Map 13 F2**

The menu at this friendly, relaxed restaurant is mostly fish and shellfish, simply prepared as ordered to bring out all the freshness and flavour. On the regular side you might find whitebait, grilled sardines, West Bay scallops, crab, cod, haddock, lemon sole plus lobster heading the luxury stakes on the regular menu; however, daily specials are the most interesting dishes with grilled black bream, steamed oysters with spinach, red mullet with a spicy salsa, poached turbot and langoustines showing that the style extends way beyond fish and chips. Banana and butterscotch crumble or tiramisu will make a splendid end to a meal. Also served are late breakfasts, snacks and teas. In good weather eight tables are set on a patio overlooking the river. Facilities for families; children's portions attract a 20% price reduction. Hours are extended in high season. ***Seats** 80. L 11.30-3 (Sat & Sun to 4) D 6.30-8.30. Closed D Sun, all Mon (except Bank Holidays & high season), early Dec-early Mar. Access, Visa.*

Bridport Places of Interest

Mapperton House Tel 0308 862645.
Parnham House & Gardens Tel 0308 862204.

Brierley Hill Copthorne Hotel 71% NEW £118

Tel 0384 482882 Fax 0384 482773 **H**

The Waterfront Level Street Brierley Hill West Midlands DY5 1UR **Map 6 C4**

Located next to the Merry Hill shopping complex, this, the newest Copthorne Hotel, opened in April 1993, combines stylish public areas with well-designed bedrooms. The large, circular, marble-floored lobby with a few scattered groups of lounge seating leads on to the combined bar/restaurant/coffee shop area which is on several split levels overlooking a stretch of canal. Mirrors in bedrooms are cleverly placed to give both front and rear views (in 'lady' rooms one conceals an iron and ironing board) and for the truly narcissistic the polished granite vanitory unit in the bathroom is set into a mirrored alcove. Connoisseur rooms get various extras, evening turn-down service and use of the Connoisseur lounge with complimentary Continental breakfast and beverages throughout the day. There are also eight full suites. Extensive 24hr room service. ***Rooms** 138. Indoor swimming pool, gymnasium, sauna, spa bath, solarium.* AMERICAN EXPRESS *Access, Diners, Visa.*

Brighouse **Forte Crest** **68%** **£98**

Tel 0484 400400 Fax 0484 400068 **H**

Coalpit Lane Clifton Village Brighouse West Yorkshire HD6 4HW **Map 6 C1**

Close to Junction 25 of the M62, the hotel sports a refreshingly different Italianate decor. Two-thirds of the bedrooms are designated non-smoking. Good leisure facilities; seven meeting/banqueting rooms accommodating 20-200. ***Rooms** 94. Garden, indoor swimming pool, sauna, spa bath, solarium, beauty salon, coffee shop (8am-11pm).* AMERICAN EXPRESS *Access, Diners, Visa.*

Brightling **Jack Fuller's** **£35**

Tel 042 482 212 **R**

Brightling nr Robertsbridge East Sussex TN32 5HD **Map 11 B6**

The name is visible only on the road from Robertsbridge to Brightling, so otherwise this former pub is easy to miss. It's fronted by a well-kept garden, and patio doors lead from the restaurant to a wide terrace (outside eating in summer). Inside it's cosy and cheerful, and the owners add to the jolly atmosphere. Good local produce goes into the mainstay of the menu – steamed savoury puddings and flaky pastry pies served in generous measure with equally hearty vegetable bakes. Nursery puds like Spotted Dick or syrup sponge demand cream or lovely thick custard. ***Seats** 72. Parties 35. Private Room 25. L 12-3 (Sun till 4) D 7-11. Closed D Sun, all Mon, also Tue & Wed in winter.* AMERICAN EXPRESS *Access, Diners, Visa.*

Brighton **Bedford Hotel** **66%** **£128**

Tel 0273 329744 Fax 0273 775877 **H**

King's Road Brighton East Sussex BN1 2JF **Map 11 B6**

On the lower five floors of a tall apartment block on the seafront, a modern establishment with spacious public areas. The Garden Room restaurant is the focal point of the day rooms. Bedrooms are large, with quality modern furniture and compact bathrooms, all with showers. Guests may use the leisure facilities of the *Metropole Hotel*, just 100 yards away. Car park for 50 cars. Eight conference suites provide versatile facilities for up to 450 delegates. ***Rooms** 129.* AMERICAN EXPRESS *Access, Diners, Visa.*

Brighton **Black Chapati** **£43**

Tel 0273 699011 **R**

12 Circus Parade New England Road Brighton East Sussex BN1 4GW **Map 11 B6**

The decor is plain and minimalist, the only colour other than black being provided by a few abstract prints. Stephen Funnell's Indian-and Thai-inspired food is equally free of clichés, and Brighton is certainly the richer for it. Some dishes have a familiar ring – onion bhaji, Madras lamb curry – while others probably don't appear on any other restaurant's menu: sautéed lamb's kidneys in a tamarind sauce, Goan pork sausage served on a bed of lentils with a red pepper chutney, lemon-marinated roast haddock fillet with kudhi and a Gujarati salad. The chef's favourite drink, Breton cider, is an excellent accompaniment. Sunday lunch is a buffet. ***Seats** 30. Parties 15. L Sun 1-3 otherwise by arrangement D 7-10.30. Closed D Sun, all Mon & Bank Holidays. Set L £7.95. Access, Visa.*

Brighton **Brighton Metropole** **70%** **£160**

Tel 0273 775432 Fax 0273 207764 **H**

King's Road Brighton East Sussex BN1 2FU **Map 11 B6**

Geared to the business executive, the Metropole boasts massive and diverse conference facilities (for up to 1800 delegates) and vast exhibition space. The broad, deep foyer leads to an elegant drawing room with crystal chandeliers, finely detailed plasterwork and settees and armchairs round marble-topped tables. There is a second peaceful lounge and a dark,

See over

atmospheric cocktail bar. Good-size bedrooms, furnished in smart lightwood, include 16 suites with sea-facing balconies. Some rooms are large enough for settees as well as the standard two chairs and table. Children up to 16 stay free in parents' room. ***Rooms** 328. Indoor swimming pool, sauna, solarium, spa bath, gymnasium, beauty salon, hairdressing, night club.* AMERICAN EXPRESS *Access, Diners, Visa.*

Brighton — Browns — £35

Tel 0273 323501 — R

3-4 Duke Street Brighton East Sussex BN1 1AH — **Map 11 B6**

An ultra-busy, good-value brasserie on the edge of the Lanes offering everything from breakfast to afternoon tea and dinner in informal style. Spaghetti, pizza, salads, hot sandwiches, straightforward meat and fish dishes and daily blackboard specials. Good-value house wines. Children's menu and mother's room make this a good family destination. *Also at:* Browns Bar 34 Ship Street plus outlets in Oxford, Cambridge and now Bristol (see entries). ***Seats** 140. Parties 30. Private Room 50. Meals 11am-11.30pm (Sun & Bank Holidays 12-11.30). Closed 25 & 26 Dec.* AMERICAN EXPRESS *Access, Diners, Visa.*

Brighton — China Garden — £55

Tel 0273 25124 — R

88 Preston Street Brighton East Sussex BN1 1HG — **Map 11 B6**

The 100-item menu at this smart roomy restaurant near the West Pier includes many Peking and Cantonese favourites: roast Peking duck for four (order 12 hours in advance), salt and pepper lobster, sole with garlic, ginger and sping onions, grilled pork dumplings, iron-griddle sizzlers. ***Seats** 130. Private Room 40. Meals noon-11pm. Closed 25 & 26 Dec. Set meals from £14.50.* AMERICAN EXPRESS *Access, Diners, Visa.*

Brighton — Grand Hotel — 74% — £160

Tel 0273 321188 Fax 0273 202694 — H

King's Road Brighton East Sussex BN1 2FW — **Map 11 B6**

Brighton's best-known hotel – right on the seafront – is splendidly equipped for both the leisure and the conference markets. Hobden's Health Spa and the Midnight Blues night club are smartly contemporary, while the original luxury and grandeur survive in the coloured marble columns, the polished marble floors, the moulded plaster ceiling and the magnificent central staircase. In the lounge, heavy drapes, wing chairs, sofas, ornaments and paintings give an elegant Victorian feel. Handsome furnishings and chintzy decor distinguish the bedrooms, which all offer full 24hr room service; de luxe rooms have sea views. There are rooms especially designed for lady executives, rooms with additional facilities for the disabled, 'romantic' rooms with double whirlpool baths and eight splendid suites. Afternoon tea is served in the airy conservatory, also overlooking the sea. De Vere Hotels. ***Rooms** 200. Indoor swimming pool, keep-fit equipment, sauna, spa bath, solarium, beauty & hair salon.* AMERICAN EXPRESS *Access, Diners, Visa.*

Brighton — Hospitality Inn — 77% — £155

Tel 0273 206700 Fax 0273 820692 — HR

Kings Road Brighton East Sussex BN1 2GS — **Map 11 B6**

Centrally located on the promenade, a strikingly modern exterior commands an equally impressive interior with a large atrium lounge, under a glass roof four storeys above, filled with plants and trees that is cleverly lit at night. Off to one side Bart's café-style bar offers a change of mood. Good, if unexciting, standardised bedrooms are properly serviced in the evening and offer pleasing little extras like bathrobes, slippers and a bowl of fresh fruit. Notably smart staff are both friendly and helpful. Extensive 24hr room service. Free parking (for diners as well as residents) by voucher valid for the Town Hall car park under the hotel. ***Rooms** 204. Indoor swimming pool, gymnasium, sauna, solarium, hairdressing.* AMERICAN EXPRESS *Access, Diners, Visa.*

La Noblesse Restaurant £80

Subdued yet rich decor creates an atmosphere of quiet luxury here. Short – just four main dishes on both the à la carte and good value table d'hote – but well-balanced menus offer simple, soundly cooked dishes: cream of parsnip soup, salad of stuffed artichokes glazed with hollandaise sauce, pan-fried halibut with Café de Paris butter, rack of lamb with garlic and parsley sauce, chocolate truffle torte, banoffi pie. Service is willing but lacks polish notwithstanding the waiters' tail-coats. Short wine list. ***Seats** 50. L 12-2.15 D 7-10.15. Closed L Sat, all Sun, some Bank Holidays. Set L & D £13.50/£16.99.*

Brighton Langan's Bistro £62

Tel 0273 606933 **R**

1 Paston Place Brighton East Sussex BN2 1HA **Map 11 B6**

Away from the centre and close to the marina, this is one of Brighton's best restaurants. Chic, colourful and relaxed, it offers a short menu (half a dozen choices for each course) of simply prepared, easy-to-enjoy dishes such as crab bisque, bacon and artichoke salad, Dover sole fillets with tapénade, calf's liver with sage sauce and tournedos with red wine. Orange and Grand Marnier crème brulée is a typical dessert. Also a three-course lunch menu with two choices per course. ***Seats** 42. Parties 10. L 12.30-2.15 D 7.30-10.15. Closed L Sat, D Sun, all Mon, 26 Dec, 2 weeks Jan, 2 weeks Aug. Set L £14.50.* AMERICAN EXPRESS *Access, Diners, Visa.*

Brighton La Marinade £45

Tel 0273 600992 **R**

77 St George's Road Kemp Town Brighton East Sussex BN2 1EF **Map 11 B6**

Popular, unpretentious little restaurant (now under new ownership, but with the same chef since 1976) serving straightforward bistro food. Coarse paté, garlicky snails, pastry-encased fillet of lamb with mushroom stuffing and pork in a cream sauce with potatoes, ham and celery are typical choices. Always a daily fish special. Good-value Sunday roast/fish lunch. "Café avec mints" to finish. No smoking in the upstairs dining room. ***Seats** 36. Private Room 35. L 12.15-2 D 7.15-10. Closed L Sat, D Sun, all Mon. Set L £12.50 (inc Sun) Set D from £16.95.* AMERICAN EXPRESS *Access, Diners, Visa.*

Brighton Old Ship Hotel 65% £105

Tel 0273 329001 Fax 0273 820718 **H**

King's Road Brighton East Sussex BN1 1NR **Map 11 B6**

A hotel of considerable charm and history – Paganini played in the ballroom here and a former owner saved the life of Charles II by transporting him to France in his boat – the Old Ship dates in part to the 15th century. A central location on the seafront is a big plus as is secure parking for 70 cars. Public areas include a surprisingly spacious oak-panelled lobby dotted with antiques, a pair of quiet lounges with Adam-style ceilings and the panelled Tettersell's Bar. About two-thirds of the bedrooms (mostly those in the east wing) are smartly furnished with freestanding darkwood furniture, matching floral fabrics, breakfast table, good armchairs and up-to-date bathrooms. The remainder vary somewhat in age and style but all are at least acceptable. Friendly staff. 24hr room service. Children under 16 stay free in parents' room. ***Rooms** 152.* AMERICAN EXPRESS *Access, Diners, Visa.*

Brighton Topps Hotel 69% £79

Tel 0273 729334 Fax 0273 203679 **HR**

17 Regency Square Brighton East Sussex BN1 2FG **Map 11 B6**

Two Regency properties overlooking a square 100 yards from the seafront make a fine setting for a very friendly, agreeable hotel that tries to provide a real home from home. There's a simple lounge/reception where drinks are served and, upstairs, well-appointed bedrooms with fabric-lined walls and antiqued pine furniture offer a touch of luxury. All have armchairs or sofas, flowers, drinks trays and excellent bathrooms; five have seating areas, and the stars of the show are two four-poster rooms with balconies – perfect to catch the sun with breakfast. No dogs. Parking is charged. *Rooms 14. AMERICAN EXPRESS Access, Diners, Visa.*

Bottoms Restaurant £48

Pauline Collins prepares unpretentious English cooking in the small, pretty basement restaurant. A typical fixed-price dinner menu might offer a thick vegetable soup, potted pork and duck or leek and ham tartlet to start followed by a potato-topped vegetarian hotpot, prawn, scallop and sole pie or venison in filo pastry with a chestnut and Madeira sauce. "Steak and kidney pie is always available", even though the menu changes every six weeks. ***Seats** 24. Parties 10. Private Room 10. D only 7-9.30. Closed Sun & Wed, Jan. Set D £18.95.*

Brighton (Hove) Sackville Hotel 61% £75

Tel 0273 736292 Fax 0273 205759 **H**

189 Kingsway Hove Brighton East Sussex BN3 4GU **Map 11 B6**

A fresh coat of paint outside and some refurbishment within is maintaining standards at this seafront hotel. A visit by Winston Churchill during the war, when the hotel was a convalescent home for wounded soldiers, is commemorated by various photographs and Churchilliana in the panelled bar-lounge with its leather chesterfields and there is a small rattan-furnished sun lounge. Well-kept bedrooms mostly feature darkwood furniture and soft colour schemes. Two rooms have antiques and eight have sea-facing balconies. ***Rooms** 45. AMERICAN EXPRESS Access, Diners, Visa.*

Brighton (Hove) Whitehaven Hotel 56% £70

Tel 0273 778355 Fax 0273 731177 **H**

Wilbury Road Hove East Sussex BN3 3JP **Map 11 B6**

Standards of cleanliness and repair are high at this small, modestly comfortable hotel in a quiet street a short stroll from the sea-front. Unrestricted street parking is another plus. No children under 8. No dogs. ***Rooms** 17. Garden, solarium. AMERICAN EXPRESS Access, Diners, Visa.*

Brighton Places of Interest

Tourist Information Tel 0273 323755.
Sallis Benney Theatre Grand Parade Tel 0273 604141.
Theatre Royal Tel 0273 328488.
The Brighton Concert Centre Tel 0273 203131.
The Dome Complex Tel 0273 674357.
Royal Pavilion Tel 0273 603005.
Brighton Museum and Art Gallery Church Street Tel 0273 603005.
Brighton Cricket Ground Eaton Road, Hove Tel 0273 732161.
Brighton Football Ground Tel 0273 739535.
Brighton Racecourse Tel 0273 682912/603580.
Brighton Ice Rink Tel 0273 324677.
Euroski Dry Ski Slope Tel 0273 688258.

Brimfield — Poppies Restaurant — £67

Tel 0584 711230 Fax 0584 711654 — RR

The Roebuck Hotel Brimfield nr Ludlow Shropshire SY8 4NE — Map 14 B1

The bright, cheery restaurant with block floor and cane-back chairs is an extension of Brimfield's renowned village local. A self-taught cook, Carole Evans displays a fine command of compositions, colours and textures: spinach soufflé served with anchovy hollandaise, duck breast with a white port and Seville orange sauce, fillet of Hereford beef on celeriac purée with a red wine and shallot sauce. There's a long sweets list and a fine variety of farmhouse cheeses. A lighter blackboard menu operates in the Roebuck bar. Service shines. ***Seats** 36. Private Room 16. L 12-2 D 7-10. Closed Sun & Mon, Christmas, 2 weeks Feb, 1 week Oct.* AMERICAN EXPRESS® *Access, Visa.*

Rooms — £60

Three lovely cottage bedrooms, two doubles with WC/shower only and a twin with full bathroom, contain limed-oak furniture and pretty floral fabrics. Fine country breakfasts include Herefordshire apple juice, honey from their own bees and home-made sausages. No children under eight.

Brimfield — Place of Interest

Burford House Gardens Tel 0584 810777.

Bristol — Aztec Hotel — 74% — £96

Tel 0454 301090 Fax 0454 201593 — H

Aztec West Business Park Almondsbury Bristol Avon BS12 4TS — Map 13 F1

A smart, professionally run, purpose-built, modern hotel in the Shire Inns group, owned by brewers Daniel Thwaites. It provides a good balance of facilities between mid-week conferences and weekend family breaks. All bedrooms are of Executive standard with coffee tables, writing desk and fax point; children under 16 are accommodated free in their parents' rooms; 18 rooms are reserved for non-smokers. Syndicate rooms convert to family use at weekends with wall-mounted let-down beds. Day rooms are more than adequate, with lounges on two levels in the central 'lodge' and a smart snooker room. The hotel also has a fine leisure club and its own Black Sheep pub. Light meals and snacks are served in Danby's Bar; more formal dining in Quarterjacks restaurant. Regional specialities at breakfast include Somerset venison sausages and Alderley trout served with scrambled eggs. In a modern business park near Junction 16 of the M5 (south of the M4/M5 interchange). ***Rooms** 88. Garden, indoor swimming pool, gymnasium, squash, sauna, solarium, steam room, children's playground.* AMERICAN EXPRESS® *Access, Diners, Visa.*

Our inspectors *never* book in the name of Egon Ronay's Guides. They disclose their identity only if they are considering an establishment for inclusion in the next edition of the Guide.

Bristol — Berkeley Square Hotel — 69% — £104

Tel 0272 254000 Fax 0272 252970 — H

15 Berkeley Square Bristol Avon BS8 1HB — Map 13 F1

Adjacent to Bristol Museum and Art Gallery, the elegant Georgian Berkeley overlooks a quiet tree-lined square. Well-equipped bedrooms vary from practical singles to spacious suites, their names drawn from eminent Bristolians. Nine rooms are designated non-smoking. Small lounge and restaurant at street level, with a state-of-the-art basement bar and café (7.30am-10pm). ***Rooms** 43. Closed Christmas.* AMERICAN EXPRESS® *Access, Diners, Visa.*

Bristol **Blue Goose** **£45**

Tel 0272 420940 **R**

344 Gloucester Road Bristol Avon **Map 13 F1**

Unusual bistro dishes: grilled polenta and Parma ham, chicken tikka kebabs with Thai rice, roast fillet of Nile perch, pissaladière of salmon, pithiviers of vegetables, pear fritters, raspberry brulée. Sensibly-priced wines: 43 under £15! Spot the large blue goose above the entrance. ***Seats** 80. D only 6.30-11.45. Closed Sun. Set D £12.50. Access, Visa.*

Bristol **Bristol Marriott Hotel** **73%** **£136**

Tel 0272 294281 Fax 0272 225838 **H**

Lower Castle Street Bristol Avon BS1 3AD **Map 13 F1**

City centre high-rise recently rebranded Marriott (formerly Holiday Inn) after major refurbishment. Public areas are spacious and well laid-out. Good-sized, air-conditioned bedrooms offer large beds (two doubles in the twin-bedded rooms) and ample work space. Executive floor rooms are similar but with various extras – second telephone at the desk, mini-bar, bathrobe – and an exclusive Executive lounge with complimentary Continental breakfast and beverages. Obliging staff and extensive 24hr room service which includes 'sous-vide' dishes from the Roux Brothers. Free parking in an adjacent multi-storey car park. ***Rooms** 289. Indoor swimming pool, gymnasium, sauna, spa baths, steam room, solarium, brasserie 7am-11pm.* AMERICAN EXPRESS *Access, Diners, Visa.*

Bristol **Browns** **NEW** **£35**

Tel 0272 304777 **R**

38 Queen's Road Bristol Avon BS8 1RE **Map 13 F1**

Housed in the former University Refectory building at the top of Park Street, this fourth in the chain of American-style brasseries has been an instant hit both with students and city types. A busy bar and fully 200 seats still leave room for a central grand piano and ubiquitous aspidistras, amongst which diners all day choose from pasta, burgers, chargrilled chicken and puddings from pecan pie to chocolate mousse cake. Start the day with an English breakfast or drop by for cucumber sandwiches and scones at tea-time. At night it's very much a see-and-be-seen scene with fancy shaken cocktails. ***Seats** 200. Parties 30. Private Room 230. Meals 11am-11.30pm (Sun & Bank Holidays from noon). Closed 25 Dec.* AMERICAN EXPRESS *Access, Diners, Visa.*

Bristol **Forte Crest** **67%** **£107**

Tel 0272 564242 Fax 0272 569735 **H**

Filton Road Hambrook Bristol Avon BS16 1QX **Map 13 F1**

City fringe hotel in 16 acres with its own lake. Health and fitness club; large conference trade, with facilities for up to 500 delegates. Close to the M32 (J1, take A4174) and M4 (from J19). Parking for 300 cars. ***Rooms** 197. Indoor swimming pool, gymnasium, sauna, spa bath, solarium.* AMERICAN EXPRESS *Access, Diners, Visa.*

Bristol **Grand Hotel** **62%** **£96**

Tel 0272 291645 Fax 0272 227619 **H**

Broad Street Bristol Avon BS1 2EL **Map 13 F1**

No longer the grandest hotel in town – although the Italianate facade still looks good, especially when floodlit at night – but a central location, friendly staff, good porterage and, most notably, valet parking is all in its favour. Go for the refurbished bedrooms – about 25% of the total and worth the small extra charge – which offer a good standard of comfort and pleasing colour schemes. Older rooms are more variable with cheaper toiletries and often without hairdryer or trouser press. Singles on the top floor are compact. Good breakfasts. Mount Charlotte Thistle. ***Rooms** 170.* AMERICAN EXPRESS *Access, Diners, Visa.*

Bristol **Harveys Restaurant** **£80**

Tel 0272 277665 **R**

12 Denmark Street Bristol Avon BS1 5DQ **Map 13 F1**

Beneath Harveys of Bristol's head office the 13th-century cellars, where the wine merchant first opened for business in 1796, now house a comfortable, air-conditioned restaurant and fascinating, labyrinthine wine museum. Chef Ramon Farthing's sound cooking is rather more up-to-date, however, with the likes of John Dory coated with strips of celeriac on a bed of sweet onions with sun-dried tomatoes; olive and basil-infused ratatouille with noisettes of lamb and breast of baby chicken with vegetables pickled in tarragon. Oysters come *au naturel* or glazed with a champagne and shallot sabayon with dill. Good puds, sadly not included on the two-course set lunch, might include a traditional bread-and-butter pudding given a new twist with apricot glaze and mascarpone cream, or a well-made hot soufflé. The marvellous wine list (regional winner Cellar of the Year) has great depth, especially in France (26 vintages of Ch Latour), but also offers good choices from the rest of the world. Note the exceptional sherries and ports. Fair prices, so indulge! ***Seats** 100. Parties 75. Private Room 60. L 12-1.45 D 7-10.45. Closed L Sat, all Sun and Bank Holidays. Set L £16.50 Set D £29.* AMERICAN EXPRESS *Access, Diners, Visa.*

Bristol **Hilton Hotel** **69%** **£110**

Tel 0272 260041 Fax 0272 230089 **H**

Redcliffe Way Bristol Avon BS1 6NJ **Map 13 F1**

Easy to find on the city's inner ring road near Temple Meads British Rail station. The first-floor, open-plan reception area incorporates the bar and lounge and there is a good business centre and small, unmanned leisure centre on the same level. A programme to upgrade the standard chain hotel bedrooms has begun and it is the new rooms with fine figured walnut furniture, air-conditioning and marble bathrooms that are particularly recommended. A buffet breakfast is served in a historic room built originally as a kiln for the Phoenix glassworks in 1785. Children up to 16 stay free in parents' room. ***Rooms** 201. Indoor swimming pool, keep-fit equipment, sauna, spa bath, steam room, solarium.* AMERICAN EXPRESS *Access, Diners, Visa.*

Bristol **Holiday Inn Crowne Plaza** **72%** **£105**

Tel 0272 255010 Fax 0272 255040 **H**

Victoria Street Bristol Avon BS1 6HY **Map 13 F1**

Previously the *Bristol Moat House*, a strikingly modern, redbrick building standing on the site of the Old City Wall, on the corner of Victoria Street and Temple Way, in the milieu of Bristol's rapidly expanding, high-tech business quarter. Catering mainly for the executive and conference market (for up to 200 delegates), the modern bedrooms mix well-lit desk space, multipoint telephone and fax line with uninspiring decor and plastic marble-look units in the bathrooms. 40 bedrooms are designated non-smoking and two are specially fitted for the disabled; four air-conditioned, spacious suites have spa baths and bathrobes provided. An open-plan foyer/lounge is noisy but reception and porterage are effectively run. Children under 16 stay free in parents' room; seven family rooms. Free underground parking with direct lift access to bedroom floors poses a security problem. No dogs. Queens Moat Houses. ***Rooms** 132. Keep-fit equipment, solarium, news kiosk.* AMERICAN EXPRESS *Access, Diners, Visa.*

Bristol — Howard's — £50

Tel 0272 262921 — **R**

1a Avon Crescent Bristol Avon BS1 6XQ — **Map 13 F1**

Cross the old Hotwells swing bridge (following signs to the *SS Great Britain*) to find this charming restaurant in a Georgian building. Hot and cold smoked fish is always a popular choice and other possibilities on the table d'hote menu and seasonal à la carte include a warm salad of chicken livers and smoked bacon, hot Stilton beignets, fresh Cornish fish and rich venison and oyster mushroom pie. Vegetarian dishes are always available. ***Seats** 60. Parties 25. Private Room 40. L 12-2.30 D 7-11.30 Closed L Sat, all Sun, 25 & 26 Dec. Set L £13 Set D £15.* AMERICAN EXPRESS *Access, Diners, Visa.*

Bristol — Hunt's — £60

Tel 0272 265580 — **R**

26 Broad Street Bristol Avon BS1 2HG — **Map 13 F1**

The former partners at *Markwick's*, Andy and Anne Hunt, operate in small, intimate surroundings a stone's throw away by St John's Gate (parking is tricky). Daily menus feature fish according to the market, and alternatives could include feta cheese and courgette tart with orange and fennel salad, calf's kidney with gin and juniper, and medallions of venison with sweet gherkins and sour cream. Among the desserts you might well find a hot prune and armagnac tart with vanilla cream. ***Seats** 40. Parties 26. L 12-2 D 7-10. Closed L Sat, all Sun & Mon, Bank Holidays, 2 weeks Aug. Set L £11.95. Access, Visa.*

Bristol — Jameson's Restaurant — £50

Tel 0272 276565 — **R**

30 Upper Maudlin Street Bristol Avon BS2 8DJ — **Map 13 F1**

Opposite the Royal Infirmary, Carole Jameson's well-patronised, lively and informal bistro now has earlier evening opening and offers better value menus than last year. The latter now include Sunday lunch (children's portions) and imaginative vegetarian selections throughout the week. Listed on a blackboard are the day's fresh fish dishes often featuring sardines, sea bream, monkfish and a Mediterranean fish soup. Otherwise, the style of the menu follows the lines of smoked fish terrine, goat's cheese in filo pastry, fresh soup, beef Wellington, rack of lamb and roast duckling with orange and port wine sauce. Accomplished cooking and an evolving wine list with good Australian bottles. Service is friendly and the music at times equally lively. ***Seats** 70. Private Room 40. L 12-2 (to 4 Sun) D 6.30-11.30. Closed L Mon & Sat, D Sun. Set L from £5.50 Set D £12.95/£14.95. Access, Visa.*

Bristol — Restaurant Lettonie ★ — £80

Tel 0272 686456 — **R**

9 Druid Hill Stoke Bishop Bristol Avon BS9 1EW — **Map 13 F1**

Martin Blunos combines natural talent with true dedication to produce the kind of cooking that makes the effort of finding this small restaurant (just seven tables) in a shopping parade on the outskirts of Bristol well worthwhile. The timing of table reservations is carefully spaced to enable the kitchen to give individual attention to dishes like scallops baked in their shell with shredded vegetables, just a hint of ginger and a butter sauce, the whole sealed with pastry and served on a bed of seaweed, or pig's trotters stuffed with a delicate mousse on a rich Madeira sauce. Oyster, potato and leek soup scented with cumin, and cabbage and wild mushroom cannelloni with a creamed leek sauce tempt from the fixed-price menu, which also offers a savoury like goat's cheese ravioli with lemon butter sauce as an alternative to desserts such as freshly-baked apple croustade with caramel ice cream and glazed pineapple with a Kirsch and pistachio ice cream.

Attention to detail extends to baking the varied petits fours freshly each day – a lot of work for the kitchen but it makes all the difference. The simpler lunch menu offers a choice of just two dishes in each course. Good wine list is full of interest with excellent house wine from Bordeaux. ***Seats** 24. Parties 16. L 12.30-1.30 D 7-9.30. Closed Sun & Mon. Set L £15.95 Set D £29.95.* AMERICAN EXPRESS *Access, Visa.*

Bristol **Markwick's** **£65**

Tel 0272 262658 **R**

43 Corn Street Bristol Avon BS1 1HT **Map 13 F1**

A former bank vault in the commercial district makes a surprisingly elegant setting – coffered ceiling, Adam-style plaster decoration on the walls and some fun 'bunch of grape' light fittings – for Stephen Markwick's interesting yet uncomplicated cooking. Scallops and mussels with saffron and parsley noodles, grilled goat's cheese with pimento and hazelnuts, guinea fowl with apples and Calvados, rack of lamb with herb crust, leeks and sherry vinegar sauce demonstrate the style. A separate fish menu depends on the previous day's catch – delivered to the door from Cornwall at 4 each morning. Sweets like pistachio and almond loaf with apricot sauce and nougat of orange and Grand Marnier with chocolate sauce are the responsibility of Stephen's first assistant, Sara Ody. Two charming side rooms provide for private parties. Sadly, the service sometimes fails to live up to the cooking and the surroundings. There's a very reasonably priced house selection on a carefully compiled wine list that includes some worthy bin ends. ***Seats** 50. Private Room 20. L 12-2 D 7-10. Closed L Sat, all Sun, Bank Holiday Mondays, 1 week Easter, 2 weeks Aug, 1 week Christmas. Set L £8.50/£10.50 Set D £19.50.* AMERICAN EXPRESS *Access, Visa.*

Bristol **Michael's Restaurant** **£60**

Tel 0272 276190 **R**

129 Hotwell Road Bristol Avon BS8 4RU **Map 13 F1**

Long-established and popular west-of-centre venue where notable Victorian decor and informal atmosphere contribute to the sense of occasion. Excellent lunchtime value; more ambitious dinners with eclectic menu: smoked tuna with horseradish mayonnaise and redcurrant salad, boned stuffed quail with a basil and tomato sauce, venison cooked in beer, cranberry meringue tart. No smoking in main dining room. ***Seats** 50. Private Room 38. L 12.30-2 D 7-11. Closed L Sat, all Sun & Mon, Bank Holidays. Set L from £12.50 Set D £22.50.* AMERICAN EXPRESS *Access, Visa.*

Bristol **Rajdoot** **£40**

Tel 0272 268033 **R**

83 Park Street Bristol BS1 5PJ **Map 13 F1**

Part of a small group of Indian restaurants offering comfort, good service and a consistently high standard of cooking. ***Seats** 60. Parties 30. L 12-2.15 D 6.30-11.30. Closed L Sun, Bank Holidays, 25 & 26 Dec, 1 Jan. Set L from £8.* AMERICAN EXPRESS *Access, Diners, Visa.*

Bristol **Redwood Lodge Hotel & Country Club 64%** **£85**

Tel 0275 393901 Fax 0275 392104 **H**

Beggar Bush Lane Failand Bristol Avon BS8 3TG **Map 13 F1**

Barely ten minutes from the city centre (via Clifton Bridge) Redwood Lodge offers conference facilities (for up to 175 delegates) and an impressive choice of leisure activities. Individual residents may lose out on quiet corners, bedroom space and room service, which is sporadic at best. Weekenders with families fare better, as there's plenty to do: an all-day coffee shop, 175-seat cinema and regular crèche facilities are available (10am-1pm). Children up to 16 stay free in parents' room. Country Club Hotels. ***Rooms** 108. Garden, indoor, outdoor & children's swimming pools,*

See over

keep-fit equipment, sauna, solarium, beauty & hair salon, tennis, squash, badminton, snooker, cinema, children's playroom & playground, coffee shop (11am-10.30pm). AMERICAN EXPRESS *Access, Diners, Visa.*

Bristol **Rodney Hotel** **64%** **£87**

Tel 0272 735422 Fax 0272 741082 **H**

4 Rodney Place Clifton Down Road Bristol Avon BS8 4HY **Map 13 F1**

Part of a Georgian terrace in the heart of Clifton village, the Rodney is just a stone's throw from Brunel's famed suspension bridge. At ground level, lounge, bar and restaurant are small and intimate, with mainly female staff to contribute a friendly welcome. Among the 50% of single bedrooms choose a "Superior" for extra space and a larger bed. The rooms take their names from the ships of Admiral Rodney's fleet at Saints in 1782. Children up to 12 stay free in parents' room. ***Rooms** 31.* AMERICAN EXPRESS *Access, Diners, Visa.*

Bristol **Stakis Bristol Hotel** **61%** **£109**

Tel 0454 201144 Fax 0454 612022 **H**

Woodlands Lane Patchway Bristol Avon BS12 4JF **Map 13 F1**

Modern low-rise hotel near junction 16 of the M5. Good-sized bedrooms, with one papered and one painted breeze-block wall, have all the usual amenities. Club rooms are standard rooms with a few extras added: miniature of whisky, mineral water, fruit, chocolate. Open-plan public areas offer plenty of comfortable seating for meeting and greeting. 24hr room service. ***Rooms** 111. Garden, indoor swimming pool, keep-fit facilities, sauna, spa bath. solarium.* AMERICAN EXPRESS *Access, Diners, Visa.*

Bristol **Swallow Royal Hotel** **77%** **£118**

Tel 0272 255100 Fax 0272 251515 **HR**

College Green Bristol Avon BS1 5TA **Map 13 F1**

Swallow's newly-renovated hotel, faced in Bath stone, dominates approaches to College Green and Bristol Cathedral. Equally impressive, on arrival, is the Spanish marble hall flanked by country house elegance in the drawing room and Club Bar, and a basement leisure club of Roman bath design. Secure covered parking is a bonus. Generous space, stylish individual decor and air-conditioning establish bedrooms high in the comfort category; marble bathrooms are well lit. Staff are smart, attentive and motivated; company policy, it appears, is responsible for some lapses in service (no evening turn-down for instance) which such a standard of hotel deserves. Banqueting and conference facilities for up to 250. ***Rooms** 242. Indoor swimming pool, sauna, solarium, spa bath, beauty salon, hairdressing, keep-fit equipment. Closed 2 dyas Christmas.* AMERICAN EXPRESS *Access, Diners, Visa.*

Palm Court Restaurant **£65**

The grand Palm Court extends up through three floors lined in Bath stone with curved balustrades and topped by stained-glass skylights. Menus follow the grand format while the service is formal yet unfussy. A fixed-price "Concept of the Kitchen" may run through glazed asparagus with salmon tartare, poached oysters, rosemary-infused lamb and summer pudding, supplemented by a seasonal à la carte. The disappointing wine list would benefit from more half bottles. ***Seats** 60. Parties 8. D only 7.30-10.30. Closed Sun & Mon, 27-29 Dec. Set D £23 (£25 Fri & Sat).*

Terrace Restaurant **£50**

Almost as grand as the Palm Court, the Terrace is surprisingly formal for a hotel's 'second' restaurant; main courses arrive *sous cloche* and the sommelier comes complete with *tastevin* hanging from a chain around his neck. The menu is rather less daunting with the à la carte including simple grills, liver and bacon with mashed potatoes and onion gravy, and crispy leg of duck with mushy peas along with the likes of red mullet glazed with endive and orange, and braised lamb with aubergine purée and gremolata. Overlooking Cathedral Square. ***Seats** 150. L 12.30-2.30 D 7-10.30. Set L £12.50/£15 Set D £15.50/£19.*

Bristol Unicorn Hotel 63% £70

Tel 0272 230333 Fax 0272 230300 **H**

Prince Street Bristol Avon BS1 4QF **Map 13 F1**

City-centre hotel on the old quayside, overlooking the historic harbour. Standard rooms are compact and cheaper than the 80 Superior rooms, many of which have fine views and all of which were refurbished recently. Children up to 16 stay free in parents' room. Separate conference facilities for up to 360 delegates. Rank Hotels. ***Rooms** 245. Coffee shop (7am-2.30pm & 6-10.15pm, all day at weekends).* AMERICAN EXPRESS *Access, Diners, Visa.*

Bristol Places of Interest

Tourist Information Tel 0272 260767.
Algars Manor Iron Acton Tel 045422 372.
Bristol Cathedral Tel 0272 264879.
Phoenix County Cricket Ground Tel 0272 245216.
Mecca Leisure Centre - Ice Rink Tel 0272 260343.
Bristol Zoo Tel 0272 738951.
Theatres and Concert Halls
Bristol Hippodrome St. Augustine's Parade Tel 0272 265524.
Bristol New Vic and Bristol Old Vic Theatre Royal King Street Tel 0272 277466.
Museums and Art Galleries
Arnolfini Gallery Tel 0272 299191.
Bristol Industrial Museum Tel 0272 251470.
Bristol Museum and Art Gallery Tel 0272 223571.
Maritime Heritage Centre and SS Great Britain Tel 0272 260680.

Brixham Quayside Hotel 59% £76

Tel 0803 855751 Fax 0803 882733 **H**

King Street Brixham Devon TQ5 9TJ **Map 13 D3**

The charming if maze-like feel given by narrow hallways and variously sized rooms betrays the hotel's origins as six fisherman's cottages. The former inhabitants would have approved of the little nautically-themed bar sharing downstairs space with a simple, 70s-furnished lounge. Upstairs, two bedrooms have four-poster beds while the best of the rest share a view over the picturesque inner harbour. Mainly very small bathrooms. The hotel's car park is 400 yards away in Ranscombe Road. ***Rooms** 29.* AMERICAN EXPRESS *Access, Diners, Visa.*

Broadhembury Drewe Arms NEW £50

Tel 040 484 267 **R**

Broadhembury Devon EX14 0NF **Map 13 E2**

Simplicity is the keynote of Kerstin Burge's cooking with a blackboard menu offering fresh, accurately cooked fish – Scottish salmon with sorrel butter, turbot hollandaise, monkfish with mustard sauce – served with simply cooked vegetables on the plate. Fishy starters might include gravad lax, anchovy and onion bake, and half a pint of prawns. A couple of meat dishes cater to carnivores and treacle tart, hazelnut meringue and chocolate marquise to the sweet-toothed. The setting is equally unpretentious, being just one room of a small 15th-century thatched pub with boarded walls, plastic tablecloths and dried flowers hanging from the ceiling. Short, reasonably-priced selection of wines. ***Seats** 25. Parties 33. L 12-2 D 7-10. Set L £16.95 Set D £16.95. Closed D Sun & 25 Dec. No credit cards.*

Broadway — Broadway Hotel — 60% — £86

Tel 0386 852401 Fax 0386 853879 — **H**

The Green Broadway Hereford & Worcester WR12 7AA — **Map 14 C1**

Once a 15th-century inn and monastic guest house, now a hotel of charm and comfort. Behind the mellow stone walls the day rooms include a small galleried lounge with a high timbered ceiling and leaded light windows; the Jockey Club bar is a popular meeting place. Bedrooms, by contrast, are generally simple and modern, although the Abbots Room features a four-poster; the Garden room, predictably but usefully, has direct access to the garden. All are well kept, with impeccably tiled bathrooms also benefiting from good housekeeping. Children up to 12 stay free in parents' room. No dogs. ***Rooms** 20. Garden, fishing, riding.* AMERICAN EXPRESS *Access, Diners, Visa.*

Broadway — Collin House — 65% — £88

Tel 0386 858354 — **HR**

Collin Lane Broadway Hereford & Worcester WR12 7PB — **Map 14 C1**

A Cotswold-stone house about a mile north-west of Broadway signposted off the A44 Evesham road (turn right at Collin Lane). John Mills and his friendly staff offer a warm welcome and plenty of advice on what to see and do in the neighbourhood (a book of handwritten notes is placed in each bedroom). Rooms are spacious and have a cottagey feel with country furnishings and pretty floral fabrics. In the winter months blazing log fires bring cheer to the lounge and bar. ***Rooms** 7. Garden, outdoor swimming pool. Closed 24-29 Dec. Access, Visa.*

Restaurant — £60

In the oak-beamed restaurant great store is set by fresh local ingredients. Duck is something of a speciality: on a spring menu it appeared with chicken and pork in a terrine served with quince jelly and crisply roasted breast with a honey, ginger and kumquat sauce. On the same menu were pan-fried salmon croquettes, veal Holstein, grilled halibut steak and carpetbagger steak. Tempting puddings include treacle tart, date sponge pudding with butterscotch sauce and damson ice cream with an almond meringue. Bar and garden lunches are an alternative to the fixed-price menu, and there's a traditional Sunday lunch (children welcome). The price of the three-course dinner is shown against the main course. Short wine list with all areas represented at fair prices. 'Fine wine' dinners are held every couple of months. ***Seats** 24. Parties 32. L 12-1.30 D 7-9. Set L £14.50 Set D from £18.*

Broadway — Dormy House — 69% — £110

Tel 0386 852711 Fax 0386 858636 — **HR**

Willersey Hill Broadway Hereford & Worcester WR12 7LF — **Map 14 C1**

Just off the A44, on an escarpment above Broadway and with views over the local golf course and the Vale of Evesham, Dormy House is an extended 17th-century farmhouse. Beams, exposed stonework and tiled floors set the tone in the main house, whose two homely lounges have fine bay windows. Converted outbuildings house cottagey, comfortable bedrooms, many also with timbered ceilings; two rooms have four-posters. Delegates at the purpose-built conference centre seem to appreciate the rustic, Cotswold-stone Barn Owl bar where less formal lunch and dinner menus are available (as well as afternoon tea). Families welcome; baby-sitting by arrangement; children's supper menu (£7.50) served from 5pm. ***Rooms** 49. Garden, table tennis.* AMERICAN EXPRESS *Access, Diners, Visa.*

Restaurant — £88

A conservatory overlooks the garden and surrounding countryside, giving a brighter alternative to the more formal, dimly-lit dining room, where John Sanderson produces à la carte, table d'hote, vegetarian and gourmet menus that all display a modern leaning in both presentation and content. Salad of lamb's tongue, snails, lardons, button onions and mushrooms with hazelnuts, feuillette of steamed leeks with pan-fried scallops, steak tartare, pot au feu of seafood with salmon, turbot and sea bass and salmon and crab ravioli are all typical of the style. Leave room for the sharp lemon soufflé served with a lime sorbet in a brandy snap basket – worth the 30-minute wait, or good French cheeses from Pierre Androuët served with walnut and raisin bread. An improved wine list has a good selection of half bottles, and plenty of choice under £20. ***Seats** 80. Parties 20. Private Room 40. L 12.30-2 D 7.30-9.30 (Fri & Sat from 7, Sun to 9). Closed L Sat, 3 days Xmas. Set L £14/£16 Set D £25.50/£33.*

Broadway Hunters Lodge £47

Tel 0386 853247 **R**

High Street Broadway Hereford & Worcester WR12 7DT **Map 14 C1**

Kurt and Dottie Friedli are the most welcoming of hosts at their mellow 19th-century Cotswold-stone house. Kurt's à la carte and fixed-price menus (no main-course choice on the latter in the evening) tempt with straightforward dishes such as fish cake with tomato coulis, quail in cider cream, monkfish with courgettes and herbs or devilled best end of lamb. Leave room for desserts, displayed on the sideboard. Note reduced opening hours. ***Seats** 50. Parties 40. L (Sat & Sun only) 12.30-2 D 7.30-10. Closed D Sun, all Mon & Tues, 3 weeks Aug. Set L £13.50 Set D £15.* AMERICAN EXPRESS *Access, Diners, Visa.*

Broadway Lygon Arms 78% £171

Tel 0386 852255 Fax 0386 858611 **HR**

High Street Broadway Hereford & Worcester WR12 7DU **Map 14 C1**

World-renowned, naming Oliver Cromwell and Charles I among its historic clientele since 1532. Quietly dominating the high street, the frontage is deceptive, as extensions over the years have taken it back some distance to the rear and include a magnificent Country Club leisure complex with a grand, galleried swimming pool. A very 'English' hotel, with beautiful old-world charm in its polished stone floors, low-beamed ceilings, wood panelling, magnificent open fireplaces and bedrooms furnished with antiques. The unique combination of modern hotel and characterful inn is exemplified by the contrast between the creaking, uneven floors in the main house and marble floors of the bathrooms. Staff manage to be helpful and friendly at the same time as being discreet and professional. Elegant conference facilities for up to 80. Informal eating in the cosy and atmospheric Goblets wine bar. Full room service includes 24hr cold snacks, full afternoon tea and night caps. A gem of a hotel under the ownership of the Savoy Group. ***Rooms** 65. Garden, valeting, helipad, indoor swimming pool, spa bath, beauty salon, fitness studio, roof garden, sauna, solarium, steam room, tennis, snooker, lock-up garage, wine bar.* AMERICAN EXPRESS *Access, Diners, Visa.*

The Great Hall Restaurant £80

Chef Clive Howe offers a mixture of traditional and more modern styles that admirably suits the mood of the hotel. An open fire, flickering candle-light and elegant table settings similarly enhance the historic ambience of the panelled and high-ceilinged Great Hall. Three-course tables d'hote are offered as well as an à la carte menu that features chargrilled meats. Traditional offerings include roast sirloin of beef glazed with horseradish and meat marrow crust (for two), Dover sole and grilled calf's liver and bacon; more unusual dishes range from raised guinea fowl and apricot pie with pickled quail's eggs and apricot and raisin relish to saddle of Cotswold lamb with an onion and lentil sauce and minted cracked wheat. There's always a separate Traditional menu (£47.50) and a four-course vegetarian menu (£29.75) plus 30 or so British and Irish farmhouse cheeses (served with walnut bread) to finish, earning the British Cheeseboard of the Year award; a daily traditional pudding, perhaps clotted cream rice pudding

See over

with dried fruit compote, and mother's favourite "Wait'n'See" are among the desserts. The helpful wine list has a good selection of half bottles. ***Seats** 120. Parties 100. Private Room 60. L 12.30-2 D 7.30-9.15. Set L £19.50 Set D £29.75.*

Brockenhurst **Balmer Lawn Hotel** **65%** **£90**

Tel 0590 23116 Fax 0590 23864 **H**

Lyndhurst Road Brockenhurst Hampshire SO42 72B **Map 14 C4**

A much-extended former coaching inn and later hunting lodge in the heart of the New Forest, with plenty of leisure facilities both inside and out. It stands on the A337 from Lyndhurst, half a mile from Brockenhurst. Children up to 16 stay free in parents' bedrooms. ***Rooms** 58. Garden, indoor & outdoor swimming pools, keep-fit equipment, squash, sauna, spa bath, tennis.* AMERICAN EXPRESS *Access, Diners, Visa.*

Brockenhurst **Careys Manor** **67%** **£89**

Tel 0590 23551 Fax 0590 22799 **H**

Brockenhurst Hampshire SO42 7QH **Map 14 C4**

A mellow brick manor house set in landscaped grounds eight miles from Junction 1 of the M27 (follow signs on the A337 for Lyndhurst and Lymington). In the splendidly airy lounge deep-cushioned seating offers relaxation, while more active moments can be passed on the hotel's mountain bikes or in the supervised gym. Most of the accommodation is in the garden wing and includes the spacious Knightwood rooms with balconies or patios overlooking the walled garden. There are six four-posters. ***Rooms** 80. Indoor swimming pool, sauna, spa bath, steam room, solarium, beauty therapy, putting.* AMERICAN EXPRESS *Access, Diners, Visa.*

Brockenhurst **Le Poussin** ★ **£75**

Tel 0590 23063 **R**

The Courtyard 49-55 Brookley Road Brockenhurst Hampshire SO42 7RB **Map 14 C4**

The 'poussin' theme extends to glass and silver cruets on elegantly-laid tables and framed 'poultry prints' around the walls of this charmingly intimate restaurant off a courtyard (there are four tables for alfresco dining) reached via a passageway from the main street of the village. Very much a family affair with Alex Aitken working single-handed in the kitchen while his wife Caroline and son Justin (who is also responsible for the good, interesting wine list) run front of house in correct but friendly fashion. Just two choices at each stage of a daily-changing menu that concentrates on good local produce – game, seafood from Lymington and Keyhaven, wild mushrooms collected from the New Forest on their days off – in interesting but unfussy dishes that are both well conceived and well executed: tagliatelle with lardons, forest mushrooms, rosemary and cream; fillet of sea-trout with laver bread and butter sauce; fennel-flavoured fish cake with freshwater crayfish sauce; haunch of venison with creamed cheese potato; terrine of white chocolate and strawberries. Note the cheeses (British Cheeseboard of the Year regional winner). Good coffee comes with irresistible petits fours. No smoking. ***Seats** 24. Parties 10. L 12-2 D 7-10.30. Closed D Sun, all Mon & Tues, (in Jan Mon-Thur & Sun D). Set L £10/£13.50/£20 Set D £20-£30. Access, Visa.*

Brockenhurst **Rhinefield House Hotel** **68%** **NEW** **£95**

Tel 0590 22922 Fax 0590 22800 **H**

Rhinefield Road Brockenhurst Hampshire SO42 7QBH **Map 14 C4**

A splendid neo-Elizabethan house built in the 1890s in the heart of the New Forest, reached via a long ornamental drive signposted Rhinefield from the A35 west of Lyndhurst. The original building houses time-share apartments and some impressive public rooms used for meetings during the week and weddings at weekends. All but two of the hotel bedrooms – large but comfortable rather than luxurious – are in a low-rise extension. Rooms looking out over the fine formal gardens, which feature 'canals' and a maze (not yet fully grown) in the style of Hampton Court Palace, are charged at a higher rate. The main bar/lounge is spacious, with some of the soft furnishings in need of refurbishment, links the new and the old. An attractive rattan-furnished Orangery offers additional lounge seating. Service from friendly staff includes 24hr room service and one's bed turned down in the evenings. The leisure club has striking decor based on the lost city of Atlantis. Good breakfasts. ***Rooms** 34. Garden, indoor & outdoor swimming pools, gymnasium, sauna, spa bath, steam room, solarium, tennis, games room.* AMERICAN EXPRESS *Access, Diners, Visa.*

Brome — Oaksmere — 67% — £80

Tel 0379 870326 Fax 0379 870051 — H

Brome Eye Suffolk IP23 8AJ — **Map 10 C2**

Ancient box and yew topiary surrounds this part-Tudor, part-Victorian hotel. Stately oaks stand proudly, and the driveway is lined with lime trees. Old rough-hewn beams, time-worn tiled floor and rustic furniture feature in the atmospheric bar and the rebuilt Victorian conservatory makes a most appealing lounge and morning coffee room. Bedrooms in the Tudor part have exposed timbers and oak furniture while those in the Victorian half are furnished with antiques. Each has its own individual appeal; smart bathrooms include wood-panelled baths and brass fittings. ***Rooms** 11. Garden.* AMERICAN EXPRESS *Access, Diners, Visa.*

Bromley — Bromley Court — 66% — £89

Tel 081-464 5011 Fax 081-460 0899 — H

Bromley Hill Bromley Kent BR1 4JD — **Map 11 B5**

A large modern accommodation and conference block adjoins the original 1820s building at a popular hotel alongside the A21. The foyer serves as an airy lounge, and there's a choice of attractive bars (one opens on to a patio overlooking the gardens), plus a conservatory and coffee shop. Bedrooms of varying sizes are smartly furnished in light wood or rattan, and bathrooms with tubs also have shower risers. Families are well catered for with baby-sitting, baby-listening and children's play area during family Sunday lunch; children up to the age of 8 free in parents' room. Free membership of a local health club, snooker club and night club. ***Rooms** 119. Garden, putting, driving net.* AMERICAN EXPRESS *Access, Diners, Visa.*

Bromsgrove — Grafton Manor — 70% — £105

Tel 0527 579007 Fax 0527 575221 — HR

Grafton Lane Bromsgrove Hereford & Worcester B61 7HA — **Map 14 B1**

Water gardens, a lake and a formal herb garden are all part of the six acres of well-tended grounds surrounding this Elizabethan manor house. Personally run by the Morris family, the whole place feels warm and lived-in. The sole day room is the Great Parlour with ornate ceiling, open fireplace, comfortable sofas and, in one corner, the hotel's bar. Bedrooms vary in size, but not in standard; all are restored and decorated in traditional style and, in winter, some have their own open fires. No dogs. ***Rooms** 9. Garden.* AMERICAN EXPRESS *Access, Diners, Visa.*

Restaurant — £75

Simon Morris's English style of cooking is quite distinctive, not only in the judicious use of some of the 100 fresh herbs to be found in the garden here, but also in his fresh, unblinkered approach that offers dishes such as lamb's kidneys cooked in butter served on toast and accompanied by streaky bacon and a fresh oyster or fillet of pork served on a bed of Puy lentils with cherry apples. Gravlax, grilled goat's cheese and Parma ham salad, loin of lamb with flageolet beans and quince jelly, crisply-roasted duck served with kumquat and apricot sauce might also feature. Vegetarians are offered

See over

their own separate four-course menu. ***Seats** 45. Parties 14. Private Room 12. L 12.30-1.45 D 7.30-9 (Sat to 9.30, Sun at 7.30 only). Closed L Sat. Set L £20.50 Set D £22.80.*

Bromsgrove Perry Hall 56% £93

Tel 0527 579976 Fax 0527 575998 **H**

Kidderminster Road Bromsgrove Hereford & Worcester B61 7JN **Map 14 B1**

In the centre of Bromsgrove, creeper-covered Perry Hall was once the home of the poet AE Housman (who wrote *A Shropshire Lad*). Bedrooms provide all the usual modern amenities. Free membership of local leisure club. Jarvis Hotels. ***Rooms** 58. Garden.* AMERICAN EXPRESS *Access, Diners, Visa.*

Changes in data sometimes occur in establishments after the Guide goes to press. Prices should be taken as indications rather than firm quotes.

Bromsgrove Stakis Country Court 69% £116

Tel 021-447 7888 Fax 021-447 7273 **H**

Birmingham Road Bromsgrove Hereford & Worcester B61 0JB **Map 14 B1**

Modern hotel built around a charming garden courtyard, complete with fountains and ponds, and offering large, well-designed bedrooms which include (with the businessman in mind) a spacious well-lit work desk with second telephone, a comfortable sofa, glass-topped coffee table and mini-bar. Good bathrooms with marble vanity units have generous towelling. Some rooms are adapted for disabled guests; there are no stairs at the hotel entrance, and a ramp gives access to the bar, where a white grand player-piano tinkles away. ***Rooms** 141. Garden, indoor swimming pool, sauna, steam room, solarium, whirlpool bath, kiosk.* AMERICAN EXPRESS *Access, Diners, Visa.*

Bromsgrove Places of Interest

Forge Mill Museum and Bordesley Abbey Needle Mill Lane Tel 0527 62509.
Avoncroft Museum of Buildings Stoke Heath Tel 0527 31363/31886.

Broughton Broughton Park 65% £94

Tel 0772 864087 Fax 0772 861728 **HR**

418 Garstang Road Broughton nr Preston Lancashire PR3 5JB **Map 6 B1**

Just half a mile from Junction 1 of the M55 Broughton Park is based on a handsome redbrick Victorian manor house. An open-plan bar/lounge on three different levels serves equally well for the informal business meeting or a convivial drink before dinner. Bedrooms in the newer south wing are slightly to be preferred to those in the somewhat more dated east wing, though all are equally well equipped. Nine Executive rooms, three with four-poster beds, are the most spacious. ***Rooms** 98. Garden, indoor swimming pool, gymnasium, squash, sauna, spa bath, steam room, solarium, beauty & hair salon, snooker.* AMERICAN EXPRESS *Access, Diners, Visa.*

Courtyard Restaurant £65

Within the original building, with a fine white marble fireplace, this pretty restaurant offers attentive service and competent cooking. The evening à la carte ranges from feuilleté of woodland mushrooms, mussel and spinach filo parcels and gratin of lemon sole and lobster to traditional mutton broth and simply grilled fillet of beef or loin of lamb. Good puds might include a ginger biscuit house (filled with white chocolate and peach mousse and pistachio praline) and rhubarb custard flan with ginger sauce. Just a short table d'hote at lunchtime with the four main dishes always including a fish dish and daily roast. No smoking. ***Seats** 60. Private Room 50. L 12-2 D 7-10 (Sun to 9.30). Closed L Sat. Set L £13.25 Set D £17.95.*

Broxbourne **Cheshunt Marriott Hotel** 66% NEW £93

Tel 0992 451245 Fax 0992 440120 **H**

Halfhide Lane Turnford Broxbourne Hertfordshire EN10 6NG **Map 15 F2**

Three miles north of the M25 alongside the A10 and approached via the Broxbourne exit this relatively new hotel offers smart open-plan public areas and bedrooms with either a king-size or two queen-size beds. Half overlook a pretty and peaceful inner courtyard with ground floor rooms having patios. Power showers are a plus in the compact bathrooms. 24hr room service. ***Rooms** 150. Garden, indoor swimming pool, keep-fit equipment, spa bath, Washington Lounge (11am-1am).* AMERICAN EXPRESS *Access, Diners, Visa.*

Broxted **Whitehall** 72% £105

Tel 0279 850603 Fax 0279 850385 **HR**

Church End Broxted Essex CM6 2BZ **Map 10 B3**

Leave the M11 at Junction 8 and take the road to Stanstead Airport; at the terminal building roundabout follow signs to Broxted. Look out for the village church and this gabled, 15th-century Elizabethan manor house is next door. Attention to detail is the keynote here, from the comfortable lounge with a log fire and views of the garden, to the spectacular timbered dining room. Bedrooms are all of a good size and are bright and cheerful with modern fabrics, table lamps and Oriental rugs. Staff are friendly and housekeeping throughout is faultless. The beamed and galleried Barn House is a most characterful function room, holding up to 120 people. ***Rooms** 25. Garden, outdoor swimming pool, tennis.* AMERICAN EXPRESS *Access, Diners, Visa.*

Restaurant £80

Full of crooked timbers, the 600-year-old vaulted dining room is splendidly atmospheric in contrast with young Liverpudlian Paul Flavell's cooking, which is modern in style with light, delicate saucing and artistic, yet unfussy, presentation. Typical dishes might be terrine of calf's liver with truffle and bacon or flakes of smoked haddock with champ and Meaux mustard sauce to start, followed by baked salmon with a crab and herb crust in a mussel and chive sauce or pan-fried slices of pork on a sage risotto and light Marsala jus; brown bread and strawberry soufflé with brandy or hot spiced apricot and plum pithiviers complete the picture. One can choose between a six-course *menu surprise*, a conventional three-course, multi-choice menu or a short 3-course table d'hote (not available Sat or Sun) with alternatives at each stage. Sunday lunch offers four choices at each stage. A good wine list, though unusually even non-French wine-producing countries are presented in French, the exception being 'Espania'. ***Seats** 60. L 12.30-2 D 7.30-9.30 (Sun to 8.30). Closed L Sat, 26-30 Dec. Set L £15/£19.50 (Sun £19.50) Set D from £29.50.*

Buckland **Buckland Manor** 79% £145

Tel 0386 852626 Fax 0386 853557 **HR**

Buckland nr Broadway Hereford & Worcester WR12 7LY **Map 14 C1**

A magnificent Cotswold-stone manor house dating in part from the 13th century and set in 10 acres of beautiful grounds. Its immaculately maintained interior holds real character and not a little luxury, with antique furniture used throughout. Panelling, portraits and pot plants adorn the access to every bedroom; these vary from smallish to palatial and all are enhanced by deep-pile carpets, fine soft furnishings and really comfortable beds. Bathrooms, some with separate walk-in showers, offer high-class toiletries, bathrobes and thick towels. Excellent housekeeping and friendly, willing staff. No children under 12. No dogs. ***Rooms** 11. Garden, putting, outdoor swimming pool, tennis.* AMERICAN EXPRESS *Access, Visa.*

Restaurant £110

Seasonal à la carte dinners and a fixed-price Sunday lunch, both with

See over

a good choice of dishes. Interesting desserts like hot apple feuilleté with cinnamon ice cream and light mousse of coffee and hazelnut in a tulip basket. English regional cheeses. Many fine wines on the serious list that includes helpful notes; several good bottles under £20. No smoking. Light snacks served in the lounge. ***Seats** 38. Parties 10. L 12.30-1.45 D 7.30-8.45. Set L £18.50 (Sun).*

Buckler's Hard — Master Builder's House — £80

Tel 0590 616253 Fax 0590 616297 — **I**

Buckler's Hard nr Beaulieu Hampshire SO42 7XB — **Map 15 D4**

An 18th-century hotel in a village famed for shipbuilding (the master builder commemorated is Henry Adams). Heavy beams and rustic furnishings make the welcoming bars popular with yachtsmen and tourists alike, and residents have their own homely lounge with easy chairs, period furniture and a large inglenook fireplace. Creaky floorboards and old-world charm make the six bedrooms in the main house appealing; rooms in a purpose-built block are plainer but well equipped. The hotel's grounds run down to the river Beaulieu. ***Rooms** 23. Garden.* AMERICAN EXPRESS *Access, Diners, Visa.*

Bucklow Hill — The Swan — 62% — £52

Tel 0565 830295 Fax 0565 830614 — **H**

Bucklow Hill Knutsford Cheshire WA16 6RD — **Map 6 B2**

A mix of old and new coaching inn, with modern bedrooms and the odd beam for character. 10 minutes from Manchester Airport and close by the M6 (J19) and M56 (J7). Executive rooms have king-size beds and whirlpool baths; family rooms are around a courtyard. ***Rooms** 70. Garden.* AMERICAN EXPRESS *Access, Diners, Visa.*

Bunbury — Wild Boar — 67% — £78

Tel 0829 260309 Fax 0829 261081 — **H**

Whitchurch Road Bunbury nr Tarporley Cheshire CW6 9NW — **Map 6 B3**

On the A49 Whitchurch to Warrington road, in the shadow of Beeston Castle, the Wild Boar is a handsome 17th-century hunting lodge with impressive, black and white timbered exterior. A lofty foyer-lounge and decent-sized bedrooms are in a modern, sympathetically designed building that adjoins the original. Several bedrooms are reserved for non-smokers. Rank. ***Rooms** 37.* AMERICAN EXPRESS *Access, Diners, Visa.*

Bunbury — Places of Interest

Beeston Castle Nr Bunbury Tel 0829 260464.
Peckforton Castle Tel 0829 260930.
Cholmondeley Castle Gardens Malpas Tel 0829 720383.
Cheshire Polo Club Mill Pool House, Park Road, Oulton Tel 0829 760650.
Oulton Park Motor Racing Circuit Little Budworth Tel 0829 760301.

Burford — Bay Tree — 67% — £97

Tel 099 382 2791 Fax 099 382 3008 — **H**

Sheep Street Burford Oxfordshire OX8 4LW — **Map 14 C2**

Situated just off the main street, the charming Bay Tree has its origins in the 16th century and has been run as a hotel since 1938. Oak beams, flagstones and good solid furnishings give the day rooms a homely, traditional feel and bedrooms are in keeping (some have four-posters that are said to have never left the building). Ten rooms are in a cottage, while others overlook an attractive terraced garden; there are also two suites and three junior suites. ***Rooms** 23. Garden.* AMERICAN EXPRESS *Access, Diners, Visa.*

Burford — Lamb Inn — £75

Tel 0993 823155 Fax 0993 822228 — IR

Sheep Street Burford Oxfordshire OX18 4LR — **Map 14 C2**

It's difficult to exaggerate the mellow charm of the 14th-century Lamb Inn, tucked down a quiet side street in one of the Cotswolds' most attractive towns. Public rooms range from a rustic bar at one end of the building to a chintz lounge at the other with in between a combination of the two featuring rugs on flagstone floor, a collection of brass ornaments over the fireplace, a display of china figurines on a window shelf, fresh flowers and antique furniture – all polished and buffed to please the most exacting housekeeper. Real log fires burn for most of the year and there is a very pretty walled garden to take advantage of the elusive English summer. Cottagey, antique-furnished bedrooms are equally appealing with old beams or pretty floral wall coverings and matching curtains at the generally small windows. Bathrooms vary from spacious to miracles of compactness, mostly with Victorian-style brass fittings and wood-panelled tubs but only unwrapped soap (no extras) and rather mean towelling. TVs but no telephone to disturb the peace. ***Rooms** 15. Garden. Access, Visa.*

Restaurant — £55

The price of a three-course meal is determined by the choice of main dish (from about seven options) – loin of pork with apricot sauce; trio of salmon, monkfish and bream with lemon ginger sauce; wild mushroom stroganoff on buttered noodles. Generally acceptable cooking would benefit from a little more attention to seasoning. ***Seats** 45. Parties 20. L (Sun only) 12-2 D 7.30-9. Closed 25 & 26 Dec. Set Sun L £15 Set D from £17.50.*

Burford — Places of Interest

Royal Air Force Polo Association RAF Brize Norton, Carterton Tel 0993 842551 Ext 547.
Brize Norton Ski Slope Carterton Tel 0993 824924.
Cotswold Wildlife Park Tel 099 382 3006.

Burley — Burley Manor — 61% — £70

Tel 0425 403522 Fax 0425 403227 — H

Burley nr Ringwood Hampshire BH24 4BS — **Map 14 C4**

A Victorian manor house surrounded by 54 acres of parkland in the heart of the New Forest. Families and dogs are encouraged. Period decor includes stone fireplaces, a creaky staircase with carved balustrade and unusual commode side-tables. Bedrooms are simply decorated and have smart, tiled bathrooms; converted stable-block rooms are the largest and have the best views, plus steps leading directly down to the lawns. Riding stables in the grounds offer rides in the New Forest for both novices and experts. ***Rooms** 30. Garden, outdoor swimming pool, hairdressing, putting, coarse fishing.* AMERICAN EXPRESS *Access, Diners, Visa.*

Consult page 16 for a full list of starred restaurants

Burnham — Burnham Beeches Moat House — 68% — £98

Tel 0628 603333 Fax 0628 603994 — H

Burnham Buckinghamshire SL1 8DP — **Map 15 E2**

An elegant Georgian building in ten acres of lawns, with period public areas and smart modern bedrooms (children up to 16 stay free in parents' room). There are two four-poster rooms in the Georgian part. ***Rooms** 73. Garden, indoor swimming pool, keep-fit equipment, sauna, spa bath, solarium, tennis.* AMERICAN EXPRESS *Access, Diners, Visa.*

Burnham **Grovefield Hotel** **63%** **£55**

Tel 0628 603131 Fax 0628 668078 **H**

Taplow Common Road Burnham Buckinghamshire SL1 8LP **Map 15 E2**

Built in 1904 for a member of the Fuller brewing family, the house stands in seven well-kept acres. The setting is one of its main assets, and the fine new Huntswood function suite (banqueting up to 120, conferences for 50) and some of the well-appointed bedrooms open on to the grounds. The John Fuller room is suitable for smaller meetings and private dinners. The cocktail bar and lounge provide ample space for guests to relax. ***Rooms** 38. Garden, putting, bowling. Closed Christmas/New Year.* AMERICAN EXPRESS *Access, Diners, Visa.*

Burnley **Forte Travelodge** **£42**

Tel 0282 416039 **L**

Cavalry Barracks Barracks Road Burnley Lancashire BB11 4AS **Map 6 B1**

At the junction between A671 and A679 on the outskirts of Burnley, close to Junction 10 of the M65. ***Rooms** 32.* AMERICAN EXPRESS *Access, Visa.*

Burnley **Oaks Hotel** **63%** **NEW** **£88**

Tel 0282 414141 Fax 0282 33401 **H**

Colne Road Reedley Burnley Lancashire BB10 2LF **Map 6 B1**

A grand Victorian town house standing back from the A56 between Brierfield and Burnley, a short distance from Junction 12 of the M65. Surrounded by four acres of gardens the house was originally built for a tea and coffee merchant. The impressive staircase hall, one of the principal day rooms, features a magnificent stained-glass window depicting the coffee and tea trades. Other rooms, many still with original decorative features, including fine panelling, are very traditional with red leather chesterfields. A galleried first-floor lounge area offers a greater degree of peace and quiet than some of the ground-floor rooms. Author's Bar has winged chesterfield armchairs creating a clubby ambience. Executive bedrooms are the best appointed having a small sitting area as well as additional offerings such as mineral water and chocolates. All rooms have queen-size beds and satellite TVs. ***Rooms** 56. Garden, indoor swimming pool, keep-fit equipment, squash, sauna, spa bath, solarium, beauty salon, snooker.* AMERICAN EXPRESS *Access, Diners, Visa.*

Burton-on-Trent **Dovecliffe Hall 68%** **£85**

Tel 0283 31818 Fax 0283 516546 **H**

Dovecliffe Road Stretton nr Burton-on-Trent Staffordshire DE13 0DJ **Map 6 C3**

A Georgian-style period house set in its own attractive gardens and seven acres of pasture by the River Dove. Extensive refurbishment last year saw improved public areas (including a fine staircase) and bedrooms; the latter offer mineral water, sweets, pot-pourri and quality toiletries among the thoughtful extras. No dogs. 7 miles from the M42, 15 miles from the M1. ***Rooms** 7. Garden. Access, Visa.*

Burton-on-Trent **Riverside Inn** **£68**

Tel 0283 511234 Fax 0283 511441 **I**

Riverside Drive Branston Burton-on-Trent Staffordshire DE14 3EP **Map 6 C3**

The hotel stands on the banks of the river Trent, where it has fishing rights. Day rooms make good use of beams, linenfold panelling, copperware and greenery, and the bar has a little thatched roof. Modestly furnished bedrooms are not large but are very well kept, with pretty floral fabrics and the immaculate bathrooms (all with showers over tubs) boast quality toiletries. Friendly staff enhance the inn's appeal. Conference facilities for up to 150 delegates. ***Rooms* 22.** *Garden, fishing.* AMERICAN EXPRESS *Access, Visa.*

Burton-on-Trent Places of Interest

Tourist Information Tel 0283 45454.
Bass Museum, Visitor Centre and Shire Horse Stables Tel 0283 511000.
Heritage Brewery Museum Tel 0283 69226.
Swadlincote Tel 0283 217200.

Burtonwood Forte Travelodge £42

Tel 0925 710376 **L**

Burtonwood Warrington Cheshire WA5 3AX **Map 6 B2**

On the westbound carriageway of the M62 at the Welcome Break Service Area between Junctions 7 and 9. ***Rooms* 40.** AMERICAN EXPRESS *Access, Visa.*

Bury Normandie Hotel 64% £83

Tel 061-764 3869 Fax 061-764 4866 **HR**

Elbut Lane Birtle nr Bury Greater Manchester BL9 6UT **Map 6 B1**

A narrow lane off the B6222 leads to the Normandie, standing in the shadow of the Pennines. Run by enthusiastic mother and son team, Gill and Max Moussa, it provides comfortable, up-to-date accommodation. Luxury rooms are the best, with rural views, attractive fabrics and plenty of work space. Bathrooms are fully tiled and have splendid showers. Standard rooms are more modest. Day rooms include a homely lounge and a small bar. Staff are genuine, helpful and friendly. ***Rooms* 23.** *Garden.*
Closed 1 week Easter, 2 weeks Christmas. AMERICAN EXPRESS *Access, Diners, Visa.*

Restaurant ★ £65

Burgundian chef Pascal Pommier cooks in a fashionably modern, down-to-earth, rustic style offering both a seasonal carte and a *menu du jour*, while Max is a most welcoming maitre d', overseeing very correct, yet friendly service. Simpler dishes on the daily fixed-price dinner might include fish terrine with pickled vegetables, cod with a saffron sauce and hot sponge pudding with caramel sauce and apples. A la carte is more involved, but with a similar mix of French and English influences: confit of duck, bisque of Dublin Bay prawns, mushroom and snail ravioli, Dover sole meunière, loin of pork with smoked bacon and prunes, red mullet fillets in a lemon and coriander sauce – fine stuff and invariably well executed. Desserts are always a high point, with maybe an individual hot prune tart with rum and raisin ice cream, *délice au cassis* or iced rosewater-scented mousse with apricot coulis. Lunch is a 2- or 3-course, fixed-price affair with a choice of two dishes per course: perhaps creamed smoked haddock with a salad of green beans, casserole of lamb with lentils and baby vegetables and hot orange pudding. Extensive tasting notes on the sound wine list, with reasonable prices; note the number of cognacs and liqueurs. ***Seats* 50.**
L 12-2 D 7-9.30 (Sat to 10). Closed L Sat & Mon, all Sun, Bank Holidays (except 25 Dec). Set L £12.50/£15 Set D £18.95.

Bury Place of Interest

Rochdale Art Gallery Tel 0706 342154.

Bury St Edmunds Angel Hotel 66% £99

Tel 0284 753926 Fax 0284 750092 **H**

Angel Hill Bury St Edmunds Suffolk IP33 1LT **Map 10 C2**

In continuous use as a hotel since 1452, the Angel is made up of several adjacent buildings (the oldest part dating back to the 12th century) that gained a unifying facade in Georgian times, now completely covered

See over

in Virginia creeper. Public areas are beginning to look a little tired and some of the soft furnishings need attention, but notably friendly staff create a welcoming atmosphere. Bedrooms come in all shapes and sizes from large rooms with four-poster beds and antique furniture to small singles with simple white-painted fitted units; all are in good order and individually decorated – often quite stylishly. Bathrooms, decorated to match each room, generally only have hand-held showers attached to the tubs but some fixed overhead showers are beginning to be introduced. 24hr room service. Ample parking. ***Rooms** 42.* AMERICAN EXPRESS *Access, Diners, Visa.*

Bury St Edmunds — Butterfly Hotel — 62% — £61

Tel 0284 760884 Fax 0284 755476 — H

Symonds Road Bury St Edmunds Suffolk IP32 7BW — **Map 10 C2**

Take the Bury East exit from the A45 to the Butterfly, a modern low-riser with modest accommodation. Delegate and private dining rooms for up to 50/30. Under-8s free in parents' room. No dogs. ***Rooms** 66.* AMERICAN EXPRESS *Access, Diners, Visa.*

Bury St Edmunds — Suffolk Hotel — 59% — £93

Tel 0284 753995 Fax 0284 750973 — H

38 Buttermarket Bury St Edmunds Suffolk IP33 1DL — **Map 10 C2**

Handsome town-centre inn, formerly the *Greyhound*, with all-day Suffolk pantry and Viking bar. Half the rooms are designated non-smoking. Under-16s free in parents' room. Forte Heritage. ***Rooms** 33. Coffee shop (9am-4pm).* AMERICAN EXPRESS *Access, Diners, Visa.*

Bury St. Edmunds — Places of Interest

Tourist Information Tel 0284 764667.
Ickworth House and Gardens (NT) Tel 0284 735270.

Calbourne — Swainston Manor — 66% — £76

Tel 0983 521121 Fax 0983 521406 — H

Calbourne Isle of Wight PO30 4HX — **Map 15 D4**

Set in 32 acres of parkland, the manor is Georgian in appearance although much older in parts. Classical columns grace the spacious entrance hall and brown plush bar and there is an elegantly proportioned drawing room. Bedrooms are of a good size and feature mahogany furniture and plenty of little extras. Receptions are held in a 12th-century chapel adjoining the main building. Children up to 11 stay free in parents' room. ***Rooms** 17. Garden, indoor swimming pool, fishing.* AMERICAN EXPRESS *Access, Diners, Visa.*

Calstock — Danescombe Valley Hotel — 72% — £175*

Tel 0822 832414 — HR

Lower Kelly Calstock Cornwall PL18 9RY — **Map 12 C3**

Martin and Anna Smith run a romantic haven of tranquillity in a "hidden valley" near a sleepy Cornish village. Originally built for Lord Ashburton, who chose a beautiful site overlooking the tidal river Tamar, it lies in a lane parallel to the river, half a mile west of Calstock village. The lounge is particularly attractive, with deep-cushioned settees, lots of books and magazines, fine artwork and fresh flowers; the intimate, slate-floored bar has Lloyd Loom chairs, a wood stove in spring and autumn and a terrace. Three bedrooms have French doors opening on to a shared verandah running around three sides of the house; all rooms have views over the river and boast a mixture of antiques and fine traditional furniture, sofas and excellent bathrooms. Breakfasts are "long, light and lazy affairs to provide a gentle start to the day". *Half-board terms only. Note unusual closing times. No children under 12. No dogs. ***Rooms** 5. Garden, mooring. Closed Wed & Thu, also Nov-end Mar (but open 4 days Christmas)* AMERICAN EXPRESS *Access, Diners, Visa.*

Restaurant

£66

Dinner is always a highlight of a stay at Danescombe. Anna Smith cooks balanced four-course, fixed-price dinners (no choice, but discussion welcome) that are largely Italian-inspired; fresh, abundant local ingredients are treated simply, but carefully, to enhance flavours. Typical dishes might include goat's cheese soufflé or roast tomato soup to start, followed by roast duck breast with balsamic vinegar and spring onion sauce or salmon fishcake with sorrel sauce; fine West Country unpasteurised farmhouse cheeses next, then perhaps olive oil and Marsala cake served with Calstock soft fruit and crème fraiche or tiramisu. The very personal and well-presented wine list is arranged by grape variety, with an excellent Italian selection, and more than reasonable prices. Booking is essential.
No smoking in the dining room. 3% surcharge for credit card payments.
***Seats** 10. Parties 10. D only at 7.30 for 8. Set D £27.50.*

Calstock Place of Interest

Cotehele House (NT) Tel 0579 50434.

Camberley Frimley Hall 68%

£122

Tel 0276 28321 Fax 0276 691253

H

Portsmouth Road Camberley Surrey GU15 2BG

Map 15 E3

A short distance from Junction 3 of the M3, a turn-of-the-century Victorian manor house surrounded by splendid grounds that are floodlit at night. Magnificent stained-glass windows overlook an impressive carved wooden staircase – Victorian style that is carried through to the traditionally furnished bedrooms in the main house, two of which have four-poster beds. However, most of the bedrooms are located in a modern extension and are smaller, but equally appealing; 16 are designated non-smoking. Families are well catered for, particularly at weekends when rates are reduced. Children up to 16 stay free in parents' room. Conference and meeting rooms have Victorian character as well and cater for up to 60 delegates. Forte Heritage. ***Rooms** 66. Garden.* AMERICAN EXPRESS *Access, Diners, Visa.*

Camberley Tithas

£30

Tel 0276 65803

R

31 High Street Camberley Surrey GU15 3RE

Map 15 E3

Mildly spicy, north Indian/Bengali cooking in modest surroundings. Meat and vegetarian set meals (thali) offer particularly good value. Specials include garlic chicken and lamb tikka masala. ***Seats** 65. Private Room 16. L 12-2.30 D 6-12. Closed 25 & 26 Dec. Set meals from £9.95.*
AMERICAN EXPRESS *Access, Diners, Visa.*

Cambridge Arundel House 60%

£57

Tel 0223 67701 Fax 0223 67721

H

53 Chesterton Road Cambridge Cambridgeshire CB4 3AN

Map 15 F1

Overlooking the river Cam and open parkland Arundel House is popular with business people as well as tourists. Privately owned, the hotel is well-maintained throughout with pleasing traditional standards of accommodation. There is however, no provision of room service and no lifts, though the top floors enjoy splendid views. Two adjacent houses have been acquired creating a larger bar in the basement and more bedrooms furnished to the same standard as the rest. ***Rooms** 88. Garden. Closed 25 & 26 Dec.* AMERICAN EXPRESS *Access, Diners, Visa.*

Cambridge — Browns — £30

Tel 0223 461655 Fax 0223 460426 — R

23 Trumpington Street Cambridge Cambridgeshire CB2 1QA — Map 15 F1

In the old Addenbrookes building opposite the Fitzwilliam Museum. The all-day menu spans hot sandwiches, spaghetti, salads, savoury pies, burgers, ribs, steaks, daily fish specials and puddings. Half the tables are designated non-smoking. Separate children's menu. ***Seats** 240. Parties 30. Private Room 50. Meals 11am-11.30pm (Sun & Bank Holidays 12-11.30pm). Closed 25 & 26 Dec. Access, Diners, Visa.*

Cambridge — Cambridge Lodge Hotel — 58% — £80

Tel 0223 352833 Fax 0223 355166 — H

Huntingdon Road Cambridge Cambridgeshire CB3 0DQ — Map 15 F1

A mock-Tudor building standing in a secluded garden on the outskirts of the city. Three of the bedrooms have shower/washbasin only; top of the range is the bridal suite. Children stay free in parents' room up to ten years of age. The Garden Room is used for small meetings or conferences. ***Rooms** 11. Closed Christmas/New Year. Access, Diners, Visa.*

Cambridge — Cambridgeshire Moat House — 63% — £78

Tel 0954 780555 Fax 0954 780010 — H

Bar Hill Cambridge Cambridgeshire CB3 8EU — Map 15 F1

The grounds of this well-designed modern hotel on the A604 include a golf course. There's also a leisure centre (including a children's paddling pool) and numerous conference suites, the largest with a capacity of 180, theatre-style. Several bedrooms are suitable for family use, and baby-listening and baby-sitting can be organised. Children up to 16 stay free in parents' room. ***Rooms** 100. Garden, indoor swimming pool, keep-fit equipment, squash, spa bath, steam room, solarium, tennis, pool table. Closed 25 & 26 Dec. Access, Diners, Visa.*

Cambridge — Charlie Chan — £44

Tel 0223 61763 — R

14 Regent Street Cambridge Cambridgeshire CB1 2DB — Map 15 F1

The simply appointed ground-floor dining room and the much plusher Blue Lagoon upstairs offer the same selection of Chinese dishes. There are set meals for two or more, and the lengthy à la carte runs the gamut from bang-bang chicken and barbecued spare ribs to crispy duck, Szechuan-style prawns, steamed Dover sole and sizzling beef with green peppers and black bean sauce. Reliable cooking, good serving staff. The Blue Lagoon provides a night-club ambience, with musical entertainment at weekends. ***Seats** 120. Parties 100. L 12-2.15 D 6-11.15. Closed 25 & 26 Dec. Set meals from £10. Access, Visa.*

> Many hotels offer reduced rates for weekend or out-of-season bookings. Always ask about special deals.

Cambridge — Forte Posthouse — 67% — £68

Tel 0223 237000 Fax 0223 233426 — H

Lakeview Bridge Road Cambridge Cambridgeshire CB4 4PH — Map 15 F1

Well geared to the needs of private guests, families and business people, this smart modern hotel stands at the junction of the A45 and B1049. Half the bedrooms are designated non-smoking. ***Rooms** 118. Garden, indoor swimming pool, keep-fit equipment, sauna, spa bath, solarium. Access, Diners, Visa.*

Cambridge **Garden House** 69% £135

Tel 0223 63421 Fax 0223 316605 **H**

Granta Place Mill Lane Cambridge Cambridgeshire CB2 1RT **Map 15 F1**

A modern hotel near the city centre, yet enjoying ample parking and riverside frontage; the hotel also owns the adjacent boatyard which hires out most of the punts to be seen on the river Cam. The smart cocktail bar and lounge take full advantage of the setting, with the conservatory extensions and patio beyond. Standardised bedrooms offer good levels of comfort and most overlook the river and meadows. Friendly staff, many of whom are long-serving, provide good service which extends to the polishing of shoes left outside rooms at night. Meeting rooms for up to 250 – the River Suite has its own entrance from the car park. Queens Moat Houses. ***Rooms** 118. Garden, punting.* AMERICAN EXPRESS *Access, Diners, Visa.*

Cambridge **Gonville Hotel** 62% £82

Tel 0223 66611 Fax 0223 315470 **H**

Gonville Place Cambridge Cambridgeshire CB1 1LY **Map 15 F1**

Overlooking the 25-acre green expanse of Parker's Piece, the Gonville is an extended Victorian house, now gradually undergoing a transformation. Public rooms have been completed and bedrooms are following in stages. The ground floor is smartly attired in emerald green, brick red and cherry with a new open-plan reception leading to a spacious and attractively bright and airy, Lloyd Loom-furnished bar/lounge at the rear. Smart, colourful bedrooms are up-to-date with chintzy fabrics and well-co-ordinated decorative schemes; older rooms look tired by comparison. The hotel has its own parking. Children under 12 free in parents' room. ***Rooms** 64.* AMERICAN EXPRESS *Access, Diners, Visa.*

Cambridge **Holiday Inn** 68% £115

Tel 0223 464466 Fax 0223 464440 **H**

Downing Street Cambridge Cambridgeshire CB2 3DT **Map 15 F1**

Modern behind its neo-classical facade, the Holiday Inn stands right in the heart of the city (follow signs towards Lion Yard). An escalator leads up from the marble-floored lobby to the first-floor reception desk and atrium-style, open-plan public areas. Air-conditioned bedrooms are the standard Holiday Inn product, combining comfort with practicality. Executive rooms get various extras plus the beds turned down in the evening. Free parking for 60 cars. Children up to 19 stay free in parents' room. ***Rooms** 199. Courtyard garden, indoor swimming pool.* AMERICAN EXPRESS *Access, Diners, Visa.*

Cambridge **Midsummer House** ★ £110

Tel 0223 69299 **R**

Midsummer Common Cambridge Cambridgeshire CB4 3AE **Map 15 F1**

Take Ferry Path off Chesterton Road and turn into Pretoria Road for the simplest access to this restaurant located in a splendid Victorian house overlooking Midsummer Common. Approached over a footbridge across the Cam it comprises a delightful conservatory surrounded by a neat and, at night, floodlit walled garden as well as the Blue Room – a pretty, chintzy dining room, filled, as is the conservatory, with fresh flowers and potted plants. There's also a first-floor conservatory dining room overlooking the river. Hans Schweitzer, chef/proprietor, cooks very much in the modern manner incorporating highly imaginative touches in a classically based repertoire. Results are both exciting and very enjoyable. The menu is priced from 2 courses up to 6, the latter comprising a starter, soup course, and sorbet which precede the main dish which in turn is followed by a superb cheese selection and finally some fine desserts: Cromer crab paté or roast pigeon breast with pine kernels and beetroot are typical starters as is a tea-smoked seafood brochette on an avocado and papaya salsa and lettuce leaves. The pieces of salmon, monkfish and prawns are very subtly flavoured and deliciously moist. Soup is served from a tureen brought to the table, so, a cream of asparagus arrives with a quenelle of cream crossed by asparagus spears and the soup is ladled on to this presentation. Main courses range from a supreme of chicken à l'armoricaine with a lobster and shrimp sauce or aiguillete of beef with roasted garlic mashed potato and a red wine sauce to tender venison medallions with wild mushrooms and a juniper berry sauce. A Victorian sponge pudding with custard, pistachio parfait with marinated strawberries and two tiny soufflés served together in separate ramekins, the one flavoured with passion fruit, the other with lemon grass and lime are well-executed desserts. Service is knowledgeable and attentive. ***Seats** 65. Private Room 50. L 12.15-1.45 D 7.15-9.30. Closed L Sat, D Sun & all Mon, 26 Dec, 1 Jan. Set L £17/£23 Set D £24/£30.* AMERICAN EXPRESS *Access, Diners, Visa.*

Cambridge — University Arms — 65% — £110

Tel 0223 351241 — **H**

Regent Street Cambridge Cambridgeshire CB2 1AD — **Map 15 F1**

Edwardian splendour lives on in the public rooms at this imposing city-centre De Vere hotel. Conference facilities include a ballroom accommodating 300. Children under 14 free if sharing parents' room. ***Rooms** 117.* AMERICAN EXPRESS *Access, Diners, Visa.*

Cambridge — Places of Interest

Tourist Information Tel 0223 322640.
Cambridge and Newmarket Polo Club Botolph Lane Tel 0223 314010.
Linton Zoo Linton Tel 0223 891308.

Theatres and Concert Halls

ADC Theatre Park Street Tel 0223 355246.
Arts Theatre St. Edward's Passage Tel 0223 355246.
Corn Exchange Parsons Court, Wheeler Street Tel 0223 358977.
The Junction Clifton Road Tel 0223 412600.

Historic Houses, Castles and Gardens

Anglesey Abbey (NT) Tel 0223 811200.
University Botanic Garden Tel 0223 336265.
Wimpole Hall (NT) Tel 0223 207257.

Museums and Art Galleries

Cambridge and County Folk Museum Tel 0223 355159.
Fitzwilliam Museum Tel 0223 332900.
Kettles Yard Tel 0223 352124.
The Scott Polar Research Institute Tel 0223 336540.
Imperial War Museum Duxford Airfield. Tel 0223 833963 or 835000 (*information line*).

Campsea Ashe — Old Rectory — £50

Tel 0728 746524 — **RR**

Campsea Ashe nr Woodbridge Suffolk IP13 0PU — **Map 10 D3**

Stewart Bassett opens his 17th-century house next to the church to both diners and overnight guests. The welcome is genuinely warm (except from Daisy, a caged parrot of malevolent aspect and disposition who can growl like a dog), and guests are shown into a drawing room where drinks are ordered and the meal announced. There's no choice about what you eat, so you should deal with any dislikes when booking. The meal is served by affable young girls in a conservatory-style room overlooking the gardens; Stewart himself does the rounds towards the end of the evening. His dishes are interesting without being complicated – the best sort of 'special occasion' home cooking – and a dinner here is a time for quiet, civilised enjoyment. An early-summer meal started with a dainty steak of halibut lapped by an unusual and very suitable smoked prawn sauce; this was followed by boned leg of lamb stuffed with a slightly salty bacon and garlic forcemeat, accompanied by sliced potatoes cooked in stock and braised fennel. Next came a trio of cheeses with a small salad, and lastly strawberries and light cream piled into a brandy snap tuile. There's a carefully chosen wine list, decently priced, with helpful notes to introduce each section and a growing choice of half bottles. No smoking in the dining room. Campsea Ashe is on the B1078 (from the A12). ***Seats** 30. Private Room 30. D only 7.30-8.30 (make prior arrangements on Sunday), Christmas. Set D £18.50.* AMERICAN EXPRESS *Access, Diners, Visa.*

Rooms **£45**

The seven bright, comfortable bedrooms include a Victorian room and a four-poster. Fine antiques, drawings and prints are featured. No smoking.

Cannock **Travel Inn** **£43**

Tel 0543 572721 Fax 0543 466130 **L**

Watling Street Cannock Staffordshire WS11 1SJ **Map 6 C3**

***Rooms** 38.* AMERICAN EXPRESS *Access, Diners, Visa.*

Canterbury **Canterbury Hotel** **58%** **£50**

Tel 0227 450551 Fax 0227 780145 **H**

71 New Dover Road Canterbury Kent CT1 3DZ **Map 11 C5**

The Cathedral is just ten minutes walk from this small privately-owned hotel, which offers reasonable accommodation in pine-furnished rooms. Children up to 12 stay free in parents' room. ***Rooms** 27. Closed Jan-Feb.* AMERICAN EXPRESS *Access, Diners, Visa.*

Canterbury **Chaucer Hotel** **61%** **£98**

Tel 0227 464427 Fax 0227 450397 **H**

63 Ivy Lane Canterbury Kent CT1 1TT **Map 11 C5**

A large, traditional bar also serves as the lounge in a comfortable Forte Heritage hotel created from an extended Georgian house. Close to the city centre, just off the Ring Road. Conference/banqueting facilities for 100. Children up to 16 stay free in parents' room. ***Rooms** 42.* AMERICAN EXPRESS *Access, Diners, Visa.*

Canterbury **County Hotel** **68%** **£105**

Tel 0227 766266 Fax 0227 451512 **HR**

High Street Canterbury Kent CT1 2RX **Map 11 C5**

A civilised, privately-owned city-centre hotel steeped in history, dating back to 1588. Original timbers and Tudor panels are used to good effect in ground-floor day rooms, and there's a particularly appealing residents' lounge on the first floor housing the best, heavily-carved antique pieces. Decent-sized bedrooms are disparate in style – Tudor, Georgian and Colonial – many with sitting areas and all now sporting smartly tiled bathrooms; there is one suite. The pedestrianised High Street allows general peace and quiet at night. Drivers should obtain directions to the rear (Stour Street), where covered parking is available at a supplementary charge. No dogs. ***Rooms** 74. Coffee shop (10.30am-11pm).* AMERICAN EXPRESS *Access, Diners, Visa.*

Sully's Restaurant **£60**

Elaborate modern lighting and mirror-panelled walls are in marked contrast to the timbered foyer and Tudor bar. Eric Gavignet's menus are in a similarly modern vein, although the lunchtime table d'hote includes a roast served from a carving trolley. A la carte extends from a meli-melo of fresh noodles with a curry jus, oysters and caviar to noisettes of venison with poivrade sauce and polenta, plus a speciality of millefeuille of bitter

See over

chocolate leaves and white chocolate mousse on a coffee sauce to finish. ***Seats** 50. Parties 18. Private room 150. L 12.30-2.30 D 7-10. Set L £12/£14.50 Set D £14.50-£18.50.*

Canterbury — Ebury Hotel — 59% — £60

Tel 0227 768433 Fax 0227 459187 — **H**

65 New Dover Road Canterbury Kent CT1 3DX — **Map 11 C5**

Two Victorian houses, standing just back from the road, with a large garden, an antique-furnished lounge and an indoor swimming pool. Light, airy bedrooms have recently been refurbished in mahogany and largely re-carpeted. Family owned and run. ***Rooms** 15. Garden, indoor swimming pool. Closed 24 Dec-14 Jan.* AMERICAN EXPRESS *Access, Visa.*

Canterbury — Falstaff Hotel — £85

Tel 0227 462138 Fax 0227 463525 — **I**

8 St Dunstan's Street Canterbury Kent CT2 8AF — **Map 11 C5**

A centuries-old coaching inn whose day rooms get character from original beams, leaded windows and polished oak tables. Bedrooms are neat and pretty and the majority use solid modern furniture that suits the feel of the place perfectly. Children under 14 are accommodated free – with a full traditional English breakfast – when sharing with an adult. Six rooms are reserved for non-smokers. Within easy walking distance of the town centre, next to the Westgate Towers. No dogs. Whitbread. ***Rooms** 25.* AMERICAN EXPRESS *Access, Diners, Visa.*

Canterbury — Howfield Manor — 68% — £85

Tel 0227 738294 Fax 0227 731535 — **H**

Chartham Hatch Canterbury Kent CT4 7HQ — **Map 11 C5**

An attractive old manor house on the A28 to the west of Canterbury, with interesting architectural features. Evidence of its long history can be seen in features like the huge inglenook fireplace in the lounge and priest hole in the bar. New-wing bedrooms are spacious and have good solid oak furniture, but those in the original house are more characterful with some exposed beams; all offer numerous little comforts and have smart, well-kept bathrooms. Conference/banqueting for 80. No children under 10. No dogs. ***Rooms** 13. Garden.* AMERICAN EXPRESS *Access, Visa.*

Canterbury — River Kwai — £40

Tel 0227 462090 — **R**

49 Castle Street Canterbury Kent CT1 2PY — **Map 11 C5**

Thai restaurant with the usual range of spicy salads, fiery curries and a range of one-dish rice or noodle dishes. *Pud Thai* – fried rice noodles with shrimps, crab meat, bean sprouts, ground peanuts, egg and chopped salted turnips – is a speciality. Reduced, but good value fixed-price menu at lunchtime. ***Seats** 70. Parties 30. L 12-2.30 D 6-11. Closed L Mon, all Sun, 25 & 26 Dec. Set L £6.50 Set D from £12.50.* AMERICAN EXPRESS *Access, Diners, Visa.*

Canterbury — Slatters Hotel — 57% — £75

Tel 0227 463271 Fax 0227 764117 — **H**

St Margarets Street Canterbury Kent CT1 2DR — **Map 11 C5**

Close to the city centre and cathedral, a Queens Moat Houses hotel with facilities for families (extra beds, baby-sitting) and business people (meeting rooms for up to 100). Small car park to the rear. ***Rooms** 31.* AMERICAN EXPRESS *Access, Diners, Visa.*

Canterbury Places of Interest

Tourist Information Tel 0227 766567.
Marlowe Theatre St. Peter's Street Tel 0227 67246.
Canterbury Cathedral Tel 0227 762862.
St. Lawrence Cricket Ground Tel 0227 456886.
Lydden Hill Motor Racing Circuit Tel 0304 830557.
Model Village Westcliff, Ramsgate Tel 0843 592543 *15 miles.*
Historic Houses, Castles and Gardens
Quex House Birchington Tel 0843 42168.
Goodnestone Park Gardens Nr Wingham Tel 0304 840218.
Chilham Castle Nr Canterbury Tel 0227 730319.
Zoos and Wildlife Parks
Howletts Zoo Park Bekesbourne Tel 0227 721286.
Blean Bird Park Honey Hill Tel 0227 471666.
Wingham Bird Park Little Rusham Bird Farm, Wingham Tel 0227 720836.

Carcroft Forte Travelodge £42

Tel 0302 330841 — L

Great North Road Carcroft nr Doncaster South Yorkshire — Map 7 D2

On the A1 northbound, 6 miles north of Doncaster. ***Rooms** 40.*
AMERICAN EXPRESS *Access, Visa.*

Carlisle Granada Lodge £45

Tel 069 74 73131 Fax 069 74 73669 — L

M6 Junction 41/42 Southwaite Carlisle Cumbria CA4 0NT — Map 4 C2

***Rooms** 39.* AMERICAN EXPRESS *Access, Diners, Visa.*

Carlisle Swallow Hilltop 59% £70

Tel 0228 29255 Fax 0228 25238 — H

London Road Carlisle Cumbria CA1 2PQ — Map 4 C2

Leave the M6 at Junction 42 and take the A6 to find a practical, if unexceptional, modern hotel with conference rooms for up to 500 and many leisure facilities. ***Rooms** 92. Garden, indoor swimming pool, keep-fit equipment, sauna, spa bath, golf practice net, putting.* AMERICAN EXPRESS *Access, Diners, Visa.*

Carlisle Places of Interest

Tourist Information Tel 0228 512444.
Carlisle Castle Tel 0228 31777.
Carlisle Cathedral Tel 0228 48151.
Carlisle Racecourse Tel 0228 22504.
Carlisle Ski Club Tel 0228 31607.

Carlyon Bay Carlyon Bay Hotel 68% £122

Tel 0726 812304 Fax 0726 814938 — H

Sea Road Carlyon nr St Austell Cornwall PL25 3RD — Map 12 B3

Set in 250 acres of sub-tropical gardens and grounds, the hotel enjoys superb views over the bay. It was built in 1930, and, while still admirably fulfilling its role of family holiday hotel, it also offers extensive conference/function facilities (for up to 200/250 delegates) and a weekly dinner dance (Saturday). Large-windowed lounges, furnished in traditional style, make the most of the splendid setting, as do most of the light, attractive bedrooms (a supplement is charged for sea-facing rooms). Families are particularly well catered for, with good outdoor facilities and an indoor pool for youngsters. ***Rooms** 73. Garden, 18-hole golf course, 9-hole*

See over

approach golf course, tennis, helipad, indoor & outdoor swimming pools, spa bath, sauna, solarium, snooker, children's playground. AMERICAN EXPRESS *Access, Diners, Visa.*

Carlyon Bay — Porth Avallen Hotel — 60% — £79

Tel 0726 812802 Fax 0726 817097 — **H**

Sea Road Carlyon Bay nr St Austell Cornwall PL25 3SG — **Map 12 B3**

Built as a private house in the 1930s, the now somewhat extended Porth Avallen enjoys some splendid views from its vantage point high above St Austell Bay. The aim of the Perrett and Sim families is to offer peace and tranquillity in a well-ordered and modestly comfortable hotel. A small sun lounge beyond the brown velour-furnished, oak-panelled lounge takes full advantage of the view. Bedroom decor and furnishing varies in style considerably from one room to another. Best are the five de luxe rooms which are larger, each boasting a pair of proper armchairs. No dogs. ***Rooms** 24. Garden. Closed 1 week Christmas.* AMERICAN EXPRESS *Access, Visa.*

Cartmel — Aynsome Manor — 60% — £102*

Tel 053 95 36653 Fax 053 95 36016 — **H**

Cartmel nr Grange-over-Sands Cumbria LA11 6HH — **Map 4 C4**

Half a mile north of the village is a welcoming house of 16th-century origins, run by the Varley family for over a decade. Open fires, magazines and a porcelain doll collection create a homely atmosphere. Accommodation, divided between main house and converted stables across a cobbled courtyard, has an equally traditional feel; some rooms have recently been redecorated. Adequate, modest bathrooms. *Half-board terms only. ***Rooms** 13. Garden. Closed 2-28 Jan.* AMERICAN EXPRESS *Access, Visa.*

Cartmel — Uplands — £65

Tel 053 95 36248 — **RR**

Haggs Lane Cartmel Cumbria LA11 6HD — **Map 4 C4**

A charming country house, some two miles from Grange-over-Sands, stands on a hillside with distant views over Morecambe Bay. The spacious and comfortable lounge and the dining room next door are decorated in shades of pale pink, grey and blue. Walls are hung with large, mainly impressionist prints from the New York Metropolitan Museum of Art. Pine tables and attractive pickled pine chairs create an informal backdrop to Tom Peter's delicious, well-cooked three-course luncheons or four-course dinners. Meals commence with a freshly baked, warm malty-sweet brown loaf brought to the table with a board and bread-knife. The style is simple but flavours are carefully thought-out, complementing one another succesfully. The choice is limited to no more than one or two but menus are very well balanced. For lunch tiny tender Morecambe Bay shrimps in a lightly curried mayonnaise are served in a Galia melon. There's always a soup and this comes to the table in a tureen. Jerusalem artichoke and tarragon is typical. Main courses could be fillet of lemon sole stuffed with smoked salmon and asparagus with a chive and vermouth sauce or a truly delicious breast of chicken stuffed with a cheese and herb paté and served with a creamy tomato and grain mustard sauce. Excellent vegetables, too, and to finish some well-prepared sweets. Service by Diana Peters is relaxed and attentive. ***Seats** 28. Parties 12. L 12.30 for 1 D 7.30 for 8. Closed Mon, Jan & Feb. Set L £13.50 Set D £24.* AMERICAN EXPRESS *Access, Visa.*

Rooms — £76

Upstairs are five fine bedrooms all brightly decorated having white-painted furniture and light colour schemes. They are also well equipped – remote TVs, hairdryers, games and books. All are en suite, three having showers only.

Cartmel Places of Interest

Holker Hall and Lakeland Motor Museum Cark-in-Cartmel Tel 05395 58328.
Cartmel Racecourse Tel 05395 36340.

Castle Ashby Falcon Hotel £72

Tel 0604 696200 Fax 0604 696673 **I**

Castle Ashby Northamptonshire NN7 1LF **Map 15 E1**

The balance of its historic setting and up-to-date appointments marks out the Falcon as both modern cottage hotel and traditional country inn. Residents relaxing in the restful garden lounge with its attendant restaurant or in the stone-vaulted basement bar enjoy high-quality yet informal service from Neville Watson and his staff. Choice of accommodation lies between brightly modernised hotel bedrooms and those in a sleepy adjacent cottage which offers, perhaps, the ultimate country village retreat. Super breakfasts and home-made preserves. ***Rooms*** *14. Garden.* AMERICAN EXPRESS *Access, Visa.*

Castle Cary Bond's 63% £60

Tel 0963 350464 **HR**

Ansford Hill Castle Cary Somerset BA7 7JP **Map 13 F2**

Formerly the Half Moon coaching inn, Bond's is a listed Georgian house just off the A371, 300yds from Castle Cary station. Creeper-clad without and cosily cosseting within, its emphasis on informal good living is epitomised by glowing log fires in bar and lounge, and period bedrooms, each with its own personal appeal, which lack nothing in comfort. True personal service from Kevin and Yvonne Bond sets the seal on guests' well-being. Good breakfasts amd light lunches (both now served to non-residents). No children under 8, but babies welcome. No dogs. ***Rooms*** 7. *Garden. Closed 1 week Christmas. Access, Visa.*

Restaurant £55

Yvonne's weekly-changing menu and nightly table d'hote contain a few surprises and a good choice; her cooking is substantial and nourishing, the dishes attractive. *Cioppino* – an Italian tomato and fish stew, duo of cheese soufflés with apple and celery sauce, herb-crusted monkfish tails with lemon butter, puff-pastry-wrapped, boned quail stuffed with apricots and rice all featured on a recent menu. Plenty of puddings (perhaps Italian trifle with Marsala, orange and amaretti or a plate of chocolate temptations) and a good cheese selection extend the options to four or five courses. If you feel indulgent try a bottle of the unusual *reciota della valpolicella classico* red dessert wine from the very carefully selected wine list. Light lunches. No smoking. ***Seats*** *20. Parties 10. L by arrangement D 7-9.30. Set D £15.50-£23.25.*

Castle Combe Manor House 79% £115

Tel 0249 782206 Fax 0249 782159 **HR**

Castle Combe nr Chippenham Wiltshire SN14 7HR **Map 14 B2**

This is a well-run and charming country house hotel in an exceedingly attractive and popular tourist village location. It was a manor house in Norman times and parts of the current house date back to the 14th century. The surrounding 26 acres of grounds, gardens, river and woodland walks provide much of the pleasure of staying here. Lounges and bar with log fireplaces give it a cosy and relaxing air. This is matched in bedrooms divided between the main building, and, by the driveway, a row of picturesque cottages. All are charmingly decorated with individual style, antique furniture and comforts in abundance. Comfortable armchairs and plenty of reading material all help to enchant you and two 'extras' which could combine happily are decanters of sherry and remote-control teletext TVs. Bathrooms are up-to-date with a profusion of toiletries, thick towels and bathrobes, good showers and extra telephones. Staff and management are friendly and eager to please. Such careful thought in so many aspects of this hotel makes it one to admire and appreciate. ***Rooms** 36. Garden, outdoor swimming pool, tennis, fishing, helipad.* AMERICAN EXPRESS *Access, Diners, Visa.*

Restaurant £95

Chef Mark Taylor continues to offer some very high quality food complemented by the professional service of restaurant manager Franco Campionni. Soufflés in the classic mould are specialities but they also rise in a variety of modern ways such as the one served on top of a fillet of Finnan haddock. The kitchen attempts at times to push its capabilities too far, resulting in some disappointments. Some combinations would work as well or better with a simpler approach. Hot-smoked salmon with mint and pink peppercorns and a caramel parfait with chocolate brownie are noteworthy recommendations. Food can be of outstanding quality, and some careful balancing of the menu and reworking of ideas could make it a starworthy prospect. Interesting wines but at a price. ***Seats** 70. Parties 10. Private Room 20. L 12.30-2 D 7.30-10. Set L £16.95 Set D £32.*

Castle Combe — Place of Interest

Castle Combe Motor Racing Circuit Tel 0249 782417.

Castle Donington — Donington Thistle — 70% — £118

Tel 0332 850700 Fax 0332 850823 — **H**

East Midlands Airport Castle Donington Derbyshire DE74 2SH — **Map 7 D3**

Located within the perimeter of the East Midlands Airport, this modern two-storey redbrick hotel is also close to Donington Park motor racing circuit and the M1. A stone-tiled floor features in the spacious foyer and pine furniture in the bar. Bedrooms are decorated in restful shades with floral fabrics and lightwood units. Executive bedrooms, and the four suites, have mini-bars and various extras in the bathrooms like towelling robes and more luxurious toiletries. 24hr room service can rustle up a hot meal in the middle of the night. Children up to 16 stay free in parents' room. Conference/banqueting facilities for 200/180. ***Rooms** 110. Indoor swimming pool, keep-fit equipment, sauna, spa bath, solarium, airport courtesy bus.* AMERICAN EXPRESS *Access, Diners, Visa.*

> Never leave money, credit cards or valuables lying around in your hotel room. Use the hotel safe or the mini-safe in your room.

Castle Donington — Places of Interest

The Donington Motor Museum Donington Park Tel 0332 810048.
Donington Park Motor Racing Circuit Tel 0332 810048.

Cavendish — Alfonso's — £60

Tel 0787 280372 — **R**

Cavendish nr Sudbury Suffolk CO10 8BB — **Map 10 C3**

Alfonso and Veronica Barricella have been providing authentic Italian food in their restaurant opposite the village green for more than 20 years. Among the favourites in their repertoire are lasagne, minestrone, *pollo alla cacciatora, vitello alla milanese* and (a house creation) fillet steak served on a crouton with paté, artichokes, olive and brandy sauce. For dessert they whisk up an excellent zabaglione. No smoking (puffers can go to the bar). ***Seats** 30. Private Room 30. L 12-2.30 D 7-9.30 (Sat to 10). Closed L Mon-Fri, D Sun. Set L £12.50/£15 Set D £15.* AMERICAN EXPRESS *Access, Diners, Visa.*

Cawston Grey Gables £48

Tel 0603 871259 **RR**

Norwich Road Cawston Norwich Norfolk NR10 4EY **Map 10 C1**

A small Georgian house with a Victorian facade, about a mile south of Cawston, provides a homely setting for Rosalind Snaith's wholesome cooking. The short, fixed-price menu of three, four or five courses makes good use of seasonal produce in dishes such as Norfolk ham with pease pudding, trout with almonds, Stilton and vegetable puff pastry parcels and sautéed turkey with a green peppercorn sauce. The good all-round wine list deserves careful scrutiny, as there are several bargains to be found, with an excellent choice under £20. No children under 5. ***Seats** 30. Private Room 22. L by arrangement D 7-8.30. Closed 24-26 Dec. Set D from £17. Access, Visa.*

Rooms £52

Six peaceful bedrooms offer traditional furnishings together with hotel comforts like direct-dial telephone, TV, radio, and en-suite, carpeted bathrooms. Children up to 10 stay free in parents' room. Bedroom number 1 is the best and carries a small supplement. *Garden, tennis.*

Chaddesley Corbett Brockencote Hall £90

Tel 0562 777876 Fax 0562 777872 **HR**

Chaddesley Corbett nr Kidderminster Hereford & Worcester DY10 4PY **Map 6 B4**

Surrounded by 70 acres of its own parkland, mostly let as grazing and full of sheep, Joseph and Alison Petitjean's classically-styled house formerly had very much the atmosphere of a *restaurant avec chambres* but a new extension (completed just too late for us to grade this year) has doubled the number of bedrooms and extended the previously limited public areas. Judging by the spacious, pre-existing bedrooms the style will be most comfortable and civilised. Graded at 75% in our 1993 Guide. No dogs. ***Rooms** 17. Garden.* AMERICAN EXPRESS *Access, Diners, Visa.*

Restaurant £80

The heart of the hotel remains the elegant restaurant with its Italian chandeliers, stylish fabrics and pastoral outlook. There are also several private dining rooms. Head chef Eric Bouchet's cuisine is very French, as is the menu format with three separate fixed-price menus – although one can mix and match. At lunchtime the price of the least expensive menu is reduced. The best of ingredients are used in dishes like prawn mousse with chilled cucumber coulis; cassolette of lamb kidneys *à l'ancienne* in a puff pastry case; veal escalope rolled with a spinach mousse, roasted in walnut oil and served with a foie gras sauce; sea bass stuffed with scallops on a sorrel sauce. A serious restaurant with a high degree of professionalism in the kitchen matched by service which is personally overseen by the proprietor. A good cheese trolley features both English and French cheeses. No smoking. ***Seats** 50. Private Room 50. L 12.30-1.45 D 7.30-9.30. Closed L Sat. Set L from £15.50 Set D from £19.50.*

Chadlington The Manor 76% £100

Tel 0608 76711 **HR**

Chadlington Oxfordshire OX7 3LX **Map 14 C1**

David and Chris Grant's mellow stone house, set in extensive grounds in a pretty Cotswold village, has a wonderfully relaxing atmosphere and the owners and staff couldn't be more helpful and attentive. Beyond the panelled entrance lounge is a second lounge with an open fire where drinks are served in the absence of any bar. Splendid bedrooms are the high point: individually designed and tastefully furnished with antiques and period pieces, they're full of little indulgences like fresh fruit and mineral water, plus plentiful bath foam in the gold-tapped bathrooms. ***Rooms** 7. Garden. Access, Visa.*

Restaurant £60

Chris Grant's dinner reflects what's best in the daily market, although favourite dishes often recur; space is limited and non-residents should book. Soup, perhaps broad bean and hazelnut, is followed by an intermediate course such as warm pigeon breast salad, grapefruit soufflé or baked mussels stuffed with herbs; for main course duck breast with orange, honey and ginger, pork fillet with sage and mustard or salmon baked in wine. Home-made sweets (rich chocolate pavé with praline cream sauce, sticky toffee pudding) continue to be a strong point, with cheeses and biscuits following. Fabulous wines on the exceptional wine list, many of which are ridiculously cheap! Also note the fine selection of half bottles and vintage ports. ***Seats** 25. Parties 8. Private Room 10. D only 7-9. Set D £25.50.*

Chagford Gidleigh Park 82% £260*

Tel 0647 432367 Fax 0647 432574 **HR**

Chagford Devon TQ13 8HH **Map 13 D2**

The quintessential country house hotel, Gidleigh nestles in a sheltered fold of the Teign valley with splendid views of Nattadon and Meldon hills. Paul and Kay Henderson's years of dedication and unstinting hard work won for them our Hotel of the Year award in 1990; their constant improvements have produced a dozen extremely comfortable bedrooms in the main house, two exquisite suites, and a separate three-room cottage standing in woodland across the river. Quality antiques, deep enormous sofas and pleasing floral arrangements are features of the panelled lounge and luxurious bar (where fine wines are served by the glass from the Cruvinet machine): discreet good taste is evident at every turn and service from the delightful staff is exceptional. Corned beef hash with poached egg, kedgeree and black pudding with boudin blanc and a herb mustard sauce are among Shaun Hill's interesting breakfast offerings. The tiny hamlet of Gidleigh, settled by King Harold's mother, Gydda, dates from the eleventh century, but to find the hotel don't go there. Take Mill Street out of Chagford Square. 150 yards past Lloyds Bank, fork right. Straight on for two miles to the end of the lane. *Half-board terms only. ***Rooms** 15. Garden, bowls, game fishing, tennis. Access, Visa.*

Restaurant ★★ £115

Shaun Hill's cooking perfectly complements the style, decor and location of the hotel. His choice of suppliers confirms that he has a healthy attitude towards our environment and his dishes reflect the superb raw materials that he seeks out – from Brixham crab served as a salad with herb mayonnaise to Dart river salmon, grilled and served with basil and tomato. The fixed-price menus are, refreshingly, written in straightforward, unpretentious English, giving little indication of the involved nature of the dishes; lunch (steeply priced, even for the captive resident market) might see a choice of only two dishes to start (crab salad or saffron risotto) and for the main course (the aforementioned salmon or ragout of spring lamb and vegetables), but extends to cheeses and good desserts afterwards. Forty pence per meal is added to each account (unless requested not) and donated to a local charity – Farms for City Children. Dinner, also only at fixed prices, sees alternatives of four-course or a speciality seven-course menu for the whole table; the choice might range from salad of lettuces with grilled Dover sole and herb dressing, grilled red mullet with ginger, garlic and tomato or grilled rabbit with pasta and sage to start, followed by roast corn-fed pigeon with gnocchi, sautéed monkfish with aubergine and red pepper or ragout of local lamb and spring vegetables. Desserts could include lemon tart with caramelised banana, chocolate and cherry parfait with port sabayon and cinnamon ice cream with mango coulis. A speciality menu in June covered sautéed scallops with lentil and coriander sauce, saffron risotto with steamed vegetables and grilled wood pigeon with wild mushroom essence. Some advice on the wine list, which has previously been awarded both Cellar, and California Cellar of the Year: you must a) read Paul Henderson's notes and b) scan both the Italian and American sections very carefully – in fact dwell on the entire list for a long time! The more expensive the wine, the better the value. ***Seats** 40. Parties 8. Private Room 24. L 12.30-2 D 7-9. Set L £35/£45 Set D £45 & £50.*

Chagford — Great Tree Hotel — 61% — £76

Tel 0647 432491 Fax 0647 432562 — **H**

Sandy Park Chagford Devon TQ13 8JS — **Map 13 D2**

A driveway leads off the A382 two miles north of Chagford to the Eaton-Grays' relaxed hotel, a former hunting lodge in 18 acres of gardens and woodland, commanding splendid views of Dartmoor and the surrounding countryside. There's an old, rather Colonial character to the entrance hall with its ornate fireplace and a carved wooden staircase leading down to a raftered bar and lounge. Most of the bedrooms are at ground level with south-facing French windows. The Great Tree ambience is epitomised by complimentary sherry on arrival. Dogs welcome but must be accompanied by valid vaccination certificates. ***Rooms** 12. Garden.* AMERICAN EXPRESS *Access, Diners, Visa.*

Chagford — Mill End — 63% — £80

Tel 0647 432282 Fax 0647 433106 — **H**

Sandy Park Chagford Devon TQ13 8JN — **Map 13 D2**

The old flour mill, whose wheel still turns in the courtyard, has been a hotel since about 1929. It stands on the edge of Dartmoor in the beautiful valley of the river Teign, on whose banks the hotel has fishing rights. Shooting is another popular pastime, while for quiet relaxation the chintzy sitting rooms have the appeal of a well-loved private house. Bedrooms are furnished with a mixture of traditional, antique and modern pieces. Children up to 15 sharing their parents' room are accommodated free; good facilities for young families. The hotel is on the A382 (don't turn off towards Chagford). ***Rooms** 17. Garden, fishing, shooting. Closed 10 days mid-Dec, 10 days mid-Jan.* AMERICAN EXPRESS *Access, Diners, Visa.*

Chagford — Places of Interest

Okehampton Tourist Information Tel 0837 53020.
Museum of Dartmoor Life Tel 0837 522951.

Chapeltown — Greenhead House — £65

Tel 0742 469004 — **R**

84 Burncross Road Chapeltown nr Sheffield South Yorkshire S30 4SF — **Map 6 C2**

Neil and Anne Allen's pretty little restaurant north of Sheffield offers an absorbing monthly-changing menu that might range from terrine of venison with prune and apples or smoked salmon and chive creams to calf's liver with pasta and mushrooms or monkfish with mustard sauce. To finish, perhaps rhubarb chiffon pie or a selection of English farmhouse cheeses. Your choice of main course determines the overall meal price. Robust, careful cooking by Neil. No smoking. ***Seats** 30. L by arrangement D 7-9. Closed Sun & Mon, Bank Holidays, 2 weeks Apr, 2 weeks Aug. Set D from £26. Access, Visa.*

Charingworth — Charingworth Manor — 79% — £110

Tel 038 678 555 Fax 038 678 353 — **HR**

Charingworth nr Chipping Campden Gloucestershire GL55 6NS — **Map 14 C1**

An idyllic setting, especially on a balmy summer's day, offering a delightful taste of gracious living. The present building is set in 54 acres and dates back to the 14th century, with beams showing the original medieval decoration still to be seen. Both the sitting room and dining room have mullion windows and oak beams; the former also has hand-stencilled walls, rugs on the polished wood floor and a stone fireplace. There's no formal bar – drinks are served direct from the cellar. Individually decorated bedrooms and suites in the main house have good furnishings and thoughtful touches such as fresh fruit, home-made biscuits and glasses of Madeira awaiting guests on arrival; they vary from a cosy twin under the eaves to one with an impressively-carved four-poster bed. Courtyard and Cottage bedrooms, created from the original stables and farm buildings, are smaller, but benefit from splendid marble bathrooms and a separate shower; all rooms feature comfortable seating and stylish furniture. Willing staff ensure an enjoyable stay here, and the romantic setting should suit honeymooning couples – the view over the gently rolling Cotswold countryside from the wooden bench at the bottom of the immaculately-kept garden is serene. An elegant, kidney-shaped swimming pool in the new leisure spa and an all-weather tennis court in the grounds should keep the more active happy. The beamed Long Room is a characterful venue for private functions. ***Rooms** 24. Garden, indoor swimming pool, sauna, steam room, solarium, billiards, tennis.* AMERICAN EXPRESS *Access, Diners, Visa.*

John Greville Restaurant £80

A series of low-ceilinged, beamed rooms with pink and green decor makes an intimate setting. New chef Bill Marmion offers an à la carte (written in refreshingly straightforward English) with a handful of daily additional dishes. Start, perhaps, with onion tart with tomato sauce or duck leg confit with French beans and endive, followed by saddle of venison with roast parsnips or seared fillet of brill served with ratatouille. Leave room for a gratin of fresh fruits with rum sabayon, banana millefeuille with butterscotch sauce or good English cheeses. A splendidly balanced wine list, offering both young and mature wines, includes a good selection available by the glass (even Krug champagne). ***Seats** 50. Parties 40. Private Room 35. L 12.30-2 D 7-9 (Sat to 10). Set L £15.50 Set D £28.*

Charlbury — Bell Hotel £75

Tel 0608 810278 Fax 0608 811447 — I

Church Street Charlbury Oxfordshire OX7 3PP — **Map 14 C1**

Once a coaching inn, the Bell stands in the centre of town on the banks of the Evenlode. Day rooms, including a flagstoned bar, have a comfortable, traditional appeal, and bedrooms offer adequate accommodation. Small functions are catered for (up to 55 people) and the hotel can organise many leisure/sporting activities in the locality. Children up to 16 stay free in parents' room. ***Rooms** 14. Garden.* AMERICAN EXPRESS *Access, Diners, Visa.*

Charlbury — The Bull at Charlbury £40

Tel 0608 810689 — R

Sheep Street Charlbury Oxfordshire — **Map 14 C1**

Almost totally rebuilt by the Wearings in the last couple of years, the ground floor of this town-centre, Cotswold stone pub is mainly devoted to its bistro/restaurant. More or less the same main dishes – noisettes of lamb with rosemary and garlic, poached salmon with a lemon dill cream sauce, Aylesbury duck with berries and cassis, sirloin steak with burgundy and shallots – appear on both the à la carte and the weekend five-course set-price menus. The latter begins with an hors d'oeuvre of fruit, seafood and vegetables served on crushed ice and a soup and ends with cheese and desserts. Bar snacks at lunchtime. Upstairs six smart bedrooms with exposed beams, natural stone features and carpeted bathrooms offer good overnight accommodation (£50 double). Check-in by arrangement (there's not always someone there in the afternoon). ***Seats** 50. Parties 25. D 7-9. Closed Mon, 4 days Christmas. Set menu £19.95 (weekends only). Access, Visa.*

Charlecote — Charlecote Pheasant — 62% — £85

Tel 0789 470333 Fax 0789 470222 — **H**

Charlecote nr Warwick Warwickshire CV35 9EN — **Map 14 C1**

Public rooms are in old beamed farmhouse buildings, bedrooms (including seven Executive rooms) in a modern block. Conference and banqueting facilities up to 120. Children up to 16 stay free in parents' room. Five miles from M40 junction 15 (Stow). Queens Moat Houses. ***Rooms*** *67. Garden, outdoor swimming pool, keep-fit equipment, steam room, solarium.* AMERICAN EXPRESS *Access, Diners, Visa.*

Chartham — Thruxted Oast — £73

Tel 0227 730080 — **PH**

Mystole Chartham nr Canterbury Kent CT4 7BX — **Map 11 C5**

In peaceful countryside four miles from Canterbury, Tim and Hilary Derouet's characterful little hotel started life in 1792 as a cluster of oast houses. There are just three bedrooms (non-smoking) with beams, pine roofs, pine furniture, patchwork quilts and many thoughtful little extras. There's a very comfortable lounge, and breakfasts are served in the farmhouse kitchen. The Oast is also home to the owners' picture-framing business. No children under 8. No dogs. Check directions, as it's slightly off the beaten track. ***Rooms*** *3. Garden.* AMERICAN EXPRESS *Access, Diners, Visa.*

Chedington — Chedington Court — 71% — £140*

Tel 0935 891265 Fax 0935 891442 — **HR**

Chedington nr Beaminster Dorset DT8 3HY — **Map 13 F2**

Most country houses have a history and this handsome Jacobean manor is no exception, having once belonged to entrepreneur Peter de Savary's parents. Now owned by Hilary and Philip Chapman, it is in a beautiful setting, overlooking ten acres of fabulous gardens (perhaps at their very best and most colourful in spring) and commands magnificent views of the surrounding countryside. The house is full of character, with solid antiques (note the carved oak dresser in the entrance hall) and open log fires; the comfortable lounge is both cosy and peaceful. Charming bedrooms, one with a four-poster bed and jacuzzi bath, provide thoughtful extras such as good books and bottles of mineral water; there are nice toiletries in the bathrooms, some of which have both bath and separate shower. Last year the Guide was perhaps unjustly critical, and as Mr Chapman points out "guests can have, within reason, whatever they want, wherever they want and whenever they want and if we can't provide something today, we will try and do so tomorrow". The hotel's own 9-hole golf course is nearby – no green fees during the week, and only a nominal charge at weekends. *Half-board terms only, though if notified by 10am that dinner is not required, a reduction of 20% is made; "no service charge is added and none is expected". The hotel is situated just off the A356, 4½ miles SE of Crewkerne at Winyard's Gap. ***Rooms*** *10. Garden, snooker, 9-hole golf. Closed Jan and early Feb.* AMERICAN EXPRESS *Access, Visa.*

Restaurant — £65

Eat in the airy dining room or lovely conservatory, resplendent with flowers and shrubs, where you'll be offered a nightly-changing five-course dinner (including the cheeseboard which offers many British cheeses) with four choices of both starters and main courses. A typical menu might consist of twice-baked Swiss-style cheese soufflé, grilled fillet of red mullet with a basil sauce, and roast noisettes of local spring lamb with a casserole of flageolet beans. There's always a vegetarian dish, say, a broccoli roulade with curry sauce, and sweets come from the trolley. The very fine wine list is fairly priced with countries outside France well represented plus exceptional Australian and German selections. ***Seats*** *26. Parties 8. Private Room 22. D only 7-9. Set D £27.50.*

Chedington — Hazel Barton — £95

Tel 0935 891613 Fax 0935 891370 — **PH**

Chedington nr Beaminster Dorset DT8 3HY — **Map 13 F2**

Built in the mid-19th century, the house stands in immaculately-kept gardens with lovely views across the countryside. Not a hotel in the strictest sense – perhaps the poshest of posh B&Bs would best describe it, with dinner required if desired – it is nevertheless a fine place in which to stay. Stylishly designed by patronne Beryl Schiller, it's beautifully and comfortably furnished, full of genuine antiques, fine paintings and tasteful fabrics, and the home-from-home feel is further enhanced by open log fires and flower arrangements. The four individually decorated bedrooms offer comfort and luxury in abundance, with bathrooms (some with separate showers) to match – note the fine toiletries, bathrobes and large, soft towels. A super breakfast, *really* cooked to order, will start the day off in the best possible manner. Discreet meetings (up to 12) can be held in the wood-panelled boardroom, and the dining room table expands to seat 20 for a private party. No dogs. ***Rooms** 4. Garden, snooker. Access, Visa.*

Cheltenham — Hotel de la Bere — 64% — £98

Tel 0242 237771 Fax 0242 236016 — **H**

Southam Cheltenham Gloucestershire GL52 3NH — **Map 14 B1**

Three miles out of town on the Winchicombe road, convenient for the racecourse. Lots of historic interest in a much-extended Tudor mansion, including a cellar bar. Conference and leisure facilities show the modern side. ***Rooms** 57. Garden, outdoor swimming pool, squash, sauna, solarium, tennis, badminton, snooker.* AMERICAN EXPRESS *Access, Diners, Visa.*

Cheltenham — Bonnets Bistro at Staithes — £50

Tel 0242 260666 — **R**

12 Suffolk Road Cheltenham Gloucestershire GL50 2AQ — **Map 14 B1**

Formerly called just Staithes, the change of name reflects a change of style and lower prices, although the cooking by chef/proprietor Paul Lucas is still very acceptable. Decor remains quite posh but the menu is now bistroish with everything, including a couple of dozen lower-priced wines, fitting on one side of the handwritten menu card. Some 'bin ends' left from the previous wine list are also still available. Cream of onion soup, lemon sole and prawn mousse with lemon butter sauce, ragout of lamb, salmon en croute, peppered steak, mango parfait and individual baked Alaska give the new style. No smoking. ***Seats** 28. Private Room 12. L 12-1.30 D 7-9.45. Closed L Sat, all Sun, 3 weeks June, 4 days Christmas, Bank Holiday Mon.* AMERICAN EXPRESS *Access, Diners, Visa.*

Cheltenham — Le Champignon Sauvage ★ — £75

Tel 0242 573449 — **R**

24-26 Suffolk Road Cheltenham Gloucestershire GL50 2AQ — **Map 14 B1**

An antidote to the currently fashionable eclectic style, David Everitt-Matthias finds ample scope for his well-disciplined culinary imagination in what is essentially the classic French canon. A complimentary starter might be spiced pigeon breasts on a bed of beetroot and barley and chocolate-enhanced sauce; David's skills in all areas of the kitchen are demonstrated by dishes such as rillettes of pork with pickled vegetables and pear, brandade of naturally-coloured smoked haddock with supreme of salmon cooked in goose fat on a carrot butter sauce, millefeuille of aubergine and ox tongue with a balsamic vinegar jus, a classic *tarte au citron* and *composition brésilienne* (a veritable tour de force in coffee with cappuccino crème brulée, bitter espresso sorbet in brandy snap cup and perfect mini Tia Maria-flavoured hot soufflé). To experience the full range of his talents go for the Tasting Menu – available until 8.30pm. Unobtrusive decor in pale grey with a hint of pink is enlivened by a changing selection of modern prints courtesy of a neighbouring gallery. Three courses on the good-value fixed-price lunch menu might offer cream of white onion soup studded with mussels, roast leg of lamb with aubergine and lamb's liver, and warm chocolate tart with home-made chocolate ripple ice cream, or French cheeses. Dishes are presented in both French and English on the clearly laid-out menus. The intelligently compiled wine list comes with useful tasting notes by David (on the reds) and his wife Helen (on the whites). ***Seats** 30. L 12.30-1.30 D 7.30-9.30. Closed L Sat, all Sun, Bank Holidays, 1 week Christmas, 2 weeks Jun. Set L from £17.50 Set D £27/£30 & £45.* AMERICAN EXPRESS *Access, Visa.*

See the Conference and Banqueting section for lists of hotels arranged by county.

Cheltenham — Cheltenham Park — 68% — £115

Tel 0242 222021 Fax 0242 226935 — **H**

Cirencester Rd Charlton Kings Cheltenham Gloucestershire GL53 8EA — **Map 14 B1**

South of town on the A435, a predominantly conference hotel based on a Georgian house which gives considerable style to smart public areas, particularly the foyer/reception and bar/lounge, both of which feature marbled columns. Good, well-equipped bedrooms featuring solid lightwood furniture are mostly in a new wing. The main meeting rooms have glass doors opening on to a patio enjoying fine views (shared by some bedrooms) across the adjacent golf course to hills beyond – an ideal 'break-out' area for conferences in the summer months. 24hr room service. ***Rooms** 153. Garden.* AMERICAN EXPRESS *Access, Diners, Visa.*

Cheltenham — Epicurean — ★ — £70

Tel 0242 222466 — **R**

On The Park Evesham Road Cheltenham Gloucestershire GL52 2AH — **Map 14 B1**

Incorporated within the *On the Park* hotel (see below) but run separately by chef/patron Patrick MacDonald, the Epicurean combines elegant, stylish decor – an arty floral display (from Claire MacDonald) at one end of the room is reproduced in miniature on each table atop wrought-iron candelabra – with a highly refined style of cooking that Patrick feels is best described as 'neo-classical'. Simplicity (of the sort only achieved after much effort – like Hemingway's prose) is the aim in constantly evolving dishes that frequently employ 'luxury' ingredients – white truffle with beef carpaccio, generous amounts of fresh foie gras with a poussin dish, Sevruga caviar decorating oysters with scrambled egg – with classy, richly indulgent results. Perfection is what MacDonald aims for and his confidence exudes in long-standing, popular dishes like parsley soup with scallops and oysters and pig's trotter with sage, onion and truffle. Tip-top desserts might include a lemon tart, hazelnut soufflé and raspberry condé (Regional winner: see earlier pages); a single fine cheese is served plated with salad. There are various menu options, all refreshingly written in straightforward English – a set (no-choice) four-course menu (plus a good-value, two-course set 'business' lunch that includes coffee and a glass of wine), a fixed-price menu with half-a-dozen choices at each stage, or the whole hog with the 'Gourmet' eight-course tasting menu (for a whole table party only) that leaves the choice of dishes safely in Patrick's hands. Wonderful petits fours served with coffee almost constitute a course on their own. The wine list includes some decent bottles under £20, enabling the final bill to be kept in check. ***Seats** 32. Parties 16 Private Room 18. L 12.30-2.30 D 7.30 (Fri & Sat from 7)-9.30 (later by arrangement). Closed D Sun, all Mon, 2-3 weeks Jan. Set L £12.50-£15 Set D £17.50 (residents), £22.50-£45.* AMERICAN EXPRESS *Access, Diners, Visa.*

Cheltenham — Golden Valley Thistle — 69% — £90

Tel 0242 232691 Fax 0242 221846 — **H**

Gloucester Road Cheltenham Gloucestershire GL51 0TS — **Map 14 B1**

A 70s' hotel on the outskirts of Cheltenham, one mile from junction 11 of the M5 (next to GCHQ) and two miles from the town centre. The bright, modern Garden Lounge has wicker furniture and its own patio. Extensive conference facilities (up to 220 delegates accommodated theatre-style) and a good modern leisure club. ***Rooms** 124. Garden, indoor swimming pool, sauna, spa bath, solarium, beautician, tennis.* American Express *Access, Diners, Visa.*

Cheltenham — Greenway — 80% — £120

Tel 0242 862352 Fax 0242 862780 — **HR**

Shurdington Cheltenham Gloucestershire GL51 5UG — **Map 14 B1**

Actually at Shurdington a mile or two south west of town on the A46, the Greenway has been run by the omnipresent Tony Elliott in a thoroughly professional manner for the last 14 years, backed up by a smart young team who are both attentive and friendly. The other great strength at this creeper-clad Elizabethan manor is in the bedrooms which, whether in the main house or in the converted stable block, are spacious and comfortable with antique furniture, stylish fabrics and good bathrooms, almost all with both hand and wall shower over the tub, Floris toiletries and generous towelling. Rooms are fully serviced at night and there's room service of drinks and light snacks throughout the day and evening. Day rooms, which also feature the occasional highly polished antique, consist of a welcoming entrance hall/lounge, large drawing room (both warmed by real log fires in winter) and separate bar. No children under seven. No dogs. ***Rooms** 19. Garden. Closed 5 days early Jan.* American Express *Access, Diners, Visa.*

Restaurant — £85

The conservatory with delightful views of the sunken garden and lily pond forms the large part of the dining room, where service is correct yet friendly. Chris Colmer's menus are equally approachable with dishes that avoid gimmicky without sacrificing interest. The sensibly short evening à la carte, which has a good vegetarian section, might include duck and guinea fowl rillettes with red cabbage and an apple and clove dressing; smoked chicken consommé infused with tarragon; a timbale of sole and scallops with cucumber pickle; saddle of lamb with roasted peppers, sun-dried tomatoes and pot-roasted vegetables; and a plate of apple puddings or a citrus tart to finish. Steak and kidney pudding and a smoked haddock and cod bake might feature on the shorter fixed-price luncheon menu. Excellent petits fours come with the equally good coffee. The New World features well alongside a traditional wine list with some good drinking under £20. No children under seven. ***Seats** 50. Private Room 18. L 12.30-2 D 7-9.30. Closed L Sat, Bank Holidays. Set L £15/£17 Set D £25.*

Cheltenham — On The Park — £64

Tel 0242 518898 Fax 0242 511526 — **H**

Evesham Road Cheltenham Gloucestershire GL52 2AH — **Map 14 B1**

Darryl and Lesley-Ann Gregory have turned this fine Regency house to the north of the town centre into a most civilised town house hotel. Spacious, antique-furnished bedrooms are individually decorated in considerable style with good bathrooms to match. Day rooms include an elegant, comfortably furnished drawing room, which also houses the bar, and new library room; the latter and six new bedrooms completed just too late for us to grade this year but the former grading of 68% is likely to rise. The sympathetic new addition includes a smart new hotel entrance making it separate from that of the starred Epicurean restaurant (see above) that is within the hotel but run separately – a special fixed-price three-course dinner at £17.50 is exclusively available to residents. ***Rooms*** *8.* AMERICAN EXPRESS *Access, Diners, Visa.*

Cheltenham **Queen's Hotel** **69%** **£119**

Tel 0242 514724 Fax 0242 224145 **H**

The Promenade Cheltenham Gloucestershire GL50 1NN **Map 14 B1**

Built in 1838, early in Queen Victoria's reign, and named in her honour, this imposing white colonnaded hotel overlooks the Imperial Gardens. The lofty foyer/lounge creates an air of Regency elegance echoed in the magnificent stairwell and Napier Bar. Bedrooms (the best of which are on the first floor) include six suites and several Executive rooms; two rooms feature four-posters. All are neatly maintained and have desk space, armchairs and the usual extras. Extensive conference and banquet trade, catering for up to 200. 24hr room service. Free parking. Forte Grand. ***Rooms*** *74.* AMERICAN EXPRESS *Access, Diners, Visa.*

Cheltenham **Redmond's** ↑ **£75**

Tel 0242 672017 **RR**

Cleeve Hill Cheltenham Gloucestershire GL52 3PR **Map 14 B1**

Out of town (take the B4632 Broadway road) Redmond's is high up on Cleeve Hill with splendid views across the valley to the Malvern Hills. The atmosphere is informal and relaxing with a spacious, comfortable lounge in which to enjoy pre-dinner drinks while perusing Redmond's approachable menu of dishes that are full of interest without unnecessary complication. Open spinach ravioli with roast peppers, grilled aubergine and fresh Parmesan, hot chicken liver mousse tartlet with green salad, cod fillet with a parsley brioche crust and anchovy sauce, duck with whole roast shallots and a honey thyme sauce and a ragout of seafood with tomato and basil demonstrate the range. A good selection of mostly British farmhouse cheeses or puds like hot rhubarb soufflé with honey and cinnamon ice cream and baked vanilla egg custard tart with nutmeg crème fraiche round off a thoroughly satisfying meal. A very selective and keenly-priced wine list, with lots of half bottles, groups wines according to style or grape variety. No smoking. ***Seats*** *36.* ***Parties*** *10.* ***Private Room*** *28.* *L 12.30-2 D 7.15-10. Closed L Sat, D Sun, all Mon, 24, 25 & 26 Dec, 1 week Jan. Set L £17.50 (£22 on Sun) Set D £32/£35.* AMERICAN EXPRESS *Access, Visa.*

Rooms **£51**

Five en-suite bedrooms with remote-control TVs but no phones, offer modestly comfortable overnight accommodation. No dogs.

Cheltenham **Travel Inn** **£43**

Tel 0242 233847 Fax 0242 244887 **L**

Tewkesbury Road Uckington Cheltenham Gloucestershire GL51 9SL **Map 14 B1**

10 minutes' drive from Cheltenham race course. ***Rooms*** *40.* AMERICAN EXPRESS *Access, Diners, Visa.*

Cheltenham **Places of Interest**

Tourist Information Tel 0242 522878.
Sudeley Castle Winchcombe Tel 0242 602308.
Chedworth Roman Villa (NT) Yanworth, Nr Cheltenham Tel 024289 256.
Cheltenham Art Gallery and Museum Tel 0242 237431.
Pittville Pump Room Museum Gallery of Fashion Pittville Tel 0242 512740.
Cheltenham Racecourse Tel 0242 513014.
Theatres and Concert Halls
Everyman Theatre Tel 0242 512515.

Pittville Pump Room Tel 0242 523690.
Playhouse Theatre Tel 0242 522852.
Shaftesbury Hall Theatre Tel 0242 22795.

Chelwood — Chelwood House — 63% — £75

Tel 0761 490730 Fax ext 504 — **HR**

Chelwood Bristol Avon BS18 4NH — **Map 13 F1**

A former dower house, dating from the reign of Charles II, with lovely, unspoilt views across rolling countryside towards Bath, some 10 miles away. Owners Jill and Rudi Birk, who clearly love the place, have created a warm and welcoming atmosphere. The lounge, boasting fine listed panelling, opens to an attractive staircase leading to individually styled bedrooms which some may find over-fussy. The French, Chinese and Victorian themed rooms all have four-posters, and some humour is shown in naming the smallest one Lilliput. Home-made fruit compote is a feature of good, traditional breakfasts served in the sunny dining room.
No children under 10. No dogs. 200 yards south of the junction of A37 and A368. ***Rooms** 11. Garden.* AMERICAN EXPRESS *Access, Diners, Visa.*

Garden Restaurant — £50

The conservatory-style "restaurant in a garden", with plants and fountain, is decorated with murals. Typical offerings from Rudi, a Bavarian by birth, might include pork liver paté with spicy apple chutney, smoked haddock in a cream sauce with spätzle topped with cheese and garnished with mussels, a brace of roast quails served with wild mushroom sauce, Hungarian pork goulash, zabaglione and Scotch Mist. Friday nights see a popular 'Taste of Bavaria' menu. Set Sunday lunch and table d'hote lunches through the week. No smoking. ***Seats** 24. Parties 16. L 12.30-1.15 D 7.30-9 (Sun to 8, residents only). Closed 2 weeks Christmas/New Year. Set L £13.50.*

Chenies — Bedford Arms Thistle — 64% — £108

Tel 0923 283301 Fax 0923 284825 — **H**

Chenies nr Rickmansworth Buckinghamshire WD3 6EQ — **Map 15 E2**

Redbrick hotel on the edge of the village, two miles from junction 18 of the M25. Banqueting facilities for 65, conferences up to 30. Two bars. ***Rooms** 10.* AMERICAN EXPRESS *Access, Diners, Visa.*

Chenies — Place of Interest

Moor Park Mansion Rickmansworth Tel 0923 776611.

Chessington — Travel Inn — £43

Tel 0372 744060 Fax 0372 720889 — **L**

Leatherhead Road Chessington Surrey KT9 2NE — **Map 15 E3**

Adjacent to Chessington World of Adventure, 10 minutes' drive from Hampton Court and both Sandown and Epsom race courses. ***Rooms** 42.* AMERICAN EXPRESS *Access, Diners, Visa.*

Chester — Abbots Well — 62% — £85

Tel 0244 332121 Fax 0244 335287 — **H**

Whitchurch Road Christleton Chester Cheshire CH3 5QL — **Map 6 A2**

One mile from the M53, an angular, low-rise modern hotel standing in spacious grounds on the A41 east of Chester. Conference/banqueting facilities for 230/180. Jarvis. ***Rooms** 127. Garden, indoor swimming pool, gymnasium, sauna, spa bath, solarium, snooker.* AMERICAN EXPRESS *Access, Diners, Visa.*

Chester — Blossoms Hotel — 63% — £107

Tel 0244 323186 Fax 0244 346433 — **H**

St John Street Chester Cheshire CH1 1HL — **Map 6 A2**

A characterful mix of 18th-century charm and modern refurbishment. Just off one of Chester's main shopping streets. Banqueting facilities for up to 50, conferences for 100. Forte. ***Rooms** 64.* AMERICAN EXPRESS *Access, Diners, Visa.*

Chester — Chester Grosvenor — 84% — £195

Tel 0244 324024 Fax 0244 313246 — **HR**

Eastgate Street Chester Cheshire CH1 1LT — **Map 6 A2**

Situated in the city centre adjacent to the city walls and the Eastgate Clock last year's worthy Hotel of the Year is owned by the Duke of Westminster's Grosvenor Estates. Always in the forefront of Cheshire life, no expense has been spared in the recent restoration of the distinctive Bath stone and mock-Tudor half-timbered frontage dating back to 1866, and the reconstruction of the interior, which includes an imposing marble-floored lobby (use the lifts and you'll miss the magnificent central staircase and glittering chandelier), a Bernard Grenot-designed half-panelled library and smart Parisian brasserie (where breakfast is served) with a polished wood floor and high-backed leather banquette seating. Styles throughout the smart air-conditioned bedrooms (with large beds) are highly individual in mahogany, yew or pickled pine; antiques abound and the quality of fabrics is kept to the highest standards. Much attention to detail is in evidence – comfortable seating, wardrobes with internal lighting, turn-down service, telephone extension in the marble bathrooms with smart floor tiles, large towels and bathrobes, powerful showers and Floris toiletries. Corridor call bells and coded keys ensure the utmost privacy, and garage security (direct access from the Newgate St car park) has also been enhanced. Service sets a benchmark under the supervision of managing director Jonathan Slater and super staff. Stylish banqueting and conference facilities. Children up to the age of 12 stay free in parents' room; informal eating in La Brasserie. ***Rooms** 86. Sauna, solarium, gymnasium, brasserie (7am-11pm), valeting.* AMERICAN EXPRESS *Access, Diners, Visa.*

Arkle Restaurant ★ — £110

Sophisticated dining with service to match makes for a first-class act in this stylish and elegant room. Polished mahogany tables boast sparkling silver and fine wine glasses, and the generous amuse-gueule, offered in the library, followed by the chef's appetiser, are almost meals in themselves. Assorted breads, baked daily on the premises, cannot be bettered, and despite hard times the best Echiré butter is still served. For lunch there's a *menu du marché* and *petite carte,* in the evening a more elaborate *à la carte,* or six-course *menu gourmand* painstakingly explained by the restaurant manager. Executive chef Paul Reed and head chef Simon Radley execute dishes in a modern style, though many are firmly rooted in classical techniques: goat's cheese and cured ham with olive bread, compote of lobster with a creamed soup of spinach and nutmeg, beef fillet with flaked oxtails in red wine and roast vegetables, Gressingham duck breast with mushroom and liver risotto. Daily fish dishes (bass, brill or turbot perhaps), irresistible desserts, fine cheeses (French and British) and sweetmeats with coffee complete the picture. A long wine list, with many classics, though at a hotel of this class one would expect the é accent to be the right way round! ***Seats** 45. L 12-2.30 D 7-10.30. Closed L Mon, all Sun, Bank Holidays. Set L £18/£22.50 Set D £25/£37.*

If we recommend meals in a hotel or inn a separate entry is made for its restaurant.

Chester **Chester International** **69%** **£145**

Tel 0244 322330 Fax 0244 316118 **H**

Trinity Street Chester Cheshire CH1 2BD **Map 6 A2**

Centrally located, large modern hotel with good conference and leisure facilities (for around 400). Unexceptional bedrooms and bathrooms. Queens Moat Houses. ***Rooms** 152. Gymnasium, sauna, spa bath, solarium. Closed 3 days Christmas.* AMERICAN EXPRESS *Access, Diners, Visa.*

Our inspectors are full-time employees; they are professionally trained by us.

Chester **Chester Resort Hotel** **62%** **£60**

Tel 0244 851551 Fax 0244 851089 **H**

Backford Cross Chester Cheshire CH1 6PE **Map 6 A2**

North of the city at the A41/A5117 junction, this is a popular modern conference hotel, with facilities for 180 theatre-style. Children up to 16 stay free in parents' room. ***Rooms** 113.* AMERICAN EXPRESS *Access, Diners, Visa.*

Chester **Crabwall Manor** **76%** **£125**

Tel 0244 851666 Fax 0244 851400 **H**

Parkgate Road Mollington Chester Cheshire CH1 6NE **Map 6 A2**

Extended from an original Victorian Tudor manor the hotel stands surrounded by rolling farmland just north of the city limits on the A540. Somewhat rambling public areas are attractively decorated in soft colours and offer lots of comfortable seating and quiet corners. A splendid stone staircase leads up to the individually decorated bedrooms which are unusually spacious and comfortable, all with sofa or pair of substantial armchairs plus proper breakfast table and good work space. Even more impressive are the large bathrooms, most with separate shower cubicle in addition to extra large bath tub and twin washbasins. All have bidets and good towels including bath robes. There is evening turn-down service and 24hr room service. Decent breakfasts although the restaurant can otherwise be rather disappointing. No dogs. ***Rooms** 48. Garden, snooker, helipad.* AMERICAN EXPRESS *Access, Diners, Visa.*

Chester **Forte Posthouse** **62%** **£68**

Tel 0244 680111 Fax 0244 674100 **H**

Wrexham Road Chester Cheshire CH4 9DL **Map 6 A2**

Modern redbrick hotel on the A483, two miles south of the city centre. Amenities include a health and fitness club, ample car parking and five conference rooms (100+ capacity). ***Rooms** 105. Indoor swimming pool, gymnasium, sauna, spa bath, solarium.* AMERICAN EXPRESS *Access, Diners, Visa.*

Chester **Francs** **£40**

Tel 0244 317952 Fax 0244 340690 **R**

14 Cuppin Street Chester Cheshire CH1 2BN **Map 6 A2**

Cheerful, bustling brasserie with old timber beams, ceiling fans and French rock music. The eating choice is wide, with anything from a quick snack to a grande bouffe on offer, and classics like oeufs florentine, moules bretagne, cassoulet, bouillabaisse and boeuf bourguignon. Sunday lunch is a family affair with special deals for youngsters and a no smoking rule. ***Seats** 110. Private Room 60. L 12-3 D 6-11 (plats du jour 12-7). Set L £7.95 Set D £9.85.* AMERICAN EXPRESS *Access, Visa.*

Chester **Mollington Banastre** 67% £95

Tel 0244 851471 Fax 0244 851165 **H**

Parkgate Road Chester Cheshire CH1 6NN **Map 6 A2**

Comfortable accommodation, plus good leisure and conference facilities (for up to 250 delegates) in an extended Victorian mansion surrounded by gardens. It stands a mile and a half from junction 16 of the M56. Ample free car parking. ***Rooms** 66. Garden, indoor swimming pool, gymnasium, squash, sauna, solarium, whirlpool bath, beauty salon, hairdressing, coffee shop (11am-10pm).* *Access, Diners, Visa.*

Chester **Rowton Hall** 64% £88

Tel 0244 335262 Fax 0244 335464 **H**

Whitchurch Road Chester Cheshire CH3 6AD **Map 6 A2**

Built as a private residence in 1779, the hall stands three miles out of Chester on the A41, on the site of a Civil War battle. There's a spacious reception area and a lounge bar looking out on to the smart indoor pool. Rooms in the old house are stylish and individual, those in the adjoining wing more functional. Good amenities (Hamiltons Leisure Club) and conference facilities for up to 200. ***Rooms** 42. Garden, indoor swimming pool, gymnasium, sauna, spa bath, solarium, squash, coffee bar (9am-11pm). Closed 25 & 26 Dec.* *Access, Diners, Visa.*

Chester **Places of Interest**

Chester Visitor Centre Tel 0244 351609.
Town Hall Tel 0244 313126.
Gateway Theatre Hamilton Place Tel 0244 340392.
The Boat Museum Ellesmere Port Tel 051 355 5017 *Britain's premier canal museum.*
Grosvenor Museum Grosvenor Street Tel 0244 321616.
Chester Cathedral Tel 0244 324756.
Chester Racecourse Tel 0244 323170.
Chester Zoo Upton-by-Chester Tel 0244 380280.

Chester-le-Street **Lumley Castle** 69% £98

Tel 091-389 1111 Fax 091-387 1437 **H**

Chester-le-Street Co Durham DH3 4NX **Map 5 E2**

Set in spacious grounds, high above nearby Chester-le-Street (take the A167 towards Durham off the A1M North), parts of the castle date back to the 9th Century. Authenticity abounds (have a look at the dungeons and the medieval banquet hall which is dominated by a giant stone fireplace and minstrel's gallery) and the interior oozes character, with furnishings that have been carefully chosen to harmonise. The lounge has period furniture, oil paintings and ornaments, and there are some 3000 books in the elegant library. Illuminated statues line the passage that leads to the function rooms, and the pillared and multi-domed Black Knight restaurant, which serves a good breakfast. Main bedrooms are spacious and appealing, with heavy drapes and beautiful decor combined with good antique furniture; feature Castle rooms have some added attractions like a raised sleeping area or a Queen Anne four-poster. The King James suite has a 20' high four-poster and a whirlpool bath. Most rooms, however, are in the courtyard and are smaller, quite musty and can suffer from noise from either adjoining rooms or those above, but they are equally stylish with decent bathrooms. Helpful and pleasant staff in period costume. Children up to 12 stay free in parents' room. ***Rooms** 65. Garden, snooker, helipad. Closed 25 & 26 Dec, 1 Jan.* *Access, Diners, Visa.*

Chester-le-Street Places of Interest

The North of England Open Air Museum Beamish, Nr Chester-le-Street Tel 0207 231811.
Lambton Park Showground Tel 091 388 5459.

Chesterfield Chesterfield Hotel 59% £70

Tel 0246 271141 Fax 0246 220719 **H**

Malkin Street Chesterfield Derbyshire S41 7UA **Map 6 C2**

Central former Victorian railway hotel, just off the by-pass. Purpose-built Peak Leisure Centre and conference suite for up to 230 delegates. Children under 16 stay free in parents' room. No dogs. ***Rooms** 73. Indoor swimming pool, gymnasium, sauna, spa bath, steam room, solarium, beauty salon, snooker.* AMERICAN EXPRESS *Access, Diners, Visa.*

Chesterfield Forte Travelodge £42

Tel 0246 455411 **L**

Brimington Road North Wittington Moor Chesterfield Derbyshire **Map 6 C2**

By the A61 Chesterfield inner ring road on the northern outskirts of the town. ***Rooms** 20.* AMERICAN EXPRESS *Access, Visa.*

Chesterfield Places of Interest

Tourist Information Tel 0246 207777.
Bolsover Castle Tel 0246 823349.
Hardwick Hall (NT) Tel 0246 850430.
Theatres and Concert Halls
Chesterfield Arts Centre Tel 0246 208061.
Pomegranate Theatre Tel 0246 232901.
The Winding Wheel Tel 0246 209552.

Chichester Comme Ca £55

Tel 0243 788724 **R**

67 Broyle Road Chichester West Sussex **Map 11 A6**

North of town on the A286, and close enough to the Festival Theatre (3 minutes walk) to offer a straightforward pre-and post-theatre menu, this French restaurant with a bar is in a converted pub. Chef-patron Michel Navet cooks in a sound, classically-based style, offering a good choice of dishes to please most palates – from fresh pasta with salmon and basil in a creamy sauce and smoked ham with melon to flambéed fillet of beef, grilled lamb chops with mint hollandaise, and fresh fish dishes. Popular family Sunday lunches (when there's a children's menu and a lone high-chair provided) and bar lunches. Six tables in the garden in good weather. Large car park. ***Seats** 42. L 12-2 D 7-10 (6-10.30 on theatre nights). Closed D Sun, all Mon, Bank Holidays. Set L £10.50/£14.50 Set D £14.50/£16.50. Access, Visa.*

Chichester Dolphin & Anchor 63% £102

Tel 0243 785121 Fax 0243 533408 **H**

West Street Chichester West Sussex PO19 1QE **Map 11 A6**

Built in the 17th century, the Dolphin and the Anchor were rivals until united in 1910. Best bedrooms (which attract a supplementary charge) are at the front, with views of the cathedral opposite. Children up to 16 stay free in parents' room. Conference and banqueting ballroom (once the Liberal Assembly Rooms) caters for up to 180. Forte Heritage. ***Rooms** 49.* AMERICAN EXPRESS *Access, Diners, Visa.*

Chichester — The Droveway — £65

Tel 0243 528832 — **R**

30a Southgate Chichester West Sussex PO19 1DR — **Map 11 A6**

Thompson's has been renamed but stays in the same ownership with the same chef. It's a smart, spacious, first-floor room with a non-smoking section. Menus combine classical and modern elements, with simpler dishes at lunchtime. On an early menu were conger and fennel soup, terrine of lamb with sun-dried tomatoes, escalope of salmon *poivre vert* and honeyed magret of duck with burnt orange. ***Seats** 40. Private Room 12. L 12.30-2 D 7-10. Set L £11.50/£14. Closed D Sun, all Mon, 2 weeks Jan. Access, Visa.*

Chichester — Places of Interest

Tourist Information Tel 0243 775888.
Chichester Festival Theatre Oaklands Park Tel 0243 781312.
West Dean Gardens Tel 0243 63301.
Chichester Cathedral Tel 0243 782595.
The Roman Palace Fishbourne Tel 0243 785859.
Royal Military Police Museum Roussillon Barracks Tel 0243 786311.
Weald and Downland Open Air Museum Singleton Tel 024 363 348.
Chichester Harbour Area of outstanding natural beauty.

Chiddingfold — Crown Inn — £57

Tel 0428 682255 Fax 0428 685736 — **I**

The Green Chiddingfold Surrey GU8 4TX — **Map 11 A6**

Established as a hostelry in 1285, the mellow half-timbered Crown is one of the oldest recorded inns in England. Linenfold panelling, stained glass in mullioned windows, creaking stairs and passages leading to atmospheric bedrooms with sloping floors, bowed walls, beams and solid furniture show its age. Annexe rooms are contrastingly light and modern. ***Rooms** 8.*
AMERICAN EXPRESS *Access, Diners, Visa.*

> Any person using our name to obtain free hospitality is a fraud.
> Proprietors, please inform the police and us.

Chilgrove — White Horse Inn — £60

Tel 0243 59219 Fax 0243 59301 — **R**

High Street Chilgrove nr Chichester West Sussex PO18 9HX — **Map 15 E4**

The wine cellar alone is worth the trip, but the setting of this old, cottagey inn amid the glorious countryside of the Sussex Downs is another major attraction. Wine expert Barry Phillips has been here for more than 20 years and chef-partner Neil Rusbridger cooks in a robust style harmonious with the oenological attractions. Fine, fresh ingredients feature in appealing dishes like ravioli of fresh crab on a watercress sauce, warm salad of lamb's kidneys with balsamic vinaigrette, home-made soups, braised knuckle of lamb with chicory, daube of beef with a hint of orange, and poached saddle of English lamb with apricots. Daily fish dishes always feature on the handwritten menus. Desserts include a variety of home-made ice creams. Outdoor eating for 12 on a patio in good weather. Dishes are now individually priced and may be selected for lighter meals. Twice winner of our Cellar of the Year award, the wine list is quite extraordinary, with a fabulous world-wide choice. An exceptional German selection, amazing Californian reds, classic clarets and burgundies – you'll drool wherever you look! ***Seats** 70. Private Room 20. L 12-1.45 D 7-9.30 (Sat to 10). Closed D Sun, all Mon, Feb, last week Oct. Set L £17.50 Set D £23 (4-course). Access, Diners, Visa.*

Chinnor — Sir Charles Napier Inn — £70

Tel 0494 483011 — R

Sprigg's Alley nr Chinnor Oxfordshire OX9 4BX — **Map 15 D2**

A fine country restaurant in an old village inn is only ten minutes drive from the M40 (Junction 6 into Chinnor, turn right at roundabout and carry on up the hill for 2 miles to Sprigg's Alley). On arrival you'll find a merry jumble of furniture and similarly informal atmosphere and service. Seasonal produce, much of it from the Griffiths' own vegetable garden, features prominently on the hand-written menus and is handled with care and respect by Sardinian chef, Batiste Tolu, here since 1980. From a recent à la carte selection come pigeon breast with braised red cabbage and apple; baked mussels with basil and chervil pesto; chargrilled fish with aubergine, peppers and courgettes; calf's liver and bacon with onion gravy; chicken with chili, garlic and ciabatta. Roasts among the Sunday lunch offerings; always a separate vegetarian selection. A very fine wine list, constantly evolving, offers some real gems at very fair prices. The New World is particularly well-represented with the Australian house white under £10. ***Seats** 80. Private Room 45. L 12-2 (Sat & Sun 12.30-3.30) D 7.30-10 (Sat to 10.30). Closed D Sun, all Mon & Bank Holidays (exc Bank Holiday Mon L). Set L £13.50 Set D £15. Access, Diners, Visa.*

Chippenham — Granada Lodge — £45

Tel 0666 837097 Fax 0666 837112 — L

M4 Junction 17/18 Leigh Delamere Chippenham Wiltshire SN4 6LB — **Map 14 B2**

***Rooms** 35.* AMERICAN EXPRESS *Access, Diners, Visa.*

Chipping — Gibbon Bridge Hotel 70% NEW — £76

Tel 0995 61456 Fax 0995 61277 — H

The Forest of Bowland Chipping Lancashire PR3 2TQ — **Map 6 B1**

Owned by the Simpson family for over 30 years, Gibbon Bridge, in the remote Lancashire fells, was once a farmhouse. Converted to a hotel more recently, it stands on the banks of the River Loud and is surrounded by 20 acres of well-cared-for grounds. Spaciousness is the keynote of both the public areas and bedrooms, the style being reminiscent of a smart, modern hunting lodge. It is almost Bavarian in design and concept. The bar is vast, one section with a flagstone floor, the rest laid with Oriental carpets. Stone walls and richly coloured upholstery create a sophisticated and comfortable environment for either a drink or relaxation. Eighteen of the bedrooms are magnificent, covering two floors with a large ground-floor lounge and a separate upstairs bedroom. Some are galleried and one has its own completely secluded and very private garden. Beds are king-size with brass bedsteads, half-testers and four-posters being almost standard. Excellent bathrooms with pretty floral suites are as thoughtfully equipped as the bedrooms. ***Rooms** 30. Garden, gymnasium, steam room, solarium, beauty salon, tennis.* AMERICAN EXPRESS *Access, Diners, Visa.*

Chipping Campden — Cotswold House 69% — £90

Tel 0386 840330 Fax 0386 840310 — H

The Square Chipping Campden Gloucestershire GL55 6AN — **Map 14 C1**

Robert and Gill Greenstock's civilised 17th-century hotel overlooks the town square, one mile north of A44 between Moreton-in-Marsh and Broadway on the B4081. Under a crystal chandelier, a fine spiralling staircase leads up from the stone-floored entrance hall to appealing accommodation with individually themed bedrooms. These include a Garden Room with views over the garden, the quaintly named Aunt Lizzie's room and a Colonial Room resplendent with four-poster bed and pineapple-based decor. Public areas have an understated elegance, with well-chosen antique furniture and complementary, strong-patterned fabrics. The small drawing room is particularly fine. The partly tile-floored *Greenstock's* is an informal, all-day café/bar that leads out on to a willow-shaded courtyard; there's also a formal restaurant. Cheerful and friendly staff try hard to give personal attention to their customers. No children under eight. No dogs. ***Rooms** 15. Garden, café/bar (9.30am-11pm). Closed 25 & 26 Dec.* AMERICAN EXPRESS *Access, Diners, Visa.*

Chipping Campden — Noel Arms 61% — £78

Tel 0386 840317 Fax 0386 841136 — **H**

High Street Chipping Campden Gloucestershire GL55 6AT — **Map 14 C1**

Bedrooms at the town's oldest hostelry are divided more or less evenly between those in a rustic style with antique furniture in the main part to a modern look in the wing. Some rooms have four-poster beds. Among the day rooms are a foyer decked with swords, shields and muskets, a conservatory adjoining the restaurant and stone-walled bar and conference facilities for 60. Children up to 10 stay free in parents' room. ***Rooms** 26.* AMERICAN EXPRESS *Access, Visa.*

Chipping Campden — Seymour House 66% — £91

Tel 0386 840429 Fax 0386 840369 — **H**

High Street Chipping Campden Gloucestershire GL55 6AH — **Map 14 C1**

A listed 18th-century high street hotel (built of mellow Cotswold stone) whose first-class bedrooms are the strong point, employing quality Italian furniture to offset the original stonework and exposed beams. A 90-year-old vine features in the restaurant and a 500-year-old yew tree in the small garden at the rear; the latter is overlooked by a charming patio. A garden cottage holds further bedrooms. Children up to 14 stay free in parents' room. The Malt House to the rear has been converted for function use. ***Rooms** 15. Garden.* AMERICAN EXPRESS *Access, Visa.*

Chipping Campden — Places of Interest

Tourist Information Tel 0386 840101.
Hidcote Manor Garden (NT) Hidcote Bartrim Tel 0386 438333.
Kiftsgate Court Garden Tel 0386 438777.

Chipping Norton — Crown & Cushion — £75

Tel 0608 642533 Fax 0608 642926 — **I**

High Street Chipping Norton Oxfordshire OX7 5AD — **Map 14 C1**

Accommodation at this privately owned former coaching inn (dating in parts from 1497) ranges from budget rooms in the annexe up to suites with separate lounge, writing bureau, sofa and traditional cast-iron bath. There are also some rooms with four-poster/half-tester beds. Public areas include a cosy lounge, beamed bar, numerous conference rooms (for up to 200) and a leisure club. ***Rooms** 40. Indoor swimming pool, gymnasium, squash, sauna, solarium, snooker.* AMERICAN EXPRESS *Access, Diners, Visa.*

Chiseldon — Chiseldon House 67% — £85

Tel 0793 741010 Fax 0793 741059 — **HR**

New Road Chiseldon nr Swindon Wiltshire SN4 0NE — **Map 14 C2**

Behind its listed Regency frontage, this former doctor's house has been considerably remodelled within to create a hotel of some charm but many contrasts. The original lounge and balconied bedrooms above are the pick for both comfort and outlook, while the bar and restaurant are condensed less sympathetically to the rear. Two stylish private rooms with seating for 16 to 20 are offered for seminars and dining. ***Rooms** 21. Garden, indoor swimming pool.* AMERICAN EXPRESS *Access, Diners, Visa.*

Orangery Restaurant — £65

Fixed-price dinner and business lunch menus, plus a lighter lunch menu. Tartlet of smoked chicken with ginger butter sauce, confit of duck leg with

See over

sauerkraut and onions, pastry-puff of pigeon breasts with chorizo sausage and lentils and gratin of Agen prunes with muesli ice cream are typical dishes. British farmhouse cheeses. Occasional Sunday jazz brunches. ***Seats** 48. Private Room 20. L 12-2 D 7-9.30. Set L £11.95/£14.95 (£9.95 Sun) Set D £17.95/£21.50.*

Chittlehamholt Highbullen 60% £105

Tel 0769 540561 Fax 0769 540492 **H**

Chittlehamholt nr South Molton Devon EX37 9HD **Map 13 D2**

A splendid Victorian mansion standing in parkland on high ground between Exmoor and Dartmoor (M5 junction 27, A361 to South Molton, B3226 5 miles, turn right to Chittlehamholt, through village half a mile to hotel). Bedrooms in comfortably traditional style are in the main house, an adjoining property in a country-style garden and a group of nearby cottages. Sports and leisure facilities are excellent (unlimited free golf, and a resident professional) while for less active moments the drawing room, conservatory and library are ideal spots. There's always plenty to do, but there are also restrictions – no children under eight, no dogs, no smoking in the restaurant or breakfast room, no credit cards. ***Rooms** 35. Garden, indoor & outdoor swimming pools, squash, sauna, spa bath, steam room, massage, solarium, hair salon, beauty salon, indoor & outdoor tennis, 9-hole golf course with resident professional, indoor putting, snooker, sports shop, helipad.*

Chobham Quails Restaurant £55

Tel 0276 858491 **R**

1 Bagshot Road Chobham Surrey GU24 8BP **Map 15 E3**

Very much a family affair with Chris and Debbie Wale in the kitchen and Carol and Robert Wale looking after front of house. The interior is light and airy (and air-conditioned) with sturdy country chairs around crisply-clothed tables, each sporting a mini-parlour plant. Choose from an interesting, monthly-changing à la carte menu – Roquefort mousse with a grape and Sauternes chutney, fillet of salmon with tapénade, filo-wrapped saddle of lamb with pesto, ragout of hare and wild boar – or a short *prix fixe* menu (not Sat & Sun) that features a different region of France each month, and includes two glasses of regional wine. Good Sunday lunches. ***Seats** 40. L 12-2 D 7-10. Closed L Sat, D Sun, all Mon, 26 Dec, 1 Jan. Set meals £14.95.* AMERICAN EXPRESS *Access, Diners, Visa.*

Chollerford George Hotel 59% £95

Tel 0434 681611 Fax 0434 681727 **H**

Chollerford nr Hexham Northumberland NE46 4EW **Map 5 D2**

A riverside setting with delightful gardens and good leisure facilities. Most bedrooms have garden or river views and are furnished in an up-to-date fashion. Swallow Hotels. ***Rooms** 50. Garden, indoor swimming pool, spa bath, sauna, solarium, fishing, putting.* AMERICAN EXPRESS *Access, Diners, Visa.*

Chollerford Place of Interest

Chesters Museum (EH) Hadrian's Wall Tel 043 681 379.

Christchurch Splinters NEW £55

Tel 0202 483454 Fax 0202 483454 **R**

11 Church Street Christchurch Dorset BH23 1BW **Map 14 C4**

A "Splinters" has existed here for over twenty years near the Priory in central Christchurch. Now owned by Timothy Lloyd and Robert Wilson, the present restaurant has been tastefully refurbished. Modern pastel colour schemes, polished wooden floors and alcove-style seating plus even a table in their wine cellar create a cosy ambience to enjoy some quality cooking by chef Robert Rees. Lunchtime has a simpler choice plus a range of specials whilst the evening menu has a seasonally changing carte, again with special dishes. Good straightforward presentation is matched by some imaginative food such as salmon steak with samphire and lemon grass or for pudding a traditional steamed chocolate sponge with chocolate sauce. A self-contained function room has a similar modern designer theme and a small bar area also serves morning coffee, light lunches and in the summer months afternoon teas (Saturdays only). Upstairs is a drawing room lounge where coffee or pre-meal drinks can be taken. ***Seats** 40. Parties 12. Private Room 22. L 12-2.30 D 7-10.30. Set L £8.60. Closed Sun, 2 weeks Jan.* AMERICAN EXPRESS *Access, Diners, Visa.*

Christchurch **Travel Inn** **£43**

Tel 0202 485376 Fax 0202 474939 **L**

Somerford Road Christchurch Bournemouth Dorset BH23 3QG **Map 14 C4**

Situated a few miles from both Mudeford and Boscombe beaches. ***Rooms** 38.* AMERICAN EXPRESS *Access, Diners, Visa.*

Churt **Frensham Pond Hotel** **62%** **£88**

Tel 0252 795161 Fax 0252 792631 **H**

Churt nr Farnham Surrey GU10 2BQ **Map 11 A5**

In a picturesque setting overlooking the pond (actually the size of a large lake with a busy weekend dinghy sailing club), the hotel caters well for both business and private visitors. Features include four conference suites and a leisure club with its own bar and restaurant. Most of the bedrooms are in a recent extension in the gardens to the rear. 24hr room service. No dogs. ***Rooms** 53. Garden, indoor swimming pool, sauna, solarium, squash, spa bath, keep-fit equipment, beauty salon, squash, games room, coffee shop (8am-10pm).* AMERICAN EXPRESS *Access, Diners, Visa.*

Cirencester **Fleece Hotel** **64%** **£80**

Tel 0285 658507 Fax 0285 651017 **H**

Market Square Cirencester Gloucestershire GL7 4NZ **Map 14 C2**

Five bedrooms have been added at this timber-fronted Tudor coaching inn in the town centre. Resort Hotels. ***Rooms** 30. Coffee shop (10am-3pm).* AMERICAN EXPRESS *Access, Diners, Visa.*

Cirencester **Stratton House** **64%** **£66**

Tel 0285 651761 Fax 0285 640024 **H**

Gloucester Road Cirencester Gloucestershire GL7 2LE **Map 14 C2**

On the A417 to the north of town this former wool merchant's house (recently extended in sympathetic fashion) dates back at least to the 17th century. The period feel has been retained in public areas like the flagstoned entrance hall, the beamed bar with real log fire and leather tub chairs and the comfortable lounge overlooking a walled garden. Pretty bedrooms are individually decorated, those in the original building often retaining original fireplaces. All have poly-cotton duvets. Good bathrooms offer large jars of shampoo and bath essence. No room service. ***Rooms** 41. Garden.* AMERICAN EXPRESS *Access, Diners, Visa.*

Cirencester **Tatyan's** **£45**

Tel 0285 653529 **R**

27 Castle Street Cirencester Gloucestershire GL7 1QD **Map 14 C2**

Szechuan, Hunan and Peking regional cooking provide the specialities on a wide-ranging evening menu; lunches are more limited, but good value nonetheless. Set meals include a gourmet dinner for a minimum of four. Friendly and helpful service. ***Seats** 64. Parties 40. L 12-2 D 6-10.30 (Sat to 11). Closed L Sun, 5 days Christmas. Set L £8.50 Set D £12.50/£15.* AMERICAN EXPRESS *Access, Diners, Visa.*

Cirencester Places of Interest

Tourist Information Tel 0285 654180.
Barnsley House Garden Barnsley Tel 028574 281.
Rodmarton Manor Garden Tel 028584 219.
Cirencester Park Polo Club The Old Kennels, Cirencester Park Tel 0285 653 225.

Clanfield The Plough at Clanfield

£80

Tel 036 781 222 Fax 036 781 596

IR

Bourton Road Clanfield Oxfordshire OX8 2RB **Map 14 C2**

Roses and wisteria clinging to the Cotswold stone walls of this small 16th-century manor house make a pretty picture and the atmosphere within is more that of an inn than a hotel; a single bar/lounge has a few old beams and posts and draylon-covered wing chairs and settees in pink and blue. Cosy bedrooms come with baby teddy bears to keep you company and bathrooms – four with whirlpool tubs, two with shower and WC only – are shared with families of plastic ducks along with towelling robes and good toiletries. No dogs. ***Rooms** 6. Garden.* AMERICAN EXPRESS *Access, Diners, Visa.*

Tapestry Room Restaurant

£70

Four different fixed-price menus to choose from at dinner, although one can also 'mix n' match', ranging from the House menu with the likes of breast of chicken with forest mushroom sauce and minute steak with port and Stilton butter to the seven-course Gourmand that might include a smoked chicken consommé with basil dumplings, fillet of venison with green peppercorn sauce and sablé of strawberries with clotted cream. Most menus come together for 'afters' which include a couple of savouries and a good selection of mostly British cheeses along with puds such as hot passion fruit soufflé and tangy, individually-baked lemon tart. Lunch brings a single set-price menu or one can choose from the light lunch menu that is also served in the bar. Three framed tapestries on the walls are a token justification for the name of the comfortably pleasant dining room.
***Seats** 35. Private Room 12. L 12-2 D 7-10 (Sun to 9.30).*
Set L £10.95/£14.50 Set D from £19.50.

Clawton Court Barn 61%

£70

Tel 040 927 219

H

Clawton Holsworthy Devon EX22 6PS **Map 12 C2**

Five acres of garden surround a delightful manor house three miles south of Holsworthy (follow the A388) and next to Clawton's 12th-century church. Day rooms like the two lounges and tiny bar are easy places to relax. The bedrooms are simple but individual in feel with a number of thoughtful extras. Three rooms are suitable for family use, and children up to 14 stay free in parents' room. Cots, high-chairs and baby-listening are available. The exceptional and somewhat eccentric wine list overshadows the restaurant menu. Look out for some real bargains. ***Rooms** 8. Garden, badminton, pitch & putt, putting. Closed 1 week Jan.* AMERICAN EXPRESS *Access, Diners, Visa.*

Claygate Les Alouettes

£70

Tel 0372 464882

R

7 High Street Claygate Surrey KT10 0JW **Map 15 E2**

Pretty in pink with cut glass and gilt wall lights, bone china and crisp linen, Les Alouettes remains quite luxurious and very French but since Thierry Obitz, the former sous chef here, has taken over the reins in the kitchen the menu has become a little simpler and considerably less expensive. Warm asparagus with mousseline sauce, braised monkfish with leeks and a tomato butter sauce, escalope of veal with tagliatelle and sauce normande give the style. The format of the wine list has changed too, with a less daunting list. The more modest wines are offered initially and the pricier items reserved for a separate list available on request. ***Seats** 60. Parties 65. L 12-2.15 D 7-9.30 (Sat till 10). Set L £13.95/£17.95 Set D £20. Closed L Sat, all Sun, Bank Holidays, 2 weeks summer & 1 week Christmas.* AMERICAN EXPRESS *Access, Visa.*

Clayton-le-Woods — Pines Hotel — 65% — £65

Tel 0772 38551 Fax 0772 629002 — **H**

Preston Road Clayton-le-Woods nr Chorley Lancashire PR6 7ED — **Map 6 B1**

Though the decor and furnishings are somewhat dated at this much-extended Victorian house on the A6, just off the M6 (Junction 28/29), the bedrooms are spacious and offer all modern facilities. Baskets of 'help-yourself' fresh fruit are provided on bedroom landings. Four acres of wooded grounds, ideal for business meetings and conferences (100), live cabaret at weekends in the Dixon suite. No dogs. ***Rooms** 39. Garden. Closed 25 & 26 Dec.* AMERICAN EXPRESS *Access, Visa.*

Clearwell — Clearwell Castle — 69% — £85

Tel 0594 832320 Fax 0594 835523 — **H**

Clearwell nr Coleford Gloucestershire GL16 8LG — **Map 14 B2**

The site dates back to Roman times, but the current castle is of 18th-century origins, in Gothic Revival style, with a castellated exterior and stately halls. The bar is less stately, having instead a clubby appeal. Bedrooms combine four-posters and half-testers with up-to-date amenities. ***Rooms** 16. Garden, fishing, riding.* AMERICAN EXPRESS *Access, Diners, Visa.*

Cleethorpes — Kingsway Hotel — 62% — £80

Tel 0472 601122 Fax 0472 601381 — **H**

Cleethorpes Humberside DN35 0AE — **Map 7 F2**

A traditional seafront hotel, run by the Harris family for four generations. Regular refurbishment keeps things smart in the day rooms and in the bedrooms, most of which have solid reproduction furniture. One of the lounges is non-smoking. No children under five (5-14s free in parents' room). No dogs. ***Rooms** 50. Roof garden, garage. Closed 25 & 26 Dec.* AMERICAN EXPRESS *Access, Diners, Visa.*

Climping — Bailiffscourt — 69% — £125

Tel 0903 723511 Fax 0903 723107 — **H**

Climping nr Littlehampton West Sussex BN17 5RW — **Map 11 A6**

Constructed almost entirely of recycled 13th-century building materials, the 'medieval manor', built by Lord Moyen in 1930, creates a genuinely mellow atmosphere with lots of old timbers, heavy iron-studded doors and old stone fireplaces. Old oak furniture and appropriate fabrics match the mood in bedrooms which, nonetheless, combine plenty of modern comforts; several boast real fires in winter – a rare luxury. Private dining and boardrooms can seat up to 65 for formal meals and 26 for conferences. No children under 9. ***Rooms** 20. Garden, outdoor swimming pool, tennis, pool table.* AMERICAN EXPRESS *Access, Diners, Visa.*

Clitheroe — Browns Bistro — £52

Tel 0200 26928 — **R**

10 York Street Clitheroe Lancashire BB7 2DL — **Map 6 B1**

Bare boards and check cloths lend Browns a French café atmosphere, while daily-changed blackboards emphasise the freshness of supplies. Fish from Manchester markets, Angus beef, complimentary *petits pains* and salad bowl, gargantuan portions – all enlivened by a general sense of fun. Laconic

See over

wine list (and menu) with a good selection of budget Italian wines. *Seats 68. Parties 20. Private Room. L 12-2 D 7-10. Closed L Sat, all Sun, 25 & 26 Dec, 1 Jan. Access, Visa.*

Clitheroe — Place of Interest

Browsholme Hall Tel 025486 330.

Coatham Mundeville — Hall Garth — 68% — £90

Tel 0325 300400 Fax 0325 310083 — H

Coatham Mundeville nr Darlington Co Durham DL1 3LU — **Map 5 E2**

A solid stone hotel standing in lovely gardens just minutes from the A1/A167 intersection. Accommodation ranges from rooms in the old house furnished in period style (some with four-poster beds) to modern rooms in a separate block. Lounges offer a choice of decor and style, but consistent comfort. The Stables bar has a pubby atmosphere and offers snacks and real ales. Conference/banqueting facilities for 300/250 in the Brafferton Suite. The leisure facilities were being greatly improved with a new leisure centre and 9-hole golf course as we went to press. ***Rooms** 40. Garden. Closed 24-26 Dec.* AMERICAN EXPRESS *Access, Diners, Visa.*

Cobham — Hilton National — 65% — £110

Tel 0932 864471 Fax 0932 868017 — H

Seven Hills Road South Cobham Surrey KT11 1EW — **Map 15 E3**

Set in 27 acres, just off the A3 (junction 10 Cobham exit), Neville Chamberlain's original house has been swallowed into new wings. Bedrooms, which feature plenty of work space, continue to be refurbished. ***Rooms** 152. Garden, indoor swimming pool, tennis, squash, sauna, solarium, spa bath, steam room, keep-fit equipment.* AMERICAN EXPRESS *Access, Diners, Visa.*

Cobham — Woodlands Park — 69% — £147

Tel 0372 843933 Fax 0372 842704 — H

Woodlands Lane Stoke d'Abernon Cobham Surrey KT11 3QB — **Map 15 E3**

The carefully restored (and much extended) former home of the match-making Bryant family is a magnificent example of late-Victorian country house style, set in ten acres of lawns. Particularly striking is the grand hall with its galleried landing, panelled walls and stained-glass ceiling. This fine room is the only residents' lounge and conference delegates (up to 300) sometimes spill over from the bar. Bedrooms range from handsome suites with original built-in furniture in the main house to smaller but equally comfortable rooms in the wing; all offer an array of extras. The buffet breakfast provides decent quality and variety. ***Rooms** 58. Tennis, putting.* AMERICAN EXPRESS *Access, Diners, Visa.*

Cobham — Place of Interest

Painshill Park and Gardens Tel 0932 868113.

Cockermouth — Quince & Medlar — £30

Tel 0900 823579 — R

13 Castlegate Cockermouth Cumbria CA13 9EU — **Map 4 C3**

Next to Cockermouth Castle, a candle-lit vegetarian restaurant run on informal lines by Colin and Louisa Le Voi. Some of Colin's inventive dishes: mushroom and watercress soup with home-made bread, parsnip and apple mousse wrapped in spinach with a filling of wild mushrooms and pine kernels, potato and green lentil galette, crusty nut rings, Jerusalem artichoke and aduki bean bake. Try the mixed dried fruit compote or warm prune and armagnac tart with vanilla sauce to finish.
No smoking. ***Seats** 26. Parties 14. D only from 7. Closed Mon, Bank Holidays, 24-26 Dec, 3 weeks Jan/Feb, 1 week Oct/Nov. Access, Visa.*

Cockermouth Place of Interest

Wordsworth House (NT) Tel 0900 824805.

Coggeshall White Hart 69% £82

Tel 0376 561654 Fax 0376 561789 **HR**

Market End Coggeshall Essex CO6 1NH **Map 10 C3**

A centuries-old inn that still retains all its character with flagstone floors, low beams, inglenook fireplace and not one but two resident ghosts. Careful renovation and refurbishment in recent years have added style and comfort to the atmospheric surroundings. Individually decorated bedrooms, 12 in a new extension, offer little extras like fresh fruit and mineral water. Room service is limited to Continental breakfast. 20% tariff reduction for two-night weekend stays. ***Rooms** 18. Garden,* AMERICAN EXPRESS *Access, Diners, Visa.*

Restaurant £60

A long, low and narrow dining room with sturdy beams and cheerful staff. An Italian menu ranges from a variety of pasta dishes to supreme of guinea fowl flamed in Madeira and cream, and chargrilled steaks. Traditional Sunday lunch and a good selection of desserts – tiramisu is a speciality. ***Seats** 70. L 12-2 D 7-9.45. Closed D Sun.*

Coggeshall Places of Interest

Braintree Tourist Information Tel 0376 550066
Paycocke's Tel 0376 561305.

Colchester Butterfly Hotel 61% £61

Tel 0206 230900 Fax 0206 231095 **H**

Old Ipswich Road Ardleigh Colchester Essex CO7 7QY **Map 10 C3**

Part of a small chain offering practical accommodation (there is separate work space in all the bedrooms) and conference facilities for up to 80 delegates. Located on the A12/A120 near the Business Parks. No dogs. ***Rooms** 50.* AMERICAN EXPRESS *Access, Diners, Visa.*

Colchester Places of Interest

Tourist Information Tel 0206 712920.
Colchester Arts Centre St. Marys-at-the-Walls, Church Street Tel 0206 577301.
Mercury Theatre Balkerne Gate Tel 0206 577301.
Colchester Museums Tel 0206 712931.
Castle Park Cricket Ground Tel 0206 574028.
Colchester Garrison Polo Club East Mersea Tel 0206 383049.
Colchester Zoo Stanway Tel 0206 331292.
Clacton Beach *13 miles SE Colchester.*
Historic Houses, Castles and Gardens
Beth Chatto Gardens Elmstead Market Tel 0206 822007.
Layer Marney Tower Tiptree Tel 0206 330784.
St. Osyth Priory St. Osyth Tel 0255 820492.

Colerne Lucknam Park 83% £150

Tel 0225 742777 Fax 0225 743536 **HR**

Colerne Wiltshire SN14 8AZ **Map 14 B2**

Approached by a straight mile of beech-lined drive, Lucknam is a gracious Georgian house in a tranquil setting six miles from Bath on the southern edge of the Cotswolds. The house has a particularly English feel and is luxuriously fitted with sound taste. Day rooms are spacious and extremely elegant with soft colours, choice antiques and oil paintings plus deep-cushioned sofas. Sumptuously comfortable bedrooms are appointed *See over* to the highest standards with handsome furnishings and fittings befitting a house of this stature. Each is individually decorated in quintessential English style and most of the marble-tiled bathrooms boast double basins. Housekeeping is immaculate. In addition to the leisure spa (conceived in the style of a Roman villa and set in the old walled garden) there are two floodlit tennis courts. Impeccably dressed young staff. No dogs, but kennelling can be arranged. ***Rooms** 42. Garden, tennis, helipad, indoor swimming pool, spa bath, sauna, steam room, keep-fit equipment, beauty salon, hairdressing, snooker.* AMERICAN EXPRESS *Access, Diners, Visa.*

Restaurant £90

Discreet, polished service and a truly elegant dining room certainly set expectations high and chef Michael Womersley's cooking strives hard to match the surroundings. His menus are fixed-price, offering an interesting selection of dishes with a strong English bias and a heavy reliance on fresh local ingredients. Typical dinner dishes might be a gateau of foie gras, truffle, chicken and pistachio served with a morille Chantilly and brioche toast or millefeuille of lamb sweetbreads, kidney and tongue with roasted shallots to start, followed a galette of Cornish crab and scallops on a bed on onions in cream, rabbit with Pomerol sauce, tenderloin of pork scented with lemon and caraway. Leave room for chocolate cannelloni with pears, hot apple and quince soufflés, or chocolate pudding with vanilla sauce and caramelised fruits. Lunch is a two-or three-course affair offering equally involved dishes – perhaps salad of confit rabbit leg and its saddle pan-fried, served with pickled cucumber and carrot with a truffle vinaigrette or braised, chargrilled and fried calamares with Provençal sauce. Gentlemen are required to wear a jacket and tie in the evenings. There are no guidance notes on the wine list which is presented mostly by year, so knowledge of which vintages are good or bad is an advantage. No children under 10 for dinner (families can eat informally in the Leisure Spa). ***Seats** 75. Parties 12. Private Room 30. L 12.30-2 D 7.30-9.45 (Sat to 10). Set L £12.50/£22 Set D £37.50.*

> Many establishments are currently on the market, so ownership could change after we go to press.

Colsterworth — Forte Travelodge £42

Tel 0476 861181 — **L**

Colsterworth Nr Grantham Lincolnshire NG33 5JJ — **Map 7 E3**

Located at the roundabout of the junction of the A1 (southbound) with A151, 8 miles south of Grantham. ***Rooms** 32.* AMERICAN EXPRESS *Access, Visa.*

Coniston — Sun Hotel 63% £70

Tel 053 94 41248 — **H**

Coniston Cumbria LA21 8HQ — **Map 4 C3**

The Old Man of Coniston creates a spectacular backdrop to this handsome Victorian house in a hillside setting overlooking the village. Views from a stylish, book-filled lounge are conducive to relaxation, while the adjacent 16th-century inn will appeal to the more convivial. Generally spacious bedrooms incorporate seating areas and are carpeted through to bright, airy bathrooms. ***Rooms** 11. Garden. Closed Christmas, Jan. Access, Visa.*

Coniston — Places of Interest

Ravenglass Tourist Information Tel 0229 717278.
Muncaster Castle and Gardens Tel 0229 717614 *28 miles.*
The Owl Centre Muncaster Castle Tel 0229 717393 *28 miles.*
Beatrix Potter Gallery (NT) Main Street, Hawkshead Tel 09666 355.
Brantwood House and Garden (Home of John Ruskin) Coniston Tel 05394 41396.

Constantine Bay — Treglos Hotel — 65% — £138*

Tel 0841 520727 Fax 0841 521163 — H

Constantine Bay St Merryn Padstow Cornwall PL28 8JH — **Map 12 B3**

In the same ownership since 1965, this is a friendly, well-run hotel just five minutes from the sea, overlooking Constantine Bay and Trevose Golf Course. It's a popular place with many regular visitors, so balcony rooms are booked well in advance. All the public rooms except the bar have sea views; the three comfortable and traditional lounges are bright and airy. Bedrooms have simple white laminate units, large windows and compact bathrooms. There are four flats in the grounds. In the hotel jackets and ties are requested after 7pm. *Half-board terms only. ***Rooms** 44. Garden, indoor swimming pool, spa bath, games room, snooker, lock-up garages. Closed early Nov-early Mar. Access, Visa.*

Constantine Bay — Place of Interest

Constantine Bay, Harlyn Bay and Treyarnon Bay Beaches.

Cooden — Cooden Resort Hotel — 60% — £75

Tel 0424 842281 Fax 0424 846142 — H

Cooden Sea Road Bexhill-on-Sea East Sussex TN39 4TT — **Map 11 B6**

Right on the beach, with views across Pevensey Bay, this 30s' hotel caters well for both leisure and business guests. There are facilities for up to 200 conference delegates, a health and leisure club, a modern lounge, a cocktail bar and a tavern serving real ale. One of the bedrooms has been adapted for disabled guests; 12 are suitable for family use. ***Rooms** 41. Garden, indoor & outdoor swimming pools, keep-fit equipment, squash, sauna, spa bath, solarium, beauty & hair salon.* AMERICAN EXPRESS *Access, Diners, Visa.*

Cooden — Place of Interest

Bexhill Beach.

Copdock — Ipswich Moat House — 64% — £68

Tel 0473 730444 Fax 0473 730801 — H

London Road Copdock nr Ipswich Suffolk IP8 3JD — **Map 10 C3**

Friendly modern hotel set in four acres of grounds just off the A12, three miles south of Ipswich. Besides practical, up-to-date accommodation the hotel offers extensive conference facilities (up to 500 delegates) and a well-equipped health and fitness club. ***Rooms** 74. Indoor swimming pool, keep-fit equipment, sauna, spa bath, solarium.* AMERICAN EXPRESS *Access, Diners, Visa.*

Corfe Castle — Mortons House Hotel — 62% — £80

Tel 0929 480988 Fax 0929 480820 — H

45 East Street Corfe Castle Dorset BH20 5EE — **Map 14 C4**

An Elizabethan manor house, almost in the shadow of the castle, enlarged in 1666 and again more recently with a sympathetic bedroom extension. Day rooms include a fine oak-panelled drawing room (warmed by an open log fire in winter), an entrance hall with an old stone fireplace and a pleasant little bar. Conference facilities for up to 45 delegates. ***Rooms** 17. Walled garden.* AMERICAN EXPRESS *Access, Visa.*

Corfe Castle — Place of Interest

Corfe Castle (NT) Nr Wareham Tel 0929 480921.

Cornhill-on-Tweed   Tillmouth Park   68%   £86

Tel 0890 882255   H

Cornhill-on-Tweed Northumberland TD12 4UU   **Map 5 D1**

High above the river Till this solid Victorian mansion has benefited greatly from a major refurbishment undertaken by welcoming new owners Ronald and Sandra Dollery. There's a fine new marble fireplace in the stylishly decorated drawing room, numerous oil paintings and a real log fire burning for most of the year in the grand, galleried central hall. Stuffed birds dotted about the place, a stag's head, fishing rods in the entrance hall and fishing photos in the bar all indicate that this is very much a shooting and fishing hotel; there's a proper room for rods and guns and a drying room. Individually decorated, antique-furnished bedrooms (the best, including two garden rooms at a little distance from the main house, are very spacious) combine comfort with modern amenities and good bathrooms with wood-panelled tubs. ***Rooms** 13. Garden, snooker. Closed first two week Feb.* AMERICAN EXPRESS *Access, Diners, Visa.*

is our symbol for an outstanding wine list.

Corse Lawn   Corse Lawn House   71%   £90

Tel 0452 780479 Fax 0452 780840   HR

Corse Lawn nr Gloucester Gloucestershire GL19 4LZ   **Map 14 B1**

Laid back from the B4211 behind its own pond, this sympathetically extended Queen Anne house is run in approachable fashion by the Hine family combining day rooms designed in a country house style with a comfortable bistro/bar (sofas and armchairs around red check-clothed tables) that also attracts local custom. Spacious bedrooms (just two are rather smaller) are individually decorated, with plain walls and attractive matching bedcovers, curtains and bedhead drapes and furnished with antiques which include marble-topped washstands to house beverage equipment (cafetière, ground coffee, loose tea, vacuum flask of fresh milk and home-made biscuits). Full room service is also available (except kippers for breakfast!). The rooms are practical, as well as pretty: there's a proper leather-topped desk near a light fitting and extras like fruit, mineral water and satellite TV. Good bathrooms, with ruffled blinds to match the room, offer generous towelling and bathrobes. Breakfasts include home-made marmalade and sausages plus home-cured bacon – the sort of attention to detail one might expect from a place with such an emphasis on good food. ***Rooms** 19. Garden, tennis, outdoor swimming pool.* AMERICAN EXPRESS *Access, Diners, Visa.*

Restaurant   £75

Everything from the bread to delicious chocolates served with coffee is home-made by Baba Hine and her team here, using only the best of fresh ingredients to produce some thoroughly satisfying dishes. Menus in the elegant L-shaped dining room offer classic combinations – goujons of cod with tartare sauce, roast duckling with Calvados and thyme, calf's brains with black butter – and more unusual items such as cassoulet of rabbit with white beans and garlic sausage, guinea fowl with champagne sauce, haunch of venison with roebuck sauce and lentils, and the odd exotic touch like soy and Madeira sauce with a millefeuille of wild mushrooms.
A particularly good and varied pudding menu might include a hot butterscotch sponge pudding and a super light and fruity hot passion fruit soufflé. Less formal but equally good eating is to be had in the bar/bistro which offers two menus – 'Baba's British Bill of Fare' (she's English) and 'Denis's Menu Français' (he's French). There are personal notes at the head of each section on the comprehensive wine list, that includes an excellent house selection. ***Seats** 50. Private Room 40. L 12-2 D 7-10. Set L £15.95. Set D £23.50*

Corsham — Methuen Arms — £65

Tel 0249 714867 Fax 0249 712004 — **I**

2 High Street Corsham Wiltshire SN13 0HB — **Map 14 B2**

Exposed oak beams and 500-year-old rubble-stone walls in the 100-foot Long Bar attest to the antiquity of this old town-centre inn and add to its special character. Main building bedrooms include two of family size: twelve further rooms, some with showers only, are in a loft conversion and an adjoining cottage. No dogs. ***Rooms** 25. Garden, skittle alley. Closed 26 Dec, 1 Jan. Access, Visa.*

Corsham — Rudloe Park — 64% — £80

Tel 0225 810555 Fax 0225 811412 — **H**

Leafy Lane Corsham Wiltshire SN13 0PA — **Map 14 B2**

The Park's wooded drive leads off the A4 between Chippenham and Bath, at the top of Box Hill. Marion and Ian Overend's handsome Bath-stone manor house stands in ten acres of award-winning gardens. Decor within is fittingly traditional, and the lounge-bar makes a comfortable setting in which to enjoy one of the impressive range of whiskies and cognacs. Bedrooms, with four-posters, half-testers or crown canopies, are traditionally furnished and full of homely touches like fresh fruit and complimentary sherry. No children under 10. No dogs in public rooms; £5 charge for dogs in bedrooms. ***Rooms** 11. Garden, bowls.* AMERICAN EXPRESS *Access, Diners, Visa.*

Corsham — Places of Interest

Chippenham Tourist Information Tel 0249 657733.
Bowood House and Gardens Calne Tel 0249 812102.
Corsham Court Tel 0249 712214.
Sheldon Manor Tel 0249 653120.

Cosham — Barnard's — £45

Tel 0705 370226 — **R**

109 High Street Cosham Hampshire PO6 3BB — **Map 15 D4**

David and Sandie Barnard's tiny, high-street restaurant hides behind heavy red curtains. Don't be misled by the rather sparse decoration for the real appeal lies in the kitchen, where David cooks single-handedly with obvious confidence and enthusiasm, producing a menu that requires varied skills and disciplines and which is worth a detour to investigate. Omelette Arnold Bennett is a popular starter alongside, perhaps, twice-baked goat's cheese soufflé and pastry-encased fresh scallops baked with vermouth and a julienne of vegetables among the six or so à la carte starters; fresh fish main courses are written on a blackboard and a small selection of meat dishes might include steaks and guinea fowl (the good-value table d'hote always offers a further choice). Passion fruit tart, lemon cheesecake and home-made ice creams offer simpler options at dessert stage than a 'thin pancake filled with a Pernod custard, chopped hazelnuts, marzipan and kiwi fruit topped with meringue and then baked and served with a raspberry sauce'. The choice, as always, is yours... Keenly-priced and carefully-chosen wines. Good-value weekday fixed-price lunches with small choice. ***Seats** 24. L 12-2 D 7.30-9.30. Closed L Sat, all Sun & Mon, Bank Holidays, 1 week Christmas, 2 weeks Aug. Set L & D £13.50. Access, Visa.*

Coventry — Chace Hotel — 61% — £98

Tel 0203 303398 Fax 0203 301816 — **H**

London Road Willenhall Coventry West Midlands CV3 4EQ — **Map 6 C4**

On the A423, a Victorian main building with modern extensions and conference facilities. Children up to 14 stay free in parents' room. Forte. ***Rooms** 67. Garden, children's playground.* AMERICAN EXPRESS *Access, Diners, Visa.*

Coventry — De Vere Hotel — 69% — £85

Tel 0203 633733 Fax 0203 225299 — H

Cathedral Square Coventry West Midlands CV1 5RP — **Map 6 C4**

A large modern hotel, which enjoys direct access to the Cathedral square through a conservatory. Attractive public areas include a spacious foyer (staff are welcoming and helpful) and the popular Daimler bar-lounge (food available all day) decorated with pictures of one of Coventry's most famous cars. Generously-sized bedrooms with cathedral views are smart and well equipped, with plenty of working space and colourfully tiled bathrooms. Conference and banqueting facilities for up to 450. Children up to 14 stay free in parents' room. ***Rooms** 190.* AMERICAN EXPRESS *Access, Diners, Visa.*

Coventry — Forte Crest — 66% — £98

Tel 0203 613261 Fax 0203 614318 — H

Hinckley Road Coventry West Midlands CV2 2HP — **Map 6 C4**

Purpose-built business centre and a fully equipped leisure club go with the modern amenities in the bedrooms. Parking for 200 cars. ***Rooms** 147. Gymnasium, sauna, spa bath, steam room, solarium, beauty salon, putting, games room, coffee shop (7am-11pm).* AMERICAN EXPRESS *Access, Diners, Visa.*

Coventry — Forte Posthouse — 60% — £68

Tel 0203 402151 Fax 0203 402235 — H

Rye Hill Allesley Coventry West Midlands CV5 9PH — **Map 6 C4**

High-riser just outside the city on the A45. Conference facilities for 120. ***Rooms** 184.* AMERICAN EXPRESS *Access, Diners, Visa.*

Coventry — Novotel — 62% — £78

Tel 0203 365000 Fax 0203 362422 — H

Wilsons Lane Longford Coventry West Midlands CV6 6HL — **Map 6 C4**

Practical, modern accommodation close to Junction 3 of the M6. ***Rooms** 100. Outdoor swimming pool, boules, children's playground.* AMERICAN EXPRESS *Access, Diners, Visa.*

Coventry (North) — Campanile Hotel — £44

Tel 0203 622311 Fax 0203 602362 — L

Wigston Road Walsgrave Coventry West Midlands CV2 2SD — **Map 6 C4**

Off the A4600 Hinckley Road, from Junction 2 of the M6. ***Rooms** 50.* AMERICAN EXPRESS *Access, Diners, Visa.*

Coventry (South) — Campanile Hotel — £44

Tel 0203 639922 Fax 0203 306898 — L

Abbey Road Whitley Coventry West Midlands CV3 4BJ — **Map 6 C4**

Close to the A45 and A423, off the A46. ***Rooms** 50.* AMERICAN EXPRESS *Access, Diners, Visa.*

Coventry — Places of Interest

Tourist Information Tel 0203 832303/832304.
Belgrade Theatre Belgrade Square Tel 0203 553055.
Coventry Arts Centre University of Warwick Tel 0203 417417.
Herbert Art Gallery and Museum Jordan Well Tel 0203 832381.
Coventry Cathedral Tel 0203 227597.
Coventry City Football Ground Tel 0203 257171.
Coventry Sports Centre 0203 228601.

Cowan Bridge — Cobwebs

£60

Tel 052 42 72141

RR

Leck Cowan Bridge nr Kirkby Lonsdale Lancashire LA6 2HZ — Map 4 C4

Turn off the A65 at Cowan Bridge and follow the sign to Leck and you'll come upon a charming Victorian house in a picturesque rural setting. Yvonne Thompson single-handedly cooks a balanced fixed-price, five-course dinner that might offer a mix of beetroot plus apple and leek soups (cleverly served in one bowl), warm salmon and almond profiteroles with minted yoghurt sauces and then sorbet, before a main course of chicken, duck, turkey and spinach rolled together, sliced and served with shellfish and leek sauces; finally, perhaps a baked baby pineapple filled with banana, pineapple, cherries and rum, followed by cheese and biscuits. Paul Kelly plays host and enthuses over a collector's wine list that's particularly strong on Alsace and the New World, with excellent-value house selections and half bottles. Booking essential. ***Seats** 24. D only 7.30 for 8.*
Closed Sun & Mon, also end Dec-mid Mar. Set D £24. Access, Visa.

Rooms

£56

Five bedrooms in individual colour schemes are Victorian-style and charming. Bathrobes and bespoke toiletries add the pampering touches. Classy country breakfasts.

Cowan Bridge — Hipping Hall Hotel — 64%

£69

Tel 052 42 71187 Fax 052 42 72452

H

Cowan Bridge nr Kirkby Lonsdale Lancashire LA6 2JJ — Map 4 C4

Ian Bryant and Jocelyn Ruffle pride themselves on creating a relaxed country-house atmosphere; guests meet for drinks round the fire and dine together at one table in the characterful, beamed Great Hall, complete with minstrel's gallery. There is also a help-yourself bar in the old stone-flagged conservatory. Bedrooms are bright, pretty and comfortable, with gleaming bathrooms. The hall is the sole survivor of a 15th-century hamlet and stands on the A65 three miles east of Kirkby Lonsdale.
No children under 12. ***Rooms** 7. Garden. Closed Jan. Access, Visa.*

Cranbrook — Hartley Mount — 62%

£70

Tel 0580 712230 Fax 0580 712588

H

Hartley Road Cranbrook Kent TN17 3QX — Map 11 C5

Lionel and Lee Skilton run a friendly hotel in a large, converted Edwardian manor house, set back off the A229, within walking distance of town. There are views over farmland and the Weald of Kent from the hotel and a non-smoking policy in all rooms but the conservatory (where breakfast is served). An informal atmosphere pervades, exemplified by a lack of formal reception facilities, as the owners prefer to greet guests personally. Bedrooms include a four-poster room with period bathroom and a very large family room. No dogs. ***Rooms** 7. Garden, tennis, mini-golf, pétanque.*
AMERICAN EXPRESS *Access, Visa.*

Cranbrook — Kennel Holt Hotel — 66%

£98

Tel 0580 712032 Fax 0580 715495

H

Goudhurst Road Cranbrook Kent TN17 2PT — Map 11 B5

Fine gardens surround this small, family-run Elizabethan manor house with distinctive brick chimneys, off the A262, three miles from Goudhurst. There are two beamed lounges, one with floral sofas and brick inglenook fireplace, the other, with oak panelling, acting as the bar. Bedrooms, mostly with plain woodchip walls, are variously furnished with antiques or new pine pieces and have pretty fabrics. Bathrooms boast good toiletries and towelling; three have shower and WC only and two are not en suite.

See over

Popular for weddings, with a marquee in the garden for larger affairs, and also well set up for small business meetings. New owners. ***Rooms** 10. Garden, putting.* AMERICAN EXPRESS *Access, Diners, Visa.*

Cranbrook — Place of Interest

Sissinghurst Castle Garden (NT) Tel 0580 712850.

Cranleigh — La Barbe Encore — £55

Tel 0483 273889 — R

High Street Cranleigh Surrey GU6 8AE — **Map 15 E3**

A change of name (formerly *Restaurant Bonnet*) and decor (the old black beams are now brown and the walls have been warmed-up with bright orange paint) but the bistroish atmosphere remains as does Jean-Pierre Bonnet who can still be seen in the kitchen producing his generally mainstream French dishes – snails in garlic butter, game paté with onion compote, confit of duck with red wine sauce, chicken with tarragon, tarte aux pommes with cinnamon ice cream, meringue glacé. The fixed-price menu no longer includes an aperitif or wine. Notably friendly service. There's a large municipal car park to the rear. Sister restaurant to *La Barbe* in Reigate (qv) and *La Bonne Auberge* in South Godstone (qv). ***Seats** 60. L 12-2 D 7-10. Closed L Sat, D Sun, all Mon, Bank Holidays. Set L £13.95/£16.95 Set D £16.95/£18.95.* AMERICAN EXPRESS *Access, Visa.*

Set menu prices may not always include service or wine.

Crathorne — Crathorne Hall — 72% — £110

Tel 0642 700398 Fax 0642 700814 — H

Crathorne nr Yarm Cleveland TS15 0AR — **Map 5 E3**

Set in 15 acres of grounds not far from the village centre and a short distance from the A19, Crathorne Hall was the last of the great stately houses built in the Edwardian era. Public rooms and the best of the bedrooms enjoy an elevated view over parkland with not a human habitation in sight. The drawing room is of classical proportions with a fine carved overmantel, large portraits in oil and brass chandeliers. Knoll sofas and buttoned leather Queen Anne style armchairs form part of a comfortable and very traditional decor. The cocktail bar has the air of a gentleman's club with its bottle-green walls, mahogany panelling and pillars and plush red velour chairs. Bedrooms are splendid though top floor and back rooms are smaller. Furniture is period style in keeping with the character of the building and all rooms are well equipped, superior rooms in particular. Bathrooms, some with bidets, have quality toiletries and bathrobes. Quite reasonable breakfasts. ***Rooms** 37. Garden.* AMERICAN EXPRESS *Access, Diners, Visa.*

Crawley — George Hotel — 64% — £76

Tel 0293 524215 Fax 0293 548565 — H

High Street Crawley West Sussex RH10 1BS — **Map 11 B5**

An old gallows sign announces this town-centre coaching inn in the Forte Heritage group. Some parts are beamed and atmospheric, others modern. ***Rooms** 86.* AMERICAN EXPRESS *Access, Diners, Visa.*

Crawley — Places of Interest

Leonardslee Gardens Lower Beeding Tel 0403 891212.
Gatwick Zoo Charlwood Tel 0293 862312.

Crewe **Forte Travelodge** **£42**

Tel 0270 883157 **L**

Alsager Road Barthomley Nr Crewe Cheshire CW2 5PT **Map 6 B3**

At Junction 16 of the M6 and A500 between Nantwich and Stoke-on-Trent, off the junction roundabout signposted to Alsager. ***Rooms** 42.*
AMERICAN EXPRESS *Access, Visa.*

Crick **Forte Posthouse Northampton/Rugby** **64%** **£68**

Tel 0788 822101 Fax 0788 823955 **H**

Crick Northamptonshire NN6 7XR **Map 7 D4**

Low-rise modern hotel near junction 18 on the M1, 7 miles from Rugby. 14 meeting rooms, conference facilities for 185. ***Rooms** 88. Garden, indoor swimming pool, gymnasium, sauna, solarium, coffee shop (7am-10.30pm, till 7pm weekends).* AMERICAN EXPRESS *Access, Diners, Visa.*

Crook **Wild Boar Hotel** **60%** **£110**

Tel 0539 445225 Fax 0539 442498 **H**

Crook nr Windermere Cumbria LA23 3NF **Map 4 C3**

Abundant character still pervades the coaching inn where, reputedly, Westmorland's last wild boar was killed (in King John's time), though today's building is predominantly Victorian. Public rooms are a mass of blackened beams, log fires and ancient oak furniture, the oldest dating from 1635. Much of this character is reflected in the main-house bedrooms with four-posters and two suites, one with a spa bath. A more modern wing offers rooms for non-smokers; bathrooms are generally on the small side. Free leisure facilities at a sister hotel (7 miles away), discounted green fees at Windermere golf club (1 mile away). ***Rooms** 36. Garden.*
AMERICAN EXPRESS *Access, Diners, Visa.*

Crooklands **Crooklands Hotel** **60%** **£84**

Tel 053 95 67432 Fax 053 95 67525 **H**

Crooklands nr Kendal Cumbria LA7 7NW **Map 4 C4**

Minutes from the M6 (junction 36) on the A65 in a peaceful rural location; a collection of farm buildings adjoining an original ale house contain the public rooms where exposed beams are still a feature. Best accommodation, with neat, well equipped bathrooms, is in the recently-built 16-bedroom extension. Choice of restaurants. ***Rooms** 30. Garden, snooker, coffee shop (7.30am-10pm).* AMERICAN EXPRESS *Access, Diners, Visa.*

Crosby-on-Eden **Crosby Lodge** **66%** **£85**

Tel 0228 573618 Fax 0228 573428 **HR**

High Crosby Crosby-on-Eden nr Carlisle Cumbria CA6 4QZ **Map 4 C2**

Follow the A689 up the Eden valley from Carlisle; Patricia and Michael Sedgwick's Georgian country house with Victorian embellishments overlooks mature parkland and the river. The elegant entrance hall contains Oriental carpets, antiques and a welcoming open fire and sets the tone; a carved staircase leads up to spacious, well-proportioned bedrooms with luxury fabrics used throughout; one room features a half-tester. By comparison, the converted stable block offers accommodation on an altogether more modest scale. ***Rooms** 11. Garden. Closed 24 Dec-mid Jan.*
AMERICAN EXPRESS *Access, Visa.*

Restaurant **£65**

Michael Sedgwick has spent twenty years here indulging his house guests with traditional cooking (chicken liver paté laced with brandy, Stilton and port paté with toast, snails in garlic butter, pickled herring fillet, duckling with orange sauce, saltimbocca), but has not entirely overlooked modern *See over* influences, so some dishes are given a slight twist. Seafood and seasonal game are specialities, and everything is home-made – from amuse-gueule to petits fours. No smoking. Helpful notes against each wine on the diverse list. No children under 5 after 7.30pm. Jacket and tie required for gentlemen. ***Seats** 50. Parties 25. Private Room 16. L 12.15-1.30 D 7.30-9 (Sun to 8). Set L £15 Set D £25.*

Croydon — Croydon Park — 69% — £126

Tel 081-680 9200 Fax 081-760 0426 — H

7 Altyre Road Croydon Surrey CR9 5AA — **Map 11 B5**

A roomy hotel opposite the Law Courts, with plenty of covered parking. The foyer is spacious but offers only limited seating, while the gas-lit Whistlers Bar (open 10am-11pm) is a more intimate spot. Bedrooms have queen-size beds and uniform decor, air-conditioning and compact bathrooms. Two floors are designated no smoking. There's a leisure centre, and conference/banqueting facilities for up to 300. Children up to 14 are accommodated free in parents' room. ***Rooms** 214. Garden, indoor swimming pool, gymnasium, squash, sauna, spa bath, solarium.* AMERICAN EXPRESS *Access, Diners, Visa.*

Croydon — Forte Posthouse — 61% — £68

Tel 081-688 5185 Fax 081-681 6438 — H

Purley Way Croydon Surrey CR9 4LT — **Map 11 B5**

Convenient location, aside the A23, with flexible conference facilities for 40 to 170 delegates. Half the bedrooms are designated non-smoking. ***Rooms** 83. 24hr coffee shop.* AMERICAN EXPRESS *Access, Diners, Visa.*

Croydon — Hilton National — NEW — 69% — £105

Tel 081-680 3000 Fax 081-681 6171 — H

Waddon Way Purley Way Croydon Surrey CR9 4HH — **Map 11 B5**

Smart, new polished granite hotel with plenty of parking at the Croydon end of Purley Way. Quality public areas combine comfort and space with a considerable sense of style. Good bedrooms offer large beds and ample work space plus wing armchairs and proper breakfast table. White marble features in equally good bathrooms. Suites (actually just large rooms) have sophisticated TVs that incorporate CD players and a video games feature, spa baths and separate shower cubicles in addition to the tub. ***Rooms** 168. Indoor swimming pool, gymnasium, sauna, spa bath, steam room, solarium, coffee shop (10.30am-10.30pm).* AMERICAN EXPRESS *Access, Diners, Visa.*

Croydon — Selsdon Park — 68% — £120

Tel 081-657 8811 Fax 081-651 6171 — H

Addington Road Sanderstead Croydon Surrey CR2 8YA — **Map 11 B5**

The leisure facilities, inside and out, are a great attraction at this impressive-looking ivy-clad hotel of neo-Jacobean appearance, set in 200 acres of undulating parkland. The baronial-style entrance hall has stone walls, an elaborate plaster ceiling and leather armchairs that are also to be found in the oak-panelled bar-lounge with its heavily carved antique furniture and brass ornaments. Bedrooms come in a variety of sizes and styles from freestanding lightwood furniture to fitted units, and soft floral to bright fabrics. All have mini-bars and room safes in addition to the usual extras. The very best rooms enjoy views across the Surrey Hills. The hotel has a large conference trade, with excellent amenities and a maximum capacity of 150. Families are well catered for at weekends when special rates apply (regular dinner dances and baby-sitting by prior arrangement); golf-and tennis-mad parents will be in seventh heaven (coaches on site). Unusual 40m circuit indoor swimming pool. Reservable lock-up garages and car service to East Croydon station. ***Rooms** 170. Garden, golf (18-hole), putting* *green, driving range, indoor & outdoor swimming pools, gymnasium, spa bath, sauna, solarium, beauty salon, tennis (grass & all-weather), squash, snooker, children's playground, helipad.* AMERICAN EXPRESS *Access, Diners, Visa.*

Croydon Travel Inn

£43

Tel 081-686 2030 Fax 081-686 6435

L

Coombe Road Croydon Surrey CR0 5RB

Map 11 B5

Rooms 40. AMERICAN EXPRESS *Access, Diners, Visa.*

Cuckfield Murray's

£55

Tel 0444 455826

R

Broad Street Cuckfield West Sussex RH17 5LJ

Map 11 B6

Several cottagey rooms provide a cosy setting for enjoying Sue Murray's skilled and imaginative cooking. Influences from Europe and beyond appear in dishes on the seasonal menu: mussel ravioli, pigeon casserole in stock and Marsala, salmon baked with raisins, almonds and ginger in a puff pastry parcel, fillet steak topped with goat's cheese. Short wine list with many bottles under £15. One room reserved for non-smokers. ***Seats** 30. Private Room 18. L 12-1.30 D 7.15-9.30. Closed L Sat, all Sun, Bank Holidays, 2 weeks Feb, 2 weeks Sep. Access, Visa.*

Cuckfield Ockenden Manor 71%

£98

Tel 0444 416111 Fax 0444 415549

H

Ockenden Lane Cuckfield West Sussex RH17 5LD

Map 11 B6

Fresh flowers and a real log fire feature in the beamed entrance hall of an original Tudor building that has been sympathetically extended in the 19th and 20th centuries, the most recent addition being a block of eight bedrooms. There are attractive views of the South Downs from the rear of the hotel, which overlooks a grand garden. Day rooms include a pub-like, oak-panelled bar, a sunny sitting room and a non-smoking dining room. Bedrooms, five of which have four-poster beds, come in a variety of styles and include both reproduction and original antiques and many extras. ***Rooms** 22. Garden.* AMERICAN EXPRESS *Access, Diners, Visa.*

Cuckfield Places of Interest

Wakehurst Place Garden (NT) Tel 0444 892701 *7 miles.*
South of England Showground Tel 0444 892700 *5 miles.*
All England Jumping Course Hickstead Tel 0273 834315.

Dane End Green End Park 62%

£95

Tel 0920 438344 Fax 0920 438523

H

Dane End nr Ware Hertfordshire SG12 0NY

Map 15 E2

Off the A602 between Ware and Stevenage, this 18th-century house stands peacefully in eight acres of gardens. There's an elegant style to the day rooms, which include an impressive bar with a patio, and a conference facility for up to 100 delegates. The 10 bedrooms include two suitable for family occupation. ***Rooms** 10. Garden, tennis, putting.* AMERICAN EXPRESS *Access, Diners, Visa.*

Darlington Blackwell Grange Moat House 62%

£98

Tel 0325 380888 Fax 0325 380899

H

Blackwell Grange Darlington Co Durham DL3 8QH

Map 5 E3

17th-century mansion set in 15 acres of parkland. Contemporary comforts in the bedrooms, which include 11 grand, Georgian state rooms. 24hr room service. Good Locomotion Leisure Club and conference and banqueting suites (including the characterful Jacobean suite with high,

See over

vaulted and beamed ceiling) for up to 300. Dinner dances on Saturdays. ***Rooms** 99. Garden, indoor swimming pool, spa bath, sauna, solarium, gymnasium, putting, pétanque.* AMERICAN EXPRESS® *Access, Diners, Visa.*

We do not accept free meals or hospitality – our inspectors pay their own bills.

Darlington — St George Thistle — 56% — £79

Tel 0325 332631 Fax 0325 333851 — H

Teesside Airport nr Darlington Co Durham DL2 1RH — **Map 5 E3**

Redbrick, two-storey hotel. Smart, modern bedrooms. Banqueting facilities for 120, conferences for 160. Friday and Saturday night tariff rates are nearly 40% lower than weekday rates. ***Rooms** 59. Sauna, solarium.* AMERICAN EXPRESS® *Access, Diners, Visa.*

Darlington — Sardis — £50

Tel 0325 461222 — R

196 Northgate Darlington Co Durham DL1 1QU — **Map 5 E3**

There are always plenty of reliable Italian dishes on the menu at this Sardinian-owned town-centre restaurant. Pasta with ham and cream sauce, mixed fish pancake, roast duckling with maraschino and cherry sauce, rack of lamb with rosemary and honey, and grilled veal Sicilian-style (garlic, onion, parsley, white wine) show the range of generally traditional cooking. ***Seats** 50. L 12-2 D 7-10. Closed Sun, Bank Holidays. Set L £9.50 Set D (Mon-Fri) £16 (incl wine). Access, Visa.*

Darlington — Swallow King's Head — 57% — £86

Tel 0325 380222 Fax 0325 382006 — H

Priestgate Darlington Co Durham DL1 1LW — **Map 5 E3**

Victorian hotel located above shops in the town centre. Conference and banquets are big business (up to 250 in the Wellington Suite) and guests have free use of the nearby Dolphin Leisure Centre. ***Rooms** 85.* AMERICAN EXPRESS® *Access, Diners, Visa.*

Darlington — Victor's — £55

Tel 0325 480818 — R

84 Victoria Road Darlington Co Durham DL1 5JW — **Map 5 E3**

To the west and north of the station just off one of the inner ring road roundabouts, Victor's is a friendly, informal and totally unpretentious restaurant decorated in palest grey with simple lighting. While Jayne Robinson does the cooking, husband Peter offers chatty, relaxed service to the diners. The three-course lunch at £8.50 represents excellent value. Dinner consists of four courses with a little more choice and elaboration. Cooking is honest with unfussy clear flavours and accurate seasoning. Everything, including the bread rolls, is home-made. Starters range from fresh asparagus with butter to stir-fried five-spice beef with watercress and a timbale of spinach with quail's eggs and a velvety cheese sauce. After a middle course of say carrot and orange soup, main courses could be poached fillets of lemon sole with a textured crab sauce, loin of lamb in puff pastry with a Madeira sauce, braised ox tongue with caper sauce or roast duckling with a lime and almond stuffing. Home-made ices are in some exotic flavours – cardamom or green Chartreuse, the latter particularly delicious – otherwise the puddings are familiar and homely, plum crumble and strawberry pavlova for instance. ***Seats** 30. L 12-2 D 7-10.30. Closed Sun & Mon, 1 week Christmas.Set L £8.50 Set D £20.* AMERICAN EXPRESS® *Access, Diners, Visa.*

Darlington — Places of Interest

Tourist Information Tel 0325 382698.
Darlington Arts Centre Vane Terrace Tel 0325 483168.
Darlington Civic Theatre Parkgate Tel 0325 486555.
Darlington Railway Centre and Museum North Road Station Tel 0325 460532.
Catterick Indoor Ski Slope Tel 0748 833788.

Dartmouth — Carved Angel ★★ £90

Tel 0803 832465 **R**

2 South Embankment Dartmouth Devon TQ6 9BH **Map 13 D3**

Winner of our Restaurant of the Year award last year, Joyce Molyneux's inviting restaurant is in a delightful quayside setting overlooking the harbour. Outside, the black-and-white timbered building is commanding, while inside all is calm, including Joyce who can be seen lovingly beavering away in her open-to-view kitchen (as she has done since 1974). The unpretentious, yet calmly stylish, interior is as likely to attract yachting types (who might arrive in oilskins by dinghy from a boat in the harbour) as it is a local family or businessmen out for a celebratory meal. And what a place in which to celebrate! Fixed-price-only dinners (including mineral water, sorbet or cheese, coffee and petits fours, and service charge) encompass superb seafood: from stir-fried cuttlefish with peppers, coriander and noodles to fillets of Dover sole with chervil butter, fennel and cucumber, or Dartmouth crab with herb mayonnaise and guacamole, and tip-top meats: a puff of lamb's kidneys and sweetbreads with mushrooms and Marsala, pan-fried calf's liver with gin and lime sauce, chargrilled marinaded venison brochette on a bed of lentils with pears in red wine. Simpler tastes are always catered for with the likes of avocado and melon salad with elderflower dressing and steamed Dart salmon trout with sorrel cream, while vegetarians are unlikely to leave hungry (typically, a watercress, chive and almond pie with leek sauce appeared on a recent table d'hote lunch). French provincial may be the base from which Joyce works, but her influences continue to come from far and wide; popular dishes remain on the menu until superseded. Her attention to detail includes the very best locally-grown vegetables and cheeses. Desserts certainly don't get overlooked, with the likes of coconut cream with lime, grapefruit and mango, tiramisu (as far from the typical hackneyed trattoria offering as you can imagine), hot Grand Marnier soufflé with clotted cream ice cream and an ever-popular plate of chocolate puddings (choc ice, coffee parfait, pithiviers, brandy snap with chocolate cream). Both good-value table d'hote and à la carte menus are offered at lunchtime. Confident and friendly service from smartly dressed, charming staff. An excellent all-round list includes good house wines, a good New World selection and a red and white of the month. ***Seats** 45. Parties 38. Private Room 18. L 12.30-2 D 7.30-9. Closed D Sun, all Mon, Bank Holidays except Good Friday, 6 weeks Jan/Feb, 1st week Oct. Set L £22.50/£27.50 (Sun £30) Set D £37.50/£42.50. No credit cards.*

Dartmouth — Royal Castle Hotel £74

Tel 0803 833033 Fax 0803 835445 **I**

11 The Quay Dartmouth Devon TQ6 9PS **Map 13 D3**

Right on the the quay, in the centre of town, two Tudor merchants' houses became a hostelry in the early 1700s and the castellated facade (a Regency addition) explains the name. Antique furniture, Tudor fireplaces, oak beams fashioned from ships' timbers and a 300-year-old cooking range are among many reminders of the past, and in some of the bedrooms four-poster and brass beds are in use. River-view rooms are the most sought after (and attract a supplement). Children sharing their parents' room enjoy reduced rates. ***Rooms** 25. Garage parking.* AMERICAN EXPRESS *Access, Diners, Visa.*

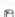

Dartmouth — Stoke Lodge — 60% — £67

Tel 0803 770523 — **H**

Stoke Fleming Dartmouth Devon TQ6 0RA — **Map 13 D3**

Family-run, and with family holidays very much in mind, the hotel overlooks the village and the sea. There are good views from the large sun terrace which overlooks the swimming pool and is a popular spot when the weather's kind. Inside, are homely, unpretentious lounges and neat bedrooms; of the latter, those with sea views attract a small supplement. ***Rooms** 24. Garden, indoor & outdoor swimming pools, tennis, putting, keep-fit equipment, giant chess. Access, Visa.*

Dartmouth — Places of Interest

Tourist Information Tel 0803 834224.
Coleton Fishacre Garden (NT) Coleton Tel 080425 466.

Daventry — Daventry Resort Hotel — 70% — NEW — £100

Tel 0327 301777 Fax 0327 706313 — **H**

Ashby Road Daventry Northamptonshire NN11 5SG — **Map 14 D1**

Located due north of Daventry town centre off a roundabout on the A361 and some 8 miles south of junction 18 of the M1. This, one of the latest additions to the Resort Hotel group, is a large, sprawling, low-rise modern building geared almost exclusively to a business clientele – a business centre is located in one corner of the reception area. Automatic doors lead into a vast and elegant American-style lobby with highly-polished coloured marble floors, Chinese-style rosewood furniture and dark, flame-patterned long settees. Numerous Chinese table lamps provide low-key lighting, recessed lights and spots adding soft background illumination. The Cat's Whiskers Bar, although spacious, has a warm, clubby atmosphere created by effective soft lighting and attractive rosewood panelling. Richly coloured upholstery here too. Bedrooms range from good-sized standard to Executive and suites. All have up-to-date quality fittings and are provided with useful extras. Bright, modern leisure facilities and a selection of conference and function rooms for 10 to 600 people. ***Rooms** 138. Indoor swimming pool, children's swimming pool, gymnasium, sauna, spa bath, solarium, beauty salon.* AMERICAN EXPRESS *Access, Diners, Visa.*

Dedham — Dedham Vale Hotel — 67% — £70

Tel 0206 322273 Fax 0206 322752 — **H**

Stratford Road Dedham nr Colchester Essex CO7 6HW — **Map 10 C3**

Located a short walk from the Talbooth and Maison (in the same group), this is a neat Edwardian house set in three acres of terraced gardens. The charming lounge is comfortable and tastefully furnished, and the atmosphere throughout is pleasantly relaxing. The Terrace Restaurant is in conservatory style. Individually furnished bedrooms have enormous bath towels. No dogs. ***Rooms** 6. Garden.* AMERICAN EXPRESS *Access, Visa.*

Dedham — Fountain House & Dedham Hall — £50

Tel 0206 323027 — **RR**

Brook Street Dedham nr Colchester Essex CO7 6AD — **Map 10 C3**

Just outside the village, Dedham Hall stands in 5 acres of grounds. A loud clanging bell announces your arrival with drinks taken in a tiny, cosy front lounge. The dining room has a charming, country cottage air of informality with its wheelback chairs and pretty pink decor. Tables have Wee Willie Winkie candle-holders and fresh flowers. The fixed-price menu changes weekly offering a choice of extremely simple but carefully prepared dishes. A typical menu would begin with avocado with smoked mackerel mousse, fresh dressed crab or gaspacho then, to follow, breaded chicken breast with mustard, sirloin steak with garlic butter, pan-fried skate with tartare sauce or slices of beef with Madeira. Simple sweets too. Service is relaxed and very low-key. Serious and well-balanced wine list with a good New World selection and plenty of half bottles. ***Rooms** 12. Seats 37. L 12.15-3 Sun only D 7.30-10. Closed D Sun, all Mon, Bank Holidays. Set L £14.50 Set D £16.50. Access, Visa.*

Bedrooms

£57

There are 12 neat, homely bedrooms (some upstairs) with residents having their own lounge and a convivial breakfast room. The accommodation is wholly taken up by residential painting courses for 8/10 weeks mid-summer.

Dedham — Maison Talbooth — 78%

£133 — **H**

Tel 0206 322367 Fax 0206 322752

Stratford Road Dedham nr Colchester Essex CO7 6HN — **Map 10 C3**

In the north-east corner of Essex, where the river Stour forms the boundary with Suffolk, Maison Talbooth stands in an area of great beauty immortalised in the paintings of John Constable. Gerald Milsom's Talbooth started as a simple tea room and has progressed to today's tranquil hotel and riverside restaurant (see entry below). All is calm and restful in the sunny lounge with its deep-cushioned armchairs, profusion of fresh flowers and views down Dedham Vale. The bedrooms, suites almost, strike a happy balance between the shameless luxury of fine co-ordinated fabrics and crown canopied beds and the quiet homeliness of abundant magazines, fresh fruit and a drinks tray. Bathrooms are superb, some with vast sunken tubs, all containing quality bath sheets and bespoke toiletries. ***Rooms** 10. Garden, giant chess.* American Express *Access, Diners, Visa.*

Dedham — Le Talbooth

£100 — **R**

Tel 0206 323150

Gunhill Dedham nr Colchester Essex CO7 6HP — **Map 10 C3**

Alfresco dining under large canvas parasols is now a fine summertime option at this beautifully located restaurant housed in a splendidly preserved half-timbered Tudor building right on the banks of the river Stour. The bar and lounges are very traditional, comfortable and welcoming, having fires burning even in the summer. The dining room overlooks the terrace and river. Redecorated in soft pastel shades, its decor complements the ancient beams and timbers. A fixed-price menu of two or three courses is available all week except Saturday night and Sunday lunchtime while the à la carte offers a choice of some eleven starters, mains and desserts. The cooking style is modern without any great surprises or innovations. There are a few traditional elements as in steak and kidney pudding and chateaubriand, the latter unusually available for one as well as two. Cooking generally is at a competent though rather pedestrian level, sweets faring marginally better. An informed wine list with background notes on styles, growers and vintages has a splendid world-wide selection at fair prices – a grande marque champagne under £25. ***Seats** 70. Private Room 24. L 12-2 D 7-9.30. Set L & D £16.50/£19.50.* American Express *Access, Visa.*

Dedham — Place of Interest

Castle House (Home of painter Sir Alfred Munnings) Tel 0206 322127.

Derby — Forte Posthouse — 61%

£68 — **H**

Tel 0332 514933 Fax 0332 518668

Pastures Hill Littleover Derby Derbyshire DE3 7BA — **Map 6 C3**

Neat, unfussy businessman's accommodation three miles west of the city centre on the A5250. Extensive grounds include a children's play area. Conference and banqueting for up to 60. ***Rooms** 62.* American Express *Access, Diners, Visa.*

Derby International Hotel 62% £60

Tel 0332 369321 Fax 0332 294430 **H**

Burton Road Derby Derbyshire DE3 6AD **Map 6 C3**

On the A5250 south-west of the city centre, the privately owned International, once a Victorian school, concentrates very much on conference and exhibition business. Bedrooms offer many extras and the suites boast spa baths. ***Rooms 62.*** AMERICAN EXPRESS *Access, Diners, Visa.*

Derby Places of Interest

Tourist Information Tel 0332 255802.
Derby Playhouse Eagle Centre Tel 0332 363275.
Guildhall Theatre Market Place Tel 0332 255447.
Derby Cathedral Tel 0332 41201.
Elvaston Castle Museum Tel 0332 571342.
Royal Crown Derby Museum Tel 0332 47051.
Derby Cricket Ground Tel 0332 383211.
Derby County Football Ground Tel 0332 40105.
Wingfield Park Showground Belper Tel 0602 324653.
Historic Houses, Castles and Gardens
Calke Abbey and Park (NT) Tel 0332 863822.
Kedleston Hall Tel 0332 842191.
Melbourne Hall and Gardens Melbourne Tel 0332 862502.
Sudbury Hall (NT) Tel 0283 585305.

Desborough Forte Travelodge £42

Tel 0536 762034 **L**

Harborough Road Desborough Northamptonshire **Map 7 D4**

On the A6 southbound, 4 miles south-east of Market Harborough and 5 miles north of West Kettering. Close to the A14 – the new A1/M1 link road. ***Rooms 32.*** AMERICAN EXPRESS *Access, Visa.*

Dinnington Dinnington Hall 65% £45

Tel & Fax 0909 569661 **H**

Falcon Way Dinnington nr Sheffield South Yorkshire S31 7NY **Map 7 D2**

Dinnington Hall is a Georgian manor house standing in three acres of gardens amid a council development in a mining village. Once derelict, it is now comfortable and homely, with a parquet-floored lounge where chintzy chairs are arranged around a log fire, and a pubby bar. Bedrooms range from single to an Executive suite with a sunken bath. One room has a four-poster. Call hotel for exact directions. ***Rooms 10. Garden.*** AMERICAN EXPRESS *Access, Diners, Visa.*

Dinnington Places of Interest

Clumber Park (NT) Nr Worksop Tel 0909 476592.
Hodsock Priory Blyth Tel 0909 591204.
Roche Abbey Maltby Tel 0709 812739.

Diss Weavers £45

Tel 0379 642411 **R**

Market Hill Diss Norfolk IP22 3JZ **Map 10 C2**

Built in the 15th century as a chapel for the Weavers' Guild, this characterful town-centre restaurant is oak-timbered inside with original paintings on the walls. Lunch offers a good-value wine-bar-like menu, while dinner is more conventional and a little more expensive. There's usually a good choice of starters like Brancaster mussels with shallots, white wine and cream, or hare, pheasant, pork and walnut terrine with a green

ginger wine dressing, followed by main dishes such as medallions of venison with a filo parcel of Brie and a crème de Cassis sauce or cabbage-wrapped monkfish tail layered with smoked haddock parfait. Chef-patron William Bavin's cooking is robust, hearty, generously-portioned and sometimes adventurous – a whole teal is boned and stuffed with dates and almonds and then served with a bitter orange sauce. Interesting vegetarian dishes. No smoking before 2pm at lunchtime or 9.30pm in the evening. Extensive wine list with a few bargains to be had. ***Seats 80.***
Private Room 45. L 12-2 D 7-9.30. Closed L Sat, all Sun, Bank Holidays, Xmas, 1 week end Aug. Set L £7.50/£10 Set D £14/£17.50. Access, Diners, Visa.

Diss Places of Interest

Bressingham Live Steam Museum and Gardens Tel 0379 88 386/0379 88 382.
Banham Zoo Banham Tel 095 387 476.

Doncaster Campanile Hotel £44

Tel 0302 370770 Fax 0302 370813 **L**

Doncaster Leisure Park Bawtry Doncaster South Yorkshire DN4 7PD **Map 7 D2**

Close to the race course, off the A638. Closest motorway junction is Junction 3 of the M18, off Junction 2 of the A1(M). ***Rooms 50.***
AMERICAN EXPRESS® *Access, Diners, Visa.*

Doncaster Danum Swallow Hotel 64% £86

Tel 0302 342261 Fax 0302 329034 **H**

High Street Doncaster South Yorkshire DN1 1DN **Map 7 D2**

An Edwardian building in the centre of town; inside it's been thoroughly modernised (except for the Crystal Suite which can accommodate up to 350 delegates in period style) with comfortable, spacious public areas and bedrooms which boast irons and ironing boards in addition to the usual amenities. ***Rooms 66.*** *Hairdressing, coffee shop (9am-5pm).*
AMERICAN EXPRESS® *Access, Diners, Visa.*

Doncaster Grand St Leger 64% £80

Tel 0302 364111 Fax 0302 329865 **H**

Bennetthorpe Doncaster South Yorkshire DN2 6AX **Map 7 D2**

With the racecourse opposite and bloodstock sales yard behind, this 19th-century building was once used as a hostelry for stable lads, but today, it provides comfortable, unassuming accommodation. Pretty floral fabrics and freestanding furniture feature in the cosy bedrooms. Day rooms include a bar-lounge with a host of racing prints and photos. ***Rooms 20.***
AMERICAN EXPRESS® *Access, Diners, Visa.*

Doncaster Moat House 68% £88

Tel 0302 310331 Fax 0302 310197 **H**

Warmsworth Doncaster South Yorkshire DN4 9UX **Map 7 D2**

Hard by the A1(M), $2\frac{1}{2}$ miles from the centre of Doncaster on the A630. Modern hotel developed around the original 17th-century Warmsworth Hall; good leisure amenities. Conference/banqueting facilities for 400/350. Children up to 14 stay free in parents' room. ***Rooms 100.*** *Indoor swimming pool, keep-fit equipment, sauna, spa bath, steam room, solarium.* AMERICAN EXPRESS® *Access, Diners, Visa.*

Doncaster Places of Interest

Tourist Information Tel 0302 734309.
Civic Theatre Waterdale Tel 0303 322817.
Comisbrough Castle Tel 0709 863329.
Doncaster Racecourse Tel 0302 320066.

Donnington Donnington Valley Hotel 74% NEW £95

Tel 0635 551199 Fax 0635 551123 **H**

Old Oxford Road Donnington nr Newbury Berkshire RG16 9AG **Map 15 D2**

Alongside its own golf course this newly-built, privately-owned hotel conceals a surprisingly stylish interior behind a rather less remarkable redbrick exterior. Beneath a vast, steeply-pitched timber ceiling the main, split-level public areas boast a real log fire, Oriental carpets over parquet floor and numerous comfortable sofas and armchairs with intriguing antique knick-knacks dotted about. The effect created is one of Edwardian elegance (though with modern comfort as the whole hotel is air-conditioned), a theme that extends to the bedrooms, many of which have period-style inlaid furniture and hand-painted tiles in the good bathrooms. There is a turn-down service in the evenings and extensive 24hr room service. ***Rooms** 58. Garden, golf (18), putting, fishing, shooting.*
AMERICAN EXPRESS *Access, Diners, Visa.*

Dorchester The Mock Turtle £54

Tel 0305 264011 **R**

34 High West Street Dorchester Dorset DT1 1UP **Map 13 F2**

A charming restaurant formed from a number of interconnecting rooms (one for smokers) in a town house dating back to the late 17th century. Decor is predominantly green with exposed stonework here and there, old photographs, crisp white napery and a welcoming fire in the comfortable lounge area. The fixed-price dinner menu offers a varied choice – Cajun blackened halibut; duck liver with bacon and gherkin sauce; rabbit, bacon and mushroom pie; magret of Barbary duck; vegetarian five nut curry – supplemented by a dozen or so fish dishes of the day. Sound cooking is complemented by friendly service. Lunchtime brings a shorter, less expensive version of the evening fare. Afters range from strawberry meringue Romanoff and chocolate pecan pie to a plate of English and Continental cheeses. No children under 10. ***Seats** 60. Parties 22. Private Room 14. L 12-2 D 7-10. Closed all Sun, L Mon (except Bank Holiday weekends) & 26 Dec. Set L £9.50 Set D £15.95/£18.95. Access, Visa.*

Dorchester Yalbury Cottage £55

Tel 0305 262382 Fax 0305 266412 **RR**

Lower Bockhampton nr Dorchester Dorset DT2 8PZ **Map 13 F2**

Well signed from the A35 roundabout on the new Dorchester by-pass. The Vosses' delightful thatched cottage with beamed ceilings and inglenook fireplaces is a comfortable restaurant setting. Fixed-price menus of four courses change daily and offer the likes of carrot and marjoram soup, tartlette of creamed leeks and poached quenelles of salmon, honey-glazed Barbary duck breast on an orange sauce, and baked egg custard with caramelised apricot sauce. Special two-night rate offers all-inclusive terms with a 4-course table d'hote menu included. ***Seats** 26. Parties 8. L 12-2 (Sun only) D 7-9 (Sat 9.15). Closed 2 weeks mid-winter. Set D £22.50.*
AMERICAN EXPRESS *Access, Visa.*

Rooms £84

Eight peaceful, cottage-style bedrooms are housed in a carefully concealed, single-storey extension to the lovely thatched cottage and are variously furnished in pine, rosewood, oak and mahogany. Undisturbed slumber is certainly likely as no children under 14 (or pets) are allowed; awaken to the timeless beauty of Hardy country.

Dorchester Places of Interest

Tourist Information Tel 0305 267992.
Dorchester Arts Centre Tel 0305 66926.
The Giant (NT) Cerne Abbas *8 miles North.*
Pavillion Theatre Tel 0305 783225.
Abbotsbury Swannery & Sub-Tropical Gardens Abbotsbury Tel 0305 871387.

Historic Houses, Castles and Gardens

Danway House Puddletown Tel 0305 269741.
Hardy's Cottage (NT) Higher Bockhampton Tel 0305 262366.
Minterne Gardens Minterne Magna Tel 0300 341370.
Wolfeton House Tel 0305 263500.

Museums and Art Galleries

The Dinosaur Museum Icen Way Tel 0305 269741.
Tutankhamun Exhibition Tel 0305 269741.
Dorset County Museum Includes Thomas Hardy memorial room Tel 0305 262735.
Warmwell Leisure Resort Dry Ski Slope Tel 0305 852911.

Dorchester-on-Thames George Hotel

£75

Tel 0865 340404 Fax 0865 341620

I

High Street Dorchester-on-Thames Oxfordshire OX10 7HH

Map 15 D2

With a history spanning more than 500 years, the George is one of the oldest inns in the land. Focal point of the public area is a fine beamed bar. Bedrooms in the main building have a solid, old-fashioned feel, some cosy and snug under oak beams, two with four-posters. Other rooms have less character but are still very adequate. Small meetings and seminars are held in the two rooms of a self-contained annexe; the beamed Stable room is particularly characterful. ***Rooms** 18. Garden. Closed 1 week Christmas.* AMERICAN EXPRESS *Access, Diners, Visa.*

Dorking Forte Travelodge

£42

Tel 0306 740361

L

Reigate Road Dorking Surrey RH4 1QB

Map 15 E3

Half a mile east of Dorking town centre and 6 miles west of Reigate on the A25. Close to the M25. ***Rooms** 29.* AMERICAN EXPRESS *Access, Visa.*

Dorking Partners West Street

£80

Tel 0306 882826

R

2-4 West Street Dorking Surrey RH4 1BL

Map 15 E3

A 16th-century buiding, just off the main street, where partners Andrew Thomason (front of house) and Tim McEntire (in the kitchen) have created a charmingly intimate restaurant. Typical offerings on the fixed-price dinner menu might include boudin noir with apples and sage or smoked pink trout mousse with horseradish vinaigrette to start, followed by casserole of Cornish mullet and squid with tomato, garlic and basil or medallions of pork and lamb with mustard sauce and mint butter; brandy snap cigars filled with chocolate mousse or William pears in red wine jelly to finish. A la carte extends to more involved dishes such as soufflé and soup of smoked Finnan haddock, ravioli of mushrooms and herbs with vegetable spaghetti, and duck breast marinated with mango and soy and served with stir-fried Oriental vegetables and noodles. Lunchtime menus offer particularly good value. No-smoking area (dinner only). Seven dessert wines are served by the glass. ***Seats** 45. Private Room 30. L 12.30-2 D 7.30-9.30. Closed L Sat, D Sun, all Mon, Bank Holidays. Set L £9.95 Set D £19.95.* AMERICAN EXPRESS *Access, Diners, Visa.*

Dorking — White Horse — 62% — £80

Tel 0306 881138 Fax 0306 887241 — **H**

High Street Dorking Surrey RH14 1BE — **Map 15 E3**

Town-centre hotel developed from an old coaching inn. Oak beams and log fires give a cosy, traditional feel to the day rooms, while in summer the patio comes into its own. Good modern bedrooms. Families are well catered for. There's a choice of meeting and syndicate rooms holding up to 60 delegates. Leave the M25 at Junction 9 on to the A24. Forte Heritage. ***Rooms** 68. Garden, outdoor swimming pool.* AMERICAN EXPRESS *Access, Diners, Visa.*

Dorking — Places of Interest

Polesden Lacey (NT) Nr Dorking Tel 0372 58203 or 52048.
Thorndike Theatre Leatherhead Tel 0372 376211.

Dorrington — Country Friends — £65

Tel 0743 718707 — **RR**

Dorrington nr Shrewsbury Shropshire SY5 7JD — **Map 6 A4**

A half-timbered house turned into a comfortable restaurant with rooms. Chef-patron Charles Whittaker cooks with Timothy Greaves, producing such dishes as a trio of salmon (smoked, marinated and roasted), smoked goose with mango and an onion marmalade, spinach-stuffed rabbit with a redcurrant sauce, calf's liver with balsamic vinegar sauce and a daily fish dish. Puddings are typified by queen of puddings with a gin and lime ice cream, banoffi pie, pecan and maple syrup ice cream, and hot white chocolate soufflé. Good British cheeses are served with home-made walnut and sultana bread. Simple, no-choice (except at pudding stage) fixed-price menu might include blue cheese soufflé and strips of chicken in a mushroom sauce accompanied by pasta. Particularly good light lunches are served in the bar. No smoking in restaurant while others are eating. ***Seats** 45. Parties 60. L 12-2 D 7-9. Closed Sun & Mon, Bank Holidays, last week Jul, first week Oct. Set meals £16.90.* AMERICAN EXPRESS *Access, Visa.*

Rooms — £45

Three good-quality coach-house bedrooms are attractive with antiques, if sparing with extras. Two are not en suite. None have phones or TVs. Room price includes breakfast of Bucks Fizz and scrambled eggs with smoked salmon.

Dovedale — Izaak Walton Hotel — 59% — £95

Tel 033 529 555 Fax 033 529 539 — **H**

Dovedale nr Ashbourne Derbyshire DE6 2AY — **Map 6 C3**

A splendidly located hilltop hotel on the Duke of Rutland's estates; its 17th-century farmhouse building, where Izaak Walton once stayed, affords rolling views of Thorpe Cloud and Dovedale in the Peak District Park. Fly fishing is available on the River Dove which flows through the estate. Leather chesterfield sofas and open fires add comfort and warmth to the public rooms; bedrooms are more noteworthy for the vistas without than the space within. Conference suite for 60. Under-16s stay free in parents' room. ***Rooms** 34. Helipad.* AMERICAN EXPRESS *Access, Diners, Visa.*

Dovedale — Peveril of the Peak — 60% — £102

Tel 033 529 333 Fax 033 529 507 — **H**

Thorpe Dovedale nr Ashbourne Derbyshire DE6 2AW — **Map 6 C3**

At the foot of the 900ft Thorpe Cloud mountain in the heart of the Peak District, Peveril of the Peak has been attracting ramblers and country lovers for over 100 years. Probably the original Thorpe Rectory, its origins are obscure, but much local Derbyshire stone is evident in the public rooms. Bedrooms are traditional. The Dovedale Centre caters for meetings of up to 45. Forte Heritage. ***Rooms** 47. Garden.* AMERICAN EXPRESS *Access, Diners, Visa.*

Dover **Forte Posthouse** **63%** **£68**

Tel 0304 821222 Fax 0304 825576 **H**

Singledge Lane Whitfield Dover Kent CT16 3LF **Map 11 D5**

Modern low-riser on the Whitfield roundabout alongside the A2, 3 miles from the ferry terminal. Children up to 16 stay free in parents' room. 24hr lounge menu. ***Rooms** 67. Garden.* AMERICAN EXPRESS *Access, Diners, Visa.*

Dover **Moat House** **66%** **£75**

Tel 0304 203270 Fax 0304 213230 **H**

Townwall Street Dover Kent CT16 1SZ **Map 11 D5**

A seafront hotel catering well for both business and leisure visitors. Large beds in spacious bedrooms. Banqueting/conference facilities for 120/150. ***Rooms** 79. Indoor swimming pool.* AMERICAN EXPRESS *Access, Diners, Visa.*

Dover **Travel Inn** **£43**

Tel 0304 213339 Fax 0304 214504 **L**

Folkestone Road Dover Kent CT15 7AB **Map 11 D5**

Less than 10 minutes drive from the cross-Channel Ferry Port. ***Rooms** 30.* AMERICAN EXPRESS *Access, Diners, Visa.*

Dover **Places of Interest**

Tourist Information Tel 0304 205108.
Dover Castle Tel 0304 201628.

Driffield **Bell Hotel** **£91**

Tel 0377 46661 Fax 0377 43228 **I**

Market Place Driffield Humberside YO25 7AP **Map 7 E1**

Period charm and modern amenities combine in a coaching inn that's more than 250 years old. Large conference and function facilities are in the restored Old Town Hall, and further conversion houses a leisure complex with a small pool. Day rooms include the 18th-century wood-panelled Oak Room, the flagstoned Old Corn Exchange buffet/bar and a residents' lounge. Bedrooms boast antique furniture and up-to-date comforts. No children under 12. No dogs. ***Rooms** 14. Garden, indoor swimming pool, spa bath, steam room, sauna, solarium, squash. Closed 25-27 Dec.* AMERICAN EXPRESS *Access, Diners, Visa.*

Driffield **Places of Interest**

Burton Agnes Hall Tel 026 289 324.
Sledmere House and Gardens Sledmere Tel 0377 86208.

Droitwich **Forte Travelodge** **£42**

Tel 0527 86545 **L**

Rashwood Hill Droitwich Hereford & Worcester WR9 8DA **Map 14 B1**

Half a mile west of Junction 5 on the M5 and 2 miles north of Droitwich on the A38. ***Rooms** 32.* AMERICAN EXPRESS *Access, Visa.*

Droitwich Spa — Chateau Impney — 70% — £80

Tel 0905 774411 Fax 0905 772371 — **H**

Droitwich Spa Hereford & Worcester WR9 0BB — **Map 14 B1**

Chateau Impney was built in the French style around 1875, but while the well-tended gardens and surrounding 120 acres of parkland buttress an impressive grandeur, all other associations with things pastoral and aristocratic no longer apply. Proximity to Junction 5 of the M5 has pushed the premises here almost exclusively towards large residential conferences and functions (for up to 500 delegates). A few fine features survive, noticeably a magnificent carved wood staircase and high ceilings supported by marble columns. Main-house bedrooms, though spacious, are bland and have incongruously compact bathrooms while the separate Impney Court building offers newer but smaller accommodation. Nine apartments are also in a separate block. Banqueting facilities (for up to 400) are on a grand scale. Children and dogs are not really welcomed. Impney Hotels. ***Rooms*** *114. Garden, sauna, solarium, gymnasium, tennis, games room, helipad. Closed Christmas.* AMERICAN EXPRESS *Access, Diners, Visa.*

Droitwich Spa — Raven Hotel — 66% — £140

Tel 0905 772224 Fax 0905 772371 — **H**

St Andrews Street Droitwich Spa Hereford & Worcester WR9 8DU — **Map 14 B1**

Specialising in conferences and banqueting (for up to 150/250), the Raven also takes very good care of private guests, putting a premium on courtesy and professionalism. It's a handsome timber-framed building, parts of it going back to the 16th century. Overnight accommodation is more up-to-date than the exterior might suggest. All the bedrooms have recently been refurbished. ***Rooms*** *72. Garden.* AMERICAN EXPRESS *Access, Diners, Visa.*

Droitwich Spa — Places of Interest

Norbury Theatre Friar Street Tel 0905 770154.
Hanbury Hall (NT) Tel 052 784 214.
Droitwich Heritage Centre Tel 0905 774312.

Dudley — Forte Travelodge — £42

Tel 0384 481579 — **L**

Dudley Road Dudley West Midlands DY5 1LQ — **Map 6 B4**

Situated on the A461 at Brierley Hill, 3 miles west of Dudley towards Stourbridge, very close to Merry Hill centre. No adjacent restaurant facilities. ***Rooms*** *32.* AMERICAN EXPRESS *Access, Visa.*

Dulverton — Ashwick House — 68% — £112*

Tel 0398 23868 — **HR**

Dulverton Somerset TA22 9QD — **Map 13 D2**

Richard Sherwood runs the quietest of houses in deep country on the fringe of Exmoor – turn left at the Post Office in Dulverton, drive up to the moor, turn left after the cattle grid and follow the hotel sign. Constructed of Wellington brick in 1901, the house has a William Morris interior still boasting original wallpapers; although the present reconstruction dates only from 1980, an evocative Edwardian atmosphere has carefully been retained. Thus, beside your turned-down bed you'll find a goodnight sweet and an Edward Bear hot-water bottle. Bedrooms are spacious, with lovely parkland views and rather dated, chintzy decor. Fine days start with breakfast on the terrace. Sweeping lawns lead down to water gardens, thus no children under 8. No dogs. *Half-board terms. ***Rooms*** *6. Garden. No credit cards.*

Restaurant — £60

Richard's capable one-man show extends to the kitchen and dinner, when a named, hand-written scroll menu is presented to each diner. A typical recent meal comprised tomato and corn soup (Roquefort mousse as an alternative) preceding boned quail in a pastry nest, pork fillet stuffed with sorrel and spinach, then a choice of two puddings or cheese. Far from grand, the food mirrors the intimacy of the surroundings, as residents readily become acquainted. Non-residents should book early and discuss requirements. ***Seats** 30. Private Room 12. L (Sun only) 12.30-1.45 D 7.15-8.30. Set Sun L £12.75 Set D £18.95.*

Dulverton — Carnarvon Arms — 60% — £90

Tel 0398 23302 Fax 0398 24022 — **H**

Dulverton Somerset TA22 9AE — **Map 13 D2**

Purpose-built for the 4th Earl of Carnarvon in 1874, the Carnarvon Arms is very much geared to walkers, horse-riders (stabling if you bring your own, hunters and ponies available at a nearby establishment) and particularly fishermen, with just over five miles of trout and salmon fishing on the rivers Exe and Barle. The lounges are large, old-fashioned and relaxing, with open fires, splendid views and flower displays. Bedrooms are modest but comfortable enough. Families can eat informally in the Buttery Bar and children up to 15 stay free in their parents' room between October and May; early supper (5pm) in the Gun Room for juniors. ***Rooms** 25. Garden, outdoor swimming pool, tennis, fishing, stabling, snooker. Access, Visa.*

Dunbridge — Mill Arms Inn — £50

Tel 0794 340401 — **R**

Dunbridge nr Romsey Hampshire SO51 0LF — **Map 4 C3**

New owners have brought a smart new cream and green facelift to this village pub opposite the Mottisfont (Dunbridge) railway station. The refurbishment extends to the restaurant with its non-smoking conservatory extension, where new young chef David Mitchell produces good, freshly cooked dishes – even if garnishes can sometimes be a bit pub-like with cress on all the main dishes. Chicken and pork terrine with redcurrant jelly, Caesar salad, monkfish with white wine sauce, magret of duck with port and grape sauce, rack of lamb with herb crust and tarragon and tomato jus and steaks show the range. ***Seats** 60. Private Room 40. L 12-2 (Sun to 2.30) D 7-10 (Fri & Sat to 10.30).* AMERICAN EXPRESS *Access, Diners, Visa.*

Dunchurch — Forte Travelodge — £42

Tel 0788 521538 — **L**

A45 London Road Thurlaston Dunchurch nr Rugby Warwickshire CV23 9LG — **Map 7 D4**

Off the M45, on the A45 westbound, 3 miles south of Rugby town centre; 8 miles east of Coventry. ***Rooms** 40.* AMERICAN EXPRESS *Access, Visa.*

Consult page 16 for a full list of starred restaurants

Dunkirk — Petty France Hotel — 65% — £94

Tel 0454 238361 Fax 0454 238768 — **H**

Dunkirk Badminton Avon GL9 1AF — **Map 13 F1**

Eye-catching gardens alongside the A46 (4 miles north of M4 junction 18) provide both the setting for Petty France's well-proportioned Georgian house and the floral displays which adorn the hall and lounge. Accommodation is divided between the main house and a converted stable block; a traditional feel with period furniture and floral fabrics in the former gives way to cottagey curtains and lightwood fittings in the stable rooms. ***Rooms** 20. Garden.* AMERICAN EXPRESS *Access, Diners, Visa.*

Dunstable **Forte Travelodge** **£42**

Tel 0525 211177 **L**

A5 Watling Street Hockliffe Dunstable Bedfordshire LU7 9LZ **Map 15 E1**

On the A5, 3 miles north of Dunstable. ***Rooms** 28.* AMERICAN EXPRESS *Access, Visa.*

Dunstable **Places of Interest**

Tourist Information Tel 0582 471012.
Whipsnade Wildlife Park Tel 0582 872171.

Dunstable **Old Palace Lodge** **66%** **£100**

Tel 0582 662201 Fax 0582 696422 **H**

Church Street Dunstable Bedfordshire LU5 4RT **Map 15 E1**

Creeper climbs thickly over a hotel developed from a building believed to date back to the Lodge of the Royal Palace of Dunstable, around 1100. In the absence of a lounge, the comfortably furnished bar is the focal point of the day rooms. Bedrooms have good darkwood furniture, breakfast or coffee tables and armchairs or sofas. Leave the M1 at junction 11. ***Rooms** 49.* AMERICAN EXPRESS *Access, Diners, Visa.*

Dunster **Luttrell Arms** **64%** **£107**

Tel 0643 821555 Fax 0643 821567 **H**

High Street Dunster nr Minehead Somerset TA24 6SG **Map 13 E1**

A creeper-clad hotel of great historical interest, built in the 15th century as a guest house for the monks of Cleeve Abbey. Impressive architectural features include a superb Gothic hall (now the lounge) with hammer-beam roof and gargantuan fireplace, and a timbered Tudor bar in the former kitchen. Bedrooms offer solid 20th-century comforts and functional modern bathrooms. Forte Heritage. ***Rooms** 27. Garden, garage.* AMERICAN EXPRESS *Access, Diners, Visa.*

Dunster **Place of Interest**

Dunster Castle and Gardens (NT) Nr Minehead Tel 0643 821314.

Durham **Royal County Hotel** **67%** **£110**

Tel 091-386 6821 Fax 091-386 0704 **H**

Old Elvet Durham Co Durham DH1 3JN **Map 5 E3**

A large business-orientated hotel created from a series of Jacobean town houses, close to the cathedral and castle. Attractively-decorated bedrooms all have a mini-bar and a trouser press among the usual extras. Fine leisure facilities (with views over the River Wear) attract weekend guests. Children under 14 free in parents' room. Swallow Hotels. ***Rooms** 150. Indoor swimming pool, spa bath, sauna, solarium, gymnasium, beauty and hair salons, coffee shop (7am-9.30pm).* AMERICAN EXPRESS *Access, Diners, Visa.*

Durham **Places of Interest**

Tourist Information Tel 091-384 3720.
Auckland Castle Bishop Auckland Tel 0388 601627.
Spectrum Leisure Centre Dry Ski Slope Willington Tel 0388 747000.
Botanic Garden University of Durham Tel 091-374 2671.
Durham Castle Tel 091-374 3863.
Durham Light Infantry Museum and Durham Arts Centre Tel 091-384 2214.
Durham Cathedral Tel 091-386 4266.
Durham Ice Rink Tel 091-386 4065.
Durham Country Cricket Club Houghton-le-Spring Tel 091-512 0178.

Duxford — Duxford Lodge — 65% — £85

Tel 0223 836444 Fax 0223 832271 — HR

Ickleton Road Duxford nr Cambridge Cambridgeshire CB2 4RU — Map 15 F1

The hotel enjoys a peaceful setting in its own well-tended grounds in the sleepy village of Duxford, a short distance south of Cambridge and one mile from Junction 10 of the M11. The exterior is as inviting as the interior is comfortable and homely. The spacious bar contrasts with the small residents' lounge, both of which are furnished in attractive soft autumnal colour schemes. Walls are decorated with an extensive collection of fighter aircraft pictures – both prints and paintings, appropriate as the Imperial War Museum's Duxford Airfield is only a short distance away. Bedrooms, of which four are in an attractive garden wing, are all of a good size and neatly furnished. Colour schemes are restful and decor well maintained. Top-floor bedrooms have characterful sloping ceilings. Four of the bathrooms have bidets. Staff try their best to please. ***Rooms** 15. Garden. Closed 26-31 Dec.* AMERICAN EXPRESS *Access, Diners, Visa.*

Restaurant — £50

A handsome light-oak dado-panelled dual-aspect dining room where Ron Craddock, formerly at the *Saffron Hotel*, Saffron Waldon, produces a menu that is wide-ranging, mostly of classical French bourgeois cooking but with a few Far Eastern touches such as deep-fried crab croquettes served on a bed of mango and lime fired with a hint of chili. Combinations and flavours are carefully thought out as in a tender, plump supreme of chicken cooked in a white wine and cream sauce infused with a fragrantly subtle hint of lavender. Other dishes are more familiar: Bressingham duckling with a tangy Cointreau and orange sauce or a pink-roasted rack of lamb with a redcurrant, orange and port wine sauce. Excellent desserts include a selection of home-made ice creams of which the English lavender is quite outstanding (see Dessert of the Year regional winners pages). ***Seats** 36. Parties 12. Private Room 36. L 12-2 D 7-9.30. Closed L Sat. Set L £9 (Sun) & £13 Set D £13.*

Easington — Grinkle Park — 70% — £80

Tel 0287 640515 Fax 0287 641278 — H

Easington Loftus nr Saltburn-by-Sea Cleveland TS13 4UB — Map 5 E5

Sweeping lawns and mature pines and rhododendrons surround a formidable mansion set in parkland just off the A174. The atmosphere inside is refined and quietly elegant. The delightful Camellia Room, with picture windows, festoon blinds and wicker seating, has camellias actually growing up through the floor, and in the foyer-bar the roaring winter fire is reflected in the darkwood panelling. Bedrooms are named after local flora, birds and places; they're stylishly decorated, with light, restful colour schemes. ***Rooms** 20. Garden, tennis, fishing, snooker.* AMERICAN EXPRESS *Access, Diners, Visa.*

East Boldon — Forsters — £62

Tel 091-519 0929 — R

2 St Bedes Station Road East Boldon Tyne & Wear NE36 0LE — Map 5 E2

Close to the A814 Sunderland to Gateshead road in the centre of Boldon, Barry Forster's eponymous restaurant with a distinctive bottle-green exterior stands in a small row of shops with limited parking at the front. Comprising a single room with a bar occupying the corner, it has pretty, peachy pastel decor. The few tables are quite closely spaced but this does not detract from the place's comfort and appeal. An eclectic menu of imaginative and enjoyable food is offered. Starters range from a toasted muffin with smoked salmon, poached egg and hollandaise to chicken liver parfait with brandy, herbs and a Cumberland sauce. Main dishes include roast medallions of venison with peppercorns and redcurrants, best end of lamb with herbs and French mustard and a selection of fresh fish. Good cheeses come with grapes, celery and walnuts as well as a glass of port.

See over

Sweets include a traditional crème brulée or warm sponge pudding with hot toffee sauce and vanilla ice cream. Friendly service is provided by Sue Forster. ***Seats** 28. D 7-10.30. Closed Sun & Mon.* AMERICAN EXPRESS *Access, Diners, Visa.*

East Boldon Places of Interest

South Shields Tourist Information Tel 091-454 6612.
Old Customs House Tel 091-454 0269.
Souter Lighthouse (NT) Whitburn Tel 091-529 3161.

East Buckland Lower Pitt £50

Tel & Fax 0598 760243 **RR**

East Buckland Barnstaple Devon EX32 0TD **Map 13 D2**

"A retreat from modern living in a peaceful location", run by Suzanne and Jerome Lyons since 1978, Lower Pitt is an old stone farmhouse two miles off the A361 North Devon link road. Suzanne uses vegetables from her own garden in season on tempting dinner menus (served in a bright conservatory dining room extension) that offer an unusually wide choice of dishes (eight at each stage). Local farm ingredients are put to good use in dishes such as pan-fried loin of pork with apples, shallots and a cider and cream sauce, plus there are diverse influences ranging from Kashmiri lamb to stir-fried prawns and Sicilian cassata cake. Good West Country cheeses and sticky toffee and date pudding with butterscotch sauce. Over twenty half bottles on the wine list. Three tables outside on a terrace in good weather. No smoking in restaurant. No children under 5 after 8.30pm. ***Seats** 32. Private Room 14. D only 7-8.30. Closed Sun & Mon (except residents), 25 & 26 Dec.* AMERICAN EXPRESS *Access, Visa.*

Rooms £100*

Three double rooms, one with bath, two with shower, are available for diners. Home-made muesli and maramalade plus local sausages for breakfast. No phones, TVs, children under 5 or dogs. *Half-board only.

East Dereham King's Head £48

Tel 0362 693842 Fax 0362 693776 **I**

Norwich Street East Dereham Norfolk NR19 1AD **Map 10 C1**

A modest, but immaculately kept 17th-century coaching inn near the town centre. A cosy red-carpeted bar, busy with locals, looks out past the patio to a bowling green beyond. Spotless bedrooms, some in a converted stable block, offer tea-making kits, and remote-control TVs; twelve of the rooms have neat en-suite bathrooms. ***Rooms** 15. Garden, tennis, bowling.* AMERICAN EXPRESS *Access, Diners, Visa.*

East Dereham Phoenix Hotel 59% £77

Tel 0362 692276 Fax 0362 691752 **H**

Church Street East Dereham Norfolk NR19 1DL **Map 10 C1**

Bright redbrick 60s' hotel in the centre of town. Neat, practical bedrooms and function/conference suite accommodating up to 160. Forte Heritage. ***Rooms** 23.* AMERICAN EXPRESS *Access, Diners, Visa.*

East Grinstead Gravetye Manor 84% £200

Tel 0342 810567 Fax 0342 810080 **HR**

Vowels Lane East Grinstead West Sussex RH19 4LJ **Map 11 B5**

The civilised hospitality and gracious charm of Peter Herbert and staff (for whom nothing is too much trouble) continue to provide an object lesson in how a country house hotel should be run. The care and attention to every last detail both within the splendidly transformed Elizabethan stone mansion (built in 1598) and in the 1000 acres of grounds is perfectly illustrated in the new wing (where four immaculate bedrooms were recently added) and in the time and expense involved in restoring the William Robinson English garden to its former glory. Flower displays grace the gracious day rooms, which include a really delightful sitting room with oak panelling and an ornate moulded ceiling, and the entrance hall – now much brighter than in the past – with carefully selected chair patterns. Supplementing the delightful bedrooms (several of which have almost doubled in size and hugely benefited from recent refurbishment), the spacious new rooms, beautifully designed and each with its own personal style, are named after trees; the comfortable beds, antique furniture and sumptuous fabrics are models of good taste; books, magazines, post cards, bedside radios and TVs concealed behind tapestry screens are among a long list of thoughtful extras. The new bathrooms, too, with his and her washbasins, bidet and power shower over the bath provide every conceivable need, and are havens of comfort. No children under 7, but babes in arms welcome – cots and baby-listening provided. Fly fishing on the lake between May and September. No dogs in the hotel; kennels at the head of the drive. The hotel stands 5 miles south-west of East Grinstead off the B2110 at West Hoathly sign. ***Rooms** 18. Garden, fishing. Access, Visa.*

Restaurant ★↑ £105

Chef Stephen Morey continues Gravetye's tradition of consistency, set by the many eminent chefs who have worked here over the years. He achieves admirable results with menus that are a delightful balance of the modern and the traditional, offering light and robust dishes with natural and complex flavours, plus attention to detail, both in presentation and accuracy of cooking; descriptions are, refreshingly, all in plain English. Fish always features prominently – perhaps a ragout of seafood with Sauternes and grapes or a salad of shrimps with olive oil, garlic, courgettes and peppers to start, followed by grilled pavé of cod with fennel sauce or poached fillet of brill in red wine on daily table d'hote menus. Smoked salmon is from their own smoke-house and a dish of poached hen's eggs with pan-fried foie gras, truffles and Madeira sauce shows that there is no shying away from luxurious ingredients. Quail and pigeon paté en croute is likely to reward the adventurous and traditional main courses – from steamed skate wing with caper and tarragon mousse to roast fillet of Scottish beef topped with bone marrow and served with a rich burgundy jus – are well executed. Leaving room for desserts will also reap dividends: passion fruit soufflé is worth the 20 minutes' wait and crisp chocolate leaves layered with chestnut mousse and served on a caramel sauce shows that the attention to detail carries right on to the end of a meal; angels on horseback (oysters and bacon on toast with cayenne pepper) is among the savouries and cheeses are exceptional. To crown such a wonderful, ceremoniously grand meal there are aged ports and dessert wines by the glass. The marvellous wine list has been carefully compiled and nurtured over the years, and offers the very best. Perhaps surprisingly (for a hotel of this class), there are several excellent bottles under £20; winner of this year's Cellar of the Year, following last year's Californian Cellar of the Year award. Service is outstanding – the staff are immaculate in every sense. Note the addition of 17½% value added tax; all menu prices exclude vat but *do* include service. No smoking. ***Seats** 42. Parties 8. Private Room 18. L 12.30-2 D 7.30-9.30 (Sun to 9). ClosedD 25 Dec. Set L £20 (+vat) Set D £24 (+vat).*

East Grinstead — Woodbury House — 67% — £75

Tel 0342 313657 Fax 0342 314801 — **H**

Lewes Road East Grinstead West Sussex RH19 3UD — **Map 11 B5**

Half a mile south of the town, on the main A22, stands this small and attractively decorated hotel, under new management this year. Late-Victorian in construction, it now boasts a chintzy lounge and conservatory dining room with a lovely summer patio, a private boardroom for meetings or dinners (max 20), and gracious bedrooms, each individual

See over

in style and decor and most with garden and countryside views. Children under 7 stay free in parents' room. ***Rooms** 14. Garden, coffee shop (9.30am-10pm).* AMERICAN EXPRESS *Access, Diners, Visa.*

East Grinstead — Places of Interest

Hammerwood Park Tel 0342 850594 or 088 385 2366.
Lingfield Park Racecourse Tel 0342 834800.

East Horsley — Thatchers Resort Hotel — 62% — £100

Tel 0483 284291 Fax 0483 284222 — **H**

Epsom Road East Horsley Surrey KT24 6TB — **Map 15 E3**

Weddings and conferences are the staple business at this attractive mock-Tudor hotel set back from the road behind a lovely garden. Main public area is a comfortable open-plan bar lounge beyond a spacious parquet-floored reception area. Choose from prettily decorated accommodation in the main house, smaller motel-style rooms around the open-air pool and a few more cottagey bedrooms in an adjacent building. ***Rooms** 59. Garden, outdoor swimming pool, helipad.* AMERICAN EXPRESS *Access, Diners, Visa.*

East Stoke — Kemps Country House Hotel — 56% — £64

Tel 0929 462563 Fax 0929 405287 — **H**

East Stoke nr Wareham Dorset BH20 6AL — **Map 14 B4**

A quiet country hotel converted from a Victorian rectory, situated on the A352 between Wareham and Wool. Best accommodation is provided by six spacious pine-furnished rooms in a separate block. Some have whirlpool baths, and one boasts a modern four-poster. Children up to seven stay free in parents' room. Banqueting/conference facilities for 120/60. No dogs. ***Rooms** 15. Garden.* AMERICAN EXPRESS *Access, Diners, Visa.*

East Stoke — Places of Interest

Athelhampton House and Gardens Athelhampton Tel 0305 848363.
Clouds Hill (NT) Near Wool Tel 0305 267992 *Cottage home of T E Lawrence.*
The Tank Museum Bovington Camp Nr Wool Tel 0929 403329 or 403463.

Eastbourne — Cavendish Hotel — 68% — £70

Tel & Fax 0323 410222 — **H**

Grand Parade Eastbourne East Sussex BN21 4DH — **Map 11 B6**

Well-maintained and imposing seafront hotel with an unsympathetic balconied modern corner extension. Large banqueting facilities (for up to 350) plus conferences for up to 150. Guests have complimentary use of the nearby David Lloyd sports and leisure club. Families are made welcome with helpful amenities provided; children up to the age of 7 are accommodated free in parents' room. ***Rooms** 112. Games room.* AMERICAN EXPRESS *Access, Diners, Visa.*

Eastbourne — Grand Hotel — 75% — £120

Tel 0323 412345 Fax 0323 412233 — **HR**

King Edward's Parade Eastbourne East Sussex BN21 4EQ — **Map 11 B6**

Sound management and smart, committed staff try hard to keep up the grand image and reputation for good service at a whitewashed, seafront establishment that dates back to Victorian times. Marble pillars, crystal chandeliers, vast corridors and high-domed day rooms evoke a more leisurely, bygone age of spacious and gracious hotels. Some of the sea-facing bedrooms have balconies and are huge, with bright furniture and up-to-date fabrics, but not all are as smart or as generous in size. 24hr room service, comprehensive leisure and exercise facilities, themed weekend breaks and children's hostesses keep the Grand apace with its more modern competitors. Families are well catered for. Function facilities for up to 400. De Vere Hotels. ***Rooms** 164. Garden, indoor & outdoor swimming pools, spa bath, sauna, solarium, beauty & hairdressing salons, keep-fit equipment, snooker.* AMERICAN EXPRESS *Access, Diners, Visa.*

Mirabelle Restaurant

£67

Imaginative menus executed with flair and served by polished and professional staff in elegant surroundings. Fixed-price lunch (2-or 3-course) and dinner (4-course, priced by choice of main course) menus offer a small choice of dishes that include a daily roast served from a silver trolley. In addition, an à la carte offers classic dishes with modern touches. Cheeses are accompanied by home-made bread and there's a choice of traditional desserts. Longish list of wines includes half a dozen English wines and a choice of 16 brandies. ***Seats** 50. Private Room 20. L 12.30-2.30 D 7-10.30. Closed Sun & Mon, Bank Holidays, 2 weeks Jan, 2 weeks Aug. Set L £14/£17.50 Set D £27.50.*

is our symbol for an outstanding wine list.

Eastbourne — Queen's Hotel — 67%

£80 **H**

Tel 0323 722822 Fax 0323 731056

Marine Parade Eastbourne East Sussex BN21 3DY — **Map 11 B6**

Large white Victorian-built hotel overlooking the pier, sea and Carpet Gardens. Equally popular for conferences (up to 300 delegates) and leisure visits. Children up to 12 free in parents' room. Good free parking. De Vere. ***Rooms** 108. Games room (summer).* AMERICAN EXPRESS *Access, Diners, Visa.*

Eastbourne — Wish Tower Hotel — 66%

£80 **H**

Tel 0323 722676 Fax 0323 721474

King Edward's Parade Eastbourne East Sussex BN21 4EB — **Map 11 B6**

The hotel stands on the seafront opposite the Wish Tower, a martello tower that is now a Napoleonic and World War II museum. Bedrooms are in attractively up-to-date style, with modern comforts like double-glazing, and many enjoy sea views. Children up to 14 stay free in parents' room. Residents have free membership of the David Lloyd Tennis and Sports Leisure Centre. Principal Hotels. ***Rooms** 65.* AMERICAN EXPRESS *Access, Diners, Visa.*

Eastbourne — Places of Interest

Tourist Information Tel 0323 411400.
Michelham Priory Upper Dicker, Nr Hailsham Tel 0323 844224.
Towner Art Gallery and Local History Museum Tel 0323 411688.
Tower No 73 (The Wish Tower) Tel 0323 410440.
Eastbourne and Bexhill Beaches.
Devonshire Park Centre (Tennis) Tel 0323 415400.
Theatres and Concert Halls
Congress Theatre Devonshire Park Tel 0323 410000.
Devonshire Park Theatre Tel 0323 410000.
Drusillas Zoo Alfriston Tel 0323 870234.
Royal Hippodrome Theatre Tel 0323 410000.

Eastleigh — Forte Crest Southampton — 66%

£95 **H**

Tel 0703 619700 Fax 0703 643945

Leigh Road Eastleigh Hampshire SO5 5PG — **Map 15 D3**

Modern low-rise hotel just off A34. Features include a business centre and a leisure centre. Children's playground. ***Rooms** 120. Indoor swimming pool, spa bath, steam room, beauty salon.* AMERICAN EXPRESS *Access, Diners, Visa.*

Eastleigh Forte Travelodge

£42

Tel 0703 616813

L

Twyford Road Eastleigh nr Southampton Hampshire

Map 15 D3

On the Twyford Road, off the A335. 5 miles north of Southampton and 6 miles south of Winchester. ***Rooms*** *32.* AMERICAN EXPRESS *Access, Visa.*

Easton Grey Whatley Manor 73%

£112

Tel 0666 822888 Fax 0666 826120

H

Easton Grey Malmesbury Wiltshire SN16 0RB

Map 14 B2

Fine gardens, a terrace looking down the Avon valley and various leisure facilities in the grounds are among the many attractions of this delightful ivy-clad Cotswold manor house. A flagstone-floored foyer, library bar and a spacious pine-panelled drawing room are stylish without being intimidating, with log fires, antiques and scatter rugs contributing to the country house charm. Private dining areas accommodate 80 (conferences for 65), discreetly separate from the day rooms. Manor House, Tudor and Terrace wings accommodate a dozen of the best bedrooms, while in the more secluded Court House (where tea-makers replace room service) ten are conveniently located on the ground floor. ***Rooms*** *29. Garden, outdoor swimming pool, sauna, solarium, spa bath, games room, helipad.* AMERICAN EXPRESS *Access, Diners, Visa.*

Eccleshall St George Hotel

£55

Tel 0785 850300 Fax 0785 851452

I

Castle Street Eccleshall Staffordshire ST21 6DF

Map 6 B3

Behind the white-painted frontage of this 17th-century coaching inn is a mixture of modern and old that includes a well-equipped business centre and an inglenook fireplace in the bar – the focal point of the inn, with old beams and copper-topped tables. Bedrooms are kept in immaculate order and have plenty of character, some with fireplaces and exposed timbers. Small conferences are held in the first-floor Old Library room with bare brick walls and beams. ***Rooms*** *10.* AMERICAN EXPRESS *Access, Diners, Visa.*

Edenbridge Honours Mill Restaurant

£60

Tel 0732 866757

R

87 High Street Edenbridge Kent TN8 5AU

Map 11 B5

A converted mill is the charming setting for some careful French cooking from the kitchen of Martin Radmall. Well-balanced fixed-price menus are inclusive of coffee, petits fours and service; on weekday evenings an additional £25 menu is offered with simpler dishes and a smaller choice plus a half bottle of wine. Typifying the main menu are terrine of red mullet lining a salmon mousse, casserole of snails and wild mushrooms, sausage of lamb's sweetbreads on a bed of lentils, and a pot-au-feu of oxtail, salt pork, beef and confit of duck. Among the desserts you might find Sussex Pond pudding and fresh passion fruit and orange tart. The New World misses out on the otherwise decent if highly priced wine list. Children welcome for Sunday lunch. ***Seats*** *38. L 12.15-2 D 7.15-10. Closed L Sat, D Sun, all Mon, 1 week Christmas. Set L £14.50 (Sun £22.50) Set D £25.* AMERICAN EXPRESS *Access, Visa.*

We endeavour to be as up-to-the-minute as possible, but inevitably some changes to key personnel may occur at restaurants and hotels after the Guide goes to press.

Edenbridge — Places of Interest

Hever Castle Open Air Theatre Tel 0732 866114 *Open mid June-September.*
Hever Castle & Gardens Tel 0732 865224.
Chiddingstone Castle Chiddingstone Tel 0892 870347.

Egham — Great Fosters — 67% — £99

Tel 0784 433822 Fax 0784 472455 — **H**

Stroude Road Egham Surrey TW20 9UR — **Map 15 E2**

The imposing facade of this stately Elizabethan house sets the tone for the quintessentially English public rooms with their ornate plaster ceilings, oak panelling and carved antique furniture. The best are on the first floor and feature richly embroidered fabrics and tapestry wall hangings, but lack some of the extras now considered standard in this quality of country hotel. Other rooms are plainer – some in the house, others in the conference centre. Get to Egham then follow the brown Historical Interest signs marked Great Fosters. ***Rooms** 45. Garden, outdoor swimming pool, sauna, tennis, snooker.* AMERICAN EXPRESS® *Access, Diners, Visa.*

Egham — Runnymede Hotel — 74% — £145

Tel 0784 436171 Fax 0784 436340 — **H**

Windsor Road Egham Surrey TW20 0AG — **Map 15 E2**

Leave the M25 at junction 13 and follow signs on the A308 to find this modern hotel with 12½ acres of grounds on the banks of the Thames – a lovely setting. Bedrooms are either standard or Executive, the roomiest twin Executives having a double and a single bed; 47 bedrooms are in extension wings, which also house a leisure centre that includes a large pool and beauty therapy centre – popular attractions. The best rooms are those that overlook the river. Some of the superior rooms offer whirlpool baths. Public areas are open-plan, with the light, spacious lounge and the restaurant having picture windows that make the most of the setting. Large function facilities. Considerable tariff reductions at weekends, when families are well catered for. A hotel for all seasons, with a cosy warmth in winter and riverside terrace and gardens on which to enjoy the summer sun. Informal eating in Charlie Bell's brasserie includes an outdoor barbecue in summer. ***Rooms** 171. Garden, indoor swimming pool, gymnasium, spa bath, sauna, solarium, beauty and hair salon, snooker, tennis, coarse fishing, putting, helipad.* AMERICAN EXPRESS® *Access, Diners, Visa.*

Egham — Places of Interest

Guards Polo Club Windsor Great Park, Englefield Green Tel 0784 434212.
Thorpe Theme Park Chertsey Tel 0932 569393.

Elcot — Elcot Park — 67% — £100

Tel 0488 58100 Fax 0488 58288 — **HR**

Elcot nr Newbury Berkshire RG16 8NJ — **Map 15 D2**

Much-extended Georgian house set back from the A4, halfway between Newbury and Hungerford. It stands in 16 acres of Kennet Valley woodland, its latest bedroom wing and leisure centre linked to the original by an impressive south-facing conservatory. Up-to-date bedrooms rooms include some equipped for disabled guests. 18 rooms are contained in a separate mews courtyard. Under-16s stay free in parents' room. Resort Hotels. ***Rooms** 75. Garden, tennis, indoor swimming pool, spa bath, sauna, solarium, gymnasium, beauty salon, hot-air ballooning.* AMERICAN EXPRESS® *Access, Diners, Visa.*

See over

Orangery Restaurant

£70

Daily table d'hote and seasonal carte in the modern idiom from dependable chef Alex Robertson. Fresh sardines with a pesto sauce, medallions of pork with an orange and green peppercorn sauce, pot-roast pheasant, halibut with a parsley crust, brioche and sultana pudding, classic lemon tart, vegetarian choices, regional farmhouse cheeses and speciality teas. ***Seats*** *50. L 12.30-2 D 7.30-9.30. Set meals £17.*

Elton — Loch Fyne Oyster Bar & Restaurant

£40

Tel 0832 280298 — **R**

The Old Dairy Buildings Elton nr Peterborough Cambridgeshire PE8 5SG — **Map 7 E4**

100 yards from the A605 bypass to Oundle, eight miles from Peterborough, an informal seafood restaurant and retail outlet in a converted dairy building dating back to 1901. Scots pine, simple furnishings and the freshest seafood ingredients brought down from Scotland overnight. See also entries under Nottingham, and Cairndow (Scotland). ***Seats*** *85. Meals 9-9 (to 10 Fri & Sat). Closed 25 & 26 Dec, 1 Jan.* AMERICAN EXPRESS *Access, Visa.*

Ely — Forte Travelodge

£42

Tel 0353 668499 — **L**

Ely Cambridgeshire — **Map 10 B2**

On the roundabout at the junction of A10/A142. Situated on the outskirts of Ely, 15 miles north of Cambridge. ***Rooms*** *39.* AMERICAN EXPRESS *Access, Visa.*

Ely — Lamb Hotel 62%

£75

Tel 0353 663574 Fax 0353 666350 — **H**

2 Lynn Road Ely Cambridgeshire CB7 4EJ — **Map 10 B2**

Close to the Cathedral, the Lamb can trace its history back to the reign of Richard II, although the present building is of somewhat later date. Intensively refurbished in recent years, it now offers good, well-equipped accommodation in singles, doubles, family rooms and four-poster rooms. A choice of bars, one of which (the Fenman) is a popular local meeting place. Queens Moat Houses. ***Rooms*** *32.* AMERICAN EXPRESS *Access, Diners, Visa.*

Ely — Old Fire Engine House

£50

Tel 0353 662582 — **R**

25 St Mary's Street Ely Cambridgeshire CB7 4ER — **Map 10 B2**

The Old Fire Engine House was built in the 18th century, being converted into a restaurant and art gallery in 1968. The main room has an uneven tiled floor, kitchen tables and pew seating, others are more elegant. Home cooking is plain English in style and includes such stalwarts as ham and lentil soup, smoked salmon paté, pike or zander in season, chicken with sage and lemon, and hot game pie. The style continues with sweets such as syllabub or apple crumble. Few non-French wines on an inexpensive list, which is accompanied by informative notes. One room is reserved for non-smokers. ***Seats*** *55. Private Room 35. L 12.30-2 D 7.30-9. Closed D Sun, Bank Holidays, 2 weeks Christmas/New Year. Access, Visa.*

Ely — Places of Interest

Tourist Information Tel 0353 662062.
Ely Cathedral Tel 0353 667735.
Museums and Art Galleries

Ely Museum Tel 0353 666655.
The Stained Glass Museum North Triforium, Ely Cathedral Tel 0353 667735.
Oliver Cromwell's House Tel 0353 662062.

Emsworth — 36 On The Quay ↑ — £74

Tel 0243 375592 — R

The Quay South Street Emsworth Hampshire PO10 7EG — Map 15 D4

A pretty pale yellow restaurant in a cottagey old building right down by the quay. Everything is of the best quality here, from stylish silver-plated cutlery to elegant china. Chef Frank Eckermann offers fixed-price-only menus for both lunch (perhaps smoked halibut salad, chump end of lamb with tarragon cream sauce and bread-and-butter pudding) and dinner. The latter includes special dishes for two such as Gressingham duck, rib of beef bordelaise and poached lobster, all of which carry a small supplement. Desserts might include feuilleté of bananas or a hot soufflé of coconut and chocolate. ***Seats** 45. Parties 12. Private Room 12. L 12-2 D 7-10. Closed L Sat, D Sun, Bank Holidays, 1 week Jan, 2 weeks Sep. Set L £19 Set D £27.50.* AMERICAN EXPRESS *Access, Diners, Visa.*

Epping — Forte Posthouse — 63% — £68

Tel 0992 573137 Fax 0992 560402 — H

High Road Bell Common Epping Essex CM16 4DG — Map 11 B4

16th-century heritage still shows in the public rooms; bedrooms are in a modern wing. Banqueting for 85, conferences facilities for 100. ***Rooms** 79.* AMERICAN EXPRESS *Access, Diners, Visa.*

Erpingham — Ark — £45

Tel 0263 761535 — RR

The Street Erpingham Norfolk NR11 7QB — Map 10 C1

An old flint cottage set deep in rural Norfolk four miles north of Aylesham off the A140. Sheila Kidd is self-taught and her very individual cooking style shows many influences on the fixed-price, handwritten menus that change daily – from asparagus with Maltaise sauce and home-cured gravlax with dill sauce to Provençal beef daube and Turkish lamb. Aubergine three ways, hazelnut fettucine with mushroom sauce and chard, pork, duck liver and sorrel terrine with sweet and sour zucchini show that no time is wasted in the kitchen – or in the garden for that matter, where she grows many of her own vegetables and herbs. Vegetarian dishes are always available – discuss when booking. Several good bottles under £20 on the wine list and half a dozen sold by the glass. No smoking. ***Seats** 34. Private Room 20. L (Sun only) 12.30-2 D 7-9.30 (Sat to 10). Closed D Sun & Mon, all Tue in winter, part of Oct. Set L (Sun) £11.75 Set D £15/£18.50. No credit cards.*

Rooms — £95*

Three bedrooms, two with en-suite facilities, are available for overnight stays, but only to non-smokers. *Half-board terms only.

Esher — Good Earth — £55

Tel 0372 462489 — R

14-18 High Street Esher Surrey KT10 9RT — Map 15 E2

Reliable cooking in comfortable surroundings, with speedy, attentive service. The China-wide menu sticks mainly to familiar items, with the occasional slightly less usual dish such as salmon steak (steamed or pan-fried), beef with tangerine peel and hot sauce, bean curd with eight precious gems or a vegetarian combination called faked yellow fish

See over

comprising mashed split peas, Chinese mushrooms and spring onions. *See also outlets under London section. **Seats** 95. L 12-2.30 D 6-11 (Sun 12.30-10.30). Closed 24-27 Dec. Set L from £12 Set D from £16.* American Express *Access, Diners, Visa.*

Esher — Places of Interest

Chessington World of Adventures Tel 0372 727227.
Claremont Landscape Garden (NT) Tel 0372 69421.
Kempton Park Racecourse Tel 0932 782292.
Sandown Park Racecourse Tel 0372 463072.
Ham Polo Club 20 Queens Road Tel 081 398 3263.
Sandown Ski School Tel 0372 65588.

Eton — Antico — £55

Tel 0753 863977 Fax 0628 30045 — **R**

42 High Street Eton Berkshire SL4 6BD — **Map 15 E2**

The 18th-century building has been a post office, an auction room and an inn. For the past 20 years the owners have run an Italian restaurant serving a traditional menu of popular dishes, including ten variations on veal. ***Seats** 65. Parties 25. Private Room 25. L 12.30-2.30 D 7-10.30. Closed L Sat, all Sun, Bank Holidays.* American Express *Access, Diners, Visa.*

Eton — Christopher Hotel — £76

Tel 0753 852359 Fax 0753 830914 — **I**

110 High Street Eton Berkshire SL4 6AN — **Map 15 E2**

Former coaching inn on the High Street. Some bedrooms are in the main house, others in courtyard chalets all recently redecorated. Children up to the age of 12 stay free in their parents' room. Leave the M4 at junction 6 and follow Eton signs. The hotel is just beyond the College on the right. Dogs in courtyard rooms only. ***Rooms** 34.* American Express *Access, Diners, Visa.*

Evershot — Summer Lodge — 72% — £125

Tel 0935 83424 Fax 0935 83005 — **HR**

Evershot Dorchester Dorset DT2 0JR — **Map 13 F2**

Nigel and Margaret Corbett's peaceful Georgian home, with its picturesque sheltered garden, is a haven for outdoor types. There are miles of walks through Hardy country; grass and hard tennis courts and a heated outdoor swimming pool; guests can even hunt with the Cattistock. Fresh garden flowers embellish the lounge, bar and reading room, bedecked with pictures and ornaments to create a home from home. Spacious bedrooms with rattan furniture, armchair and settee have a similarly sunny feel, and the bathrooms are spotless. Arrive in time for home-baked afternoon tea and don't leave without sampling the super country breakfast. Private meetings by arrangement (max 25). Unsuitable for small children. ***Rooms** 17. Outdoor swimming pool, tennis. Closed 2 weeks Jan. Access, Visa.*

Restaurant — £78

Formal, yet relaxed dining in a series of rooms that overlook the gardens. Nigel Corbett is a welcoming host, overseeing the service from demure waitresses. Both à la carte and table d'hote menus are offered, with the likes of mussels, local Denhay ham with spiced plums, home-made soups, Gressingham duck breast on an apple and potato cake with a honey and ginger sauce, pan-fried fillet of gurnard or John Dory, kiwi fruit and almond roulade on a passion fruit sauce and farmhouse cheeses. The wine list is splendidly easy to use and has a good selection of half bottles. No smoking. ***Seats** 50. L 12.30-1.30 D 7.30-9. Set L £15 Set D £25.*

Set menu prices may not always include service or wine.

Eversley — New Mill Restaurant — £75

Tel 0734 732277 Fax 0734 328780 — **R**

New Mill Road Eversley Hampshire RG27 0RA — **Map 15 D3**

A converted riverside mill house complete with ducks, waterwheel and an idyllic setting, off the main road between Reading and Camberley. The Blackwater River runs gently by the restaurant, which boasts an open fireplace, wood-panelled ceilings and exposed beams. Robert Allen's cooking is mainly in a modern style, with dishes such as air-dried beef with chargrilled peppers and olives sitting happily alongside Loch Fyne smoked salmon and marinated herrings and crab bisque; similarly, fricassee of seafood with noodles and champagne sauce, Dover sole and ribeye steak with black peppercorn sauce are among the main courses, along with chargrilled dishes. The à la carte menu is supplemented by good-value, fixed-price lunches and dinners. British cheeses are served from a trolley with home-made walnut bread. The less formal, beamed *Grill Room* offers equally admirable food at more down-to-earth prices, including a good roast Sunday lunchtimes. Extensive, carefully-priced wine list. ***Seats** 80. Private Room 40. L 12-2 D 7-10 (Grill Room: Sun 12.30-8). Restaurant closed L Sat, all Sun & Mon. Grill Room closed L Sat, 26 & 27 Dec, 1 Jan. Set L £17.50 Set D £23.50.* AMERICAN EXPRESS *Access, Diners, Visa.*

Evesham — Evesham Hotel — 62% — £94

Tel 0386 765566 Fax 0386 765443 — **H**

Cooper's Lane off Waterside Evesham Hereford & Worcester WR11 6DA — **Map 14 C1**

The first and enduring impression of the Jenkinson family's modernised Tudor mansion set in 2½ acres (dominated by a large old cedar of Lebanon) is of fun, friendliness and a truly relaxed atmosphere. That feeling starts in the foyer, continues in the chintzy bar and is still strong in the bedrooms which are provided with all sorts of extras, from games and cards to teddy bears and rubber ducks. The whole caboodle is mildly eccentric and very friendly towards families – "well-behaved children are as welcome as well-behaved adults". Good-value buffet lunches, an unbelievably wordy, rambling carte plus a section of (their words) "plain ordinary boring (but good quality) food – it's often pleasant not to have your food mucked about". Incidentally, the wine list is also eccentric: nothing French, but everywhere else represented – even Tunisia, Brazil and Mexico. ***Rooms** 40. Garden, indoor swimming pool. Closed 25 & 26 Dec.* AMERICAN EXPRESS *Access, Diners, Visa.*

Evesham — Riverside Hotel — 68% — £72

Tel 0386 446200 Fax 0386 40021 — **HR**

The Parks Offenham Road Evesham Hereford & Worcester WR11 5JP — **Map 14 C1**

Check directions when booking, as this white pebbledash house is awkward to find. It is run by the amiable Willmotts and stands in three acres by the river Avon. On entering, a colourful fresco of river life greets guests, while downstairs an attractive lounge is decorated in corals and greens with plenty of comfortable seating. Bedrooms, with river views, are pretty and appealing, soft colours and co-ordinated fabrics being well employed. Staff are smartly attired, keen and obviously enjoy their jobs. Children up to 14 stay free in parents' room. No dogs. ***Rooms** 7. Garden. Access, Visa.*

Restaurant — £55

Fine views over the river Avon from the dining room, where Rosemary Willmott offers fixed-price, hand-written, daily-changing menus with a good choice of dishes that might encompass local black pudding with mustard sauce, cream of turbot soup with prawns, charcuterie, rack of lamb with roast parsnips, salmon grilled with lime, and venison with peppercorn, port and mushroom jus. Straightforward fare, interestingly cooked and presented – right through to puddings like treacle sponge

See over

or tangy passion fruit mousse with shortbread. Interesting British cheeses. No smoking. Lunch snacks in the bar (except Sundays). The list of liqueurs, Highland and Island malt whiskies, armagnacs and eaux de vie is exceptional. ***Seats** 40. L 12.30-2 (Sun to 1.30) D 7.30-9. Closed D Sun, all Mon. Set L £15.95 (£17.95 Sun) Set D £19.95.*

Evesham — Places of Interest

Tourist Information Tel 0386 446944.
Snowshill Manor (NT) Broadway Tel 0386 852410.

Exeter — Buckerell Lodge — 66% — £87

Tel 0392 52451 Fax 0392 412114 — H

157 Topsham Road Exeter Devon EX2 4SQ — **Map 13 D2**

A much-extended Regency house set in peaceful grounds on the B3182 a mile from the town centre. Bedrooms include Executive, Lady Executive and one with a spa bath. Children up to 12 stay free in parents' room. Two bars and several lounge areas. Meeting rooms and a purpose-built conference centre (for up to 60 delegates). ***Rooms** 54. Garden.*
AMERICAN EXPRESS Access, Diners, Visa.

Exeter — Forte Crest — 69% — £100

Tel 0392 412812 Fax 0392 413549 — H

Southernhay East Exeter Devon EX1 1QF — **Map 13 D2**

1989-built hotel with cathedral views from some of the bedrooms. Conference facilities for up to 180 delegates. 40 of the bedrooms, where children up to 16 stay free with parents, are reserved for non-smokers. ***Rooms** 110. Indoor swimming pool, gymnasium, sauna, spa bath, solarium.*
AMERICAN EXPRESS Access, Diners, Visa.

Exeter — Rougemont Hotel — 63% — £79

Tel 0392 54982 Fax 0392 420928 — H

Queen Street Exeter Devon EX4 3SP — **Map 13 D2**

Modernised Victorian hotel in the city centre. Its popular conference facilities include five suites for up to 300. Mount Charlotte Thistle. ***Rooms** 90. AMERICAN EXPRESS Access, Diners, Visa.*

Exeter — Royal Clarence — 71% — £98

Tel 0392 58464 Fax 0392 439423 — H

Cathedral Yard Exeter Devon EX1 1HD — **Map 13 D2**

On the green facing the 14th-century cathedral, the Royal Clarence claims to be the first inn in Britain to receive the title "hotel". Behind its Georgian facade the building contains several architectural styles and retains an atmosphere steeped in the past. Every one of the bedrooms is in Tudor, Georgian or Victorian style. A wealth of oak panelling, moulded friezes and covings, gilt-framed mirrors and period furniture contrive to unify the theme. By comparison, bathrooms are thoroughly modern, though smallish. The stately Georgian-style Clarence Room accommodates conferences and banquets for up to 150. No dogs. Queens Moat Houses. ***Rooms** 56. AMERICAN EXPRESS Access, Diners, Visa.*

Exeter — White Hart — 61% — £78

Tel 0392 79897 Fax 0392 50159 — H

South Street Exeter Devon EX1 1EE — **Map 13 D2**

An ancient inn at the heart of town, dating from the 15th century and originally a resting place for monks. It's built around an attractive cobbled courtyard, off which are various bars where exposed beams, timbers and bulging walls abound. The residents' lounge in the oldest part sports an uneven and unusual plasterwork ceiling. Much of the original structure of the stables can be seen in the reception area. Most bedrooms are in a modern extension and have a purpose-built look with functional fitted units. Six rooms have shower and WC only. *Bottlescrue Bill's* Wine Bar is off the car park and the cobbled wine garden comes into its own during good weather. No dogs. ***Rooms** 61.* AMERICAN EXPRESS *Access, Diners, Visa.*

Exeter Places of Interest

Tourist Information Tel 0392 265297.
The Barnfield Theatre Tel 0392 21951.
Northcott Theatre Stocker Road Tel 0392 56181.
Exeter Maritime Museum The Haven Tel 0392 58075.
Exeter Cathedral Tel 0392 55573.
Exeter Racecourse Tel 0392 832599.
Exeter Ski Club Tel 0392 211322.
Westpoint Showground Tel 0392 444777.
Historic Houses, Castles and Gardens
Killerton (NT) Tel 0392 881345.
University of Exeter Garden Tel 0392 263263.
Bickleigh Castle Tel 08845 363 *13 miles.*

Exmouth Imperial Hotel 60% £116

Tel & Fax 0395 274761 **H**

The Esplanade Exmouth Devon EX8 2SW **Map 13 E3**

Popular whitewashed Forte Heritage holiday hotel set in its own grounds on the esplanade. Children up to the age of 16 free in parents' room. ***Rooms** 57. Garden, outdoor swimming pool, tennis.* AMERICAN EXPRESS *Access, Diners, Visa.*

Exmouth Place of Interest

Budleigh Salterton Beach.

Eyton Marsh Country Hotel 67% £100

Tel 0568 613952 **HR**

Eyton Leominster Hereford & Worcester HR6 0AG **Map 14 A1**

Just north-west of Leominster, a haven of peace and tranquillity standing in an acre and a half of award-winning gardens. Martin and Jacqueline Gilleland run the house on informal and personable lines, greeting guests at their delightful home. Dating from the 14th century, the old hall is now a splendid lounge, sympathetically furnished and immensely relaxing. Bedrooms, all named after birds, are smallish but stylish, with pretty fabrics and pine furniture. The whole place has a wonderfully relaxed air and housekeeping is immaculate. No dogs. ***Rooms** 5. Garden. Access, Visa.*

Restaurant £70

Quality home cooking served in a pretty restaurant with views of the garden, where herbs are grown for the kitchen. Typical dishes on the fixed-price dinner menu include cream of seafood soup, leeks in puff pastry, sole and smoked salmon roulade and marinated saddle of venison with apple and cranberries. To finish, perhaps rhubarb tart with ginger meringue ice cream or a trio of lemon desserts. ***Seats** 24. L by arrangement D 7.30-9.30. Set D £27.50.*

Fairford Bull Hotel 60% £43

Tel 0285 712535 Fax 0285 713782 **H**

Market Place Fairford Gloucestershire GL7 4AA **Map 14 C2**

This ancient inn, once a monks' chanting house, owns private fishing rights on the river Colne, which is kept seasonally stocked with trout and grayling. Inside, there's a cosy little lounge and a stone-walled bar. *See over*

Corridors and many bedrooms feature sloping floors, oak beams and low ceilings. Owned by Arkell's Brewery. Conference facilities for up to 60 delegates. ***Rooms** 20. Garden, fishing.* AMERICAN EXPRESS *Access, Diners, Visa.*

Fairy Cross — Portledge Hotel — 62% — £67

Tel 0237 451262 Fax 0237 451717 — **H**

Fairy Cross nr Bideford Devon EX39 5BX — **Map 12 C2**

A Jacobean staircase, ancestral portraits and fine panelling and mouldings are among the period features. Boldly decorated day rooms, traditionally styled bedrooms, in which children up to 12 can stay free with parents. The Garden Restaurant is in its own seven-acre woodland site. ***Rooms** 35. Garden, outdoor swimming pool, tennis, crazy golf. Access, Visa.*

Fairy Cross — Place of Interest

Rosemoor Garden, The Royal Horticultural Society Nr Great Torrington Tel 0805 24067.

Falmouth — Falmouth Hotel — 63% — £92

Tel 0326 312671 Fax 0326 319533 — **H**

Castle Beach Falmouth Cornwall TR11 4NZ — **Map 12 B4**

Solid and imposing Victorian seaside hotel in French chateau style. Gardens are neat and trim and the day rooms, including a conservatory, are light and peaceful. Half the bedrooms have a view of the sea (other rooms overlook the river), and three Executive bedrooms have balconies and whirlpool baths. There are also self-catering cottages and apartments, and facilities for large-scale conferences and banquets (for up to 200), plus a leisure centre. Families with young children are admirably catered for. ***Rooms** 72. Garden, indoor swimming pool, sauna, spa bath, solarium, beauty & hair salon, putting, snooker.* AMERICAN EXPRESS *Access, Diners, Visa.*

Falmouth — Greenbank Hotel — 69% — £105

Tel 0326 312440 Fax 0326 211362 — **H**

Harbourside Falmouth Cornwall TR11 2SR — **Map 12 B4**

The call of the sea is strong at the Greenbank, which looks across the vast natural harbour to Flushing on the far bank. The picture-windowed bar and the traditionally appointed lounges make the most of the marvellous setting, as do the majority of the bedrooms, many of them named after former resident captains and their vessels. Children up to 10 stay free in parents' room. Directions: keep to the harbourside when approaching from Truro and follow the signs from the roundabout after Penryn. ***Rooms** 61. Garden, keep-fit equipment, sauna, solarium, beauty salon, hairdressing, sea fishing. Closed 24 Dec-6 Jan.* AMERICAN EXPRESS *Access, Diners, Visa.*

Falmouth — Pandora Inn — £37

Tel 0326 372678 — **R**

Restronguet Creek Mylor Bridge Falmouth Cornwall TR11 5ST — **Map 12 B4**

A thatched riverside pub named after the ill-fated naval ship sent to Tahiti to capture the Bounty mutineers. The captain returned to England where he bought the inn. "Catch of the day" produces a special that's always worth trying, and other dishes cover a straightforward range from chicken liver paté and baked mushrooms to pot-roasted pheasant, veal escalopes and sirloin steak. Also a bar menu daily, lunchtime and evening. Ask for directions when booking. ***Seats** 45. Private Room 10. D only 7-10 (Sun to 9.30). Access, Visa.*

Falmouth Royal Duchy Hotel 66% NEW

£99

Tel 0326 313042 Fax 0326 319420

H

Cliff Road Falmouth Cornwall TR11 4NX

Map 12 B4

Originally built in 1893, the hotel sits atop the cliffs between the town and Gyllyngvase beach commanding fine sea views. Public rooms range from sun lounge to spacious dining room with live entertainment during the summer season. A small leisure area has plenty of facilities, and bedrooms have Regency-style freestanding furniture and modern accessories (remote-control televisions). Bathrooms are clean and functional. Friendly staff and typical of the Brend hotel group. ***Rooms** 47. Garden, indoor swimming pool, children's pool, sauna, spa bath, solarium, games room.* AMERICAN EXPRESS *Access, Diners, Visa.*

Falmouth St Michael's Hotel 63%

£86

Tel 0326 312707 Fax 0326 211772

H

Stracey Road Falmouth Cornwall TR11 4NB

Map 12 B4

Located directly opposite Gyllyngvase beach this hotel provides basic yet comfortable accommodation for the tourist or business visitor. There's a spacious bar/lounge with a sun terrace which overlooks award-winning gardens. The whole place was looking a bit tired on a summer visit, and it is to be hoped that the new management will invest to restore standards. ***Rooms** 66. Garden, indoor swimming pool, keep-fit equipment, sauna, spa bath, solarium, games room.* AMERICAN EXPRESS *Access, Diners, Visa.*

Falmouth Seafood Bar

£45

Tel 0326 315129

R

Lower Quay Hill Falmouth Cornwall

Map 12 B4

Down a few steps in a steep passageway near the customs house quay, this lively bar serves the very freshest of seafood, from stir-fried crab claws and Helford oysters to lemon sole, skate, squid and lobster. Also steaks (sirloin or oyster-stuffed carpetbagger fillet) ***Seats** 24. Private Room 12. D only 7-11. Closed Sun in winter. Access, Visa.*

Falmouth Places of Interest

Tourist Information Tel 0326 312300.
Falmouth Arts Centre Church Street Tel 0326 314566.
Princess Pavillion Melville Road Tel 0326 311277.

Fareham Forte Posthouse 61% NEW

£68

Tel 0329 844644 Fax 0329 844666

H

Cartwright Drive Titchfield Fareham Hampshire PO15 5RS

Map 15 D4

One of the newest Posthouses with a leisure centre and a range of meeting rooms (up to 140 people theatre-style). Half the bedrooms are designated non-smoking. From M27 junction 9 take the A27 towards Fareham. ***Rooms** 126. Indoor swimming pool, gymnasium, sauna, solarium.* AMERICAN EXPRESS *Access, Diners, Visa.*

Fareham Red Lion Hotel 57%

£65

Tel 0329 822640 Fax 0329 823579

H

East Street Fareham Hampshire PO16 0BP

Map 15 D4

A Lansbury Group hotel equidistant from Portsmouth and Southampton. Originally a coaching inn, it still has some period character. Conference facilities for up to 80. No dogs. ***Rooms** 43. Garden, sauna.* AMERICAN EXPRESS *Access, Diners, Visa.*

Fareham **Solent Hotel** 75% £108

Tel 0489 880000 Fax 0489 880007 **HR**

Solent Business Park Whiteley Fareham Hampshire PO15 7AJ **Map 15 D4**

In a most unexpected location – adjacent to junction 9 of the M27 (10 miles from both Portsmouth and Southampton) – this modern, gabled hotel almost has the feel of a New England inn, successfully balancing wood and brick in its design and happily satisfying the contrasting needs of business and leisure guests. The functions are separated physically in the building's design, but high standards of service do not exclude one at the expense of another. All of the bedrooms are of Executive standard, in traditional style, with both working and relaxing space plus comprehensive comforts – from bathrobes to mini-bars. Suites accommodate syndicate, business and interview requirements in the week and have ample space for families at weekends; children up to 16 are accommodated free in their parents' room. Committed young staff and expert management show good direction throughout. The *Parson's Collar* pub in the grounds offers Daniel Thwaite's ales and informal eating – a place for parents to unwind while taking up the hotel's baby-listening facility. A stylish leisure club has a private membership and access from within the hotel; a floodlit tennis court was planned as we went to press. Plenty of easy parking. Shire Inns. ***Rooms** 90. Indoor swimming pool, whirlpool bath, children's splash pool, sauna, steam room, solarium, keep-fit equipment, squash, snooker.* AMERICAN EXPRESS *Access, Diners, Visa..*

Woodlands Restaurant £55

One room in the stone-floored dining area overlooks grass and woodlands beyond, carefully segregating conference diners when required, leaving other guests to enjoy the open fire in the main, split-level room. An enterprising carte and table d'hote offer familiar favourites with an interesting twist. ***Seats** 100. Private Room 30. L 12.30-2 D 7-10. Closed L Sat. Set L £14 Set D £18.*

Fareham **Places of Interest**

Tourist Information Tel 0329 221342.
Titchfield Abbey Titchfield Tel 0329 43016.
Porchester Castle Porchester Tel 0705 378291.
Royal Navy Submarine Museum Gosport Tel 0705 529217.
Fort Brockhurst Gosport Tel 0705 581059.

Farnborough **Forte Crest** 66% £119

Tel 0252 545051 Fax 0252 377210 **H**

Lynchford Road Farnborough Hampshire GU14 6AZ **Map 15 E3**

Handsome Edwardian building alongside A325. Day rooms have period appeal, bedrooms, most refurbished in 1992, are mainly modern. Banqueting and conference facilities for 200. ***Rooms** 110. Indoor swimming pool, keep-fit equipment, spa bath, solarium, health & beauty salon.* AMERICAN EXPRESS *Access, Diners, Visa.*

Farnham **Bishop's Table Hotel** 62% £85

Tel 0252 710222 Fax 0252 733494 **H**

27 West Street Farnham Surrey GU9 7DR **Map 15 E3**

A small, Georgian town-centre hotel (next to the public library) with individually decorated bedrooms, most now including some antique furniture and French pine beds. The bridal suite features a Victorian half-tester bed. Kass and Mariam Verjee, a brother and sister team, run the place in friendly style. Peaceful, secluded garden with a magnificent cedar tree to the rear. Children up to 14 free in parents' room. ***Rooms** 18. Garden. Closed 1 week Christmas/New Year.* AMERICAN EXPRESS *Access, Diners, Visa.*

Farnham **Bush Hotel** 62% £103

Tel 0252 715237 Fax 0252 733530 **H**

The Borough Farnham Surrey GU9 7NN **Map 15 E3**

17th-century buildings cluster around a cobbled courtyard at a well-kept Forte hotel in the town centre. Most bedrooms are in a newer wing that overlooks the garden. ***Rooms** 66. Garden, coffee shop (10am-6pm).* AMERICAN EXPRESS *Access, Diners, Visa.*

Farnham **Krug's** £55

Tel 0252 723277 **R**

84 West Street Farnham Surrey GU9 7EN **Map 15 E3**

A homely Austrian restaurant with a stag's head, log-burning stove and Alpine folksy tablecloths setting the scene for Gerhard Krug's competent and authentic national cooking. Dinner proceeds at a leisurely pace and dishes such as smoked bacon and cabbage soup, meat or cheese fondue and pan-fried pork fillet with soured cream and garlic sauce show the style. Fine home-cooked desserts include pancakes filled with apricot purée and praline or cinnamon-laced apfelstrüdel. The sign over the door reads "wine for truth, beer for strength and water for germs". ***Seats** 85. Private Room 40. L 12-2.30 D 7-11.30. Closed L Sat, all Sun & Mon, Bank Holidays. Set L £8. Access, Visa.*

Farnham **Trevena House** 59% £59

Tel 0252 716908 Fax 0252 722583 **H**

Alton Road Farnham Surrey GU10 5ER **Map 15 E3**

Look out for the sign and the tree-lined drive on the A31, a mile from Farnham towards Winchester. The house has a Tudor/Gothic appearance, and public areas are in a similar style with a huge stone fireplace in the foyer/lounge and a nice ribbed ceiling in the comfortable, panelled bar. Bedrooms offer modest comforts and the general atmosphere is relaxed and friendly. ***Rooms** 20. Garden, tennis.* AMERICAN EXPRESS *Access, Visa.*

Farnham **Places of Interest**

Farnham Tourist Information Tel 0252 715109.
Aldershot Tourist Information Tel 0252 20968.
Aldershot Military Museum Tel 0252 314598.
Crosswater Farm and Gardens Churt Tel 025125 2698.
Rural Life Centre Tilford Tel 025124 2300.
Birdworld Tel 0420 22140.
Aldershot Ice Rink Tel 0252 336464.
Stainforth Ski Centre Aldershot Tel 0252 25889.

Faugh **String of Horses Inn** £65

Tel 022 870 297 Fax 022 870 675 **I**

Heads Hook Faugh nr Carlisle Cumbria CA4 9EG **Map 4 C2**

Substantial white-painted coaching inn with an unbroken 300-year history, in a tiny hamlet off the A69. The rustic bar and lounges sport a plethora of panelling, oak beams, polished brass and similar trappings. Those in the bedrooms are rather more surprising: Hollywood-style brass fittings, large corner baths and proprietor Eric Tasker's complimentary hangover kit; several rooms have four-poster beds. Family facilities; popular bar snacks and Sunday lunches. ***Rooms** 14. Garden, outdoor heated swimming pool, keep-fit equipment, spa bath, sauna, solarium. Closed 25 & 26 Dec.* AMERICAN EXPRESS *Access, Diners, Visa.*

Faversham Read's £75

Tel 0795 535344 Fax 0795 591200 **R**

Painter's Forstal Faversham Kent ME13 0EE **Map 11 C5**

One and a half miles from Faversham off the old A2, Read's occupies a plain, single-storey 70s' rectangle that is reminiscent of a school building or office. Inside, great effort has been made to create a smart, welcoming ambience. Polished wood rattan screens divide the one room into a comfortable bar area with low, comfortable settees, and a spacious, pleasantly airy dining area with dark chintzy drapes and pristine, candle-lit tables. The menu changes every six weeks and the selection is varied, examples being starters such as fish cooked bouillabaisse style, duck foie gras terrine, cream of asparagus and hot soufflé of Montgomery Cheddar on a bed of smoked haddock. Main dishes could include a sautéed fillet of beef with black pudding, bacon and onions on a Guinness sauce, noisettes of Romney Marsh lamb, Provence vegetables and potatoes baked with garlic and cream, a boneless wild salmon slice with asparagus, butter sauce and Jersey Royals or sautéed loin of venison with chestnut purée, kumquat marmalade and a poivrade sauce. A typical meal could begin with a complimentary nibble of hot herring roe on toast with a garlic and parsley butter followed perhaps by two small, well-formed, carefully fried crabmeat and salmon fish cakes with a coriander butter sauce. A main course of neatly fanned sliced breast of Lunesdale duck is accompanied by Armagnac-soaked prunes and a honey-scented sauce. Sweets include a rhubarb fool and a chocoholics anonymous. David Pitchford is extremely talented, his menus comprising dishes whose ingredients are well thought-out. The cooking too is precise, the one quibble being that flavours can be a little awry. A clearly presented wine list has a super selection of over 40 wines under £16 and several big names fairly-priced. Helpful tasting notes. Service led by Rona Pitchford is exemplary. ***Seats** 40. Private Room 12. L 12-2 D 7-10. Closed Sun & Mon, Bank Holidays, 2 weeks Aug. Set L £14.50 Set D £25/£29.* AMERICAN EXPRESS *Access, Diners, Visa.*

Fawkham Brandshatch Place 66% £90

Tel 0474 872239 Fax 0474 879652 **HR**

Fawkham Valley Road Fawkham Kent DA3 8NQ **Map 11 B5**

This redbrick Georgian house built for the Duke of Norfolk stands opposite the Paddock entrance to Brands Hatch racing circuit. Plain and uninteresting public rooms range from a pale pink lounge and bar area to a selection of meeting and conference rooms. The self-contained leisure club has more appeal. Bedrooms have up-to-date decor and include small seating areas and remote-control TVs as standard features. Bathrooms are more basic and functional. Future plans for investment will be welcome. ***Rooms** 29. Garden, indoor swimming pool, gymnasium, squash, sauna, spa bath, solarium, snooker.* AMERICAN EXPRESS *Access, Diners, Visa.*

Hatchwood Restaurant £55

Appealing set-price lunch and dinner menus supplement a monthly-changing à la carte. The restaurant is divided between a panelled dining area and a pale green room which is unremarkable, like some of the cooking. This is generally sound but where ambitious can be disappointing in execution. ***Seats** 65. Parties 30. L 12.30-2 D 7-10. Set L £17.50 Set D £18.50. Closed L Sat, 26-30 Dec.*

Fawkham Places of Interest

Orchard Theatre Home Gardens Dartford Tel 0322 34333.
Hesketh Park Cricket Ground Dartford Tel 0322 225152.

Felixstowe — Orwell Moat House 69% — £85

Tel 0394 285511 Fax 0394 670687 — H

Hamilton Road Felixstowe Suffolk IP11 7DX — **Map 10 D3**

Comfortable public rooms retain many period features at this Victorian town-centre hotel opposite the railway station; bedrooms offer all the usual modern comforts, and there are conference facilities. Ample free parking. ***Rooms** 58.* AMERICAN EXPRESS *Access, Diners, Visa.*

Felsted — Rumbles Cottage — £53

Tel 0371 820996 — R

Braintree Road Felsted Essex CM6 3DJ — **Map 11 B4**

The whitewashed 16th-century cottage has low, beamed ceilings with four dining rooms run by enthusiastic chef-proprietress Joy Hadley. Her eclectic English menu offers a choice of five dishes per course and might include smoked halibut parcel, smoked chicken and sweetcorn soup or mini-meatballs to start, followed by roulade of pork with mushroom and Stilton stuffing, or strips of beef pan-fried with celery and red pepper and served with a peanut and ginger sauce. There is always an unusual vegetarian dish such as a pancake gateau layered with spinach, mushroom and grated courgette on a tomato and pesto sauce. Coffee and walnut roulade with Earl Grey sauce, pink grapefruit, lime and Tequila sorbet, or chocolate mint slice with a crème de menthe sauce, perhaps, to finish. Frequent 'guinea pig menus' for tasting experimental dishes are offered to adventurous diners. Also at: *Rumbles Castle Restaurant*, 4 St James Street, Castle Hedingham, Essex (Tel 0787 461490 Open L Sun only & D Wed-Sat). ***Seats** 50. Parties 25. Private Room 10. L Sun only 12-2 D 7-9. Closed D Sun, all Mon, Bank Holidays. Access, Visa.*

Fenstanton — Forte Travelodge — £42

Tel 0954 30919 — L

Fenstanton nr Cambridge Cambridgeshire — **Map 15 F1**

Located on the eastbound side of the A604, 4 miles south-east of Huntingdon and 10 miles north-west of Cambridge. ***Rooms** 40.* AMERICAN EXPRESS *Access, Visa.*

Ferndown — Dormy Hotel 71% — £105

Tel 0202 872121 Fax 0202 895388 — H

New Road Ferndown Dorset BH22 8ES — **Map 14 C4**

Manager Derek Silk has kept standards high here since 1977. Guests will find plenty to please them: public rooms include an all-day bar and brasserie with well-upholstered rattan furniture, and a further bar with oak-panelled walls, red plush chesterfields and a real log fire. The leisure club's facilities are extensive: there's a club room with snooker, pool, darts and table tennis, and a children's games room with supervised activities during holiday periods; both the gym and pool are wonderfully light and airy. Bedrooms offer good standards of modern comfort. Well geared-up for conferences with some 10 meeting rooms, the largest of which can accommodate up to 250 delegates in theatre style. De Vere. ***Rooms** 128. Garden, indoor swimming pool, gymnasium, squash, sauna, solarium, whirlpool bath, beauty salon, tennis, snooker, brasserie (10am-10pm).* AMERICAN EXPRESS *Access, Diners, Visa.*

Ferrybridge — Granada Lodge — £45

Tel 0977 672767 Fax 0977 672945 — L

M62/A1 Junction 33 Ferrybridge West Yorkshire WF11 0AF — **Map 7 D1**

***Rooms** 35.* AMERICAN EXPRESS *Access, Diners, Visa.*

Findon — Findon Manor — 61% — £60

Tel 0903 872733 — **H**

Findon West Sussex BN14 0TA — **Map 11 A6**

Actually a 16th-century flint rectory owned by Magdalen College Oxford until the 1930s. One enters directly into a charming beamed lounge which has just been refurbished by the Bishop-Milnes family (Lesley is an interior decorator by profession) who have only recently acquired the hotel. A small, pubby bar also serves as the village "local". Bedrooms vary in size and furnishings, mostly with atttractive matching fabrics and poly-cotton duvets. No remote control for the TV but fresh flowers add a personal touch. The two best rooms have four-posters and spa baths. In the summer the large secluded garden is just the spot for afternoon teas or an energetic game of croquet. ***Rooms** 10. Garden.* AMERICAN EXPRESS *Access, Visa.*

Fleet — Forte Travelodge — £42

Tel 0252 815578 — **L**

Hartley Wintney Basingstoke Hampshire RG27 8BN — **Map 15 D3**

Located on the westbound carriageway of the M3 at the Welcome Break Fleet service area, between Junctions 4 and 5. ***Rooms** 40.* AMERICAN EXPRESS *Access, Visa.*

Flitwick — Flitwick Manor — 73% — £135

Tel 0525 712242 Fax 0525 712242 — **HR**

Church Road Flitwick Bedfordshire MK45 1AE — **Map 15 E1**

A change of management, the second in two years, at this late 17th/early 18th-century house set in rolling parkland just a couple of minutes from the M1 (Junction 12). The high-ceilinged music room (the main day room) sets the tone of the hotel with homely touches like magazines and chessboard set up ready for play. Bedrooms come in all shapes and sizes from small singles to large four-poster with original panelling, but all get the same extras including ice and slices of lemon with the well-stocked drinks tray, mineral water, fresh fruit, home-made biscuits, books, magazines and fresh flowers. Bathrooms are equally variable – two have shower and WC only, one with his 'n' hers 'kissing' bath tubs. No children under 8. ***Rooms** 15. Garden, tennis, helipad.* AMERICAN EXPRESS *Access, Visa.*

Restaurant — £90

Between the good canapés that arrive with the menu and nicely varied petits fours with the coffee Duncan Poyser's fixed-price menu offers a selection of thoroughly modern dishes. Soup of grilled new season tomatoes and sweet garlic with griddled pesto bread; carpaccio of scallops with lemon oil, garlic, chive and tomato; baked salmon on a red bean, smoked bacon and parsley broth; roast chump of lamb with rosemary and chives, and lamb's sweetbreads glazed with an orange and tarragon sauce give the style. Vegetables do not come separately but form part of the garnish of the main dish. Plenty of interest for afters too, with the likes of a warm tart of Munster and morels with garden chive, panna cotta with seasonal berries and a twice-baked goat's cheese soufflé among the desserts. ***Seats** 40. Private Room 30. L 12-1.30 D 7-9.30 Set L £15.50/£18.50 Set D £29.50/£33.50.*

Folkestone — Paul's — £43

Tel 0303 59697 — **R**

2a Bouverie Road West Folkestone Kent CT20 2RX — **Map 11 C5**

Pastel decorations abound in Paul and Penny Hagger's converted house. A pink menu announces the uncomplicated cooking on offer from Paul: cream of broccoli soup topped with diced ham, devilled sprats, salmon filo parcels, roast duck with a sherry vinegar sauce and pineapple, sirloin steak with Stilton butter. Always a choice for vegetarians. Sweets are served from the trolley. Longish, keenly-priced wine list. ***Seats** 80. L 12-2.30 D 7.30-9.30 (Sat 7-10). Closed a few days over Christmas. Set L & D £12.90/£15.65. Access, Visa.*

Folkestone La Tavernetta £45

Tel 0303 54955 **R**

Leaside Court Clifton Gardens Folkestone Kent CT20 2EY **Map 11 C5**

Chef-partner Felice Puricelli has been providing sound Italian cuisine since 1965 in his friendly basement restaurant. The menu steers a safe course through antipasti hot and cold, soups, pasta, fish and meat main courses. The last include a wide variety of steaks both plain and sauced. ***Seats** 55. Private Room 22. L 12-2.30 D 6-10.30. Closed Sun, Bank Holidays. Set L from £9.50.* AMERICAN EXPRESS *Access, Diners, Visa.*

Folkestone Places of Interest

Tourist Information Tel 0303 58594.
Metropole Arts Centre Tel 0303 55070.
Leas Cliff Hall Tel 0303 53191.
Kent Battle of Britain Museum Tel 0303 893140.
Eurotunnel Exhibition Centre Tel 0303 270111.
Cheriton Cricket Ground Tel 0303 53366.
Folkestone Racecourse Tel 0303 66407.
Folkestone Sports Centre Trust Tel 0303 850333.
Swingfield Butterfly Centre Swingfield Tel 0303 83244.

Fontwell Forte Travelodge £42

Tel 0243 543972 **L**

A27/A29 Fontwell West Sussex BN18 0SB **Map 11 A6**

On the A27, 5 miles north of Bognor Regis. ***Rooms** 32.* AMERICAN EXPRESS *Access, Visa.*

Fossebridge Fossebridge Inn 65% £55

Tel 0285 720721 Fax 0285 720793 **H**

Fossebridge Northleach Gloucestershire GL54 3JS **Map 14 C2**

An ivy-clad coaching inn standing alongside the A429 and lying on the banks of the river Coln where it crosses the Fosse Way. Views from the bedrooms at the rear of the house overlook lawns leading down to a lake teeming with trout. The 15th-century Bridge Bar has exposed beams, stone walls and a flagstone floor. Children up to 12 stay free in parents' room. ***Rooms** 9. Garden, coarse fishing. Access, Visa.*

Framlingham The Crown 62% £103

Tel 0728 723521 Fax 0728 724274 **H**

Market Hill Framlingham Suffolk IP13 9AN **Map 10 D2**

A Forte Heritage hotel that stands out from the crowd with much 16th-century period charm. A flagstoned foyer/lounge and public bar have beamed ceilings and open fires, with a creaking staircase leading up to simple bedrooms furnished with freestanding oak units. The best bedroom has a panelled oak four-poster and floral print settee. Plenty of car parking at the back of the hotel. ***Rooms** 14.* AMERICAN EXPRESS *Access, Diners, Visa.*

Framlingham Place of Interest

Framlingham Castle Tel 0728 723330.

Freshford Homewood Park 79% £115

Tel 0225 723731 Fax 0225 723820 **HR**

Hinton Charterhouse Freshford Avon BA3 6BB **Map 13 F1**

Mainly Georgian, although the cellars date back to the 13th century, Homewood Park enjoys 10 acres of its own grounds within an area designated as being of outstanding natural beauty. Oil paintings, Oriental rugs, a collection of bronze statuettes and some framed Hermès scarves all contribute to the charm of relaxing day rooms. Bedrooms vary in size but all share the same degree of comfort and sense of style: well-chosen fabrics (often with elaborate bedhead drapes), the occasional antique, cut-glass decanter of sherry, mineral water and pretty bathrooms decorated to match the individual rooms. Frank Gueuning (the relatively new owner) is an accomplished hotelier who is maintaining high standards here. No dogs. ***Rooms*** *15. Garden, tennis, croquet.* AMERICAN EXPRESS *Access, Diners, Visa.*

Restaurant £75

There is a simple elegance to the twin dining rooms, overlooking the garden, and very comfortable chairs encourage one to linger over Tim Ford's stylish cooking. Well-balanced menus are full of interest – an individual pie of quail breast and dumplings in a rich Madeira sauce, twice-baked soufflé with a ragout of spiced seafood, roast breast of guinea fowl with a confit of the leg and black pudding and braised cabbage, apple fritters with vanilla ice cream and an apricot coulis. The fish dish of the day depends upon the market and there is a good selection of English farmhouse cheese. No smoking. ***Seats*** *50. Parties 50. Private Room 30. L 12-1.45 D 7-9.30 Set L £17.50 Set D £29.50*

Freshwater Farringford Hotel 57% £88

Tel 0983 752500 **H**

Bedbury Lane Freshwater Isle of Wight PO40 9PE **Map 14 C4**

Once the home of Alfred Lord Tennyson, this 18th-century Gothic-style house is now a peaceful holiday hotel whose neat gardens border National Trust downland. Day rooms include a French-windowed drawing room, a small bar and a library with Tennyson memorabilia. Bedrooms are modest and neat, and there are also a number of self-catering Cottage and Garden suites in the grounds. Families with children are welcome, and baby-sitting and baby-listening can be arranged. ***Rooms*** *19. Outdoor swimming pool, 9-hole golf course, putting, bowling green, tennis, children's play area.* AMERICAN EXPRESS *Access, Diners, Visa.*

Fressingfield Fox & Goose ↑ £66

Tel 037 986 247 **R**

Fressingfield nr Diss Suffolk IP21 5PB **Map 10 C2**

In a lovely old black-and-white inn by the church, cook/patronne Ruth Watson and chef Brendan Ansbro produce a menu whose inspiration is worldwide. British dishes are flanked by ethnic offerings, and Morecambe Bay potted brown shrimps, salmon fish cakes with parsley and tarragon sauce, steak and kidney pudding and Sussex Pond pudding (the latter for two diners or more require 24hrs' notice) are favourites on the fascinating menu. Culinary explorers could go for 'nearly-sashimi of scallop, salmon and pickled ginger', bruschetta, bresaola, grilled halloumi cheese, crispy Peking duck with pancakes, tofu and vegetable tempura, and even sweet and sour rabbit with prunes and bitter chocolate. Some dishes are dual-priced, either as starters or main courses. Sunday lunchtime brings roast Aberdeen Angus sirloin of beef served with Yorkshire pudding (order by midday Saturday). Cheeses are 'made as far as possible from raw milk by real people'. The outstanding wine list of 400+ bottles is accompanied by a 30-wine short-form list for easing selection. ***Seats*** *50. Parties 24. L 12-2 D 7-9.30. Closed Mon & Tue, 4 days Christmas. No credit cards.*

Frilford Heath — Dog House Hotel

£63

Tel 0865 390830 Fax 0865 390860

I

Frilford Heath nr Abingdon Oxfordshire OX13 6QJ

Map 15 D2

The 17th-century Dog House (a ten-minute drive from Oxford) has rooms in contemporary cottage style. Furniture is good-quality pine (one room has a pine four-poster), and accessories include remote-control teletext TV. Bathrooms have smart modern tiling, large mirrors and good lighting. Children's play area. ***Rooms** 19. Garden.* American Express *Access, Diners, Visa.*

Garforth — Hilton National 61%

£94

Tel 0532 866556 Fax 0532 868326

H

Wakefield Road Garforth nr Leeds West Yorkshire LS25 1LH

Map 7 D1

Stylish public areas raise expectations for the bedrooms, which although well kept, are small and fairly ordinary. Leisure centre. ***Rooms** 144. Garden, indoor swimming pool, keep-fit equipment, sauna, solarium, pool table.* American Express *Access, Diners, Visa.*

Gateshead — Forte Travelodge

£42

Tel 091-438 3333

L

A194 Leam Lane Wardley Whitemare Pool nr Gateshead Tyne & Wear NE10 8YB

Map 5 E2

On the outskirts of Newcastle-upon-Tyne, 4 miles east of Gateshead town centre and 8 miles west of Sunderland. ***Rooms** 41.* American Express *Access, Visa.*

Gateshead — Newcastle Marriott 70% NEW

£129

Tel 091-493 2233 Fax 091-493 2030

H

MetroCentre Gateshead Newcastle Tyne & Wear NE11 9XF

Map 5 E2

Adjacent to the MetroCentre (Europe's largest indoor shopping and leisure complex), the Marriott is tall and faced entirely in darkened glass. The spacious and modern white marble-floored foyer is stylishly appointed with wide brown leather settees and armchairs. There are two bars: Chesters cocktail bar and a pale pink and charcoal lounge bar. Bedrooms have smart lightwood furniture and soft pastel colour schemes; all are well equipped – even to the extent of having video recorders with a selection of video cassettes for hire. Bathrooms have power showers and good towels. Ten highly distinctive, themed rooms are very original and well thought out: four are inspired by the Wild West with a covered wagon for a bed and bathrooms done out as jails; two more are Arabian with a harem theme, two are Hollywood with large Oscar statues at the bed corners and 20s' decor; the remaining two are American-themed with an illuminated juke box offering 60s' songs and a bed resembling the back end of a Cadillac – great fun and very popular. Children up to 19 free in parents' room. Conference facilities for up to 500. ***Rooms** 150. Indoor swimming pool, spa bath, gymnasium, solarium, sauna, steam room, beauty salon.* American Express *Access, Diners, Visa.*

Gateshead — Springfield Hotel 63%

£88

Tel 091-477 4121 Fax 091-477 7213

H

Durham Road Low Fell Gateshead Tyne & Wear NE9 5BT

Map 5 E2

Jarvis business hotel by the A6127, 4 miles from A1(M) junction. Conference/banqueting facilities for 120/100. Children up to 5 stay free in parents' room. ***Rooms** 60.* American Express *Access, Diners, Visa.*

Gateshead Swallow Hotel 60% £88

Tel 091-477 1105 Fax 091-478 7214 **H**

High West Street Gateshead Tyne & Wear NE8 1PE **Map 5 E2**

A leisure club, ample secure car parking and conference facilities for up to 350 are among the amenities at this modern hotel three miles from the A1(M) and one mile from the city centre – check directions. ***Rooms*** *103. Indoor swimming pool, keep-fit equipment, sauna, spa bath, steam room, solarium.* AMERICAN EXPRESS *Access, Diners, Visa.*

Gateshead Places of Interest

Tourist Information Tel 091-477 3478.
Caedmon Hall Tel 091-477 3478.
Gibside Chapel and Grounds (NT) Gibside Tel 0207 542255.
Bede Monastery Museum Jarrow Tel 091-489 2106.
Wickham Thorns Farm Ski Slope Dunston Tel 091-460 8746.
Gateshead International Sports Stadium Tel 091-478 1687.

Gatwick Airport Chequers Thistle 63% £106

Tel 0293 786992 Fax 0293 820625 **H**

Brighton Road Horley Surrey RH6 8PH **Map 15 E3**

At a roundabout on the A23 to the north of the airport. Public areas are in the original Tudor building although only the beamed bar hints at the Chequers' coaching inn past. Standardised bedrooms, all in a two-storey 'system built' extenstion to the rear, are in good order with all the usual creature comforts and practical bathrooms. 24hr room service. ***Rooms*** *78. Outdoor swimming pool, coffee shop (10am-10pm).* AMERICAN EXPRESS *Access, Diners, Visa.*

Gatwick Airport Copthorne Effingham Park 72% £126

Tel 0342 714994 Fax 0342 716039 **H**

West Park Road Copthorne West Sussex RH10 3EU **Map 15 E3**

Follow signs to East Grinstead, off Junction 10 of the M23. Six sequoia trees originally imported from Oregon to commemorate Wellington's victory at Waterloo line the driveway. There's lots more of interest in the modernised stately home, including a large rotunda conference centre (catering for up to 500 delegates). Decent-sized bedrooms have reproduction furniture including a breakfast table. Best rooms have private balconies. ***Rooms*** *122. Garden, 9-hole golf course, indoor swimming pool, gymnasium, Turkish bath, sauna, spa bath, beautician, hairdressing.* AMERICAN EXPRESS *Access, Diners, Visa.*

Gatwick Airport Copthorne London Gatwick 69% £128

Tel 0342 714971 Fax 0342 717375 **H**

Copthorne nr Crawley West Sussex RH10 3PG **Map 15 E3**

Set in 100 acres of gardens and woodland, the Copthorne is centred round a 16th-century farmhouse. Oak beams and log fires keep the period feel in the White Swan pub, and many of the bedrooms are also in a traditional style. There are rooms for disabled guests and non-smokers, and the newest rooms in the Connoisseur wing boast corner jacuzzis. The hotel has several bars and restaurants, conference/banqueting suites (for around 120) and facilities for sport and leisure. Six minutes from the airport (not on the flight path) and just two from the M23 (junction 10, then A264 towards East Grinstead). Courtesy coach to the airport every 30mins from 6am-midnight. Families well catered for. ***Rooms*** *227. Garden, gymnasium, sauna, solarium, squash, beautician.* AMERICAN EXPRESS *Access, Diners, Visa.*

Gatwick Airport — Europa Gatwick 68% — £117

Tel 0293 886666 Fax 0293 886680 — **H**

Balcombe Road Maidenbower nr Crawley West Sussex RH10 4ZR — **Map 15 E3**

On the B2036 about 15 minutes from the airport, the Europa is a modern low-rise hotel built in an unusual hacienda style, with whitewashed walls and terracotta roofs. Inside, it's just as distinctive, and reception impresses first with its tall rafters, terrazzo marble floor and dark mahogany furniture. There are two restaurants (the *Silk Trader* serving Chinese food and the *Méditerranée*), a lounge bar for lighter meals, a cocktail bar, numerous syndicate rooms and Studio 4 – a well-equipped health and leisure centre. Smart bedrooms with polished wood and autumnal colour schemes range up to Executive rooms with sofa beds and work areas, and Club rooms with whirlpool baths. Parking for 250 cars. ***Rooms** 211. Garden, indoor swimming pool, gymnasium, spa bath, sauna, solarium, beautician, hairdressing.* AMERICAN EXPRESS *Access, Diners, Visa.*

Gatwick Airport — Forte Crest Gatwick 74% — £99

Tel 0293 567070 Fax 0293 567739 — **H**

North Terminal Gatwick Airport West Sussex RH6 0PH — **Map 15 E3**

Formerly the *Gatwick Sterling*, Gatwick's most distinctive hotel is 100 yards from the north terminal and has a covered walkway between the two, leading directly into the unusual, eight-storey-high open atrium, under which a bright cocktail bar and café take on an open-air feel. Public areas are modernistic, even a bit austere, and the uniformly furnished bedrooms are stark, though well lit and comfortable, with chrome fittings and black and white decor; striped bedcovers provide a dash of colour; glazing is thoroughly efficient with little or no air traffic noise disturbing one's night. A surprisingly easy-to-use, high-tech TV system displays messages, flight information, a running total of the bill and even a check-out facility in addition to regular viewing. It's worth the extra to stay on the Sterling Club floor with its separate lounge, complimentary cocktail, Continental breakfast and various extras in the rooms. Despite its plethora of eating facilities, ranging from an un-Viennese Café Viennois to an Original Carvery, Sampans Chinese restaurant and the 24hr room service, the quality of food on offer is in sad contrast to the accommodation which is run in exemplary style. Service throughout is helpful, knowledgeable, friendly and efficient. The Leisure Club is very well equipped, but the pool is small. Children stay free at weekends in their own room. Free parking is offered to guests for up to 15 days in the long-term car park. ***Rooms** 474. Indoor swimming pool, sauna, solarium, gymnasium, keep-fit equipment, business centre, 24hr café, news kiosk, hairdressing, British Airways ticket desk.* AMERICAN EXPRESS *Access, Diners, Visa.*

Gatwick Airport — Forte Posthouse Gatwick 63% — £68

Tel 0293 771621 Fax 0293 771054 — **H**

Povey Cross Road Horley Surrey RH6 0BA — **Map 15 E3**

On the A23 a mile north of the airport. Good modern bedrooms, choice of conference and meeting rooms (up to 150 delegates), large long-term car park. ***Rooms** 210. Outdoor swimming pool, coffee shop (7am-10pm), airport courtesy coach (from 6.15am).* AMERICAN EXPRESS *Access, Diners, Visa.*

Gatwick Airport — Gatwick Concorde Hotel 61% — £104

Tel 0293 533441 Fax 0293 535369 — **H**

Church Road Lowfield Heath Crawley West Sussex RH11 0PQ — **Map 15 E3**

Queens Moat Houses hotel off the A23. Some of the bedrooms overlook the runways. Courtesy coach from airport and station. ***Rooms** 116.* AMERICAN EXPRESS *Access, Diners, Visa.*

Gatwick Airport — Gatwick Hilton International — 72% — £159

Tel 0293 518080 Fax 0293 28980 — H

Gatwick West Sussex RH11 0PD — **Map 15 E3**

A pedestrian walkway directly connects Gatwick's south terminal with this large hotel's four-storey central atrium; a full-size replica of *Jason*, Amy Johnson's biplane, hangs from the ceiling. Good-sized bedrooms have easy chairs, breakfast tables, large beds and all the extras one would expect from an international hotel; TVs even display flight information, very useful if your plane is delayed. The Jockey Bar's horse-racing theme harks back to the days when Gatwick racecourse was on this site. Conferences for up to 500. ***Rooms** 550. Indoor swimming pool, sauna, solarium, spa bath, steam room, gymnasium, beauty salon, hairdressing, games room, kiosk, florist, business centre, 24hr coffee shop.* AMERICAN EXPRESS *Access, Diners, Visa.*

Gatwick Airport — Holiday Inn Gatwick — 68% — £118

Tel 0293 529991 Fax 0293 515913 — H

Langley Drive Crawley West Sussex RH11 7SX — **Map 15 E3**

4 miles south of the airport. Good leisure and conference facilities (for up to 300) in a modern hotel on the A23. Informal and formal restaurants. Children's splash pool and spa bath by the bright, daylight pool. ***Rooms** 223. Gymnasium, indoor swimming pool, spa bath, sauna, solarium, snooker, coffee shop (11am-11.30pm).* AMERICAN EXPRESS *Access, Diners, Visa.*

Gatwick Airport — Moat House — 62% — £74

Tel 0293 785599 Fax 0293 785991 — H

Longbridge Roundabout Horley Surrey RH6 0AB — **Map 15 E3**

Five-storey hotel by a roundabout on the A23, half a mile north of the airport. Bedrooms have individual heat and air controls. First-floor bar and brasserie. Conferences up to 180. Airport courtesy coach; long-term car parking. Children up to 12 free in parents' room. ***Rooms** 121.* AMERICAN EXPRESS *Access, Diners, Visa.*

Gatwick Airport — Ramada Hotel Gatwick — 70% — £134

Tel 0293 820169 Fax 0293 820259 — H

Povey Cross Road Horley Surrey RH6 0BE — **Map 15 E3**

Well-signposted, large modern hotel (formerly the *Gatwick Penta*) just off the A23. Spacious and stylish public areas include the Brighton Belle bar (based on an old Pullman carriage) with walls that are lined with railway memorabilia; leather sofas, large brass table lamps and a marble-tiled floor make the foyer-lounge an attractive area. The best bedrooms are spacious and well equipped, with efficient sound-proofing, good air-conditioning and neutral decor, in contrast to the standard rooms. The extensive leisure centre includes two squash courts. Good, self-contained conference facilities for up to 150 delegates. Courtesy coaches to the airport. ***Rooms** 255. Garden, coffee shop (10am-11pm), beautician, indoor swimming pool, sauna, solarium, spa bath, gymnasium, squash.* AMERICAN EXPRESS *Access, Diners, Visa.*

Gayton — Travel Inn — £43

Tel 051-342 1982 Fax 051-342 8983 — L

Chester Road Gayton Wirral Merseyside L60 3FD — **Map 6 A2**

A short drive from both Ellesmere Port and Wirral Leisure Park. ***Rooms** 37.* AMERICAN EXPRESS *Access, Diners, Visa.*

Consult page 16 for a full list of starred restaurants

Gerrards Cross — Bull Hotel — 63% — £125

Tel 0753 885995 Fax 0753 885504 **H**

Gerrards Cross Buckinghamshire SL9 7PA **Map 15 E2**

Some glimpses still of coaching days; mostly modern bedrooms which children up to 14 share free with parents. Conferences for up to 200. De Vere. ***Rooms** 95.* American Express *Access, Diners, Visa.*

Gillingham — Stock Hill House — 74% — £190*

Tel 0747 823626 Fax 0747 825628 **HR**

Stock Hill Gillingham Dorset SP8 5NR **Map 14 B3**

Deep in Hardy country, Peter and Nita Hauser's sturdy Victorian house stands in ten acres of mature grounds and woodland. Their dedication to its improvement over the years still continues, providing a haven of tranquillity to which they bring their unique brand of personal hospitality. Antiques and designer materials of the highest standard make for some splendid public rooms, the most unusual feature of which is a collection of huge carved animals. Each bedroom is individually designed, here with a carved four-poster, there a Spanish wrought-iron bed. The sumptuous Robin's Nest suite is the latest addition to the bedrooms. Try to arrive in time for afternoon tea, which is splendid, as (before you go) is the breakfast. *Half-board terms only. No children under 7. No dogs. ***Rooms** 9. Garden. Access, Visa.*

Restaurant ↑ £70

Peter Hauser not only produces elegant meals, but he also tends his own walled kitchen garden for the freshest of vegetables and personally shops around for produce from local farms and fish from the Dorset coast. His enthusiasm is evident in a carte that might offer zuppa pavese, grilled Somerset goat's cheese on Dutch cabbage vinaigrette or braised baby octopus on green noodles to start, followed perhaps by poached shin of beef in horseradish glaze with a bread dumpling, fillet of turbot topped with crab mousseline and tarragon cream or sautéed calf's kidneys with juniper berries and a mustard seed sauce. Being Austrian, Peter's emphasis is naturally on desserts and *rehrucken mit schlag* (almond-decorated chocolate cake with whipped cream) and *gratinierte topfen palatschinken* (pancakes stuffed with curd cheese) feature among them, alongside Bramley apple fritters with golden syrup and tipsy dates with coffee cream. No smoking. ***Seats** 30. Parties 12. Private Room 12. L 12.30-1.45 D 7.30-9. Closed D Sun, all Mon. Set L £18.50 Set D £26.50.*

Gittisham — Combe House — 73% — £92

Tel 0404 42756 Fax 0404 46004 **H**

Gittisham nr Honiton Devon EX14 0AD **Map 13 E2**

Thérèse and John Boswell are both very much involved in the day-to-day running of their stately Elizabethan mansion. The 3000-acre estate is predictably peaceful, and there are views of the Blackmore Hills, but it's not remote, being less than two miles from the A30 Honiton Bypass. Public rooms have carved panelling in the entrance hall, ancestral portraits in the panelled drawing room, a charming pink sitting room, a cosy bar with pictures of John's horse-racing activities (the hotel owns several racehorses trained nearby – visits to the stables can be arranged), and everywhere architectural features, antiques and personal touches by painter and sculptress Thérèse (and her mother). Bedrooms vary in size and price, larger rooms tending to have better views and more interesting furniture and pictures. Two rooms have four-poster beds. The hotel owns fishing rights on the River Otter, with a season running from April to the end of September. During January & February the hotel closes from after Sunday breakfast to teatime on Tuesday. ***Rooms** 15. Garden, fishing.* American Express *Access, Diners, Visa.*

Glastonbury No. 3 Restaurant & Hotel £75

Tel 0458 832129 **RR**

3 Magdelene Street Glastonbury Somerset BA6 9EW **Map 13 F1**

On the A39 adjacent to the ruins of Glastonbury Abbey is this fine Georgian town house. Ann Tynan serves a fixed-price menu with a good choice that might offer smoked trout with mustard and dill sauce, Roquefort and walnut parcels with watercress sauce or a timbale of chicken livers to start, followed by an inter-course sorbet and then lobster Thermidor (at a £10 supplement), a vegetarian option (perhaps walnut and cashew en croute with mushroom sauce), sautéed guinea fowl, venison à la bourguignonne, steak au poivre or monkfish provençale. Pear frangipane, brandy snap baskets with seasonal fruits and cream (or yoghurt), praline and Amaretto ice cream or cheese with celery and fruits finish off a splendid meal. Carefully selected wines on the list with distinctively rounded prices. ***Seats** 20. D only 7.30-9. Closed Sun & Mon, all Dec & Jan. Set D £26. Access, Visa.*

Rooms £70

Six stylish bedrooms with antiques and bathrooms en suite; some rooms are in a modern annexe at the bottom of the garden. No dogs.

Gloucester Forte Crest 66% £109

Tel 0452 613311 Fax 0452 371036 **H**

Crest Way Barnwood Gloucester Gloucestershire GL4 7RX **Map 14 B1**

Modern hotel on the A417, strong on conference (up to 100) and leisure facilities. Lady Crest rooms cater well for female executives. ***Rooms** 123. Indoor swimming pool, sauna, spa bath.* AMERICAN EXPRESS *Access, Diners, Visa.*

Gloucester Hatherley Manor 65% £78

Tel 0452 730217 Fax 0452 731032 **H**

Down Hatherley Lane Gloucester Gloucestershire GL2 9QA **Map 14 B1**

Forty acres of parkland and pasture surround a 17th-century manor two miles north of Gloucester (just off the A38). Private guests and conference delegates (up to 250) are both well catered for, the former in comfortable bars and a lounge, the latter chiefly in the Hatherley Suite with its own entrance, bar and servery kitchen kept well away from the hotel proper. A few standard bedrooms are in the old part, but the majority are in the 'de luxe' category with satellite TV and good work space. A few are suitable for family use (baby-listening and baby-sitting by arrangement) and there's a four-poster honeymoon suite. Plenty of free parking. ***Rooms** 55. Garden.* AMERICAN EXPRESS *Access, Diners, Visa.*

Gloucester Hatton Court 75% £90

Tel 0452 617412 Fax 0452 612945 **HR**

Upton Hill Upton St Leonards Gloucester Gloucestershire GL4 8DE **Map 14 B1**

Ignore the M5 and you can enjoy wonderful views over the Severn Valley from an extended 17th-century house set in 37 acres of greenery on a ridge alongside the B4073, three miles from Gloucester. Inside the ivy-clad building it's a refined yet busy business catering for weekday conferences of up to 30 delegates. A glass of port or sherry greets guests on arrival in the stylishly furnished foyer. Eighteen bedrooms are in the main house with further smaller (and more uniform) ones in an adjoining wing, reached from outside the house. All have the same level of extras like bathrobes, sweets, fruit and mineral water. Bathrooms (some with whirlpool baths) are bright, neat and carpeted. Terrace lunches in summer. ***Rooms** 45. Garden, outdoor swimming pool (May-Oct), keep-fit equipment, sauna, solarium.* AMERICAN EXPRESS *Access, Diners, Visa.*

Carringtons Restaurant **£75**

Choose the terrace for a panoramic view of the Severn Valley or dine within where it's all ruffled curtains, crystal chandeliers and formal service. An extensive à la carte – home-cured gravad lax with a honey, dill and mustard dressing, brill in filo with mushrooms and chives, twice roasted confit of duck with seasonal leaves and plum coulis – includes a 'taste of tradition' section – French onion soup, asparagus hollandaise, duck with orange – and is supplemented by a table d'hote with about five choices at each stage, and a serious vegetarian menu. For afters there are some good desserts – a freshly baked apple tart with crumble ice cream on a pistachio anglaise sauce was particularly good – plus hot savouries and some recherché British cheeses. Well-rounded wine list with some fairly-priced bottles, though the classics are quite pricy. The skills of new chef Tony Warburton, who comes here from a sister hotel on Jersey, are a match for the ambitious menu. No smoking. ***Seats** 80. Parties 16. Private Room 40. L 12.30-2 D 7.30-10 (Sun to 9.30). Set L £14 Set D £19.75.*

Gloucester **Travel Inn** **£43**

Tel 0452 523519 Fax 0452 300924 **L**

Tewkesbury Road Longford Gloucester Gloucestershire GL2 9BE **Map 14 B1**

***Rooms** 40. AMERICAN EXPRESS Access, Diners, Visa.*

Gloucester **Travel Inn** **£43**

Tel 0452 862521 Fax 0452 864926 **L**

Witcombe nr Gloucester Gloucestershire GL3 4SS **Map 14 B1**

***Rooms** 40. AMERICAN EXPRESS Access, Diners, Visa.*

Gloucester **Places of Interest**

Tourist Information Tel 0452 421188.
Berkeley Castle Berkeley Tel 0453 810332.
Westbury Court Garden (NT) Westbury-on-Severn Tel 045276 461.
Gloucester Cathedral Tel 0452 24167.
Gloucester Ski Centre Tel 0452 414 300.
Museums and Art Galleries
Nature in Art (The International Centre for Wildlife Art) Tel 0452 731422.
City Museum and Art Gallery Tel 0452 24131.
The Robert Opie Collection Museum of Advertising and Packaging, Gloucester Docks Tel 0452 302309.
Zoos and Wildlife Parks
National Birds of Prey Centre Tel 0531 820286.
Wildfowl and Wetlands Trust Slimbridge Tel 045 389 0827.

Goathland **Mallyan Spout** **61%** **£60**

Tel 0947 86206 **H**

Goathland Whitby North Yorkshire YO22 5AN **Map 5 F3**

In a remote village nine miles from Whitby the hotel takes its name from a waterfall flowing into a wooded valley just a short walk away. Stone-built and clad in ivy, it's a homely, welcoming place with family owners; the lounges and bars provide ample space for relaxation and have views of the garden. Cottage-style bedrooms include six rooms in a converted coach house. The two best rooms have balconies and views of the valley and moors beyond. Two studio flats are also available for self-catering. No children under six. ***Rooms** 24. Garden. AMERICAN EXPRESS Access, Diners, Visa.*

is our symbol for an outstanding wine list.

Godalming Inn on the Lake £75

Tel 0483 415575 Fax 0483 860445 **I**

Ockford Road Godalming Surrey GU7 1RH **Map 15 E3**

A charming country house inn run by Joy and Martin Cummings, set in 2 acres of lovely gardens with lawns leading down to the lake. Guests will find stylish accommodation with thoughtful extras such as magazines, sewing kits, trouser presses and hairdryers in the best bedrooms; six rooms have spa baths and balconies. There's a convivial pubby bar with a bar snack menu and a welcoming log fire in winter. Function facilities for up to 120. The inn stands on the A3100 just south of Godalming. Residents have free use of a nearby health club. ***Rooms** 20. Garden.* AMERICAN EXPRESS *Access, Diners, Visa.*

Godalming Place of Interest

Vann House Hambledon Tel 0428 683413.

Golant Cormorant Hotel 62% £84

Tel & Fax 0726 833426 **H**

Golant nr Fowey Cornwall PL23 1LL **Map 12 C3**

The riverside setting in a small fishing village just north of Fowey is a great attraction, and the bedrooms, day rooms and swimming pool all enjoy the views. Boats may be hired for sea or river fishing, and the area is also a centre for sailing and water-skiing. Bedrooms are airy, warm and comfortable, and there's a honeymoon room. The swimming pool, set higher than the hotel, has a sliding roof for summer days. No children under 12. ***Rooms** 11. Garden, indoor swimming pool.* AMERICAN EXPRESS *Access, Visa.*

Goodwood Goodwood Park 67% £94

Tel 0243 775537 Fax 0243 533802 **H**

Goodwood nr Chichester West Sussex PO18 0QB **Map 11 A6**

Within the 12,000 acre grounds of Goodwood House estate, a much modernised and extended old house plays host to hotel, golf and country club rolled into one. Residential conferences and banqueting are the mainstay of mid-week business, while weekends are busy with guests who make full use of the extensive leisure facilities. Theatre breaks include tickets to the nearby Chichester Festival Theatre and racing breaks at Glorious Goodwood are also popular. Families are well catered for; under-16s stay free in their parents' room; informal eating in the Waterbeach Grill. No dogs. Country Club Hotels. ***Rooms** 88. Garden, indoor swimming pool, sauna, solarium, spa bath, beauty salons, snooker, tennis, squash, keep-fit equipment, 18-hole golf course, driving range, coffee shop (9.30am-10.30pm).* AMERICAN EXPRESS *Access, Diners, Visa.*

Goodwood Places of Interest

Goodwood House Tel 0243 774107.
Goodwood Racecourse Tel 0243 774107.

Gordano Forte Travelodge £42

Tel 0275 373709 **L**

Gordano nr Portbury Avon BS20 9XG **Map 13 E1**

7 miles from Bristol city centre at Junction 19 of the M5 motorway by the Gordano service area. ***Rooms** 40.* AMERICAN EXPRESS *Access, Visa.*

Goring-on-Thames — The Leatherne Bottel ↑ — £70

Tel 0491 872667 — R

Goring-on-Thames Berkshire RG8 0HS — Map 15 D2

Signposted off the B4009 north of Goring, Keith Read and Annie Bonnet's delightful establishment has just about everything going for it. A little row of white-painted cottages stands on the edge of an unspoilt stretch of the Thames with a large terrace for summer eating; there's even an Edwardian launch available for charter for pre-prandial drinks on the river. Inside, the atmosphere is highly civilised yet relaxed and informal with log fire burning in the bar between two dining rooms which boast some glorious floral displays courtesy of Annie. Foodwise, Keith's department along with Clive O'Connor, it's all about quality ingredients with the main component of dishes simply cooked and served with virgin olive oil dressings, rather than sauces, that are profligate in their use of spices and home-grown herbs – guinea fowl with cumin, coriander, sun-dried tomatoes, olives, kidney beans, haricot beans and all sorts of herbs; salmon marinated in ginger and chargrilled with Norfolk samphire and a red chili and herb vinaigrette; local venison liver pan-fried with sage, tomato chutney, roquette leaves and Parmesan. Main courses come with either locally grown vegetables, 'greens' (Keith's very fond of curly kale) or a salad that will contain upwards of 20 different leaves. The menu is individually priced and they are happy to serve just a single dish. There's a variety of good home-made breads and five British and Irish cheeses. Regional British Cheeseboard of the Year winner (see earlier pages). No half bottles on the short though wide-ranging wine list, but most bottles will be opened and charged as taken. ***Seats** 45. Private Room 20. L 12.30-2 (Sat & Sun to 2.30) D 7-9.30 (Sun 7.30-9). Closed 25 Dec.*
AMERICAN EXPRESS *Access, Visa.*

Goudhurst — Star & Eagle Inn — £40

Tel 0580 211512 — I

High Street Goudhurst Kent TN17 1AL — Map 11 B5

The bedrooms at this gabled 14th-century inn come in all shapes and sizes, and one sports a restored four-poster bed. In the public areas period appeal survives in exposed beams, open brick fireplaces and old settles. No dogs. A Whitbread hotel. ***Rooms** 11. Garden.* AMERICAN EXPRESS *Access, Visa.*

Goudhurst — Place of Interest

Bedgebury National Pinetum Tel 0580 211044.

Grantham — Forte Travelodge — £42

Tel 0476 77500 — L

Grantham service area Gonerby Moor Grantham Lincolnshire NG32 2AB — Map 7 E3

At the Welcome Break service area on the A1 – 3 miles north of Grantham, 10 miles south of Newark-on-Trent. ***Rooms** 40.*
AMERICAN EXPRESS *Access, Visa.*

Grantham — Granada Lodge — £45

Tel 0476 860686 Fax 0476 861078 — L

A1/A151 Colsterworth Grantham Lincolnshire NG33 5JR — Map 7 E3

***Rooms** 38.* AMERICAN EXPRESS *Access, Diners, Visa.*

> We welcome bona fide complaints and recommendations on the tear-out pages at the back of the book for readers' comments. They are followed up by our professional team.

Grasmere Michael's Nook 79% £152*

Tel 053 94 35496 Fax 053 94 35765 **HR**

Grasmere nr Ambleside Cumbria LA22 9RP **Map 4 C3**

Originally built as a summer home in 1859 this grand Victorian house stands a short distance back off the A591 surrounded by three acres of landscaped gardens. Reg Gifford, the owner, opened it as a hotel in 1969 and since then it has firmly established itself as one of the premier country house hotels in the Lake District. The doorbell is rung to gain admittance into a beautiful entrance hall which is typical of the gracious and supremely comfortable day rooms. An Oriental carpet on the polished parquet floor, antiques, a ticking grandfather clock, potted plants and fresh flowers create an immediate sense of well-being. The drawing room, approached through double doors, is also immensely impressive, the flower arrangements arrestingly beautiful. Decor is classically elegant, with deep-cushioned well-upholstered settees and armchairs in which to relax. The bar, sometimes also visited by Reg's two loveable Great Danes, has a delightful farmhouse ambience with its china-filled antique Welsh dresser and polished oak tables and chairs. Log fires warm the bar and drawing room in inclement weather. A fine balustrade staircase leads up to the bedrooms which, again, are very traditional in character and decor. Exquisite satinwood suites grace some rooms and the original furniture has been restored in one room with mahogany, oak and even Chinese lacquer in others, together with a whole host of extras making for very comfortable rooms. Beautiful bathrooms have thick towels, flannels, bathrobes and a range of Floris toiletries. No dogs. *Half-board terms only. ***Rooms** 14. Garden.* AMERICAN EXPRESS *Access, Diners, Visa.*

Restaurant ★↑ £96

Orders and pre-dinner drinks are served in the charming, cosy bar with dinner taken in one of the two splendid dining rooms. The first room has a striking decor of red gloss walls, gilt-framed mirrors and a crystal chandelier. The red room is grander with fine oak-panelled walls. Highly polished antique mahogany tables, crystal glassware and gleaming silver create an ambience of relaxed but traditional formality. Kevin Mangeolles' cooking reflects the high quality and painstaking attention to detail exhibited in the decor and upkeep. Dinner includes a £46 six-course no-choice gourmet menu and a £38 five-course well-balanced 'recommended' menu. Additionally, a short but varied selection of seasonal alternatives can be taken. There is flexibility in that, with the exception of the gourmet menu, which is unalterable, the other menus are interchangeable. The marvellously innovative classicism of the cooking style is exemplified by: a warm chartreuse of asparagus mousse, soft and featherlight, wrapped in paper-thin slices of carrot and courgette. It is served surrounded by sprue, chicken mousse-filled ravioli and crunchy celeriac crisps. In a rich, creamy bisque the delicacy of the crab is complemented by a tiny, warm fresh tomato quiche. As a main course two small, plump, tear-shaped breasts of poussin are served on a creamy green peppercorn sauce surrounded by slices of a flavoursome ballotine of the legs. To finish, glorious desserts include a stunning praline-flavoured crème brulée baked in a fine pastry case with lightly glazed fruit and a blackcurrant and liquorice sauce. Note the inexpensive French regional wines on the well-balanced wine list, which includes plenty of half bottles. This is currently the best cooking in the Lake District. Booking is essential. ***Seats** 28. Private Room 35. L 12.30 for 1 D 7.30 for 8. Set L £27.50 Set D £38/£46.*

Grasmere The Swan 65% £148*

Tel 053 94 35551 Fax 053 94 35741 **H**

Grasmere nr Ambleside Cumbria LA22 9RF **Map 4 C3**

Wordsworth's favourite lakeland hotel: the inn-like public areas, with their carved furniture, horse brasses, copper jugs and pewter, are little changed since he mentioned The Swan in his poem *The Waggoner*. By contrast, the bedrooms, many with views of the surrounding fells, offer more up-to-date comfort; half-tester beds in five feature rooms (with views); eight courtyard rooms attract partial views and a reduced rate. On wet days walkers will appreciate the Drying Room. Forte Heritage. *Half-board terms only. ***Rooms** 36. Garden.* AMERICAN EXPRESS *Access, Diners, Visa.*

Grasmere **White Moss House** 69% £128*

Tel 053 94 35295 **HR**

Rydal Water Grasmere Cumbria LA22 9SE **Map 4 C3**

One of Lakeland's smallest hotels, built in 1730 and once owned by William Wordsworth, sets great store by its resultant intimacy, and the views over Rydal Water from its wooded hillside location are another bonus. Bedrooms in the main house are full of antique pieces, and Susan Dixon's homely touches abound. Above the hotel, in the hideaway Brockstone Cottage, two further en-suite bedrooms are let to just one party at a time (sometimes just two people – very peaceful and romantic); there are a lounge, dining area and kitchen in the cottage. Good breakfasts extend to kippers, Cumberland sausage and black pudding. *Half-board terms only. No dogs. ***Rooms** 6. Garden, game fishing, hotel boat. Closed Dec-Feb. Access, Visa.*

Restaurant £60

Consistency and continuity are Peter Dixon's watchwords; "no meal is served unless Peter is cooking". A five-course dinner is served at 8pm in a tiny cottage-style dining room in the oldest part of the house. The nightly menu is a meticulously planned affair, perhaps commencing with carrot, coriander, lentil and orange soup, followed by a bombe of brill with a centre of Bonchester brie and a red pepper sauce; roast fillet of Siga wild Westmorland venison marinated with juniper and Pomerol, served with a woodland mushroom sauce, potatoes roasted in goose fat, spiced red cabbage, purée of salsify, celeriac and parsnip with heather honey and stir-fried green beans. Dessert might offer a choice of Guardsman's pudding with raspberry sauce, apple and blueberry Grasmere or Eton Mess; finally, a selection of 13 or so unusual British cheeses with home-made oat biscuits. Fair prices on a decent wine list that features familiar names, particularly from France; useful tasting notes. No smoking. ***Seats** 18. Parties 8. D only 7.30 for 8. Closed Sun. Set D £25.*

Grasmere **Wordsworth Hotel** 72% £100

Tel 053 94 35592 Fax 053 94 35765 **HR**

Grasmere nr Ambleside Cumbria LA22 9SW **Map 4 C3**

Centrally located in Grasmere village, the Wordsworth's two acres of well-tended gardens and paddock nevertheless promise calm and tranquillity. The conservatory bar and adjacent lounge have bold floral fabrics, some cane seating and the best of the views. The more active will enjoy the well-equipped leisure centre or the Dove & Olive Branch pub. Individually decorated bedrooms vary widely in size and aspect; the best are two suites with whirlpool baths and an antique-furnished four-poster room. Many rooms are suitable for family use, and baby-sitting and baby-listening are available; there's also a children's menu. Free golf at Keswick mid-week. ***Rooms** 37. Garden, indoor swimming pool, keep-fit equipment, sauna, spa bath, solarium, games room.* AMERICAN EXPRESS *Access, Diners, Visa.*

Prelude Restaurant £74

There's a traditional feel to the dining room but many of the variations on Bernard Warne's menus have a modern ring: terrine of marinated herring, smoked salmon and potato, chilled two-tone soup, vegetable and lentil moussaka, baked tenderloin of pork wrapped in brioche with sage on a coarse broccoli and raisin sauce. To finish, perhaps a layered trio of chocolate mousses on a pistachio sauce, or cheeses from the North of England's British Cheeseboard of the Year regional winner. Note the house

See over

selection and bin ends on a well-balanced wine list which offers plenty under £20. No smoking. ***Seats** 60. L 12.30-2 D 7-9 (Fri & Sat to9.30). Set L £17.50 Set D £29.50.*

Grasmere — Place of Interest

Dove Cottage and Wordsworth Museum Tel 09665 544/547.

Grayshott — Woods Place — £50

Tel 0428 605555 — **R**

Headley Road Grayshott nr Hindhead Surrey GU26 6LB — **Map 11 A6**

There is a rustic slant to Dana and Eric Norrgren's authentic Scandinavian cooking in the unlikely bistroesque setting of a former butcher's shop in a village just off the A3 south of Hindhead. Homely cooking encompasses a range of hearty, relatively uncomplicated dishes: gravlax (try it with a glass of ice-cold akvavit), Jansson's Temptation (sliced potatoes baked with fish and cream), pike quenelles with white wine sauce and mushrooms, roast pork stuffed with prunes and served with red cabbage, preserved duck with onions cooked in red wine and honey. Leave room for upside-down apple tart or home-made hot doughnuts served with ice-cold vanilla sauce. ***Seats** 36. Parties 16. L 12-2.30 D 7-11. Closed Sun & Mon, 1 week Christmas.* AMERICAN EXPRESS *Access, Diners, Visa.*

Great Ayton — Ayton Hall — 73% — £85

Tel 0642 723595 Fax 0642 722149 — **H**

Low Green Great Ayton nr Middlesbrough North Yorkshire TS9 6PW — **Map 5 E3**

Six acres of landscaped ground surround Ayton Hall, seven miles south of Middlesbrough on the A172. Inside the Grade II listed building a Moroccan-style reception area-cum-cocktail bar gives on to a spacious, drawing room with huge picture windows, antiques and a cool pastel decor; ornaments, magazines and attractive pictures provide a homely feel. The bedrooms are equipped with antique or pine furniture; they offer an exceptional range of extras, both large and small. As we went to press there were plans for two more bedrooms and a second, brasserie-style, restaurant. No dogs. ***Rooms** 11. Garden, tennis, archery.* AMERICAN EXPRESS *Access, Diners, Visa.*

Great Baddow — Pontlands Park — 70% — £135

Tel 0245 476444 Fax 0245 478393 — **H**

West Hanningfield Road Great Baddow nr Chelmsford Essex CM2 8HR — **Map 11 B4**

An extended mid-Victorian hotel with an attractive health and leisure centre. Bedrooms in the wing are huge, with high ceilings, separate sitting areas, large beds, quality reproduction furniture and bright, stylish fabrics. Rooms in the main house are similar but smaller; all bathrooms boast bidets, high-class toiletries and good carpeting and decor. Public areas include a marble-effect entrance hall, a comfortable bar, an elegant lounge and a bright little garden coffee shop with lots of plants and Lloyd Loom chairs. Dogs in kennels only. Children not allowed in health centre during members' hours. 10% service charge is added to all accommodation, food and bar final bills (included in the room rate above). ***Rooms** 17. Garden, indoor & outdoor swimming pools, sauna, spa bath, keep-fit equipment, beauty & hair salons, dance studio. Closed 1 week Jan.* AMERICAN EXPRESS *Access, Diners, Visa.*

Great Baddow — Places of Interest

Hyde Hall Garden Rettendon Tel 0245 400256.
Chelmsford Cathedral Tel 0245 263660.
Essex County Cricket Ground (Chelmsford) Tel 0245 252420.
Riverside Ice and Leisure Centre Tel 0245 269417.
Great Leighs Showground Tel 0245 361259.

Great Dunmow **Saracen's Head** 58% £97

Tel 0371 873901 Fax 0371 875743 **H**

High Street Great Dunmow Essex CM6 1AG **Map 10 B3**

Forte hotel blending Tudor and Georgian architectural features with a modern wing of bedrooms. Banqueting and conference facilities for around 50. Families with children well catered for, with baby-sitting and listening available. ***Rooms** 24.* AMERICAN EXPRESS *Access, Diners, Visa.*

Great Dunmow **The Starr** £75

Tel 0371 874321 Fax 0371 876337 **RR**

Market Place Great Dunmow Essex CM6 1AX **Map 10 B3**

The Starr is a small restaurant housed in a 400-year-old timber-framed hostelry building overlooking Great Dunmow's market place and has been run by Brian and Vanessa Jones since 1980. London markets and local sources supply the raw materials for Mark Fisher's menus: warm salad of pigeon breast, moules marinière, scallops grilled with bacon, pan-fried skate wing with capers, rack of English lamb, braised oxtail, mixed grill. Lighter lunchtime options are available Monday to Friday. A physically small list of good-value wines is classified by style and is exceptionally well chosen, mostly French but Australia and New Zealand also make a good showing. ***Seats** 50. Parties 12. Private Rooms 36. L 12-1.30 D 7-9.30. Closed L Sat, D Sun, 1 week Jan. Set L £11 (Sun £21.50) Set D £21.50 & £32.50.* AMERICAN EXPRESS *Access, Visa.*

Rooms £75

Eight en-suite bedrooms, with names like the Oak Room, the Brass Room and the Poppy Room, are in the old stable block and individually furnished, mainly with antiques. *Rooms closed 1 week Jan.*

Great Dunmow **Place of Interest**

Saling Hall Garden Great Saling Tel 0371 850141.

Great Gonerby **Harry's Place** £80

Tel 0476 61780 **R**

17 High Street Great Gonerby Grantham Lincolnshire NG31 8JS **Map 7 E3**

Harry Hallam cooks and his wife Caroline serves a meticulously planned meal to just ten diners at their tiny restaurant set in an elegant Georgian house, one mile north of Grantham on the B474. Each session sees a separate hand-written menu of two choices per course (plus optional French and English cheeses), on which Harry's elaborate creations are carefully described. Thus, "calves' liver terrine with Madeira and black pepper jelly, served with Cumberland sauce and mixed salad leaves" may precede "sautéed fillet of wild Scottish salmon served with a sauce of white wine, cardamom, mango, tomatoes and basil", finishing with rhubarb soufflé. Other recent dishes have included a terrine of Orkney king scallops, smoked haddock soufflé, Cornish sea bass with lemon and Pernod sauce, and breast of young Yorkshire grouse roasted with red wine, Madeira, cognac, redcurrants and rosemary. Everything is cooked to order by Harry on his own in the kitchen and thus meals here can be long affairs; however, the affair is likely to develop into love at first sight as results invariably live up to their promise. For pre-booked parties, a complementary wine may be proposed to accompany each course. No smoking. ***Seats** 10. Private Room 4. L 12-2 D 7-9.30. Closed Sun & Mon (except by special arrangement), Bank Holidays, 1 week Christmas. Access, Visa.*

We publish annually, so make sure you use the current edition.
It's worth it!

Great Milton — Le Manoir aux Quat'Saisons — 85% — £184

Tel 0844 278881 Fax 0844 278847 — **HR**

Church Road Great Milton Oxfordshire OX44 7PD — **Map 15 D2**

Service and housekeeping are among the best in the country at this 15th-century manor house built by a French nobleman and set in 25 acres of grounds. A flagstoned inner foyer is a showpiece for the accolades bestowed upon Raymond Blanc for his cooking and leads into lounges that are models of restrained good taste, created by interior designer Michael Priest. Antique and immaculate reproduction furniture sets a refined tone that is echoed throughout the whole house. All the luxury extras that one might expect from an 80%+ hotel are in the bedrooms, including a comfortable settee, decanter of Madeira, sugared almonds, sewing kit with silk thread and a bowl of 14 fresh fruits. Rooms in the new wing lead out on to little patio gardens with wrought-iron furniture; each is given a certain amount of privacy and separation from the others by a hedge of shrubs. The beautiful bathrooms feature jacuzzi or whirlpool baths, gold-plated fittings, huge fluffy towels and luxurious bathrobes. Cooked breakfasts are, of course, superb. One mile from Junction 7 of the M40, 7 miles from Oxford and 40 miles from London. ***Rooms** 19. Garden, outdoor swimming pool, tennis.* AMERICAN EXPRESS *Access, Diners, Visa.*

Restaurant ★★★ — £195

Perfection is Raymond Blanc's aim in life – right from the electronically-controlled automatic gates at the entrance of the manor house down to the correct hanging of paintings and the precision growing of vegetables and herbs in the 3-acre kitchen garden. His meticulousness has involved revamping two dining rooms recently and he has grand plans for further improvements around the manor. Residents should take time to appreciate the three distinctly different dining areas: the first room as one enters is now lovely and bright (yet surprisingly intimate), featuring a pale lemon and light blue colour scheme jazzed up with half a dozen or so modern paintings, cream-painted beams and mirrored centre column; this leads through to a room that has two windows (originally the back windows of the house) looking into the conservatory, the same colour scheme, shelves with preserved fruits in glass jars and "naïf" paintings of Burgundian village scenes. The large, airy conservatory has powerful air-conditioning (it's the only dining area where smoking is permitted), cane chairs and a pink and green colour scheme matched by Sarah Goodsell's floral displays. Tables in the first room are cleverly lit by downlighters and set with greenery and fresh flowers (perhaps even chive flowers) from the garden; a pewter candle-holder adds a nice 'old' touch in keeping with the feel of the manor house. Pre-prandial drinks and canapés are taken in two elegant drawing rooms which can come under pressure – not a problem in summer when you can wander around the lovely gardens. Choosing from the large, cleverly designed, triptych-like printed menu (that evolves through the seasons) is a pleasure with so much to tempt, and the maitre d' will skilfully help with any prevarications; dishes are written in French with English translations. Head chef Clive Fretwell might commence one's meal with a typical appetiser of cubed marinated salmon in a gravad lax style or a miniature feast of Mediterranean flavours. Albert Ring, the previous head gardener, has now retired and Anne-Marie Owens is now rightfully credited on the menu; however Albert's name lives on in an *assiette de notre jardinier "Albert"*: a vivid green dish of the freshest vegetables from the garden, including asparagus, skinned broad beans, baby courgettes with a stuffed flower on a bed of creamed spinach, plus morel, miller and *trompette de mort* mushrooms. Fish soup with coconut milk and Thai spices, lamb sweetbreads with poached morels filled with chicken mousse, terrine of wild Scottish salmon, crustaceans, turbot and scallops, and roasted lobster tail and tomato bavarois with a coral vinaigrette dressing also appeared among the starters of a spring carte. Fish dishes are only priced as a main course, but should you wish (even at these prices) for an intermediate course a special portion will be happily produced of, perhaps, sea bass tied around spinach-wrapped scallops or red mullet fillets set on an interesting combination of sea urchin coulis and meat jus. Diners who wish to sample a wider range of Raymond's seasonal specialities are offered the *menu gourmand*, a seven-course tasting menu; the simpler table d'hote lunch, however, only offers a small choice. Main courses can turn into an event if you order Bresse chicken cooked *en vessie* (in a pig's bladder) and cut open from a tureen at your table, or a roast joint of Pauillac lamb, also carved at table; other temptations might be an intricate dish of pan-fried quail breasts on smoked bacon and fondant potatoes served with a miniature bird's nest of deep-fried leek and potato containing softly-cooked, breadcrumbed quail's eggs (*supremes de caille des Dombes poelés, pommes de terre fondantes au lard fumé et sauce à l'essence de cèpes et vin de Pineau des Charentes*) or corn-fed Bresse squab pigeon filled with boudin blanc and foie gras in a truffle-scented jus (*pigeonneau de Bresse farci au boudin blanc, jus parfumé aux truffes et petits légumes*). The simultaneous cloche-raising may be considered a tired old cliché in some restaurants, but here the small flourish seems perfectly apposite – an elegant touch. Among the superb desserts, *Le Café Crème* is somewhat of a trademark – concentrated espresso ice cream served in a coffee cup formed from wafer-thin Valrhona bitter chocolate topped with a Kirsch sabayon; *assiette aux parfums de caramel* offers five individual miniature dishes on a caramel theme; *fleurs d'ananas croustillantes, parfait glacé au kirsch, griottes aux épices et crème vanillée* is a clever creation with slivers of dried pineapple cut into sunflower shapes. The fine selection of petits fours served with coffee is almost a dessert in itself. Unhurried service under Alain Desenclos and Etienne Uzureau is exemplary, suitably semi-formal, smooth and efficient. There are some excellent country wines on the serious wine list, which features many of the best wine-makers worldwide; perhaps surprisingly, Italy and the New World are also well represented. After a few years when we have had some adverse criticism of *Le Manoir* it is good to see both it and Raymond himself back on tip-top form, particularly at a time when the higher end of the London restaurant scene has seen so much inconsistency. ***Seats 95.*** *Parties 64. Private Room 46. L 12.15-2.15 D 7.15-10.30. Set L £29.50 Set D £59.50.*

Great Snoring — Old Rectory — 61% — £84

Tel 0328 820597 Fax 0328 820048 — H

Barsham Road Great Snoring nr Fakenham Norfolk NR21 0HP — **Map 10 C1**

Behind the church on the Barsham road, the Old Rectory retains some pleasing architectural features, including stone-mullioned windows bordered by frieze tiles. Day rooms are peaceful and old-fashioned and there are some fine period furnishings in the handsomely proportioned bedrooms. The Shelton Suites, newly-built, brick-and-flint self-catering cottages in the grounds, offer a greater degree of privacy and seclusion, each having its own living room and kitchen. No children under 12, although families with babes in arms may find this a wonderfully relaxing country retreat. Six miles from the Norfolk coast. No dogs. ***Rooms 6.*** *Garden.* AMERICAN EXPRESS, *Diners.*

Great Yarmouth — Carlton Hotel — 67% — £79

Tel 0493 855234 Fax 0493 852220 — H

Marine Parade Great Yarmouth Norfolk NR30 3JE — **Map 10 D1**

With its fine seafront location directly opposite Wellington Pier and still fresh refurbishment, the Carlton is the flagship of East Anglia's Waveney Inns Group. An impressive interior now houses conference facilities. Bonuses for individual guests include Penny's café-bar (offering a weekday happy hour and a modern brasserie menu encompassing Tex-Mex) and a hair salon. Bedrooms have bright colour schemes and smart tiled bathrooms. Children under 12 free in parents' room; families are well catered for, with baby-sitting by arrangement and high-chairs for junior diners. ***Rooms 90.*** AMERICAN EXPRESS *Access, Diners, Visa.*

Great Yarmouth Seafood Restaurant £55

Tel 0493 856009 **R**

85 North Quay Great Yarmouth Norfolk NR30 1JF **Map 10 D1**

There's a tankful of live lobsters, and an excellent selection of seafood and shellfish, much of it arriving daily from Lowestoft. Fish can be served grilled, poached, in batter or with a sauce – prawn with lemon sole, creamy black pepper with turbot, tarragon with plaice, cheese and onion with cod. Steaks for meat-eaters, surf'n'turf for a mixed palate. Good wines include some drier Germans. The restaurant is next to the railway station. ***Seats** 40. L 12-1.45 D 7-10.30. Closed L Sat, all Sun, Bank Holidays, 3 weeks Christmas.* AMERICAN EXPRESS *Access, Diners, Visa.*

Great Yarmouth Places of Interest

Tourist Information Tel 0493 846345.
Britannia Theatre Tel 0493 842914.
Royalty Theatre Tel 0493 842043.
Great Yarmouth Racecourse Tel 0493 842527.
Thrigby Hall Wildlife Park and Gardens Tel 0493 369477.

Greta Bridge Morritt Arms £66

Tel 0833 27232 Fax 0833 27570 **I**

Greta Bridge nr Barnard Castle Durham DL12 9SE **Map 5 D3**

Twin brothers David and John Mulley, here since 1986, extend a very friendly welcome at their charming old coaching inn, which enjoys a picturesque location appropriate to its characterful interior. The lounge bar is comfortable and old-fashioned, with groups of easy chairs, an antique barrel organ and a miniature traction engine, while the famous Dickens Bar depicts various characters from the novels. Bedrooms, some of which have fine views, are quaint and homely. ***Rooms** 17. Garden, children's playground.* AMERICAN EXPRESS *Access, Diners, Visa.*

Grimsby Forte Crest 64% £67

Tel 0472 350295 Fax 0472 241354 **H**

Littlecoates Road Grimsby Humberside DN34 4LX **Map 7 F1**

Friendly and peaceful late-60s' hotel on the outskirts of town, overlooking a golf course. Business-oriented in the week (catering for conferences of up to 250 delegates), popular with families at weekends. Half the bedrooms are designated non-smoking. ***Rooms** 52.* AMERICAN EXPRESS *Access, Diners, Visa.*

Grimsby Places of Interest

Tourist Information Tel 0472 240180.
Leisure Centre Ice Rink Tel 0472 242000.
Animal Gardens Mablethorpe Tel 05074 73346.

Grimston Congham Hall 76% £101

Tel 0485 600250 Fax 0485 601191 **HR**

Lynn Road Grimston King's Lynn Norfolk PE32 1AH **Map 10 B1**

A privately-owned Georgian country house set in 40 acres of parkland, six miles east of King's Lynn. Christine Forecast's noted herb garden contributes baskets of lavender and other herbs and flowers to decorate the summery day rooms. Peace and quiet are the main attractions and there is plenty of room in which to relax; a well-proportioned sitting room is a good contrast to the bar with its cosy log fire. Staff are charming and the general feel is one of being pampered. Bedrooms are individually decorated and boast many extras that one now comes to expect in a country hotel of this standard. No children under 12. Dogs in kennels only. ***Rooms** 14. Garden, outdoor swimming pool, whirlpool bath, tennis, clay-pigeon shooting, cricket, helipad.* AMERICAN EXPRESS *Access, Diners, Visa.*

Orangery Restaurant ↑ £85

An attractive restaurant with full-length windows that overlook the lawns to parkland beyond. The glass roof in the centre of the room trails plants, giving a fine mix of the formal and informal. Chef Murray Chapman's menus are a suitable match to the venue – from light summer lunches on the lawns to more elaborate fixed-price affairs which include 'Hobson's Choice' – a set gourmet dinner of seven light, small courses. Dishes change frequently: Chilled fish terrine wrapped in trout served with a garden herb salad and tomato vinaigrette, English lamb with a wild mushroom farce, braised leeks and celeriac, and a baked vanilla soufflé scented with orange and served with raspberry ripple ice cream. ***Seats** 50. Parties 12. L 12.30-2 D 7.30-9.30. Closed L Sat & Bank Holidays. Set L £13.50/£15 Set D £21.50-£36.*

Grindleford — Maynard Arms — £60

Tel 0433 630321 Fax 0433 630445 — **I**

Main Road Grindleford Derbyshire S30 1HP — **Map 6 C2**

At the heart of the Peak National Park amid fine walking country stands this imposing Victorian house. Splendid stained-glass windows feature throughout the hotel, which has a welcoming and informal air. Bedrooms of good size are decorated and furnished in various styles. Most offer fine views over Hope Valley. Dark blue tiling in the bathrooms. Public areas include a homely residents' lounge, two bars and a ballroom. ***Rooms** 13. Garden.* AMERICAN EXPRESS *Access, Diners, Visa.*

Grizedale — Grizedale Lodge — 61% — £68

Tel 053 94 36532 — **HR**

Grizedale nr Hawkshead Cumbria LA22 0QL — **Map 4 C3**

The Lambs' hidden hotel, small and homely, welcomes so many annual returnees that you'll need to book well in advance. Comfortable rewards are found in the roomy lounge, cheery bar and spick-and-span cottage-style bedrooms; two rooms are in an extension. All have en-suite facilities (four with showers only); one is a family room with a double and two single beds; two have four-posters. No dogs. Follow the Tourist Board signs from Hawkshead or Newby Bridge for Grizedale Forest Park and the Theatre in the Forest. ***Rooms** 9. Closed Jan-mid Feb. Access, Visa.*

Restaurant in the Forest £45

Margaret Lamb's home-style cooking befits the atmosphere of a former hunting lodge. Choices on the short menu rely heavily on local produce and are substantial in both flavours and volume. Favourites include Penrith peppered lamb and Old English-style game pie with venison, guinea fowl and pheasant. One of the four main courses is for vegetarians. ***Seats** 30. L 12.15-1.45 D 7-8.30 (Sun at 7). Set D £16.95.*

Guildford — The Angel — 71% — £122

Tel 0483 64555 Fax 0483 33770 — **H**

91 High Street Guildford Surrey GU1 3DP — **Map 15 E3**

In the centre of town, halfway up the steep High Street, the Angel is a smart, privately-owned "Posting House and Livery" with much style in evidence. Nine of the eleven bedrooms are full suites and all are furnished to a high standard with reproduction antique furniture and a variety of stylish fabrics with bedhead drapes and quilted covers. Marble bathrooms boast large soft towels and bathrobes. The only day room is a small galleried lounge with ancient redbrick inglenook fireplace, old black timbers, an original 17th-century parliament clock and deep, comfortable settees and armchairs, where drinks are served to residents and diners only. Beds are turned down in the evenings and excellent breakfasts in the cosy, wood-panelled Oak Room make a fine start to the day. ***Rooms** 11.* AMERICAN EXPRESS *Access, Diners, Visa.*

Guildford Forte Crest 68% £108

Tel 0483 574444 Fax 0483 302960 **H**

Egerton Road Guildford Surrey GU2 5XZ **Map 15 E3**

Darkwood panelling and a white marble fireplace lend a very civilised air to the public areas at this smart modern hotel on the outskirts of town (follow signs for Cathedral/University then the Business Park). It's very much geared-up to the requirements of business travellers with ample free parking, secretarial services and meeting rooms and they can even provide a personal pager for use within the hotel, ensuring that you do not miss a vital call. Conference facilities for up to 200 delegates. Comprehensive 24hr room service. Children up to 16 stay free in parents' room.
***Rooms** 111. Garden, indoor swimming pool, gymnasium, sauna, solarium.*
AMERICAN EXPRESS® *Access, Diners, Visa.*

Guildford Mandarin £35

Tel 0483 572293 **R**

13 Epsom Road Guildford Surrey GU1 3JT **Map 15 E3**

Modern, cool decor with black lacquered chairs and spotlit tables add up to a quietly chic ambience in a friendly restaurant at the top of the town (opposite the Odeon cinema). Cooking covers Peking, Szechuan and Cantonese styles with both outstanding crispy aromatic duck and unusual deep-fried quail showing flair in the kitchen. Mongolian lamb and beef are filling hot pot dishes. ***Seats** 55. L 12.30-2.30 D 6-10.30 (Fri & Sat to 11). Closed L Sun, 25 & 26 Dec. Set D from £16.* AMERICAN EXPRESS® *Access, Diners, Visa.*

Guildford Places of Interest

Tourist Information Tel 0483 444007.
Yvonne Arnaud Theatre Millbrook Tel 0483 64571.
Guildford Cathedral Tel 0483 65287.
Woodbridge Road Cricket Ground Tel 0483 572181.
Combined Services Polo Committee Pirbright Tel 0483 798449.
Stoke Park Showground Tel 0483 414651.

Historic Houses, Castles and Gardens

Clandon Park and Garden (NT) Tel 0483 222482.
Coverwood Lakes Ewhurst Tel 0306 731103.
Hatchlands Park House and Gardens (NT) East Clandon Tel 0483 222787.
Loseley House Tel 0483 304440.
Wisley Garden (The Royal Horticultural Society) Wisley Tel 0938 224234.

Museums and Art Galleries

British Red Cross Museum and Archives Barnett Hill, Wonersh. Tel 0483 898595.
Gallery 90 Ward Street Tel 0483 444741.
Guildford Museum Tel 0483 444750.

Guiseley Prachee £30

Tel 0943 872531 **R**

6 Bradford Road Whitecross Guiseley West Yorkshire LS20 8NH **Map 6 C1**

Tandoori restaurant opposite Harry Ramsden's fish and chip restaurant at Whitecross. ***Seats** 56. Parties 25. L 12-2 D 6-12. Access, Visa.*

Our inspectors *never* book in the name of Egon Ronay's Guides. They disclose their identity only if they are considering an establishment for inclusion in the next edition of the Guide.

Guist **Tollbridge** £65

Tel 036 284 359 R

Dereham Road Guist Norfolk NR20 5NU **Map 10 C1**

A redbrick house on the B1110 with an open-air, floodlit terrace dining area overlooking the rushes on the banks of the river Wensum. The menu format for dinner has now changed back to à la carte only and a 'two-course lunch for a fiver' has also been introduced for only those who book on summer Thursdays and Fridays. Snacks are also available in the lounge and on two outdoor terraces at lunchtime. Straightforward, unfussy cooking with starters like a smoked haddock and cheese pot, Stilton and pecan nut salad and spicy fish cakes with tartare sauce, followed by cassoulet, fresh pasta, rack of English lamb or salmon in pastry with lemon sauce. Puddings might include a fruit pavlova, chocolate profiteroles and orange sponge with butterscotch sauce. No smoking. Concise wine list with personal notes and fair prices. Open for lunch Sunday, also Thursday and Friday in summer; open for dinner Thursday-Saturday, also Tuesday and Wednesday in summer. ***Seats** 50. Parties 60. L 12.30-1.30 D 7.30-9 (Sat from 7). Closed Mon, 3 weeks Jan. Set L £5 (Thurs/Fri summer). Access, Visa*

Gulworthy **Horn of Plenty** ★ £100

Tel & Fax 0822 832528 RR

Gulworthy nr Tavistock Devon PL19 8JD **Map 12 C3**

Signposted off the A390 to the west of Tavistock, this 200-year-old house overlooking the Tamar valley is surrounded by gardens and filled with flowers beautifully arranged by Elaine Gatehouse who, with husband Ian, provides a genuinely warm welcome. The well-balanced fixed-price menus are the responsibility of chef Peter Gordon whose skills are equally evident in all departments of the kitchen from a tiny, freshly baked pastry parcel filled with spicy minced venison amongst the canapés to a crème brulée just bursting with fresh mint flavour. In between come well-conceived dishes like buckwheat ravioli filled with wild mushrooms on a roasted red pepper sauce; guinea fowl with goat's cheese, truffles and a port sauce; a warm sausage of rabbit with mustard sauce and a fish dish of the day dependent upon what is best in the market. A selection of local cheeses offers an alternative to the delicious desserts. Good selection of house wines, all available by the glass. ***Seats** 48. Private Room 12. L 12-2 D 7-9.30. Closed L Mon, 25 & 26 Dec. Set L £14.50/£17.50 Set D £25.50.* AMERICAN EXPRESS *Access, Visa.*

Rooms £72

Six of the seven pine-furnished bedrooms, each with its own balcony overlooking the valley, are in a separate converted stable block. Direct-dial phones, remote-control TVs and well-stocked mini-bars provide the modern comforts. *Garden.*

Hackness **Hackness Grange** 61% £118

Tel 0723 882345 Fax 0723 882391 H

Hackness nr Scarborough North Yorkshire YO13 0JW **Map 5 F3**

An attractive 19th-century house standing in its own grounds by the River Derwent in the North York Moors National Park. Recent improvements include the refurbishment of the bar and most of the bedrooms, some of which are in a courtyard away from the main building. Parking for 50 cars. Dogs in kennels only. ***Rooms** 28. Garden, indoor swimming pool, tennis, putting.* AMERICAN EXPRESS *Access, Diners, Visa.*

Changes in data sometimes occur in establishments after the Guide goes to press. Prices should be taken as indications rather than firm quotes.

Hadley Wood — West Lodge Park — 66% — £106

Tel 081-440 8311 Fax 081-449 3698 — **H**

Cockfosters Road Hadley Wood nr Barnet Hertfordshire EN4 0PY — **Map 15 F2**

An extended 19th-century country house set in parkland that includes an arboretum and a lake. Inside, there's an orderly, civilised feel in the lounge, plentifully supplied with armchairs, in the brick-walled bar and in the four conference rooms (catering for up to 75 delegates). Bedrooms are individually decorated and furnished, and the majority have small entrance lobbies. The hotel is on the A111 halfway between the M25 (exit 24) and Cockfosters underground station. Free membership of, and taxi to, local leisure club. No dogs. ***Rooms 50. Garden, putting, bar billiards.***
American Express *Access, Visa.*

Hagley — Travel Inn — £43

Tel 0562 883120 Fax 0562 884416 — **L**

Birmingham Road Hagley nr Stourbridge West Midlands DY9 9JS — **Map 6 C4**

Birmingham City Centre 15 minutes' drive, Birmingham International Airport 20 minutes. ***Rooms 40.*** American Express *Access, Diners, Visa.*

Hailey — The Bird in Hand — NEW — £55

Tel 0993 868321 Fax 0993 868702 — **I**

Hailey nr Witney Oxfordshire — **Map 14 C2**

A delightful "residential country inn" in a rural setting surrounded by open fields, one mile north of Hailey on the B4022 between Witney and Charlbury. Sixteen spacious, cottage-style bedrooms (non-smoking) are in keeping with the original Cotswold-stone former coaching inn, in a U-shaped building on two storeys with wooden balconies, all overlooking an attractive grassed courtyard. Two twin-bedded, ground-floor rooms have facilities for the disabled and a couple of large family rooms sleep up to five; matching floral fabrics, pine furnishings, thoughtful touches like full-length mirrors and cotton wool plus good housekeeping bring all rooms up to a good hotel standard. Light meals can be enjoyed in the stone-walled bar rooms (one of which features a fine inglenook) and on picnic tables outside on the patio and in the walled front garden. Residential weekday conferences are popular, with one of the restaurant dining rooms doubling as a conference room (for up to 40, theatre-style). ***Rooms 16.*** *Garden. Access, Visa.*

Hailsham — Forte Travelodge — £42

Tel 0323 844556 — **L**

Hellingly Hailsham East Sussex BN27 4DT — **Map 11 B6**

9 miles north of Eastbourne on the A22 at the Boship Roundabout. ***Rooms 40.*** American Express *Access, Visa.*

Halifax — Holdsworth House — 69% — £87

Tel 0422 240024 Fax 0422 245174 — **H**

Holdsworth nr Halifax West Yorkshire HX2 9TG — **Map 6 C1**

Much period charm has been retained by the Pearson family at their 17th-century manor, which stands two miles from Halifax off the A629 Keighley road. The impressive oak-panelled restaurant is the main feature (spreading out over three rooms) and a bar-lounge provides additional space. The best bedrooms are four split-level suites and the rest are both neat and comfortable with colourful fabrics and mainly period furniture. Two rooms specially adapted for disabled guests. Good facilities for children (under-10s free in parents' room). Characterful meeting rooms hold up to 100. ***Rooms 40.*** *Garden. Closed Christmas/New Year.*
American Express *Access, Diners, Visa.*

Halifax Places of Interest

Tourist Information Tel 0422 368725.
Piece Hall Tel 0422 58087.
Playhouse Kings Cross Street Tel 0422 365998.
Toulston Polo Club Bowers Hall, Barkisland Tel 0422 372529.
Sportsman Leisure Dry Ski Slope Swalesmoor Tel 0422 40760.
Halifax RLFC Tel 0422 361026

Hampton Wick Le Petit Max NEW £42

Tel 081-977 0236 **R**

97a High Street Corner Vicarage Road Hampton Wick Surrey KT2 5NB Map 15 E2

Formerly at *Chez Max* in Kew, Max Renzland and brother Marc (in the kitchen) share these tiny, very modest premises with a daytime chips-with-everything café called *Bonzo's* (which is the large name to look for above the door) becoming *Petit Max* only at night and for Sunday lunch (same menu – two sittings at 12.30 and 3.45). Next door to a wine merchant (handily, as Petit Max is unlicensed – £1.50 corkage) close to Hampton Wick railway station, there are just seven tables squeezed inside with paper squares over red check cloths and it's only the framed menus from the likes of Girardet, Bocuse and Alain Chapel covering the bare brick walls to indicate that the food here is anything out of the ordinary. Foodie without frills (or pretension) sums up the style which is partly dictated by the smallness of the open-plan kitchen. Only the very best and freshest of raw materials are used in dishes like sautéed Bresse pigeon salad with girolles and mixed leaves; Roma tomato, rocket and basil salad with olive oil from Crete; huge pink prawns from France with a peppery mayonnaise; roasted Cornish turbot with samphire and hollandaise; pot au feu of rabbit with mustard sauce. The home-baked fleur de sel-topped olive oil bread (it comes with the finest French butter and Niçois olives) is down to talented pastry cook Matthew Jones (late of *Bibendum* and *Gidleigh Park*) whose tarte à la crème is not to be missed, but who also finds time to help Max front of house relaying tables when they are busy – which is always, so book – at this most informal of restaurants. No children under 12 and no credit cards but smoking is allowed, which can be a problem given the closeness of the tables. ***Seats** 32. L Sun only 12.30 & 3.45. D 7-11.15. Set L & D £18. Closed 4 days beginning of each month. No credit cards.*

Hampton Wick Place of Interest

Hampton Court Palace Tel 081-781 9500

Hanchurch Hanchurch Manor 74% £75

Tel 0782 643030 Fax 0782 643035 **H**

Hanchurch nr Stoke-on-Trent Staffordshire ST4 8JD Map 10 B3

An attractive driveway runs up to a fountain in front of a Tudor-style mansion and its adjacent 17th-century thatched mews cottages. It's been carefully turned into a fine hotel, and the bedrooms are a particular delight – individual decor, specially made furniture, an abundance of thoughtful little extras. Two rooms have four-poster beds. No children under 12. No dogs. ***Rooms** 9. Garden, fishing.* AMERICAN EXPRESS *Access, Diners, Visa.*

Handforth Belfry Hotel 71% £102

Tel 061-437 0511 Fax 061-499 0597 **HR**

Stanley Road Handforth nr Wilmslow Cheshire SK9 3LD Map 6 B2

The functional exterior belies a professionally run and exceptionally well-maintained hotel inside. It's mainly business oriented, and the Beech family look to provide all the modern facilities for executives. Reception is floored with pink marble, the lounge has cream-coloured silk-effect walls and the bar is strikingly up to date in shades of grey. The hotel's solid virtues are

See over

felt strongly in the spotless bedrooms, where good room service obviates the need for tea-makers. Dark mahogany furniture adds to the comfortable feel. Seven suites. Children under 10 stay free in their parents' room. Reduced tariff at weekends. Courtesy coach to Manchester airport. No dogs. ***Rooms** 81. Garden.* AMERICAN EXPRESS *Access, Diners, Visa.*

Restaurant **£60**

Smooth, professional service and a menu that makes interesting reading, particularly the "return to the traditional English table" which features poached Finnan haddock, calf's liver, bacon and onions, pan-fried whole trout with almond butter and a mixed grill London House. The carte sticks mainly with tradition (hors d'oeuvre served from a trolley, whitebait, chicken liver paté with apple and raisin chutney, Dover sole with shrimp and lemon butter, roast crispy duckling with cherry and Kirsch sauce) but ventures into occasional newer territory with Roquefort and pear strudel with aubergine and mushroom fritters and a coriander butter sauce. Good-value tables d'hote offer a choice of five or so dishes at each course; a gourmet menu completes the picture. Regular Friday night dinner-dances. There's something for everyone on the wine list, which includes many of the best French wine makers. Fair prices, and a liberal sprinkling of half bottles. ***Seats** 90. Parties 40. Private Room 180. L 12.30-2 D 7-10.30. Closed D 25 Dec, all 1 Jan, Good Friday. Set L £12 Set D £15 & £21.*

Handforth **Handforth Chinese Restaurant** **£45**

Tel 0625 531670 **R**

8a The Paddock Handforth Cheshire **Map 6 B2**

A straightforward restaurant in a parade of shops in suburban Manchester serving good, honest Chinese food. Sound cooking and professional service are matched by some interesting dishes (fish slices smoked in tea leaves, mushrooms in garlic sauce with pancake wraps) supplementing more familiar choices. ***Seats** 85. L 12-2 D 5.30-11.30. Closed L Sun, all 25 & 26 Dec. Set L from £5.50 Set D from £14.* AMERICAN EXPRESS *Access, Visa.*

Harlow **Green Man** **60%** **£102**

Tel 0279 442521 Fax 0279 626113 **H**

Mulberry Green Old Town Harlow Essex CM17 0ET **Map 11 B4**

Forte Heritage hotel with the heart of a 14th-century coaching inn and modern bedroom blocks. Two bars, but no lounge. ***Rooms** 55. Garden.* AMERICAN EXPRESS *Access, Diners, Visa.*

Harlow **Moat House** **68%** **£72**

Tel 0279 422441 Fax 0279 635094 **H**

Southern Way Harlow Essex CM18 7BA **Map 11 B4**

Modern hotel with a squat, faceless exterior close to Junction 7 of M11 (one mile). Stylish, spacious public rooms and bedrooms. Conference facilities for 220. ***Rooms** 120. Closed 24 Dec-1 Jan.* AMERICAN EXPRESS *Access, Diners, Visa.*

Harlow **Places of Interest**

The Playhouse The High Tel 0279 24391.
Epping Forest District Museum Tel 0992 716882.
Harlow Ski School Tel 0279 21792.

Many hotels offer reduced rates for weekend or out-of-season bookings.
Always ask about special deals.

Harome **Pheasant Hotel** **68%** **£110***

Tel 0439 771241 **H**

Harome nr Helmsley North Yorkshire YO6 5JG **Map 5 E3**

The village smithy, the village shop and two cottages were transformed into a comfortable and relaxed hotel by the pond and millstream. Day rooms comprise a little oak-beamed bar, a restaurant and a lounge that opens on to a flagstoned terrace. Bedrooms include three suites in buildings around a courtyard; to one side of this courtyard is a building housing a new heated swimming pool. Two cottages are also available for accommodation. No children under 12. *Half-board terms. ***Rooms** *18. Garden, indoor swimming pool. Closed Christmas Eve-end Feb.*

Harpenden **Glen Eagle Hotel** **63%** **£85**

Tel 0582 760271 Fax 0582 460819 **H**

1 Luton Road Harpenden Hertfordshire AL5 2PX **Map 15 E2**

A functional-looking redbrick hotel with ample free parking. Decent-sized bedrooms, 24hr room service, and several function rooms. The Glen Eagle stands on the A1081, near the railway station. ***Rooms** 50. Garden.* AMERICAN EXPRESS *Access, Diners, Visa.*

Harpenden **Moat House** **68%** **£95**

Tel 0582 764111 Fax 0582 769858 **H**

Southdown Road Harpenden Hertfordshire AL5 1PE **Map 15 E2**

Elegant redbrick Georgian house, just off A1081. Tastefully decorated day rooms and well-equipped bedrooms (13 of which are reserved for non-smokers). Family facilities; children under 6 stay free in parents' room. ***Rooms** 53.* AMERICAN EXPRESS *Access, Diners, Visa.*

Harrogate **Café Fleur** **£42**

Tel 0423 503034 **R**

3 Royal Parade Harrogate North Yorkshire HG1 2SZ **Map 6 C1**

Opposite the Crown Hotel, a reasonably priced French brasserie-style restaurant with a lively and informal atmosphere. Simple fare runs from grilled sardines and *frisée aux lardons* to salmon with mustard and dill sauce, vegetable pancakes and grilled steaks. Steak sandwich is a popular quick-snack speciality. Set menus include Petite Fleur, which is very cheap (and even cheaper before 7.30). No smoking. ***Seats** 56. **Parties** 14. **D only** 6-9.30. Closed 25 & 26 Dec, 1 Jan. **Set D** £4.95/£6.95/£7.95 & £15.95. Access, Visa.*

Harrogate **The Crown** **67%** **£98**

Tel 0423 567755 Fax 0423 502284 **H**

Crown Place Harrogate North Yorkshire HG1 2RZ **Map 6 C1**

Forte Heritage hotel originally built in 1740 as a coaching inn, but of the grander variety. Free use of the *Majestic's* leisure facilities. Conferences/banquets for up to 450/300. ***Rooms** 121.* AMERICAN EXPRESS *Access, Diners, Visa.*

Harrogate **Drum & Monkey** **£45**

Tel 0423 502650 **R**

5 Montpellier Gardens Harrogate North Yorkshire HG1 2TF **Map 6 C1**

Bustling fish restaurant on two floors with cramped tables. Simple dishes fare best on a menu that ranges from oysters and mussels to Dover sole and seafood pie. Lobster comes cold with salad, steamed with garlic butter,

See over

Thermidor or Drouant (cream and mustard sauce). Lunch prices lower than dinner. ***Seats** 48. Parties 8. L 12-2.30 D 7-10.15. Closed Sun, Christmas/New Year. Access, Visa.*

Harrogate **Hospitality Inn** **61%** **£98**

Tel 0423 564601 Fax 0423 507508 **H**

West Park Prospect Place Harrogate North Yorkshire HG1 1LB **Map 6 C1**

On the A61, a row of town-centre converted Georgian town houses, close to the parkland of The Stray. Children up to 14 free in parents' room. Busy conference and banqueting facilities. Mount Charlotte Thistle. ***Rooms** 71.* AMERICAN EXPRESS *Access, Diners, Visa.*

Harrogate **Imperial Hotel** **65%** **£95**

Tel 0423 565071 Fax 0423 500082 **H**

Prospect Place Harrogate North Yorkshire HG1 1LA **Map 6 C1**

In the heart of town, overlooking attractive gardens, the *Imperial* was once the home of Lord Carnarvon, discoverer of the Tutankhamen site. A programme of refurbishment includes the restaurant, day rooms and corridors. Children up to 14 stay free in parents' bedroom. Conference/banqueting for 200. ***Rooms** 85. Snooker.* AMERICAN EXPRESS *Access, Diners, Visa.*

Harrogate **Majestic Hotel** **64%** **£114**

Tel 0423 568972 Fax 0423 502283 **H**

Ripon Road Harrogate North Yorkshire HG1 2HU **Map 6 C1**

Imposing Victorian building both inside and out, with good leisure facilities and large gardens. Conference/banqueting facilities for 450/700. Children up to the age of 16 free in parents' room. Forte Grand. ***Rooms** 156. Indoor swimming pool, gymnasium, squash, sauna, spa bath, solarium, tennis, golf driving net, snooker.* AMERICAN EXPRESS *Access, Diners, Visa.*

Harrogate **Miller's, The Bistro** **£60**

Tel 0423 530708 **R**

1 Montpelier Mews Harrogate North Yorkshire HG1 2TG **Map 6 C1**

A tiny restaurant in a pretty mews complex, with accomplished cooking by chef-patron Simon Gueller. Changes have been made since last year, both to the look of the place – more seats, a new oak floor, general modernisation – and to the menu, which is now more in fancy bistro style, from gratin of crab with pink grapefruit to fillet of beef béarnaise with caramelised shallots. Outdoor eating on the cobbled courtyard. Almost all the 50-odd wines are under £20. ***Seats** 40. L 12-2 (Sun to 3.30) D 6.30-10. Closed D Sun, all Mon, Bank Holidays.* AMERICAN EXPRESS *Access, Visa.*

Harrogate **Moat House** **64%** **£125**

Tel 0423 500000 Fax 0423 524435 **H**

King's Road Harrogate North Yorkshire HG1 1XX **Map 6 C1**

Large hotel conveniently sited right next door to the Exhibition and Conference centre and linked directly to it. Modern, redbrick building with lots of mirrored glass. Conference/banqueting facilities for 400/250. ***Rooms** 214.* AMERICAN EXPRESS *Access, Diners, Visa.*

Harrogate **Old Swan Hotel** **69%** **£128**

Tel 0423 500055 Fax 0423 501154 **HR**

Swan Road Harrogate North Yorkshire HG1 2SR **Map 6 C1**

Probably the town's best hotel, an imposing ivy-clad building set in attractive private gardens near the centre of town, not far from Harrogate's exhibition and conference centre (5 minutes' walk away).

When Agatha Christie mysteriously vanished in 1926 it was here, at the Old Swan, that she was discovered some days later, making this a particularly fitting venue for the Super Sleuth weekends held from time to time for aspiring Misses Marple and Hercule Poirots. The atmosphere of Victorian times is evoked by some handsome architectural features (the Wedgwood room, where breakfast is served) and fine antiques (the grandfather clock in the main lobby). Committed staff and good housekeeping are major pluses, as is the ample parking. Conference facilities for up to 400. Children under 12 stay free in parents' room. ***Rooms*** *135. Garden.* AMERICAN EXPRESS *Access, Diners, Visa.*

Library Restaurant **£70**

An elegant and delightfully traditional room offering standards a cut above many provincial hotels of this size. Appealing, modern dishes are carried off with aplomb. Desserts are displayed on a pyramid centrepiece. Decent cheeses; the so-so wine list has helpful notes. ***Seats*** *28. Parties 40. L 12.30-2 D 7-10. Set L from £9.95 Set D £18.*

Harrogate **Hotel St George** **63%** **£105**

Tel 0423 561431 Fax 0423 530037 **H**

Ripon Road Harrogate North Yorkshire HG1 2SY **Map 6 C1**

Edwardian-styled interiors and good-sized bedrooms behind an ivy-clad facade. Extensive conference facilities (for up to 300 delegates) and a modern leisure club. Swallow Hotels. ***Rooms*** *93. Garden, indoor swimming pool, keep-fit equipment, sauna, spa bath, steam room, solarium.* AMERICAN EXPRESS *Access, Diners, Visa.*

Harrogate **Studley Hotel** **66%** **£90**

Tel 0423 560425 Fax 0423 530967 **H**

28 Swan Road Harrogate North Yorkshire HG1 2SE **Map 6 C1**

A well-run, homely hotel in a peaceful location very near the entrance to Valley Gardens. The attractive front is made up of a terrace of houses, and at the back there's an ample car park. Lounge and bar offer easy relaxation, the former containing a gallery of local artists' work. Good-quality built-in units furnish the bedrooms, whose well-co-ordinated colour schemes extend to the excellent bathrooms. ***Rooms*** *36. Garden.* AMERICAN EXPRESS *Access, Diners, Visa.*

Harrogate **Tannin Level** **£35**

Tel 0423 560595 **R**

5 Raglan Street Harrogate North Yorkshire HG1 1LE **Map 6 C1**

Basement wine bar on the corner of Raglan Street and Princes Street with brick walls, slate floors, old pews and assorted kitchen-style chairs, and green boards on which are written the daily menu. This usually includes an interesting, well-balanced mix of dishes with a French accent: home-made soups, paté and terrines, vegetarian options, good fresh fish and desserts. Simple, tasty fare, well executed. Extensive list of wines plus a dozen by the glass. One of the rooms is non-smoking. ***Seats*** *75. Parties 30. Private Room 12. L 12-2 D 5.30-10 (Sat from 6.30). Closed Sun. Access, Visa.*

Harrogate **Places of Interest**

Harrogate Tourist Information Tel 0423 525666.
Harrogate Conference and Exhibition Centre Tel 0423 500500.
Royal Pump Room Museum Tel 0423 503340.
Harrogate Theatre Tel 0423 502116.
Wetherby Racecourse Tel 0937 582035.
Harrogate Ski Centre Tel 0423 505457.
Great Yorkshire Showground Tel 0423 561536.

Hartlebury — Forte Travelodge — £42

Tel 0299 250553 — **L**

Shorthill Nurseries Hartlebury Kidderminster Hereford & Worcester DY11 6DR — **Map 14 B1**

On the southbound carriageway of the A449, 4 miles south of Kidderminster. ***Rooms** 32. American Express Access, Visa.*

Hartlepool — Grand Hotel — 59% — £63

Tel 0429 266345 Fax 0429 265217 — **H**

Swainson Street Hartlepool Cleveland TS24 8AA — **Map 5 E3**

A balconied Victorian ballroom tops the function/conference facilities at this handsome redbrick hotel opposite the main shopping centre. Children under 14 sharing parents' room are accommodated free. ***Rooms** 47. American Express Access, Diners, Visa.*

Hartshead Moor — Forte Travelodge — £42

Tel 0274 851706 — **L**

Clifton Brighouse West Yorkshire HD6 4RJ — **Map 6 C1**

Located on the eastbound carriageway of the M62 at the Welcome Break service area between Junctions 25 and 26. ***Rooms** 40. American Express Access, Visa.*

Harvington — The Mill — 67% — £85

Tel & Fax 0386 870688 — **HR**

Anchor Lane Harvington nr Evesham Hereford & Worcester WR11 5NR — **Map 14 C1**

Signposted off the A439 on the opposite side to Harvington Village, four miles from Evesham, the Mill is a stylishly converted Georgian malting mill. Created by Simon and Jane Greenhalgh, it is a civilised and peaceful place, set in eight acres of wooded parkland. Immaculate bedrooms have delightful views of the garden and willow trees by the 600ft River Avon frontage and are attractively appointed with up-to-date, carpeted bathrooms. Day rooms include a lovely lounge that opens on to the lawns. Beautifully maintained and run on friendly lines. No children under 10. No dogs, but kennelling nearby. ***Rooms** 15. Garden, outdoor swimming pool, fishing, tennis. Closed 5 days Christmas. American Express Access, Visa.*

Restaurant — £55

The pretty dining room is decorated in soft peach and grey and overlooks the lawns and river. Jane Greenhalgh and her small team cook in an admirably straightforward fashion. A 2-or 3-course table d'hote lunch is served in the restaurant or snacks in the lounge by the fire or on the terrace; Sunday lunch always features children's portions (£7.50) and a traditional roast. Dinner offers the widest choice – from chicken livers in puff pastry with orange sauce or spiced spare ribs to game pie, rabbit with mustard, herbs and tagliatelle, individual summer pudding and a slice of hot butterscotch pudding. ***Seats** 40. Private Room 14. L 12-1.45 D 7-8.45 (Sun to 8.30). Set L £11.95/£13.50 (£10.95/£12.95 Sun) Set D £15.50/£19.75.*

Harwich — Pier at Harwich — £59

Tel 0255 241212 Fax 0255 322752 — **RR**

The Quay Harwich Essex CO12 3HH — **Map 10 C3**

Overlooking the harbour (and within a mile of the ferry port), the first-floor restaurant is just the place to enjoy good, fresh seafood which comes both plain (shallow-fried Dover sole, grilled fillets of plaice) and fancy (lobster prawn and scampi thermidor, escalopes of halibut with a mousseline of salmon and prawns). The choice is extensive – from crab terrine, oysters or coquilles St Jacques mornay to fish pie and a filo pastry gateau of cod, salmon and prawns. Other, more standard fare, like melon and citrus fruit cocktail, brochette of three meat fillets and charcoal-grilled steaks should satisfy straightforward tastes. A succinct wine list at sensible prices, with a varied selection of half bottles. The *Ha'penny Pier* on the ground floor is a second, family-orientated restaurant offering a children's menu, high-chairs and a mainly fish menu. ***Seats** 70. Parties 30. Private Room 90. L 12-2 D 6-9.30 (Sun to 9). Set L £9/£11.75 Set D £16.* AMERICAN EXPRESS *Access, Diners, Visa.*

Rooms **£70**

The third-floor accommodation comprises six bedrooms of varying standards, all with a nautical theme, some with views down the estuary. All have en-suite bathrooms and televisions.

Haslemere Lythe Hill Hotel 71% £110

Tel 0428 651251 Fax 0428 644131 **H**

Petworth Road Haslemere Surrey GU27 3BQ **Map 11 A6**

1½ miles east of town on the B2131, Lythe Hill has been created from a collection of old farm buildings, which include a splendid Elizabethan house (where the five most characterful bedrooms are located), plus a few newer bits all set in 20 acres of grounds which encompass a croquet lawn, two lakes and a bluebell wood, with some glorious Surrey countryside beyond. A small lounge is now supplemented by a comfortable new cocktail bar but the great strength here are the bedrooms which include a dozen full suites from large to small, and a number of large rooms with separate sitting area. All rooms and suites are individually decorated and furnished, mostly with reproduction antiques, and boast Italian marble bathrooms with bidet, bathrobe and generous towelling. Rooms are serviced in the evening and there is 24hr room service. ***Rooms** 40. Garden, tennis, fishing, games room.* AMERICAN EXPRESS *Access, Visa.*

Haslemere Morel's ★ £90

Tel 0428 651462 **R**

23 Lower Street Haslemere Surrey GU27 2NY **Map 11 A6**

The summery blues and pale creams of the decor are complemented by large vases of mixed flowers with stylish knotted blue tablecloths, carefully fanned white napkins, gleaming glassware and shining silver cutlery – all indications of an impeccably well-run establishment. A small dish of crudités comes with aperitifs in the comfortable, beamed bar with its well-upholstered sofas and armchairs. An amuse-gueule of very fine, smooth duck liver paté, home-baked crusty white or brown rolls and butter made into a featherlight mousse show the kitchen's painstaking attention to detail. Jean-Yves Morel offers a short, classic French menu with a few innovative touches to keep abreast of fashionable trends. The overall quality is faultless though minor discrepancies can occur. A Provençal terrine of vegetables with duck confit has a refreshing mix of peppers, tomatoes and courgettes with some small pieces of duck. The "unusual dressing" mentioned on the menu is no more than a good olive oil/vinegar liaison with a few black sesame seeds sprinkled on the lettuce garnish. Main dishes include boned quail wrapped in pastry with spinach, nutmeg and mushrooms; slices of beef fillet dipped in garlic, parsley and coriander or lasagne of pigeon, mushroom duxelles and red wine sauce. Fish of the day could be a small turbot fillet with wild mushrooms – it possesses a delicately aromatic perfume that isn't quite matched on the palate, the sauce being rather bland and too creamy. Excellent desserts include a rhubarb medley – as a fool, stew and sorbet – or a sliced pear poached in Sauternes and served on a dark, rich hot chocolate and ginger sauce which though superb, lacks sufficient taste of the promised ginger. Some Australian and Spanish wines have joined the extensive French selection which offers good drinking under £25. Excellent, attentive and highly professional service. ***Seats** 50. Parties 12. Private Room 15. L 12.30-2 D 7-10.*

See over

Closed L Sat, all Sun & Mon, Bank Holidays except Good Friday, 2 weeks Feb, 3 weeks Sep. Set L £16.50 Set D £19.50. AMERICAN EXPRESS® *Access, Diners, Visa.*

Hastings — Cinque Ports Hotel — 66% — £73

Tel 0424 439222 Fax 0424 437277 — H

Summerfields Hastings East Sussex TN34 1ET — **Map 11 C6**

A hotel styled in the modern American low-rise style, with bright, spacious public areas furnished with good-quality period-style settees and armchairs. There are seven purpose-built conference rooms for up to 320 delegates. The hotel stands on the A21 leading into the town centre. Children up to 10 stay free in parents' room. No dogs. ***Rooms** 40.* AMERICAN EXPRESS® *Access, Diners, Visa.*

Hastings — Röser's — ★ — £60

Tel 0424 712218 — R

64 Eversfield Place St Leonards on Sea nr Hastings East Sussex TN37 6DB — **Map 11 C6**

A small, snug restaurant opposite the pier, with dark-panelled walls and booth seating. Seaside restaurants are not usually known for their quality, but this is certainly an exception. Gerald Röser takes his influences mainly from France and his native Germany, and many dishes show innovative touches; guinea fowl consommé with lentils, soufflé of mozzarella and Parmesan with a mixed pepper ragout, double venison saddle chop with a port and spice sauce, apple millefeuille served with a butterscotch sauce. From the set lunch menu might come seafood pancakes, chicken breast with wild mushroom sauce and braised oxtail with vegetables. Splendid wine list at fair prices, with wonderful Chablis, clarets and burgundies as well as impressive depth elsewhere. ***Seats** 40. Parties 16. Private Room 35. L 12-2 D 7-10. Closed L Sat, all Sun & Mon, Bank Holidays, 1 week Jan, 1 week Aug. Set L from £10.95/£13.95/£15.95 (incl. of glass of wine) Set D £18.95.* AMERICAN EXPRESS® *Access, Diners, Visa.*

Hastings — Royal Victoria Hotel — 70% — £75

Tel 0424 445544 Fax 0424 721995 — H

The Marina St Leonards-on-Sea nr Hastings East Sussex TN38 0BD — **Map 11 C6**

The seafront Royal Victoria retains the grand style of architecture that graced the Victorian age. An elegant marble staircase sweeps up from the foyer and in the first-floor piano lounge-cum-bar there are pillars, arches and ornate plaster mouldings, plus sea views. All the bedrooms are designated as suites, with either a separate sitting room or a large sitting area. Limited private parking. Resort Hotels. ***Rooms** 52.* AMERICAN EXPRESS® *Access, Diners, Visa.*

Hastings — Places of Interest

Tourist Information Tel 0424 718888.
Stables Theatre Tel 0424 423221.
Great Dixter House and Gardens Northiam Tel 0797 253160.
Hastings Castle and 1066 Story Tel 0424 717963.
Hastings Embroidery Town Hall Tel 0424 722022.
Shipwreck Heritage Centre Tel 0424 437452.
Sea Life Centre Tel 0424 718776.
Museum and Art Gallery Tel 0424 721202.

Never leave money, credit cards or valuables lying around in your hotel room. Use the hotel safe or the mini-safe in your room.

Hatch Beauchamp — Farthings Hotel 70% — £85

Tel 0823 480664 — H

Hatch Beauchamp nr Taunton Somerset TA3 6SG — **Map 13 E2**

Only four miles from the M5 (junction 25) and the A303, yet "miles from anywhere", the Coopers' quiet Georgian house stands in three acres of beautiful, secluded gardens. Accommodation comprises three doubles, two twins and one single bedroom with immaculately kept, cottagey decor and traditional period furniture; one room features a unique spiral mahogany staircase leading up to its bathroom. Thoughtful little touches (books, magazines, sewing kits) are found in all rooms. Open fires warm the lamp-lit lounge and bar where the accent is on friendly, personal service. ***Rooms** 6. Garden.* AMERICAN EXPRESS *Access, Visa.*

Hatfield Heath — Down Hall 71% — £138

Tel 0279 731441 Fax 0279 730416 — H

Hatfield Heath nr Bishops Stortford Hertfordshire CM22 7AS — **Map 11 B4**

Down Hall is a splendid Italianate mansion set in 100 acres of parkland. The handsome exterior is matched in the day rooms; the focal point is the main lounge with its Italian stone fireplace, huge crystal chandeliers and furniture ornate with ormolu, and the canopied bar boasts a green marble counter and matching tables. Bedrooms are divided between the main house and the sympathetically designed west wing; wing rooms have larger and more luxurious bathrooms, mini-bars and extra phones in the bathrooms and on the desks. Well geared up for conferences of up to 200. ***Rooms** 103. Garden, putting, indoor swimming pool, spa bath, sauna, tennis, snooker.* AMERICAN EXPRESS *Access, Diners, Visa.*

Hatherleigh — George Hotel — £65

Tel 0837 810454 Fax 0837 810901 — I

Market Street Hatherleigh nr Okehampton Devon EX20 3JN — **Map 13 D2**

Originally a sanctuary for monks, later brew house, tavern, coaching inn and law court. The cob-and-thatch building still has old-fashioned appeal. Bedrooms are comfortable and traditionally furnished. ***Rooms** 11. Garden, outdoor swimming pool, snooker.* AMERICAN EXPRESS *Access, Visa.*

Hathersage — Hathersage Inn — £68

Tel 0433 650259 Fax 0433 651199 — I

Hathersage Derbyshire S30 1BB — **Map 6 C2**

The ivy-clad, stone-built inn stands by Hathersage's steep main street; pub to the front where the Cricketers bar is full of local memorabilia and quietly residential to the rear with a lounge bar and cosy dining room. Bedrooms are neatly kept, with plenty of extras from TV and radio/alarm to drinks tray and fresh fruit. There's a four-poster honeymoon suite. ***Rooms** 15.* AMERICAN EXPRESS *Access, Diners, Visa.*

Havant — Bear Hotel 59% — £77

Tel 0705 486501 Fax 0705 470551 — H

East Street Havant Hampshire PO9 1AA — **Map 15 D4**

Historic town-centre coaching inn with modest accommodation and good parking. Conference facilities for up to 120, banqueting up to 100. Lansbury Hotels. ***Rooms** 42.* AMERICAN EXPRESS *Access, Diners, Visa.*

See the Conference and Banqueting section for lists of hotels arranged by county.

Havant — Forte Posthouse — 62% — £68

Tel 0705 465011 Fax 0705 466468 — **H**

Northney Road Hayling Island Havant Hampshire PO11 0NQ — **Map 15 D4**

Practical modern accommodation overlooking Langstone Harbour. ***Rooms*** *92. Indoor swimming pool, gymnasium, sauna, spa bath, solarium.* AMERICAN EXPRESS *Access, Diners, Visa.*

Hawkchurch — Fairwater Head Hotel — 65% — £106

Tel 0297 678349 — **H**

Hawkchurch nr Axminster Devon EX13 5TX — **Map 13 E2**

Loyal guests return year after year to the Austin and Lowe families' peaceful, Edwardian country house hotel with prize-winning gardens and fine views over the Axe valley. Housekeeping is diligent in both the main-house bedrooms and those in the more modern wing; attention to detail includes fresh Devon milk for the tea and coffee-making facilities. A garden wing is not connected to the house but offers the most up-to-date rooms with compact bathrooms and views over the gardens. Enjoy the lounge-bar fitted out in dark mahogany – one of many recent improvements. Guests are greeted with tea and freshly-baked cakes on arrival. ***Rooms*** *21. Garden, children's play area. Closed Jan-Feb.* AMERICAN EXPRESS *Access, Diners, Visa.*

Hawkhurst — Tudor Court — 61% — £78

Tel 0580 752312 Fax 0580 753966 — **H**

Rye Road Hawkhurst Cranbrook Kent TN18 5DA — **Map 11 C6**

On the Rye road (A268) about a mile from Hawkhurst, this well-kept redbrick hotel has equally spruce gardens. Guests can enjoy a drink on the terrace or in the oak-panelled bar, or while away an hour or two with a book in the lounge. Comfortably appointed bedrooms include some with four-posters. There's a conference suite and two syndicate rooms, catering for up to 80 delegates. There are tennis courts opposite the hotel. ***Rooms*** *18. Garden, clock golf, children's play area.* AMERICAN EXPRESS *Access, Diners, Visa.*

Hawkhurst — Place of Interest

Bodiam Castle (NT) Tel 0580 830436 *4 miles*

Haworth — Weavers — £50

Tel 0535 643822 — **RR**

15 West Lane Haworth nr Bradford West Yorkshire BD22 8DU — **Map 6 C1**

Follow signs for the Bronte Parsonage Museum (and use its car park) to find a characterful restaurant formed out of a row of old weaver's cottages. 'Yorkshire Pud wi' rich onion gravy', lamb's kidneys with lentil cakes, Pennine beefsteak and onion pie, and escalope of pork with tomato sauce are typical of dishes that are created with a light touch from mainly local produce. Afters include the likes of 'Old school Pud' and 'Nannies meringue', the latter coming with cream, brown bread ice cream and apricot sauce. Cheerful service completes the satisfying picture. ***Seats*** *45. Parties 16. L (winter Sun only) 12-1.30 D 7-9. Closed Mon (except Jun-Sept), Bank Holidays (open 25 Dec), 2 weeks Christmas, 2 weeks Jul. Set meals from £12.50.* AMERICAN EXPRESS *Access, Diners, Visa.*

Rooms — £63

Bedrooms, each with en-suite bathroom, combine antique pieces with modern touches like TV, video, direct-dial phone and trouser press. All have views over the Parsonage and village to the moors beyond.

Haworth — Place of Interest

Bronte Parsonage Tel 0535 42323.

Haydock — Forte Posthouse — 65% — £68

Tel 0942 717878 Fax 0942 718419 — **H**

Lodge Lane Newton-le-Willows Haydock Merseyside WA12 0JG — **Map 6 B2**

Smart, modern and well-organised hotel. Half the bedrooms are of the better Executive standard. Health club and children's play area and playroom at weekends. Conference/banqueting facilities for up to 200. ***Rooms** 136. Garden, indoor swimming pool, gymnasium, sauna, spa bath, solarium.* AMERICAN EXPRESS *Access, Diners, Visa.*

Haydock — Forte Travelodge — £42

Tel 0942 272055 — **L**

Piele Road Haydock St Helens Merseyside WA11 9TL — **Map 6 B2**

On the A580 westbound, 2 miles west of Junction 23 on the M6. ***Rooms** 40.* AMERICAN EXPRESS *Access, Visa.*

Haydock — Haydock Thistle — 67% — £107

Tel 0942 272000 Fax 0942 711092 — **H**

Penny Lane Haydock St Helens Merseyside WA11 9SG — **Map 6 B2**

Neo-Georgian, low-rise lodge by Junction 23 of the M6 with spacious lounge and bedrooms. Leisure spa and conference facilities for up to 200 delegates. Good-value family accommodation Fri & Sat nights. ***Rooms** 139. Indoor swimming pool, gymnasium, sauna, spa bath, solarium, snooker.* AMERICAN EXPRESS *Access, Diners, Visa.*

Haydock — Place of Interest

Haydock Park Racecourse Tel 0942 727345.

Hayes — Travel Inn — £43

Tel 081-573 7479 Fax 081-569 1204 — **L**

362 Uxbridge Road Hayes Middlesex UB4 0HE — **Map 15 E2**

10 minutes' drive from Heathrow Airport. ***Rooms** 40.* AMERICAN EXPRESS *Access, Diners, Visa.*

Hayfield — Bridge End Restaurant — £65

Tel 0663 747321 — **RR**

7 Church Street Hayfield Derbyshire SK12 5JE — **Map 6 C2**

Jonathan Holmes remembers his globe-trotting years and takes his inspiration from near and far in this appealing little restaurant opposite the village church. Menus change, at least in part, every week, tempting with the likes of Irish mussels in a nest of four-coloured pasta, twice-cooked goat's cheese soufflé and wild rabbit sausage filled with a chicken mousse, studded with smoked ham, served on a leek and mushroom sauce. And that's just for starters! Afterwards might come steamed sea bass on a sesame-scented jus, roast duck breast on a herb butter sauce and hot smoked fillet of Scotch beef on a purée of celeriac. Desserts keep up the good work, and there's a good-value wine list with many wines under £15. House policy of reduced mark-ups on fine wines – other restaurants note! ***Seats** 54. Private Room 20. Sun L 12.30-2.30 D Tue-Sat 7-10. Closed Mon.* AMERICAN EXPRESS *Access, Diners, Visa.*

Rooms — **£45**

Four en-suite bedrooms in attractive cottage style with pine furnishings and bedsteads have a secure separate entrance. 5% dinner discount for residents.

Hayfield Place of Interest

Lyme Park House and Gardens Disley Tel 0663 762023.

Haytor Bel Alp House 72% £126

Tel 0364 661217 Fax 0364 661292 **H**

Haytor nr Bovey Tracey Devon TQ13 9XX **Map 13 D3**

In a hillside location commanding splendid views over the rolling Devonshire countryside, this fine Edwardian house and its gardens have been much improved by the Curnocks since they arrived in 1983. Peace and quiet show in the antique-furnished day rooms, amply supplied with armchairs, sofas and a host of pot plants. The atmosphere is more that of being a house guest in a large family home than of staying in a hotel. Light, airy bedrooms have plain walls, matching floral fabrics, more armchairs and pot plants, and carpeted bathrooms (two with the original Edwardian tubs on marble plinths) with quality toiletries. Housekeeping and repair are immaculate throughout. Smoking discouraged. The hotel lies two and a half miles west of Bovey Tracey off the B3387 before Haytor. ***Rooms** 9. Garden, snooker. Closed Dec-Feb (except for prior bookings). Access, Visa.*

Heathrow Airport Berkeley Arms Hotel 67% £111

Tel 081-897 2121 Fax 081-897 7014 **H**

Bath Road Cranford Middlesex TW5 9QF **Map 15 E2**

On the A4 two miles from Heathrow. An agreeable Jarvis hotel set around a delightful garden complete with fountain and pond. Practical bedrooms, state-of-the-art conference facilities. ***Rooms** 56.* AMERICAN EXPRESS *Access, Diners, Visa.*

Heathrow Airport Edwardian International 76% £206

Tel 081-759 6311 Fax 081-759 4559 **H**

Bath Road Hayes Middlesex UB3 5AW **Map 15 E2**

Behind its glass and marble facade the Edwardian International offers abundant style, comfort, service and modern amenities five minutes from the airport. Public areas include a vast foyer with carpet-strewn pink marble floor, cocktail bar-cum-lounge with deep sofas in a variety of rich fabrics and polo-themed bar sporting real saddles in place of bar stools. Bedrooms, though not large, are visually appealing with decoratively painted lightwood furniture and stylishly colourful matching bedcovers and curtains. There are 17 luxurious suites with marble-lined bathrooms, spa baths, separate impulse showers and twin washbasins with gold fittings; some rooms have four-posters. 75 rooms are reserved for non-smokers. Residential conferences are an important part of the business here with a fully-equipped business centre and a theatre-style capacity of 7-450 in no fewer than 17 conference suites. ***Rooms** 459. Indoor swimming pool, gymnasium, sauna, spa bath, solarium, beauty & hair salon, news kiosk, brasserie (6am-11pm).* AMERICAN EXPRESS *Access, Diners, Visa.*

Heathrow Airport Excelsior Hotel 71% £128

Tel 081-759 6611 Fax 081-759 3421 **H**

Bath Road West Drayton Middlesex UB7 0DU **Map 15 E2**

A huge, modern hotel near the airport terminals with 248 Executive rooms, 16 suites, 100 non-smoking rooms and five equipped for wheelchair-bound guests. A spacious, marble-floored foyer sets the tone for the day rooms, which include two bars, one in plush and mahogany, and two restaurants. Children up to 14 free in parents' room. Conference/banqueting facilities for 800. Forte Grand. ***Rooms** 839. Indoor swimming pool, sauna, spa bath, solarium, beauty & hair salons, flower shop, coffee shop (noon-midnight).* AMERICAN EXPRESS *Access, Diners, Visa.*

Heathrow Airport Forte Crest 68% £99

Tel 081-759 2323 Fax 081-897 8659 **H**

Sipson Road West Drayton Middlesex UB7 0JU **Map 15 E2**

Familiar landmark by the M4 turn-off to Heathrow, ten storeys high and dating from the mid-70s. Chinese and Italian restaurants, a carvery and an informal American-style bar with juke box and pool table. Conference facilities for up to 200. ***Rooms** 572.* AMERICAN EXPRESS *Access, Diners, Visa.*

Heathrow Airport Forte Posthouse (Ariel) 65% £68

Tel 081-759 2552 Fax 081-564 9265 **H**

Bath Road Hayes Middlesex UB3 5AJ **Map 15 E2**

Previously known as the *Ariel* hotel (for thirty years), now included in the Forte Posthouse group. Meeting rooms for up to 50. ***Rooms** 180.* AMERICAN EXPRESS *Access, Diners, Visa.*

Heathrow Airport Granada Lodge £55

Tel 081-574 5875 Fax 081-574 1891 **L**

M4 Junction 2/3 Heston Middlesex TW5 9NA **Map 15 E2**

***Rooms** 46.* AMERICAN EXPRESS *Access, Diners, Visa.*

Heathrow Airport Heathrow Hilton 76% £169

Tel 081-759 7755 Fax 081-759 7579 **H**

Terminal 4 Heathrow Airport Hounslow Middlesex TW6 3AF **Map 15 E2**

Quite the most stunning of Heathrow's hotels, the former Sterling Hotel is now under the long-term management of Hilton. Its modern glass and steel exterior is strikingly angular and the interior draws inspiration from the past great Cunard liners. At ground level the main restaurant, a Continental-style brasserie and Oscar's Bar & Grill surround the open-plan lounge under a vast, lofty atrium. Designs in the bedrooms echo a shipboard theme, and modern technology is very much to the fore with flight information, account review and check-out details all appearing on the TV screen. A covered walkway affords direct access to Terminal 4. There are banqueting/conference facilities for 200/140. Children up to 18 stay free in a parent's room. ***Rooms** 400. Indoor swimming pool, gymnasium, sauna, steam room, coffee shop (24hrs).* AMERICAN EXPRESS *Access, Diners, Visa.*

Heathrow Airport Holiday Inn Crowne Plaza 74% £164

Tel 0895 445555 Fax 0895 445122 **H**

Stockley Road West Drayton Middlesex UB7 9NA **Map 15 E2**

A multi-million pound refit has turned this hotel into Holiday Inns' top-of-the-range Crowne Plaza brand offering higher levels of service – 24hr table service in the lounge/bar, extensive room service with a good range of hot meals available throughout the night, a turn-down service in the evenings, valet parking – and comfort than standard Holiday Inns. Spacious bedrooms, with a pleasing maroon and dark blue colour scheme, have proper armchairs and breakfast table plus plenty of work space – even more in the Business Study rooms that have a more masculine black and grey decor. Poly-cotton bedding and shortish baths (but with good showers above them) in otherwise well-appointed bathrooms which include face cloths and towelling robes. There's a new, larger swimming pool in the revamped leisure centre where there are also facilities for the disabled and mothers with babies. Children up to the age of 18 are accommodated free in parents' room; informal eating in the Café Galleria. Conference rooms for up to 90. Just north of the M4. ***Rooms** 375. Indoor swimming pool, children's pool & plunge pool, spa bath, leisure centre, gym,*

See over

sauna, solarium, steam room, beauty salon, golf (9), coffee shop (6.30am-midnight), news kiosk, business centre, helipad. American Express *Access, Diners, Visa.*

Heathrow Airport — Park Hotel — 61% — £111

Tel 081-759 2400 Fax 081-759 5278 — H

Bath Road Longford West Drayton Middlesex UB7 0EQ — **Map 15 E2**

Triple glazing and air-conditioning in all the bedrooms are big pluses at a low-rise Mount Charlotte hotel located between the A4 and the airport's runways. Conferences for up to 600. ***Rooms** 306. Car-hire desk, kiosk, coffee shop (10.30am-11.30pm).* American Express *Access, Diners, Visa.*

Heathrow Airport — Ramada Hotel Heathrow — 66% — £115

Tel 081-897 6363 Fax 081-897 1113 — H

Bath Road Hounslow Middlesex TW6 2AQ — **Map 15 E2**

Runway views come without the noise, thanks to sound-proofing, at a large 70s-built hotel (formerly the *Heathrow Penta*) with good leisure and up-to-date audio-visual conference facilities (for up to 500 delegates); the latter is supported by a well-equipped business centre. No dogs. ***Rooms** 636. Indoor swimming pool, gymnasium, sauna, spa bath, solarium, beauty salon, hairdressing, car-hire desk, kiosk, coffee shop (24hrs).* American Express *Access, Diners, Visa.*

Heathrow Airport — Sheraton Heathrow Hotel — 70% — £103

Tel 081-759 2424 Fax 081-759 2091 — H

Bath Road West Drayton Middlesex UB7 0HJ — **Map 15 E2**

Decent-sized bedrooms are stylishly contemporary, with good showers in the bathrooms. Bright day rooms include a long-hours coffee shop and banqueting/conference facilities for up to 80. One mile from Heathrow Airport. No dogs. ***Rooms** 415. Garden, coffee shop (6am-11.30pm), courtesy bus to airport.* American Express *Access, Diners, Visa.*

Heathrow Airport — Sheraton Skyline — 73% — £164

Tel 081-759 2535 Fax 081-750 9150 — H

Bath Road Hayes Middlesex UB3 5BP — **Map 15 E2**

The focal point of this hotel on the A4 is the most unusual Patio Caribe, a large indoor tropical garden complete with palm trees, swimming pool, bar and music. Good-sized bedrooms are right up-to-the-minute, with air-conditioning, automated mini-bars, computer links, sprinklers and smoke detector system (31 rooms are no-smoking); rooms on the third floor are designated as de luxe and the first-floor rooms have been recently refurbished. Greatly reduced weekend rates. Conference and banqueting facilities for up to 500. Children up to 16 stay free in parents' room. No dogs. ***Rooms** 353. Indoor swimming pool, florist, gift shop, coffee shop (6am-1am).* American Express *Access, Diners, Visa.*

Helford — Riverside — £80

Tel 0326 231443 Fax 0326 231103 — RR

Helford nr Helston Cornwall TR12 6JU — **Map 12 B4**

An idyllic setting on one side of a wooded creek, this is Daphne du Maurier country with Frenchman's Creek just a short walk away. The pretty, cottagey restaurant is home to Susie Darrell's essentially simple cooking that relies heavily on local produce, particularly seafood, in dishes such as clams in a parsley and cream sauce; poached fillet of brill on a bed of creamed leeks; salmon in pastry with basil butter sauce; and new-season West Country lamb with sweetbreads and a rosemary red wine sauce. Puds might include strawberry shortbread on a raspberry coulis and sliced banana glazed with an almond sabayon plus a selection of English and

French cheeses. Edward Darrell's passion for wine is reflected in a list that's both comprehensive and fairly priced, with a wide selection from the New World and plenty of half bottles. A light à la carte lunch is available from mid May to mid September only. ***Seats** 38. Parties 12. D only 7.30-9.30. Closed Nov-Feb. Set D £28. No credit cards.*

Rooms

£83

Seven luxurious bedrooms boast antiques, Oriental carpets, fresh flowers, remote-control TV, mini bar, books and magazines but very deliberately no telephones. The terrace is the perfect spot for a breakfast which now includes a cooked option and comes with home-made croissants and marmalade. No dogs. *Garden.*

Helland Bridge — Tredethy Country Hotel — 56%

£68

Tel 020 884 262/364 Fax 020 884 707

H

Helland Bridge Bodmin Cornwall PL30 4QS

Map 12 B3

Take the A389 from Bodmin, then the B3266 to Camelford to find this grey-stone country house, standing on a bank of the Camel valley, in a tranquil setting of nine wooded acres. Best bedrooms are in the light and sunny front half, whereas rooms at the back have views only of the courtyard and another wing. There are also ten self-catering cottages in the grounds. A new wheelchair ramp, giving better access to the ground floor, was installed last year. Family facilities. ***Rooms** 11. Garden, outdoor swimming pool, solarium.* AMERICAN EXPRESS® *Access, Diners, Visa.*

Helland Bridge — Places of Interest

Bodmin Tourist Information Tel 0208 76616.
Tintagel Castle (EH) Tel 0840 770328 *18 miles.*
Trebarwith Strand Beach *12 miles.*
Lanhydrock Bodmin Tel 0208 73320.
Pencarrow House and Garden Nr Bodmin Tel 020884 369.
Royal Cornwall Showground Nr Wadebridge Tel 0208 812183.

Helmsley — Black Swan — 69%

£111

Tel 0439 70466 Fax 0439 70174

H

Market Place Helmsley North Yorkshire YO6 5BJ

Map 5 E4

Standing by the market square, comprising an Elizabethan coaching inn, a Georgian house and a Tudor rectory. Day rooms, including several lounges, are all very traditional, with heavy timbers, low beamed ceilings and cottagey decor. Residents have their own bar as well as the public bar, both being small, cosy and welcoming. Bedrooms at the rear are modern and uniform in size, with good-quality Italian furniture; those at the front boast hand-built traditional oak furniture. All are individually decorated with well-co-ordinated chintzy fabrics and 12 are designated non-smoking; the restaurant is another smokeless zone. Forte Heritage. ***Rooms** 44. Garden.* AMERICAN EXPRESS® *Access, Diners, Visa.*

Helmsley — Feversham Arms — 66%

£70

Tel 0439 70766 Fax 0439 70346

H

1 High Street Helmsley North Yorkshire YO6 5AG

Map 5 E4

Rebuilt in 1855 on the site of a previous hostelry, the inn is in the capable hands of the Aragues family. Period appeal lives on, but the place also moves with the times: the most recent improvement involves the creating of an additional residents' lounge in the cottage next door. The other lounge and the bars are named after Aragues children. Bedrooms, all with little luxuries like personalised toiletries, include some with four-posters. Children under 16 stay free in parents' room. ***Rooms** 18. Garden, outdoor swimming pool, tennis.* AMERICAN EXPRESS® *Access, Diners, Visa.*

Helmsley — Places of Interest

Rievaulx Abbey Helmsley Tel 04396 228.
Rievaulx Terrace and Temples.

Henley-on-Thames — Red Lion — 62% — £111

Tel 0491 572161 Fax 0491 410039 — **H**

Hart Street Henley-on-Thames Oxfordshire RG9 2AR — **Map 15 D2**

Wisteria creeps around the frontage of a 16th-century building overlooking the finishing post of the Henley Royal Regatta rowing course, right by the bridge. Antique pine panelling is a feature in some of the day rooms, and in the bar flagstones and a log fire produce a rustic air. Two small banqueting/conference suites. Bedrooms generally combine period appeal with modern comfort. The Regatta bar offers bar snacks and the restaurant overlooks the river. Families welcome. ***Rooms 26.*** AMERICAN EXPRESS *Access, Visa.*

Henley-on-Thames — Places of Interest

Tourist Information Tel 0491 578034.
Fawley Court - Marian Fathers Historic House and Museum Tel 0491 574917.
Greys Court (NT) Rotherfield Grey. Tel 04917 529.
Stonor Park Tel 049 163 587.

Hereford — Moat House — 63% — £70

Tel 0432 354301 Fax 0432 275114 — **H**

Belmont Road Hereford Hereford & Worcester HR2 7BF — **Map 14 A1**

A mile and a half from the city centre on the Abergavenny road. Accommodation divided between discreet motel-style units and a spacious new extension. ***Rooms 60. Garden.*** AMERICAN EXPRESS *Access, Diners, Visa.*

Hereford — Travel Inn — £43

Tel 0432 274853 Fax 0432 343003 — **L**

Holmer Road Holmer nr Hereford Hereford & Worcester HR4 9RS — **Map 14 A1**

Hereford race course and leisure centre 5 minutes' walk. ***Rooms 40.*** AMERICAN EXPRESS *Access, Diners, Visa.*

Hereford — Places of Interest

Tourist Information Tel 0432 268430.
New Hereford Theatre Tel 0432 268785.
Hereford Cathedral Tel 0432 359880.
Historic Houses, Castles and Gardens
Dinmore Manor and Gardens Leominster Tel 043271 240.
Moccas Court, House and Parkland Moccas Tel 09817 381.
The Weir Garden (NT) Swainshill Tel 098122 697.
Hereford Racecourse Tel 0432 273560.
Museums and Art Galleries
Hereford City Museum and Art Gallery Tel 0432 268121 ext 207.
Cider Museum and King Offa Cider Brandy Distillery Hereford Cider Museum Trust Tel 0432 354207.
Churchill Gardens Museum Tel 0432 267409.
The Old House Tel 0432 268121.

We welcome bona fide complaints and recommendations on the tear-out pages at the back of the book for readers' comments. They are followed up by our professional team.

Herne Bay L'Escargot £55

Tel 0227 372876 **R**

22 High Street Herne Bay Kent CT6 5LH **Map 11 C5**

Alain and Joyce Bessemoulin are charming hosts and their friendly, informal restaurant has an uncomplicated appeal. Alain cooks in a competent and unfussy fashion using good fresh ingredients in largely classic dishes. Start with a home-made country-style paté or deep-fried Camembert with gooseberry sauce; move on to best end of lamb with rosemary, veal chop with a creamy mushroom sauce, or the daily fish special. *__Seats__ 40. L 12-1.30 D 7-9.30. Closed Thur, 2 weeks Jan, 2 weeks Sep. Set L £6.50 Set D £12.95. Access, Visa.*

Herne Bay Places of Interest

Brambles English Wildlife Rare Breeds Centre Wealdon Forest Park Tel 0227 7123.
Margate Tourist Information Tel 0843 220241.
Winter Gardens Tel 0843 292795.
Bembon Brothers Theme Park Tel 0843 227011.
Cliftonville Aquarium Tel 0843 221951.

Hersham The Dining Room £53

Tel 0932 231686 **R**

10 Queens Road The Village Green Hersham Surrey KT12 5LS **Map 15 E2**

A very English restaurant, from the Laura Ashley decor of the four interconnecting dining rooms to the steak and kidney, toad-in-the-hole and Spotted Dick that form the backbone of a menu that wanders freely round the English counties: hot Gloucester cheese and ale pot with toast soldiers; Norfolk turkey and leek pie with apricot stuffing; Aylesbury duckling with rum-soaked apple; Somerset lamb steak with cider, fruit and mint; Berkshire hog (pork chop with mushroom cream sauce). An excursion to Scotland finds Cowdenbeath haggis with bashed neeps, while Wales contributes Anglesey egg with smoked haddock and leek in a cream sauce. Two high-chairs provided for junior diners. *__Seats__ 90. Private Room 30. L 12-2 (Sun to 2.30) D 7-10.30 (Sat from 6.30). Closed L Sat, D Sun, Bank Holidays, 1 week Christmas.* AMERICAN EXPRESS *Access, Visa.*

Herstmonceux Sundial Restaurant £82

Tel 0323 832217 **R**

Gardner Street Herstmonceux East Sussex BN27 4LA **Map 11 B6**

In the centre of the village and now established for over 25 years, Laurette and Giuseppe Bertoli's pretty 17th-century cottage has a garden and terraces for alfresco summer lunches overlooking the Sussex countryside, and continues to be run with homely pride. Diners are treated like guests at a dinner party, and up to 20 diners can eat in a private room. Giuseppe's menu is an unusual mix of Italian, French and other varied influences: *l'oeuf à la neige Bombay* (poached egg on a bed of fine pasta in a light curry sauce) sits alongside cripsy roast duckling served with a strawberry sauce. The set dinner menu is more traditionally French. Though Italy and Germany get a look in, the wine list is predominantly French, with many fine wines; for those with short pockets, choose carefully! *__Seats__ 50. Private Room 20. L 12.30-2.30 D 7.30-9.30 (Sat to 10). Closed D Sun, all Mon, 2/3 weeks Aug/Sep, Xmas-mid Jan. Set L £15.50 Set D £26.50.* AMERICAN EXPRESS *Access, Diners, Visa.*

If we recommend meals in a hotel or inn a separate entry is made for its restaurant.

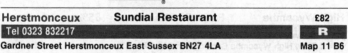

Hertingfordbury — White Horse Hotel — 63% — £90

Tel 0992 586791 Fax 0992 550809 — H

Hertingfordbury Road Hertingfordbury Hertfordshire SG14 2LB — **Map 15 F2**

Once a coaching inn on the Cambridge-Reading run, now a mix of Georgian facade, earlier interiors and modern bedroom blocks. Forte Heritage. ***Rooms** 42. Garden.* AMERICAN EXPRESS *Access, Diners, Visa.*

Hertingfordbury — Place of Interest

Hatfield House and Gardens Hatfield Tel 0707 262823.

Hethersett — Park Farm Hotel — 64% — £90

Tel 0603 810264 Fax 0603 812104 — H

Hethersett nr Norwich Norfolk NR9 3DL — **Map 10 C2**

The Gowing family's hotel stands in landscaped gardens just off the A11 five miles south of Norwich. The original Georgian farmhouse has been extended over the years to include not only accommodation in skilfully converted outbuildings but a well-equipped leisure complex, Georgian restaurant and six conference rooms. Rooms come in considerable variety, Executive rooms boasting four-poster beds and whirlpool baths. The majority of rooms are designated non-smoking. ***Rooms** 38. Garden, indoor swimming pool, keep-fit equipment, sauna, spa bath, steam room, solarium, tennis, games room, snooker, helipad.* AMERICAN EXPRESS *Access, Diners, Visa.*

Hexham — Beaumont Hotel — 58% — £75

Tel & Fax 0434 602331 — H

Beaumont Street Hexham Northumberland NE46 3LT — **Map 5 D2**

Popular business hotel just off the A69, overlooking parkland next to the abbey. Function facilities for up to 80 people. No dogs. ***Rooms** 23. Keep-fit equipment. Closed 25 & 26 Dec.* AMERICAN EXPRESS *Access, Diners, Visa.*

Hexham — Places of Interest

Museum of Border History Tel 0434 604011 *Not Weekends*
Hexham Racecourse Tel 0434 603738.

High Wycombe — Forte Posthouse — 65% — £68

Tel 0494 442100 Fax 0494 439071 — H

Crest Road High Wycombe Buckinghamshire HP11 1TL — **Map 15 E2**

Low-riser by Junction 4 of the M40, with conference and banqueting facilities for around 100. ***Rooms** 106. Garden, children's playground, snooker.* AMERICAN EXPRESS *Access, Diners, Visa.*

High Wycombe — Places of Interest

Tourist Information Tel 0494 421892.
Wycombe Sports Centre Swimming Pool Tel 0494 446324.
Historic Houses, Castles and Gardens
Hughenden Manor (NT) Tel 0494 532580 *Home of Benjamin Disraeli.*
West Wycombe Park (NT) West Wycombe Tel 0494 24411.
Chenies Manor House and Garden Little Chalfont Tel 0494 2888 *8 miles on A404.*

Highclere — The Yew Tree — NEW — £48

Tel 0635 253360 — R

Hollington Cross Andover Road Highclere nr Newbury Berkshire RG15 9SE — **Map 15 B3**

A delightful 15th-century inn just south of the village on the A343. Several cottagey interconnecting rooms form the restaurant where Jenny Wratten offers an intriguing menu. Simple dishes like grilled lemon sole and steaks share the carte with the likes of spinach and ricotta filo pastry parcels, beef in ale and recherché old-English items like crock of pheasant from an 18th-century recipe or a 15th-century Hampshire dish of meat, cheese and vegetable sticks with fruity chutney. Finish with a selection of unpasteurised farmhouse cheeses or a delicious pud like squidgy chocolate roll or walnut and honey tart. There's a pretty patio for summer eating. Six cottagey rooms offer comfortable overnight accommodation. ***Seats** 50. Parties 25. Private Room 20. L 12-2.30 D 6.30-10 (7-9.30 Sun). Access, Visa.*

Hinckley — Hinckley Island Hotel — 64% — £89

Tel 0455 631122 Fax 0455 634536 — **H**

The A5 Hinckley Leicestershire LE10 3JA — **Map 7 D4**

Adjacent to exit 1 of the M69, at the junction of the A5, this conference-oriented hotel covers some 15 acres. A huge statue of Neptune greets arrivals in the marble-floored, mirror-ceilinged foyer. Accommodation is all comfortable but the newer de luxe rooms are more spacious and more stylish than standard rooms. ***Rooms** 276. Indoor swimming pool, gymnasium, sauna, spa bath, steam room, solarium, beauty & hair salon, snooker, fishing, news kiosk, coffee shop (7am-10pm)* AMERICAN EXPRESS *Access, Diners, Visa.*

Hinckley — Places of Interest

Nuneaton Tourist Information Tel 0203 384027.
Arbury Hall Tel 0203 382804 or 0676 40259 *8 miles.*
Twycross Zoo Morton-Juxta-Twycross, Atherstone Tel 0827 880250.

Hindhead — Xian — £55

Tel 0428 604222 — **R**

9 London Road Hindhead Surrey — **Map 11 A5**

An unprepossessing redbrick facade, almost on top of the traffic lights at the Hindhead crossroads on the A3, conceals an unusually good Oriental restaurant. Oriental, because although the menu is mainly Chinese, it also includes such dishes as Vietnamese or Korean-style barbecued beef, Nabemono one-pot dishes, sukiyaki and Mongolian hot-pot. ***Seats** 60. Parties 20. D only 7-10.30. Closed Sun. Set meals from £13. Access, Visa.*

Hintlesham — Hintlesham Hall — 82% — £104

Tel 0473 652268 Fax 0473 652463 — **HR**

Hintlesham nr Ipswich Suffolk IP8 3NS — **Map 10 C3**

A well-managed and comfortable country house hotel with a symmetrical facade that dates back to Georgian times. Behind the stuccoed front is an Elizabethan house built in the 1570s with a heavily-timbered second floor and tall, distinctive redbrick chimneys. Reception rooms are both grand and welcoming: the book-lined library features an interesting hand-painted floor partially covered by rugs and a warming fire in the marble fireplace during winter. An old stable block has been transformed to accommodate bedrooms, one of which houses the workings of the estate clock. Extravagant toiletries are provided in all the bathrooms, which are mainly marble. A new 18-hole golf course and large club house are overlooked by rooms to the rear of the house. Discreet conference facilities. 10 minutes from the A45 & A12. Prior arrangement is required for "good dogs" (not in public rooms or bedrooms) and "good children". ***Rooms** 33. Garden, outdoor swimming pool, tennis, riding, game fishing, snooker, golf, sauna, steam room, spa bath.* AMERICAN EXPRESS *Access, Diners, Visa.*

Restaurant — £90

The two dining areas vary greatly: one an intimate parlour with pine panelling, the other a bright, high-ceilinged salon with ornate plasterwork and long drapes. Alan Ford's well-planned, three-course fixed-price menus include a weekday lunch menu, traditional Sunday lunch, and table d'hote

See over

dinner (Sun-Thurs) and there's also a regular carte. The latter encompasses roasted quail with red and spring cabbage with smoked pork, red onion and port soup with herb and garlic croute, grilled escalopes of salmon with a timbale of couscous and rosemary-flavoured juices, seized fillet of halibut with tiger prawns and spring onions, nougat soufflé with orange ice cream, and tarte tatin. Herbs from the famous garden are much used. A typical spring lunch menu might commence with stir-fry of brill and crisp vegetables with sesame noodles, follow with braised oxtail with red wine sauce and finish with good cheeses or warm apple tempura with a cinnamon dipping sauce. The splendid and comprehensive wine list deserves careful scrutiny – it's easy to use, contains helpful notes and offers selections to suit all pockets. No smoking. Service is their "duty and pleasure", therefore included in all prices. ***Seats*** *137. L 12-1.45 D 7-9.30. Closed L Sat. Set L £18.50 (£19.50 Sun) Set D £22.*

Hinton — Hinton Grange — 62% — £89

Tel 0272 372916 Fax 0272 373285 — **HR**

Hinton nr Dyrham Avon SN14 8HG — **Map 13 F1**

The Lindsay-Walkers' conversion of a stone farmhouse and outbuilding in six acres of grounds has brought a touch of country living only minutes from Bath and the M4 (from Junction 18). The main building comprises a 15th-century stone-flagged bar and a lounge in simple Chinese style; a conservatory houses both bar and heated swimming pool. Bedrooms in the surrounding buildings are Victorian-style recreations, with period washstands and bathing alcoves. There are antique four-posters and open fires. A lake has a tiny island with one tree and a summer house from which one can fish for trout. The Palm Court conservatory pool-side bar area is kept at tropical heat all year round, nurturing palm trees and orchids, and even providing bananas for the restaurant. No children under 14. ***Rooms*** *17. Garden, 9-hole pitch & putt, indoor swimming pool, sauna, solarium, keep-fit equipment, tennis, fishing.* AMERICAN EXPRESS *Access, Diners, Visa.*

Inglenook Restaurant — £50

Informal surroundings for sound cooking by chef Neil Cooper, who has now introduced business lunches. The short à la carte is typified by timbale of locally-smoked salmon and avocado mousses, terrine of pigeon, pistachio and sultanas, mélange of fresh fish in a pastry tartlet on a tomato and fennel coulis, grilled calf's liver with port and orange sauce, and a baked filo money bag filled with fresh fruit compote and set on a Grand Marnier sabayon; simpler dishes are always available on request, as is a good-value fixed-price menu. Vegetarians are well catered for. ***Seats*** *60. Private Room 18. L 12-2.15 D 7.30-10 (Sun to 9). Set L £14.95 Set D £16.95*

Hockley Heath — Nuthurst Grange — 74% — £117

Tel 0564 783972 Fax 0564 783919 — **HR**

Nuthurst Grange Lane Hockley Heath Warwickshire B94 5NL — **Map 6 C4**

The original redbrick house has been added to a number of times over the last 100 years, but the overall result is a surprisingly handsome building, helped by its setting in extensive landscaped grounds. David Randolph's restaurant takes pride of place on the ground floor along with a pair of plush chesterfield-furnished lounges (one for non-smokers) where drinks are also served; there is no bar. Pretty, individually-decorated bedrooms are spacious and comfortable with sofas and armchairs alongside the freestanding, darkwood furniture, and extras ranging from books, chocolates and fruit to more mundane fly-spray and shoe-cleaning kit. Poly-cotton duvets are standard but more traditional bedding is available on request. Bathrooms all have 'air spa' baths, telephone extensions and bathrobes. "Suitable for children who are well behaved." No dogs. ***Rooms*** *15. Garden, helipad. Closed 1 week Christmas.* AMERICAN EXPRESS *Access, Diners, Visa.*

Restaurant

£60

Chef-proprietor David Randolph ensures that the restaurant remains very much the centrepiece of the hotel. Fine fresh produce is handled with great care and dishes on the variety of fixed-price-only menus are notable for honest, distinctive flavours and attractive presentation: tomato and basil soup, fillet of grey mullet with Noilly Prat and cucumber sauce, lime-marinated salmon and John Dory with sea salt and sweet mustard dressing, Gressingham duck breast marinated in honey, soy and Chinese spices, and iced coffee soufflé with baby coconuts. No smoking (puffers can use the lounge if desperate). The concise wine list features clarets, burgundies and a good house selection. ***Seats** 50. Private Rooms 95. L 12-2.30 D 7-9.30. Closed L Sat. Set L £14.95 Set D £15.95/£19.95.*

Holbeton Alston Hall 65%

£75

Tel 075 530 555 Fax 075 530 494

H

Alston Cross Holbeton nr Plymouth Devon PL8 1HN

Map 13 D3

South-west of the village (best ask directions when booking) this Edwardian mansion commands some splendid views of the surrounding countryside. The galleried, wood-panelled Great Hall serves as both reception area and lounge, off which is a clubby bar. Individually decorated bedrooms have attractive matching bedcovers and curtains and smart carpeted bathrooms. All are furnished and equipped to the same standard with superior rooms (£10 supplement) being larger and having the better views. ***Rooms** 20. Garden, indoor swimming pool, keep-fit equipment, sauna, solarium, tennis.* AMERICAN EXPRESS *Access, Diners, Visa.*

Hollingbourne Great Danes 64%

£65

Tel 0622 631163 Fax 0622 735290

H

Ashford Road Hollingbourne Kent ME17 1RE

Map 11 C5

Great Danes stands in 22 acres of grounds next door to Leeds Castle off Junction 8 of the M20. It has very extensive, up-to-the-minute conference facilities and also on site is the Sebastian Coe Health Park whose attractions include a running track and floodlit tennis courts. Bedrooms are currently undergoing refurbishment. ***Rooms** 130. Garden, indoor swimming pool, gymnasium, sauna, solarium, tennis, 9-hole pitch & putt, games room, helipad.* AMERICAN EXPRESS *Access, Diners, Visa.*

Hope Cove Cottage Hotel 56%

£114*

Tel 0548 561555

H

Hope Cove nr Kingsbridge Devon TQ7 3HJ

Map 13 D3

John and Janet Ireland are the resident proprietors of this popular family holiday hotel extended, originally, from just one small cottage. It stands in a fine elevated position in gardens that descend to the beach. The main lounge is largely 30s in style, and the cocktail bar was built from the timbers of a wrecked tall ship, the *Herzogin Cecilie*. The sun terrace is the place to be in summer, when Devonshire cream teas accompany the lovely views. Accommodation includes de luxe rooms with extra accessories; just over half the rooms have en-suite facilities and some have balconies. A few singles at the back miss out on the sea views. Children up to 12 stay free in parents' room. * Half-board terms only. ***Rooms** 35. Garden, games room. Closed Jan. No credit cards.*

Hope Cove Lantern Lodge 59%

£70

Tel 0548 561280

H

Grand View Road Hope Cove nr Kingsbridge Devon TQ7 3HE

Map 13 D3

Overlooking the sea and the fishing village of Hope Cove, the Lantern Lodge is a pleasant and popular clifftop hotel. It's easy to relax in the cosy little bar or in the homely lounges with their antique pieces and choice of TV or books. Individually furnished bedrooms (three with four-posters) are well kept, with neat bath or shower rooms. There's a very fair 10% supplement for single occupancy of double rooms. No children under ten. No dogs. ***Rooms** 14. Garden, indoor swimming pool, sauna, solarium, putting. Closed Dec-Feb. Access, Visa.*

Horley — Langshott Manor — 71% — £106

Tel 0293 786680 Fax 0293 783905 — **HR**

Langshott Horley Surrey RH6 9LN — **Map 11 B5**

The considerable charm of this small Elizabethan manor house comes partly from its domestic scale (it has just five bedrooms) and partly from the relaxed, informal style in which it is run by New Zealanders Patricia and Geoffrey Noble. Family photos and fresh flowers in the oak-panelled drawing room and atmospheric entrance hall enhance the homely impression. The pretty, antique-filled bedrooms offer more home comforts: books, magazines, mineral water, bathrobes and big soft towels; the largest rooms only carry a small supplement. A courtesy Jaguar car is available for the short trip to Gatwick airport (plus two weeks' free parking), making this a popular spot from which to start a honeymoon. A real gem of a hotel in a tranquil setting with over two acres of grounds, only slightly tarnished by its proximity to modern housing on two sides. ***Rooms** 5. Garden. Closed 3 days Christmas. AMERICAN EXPRESS Access, Diners, Visa.*

Restaurant — £57

The communal dining of last year has disappeared and individual tables are now set in a new dining room; the wine list has also recently expanded. Two private rooms are also available for private parties. The fixed-price, three-or four-course lunch and dinner menus usually have a small choice of dinner-party dishes served in generous portions. Open to non-residents by prior appointment only. No smoking. ***Seats** 12. Parties 6. Private Room 12. L by arrangement D 7-9. Set L £19.50 Set D £19.50/£25.*

Horndon-on-the-Hill — The Bell Inn & Hill House — £50

Tel 0375 642463 Fax 0375 361611 — **RR**

High Road Horndon-on-the-Hill Essex SS17 8LD — **Map 11 B4**

Located in the village centre a few doors from one another, The Bell offers a blackboard menu and a friendly rustic, pubby ambience including beams, unpolished wood tables and flagstone floors, while Hill House next door has more formal dining in a pretty pastel-coloured room. The Bell menu features both simple and more unusual dishes: toad-in-the-hole, cod and chips, steaks, duck with orange sauce sit alongside the likes of guinea fowl terrine served with home-made chutney and grilled turbot with a yellow pepper sauce. At Hill House the fixed-price menu does away with the simpler, more pubby items. Starters from a choice of about nine could be a smoked salmon and vegetable strudel, or chicken liver paté with toasted orange and ginger bread. Main dishes are from an ample and varied selection of about ten including fillet of beef roasted with whole garlic, breast of duck with honey and peach or best end of lamb with a haggis mousse baked in puff pastry. This is imaginative cooking, skilfully executed and with very enjoyable results on the plate. Sweets follow in the same conservatively innovative style with apple and rhubarb crumble served with whisky anglaise, terrine of strawberries and grilled bananas with chocolate sauce or even a 'Cream Tea' – Earl Grey ice cream with shortbread and a strawberry sauce. Diverse wine list. *Bell Inn: **Seats** 35. Parties 60. Closed 4 days Christmas. Hill House: **Seats** 30. Parties 32. L 12.15-2 D 7.30-10. Closed L Sat, all Sun & Mon, Bank Holidays, 5 days Christmas. Set meals £17.95. AMERICAN EXPRESS Access, Diners, Visa.*

Rooms — £54

Above and also to the rear of Hill House are ten pretty, cottagey en-suite bedrooms, each thoughtfully equipped and neatly maintained.

Horsham — Travel Inn — £43

Tel 0403 50141 Fax 0403 270797 — L

57 North Street Horsham West Sussex RH12 1RB — **Map 11 A6**

Rooms 40. AMERICAN EXPRESS *Access, Diners, Visa.*

Horton — French Partridge — £50

Tel 0604 870033 Fax 0604 870032 — R

Horton nr Northampton Northamptonshire NN7 2AP — **Map 15 D1**

The Partridges have been serving good food at their friendly restaurant since 1963 and have many loyal customers. Bottle-green walls hung with oil paintings, black leather banquettes and polished mahogany tables create a sedate, traditional ambience. Dishes are mainly, but not exclusively, French on the four-course, fixed-price menu: cream of watercress soup, duck terrine with Cumberland sauce or home-made taramasalata with pitta bread might be followed by a lamb medley of cutlet, kidneys and sweetbreads, sliced venison steak with gin and juniper sauce or lime-marinated, breadcrumbed chicken breast with bacon and hollandaise sauce, plus an interesting course in between (fresh trout fillet with mushroom and cream sauce or warm onion and Roquefort quiche). Typically, lemon soufflé, traditional Bakewell pudding, and amaretti schokoladentorte might be among the puddings. Fair prices on the sound wine list. Smoking is discouraged. The restaurant is on the B526 Northampton-Newport Pagnell road. ***Seats** 40. Parties 10. D only 7-9. Closed Sun & Mon, 2 weeks Christmas, 2 weeks Easter, 3 weeks Jul/Aug. Set D £22. No credit cards.*

Horton-cum-Studley — Studley Priory — 64% — £98

Tel 0865 351203 Fax 0865 351613 — H

Horton-cum-Studley nr Oxford Oxfordshire OX33 1AZ — **Map 15 D2**

A striking Elizabethan manor house set in 13 acres of wooded grounds seven miles from Oxford. Impressive day rooms include a splendid hall panelled in pitch pine, a lofty drawing room and a Victorian bar with oak panelling. Six bedrooms are in the main house (antiques one with a four-poster dating from about 1700), while the majority are in the Jacobean wing reached through a labyrinth of corridors. These rooms are smaller and more modern. Small conferences are big business here, so you'll sometimes be sharing the drawing room with the delegates. ***Rooms 19.** Garden, tennis, clay-pigeon shooting.* AMERICAN EXPRESS *Access, Diners, Visa.*

Hove. For entries under Hove please refer to Brighton.

Huddersfield — George Hotel — 62% — £85

Tel 0484 515444 Fax 0484 535056 — H

St George's Square Huddersfield West Yorkshire HD1 1JA — **Map 6 C1**

In the main square opposite the railway station, a large Victorian building with sizeable conference and banqueting facilities. Refitted bedrooms are stylish with up-to-date amenities. Children under 14 stay free in parents' room. Ask about special parking arrangements in nearby car park. ***Rooms** 60.* AMERICAN EXPRESS *Access, Diners, Visa.*

Huddersfield — Pennine Hilton National — 66% — £95

Tel 0422 375431 Fax 0422 310067 — H

Ainley Top Huddersfield West Yorkshire HD3 3RH — **Map 6 C1**

Above the town centre, conveniently located by junction 24 of the M62, a modern, low-rise hotel with attractive, contemporary-style bedrooms with small, but bright, bathrooms. Children up to 12 stay free in parents'

See over

room. Leisure Centre and conference facilities for up to 450. ***Rooms** 118. Pool, sauna, steam room, gymnasium, coffee shop (7am-10pm), beautician.* AMERICAN EXPRESS *Access, Diners, Visa.*

Huddersfield Places of Interest

Tourist Information Tel 0484 430808.
Holmfirth Postcard Museum Holmfirth Tel 0484 682231.
Huddersfield Art Gallery Tel 0484 513808.

Hull Campanile Hotel £44

Tel 0482 25530 Fax 0482 587538 **L**

Beverley Road/Freetown Way Hull Humberside HU2 9AN **Map 7 E1**

Off the A63, within the city centre, near the station. ***Rooms** 50.* AMERICAN EXPRESS *Access, Diners, Visa.*

Hull Ceruttis £60

Tel 0482 28501 Fax 0482 587597 **R**

10 Nelson Street Hull Humberside HU1 1XE **Map 7 E1**

Approaching 20 years in its harbourside location (ask for the pier), the Cerutti family's friendly restaurant deals almost exclusively in fish and seafood. Dover sole is a particular favourite, served grilled, meunière or six other ways. A number of main courses are available with a reduced calorie count. ***Seats** 40. Private Room 24. L 12-2 D 7-9.30. Set D from £11.50. Closed L Sat, all Sun, Bank Holidays, 1 week Xmas. Access, Visa.*

Hull Forte Crest 69% £89

Tel 0482 225221 Fax 0482 213299 **H**

Castle Street Hull Humberside HU1 2BX **Map 7 E1**

Alongside the impressive dock development, the best rooms in this purpose-built hotel have balconies and fine views over the marina. Conferences for up to 140, banqueting for 120. ***Rooms** 99. Indoor swimming pool, gymnasium, sauna, solarium, beauty salon.* AMERICAN EXPRESS *Access, Diners, Visa.*

Hull Forte Posthouse 62% £68

Tel 0482 645212 Fax 0482 643332 **H**

Ferriby High Road North Ferriby Hull Humberside HU14 3LG **Map 7 E1**

Comfortable modern hotel outside Hull, overlooking the remarkable suspension bridge. Children's playroom and playground. About half the bedrooms are reserved for non-smokers. ***Rooms** 97.* AMERICAN EXPRESS *Access, Diners, Visa.*

Hull Places of Interest

Tourist Information Tel 0482 223559.
Burton Constable Hall and Gardens Tel 0964 562400.
Theatres and Concert Halls
New Theatre Tel 0482 20244.
Spring Street Theatre Tel 0482 20491.
Truck Theatre Tel 0482 225800.
Museums and Art Galleries
Ferens Art Gallery Tel 0482 222750.
Town Docks Museum Tel 0482 222737.
University of Hull Art Collection Tel 0482 465192.
Wilberforce House and Georgian Houses Tel 0482 222737.
Hull City Football Ground Tel 0482 51119.
Hull RLFC Tel 0482 29040
Hull Kingston Rovers RLFC Tel 0482 74648
Humberside Ice Arena Tel 0482 25252.

Hungerford **Bear Hotel** 63% £72

Tel 0488 682512 Fax 0488 684357 **H**

Charnham Street Hungerford Berkshire RG17 0EL **Map 14 C2**

On the A4 on the outskirts of town, one of England's most historic inns, once owned by Henry VIII, provides modern comforts in evocative surroundings. Guests have the use of free health facilities at the nearby Elcot Park Hotel (3 miles away, under the same ownership of Resort Hotels) and squash, gym, saunas, snooker and skittles at the Meadowview Leisure Club (50 yards away). Accommodation includes four-poster rooms and courtyard rooms looking on the river Dunn. ***Rooms** 41. Garden.*
AMERICAN EXPRESS *Access, Diners, Visa.*

Hunstrete **Hunstrete House** 72% £150

Tel 0761 490490 Fax 0761 490732 **HR**

Hunstrete Chelwood nr Bath Avon BS18 4NS **Map 13 F1**

This Georgian-style property ten miles from Bath and Bristol is set in some ninety acres of grounds. A deer park, a walled vegetable garden providing produce for the kitchen and well-tended borders provide a tranquil and relaxing setting. The hotel still has a feeling of faded elegance and better times past, with lack of attention evident in some places: stained wall coverings, faulty plumbing and bed linen of inferior quality are examples. Library and drawing room lounges, whilst well-appointed with antique furniture, have a rather tired look, and the cane-furnished bar is a touch dated – but still appealing, with access to a terrace overlooking the croquet lawn. Bedrooms all of individual style include some good period pieces of furniture; most have fine views and are generally well appointed and extras such as a decanter of sherry and cool water flask. Staff are generally cheerful and helpful and we hope that the hotel will once again start to realise its potential. No children under 9. No dogs. ***Rooms** 24. Garden, outdoor swimming pool, tennis. Access, Visa.*

Restaurant £85

The fertile gardens and the skills of chef Darren Bott provide some highly creditable cooking. The restaurant is split between the Garden Room for smokers and the main (non-smoking) dining area overlooking the courtyard. The menu has limited choice but is well thought-out in terms of balance and interest. Especially good on a summer visit were a dish of poached salmon with crispy fried oyster mushrooms and salad leaves from the garden; tender pink fillet of lamb; and an outstanding glazed lemon tart. Presentation is first rate, simple, clean and stylish. Service is friendly and helpful. ***Seats** 50. Private Room 18. L 12-2 D 7.30-9.30. Set L £15 Set D £29.50.*

Huntingdon **Old Bridge Hotel** 68% £90

Tel 0480 52681 Fax 0480 411017 **HR**

1 High Street Huntingdon Cambridgeshire PE18 6TQ **Map 10 B2**

Gardens run down to the river Ouse from this creeper-clad Georgian hotel close to the town centre (on the inner ring road). Pastel murals decorate the Terrace lounge (where informal meals are served) and in winter a log fire warms the panelled bar. Well-equipped bedrooms are individually and stylishly designed, the best being quite spacious; huge towels and plenty of toiletries in the bathrooms. Afternoon tea in the Lounge is a civilised affair. The business conference room holds up to 50. Poste Hotels. ***Rooms** 26. Garden, private jetty.* AMERICAN EXPRESS *Access, Diners, Visa.*

Restaurant £76

A comfortable, discreet, formal dining room with beautiful light oak-panelled walls where gentlemen are requested to wear a jacket and tie for dinner. This is an elegant setting for a seasonally changing, imaginative and well-executed menu. A spring carte could include sizzling tiger prawns

See over

in hot olive oil and garlic, al dente spinach and mushroom ravioli with an unusual and successful dill, lime and olive oil dressing or field and forest mushrooms stewed in Madeira and served with sweet brioche. Main dishes include roast breast of duck with Elizabethan mead and flame grapes, an escalope of salmon with cucumber, cream and basil or tender, lean and pink medallions of venison on a spaghetti of celeriac and leeks with a redcurrant and port sauce. To follow, as well as a enticing sweet menu there's a choice of fine pasteurised British cheeses from Neal's Yard – Colston Bassett Stilton, Kirkham's Lancashire and Montgomery Cheddar to name but three. Always one of the best wine lists in the country (past winner of Cellar of the Year), it continues to amaze with both its value and its quality. Expertly compiled, it offers many half bottles and champagne under £20! ***Seats** 38. Private Room 50. L 12-2.30 D 7-10.30. Set Sun L £14.95.*

Huntingdon Places of Interest

Island Hall Godmanchester Tel 0480 459676.
The Cromwell Museum Tel 0480 425830.
Huntingdon Racecourse Tel 0480 453373.

Huntsham Huntsham Court 68% £110

Tel 039 86 365 Fax 039 86 456 **HR**

Huntsham Bampton nr Tiverton Devon EX16 7NA **Map 13 D2**

A rather gaunt Victorian Gothic pile run in friendly, very casual style by owners Mogens and Andrea Bolwig. Eating is communal, there's an honour system in the bar, and you just wander into the kitchen if you need anything. There's great atmosphere in the day rooms (log fires, a panelled great hall, splendid pieces of furniture) and in the roomy bedrooms, named after composers, there are Victorian beds and baths and pre-war radios with an authentic crackle – not a teasmaid in sight! The hotel is dedicated to music, with the classical variety played *forte* in the evening. The day starts with an excellent buffet breakfast. No dogs. Children are well catered for and under-10s are accommodated free of charge if they share their parents' room; baby-sitting is available. No dogs, however "good" or "small". This is a great place for relaxing – its motto is 'dulce nihil facere'. Private house parties and group functions a speciality. ***Rooms** 17. Garden, sauna, solarium, tennis, coarse fishing, shooting, bicycles, snooker.* AMERICAN EXPRESS *Access, Diners, Visa.*

Restaurant £72

Five-course dinners (no choice, but variations possible in advance) are enjoyed in leisurely fashion at a convivial candle-lit table. Duck from a local farm, roasted crisp and escorted by a Périgord sauce, is a favourite dish, so too fillet of brill sauce américaine, and for dessert, treacle tart. Guests are welcome to browse around the wine cellars where they'll find the New World and Spain particularly well represented; fair prices and some wine charged by the glass from bottles left open on the table. ***Seats** 30. Private Room 28. D only 8-10.30. Set D £27.50.*

Huntsham Places of Interest

Tiverton Tourist Information 0884 255827.
Knightshayes Court (NT) Nr Tiverton Tel 0884 254665.
Tiverton Castle Tel 0884 253200.
The Tiverton Museum Tel 0884 256295.

Hurley Ye Olde Bell 65% £100

Tel 0628 825881 Fax 0628 825939 **H**

High Street Hurley nr Maidenhead Berkshire SL6 5LX **Map 15 D2**

A black-and-white inn which was built in 1135 as a guest house for a Benedictine monastery. You enter through a Norman arch to find a heavily beamed bar with comfortable armchairs, old brass and lots of character, while adjacent to it is the tiny Hogarth bar. The comfortable bedrooms vary from handsome, traditionally furnished rooms in the inn and neighbouring Malt House to more modern ones in an annexe. Children up to 14 stay free in parents' room. Function facilities include a 16th-century tithe barn. Resort Hotels. ***Rooms** 36. Garden, pétanque.* AMERICAN EXPRESS *Access, Diners, Visa.*

Hurstbourne Tarrant — Esseborne Manor — 72% — £95

Tel 0264 76444 Fax 0264 76473 — **HR**

Hurstbourne Tarrant nr Andover Hampshire SP11 0ER — **Map 14 C3**

An unpretentious yet stylish country house hotel lying in the heart of Watership Down country, set back off the A343 about a mile to the north of Hurstbourne Tarrant. It displays obvious attention to detail both in the public rooms and in the overnight accommodation, with fresh flowers, carved ducks, glossy magazines, family ornaments and some antiques. All the bedrooms have been decorated and furnished to a very high standard in both fabrics and materials, enjoying views of the well-kept gardens or rich farmland beyond. The six most spacious rooms are housed in a a converted stable block, just a short distance across a courtyard. Extras provided include thick bath robes, books and fresh fruit. Bathrooms benefit from full-length mirrors, spacious surfaces and vividly coloured bath toys. No children under 12. No dogs. ***Rooms** 12. Garden, tennis.* AMERICAN EXPRESS *Access, Diners, Visa.*

Restaurant — £76

New head chef Andy Norman cooks good produce with adept skill. His interesting menus range from a two-course 'Quickie' lunch to a limited choice but well-balanced dinner menu. Good warm bread rolls, friendly and cheerful service plus a cosy atmosphere make it a pleasurable environment in which to enjoy dishes such as local fresh asparagus or trio of fresh fish with a lime and coriander dressing. British cheeses including a local representative and selection of desserts from classic sherry trifle to dark chocolate marquise complete the meal. ***Seats** 30. Private Room 30. L 12.30-2 D 7.30-9.30. Set L £14/£17.50 Set D £19.50.*

Hythe — Hythe Imperial — 71% — £117

Tel 0303 267441 Fax 0303 264610 — **H**

Princes Parade Hythe Kent CT21 6AE — **Map 11 C5**

A large, family-run hotel set right on the seafront and surrounded by 50 acres of grounds. An imposing, cream-painted exterior of Victorian splendour belies the more classical air within. The polished mahogany reception area is adorned with brown leather chesterfields and leads through to comfortable bars and lounges. All bedrooms have views of the sea or gardens and are mostly of good size with a mixture of quality period furniture, although some have more ordinary darkwood pieces. Excellent, unusually pleasant staff and leisure facilities that include go-karting and a children's play area with Scalextric. Families are particularly well catered for with baby-sitting, baby-listening and crèche facilities available on Saturday mornings; they can eat informally in the leisure centre bistro. A new children's playroom is now in use as are two extensions to the conference rooms (now catering for up to 200 delegates). Sunday Plus is an interesting idea – extend a weekend stay (keeping the use of your room) until 5pm on Sunday for a nominal charge that includes Sunday lunch. No dogs. ***Rooms** 100. Garden, indoor swimming pool, gymnasium, spa bath, sauna, solarium, steam room, beauty & hair salons, squash, tennis, games room, 9-hole golf course, putting, helipad, coffee shop (8.30am-10.30pm).* AMERICAN EXPRESS *Access, Diners, Visa.*

Our inspectors are full-time employees; they are professionally trained by us.

Hythe — Stade Court — 62% — £75

Tel 0303 268263 Fax 0303 261803 — **H**

West Parade Hythe Kent CT21 6DT — **Map 11 C5**

A small, welcoming entrance hall opens out on to a bamboo-furnished bar, and there's an upstairs lounge looking out to sea. There are also Channel views from many of the traditionally-styled bedrooms, the majority of which have little sun lounges. All the bedrooms are double-glazed. Free use of the extensive leisure facilities at the Hythe Imperial 600 metres away, excluding golf (for which a green fee is charged). Families are well catered for. ***Rooms*** *42. Garden.* AMERICAN EXPRESS *Access, Diners, Visa.*

Hythe — Places of Interest

Lympne Castle Tel 0303 267571.
Port Lympne Zoo Park Lympne Tel 0303 64646.

Ide — Old Mill — £55

Tel 0392 59480 — **R**

20 High Street Ide nr Exeter Devon EX2 9RN — **Map 13 D2**

Set menus and à la carte are available both lunchtime and evening in the tranquil surroundings of a converted 16th-century mill, just off the A30 west of Exeter. Fish dishes feature prominently, with lobsters, fresh from the tank, prawn tails and lemon sole ever-popular choices. Pork cutlets, gammon steak, fillet steak and chicken with sweetcorn sauce are familiar alternatives, with pavlovas, chocolate parfait and home-made ice creams to follow. ***Seats*** *32. Private Room 8. L 12-1.30 D 7-9.30. Closed L Sat, all Sun, 25 & 26 Dec. Set L £8.95/£9.95 Set D £14.* AMERICAN EXPRESS *Access, Visa.*

Ilkley — Rombalds Hotel — 61% — £100

Tel 0943 603201 Fax 0943 816586 — **HR**

West View Wells Road Ilkley West Yorkshire LS29 9JG — **Map 6 C1**

Part of a period sandstone terrace just yards from the edge of Ilkley Moor. The main day room is a comfortable, traditionally furnished bar/lounge busy with diners having pre-and post-prandial drinks. Bedrooms, which include four suites, are modestly comfortable, mostly with inexpensive white melamine furniture and functional bathrooms – about half with shower and WC only. The coach house meeting room combines character with high-tech facilities. Friendly staff. 24hr room service. ***Rooms*** *15. Garden. Closed 27-30 Dec.* AMERICAN EXPRESS *Access, Diners, Visa.*

Restaurant — £65

There is a strong local following for Rombalds' brand of soundly based cooking which combines interest with the security of tried and trusted combinations: salmon with champagne sauce, pork fillet with apple and Calvados, veal with wild mushrooms and truffle sauce, duck with port and orange sauce. On the short but well-balanced à la carte menu they are happy to turn starters into main dishes and vice versa thus extending the choice. Lunchtimes and Monday to Friday evenings there is also a good value table d'hote. Sunday brings an 'Edwardian Breakfast' (brunch) served from 9am to 1.30pm. No smoking. ***Seats*** *36. Parties 10. Private Room 50. L 12-2 (Sun 9am-1.30pm) D 7-9.30 (Sun till 9). Set L £9.95 Set D £10/£12.95.*

Ilminster — Forte Travelodge — £42

Tel 0460 53748 — **L**

Southfield roundabout Horton Cross Ilminster Somerset PA19 9PT — **Map 13 E2**

Located on the A303 at the intersection with the Ilminster bypass, west of the town centre. ***Rooms*** *32.* AMERICAN EXPRESS *Access, Visa.*

Ingatestone — Heybridge Moat House — 68% — £85

Tel 0277 355355 Fax 0277 353288 — H

Roman Road Ingatestone Essex CM4 9AB — Map 11 B4

Motel-style rooms stand round a central courtyard, and there are purpose-built conference facilities for up to 600 delegates. Just off the A12. ***Rooms** 22. AMERICAN EXPRESS Access, Diners, Visa.*

Ipswich — Belstead Brook Hotel — 68% — £67

Tel 0473 684241 Fax 0473 681249 — H

Belstead Road Ipswich Suffolk IP2 9HB — Map 10 C3

On the southern outskirts of the city (ask for directions when booking), the 16th-century Belstead Brook is set in eight acres of gardens and woodland. Public rooms and the four-poster honeymoon suite are in the original house with most of the other well-appointed bedrooms in a modern extension. The six best suites are in a secluded garden block. Children up to 16 stay free in parents' room. Purpose-built syndicate rooms cater for meetings of up to 70. ***Rooms** 92. Garden. AMERICAN EXPRESS Access, Diners, Visa.*

Ipswich — Forte Posthouse — 63% — £68

Tel 0473 690313 Fax 0473 680412 — H

London Road Ipswich Suffolk IP2 0UA — Map 10 C3

On the A12 two miles from the centre of Ipswich, this Posthouse offers stylish public areas and decent-sized bedrooms. Families are well catered for, with reduced rates and a playroom for children at weekends. ***Rooms** 112. Outdoor swimming pool, children's play area. AMERICAN EXPRESS Access, Diners, Visa.*

Ipswich — Marlborough Hotel — 65% — £75

Tel 0473 257677 Fax 0473 226927 — H

Henley Road Ipswich Suffolk IP1 3SP — Map 10 C3

Peacefully located north of the town centre, the Marlborough (in the same ownership as the *Angel*, Bury St Edmunds) is run with care and enthusiasm by Wendy and David Brooks. The tasteful public areas and the comfortable bedrooms (the best have antique furniture) are equally well kept. 24hr room service. ***Rooms** 22. Garden. AMERICAN EXPRESS Access, Diners, Visa.*

Ipswich — Novotel — 61% — £78

Tel 0473 232400 Fax 0473 232414 — H

Greyfriars Road Ipswich Suffolk IP1 1UP — Map 10 C3

Five minutes walk from the pedestrianised town centre and only a brisk ten from the station: purpose-built facilities include all-day grill, conferences from 2 to 200 (banquets 180) and 4 bedrooms for the disabled. Under-16s stay free in parents' room, with breakfast also free. ***Rooms** 101. Patio, coffee shop (6am-midnight). AMERICAN EXPRESS Access, Diners, Visa.*

Ipswich — Places of Interest

Tourist Information Tel 0473 258070.
Christchurch Mansion and Wolsey Art Gallery Christchurch Park Tel 0473 253246.
Museum of East Anglian Life Stowmarket Tel 0449 612229.
Wolsey Theatre Tel 0473 53725.

Historic Houses, Castles and Gardens

Bucklesham Hall Gardens Bucklesham Tel 047388 263.
Helmingham Hall and Gardens Stowmarket Tel 047339 217/363
Otley Hall - House and Garden, Otley Tel 047339 264.

Ipswich Town Football Ground Tel 0473 219211.
Suffolk Ski Club Wherstead Tel 0473 36737.
Suffolk Showground Tel 0473 726847.

Ixworth Theobalds £60

Tel 0359 31707 **R**

68 High Street Ixworth Bury St Edmunds Suffolk IP31 2HJ **Map 10 C2**

Simon and Geraldine Theobald set up their restaurant in a village seven miles north of Bury St Edmunds in 1981; consistency has been the name of their game ever since their first appearance in this Guide in 1989. Oak beams and log fires make a traditional English setting for enjoying Simon's capable and confident cooking. The price of a three-course meal is still dictated by the price of the main dish (an allowance is made for any course not required); at lunchtime there is also a good-value table d'hote. The cheapest main-course option is vegetarian, continuing with the likes of skate with spinach and a white port and mustard seed sauce or sautéed noisettes of lamb with rosemary served on a bed of aubergine, pimento and tomato with a sherry sauce. Good meat dishes (game in season) and good saucing are the highlights. Some of the best-known names appear on the fine wine list, which is comprehensive, fairly priced and provides helpful notes where needed; mineral water is offered free of charge. No smoking – puffers can repair to the lounge. ***Seats** 36. L 12-2 D 7-9.30 (Sat to 10). Closed L Sat, D Sun, all Mon, Bank Holidays. Set L £11.95/£14.95 Set D from £18.50 (vegetarian) & from £23.50. Access, Visa.*

Jervaulx Jervaulx Hall 70% £130*

Tel 0677 60235 Fax 0677 60263 **H**

Jervaulx Masham nr Ripon North Yorkshire HG4 4PH **Map 5 D4**

Enjoying an attractive spot next to the ruins of the 12th-century Abbey, the Hall is run by the sociable John Sharp. A dignified yet homely atmosphere prevails with watercolours, period furnishings, ornaments and family photos in the quiet and appealing day rooms. Peace is the main objective in the bedrooms, with no TVs to intrude (although telephones are now in all rooms); an abundance of quality toiletries in the carpeted bathrooms continues the home-from-home appeal. Open for shooting and house parties only from Dec to mid March. *Half-board terms. ***Rooms** 10. Garden. Closed Dec-mid Mar. No credit cards.*

Jevington Hungry Monk £58

Tel 0323 482178 Fax 0323 483989 **R**

The Street Jevington nr Polegate East Sussex BN26 5QF **Map 11 B6**

The friendly atmosphere created by owners Nigel and Sue Mackenzie (here since 1968) is enhanced by the charming surroundings, which feature open fires and low beamed ceilings. The fixed-price menu, which always includes some vegetarian options, ranges from salad of venison sausage, chestnuts and bacon or squid stuffed with spinach and pine kernels to Madeira-sauced pigeon, breast of duck (crispy Norfolk or pink Barbary) and croustade of three fish on spinach and ginger with hollandaise. A good choice to finish might be pear clafoutis, lemon sponge pudding or a goat's cheese and sesame seed savoury. Smoking is only allowed in the sitting room. No children under 3. ***Seats** 36. Private Room 16. L Sun 12-2 (Mon-Sat by arrangement) D 7-10. Closed Bank Holiday Mons, 3 days Christmas. Set meals £19.90.* AMERICAN EXPRESS

We welcome bona fide complaints and recommendations on the tear-out pages at the back of the book for readers' comments. They are followed up by our professional team.

Kendal The Moon

£35

Tel 0539 729254

R

129 Highgate Kendal Cumbria LA9 4EN

Map 4 C3

Eye-catching bistro opposite the Brewery Arts Centre, where there is parking. Attention to quality and loyalty to local produce make for Lakeland food at its best; half the menu is vegetarian, with interesting choices such as fennel rice, mozzarella and sweetcorn-filled pancakes with a sour cream topping. From the meaty side come pork and gooseberry stroganoff, spiced lamb and apricot bobotie or chicken breast in a Thai sauce of coconut, lime and coriander. The Moon hosts a pudding club once a month so there's an ever-changing and adventurous choice of puddings. Children's portions. No smoking in the restaurant. ***Seats** 78. Private Room 40. D only 6.30-10 (Fri & Sat from 6). Closed 25 Dec, 1 Jan, 4 weeks Jan-Feb. Access, Visa.*

Kendal Posh Nosh

£35

Tel 0539 725135

R

Yard 11 Stramongate Kendal Cumbria LA9 4BH

Map 4 C3

Sophisticated family restaurant where chef-patron Stephen Burrowes, a Miller Howe emigré, provides carefully-priced daytime and night-time menus that range from carrot, lemon and cumin soup and Cumberland sausage with home-made chutney in the daytime to hot and sour Dublin Bay prawns, loin of pork with orange and hazelnut stuffing and roast beef with tarragon sauce. British farmhouse cheeses are served with home-made sesame biscuits. Scones, cakes and teas anytime Mon-Thurs. ***Seats** 52. Parties 38. Meals 9-6 (Fri & Sat 9-3 & 7-9). Closed D Mon-Thu, all Sun, Bank Holidays. Access, Diners, Visa.*

Kendal Woolpack Hotel 59%

£70

Tel 0539 723852 Fax 0539 728608

H

Stricklandgate Kendal Cumbria LA9 4ND

Map 4 C3

17th-century former coaching inn (its ground floor was once Kendal's wool auction room) with old-fashioned original bedrooms, a modern annexe and a private car park at the rear. Children up to 12 stay free in parents' room. No dogs. ***Rooms** 54. Access, Diners, Visa.*

Kendal Places of Interest

Tourist Information Tel 0539 725758.
Levens Hall Tel 05395 60321.
Sizergh Castle and Garden (NT) Tel 05395 60070.
Kendal Ski Club Tel 0539 33031.
Museums and Art Galleries
Abbot Hall Art Gallery Tel 0539 722464.
Abbot Hall Museum of Lakeland Life and Industry Tel 0539 722464.
Kendal Museum of Natural History and Archaeology Tel 0539 721374.

Kenilworth Restaurant Bosquet

£72

Tel 0926 52463

R

97a Warwick Road Kenilworth Warwickshire CV8 1HP

Map 6 C4

Bernard Lignier's superbly consistent cooking has a sound classical base. His imagination and obvious creative flair enhance daily fixed-price and seasonal à la carte menus which are full of ambition and interest; the translations from the French descriptions help considerably. Cream of pigeon soup with pigeon breast and wild mushrooms, lobster and sole terrine or a salad of several preparations of duck could precede the day's fish special, saddle of lamb or beef with a Roquefort and armagnac sauce. Dishes similar in concept appear on the shorter (three choices for starter and main) prix-fixe menu. Jane Lignier's polite, efficient service complements the

See over

serious cooking. ***Seats** 26. L by arrangement D 7-9.30. Closed Sun & Mon, 1 week Christmas, 3 weeks Aug. Set D £19.80 (exc Sat).* AMERICAN EXPRESS *Access, Visa.*

Kenilworth — Clarendon House — 60% — £77

Tel 0926 57668 Fax 0926 50669 — H

Old High Street Kenilworth Warwickshire CV8 1LZ — **Map 6 C4**

The Lea family's friendly hotel stands at the heart of the town's conservation area and was originally built in 1430 as a tavern to serve the local community. Care has been taken to retain the original character, with panelling and exposed beams much in evidence, particularly in the Royalist Retreat Bar and Castle Tavern restaurant. Bedrooms, which include some tiny singles, are furnished in a cosy, unfussy manner in a variety of styles. Each has its own en-suite bath or shower room. The hotel is not far from the NEC, and Birmingham, Leamington, Warwick, Stratford and Coventry are within easy reach. ***Rooms** 31. Access, Visa.*

Kenilworth — De Montfort Hotel — 63% — £100

Tel 0926 55944 Fax 0926 57830 — H

Kenilworth Warwickshire CV8 1ED — **Map 6 C4**

Modern De Vere hotel with spacious day rooms and a good standard of accommodation. Banqueting facilities up to 200, conferences to 350. ***Rooms** 96.* AMERICAN EXPRESS *Access, Diners, Visa.*

Kenilworth — Place of Interest

Royal Showground National Agricultural Centre, Stoneleigh Park Tel 0203 696969.

Kenton — Travel Inn — £43

Tel 081-907 1671 Fax 081-909 1604 — L

Kenton Road Kenton Middlesex HA3 8AT — **Map 15 E2**

***Rooms** 43.* AMERICAN EXPRESS *Access, Diners, Visa.*

Keswick — Keswick Hotel — 60% — £70

Tel 076 87 72020 Fax 076 87 71300 — H

Station Road Keswick Cumbria CA12 4NQ — **Map 4 C3**

Solid Victorian hotel set in four acres of gardens, an easy walk from the town. Lakeland views. Families welcome, but also a business trade. A fine Victorian conservatory has a grapevine and is an ideal place for afternoon tea. Guests can play golf free (Monday to Friday) at Keswick Club. ***Rooms** 66. Garden, putting.* AMERICAN EXPRESS *Access, Diners, Visa.*

Kettering — Kettering Park Hotel — NEW — 71% — £105

Tel 0536 416666 Fax 0536 416171 — H

Kettering Parkway Kettering Northamptonshire NN15 6XT — **Map 7 E4**

Styled inside and out in the manner of a large Jacobean manor house, Kettering Park, Shire Inns' newest hotel, stands above a roundabout south of Kettering right next to the A1/M1 link road. In winter the welcoming smell of burning log fires fills the entrance hall. Stone floors laid with Oriental carpets, oak panelling, deep-coloured, richly patterned upholstery, dark polished wood tables and furniture, tapestry wall hangings – all create an ambience that feels traditional and long-established. Public areas, structured on differing levels, flow into one another culminating in a spacious, well-laid-out bar/lounge. Bedrooms are well designed and up to date offering a good range of amenities from magazines and hairdryers to mini-bars and satellite TV. Executive rooms have a sitting area, all rooms have a writing desk. Decor features polished wood and well-matched, colourful fabrics. Bathrooms have excellent showers with a good selection of quality toiletries. The hotel's leisure facilities are magnificent. ***Rooms** 90. Garden, indoor swimming pool, children's swimming pool, gymnasium, squash, sauna, spa bath, steam room, solarium, snooker.* AMERICAN EXPRESS *Access, Diners, Visa.*

Kew **Wine & Mousaka** £35

Tel 081-940 5696 **R**

12 Kew Green nr Richmond Surrey TW9 3BH **Map 15 E2**

Sensibly-priced Greek restaurant opposite Kew Green and next to the Coach & Horses pub. The menu covers the usual favourites including both meat and vegetarian moussaka. See also entry under London W5 (Ealing). ***Seats** 52. Parties 20. L 12-2.30 D 6-11. Set L & D £6.95. Closed Sun, Bank Holidays.* AMERICAN EXPRESS *Access, Diners, Visa.*

Keyston **Pheasant Inn** £50

Tel 080 14 241 Fax 080 14 340 **R**

Village Loop Road Keyston nr Bythorn Cambridgeshire PE18 0RE **Map 7 E4**

Restaurant and bar menus have been amalgamated at this delightful thatched pub just off the A14, and guests can choose between the more formal Red room or by log fires in the bars. Chef-manager Nick Steiger offers an eclectic, daily-changing menu that takes its inspiration from far and wide: terrine of pheasant and pigeon with Cumberland sauce; latkes with smoked salmon and sour cream; tajine of vegetables with mixed lentils; wild boar sausages with mustard and onion sauce; sirloin steak bordelaise; Brazilian-style chicken with coconut milk, sweet peppers, prawns and rice. Finish with one of a dozen puddings or a selection of Neal's Yard cheeses. Enjoy all this fine food with a glass of cask-conditioned ale or something from the super wine list with some bargain prices, especially at the top end. Helpful notes are worth following. ***Seats** 30. Private Room 35. L 12-2 D 6-10. Closed D 25 & 26 Dec.* AMERICAN EXPRESS *Access, Diners, Visa.*

Kidderminster **Stone Manor** 65% £65

Tel 0562 777555 Fax 0562 777834 **H**

Stone nr Kidderminster Hereford & Worcester DY10 4PJ **Map 6 B4**

Mock-Tudor in style, the Manor dates from 1926. Space is not in short supply; newer conference complex accommodates 150; Garden Room banqueting for up to 250. Some characterful bedrooms overlooking rose gardens and swimming pool include four with four-posters. ***Rooms** 52. Garden, outdoor swimming pool, tennis, putting.* AMERICAN EXPRESS *Access, Diners, Visa.*

Kidderminster **Places of Interest**

Hartlebury Castle Tel 0229 250410.
Harvington Hall Tel 0562 777 267.
Dudmaston House and Garden (NT) Quatt, Bridgnorth Tel 0746 780866.
West Midland Safari and Leisure Park Bewdley Tel 0299 402114.

Kilve **Meadow House** 70% £80

Tel 0278 7415465 Fax 0278 741663 **H**

Sea Lane Kilve nr Bridgwater Somerset TA5 1EG **Map 13 E1**

Howard and Judith Wyer-Roberts operate a civilised home-from-home at their former rectory in the foothills of the Quantocks, five minutes from a quiet, fossil-strewn beach. Immaculate landscaped gardens with stream and duck pond provide a peaceful setting, and the main-house bedrooms are spacious, attractive and well appointed. Stable rooms across the car park

See over

have sitting rooms and a pleasant, cottagey look. Antiques, original paintings and log fires are features in the drawing room, lounge and study. Turn right off the A39 at the *Hood Arms* when coming from Bridgwater. ***Rooms** 10. Garden.* AMERICAN EXPRESS *Access, Visa.*

King's Lynn — Butterfly Hotel — 62% — £67

Tel 0553 771707 Fax 0553 768027 — **H**

Beveridge Way Hardwick Narrows King's Lynn Norfolk PE30 4NB — **Map 10 B1**

A modern, town-fringe hotel at the A10/A47 roundabout; part of a small East Anglian group aiming at the middle of the market. Conferences up to 50; private dining for 15; under-16s stay free in parents' room. ***Rooms** 50. Garden.* AMERICAN EXPRESS *Access, Diners, Visa.*

King's Lynn — Duke's Head — 60% — £93

Tel 0553 774996 Fax 0553 763556 — **H**

Tuesday Market Place King's Lynn Norfolk PE30 1JS — **Map 10 B1**

Forte Heritage hotel with an imposing 17th-century frontage. Singles, doubles and superior doubles. Conference facilites. ***Rooms** 71.* AMERICAN EXPRESS *Access, Diners, Visa.*

King's Lynn — Forte Travelodge — £42

Tel 0406 362230 — **L**

Wisbech Road Long Sutton King's Lynn Norfolk PE12 9AG — **Map 10 B1**

On the A17 at the junction with the A1101, 12 miles west of King's Lynn and 10 miles north of Wisbech. ***Rooms** 40.* AMERICAN EXPRESS *Access, Visa.*

King's Lynn — Places of Interest

Tourist Information Tel 0553 763044.
Houghton Hall Tel 0485 569.
Oxburgh Hall (NT) Swaffham Tel 036621 258.
Sandringham House and Grounds Sandringham Tel 0553 772675.
Peckover House and Garden (NT) Wisbech Tel 0945 583463.
Hunstanton Beach *14 miles King's Lynn.*

Kingham — Mill House — 66% — £100

Tel 0608 658188 Fax 0608 658492 — **H**

Kingham nr Chipping Norton Oxfordshire OX7 6UH — **Map 14 C1**

Privately owned Cotswold hotel in a quiet pastoral setting complete with trout stream. Local stone and exposed beams give character to the day rooms, and most of the prettily decorated bedrooms enjoy fine views. The hotel is situated halfway between Stow-on-the-Wold and Chipping Norton. No children under five. No dogs. ***Rooms** 24. Garden, fishing.* AMERICAN EXPRESS *Access, Diners, Visa.*

Kingston — Restaurant Gravier — £70

Tel 081-549 5557 — **R**

9 Station Road Norbiton Kingston Surrey KT2 7AA — **Map 11 A5**

Swags of hops, exposed-brick walls, smart table settings and some seriously good seafood are to be found at this well-established restaurant on the outskirts of town. The printed menu is more or less doubled by dishes of the day, recited at the table, the result of Jean-Philippe Gravier's early morning trips to Billingsgate. Madame Gravier (the only English member of an otherwise exclusively French team) rules in the kitchen with a sure touch – *homard à l'armoricaine, coquilles St Jacques meunière, filet de sole normande, choucroute de poissons, lotte à la moutarde.* Leave room for some excellent puds – *tarte aux poires glacé aux amandes sauce caramel, Far Breton aux pruneaux* – and/or some good French cheeses. A sound wine list includes, unusually for a fish restaurant, an interesting selection of clarets. ***Seats** 40. L 12-2 D 7-10. Closed L Sat, all Sun, Bank Holidays, 1 week Jan, 1 week Aug. Set L £14.50.* AMERICAN EXPRESS *Access, Diners, Visa.*

Kington Penrhos Court

£65

Tel 0544 230720 Fax 0544 230754

RR

Penrhos Kington Hereford & Worcester HR5 3LH

Map 9 D4

In six acres of grounds, standing on the hill between Lyonshall and Kington on the A44, Martin Griffiths' and Daphne Lambert's restaurant is in the beautifully restored 13th-century Cruck Hall, complete with flagstone floors and heavy beams – a characterful setting for occasional medieval banquets. Daphne offers daily-changing menus with a short choice: perhaps queen scallops grilled with laverbread or grilled goat's cheese to start, followed by pan-fried fillet of rabbit with oyster mushrooms, garlic and basil or fillet of lamb with mushroom risotto and a light curry sauce. Simple, but well-executed desserts such as blackcurrant trifle, lemon tart and chocolate truffle cake with coffee-flavoured crème anglaise. 4-course Sunday lunches offer a small choice, but always include a traditional roast. ***Seats** 50. Private Room 20. L (Sun only) 12.30-3 D 7.30-9. Closed 25 & 26 Dec, last 2 weeks Feb. Set L £12.50/£15.50 (Sun £15.50) Set D £19/£25.* AMERICAN EXPRESS *Access, Diners, Visa.*

Rooms

£110

Nineteen individually-styled bedrooms, named after birds, show some fine taste. The latest eight rooms are in converted Elizabethan barns; of a fair size, they use lightwood and mahogany furniture, co-ordinated contemporary fabrics and bright, clean decor. Bathrooms (some with shower/WC only) have attractive fittings and quality toiletries. Limited hotel-style public areas, but high bedroom standards. The Swallow Room features a four-poster bed and private balcony. Children up to 10 free in parents' room. No dogs.

Kington Place of Interest

Hergest Croft Gardens Tel 0544 230160.

Kintbury Dundas Arms

£65

Tel 0488 58263 Fax 0488 58568

IR

53 Station Road Kintbury nr Newbury Berkshire RG15 0UT

Map 14 C2

The Kennet and Avon canal runs by this 18th-century inn with roomy, traditionally-styled accommodation in a converted livery and stable block. Sliding picture windows offer access to a terrace with garden furniture; all rooms enjoy views of the ducks at play. ***Rooms** 5. Closed 25 Dec.* AMERICAN EXPRESS *Access, Visa.*

Restaurant

£65

A comfortable dining room with canal views is the stage for owner David Dalzell-Piper's cooking. Fresh local ingredients are prepared with skill, confidence and a notable lack of fuss – the food is cooked, put on a plate and served. These talents show up well on the understated, hand-written menu with dishes like home-cured gravad lax, fried lamb's sweetbreads with shallot sauce, roast Gressingham duck with sultana and jasmine sauce, fried haddock with parsley crust, cockles and mussels. Brown sugar meringues, pear in red wine with cinnamon ice cream and bread-and-butter pudding are to be found among the desserts. Fine British cheeses. Food is also served in the small 'Cocktail' bar (Mon-Sat, exc D Mon).
A drinker's wine list: for lovers of burgundy and claret it offers exceptional value for money on every page, as well as bargains galore from elsewhere – once again a regional winner of Cellar of the Year – see page 34.
***Seats** 50. Parties 20. Private Room 12. L 12.30-1.30 D 7.30-9.15. Closed Xmas/New Year, Sun & Mon, Set L £16.50.*

Kinver Berkleys £55

Tel 0384 873679 **R**

5 High Street Kinver West Midlands **Map 6 B4**

In the Piano Room (a pianist plays Fri & Sat eves) Andrew Mortimer's short menu, with explanatory notes, is cautiously contemporary: scallop kebabs with hot leek vinaigrette, sliced smoked trout with jellied lobster, noisettes of veal with Roquefort and Calvados. The bistro, with a different selection of dishes, is open lunchtime and evening. ***Seats** 35. D only 7-10 (Bistro also 12-2 & 7-10). Closed Sun, Bank Holidays, 2 weeks Feb.* AMERICAN EXPRESS *Access, Diners, Visa.*

Knaresborough Dower House 63% £66

Tel 0423 863302 Fax 0423 867665 **H**

Bond End Knaresborough nr Harrogate North Yorkshire HG5 9AL **Map 6 C1**

An ivy-decked former dower house – the main building dates from Tudor times – that retains considerable appeal in period furnishings and features (notably a handsome Georgian staircase). Some of the bedrooms have an old-fashioned feel, while others, along with the conference and leisure facilities, are modern. Children stay free in parents' room. Dogs allowed in some annexe rooms only. ***Rooms** 32. Garden, indoor swimming pool, gymnasium, sauna, spa bath, solarium.* AMERICAN EXPRESS *Access, Diners, Visa.*

Knaresborough Places of Interest

Allerton Park Tel 0423 330927.
Mother Shipton's Cave and Petrifying Well Tel 0423 864600 *Oldest tourist attraction in Britain.*

Knutsford La Belle Epoque £70

Tel 0565 633060 Fax 0565 634150 **RR**

60 King Street Knutsford Cheshire WA16 2DT **Map 6 B2**

A flamboyant art nouveau restaurant with fancy table settings, parquet flooring, cane chairs, marble columns and richly-coloured curtain drapes. The cooking, from Graham Codd and David Mooney, matches the setting with a mix of twisted traditional (faggots in cider, asparagus soufflé, salmon and tomato mousse terrine, lamb's kidneys and oxtail 'hot pot') and modern (pizza with smoked salmon, sour cream and chives, ravioli of smoked haddock, saddle of boned, roast venison with lightly peppered raspberry vinaigrette, spinach-wrapped darne of salmon filled with hake fillet and served on a citrus sauce). Good British cheeses. Outdoor eating on the roof garden in fine weather. A good all-round wine list with every bottle enthusiastically trumpeted. $1\frac{1}{2}$ miles from J19 of the M6 and 10 miles from Manchester Airport. ***Seats** 65. Private Room 100. D only 7.30-10. Closed Sun, Bank Holidays, 1 week Jan.* AMERICAN EXPRESS *Access, Diners, Visa.*

Rooms £60

Seven charmingly decorated rooms with large floral prints and a mixture of Edwardian and white reproduction furniture. All have en-suite bathrooms. No children under 10 in rooms or restaurant.

Knutsford Cottons Hotel 65% £112

Tel 0565 650333 Fax 0565 755351 **H**

Manchester Road Knutsford Cheshire WA16 0SU **Map 6 B2**

Five minutes from the M6 (junction 19) and just 15 from Manchester Airport, Cottons was designed with a New Orleans theme. There's plenty of free parking, versatile facilities for conferences (up to 200 delegates theatre-style) and a well-designed leisure club to which all guests have free membership during their stay. Two bars provide a choice for the thirsty.

Children up to 14 accommodated free in parents' room; cots and high chairs provided. Shire Inns. ***Rooms** 82. Indoor swimming pool, gymnasium, sauna, spa bath, solarium, tennis.* AMERICAN EXPRESS® *Access, Diners, Visa.*

Knutsford **Forte Travelodge** £42

Tel 0565 652187 **L**

Chester Road Tabley Knutsford Cheshire WA16 0PP **Map 6 B2**

On the A556 northbound, 15 miles south of Manchester city centre. East of Junction 19 of the M6. ***Rooms** 32.* AMERICAN EXPRESS® *Access, Visa.*

Knutsford **Places of Interest**

Tatton Park (NT) Tel 0565 564822.
Tabley House Collection Tel 0565 50888.
Tabley Showground Tel 027 073 245.

Lacock **At The Sign of The Angel** £75

Tel 0249 730230 Fax 0249 730527 **IR**

6 Church Street Lacock nr Chippenham Wiltshire SN15 2LB **Map 14 B2**

A 15th-century wool-merchant's house situated in a National Trust village and run by the Levis family since 1953. Beams, creaking floors, huge fireplaces and heavy oak furniture offer plenty of character in main-house bedrooms; a couple of rooms are in the annexe, reached by a little bridge across the garden stream. The lounge is shared by residents and diners. Not a conference delegate in sight! ***Rooms** 10. Garden. Closed 22 Dec-1 Jan.* AMERICAN EXPRESS® *Access, Visa.*

Restaurant £80

A traditional roast, with a fish alternative, is the centrepiece of set dinners served by candle-light. Typical starters are prawn and cucumber mousse, Madeira-sauced lamb's kidneys (also available for main course). To finish, perhaps almond crème brulée, spiced bread-and-butter pudding or meringues with clotted cream (this is hearty food, not for serious weight-watchers!). Also à la carte. Cold food only Saturday lunch & Sunday dinner (the latter for residents only). Several gems on a managable wine list. ***Seats** 45. Parties 20. Private Room 20. L 1-1.30 D 7.30-8.15. Closed L Sat & Mon (including Bank Holidays), D Sun. Set L £16 Set D £22.50-£30.*

Lacock **Places of Interest**

Lacock Abbey (NT) Tel 024973 227.
Fox Talbot Museum of Photography (NT) Tel 024 973 459.

Lamorna Cove **Lamorna Cove Hotel** 65% £95

Tel 0736 731411 **H**

Lamorna Cove nr Penzance Cornwall TR19 6XH **Map 12 A4**

The stunning location on one side of the steeply wooded valley, with views of the cove below, remains the same but new owners Malcolm and Lisa Gray are changing to a more country house style. The ponderous reception desk and pub-like bar counter have gone and various antiques and paintings have been introduced into the day rooms. Pine furniture is gradually replacing functional melamine pieces in bedrooms which often feature a natural stone wall or characterful black beams. 1960s' bathrooms, two with shower and WC only, are still perfectly usable. Three rooms have private balconies and all enjoy fine views. Children and dogs are accepted but not encourgaged. ***Rooms** 16. Garden, outdoor swimming pool. Access, Visa.*

Lancaster Forte Posthouse 69% £68

Tel 0524 65999 Fax 0524 841265 **H**

Waterside Park Caton Road Lancaster Lancashire LA1 3RA **Map 6 A1**

Well-designed, practical accommodation and smart public rooms in a low-rise hotel overlooking the river Lune. Banqueting and conference facilities for 100/120. ***Rooms** 110. Indoor swimming pool, gymnasium, sauna, spa bath, solarium.* AMERICAN EXPRESS *Access, Diners, Visa.*

Lancaster Places of Interest

Tourist Information Tel 0524 32878.
Judges' Lodgings Museum Tel 0524 32808.
Frontierland Western Theme Park Morecambe Tel 0524 410024.
Theatres and Concert Halls
Dukes Theatre Tel 0524 66645.
Nuffield Theatre Studio Tel 0524 39026.
Leighton Hall Carnforth Tel 0524 734474.

Land's End State House 67% £70

Tel 0736 871844 Fax 0736 871599 **H**

Land's End Sennen Cornwall TR19 7AA **Map 12 A4**

The setting is spectacular, right on the clifftop at Land's End, and the views out to sea and the Scilly Isles are truly dramatic. Day rooms include a bar serving 30 malt whiskies and a new fast food restaurant replacing the café. Bedrooms, recently re-designed and refurbished, are priced according to the view. Most rooms are available for family use and children stay free in parents' room. Conference/function facilities for 200+. ***Rooms** 34. Coffee shop 10am-5pm).* AMERICAN EXPRESS *Access, Visa.*

Lands End Places of Interest

Minack Theatre Porthcurno Tel 0736 810471.
Sennen Cove Beach.

Langar Langar Hall 70% £80

Tel 0949 60559 Fax 0949 61045 **HR**

Langar Nottinghamshire NG13 9HG **Map 7 D3**

In the heart of the Vale of Belvoir and adjacent to the village church, Langar Hall, built of sandstone in the 1830s, is the family home of Imogen Skirving and as such is crammed full of antiques and homely artefacts. Large oil paintings of past family members line the wide stone staircase in the entrance hall, which has an informality continued throughout the hotel. Public rooms comprise a dark, intimate library and bright, sunny drawing room both furnished in a comfortable, lived-in style. Bedrooms upstairs in the main house vary in size and character; the newly converted courtyard rooms are more up-to-date but all the rooms have oodles of appeal including a wide selection of books and fine views over the extensive grounds. ***Rooms** 11. Garden.* AMERICAN EXPRESS *Access, Diners, Visa.*

Restaurant £70

With pillars and a huge fireplace, the restaurant occupies what was an inner hall. Silver candelabra and fresh flowers decorate tables which are large and well-spaced. The cooking, supervised by Imogen Skirving, has a simplicity of style and content. This is hearty, wholesome country cooking, largely traditional but with a few nods to modernity. Dinner is a relaxed, informal affair beginning with tasty amuse-gueule and home-baked bread and ending with either the local Colston Bassett Stilton or a delicious chocolatey pudding. ***Seats** 30. Parties 12. Private Room 16. L 12.30-2.30 D 7.30-9.30. Closed Sun (residents only).*

Langdale **Langdale Hotel** **71%** **£130**

Tel 05394 37302 Fax 05394 37694 **H**

Great Langdale nr Ambleside Cumbria LA22 9JD **Map 4 C3**

An extensive hotel and timeshare complex in 35 acres of woodland overlooking Great Langdale Beck. Centrally, an open-plan bar-lounge and restaurant incorporate the old mill stream, while an adjacent pub bar features slate walls and a log fire. Accommodation comprises a number of satellite blocks, constructed in Lakeland stone, where there is plenty of room for families in the former self-catering chalets; baby-sitting is offered (by advance arrangement) but not baby-listening, due to the distance between rooms and dining room. Wet-weather provision includes fine leisure facilities, a Lego table in the bar and coffee shop seating by the large pool. No dogs. ***Rooms** 65. Garden, gymnasium, indoor swimming pool, children's pool, spa bath, sauna, solarium, keep-fit equipment, beauty & hair salon, tennis, squash, games room, snooker, adventure trail and play equipment, trim trail, bowling green, coffee shop (10am-10pm), news kiosk.* AMERICAN EXPRESS *Access, Diners, Visa.*

Langho **Northcote Manor** **67%** **£65**

Tel 0254 240555 Fax 0254 246568 **HR**

Northcote Road Langho nr Blackburn Lancashire BB6 8BE **Map 6 B1**

Just off the A59 and nine miles from the M6 (Junction 31), Langho was once home to a Victorian cotton luminary and today retains much of the atmosphere of a lived-in family home, although recent improvements are changing the operation into a larger and more efficiently-run business. By day, large bay windows afford fine views of the Ribble Valley, while on winter nights open log fires are warm and welcoming; a new, second lounge is decorated in calm, pastel shades and has improved pre-dinner seating. The first-floor bedrooms, reached by a carved oak staircase, are attractive and homely, with characterful, old-fashioned bathrooms; seven rooms have been added recently (only two now have just a shower en suite). The Davies Suite features a four-poster and a 6ft cast-iron tub. Children stay free in parents' room. Disabled facilities have also been greatly improved. ***Rooms** 13. Garden.* AMERICAN EXPRESS *Access, Diners, Visa.*

Restaurant **£80**

The recent refurbishment has also extended to the dining rooms and kitchens, with yellows and gold decor, a rich blue carpet and deep red chairs; the conservatory extension has increased the table capacity to 19, seating up to 80. Classically based dishes refreshed with innovative touches run through joint-owner Nigel Haworth's variety of menus which change two-monthly. Dishes might range from collared pork (rolled pork and cow heel with smoked bacon and cabbage salad, pea purée and mustard sauce) or vegetable and salmon terrine with a chive dressing to pot-roasted Pendle lamb shank with onions and crisp layers of potatoes, or grilled undercut of beef with red wine, shallots and marrowbone on a tarragon sauce. Fine fresh fish appears on a specialities list and game in season. Good vegetarian options and farmhouse cheeses; home-made breads and amuse-gueule. Traditional Sunday lunches. The concise wine list offers some good drinking under £20. The Birtwistle Room, off the drawing room, has private dining facilities for up to 40. ***Seats** 80. Private Room 40. L 12-1.45 (11.45-2 Sun) D 7-9.30. Closed 1 Jan. Set L £9.20 & £11.40.*

Langley-on-Tyne **Langley Castle** **65%** **£70**

Tel 0434 688888 Fax 0434 684019 **H**

Langley-on-Tyne nr Haydon Bridge Northumberland NE47 5LU **Map 5 D2**

Surrounded by ten acres of woodland, this resplendent castle, built in 1350, has walls that are seven feet thick and is full of architectural interest; the main staircase houses some of the best-preserved 14th-century garderobes in Europe and there's a chapel in the roof. Bedrooms are simply furnished

See over

but given individuality by stylishly-draped half-tester beds. One of the en-suite bathrooms has a sauna and another a whirlpool bath. A large, lofty drawing room boasts an open fireplace and antique furniture. The hotel is on the A686, a mile or two south of Haydon Bridge. ***Rooms** 8. Garden.* AMERICAN EXPRESS *Access, Diners, Visa.*

Lavenham Great House

£45

Tel 0787 247431

RR

Market Place Lavenham Suffolk CO10 9QZ **Map 10 C3**

The Great House is 15th-century with a Georgian facade, and stands just opposite the historic Guildhall in this well-preserved medieval town. Frenchman Régis Crépy provides excellent food served in cosy surroundings on rural French and English menus, applying a modern touch to the best local ingredients. Wide selection of French cheeses. Long brasserie-style lunch menu and both fixed-price and à la carte in the evening. A covered patio with conservatory dining was due to be completed as we went to press. No smoking. ***Seats** 40. Private Room 50. L 12-2.30 D 7-9.30 (Sat to 10.30). Closed D Sun, all Mon. Set L £9/£12 Set D £14.95.* AMERICAN EXPRESS *Access, Diners, Visa.*

Rooms

£68

There are four charming bedrooms/suites. Thick beams, antique furniture and floral fabrics create the look of village England.

Lavenham The Swan 71%

£120

Tel 0787 247477 Fax 0787 248286

HR

High Street Lavenham nr Sudbury Suffolk CO10 9QA **Map 10 C3**

A splendid example of Elizabethan architecture, the Swan has been welcoming guests since the 15th century. Bristling with timbers, the cosy alcoves meander one into another, creating charming public areas. The lounge has long been the setting for relaxing afternoon tea, while the earthy real-ale bar has the warm feel of a much-loved local. Walkways overlooking pretty little gardens lead to the variously sized bedrooms, designed to retain the period feel; stylish furniture and extras like fruit and chocolates set the the tone for the attention to detail in evidence throughout the hotel; 18 rooms are reserved for non-smokers. Breakfast is good and service is on the ball. Forte Heritage. ***Rooms** 47. Garden.* AMERICAN EXPRESS *Access, Diners, Visa.*

Restaurant

£75

Long-serving chef Andrew Barrass has a sure touch and his menus offer a good choice of carefully cooked dishes, simply conceived and elevated by imaginative touches. A recent, seasonal menu offered millefeuille of woodland mushrooms, avocado and tiger prawn salad, courgette and mint soup, grilled halibut steak with spring onion and orange butter, fresh pasta ribbons with a trio of sauces, and chicken breast simmered in mustard and cider cream. The restaurant, built in 1965, is in keeping with the hotel's origins and has an open-raftered ceiling and a minstrel's gallery. No smoking. ***Seats** 80. Parties 30. Private Room 40. L 12.30-2 D 7-9.30. Set L £12.50/£14.50 Set D £19.95.*

Lavenham Place of Interest

The Priory Lavenham Tel 0787 247417.

Our inspectors *never* book in the name of Egon Ronay's Guides. They disclose their identity only if they are considering an establishment for inclusion in the next edition of the Guide.

Leamington Spa — Courtyard by Marriott — 65% — £70

Tel 0926 425522 Fax 0926 881322 — **H**

Olympus Avenue Europa Way Leamington Spa Warwickshire CV34 6RJ — **Map 14 C1**

Roomy and practical accommodation at competitive rates aimed mainly at the business traveller. Conference and banqueting facilities for up to 50. Children free in parents' room. Located in an industrial park. Formerly a *Holiday Inn. **Rooms** 97. Keep-fit equipment.* AMERICAN EXPRESS *Access, Diners, Visa.*

Leamington Spa — Inchfield Hotel — 63% — £78

Tel 0926 883777 Fax 0926 330467 — **H**

64 Upper Holly Walk Leamington Spa Warwickshire CV32 4JL — **Map 14 C1**

A solid Victorian house, just five minutes from the town centre and about ten from the M40. Bedrooms are of a good standard, quietly stylish and equipped with the usual modern comforts. Children up to 12 stay free when sharing parents' room. No dogs. ***Rooms** 22. Garden.* AMERICAN EXPRESS *Access, Visa.*

Leamington Spa — Mallory Court — 80% — £162

Tel 0926 330214 Fax 0926 451714 — **HR**

Harbury Lane Bishop's Tachbrook Leamington Spa Warwickshire CV33 9QB — **Map 14 C1**

2 miles south of Leamington Spa, off the B4087 towards Harbury, and standing in 10 acres of beautifully landscaped gardens, Mallory Court has an air of luxury and refinement. It's one of the original country house hotels and still one of the very best, built in 1910 in the Elizabethan style of tall chimneys and stone-mullioned windows with leaded lights. A small entrance hall leads directly into the main lounge, complete with deep-cushioned couches and armchairs, quality drapes, deep carpets and fine period furniture; the drawing room boasts green leather chesterfields and there's a delightful conservatory sun-trap. Bedrooms are generally of a good size and impeccably designed, with stylish fabrics, light, fresh colours and quality freestanding furniture; some have four-posters. Extras in the rooms include bath robes, mineral water, flowers and magazines. The Blenheim suite is nothing short of luxurious with its own balcony, two tubs in the bathroom and a painted ceiling. Attentive staff and highly efficient housekeeping. Unsuitable for children under the age of nine. No dogs – kennelling nearby. ***Rooms** 10. Garden, outdoor swimming pool, squash, all-weather tennis. Access, Visa.*

Restaurant ★ — £115

The panelled dining room is at the very heart of Mallory Court, offering high-quality cooking with polished and professional service to match. Chef-proprietor Allan Holland's style is a mix of classical and modern, amply illustrated by dishes like a warm salmon mousseline filled with crab and served with a shellfish sauce and pan-fried fillet of cod with virgin olive oil, sun-dried tomatoes and creamed potatoes – two dishes that featured on a recent three-course fixed-price menu which offered alternatives only at each stage. The à la carte is most unusually priced so it's difficult to ascertain one's likely expenditure; there is a minimum charge of £31.50 (equivalent to the price of the table d'hote) plus supplements for every dish – from £2.50 for duck consommé with beetroot and ravioli to £6.50 for foie gras terrine with Sauternes jelly and toasted brioche and £9.50 for braised fillet of turbot with black taglioni and a langoustine sauce. The 2- or 3-course fixed-price lunch menu also offers a good choice of simpler but equally well-executed dishes (smoked haddock and salmon fish cakes with egg sauce, strips of calf's liver with onions and creamed potato). Excellent desserts (oeufs à la neige with crème anglaise and blackcurrant coulis, Grand Marnier soufflé with orange sorbet) and tip-top British cheeses.

See over

There are a few reasonably-priced bottles on the safe wine list. "No service charge is made or expected." ***Seats** 50. Private Room 50. L 12.30-2 D 7.30-9.45 (Sat to 10, Sun to 9). Set L £20.50/£24.50 Set D £31.50.*

Leamington Spa Regent Hotel 68% £89

Tel 0926 427231 Fax 0926 450728 **HR**

77 The Parade Leamington Spa Warwickshire CV32 4AX **Map 14 C1**

A veritable institution, the Regent was the largest hotel in the world when built in 1819 and boasts a guest list ranging from the Duke of Wellington and Ulysses S Grant to Henry Wadsworth Longfellow and Sarah Bernhardt – a comprehensive Who's Who of the last two centuries. In the same family ownership since 1904, the hotel, far from resting on its laurels, has undergone a major refurbishment over the last four years with individually-decorated bedrooms boasting smart new furniture (a few have antiques), including some deeply comfortable reclining armchairs, and with brand new bathrooms. Of the public rooms the lounge is more grand than comfortable but the bar has a remarkably fine, intriguing mural – get the barman to interpret. Charmingly 'old-fashioned' touches include eiderdowns on the beds, the overnight cleaning of shoes left outside bedroom doors at night and genuinely friendly, helpful service from often long-serving staff. Free parking. 24hr room service. ***Rooms** 80. Games room.* AMERICAN EXPRESS *Access, Diners, Visa.*

Vaults Restaurant £65

Quenelles of sole with a shrimp and brandy sauce and roast Angus beef carved from the trolley are equally safe choices at this most reliable of restaurants where head chef Roland Clark has presided for over 20 years. The fairly traditional French/English menu might include oxtail soup, lamb and beef cassoulet, fillet steak 'Café de Paris', mixed grill, duckling grand'mère, hot cabinet pudding and even Christmas pudding (not just in December). The setting, as the menu suggests, is the barrel-vaulted cellars of the hotel, most of it reserved for non-smokers. Good wine list with some bargains to be found among the erratically priced first-growth clarets. ***Seats** 50. Parties 20. Private Room 20. L 12.30-2.30 D 7.30-10.45 (Fri & Sat from 7). Closed Sun & Bank Holidays. Set L £9.75/£11.75 Set D £16.50.*

Leamington Spa Places of Interest

Tourist Information Tel 0926 311470.
Offchurch Bury Polo Club Red House Farm, Campion Hills Tel 0926 882883.

Ledbury The Feathers £85

Tel 0531 635266 Fax 0531 632001 **I**

High Street Ledbury Hereford & Worcester HR8 1DS **Map 14 B1**

Between Malvern and Ross-on-Wye, a classic timber-framed former coaching inn dating from 1564 with oddly-shaped, en-suite, double-glazed bedrooms (including one with a four-poster), original Elizabethan wall paintings, uneven, creaky floors and drunken staircases. Remote-control TV, bedside tea-tray and hair-dryers are standard. Good snacks in the hop-bedecked Fuggles bar and small rear patio in good weather. Function facilities in the ballroom complex for 130. ***Rooms** 11.* AMERICAN EXPRESS *Access, Diners, Visa.*

Ledbury Hope End 70% £119

Tel 0531 633613 Fax 0531 636366 **HR**

Hope End Ledbury Hereford & Worcester HR8 1SQ **Map 14 B1**

Elizabeth Barrett-Browning's former home, largely of 18th-century origin, is mellow rather than grand, nestling in 40 acres of wooded parkland and a Georgian landscaped garden which includes a temple, grotto and island ruin. Today's incumbents John and Patricia Hegarty run this haven of tranquillity in suitably informal fashion, setting piles of books by the deep sofas in front of the log-burning stoves. Simply decorated bedrooms have exposed beams along with country oak and antique stripped-pine furniture, fresh flowers and yet more books; nary a TV unless requested. Cork and tile bathrooms come with a selection of bath oils. No children under 12. No dogs. ***Rooms** 9. Garden. Closed mid Dec-1st week Feb. Access, Visa.*

Restaurant £70

Patricia Hegarty is the definitive home cook, her chutneys, breads and jellies as integral a part of production as her nightly fixed-price dinner. The kitchen garden provides vegetables, herbs and fruit for many dishes; a typical dinner might offer cucumber and fennel soup or tomato and oatmeal flan with anchovy dressing to start, followed by breast of chicken with lemon, ginger and parsley sauce, roast best end of lamb with glazed turnips or aubergine-stuffed courgettes with broad bean purée; ruby chard, kohlrabi and steamed new potatoes might be the accompaniment to the main course. Salad (perhaps celery and grape or cucumber and apple mint) and good farmhouse cheeses then precede the likes of demerera meringues with loganberries, chocolate marbled tart with orange custard or elderflower sorbet. An exceptional wine list is strongest in fine burgundies, best for value in the Rhone. No smoking. ***Seats** 18. Parties 8. D only 7.30. Set D £30.*

Ledbury Place of Interest

Eastnor Castle Tel 0531 2305/2894.

Leeds Adriano Flying Pizza £30

Tel 0532 666501 **R**

60 Street Lane Roundhay Leeds West Yorkshire LS8 2DQ **Map 6 C1**

Bright and cheerful with polished granite tables and smart, efficient staff coping well with the crowds. There's rather more than just pizzas on offer here. Apart from the carte of standard Italian main courses, the daily (except Monday) list of fresh fish dishes is particularly worthy of note: hake with rosemary, char-grilled salmon and delicious monkfish *provincia* – made with fresh herbs and tomatoes – along with lemon sole and *calamari fritti*. In good weather eat outside on the cobbled pavement under a colourful awning. ***Seats** 140. Parties 20. L 12-2.30 D 6-11.30. Closed Easter Sun, 25 & 26 Dec, 1 Jan.* AMERICAN EXPRESS *Access, Visa.*

Leeds Bhavani Junction £24

Tel 0532 468988 **R**

2 Eastgate Leeds West Yorkshire LS2 7JI **Map 6 C1**

An exclusively vegetarian restaurant (on the top floor of Shabab) with an interesting range of northern thalis as a complement to their Moglai menu: onion bhaji, bhindian with fresh tomato, palak allo with methi, home-made paneer korma, raita, pillau rice, puri, fresh salad and gulab jamun, an excellent value combination. Bite-sized pani puri are filled with a mixture of chick peas and spicy potatoes. ***Seats** 50. L 11.30-2.30 D 6.30-11.45. Closed L Sun, Bank Holidays. Set L from £4.45 Set D from £12. Access, Visa.*

Leeds Bibis £48

Tel 0532 430905 **R**

Minerva House 16 Greek Street Leeds West Yorkshire LS1 5RU **Map 6 C1**

Smart, yet informal restaurant in Roman forum style squeezed in between city-centre office blocks. An extensive menu – everything from lobster ravioli with shrimp sauce and *osso buco alla milanese* to pizzas – is supplemented by daily specials like fresh asparagus hollandaise, and veal and pigeon pie. Cooking is distinctly above average for an Italian restaurant,

See over

as is the service, which is particularly swift at lunchtime to meet the needs of the local business community. ***Seats** 160. L 12-2.15 D 6-11.15. Closed Sun & Bank Holidays.* AMERICAN EXPRESS *Access, Visa.*

Leeds — Brasserie Forty Four ↑ — £50

Tel 0532 343232 Fax 0532 343332 — **R**

44 The Calls Leeds West Yorkshire LS2 7EW — **Map 6 C1**

A stylishly converted grain mill (next to *42 The Calls* hotel – see entry) houses an attractive riverside brasserie, next to Leeds parish church. The wide-ranging menu shows numerous styles and influences along with a sense of adventure; thus, Yorkshire pudding with onion gravy sits happily alongside Oriental stir-fried beef; lemon and garlic marinated chicken by classic coq au vin. Also available (to end a romantic dinner?) is a Cointreau-laced chocolate fondue for two, with marshmallows and pieces of fruit for dipping. 12 tables on a balcony and patio overlooking the river Aire are popular when the weather is kind. A very fairly priced and carefully compiled wine list has as many offerings from the New World as from France. ***Seats** 125. Private Room 60. L 12-2.30 D 6.30-10.30. Closed L Sat, all Sun. Set L £7.95.* AMERICAN EXPRESS *Access, Visa.*

Leeds — Darbar — £30

Tel 0532 460381 — **R**

16-17 Kirkgate Leeds West Yorkshire LS1 6BY — **Map 6 C1**

Splendidly grand first-floor restaurant serving better-than-average Indian food with the emphasis on subtlety rather than heat. The lunchtime hot buffet offers terrific value for money. ***Seats** 92. Parties 50. L 11.30-2 D 6-11.30 (Sun 11.30-11.30). Closed 25 Dec.* AMERICAN EXPRESS *Access, Diners, Visa.*

Leeds — Dawat — £30

Tel 0532 872279 — **R**

4-6 Leeds Road Kippax nr Leeds West Yorkshire LS25 7LT — **Map 6 C1**

Indian home cooking Delhi-style – from karahi gosht to keema nan and kulfi plus tandoori specialities from owner Mrs Arora in two 19th-century cottages. ***Seats** 26. Parties 16. D only 6.30-11. Closed Sun, 25 & 26 Dec.* AMERICAN EXPRESS *Access, Visa.*

Leeds — 42 The Calls — £120

Tel 0532 440099 Fax 0532 344100 — **PH**

42 The Calls Leeds West Yorkshire LS2 7EW — **Map 6 C1**

Created from a derelict riverside grain mill, 42 The Calls provides a new level of modern, sophisticated comfort for visitors to Leeds.
In a redevelopment area, it's the brainchild of Jonathan Wix. Its strong point is the bedrooms: co-ordinated soft furnishings blend with the building's original features like painted stone walls and warehouse beams. Each room has a large work desk, three phones, a CD stereo system and coffee percolator. Bathrooms are equally impressive. Minimal day rooms include a bright foyer and small lounge. There's no restaurant, but direct billing is arranged with a number of local restaurants that include *Brasserie Forty Four* next door (see entry), which has recently doubled its dining area. Excellent staff impress greatly and free valet parking is among the services offered. The top-floor Fletland suite seats 40 boardroom style, 55 theatre. ***Rooms** 39. Coarse fishing. Closed 5 days Christmas.* AMERICAN EXPRESS *Access, Diners, Visa.*

Any person using our name to obtain free hospitality is a fraud.
Proprietors, please inform the police and us.

Leeds — Haley's Hotel — 74% — £112

Tel 0532 784446 Fax 0532 753342 — **HR**

Shire Oak Road Headingley Leeds West Yorkshire LS6 2DE — **Map 6 C1**

Two miles from the city centre, on a leafy lane just off the A660 Otley Road, stands a lovely Victorian house that has been transformed into a stylish hotel. Although not large, the individually designed bedrooms are well appointed with smart fabrics in varying styles; attention to detail extends to a phone on both bedside table and desk, shoe-cleaning service and antique pieces. Bathrooms are bright and tiled, and quality toiletries and bathrobes are provided. Smartly attired young staff; 24hr room service and good breakfasts. Children up to 14 stay free in parents' room. ***Rooms*** *22. Garden. Closed 26-30 Dec.* AMERICAN EXPRESS *Access, Diners, Visa.*

Restaurant — £52

A serious restaurant with a style and quality unusual for the Leeds area. The refined, quietly elegant atmosphere is enhanced by neat table settings, subtle lighting and well-dressed staff. New chef Chris Baxter offers a straightforward table d'hote and a more involved carte with dishes like a spicy fish soup under a pastry case, oysters glazed in their shells with a tagliatelle of vegetables, fillet of beef with Brouilly sauce and wild mushrooms and duck breasts in pastry with caramelised red cabbage and plum sauce. Chocoholics can indulge in *la folie de cinq chocolats*, a speciality of the restaurant. French and British cheeses with home-made biscuits and walnut bread, plus dessert wines by the glass (try the unusual Banyuls). ***Seats*** *50. Parties 10. Private Room 25. L 12.30-2 D 7.15-9.45. Closed L Sat, D Sun. Set L £13.95/£16.95 Set D £18.95/£23.95.*

Leeds — Hilton International — 69% — £105

Tel 0532 442000 Fax 0532 433577 — **H**

Neville Street Leeds West Yorkshire LS1 4BX — **Map 6 C1**

Escalators in glass 'antechambers' lead to the cool marble reception/lounge. A modern, well-kept, well-run hotel. Conference/banqueting facilities for 400/290. ***Rooms*** *206. Garage, coffee shop (10am-11pm).* AMERICAN EXPRESS *Access, Diners, Visa.*

Leeds — Holiday Inn Crowne Plaza — 71% — £150

Tel 0532 442200 Fax 0532 440460 — **H**

Wellington Street Leeds West Yorkshire LS1 4DL — **Map 6 C1**

Modern, redbrick, seven-storey hotel in the city centre, next to the Yorkshire Post Newspaper Group building. A marble-floored foyer leads up to meeting rooms on the mezzanine floor and the Roundhay lounge bar, which overlooks the striking swimming pool. A club-like cocktail bar adjoins Hamilton's restaurant and the lively Wig and Pen pub (open 11-11) is also on the ground floor. Bedrooms have at least one double bed, stylish furniture and individual air-conditioning. There are many thoughtful extras included and ample work space with easy chairs. 24hr room service. Large mirrors, bathrobes, slippers and toiletries in the bathrooms. Children stay free in parents' room. Staff are young, smart and quietly efficient. Conference/banqueting facilities for 200/250. Car park for 140 cars. Recently rebranded from plain *Holiday Inn*. ***Rooms*** *125. Indoor swimming pool, children's pool, keep-fit equipment, sauna, spa bath, steam room, solarium, beauty salon, snooker.* AMERICAN EXPRESS *Access, Diners, Visa.*

> Many establishments are currently on the market, so ownership could change after we go to press.

Leeds — Maxi's Chinese Restaurant — £40

Tel 0532 440552 Fax 0532 343902 — R

Bingley Street Leeds West Yorkshire LS3 1LX — **Map 6 C1**

The largest purpose-built Chinese restaurant in the North, serving Cantonese and Peking cuisine to 300 diners. Hardly worthy of a foodie pilgrimage, but worth knowing about; plenty of room for families and a couple of private suites for functions. ***Seats 300.*** *Meals 12-12. Set meals from £13.* AMERICAN EXPRESS *Access, Diners, Visa.*

Leeds — Merrion Thistle Hotel — 65% — £101

Tel 0532 439191 Fax 0532 423527 — H

Merrion Centre Wade Lane Leeds West Yorkshire LS2 8NH — **Map 6 C1**

With the new name (it was formerly just *Merrion*) has come top-to-toe refurbishment for this city-centre hotel. The small ground-floor reception/lobby now boasts a marble floor and fine wood panelling and the first floor a smart new (and enlarged) lounge plus Starlets cocktail bar featuring framed photos of former variety artists. Almost three-quarters of the bedrooms are rather small, but well designed, single rooms with good oak fitted furniture and attractive colour schemes. Large double and twin-bedded rooms are decorated and furnished in similar style. Good new bathrooms complete the picture. Free overnight parking in next door multi-storey car park. ***Rooms 120.*** AMERICAN EXPRESS *Access, Diners, Visa.*

Leeds — New Asia — £35

Tel 0532 343612 — R

128 Vicar Lane Leeds West Yorkshire LS2 7NL — **Map 6 C1**

Mr Xuan Truong Hoang produces inexpensive Vietnamese specialities in slightly old-fashioned surroundings. Fine spring rolls made to order, mung bean flour (luk dao fan) noodles and char siu. There's a long list of seafood and over a dozen soups. ***Seats 60.*** *L 12-2 D 5-12. Set L from £4.20 Set D from £9.50. Access, Visa.*

Leeds — The Olive Tree — £55

Tel 0532 569283 — R

Oaklands Rodley Lane Leeds West Yorkshire LS13 1NG — **Map 6 C1**

To the west of town where the A657 meets the ring road you can't miss this large Victorian house looking down on the roundabout. It's an incongruous setting for an extensive menu of above-average Greek cooking with even the sweet honeyed desserts being home-made. If your tooth is not so sweet try the delicately rosewater-scented Greek trifle. The à la carte is not particularly cheap but early diners (before 7.30pm Mon-Fri and all day Sun) can take advantage of a good-value set meal at £9.95. Greek coffee comes with some excellent Turkish delight. Chef/patron George Psarias has an entry in the Guinness Book of Records as having produced the world's longest kebab. Every Tuesday there is a 'Bouzouki' evening with live music and dancing at no extra charge. ***Seats 160.*** *Private Room 40. L 12-2 (Sun till 3) D 6.30-11.30. Closed L Sat, all Bank Holidays. Set L £9.95/£13.50 Set D £9.95 (till 7.30pm) & £13.50.* AMERICAN EXPRESS *Access, Visa.*

Leeds — Queen's Hotel — 70% — £119

Tel 0532 431323 Fax 0532 425154 — H

City Square Leeds West Yorkshire LS1 1PL — **Map 6 C1**

The grandest hotel in Leeds when built in the 1930s retains many of the original features in the refurbishment undertaken by Forte over the last few years. Particularly impressive are the Palm Court Lounge (returned to its first use having been a furniture room for many years), large oval lobby with domed ceiling and clubby mahogany panelled bar. Authentic 1930s furniture and light fittings distinguish bedrooms, which also offer all the modern comforts including up-to-date bathrooms. A good buffet breakfast is well tended by friendly, helpful staff. 24hr room service and free valet parking. Conference facilities for 700. Forte Grand. ***Rooms** 190. News kiosk, Palm Court Lounge (7am-11pm).* AMERICAN EXPRESS *Access, Diners, Visa.*

Leeds — Sang Sang — £50

Tel 0532 468664 — R

7 The Headrow Leeds West Yorkshire — **Map 6 C1**

Over 200 dishes are listed on the long menu at this popular Chinese restaurant. All the favourites are represented including sizzling dishes, noodles with mixed meat and Peking duck. ***Seats** 110. Parties 80. Private Room 25. L 12-2 D 5.30-11.30. Closed Bank Holidays. Set meals from £13.* AMERICAN EXPRESS *Access, Diners, Visa.*

Leeds — Sous le Nez en Ville — £40

Tel 0532 440108 — R

Basement Quebec House Quebec Street Leeds West Yorkshire LS1 2HA — **Map 6 C1**

Basement bistro with the emphasis on fresh tastes, conviviality and better-than-average desserts. Tapas in the bar. ***Seats** 75. Private Room 28. L 12-2.30 D 6-10.30. Closed L Sat, all Sun, Bank Holidays. Set D £11.95 incl ½ bottle of wine. Access, Visa.*

Leeds — Thai Siam — £40

Tel 0532 451608 — R

68-72 New Briggate Leeds West Yorkshire LS1 6NU — **Map 6 C1**

Friendly service from traditionally clad staff in simple, uncluttered first-floor surroundings. The Thai menu offers 60+ dishes, with a further two dozen in the vegetarian section. MSG-free. ***Seats** 60. L 12-2.30 D 6-11 (Sun to 10.30). Set L from £3.95 Set D from £11. Access, Visa.*

Leeds — Places of Interest

Tourist Information Tel 0532 478302.
Harewood House and Bird Garden Tel 0532 886225/886238.
The Hollies Park Tel 0532 782030.
Museum of Leeds
Middleston Railway Moor Road Railway Station Tel 0532 710320
World's oldest railway.
City Varieties Music Hall Tel 0532 430808.
Civic Theatre Tel 0532 462453.
Grand Theatre and Opera House Tel 0532 459351.
Leeds Playhouse Tel 0532 442141.
International Pool Tel 0532 438696.
Headingley Cricket Ground Tel 0532 787394.
Leeds United Football Ground Tel 0532 716037.
Leeds RLFC Tel 0532 786181
Pontefract Park Racecourse Tel 0977 703224.

Leek — Primo Piano — £40

Tel 0538 398289 — R

12 Sheepmarket Leek Staffordshire ST13 5HW — **Map 6 C3**

First-floor bistro and pizzeria above the pedestrianised Sheepmarket. Predictable menu plus some interesting breads. Children's portions. No smoking. ***Seats** 42. Parties 24. L 12-2 D 6-10 (Fri/Sat to 10.30). Closed L Mon, all Sun. No credit cards.*

Leicester **Belmont Hotel** **65%** **£80**

Tel 0533 544773 Fax 0533 470804 **H**

De Montfort Street Leicester Leicestershire LE1 7GR **Map 7 D4**

In the same family ownership for more than 50 years, the Belmont stands in a quiet street just off the A6. Good-quality darkwood furniture is used in the bedrooms, the larger of which are designated Executives. Among the day rooms are two bars: Olives in the basement has a wine bar/bistro atmosphere. Children up to 16 stay free in parents' room. ***Rooms** 68. Garden. Closed Christmas.* AMERICAN EXPRESS *Access, Diners, Visa.*

Leicester **Curry Pot** **£45**

Tel 0533 538256 **R**

78 Belgrave Road Leicester Leicestershire LE4 5AS **Map 7 D4**

Tandoori restaurant offering a short menu of Indian favourites that are a cut above the standard suggested by the dull exterior. Particularly good samosas, chicken tikka and masala, plus lamb shahi korma. ***Seats** 55. Parties 30. L 12-2 (Sat to 1.30) D 6-11 (Sat to 11.30). Closed Sun, 4 days Christmas. Set meals from £16.25.* AMERICAN EXPRESS *Access, Diners, Visa.*

Leicester **Forte Posthouse** **64%** **£68**

Tel 0533 630500 Fax 0533 823623 **H**

Braunston Lane East Leicester Leicestershire LE3 2FW **Map 7 D4**

Equidistant from Junction 21 of the M1 and the city centre, this modern low-rise hotel has seen substantial upgrading. Most of the bedrooms have been completely refurbished, and improvements have also been made to restaurant, bar, lounge and reception. Conference/banqueting facilities for 100. ***Rooms** 172. Garden.* AMERICAN EXPRESS *Access, Diners, Visa.*

Leicester **Granada Lodge** **£45**

Tel 0530 244237 Fax 0530 244580 **L**

M1/A50 Junction 22 Markfield Leicester Leicestershire LE6 0PP **Map 7 D4**

***Rooms** 39.* AMERICAN EXPRESS *Access, Diners, Visa.*

Leicester **Grand Hotel** **66%** **£102**

Tel 0533 555599 Fax 0533 544736 **H**

Granby Street Leicester Leicestershire LE1 6ES **Map 7 D4**

A city-centre Victorian building with ample parking close to the railway station. Public rooms live up to the name and bedrooms are stylish and of a good size. Two themed bars; vast banqueting and conference facilities for up to 450. 24hr room service. Jarvis Hotels. ***Rooms** 92. Coffee shop (10am-6pm Mon-Sat).* AMERICAN EXPRESS *Access, Diners, Visa.*

Leicester **Holiday Inn** **72%** **£114**

Tel 0533 531161 Fax 0533 513169 **H**

129 St Nicholas Circle Leicester Leicestershire LE1 5LX **Map 7 D4**

At the hub of a major road interchange, near Junction 21 of the M1, Leicester's Holiday Inn is a tall building reaching high over the city. The marbled reception area makes a splendid first impression, and the lounge area that adjoins it is no less appealing. The rustic-style Hayloft restaurant with beams and agricultural accoutrements is an interesting contrast to the otherwise modern decor. Bedrooms provide plenty of space, large beds, fitted units and good tiled bathrooms. 65 are designated non-smoking. The leisure centre is a great family attraction at weekends. Free covered parking for residents. Conference facilities for 300. ***Rooms** 188. Indoor swimming pool, sauna, solarium, spa bath, steam room, news kiosk, coffee shop (7am-10.15pm).* AMERICAN EXPRESS *Access, Diners, Visa.*

Leicester — Leicester Forest Moat House — 58% — £73

Tel 0533 394661 Fax 0533 394952 — **H**

Hinckley Road Leicester Leicestershire LE3 3GH — **Map 7 D4**

Alongside the A47 four miles from the city centre, 3 miles from Junction 21 interchange of M69 and M1. Well-equipped bedrooms, a choice of bars and conference rooms for up to 65. ***Rooms** 34. Garden.* AMERICAN EXPRESS *Access, Diners, Visa.*

Leicester — Man Ho — £40

Tel 0533 557700 — **R**

16 King Street Leicester Leicestershire LE1 6RJ — **Map 7 D4**

Comprising two houses in a low Georgian terrace behind New Walk Centre, Man Ho probably offers the best Chinese cooking in Leicester. Space, comfort and tastefully modern decor make a fine setting in which smartly-suited waitresses serve a mix of Peking, Cantonese and Szechuan cooking. Good choice of iron-plated sizzling dishes (including oysters, stuffed rainbow trout and prawn-filled aubergines), fresh seafood (lobster, scallops, sea bass, Dover sole), crispy aromatic duck and lamb, plus lettuce-wrapped minced chicken and seafood. ***Seats** 130. Private Room 60. L 12-2.30 D 5.30-11.30 (Sat & Sun 12-11.30). Set L from £6.50 Set D from £12.* AMERICAN EXPRESS *Access, Visa.*

Leicester — Park International — 61% — £82

Tel 0533 620471 Fax 0533 514211 — **H**

Humberstone Road Leicester Leicestershire LE5 3AT — **Map 7 D4**

Tall, imposingly modern hotel with a choice of bars and large conference suites, but no leisure facilities. ***Rooms** 209. Coffee shop (7am-10pm, from 8am weekends).* AMERICAN EXPRESS *Access, Diners, Visa.*

Leicester — Rise of the Raj — £35

Tel 0533 553885 — **R**

6 Evington Road Leicester Leicestershire LE2 1HF — **Map 7 D4**

Indian cooking in a homely restaurant on two floors. The menu is fairly standard, with many variations on lamb, chicken and prawns providing the bulk of the dishes. Specialities include chicken or king prawn masala, lamb pasanda and tandoori rainbow trout. Good-value thali (set meals), both meat and vegetarian. ***Seats** 72. Parties 40. L 12-2 D 6-11.45. Closed 25 Dec. Set meals from £8.50.* AMERICAN EXPRESS *Access, Diners, Visa.*

Leicester — Stakis Country Court — 69% — £104

Tel 0533 630066 Fax 0533 630627 — **H**

Braunstone Leicester Leicestershire LE3 2WQ — **Map 7 D4**

Ten minutes from the city centre, just off Junction 21 of the M1, at the end of the M69. A modern, business-oriented hotel offering good-sized bedrooms (all rooms have either one or two double beds), extensive range of conference facilities (for up to 90), leisure club and vastly reduced rates at off-peak weekends when businessmen are thin on the ground. Children under 16 stay free in parents' room. ***Rooms** 141. Garden, indoor swimming pool, gymnasium, sauna, spa bath, steam room, solarium, beauty salon.* AMERICAN EXPRESS *Access, Diners, Visa.*

We do not accept free meals or hospitality – our inspectors pay their own bills.

Leicester Places of Interest

Tourist Information Tel 0533 511300/511301.
Haymarket Theatre Tel 0533 539797
Phoenix Arts Theatre Tel 0533 554854.
Bosworth Battlefield Visitor Centre & Country Park Market Bosworth Tel 0455 290429.
Leicester Cathedral Tel 0533 625294.
The Leicestershire Museum and Art Gallery New Walk Tel 0533 554100.
Leicestershire Museum of Technology Tel 0530 510851.
Grace Road Cricket Ground Tel 0533 831880.
Leicester City Football Ground Tel 0533 555000.
Leicester Racecourse Tel 0533 716515.
Outdoor Pursuits Centre Dry Ski Slope Tel 0533 681426.
Braunstone Park Showground Tel 0509 231665.
Mallory Park Motor Racing Circuit Tel 0455 842931.

Leighton Buzzard The Swan 64% £80

Tel 0525 372148 Fax 0525 370444 H

High Street Leighton Buzzard Bedfordshire LU7 7EA **Map 15 E1**

A handsome Georgian coaching inn in the centre of town. Bedrooms vary in both size and decor with a mix of pine and reproduction furniture and colourful fabrics. Bathrooms are neat and unfussy. The Hunter's bar has rustic appeal with hunting prints, guns and fishing rods on the walls, and a carved-oak counter. There is also a comfortable lounge. Children up to 16 stay free in parents' room. Resort Hotels. ***Rooms 38.*** AMERICAN EXPRESS *Access, Diners, Visa.*

Leighton Buzzard Places of Interest

Library Theatre Tel 0525 378310.
Ascott (NT) House & Garden Wing Tel 0296 688242.

Lenham Chilston Park 71% £95

Tel 0622 859803 Fax 0622 858588 H

Sandway Lenham nr Maidstone Kent ME17 2BE **Map 11 C5**

Four miles from Junction 8 of M20, between Ashford and Maidstone, a remarkable hotel set in 250 acres complete with a lake. The 17th-century Grade I house contains a treasure trove of antique furniture, oil paintings, water colours, rugs and objets d'art. Over 200 candles are lit throughout the public areas at dusk, evoking a sense of the past. The Marble Hall and Drawing Room are fine examples of elegant comfort and each bedroom in the house has its own very individual style and character; some have open fires. The Hogarth Room has an 18th-century four-poster and a splendid view of the lake. Bedrooms in the stable block are simpler but not without charm. The lounge accommodation is enhanced by an Orangery. Characterful conference and meeting rooms (for up to 120). ***Rooms 40.*** *Garden, tennis, coarse fishing, snooker.* AMERICAN EXPRESS *Access, Diners, Visa.*

Letchworth Broadway Toby Hotel 59% £60

Tel 0462 480111 Fax 0462 481536 H

The Broadway Letchworth Hertfordshire SG6 3NZ **Map 15 E1**

1½ miles from Junction 9 of the M1, a smartly-kept hotel with a friendly, non-chain feel (even though it is in the Toby and Osprey chain). Well-furnished bedrooms and a calm cocktail bar-cum-lounge. Conference and banqueting facilities for up to 180. ***Rooms 35.*** AMERICAN EXPRESS *Access, Diners, Visa.*

Lewdown — Lewtrenchard Manor 73% — £95

Tel 056 683 256 Fax 056 683 332 — **HR**

Lewdown nr Okehampton Devon EX20 4PN — **Map 12 C2**

Personally run with quiet charm by James and Sue Murray, this early 17th-century mansion, overlooking a peaceful Devon valley, has been turned into an ideal country retreat. Mellow day rooms boast some fine ribbed ceilings, stone-mullioned windows, oak panelling and numerous antiques plus the sweet, welcoming smell of real log fires. Bedrooms vary in size, the larger with antique furniture including a couple with four-posters, but all benefit from well-chosen fabrics, fresh flowers, mineral water and, in the carpeted bathrooms, towelling robes, good toiletries and huge, soft bath sheets. Room service offers drinks and light snacks throughout the day and evening and beds are turned down at night. No children under eight. ***Rooms** 8. Garden, fishing, clay-pigeon shooting.* AMERICAN EXPRESS *Access, Diners, Visa.*

Restaurant — £75

A grand room with oil portraits of some of the former occupants of the house gazing down at the crisply clothed tables where today's guests are offered a choice between Patrick Salvadori's varied à la carte or the no-choice table d'hote menu. Dishes such as mussel soup with cardamom, ravioli of seafood with crab and caviar sauce, pan-fried cod with tagliatelle and sweet pepper sauce, roast grouse with bacon, chick pea and red wine sauce and chocolate chip éclair filled with banana crème patissière are all given the same care even if not all are equally successful. Service is a happy combination of friendliness and formality. ***Seats** 35. Parties 8. Private Room 30. L by arrangement & Sun 12-2.30 D 7.15-9.30. Set L £16 Set D £24.50.*

Lewes — Shelleys Hotel 60% — £118

Tel 0273 472361 Fax 0273 483152 — **H**

High Street Lewes East Sussex BN7 1XS — **Map 11 B6**

One of the original Mount Charlotte hotels, Shelleys is located on the main road through Lewes. Dating from the 17th century, it retains some old-world charm and elegance. ***Rooms** 21. Garden.* AMERICAN EXPRESS *Access, Diners, Visa.*

Lewes — Places of Interest

Historic Houses, Castles and Gardens

Bateman's (NT) Burwash Tel 0435 882302 *Rudyard Kipling lived here.*
Charleston Farmhouse Fircle Tel 032 183 265 *Home of Vanessa and Clive Bell and Duncan Grant, leaders of the Bloomsbury movement.*
Firle Place Tel 0273 858335.
Glynde Place Tel 0273 858337.
Monk's House Rodmell Tel 0273 479274 *Cottage home of Virginia and Leonard Woolf.*
Wilmington Priory and Long Man Nr Newhaven Tel 0323 870537 *10 miles.*
Borowski Centre Dry Ski Slope Newhaven Tel 0273 515402.
Drusillas Zoo Alfriston Tel 0323 870656.

Lichfield — George Hotel 59% — £90

Tel 0543 414822 Fax 0543 415817 — **H**

Bird Street Lichfield Staffordshire WS13 6PR — **Map 6 C3**

Regency style survives in the spacious, peaceful day rooms and the pastel-decorated bedrooms of this Jarvis hotel. The ballroom can accommodate up to 100 guests for a banquet or conference. Children up to 12 stay free in parents' room. ***Rooms** 38.* AMERICAN EXPRESS *Access, Diners, Visa.*

Lichfield Places of Interest

Tourist Information Tel 0543 252109.
Hanch Hall and Garden Tel 0543 490308.
Lichfield Cathedral Tel 0543 256120.
Samuel Johnson Birthplace Museum Tel 0543 264972.
Lichfield Heritage Exhibition Treasury and Muniment Room Tel 0543 256611.

Lifton Arundell Arms 65% £88

Tel 0566 784666 Fax 0566 784494 **H**

Lifton Devon PL16 0AA **Map 12 C2**

Ann Voss-Bark's lovely old creeper-covered inn has for more than 50 years been a leading fishing hotel, with 20 miles of its own water on the Tamar and its tributaries, and a 3-acre lake. Public areas include a warm, old-fashioned sitting room, a bar, a games room and a skittle alley. Bedrooms are light and cheerful, with soft colours and solid furnishings. Children up to 16 stay free in parents' room. The hotel is half a mile off the A30. ***Rooms** 29. Garden, fishing. Closed 3 days Christmas.* AMERICAN EXPRESS *Access, Diners, Visa.*

Lifton Place of Interest

Launceston Castle Launceston Tel 0566 2365.

Lincoln D'Isney Place £60

Tel 0522 538881 Fax 0522 511321 **PH**

Eastgate Lincoln Lincolnshire LN2 4AA **Map 7 E2**

A delightful garden surrounds D'Isney Place, an 18th-century building by the Cathedral offering an exceptionally warm and comfortable atmosphere. David and Judy Payne run it as an up-market bed and breakfast hotel. Well-loved antique furniture abounds and there's a homely feel throughout. The rooms vary from large, with four posters and spa baths or steam showers, to compact and charming singles, one with shower/WC only. Also available is a cottage with two double en-suite bedrooms, living room, dining room and kitchen. All the bedrooms have tables and breakfast is served to order in the rooms. Parking within the grounds. ***Rooms** 17. Garden.* AMERICAN EXPRESS *Access, Diners, Visa.*

Lincoln Forte Posthouse 63% £68

Tel 0522 520341 Fax 0522 510780 **H**

Eastgate Lincoln Lincolnshire LN2 1PN **Map 7 E2**

A modern hotel (formerly Forte Crest) right beside the cathedral and handy for visiting old Lincoln. Well-equipped bedrooms add to the convenience. Conference and function facilities for up to 80. ***Rooms** 70. Garden.* AMERICAN EXPRESS *Access, Diners, Visa.*

Lincoln White Hart 69% £90

Tel 0522 526222 Fax 0522 531798 **H**

Bailgate Lincoln Lincolnshire LN1 3AR **Map 7 E2**

An old Forte Heritage hotel in the heart of the city on a site where there has been an inn for over 600 years (Richard II stayed in 1387). Secure parking available opposite. ***Rooms** 50. Roof-top garden, orangery coffee shop (9-5.30).* AMERICAN EXPRESS *Access, Diners, Visa.*

Lincoln Places of Interest

Tourist Information Tel 0522 529828.
Theatre Royal Tel 0522 23303.
Historic Houses, Castles and Gardens
Doddington Hall Doddington Tel 0522 694308.
Lincoln Castle Castle Hill Tel 0522 511068.
Tattershall Castle (NT) Tattershall, Nr Woodhall Spa Tel 0526 42543.
The Old Hall Gainsborough Tel 0427 612669.
Lincoln Cathedral Tel 0522 530320.
City and County Museum Tel 0522 530401.
Usher Gallery Tel 0522 527890.
Market Rasen Racecourse Tel 0673 843434 *16 miles.*
Cadwell Park Motor Racing Circuit Nr Louth Tel 0507 343248.
Grange-de-Lings Showground Tel 0522 522900.

Linton Wood Hall 80%

£89

Tel 0937 587271 Fax 0937 584353

HR

Linton nr Wetherby West Yorkshire LS22 4JA

Map 6 C1

It's hard not to be impressed when first sighting this magnificent Georgian house (with an older, Jacobean wing), set in 100 acres of rolling parkland. Day rooms exude elegance, from the polished flagstone floor to the panelled bar and sumptuously furnished lounge – all appointed with great taste. Supremely comfortable, spacious bedrooms (24 were recently added), individually styled and beautifully decorated, are furnished with bold fabrics and freestanding, painted furniture. Extras provided include sherry, fruit, mineral water and a teddy bear. Carpeted bathrooms have power showers, huge towels, quality toiletries and telephone extensions. Leisure centre and free use of nearby tennis courts. ***Rooms** 44. Garden, coarse fishing, indoor swimming pool, spa bath, solarium, beauty salon, steam room, gymnasium, games room, snooker.* AMERICAN EXPRESS *Access, Diners, Visa.*

Restaurant

£80

An elegant restaurant where chef Simon Wood cooks in a style that is best described as light, modern English, with no heavily-reduced or cream sauces in evidence. Fixed-price lunches and à la carte dinners. Good local cheeses. An extensive wine list, albeit at stiff prices. Lounge menu only Saturday lunchtime. ***Seats** 65. Private Room 110. L 12.30-2 D 7-9.30. Closed L Sat. Set L £14.95 (£12.95 Sun).*

Liskeard Well House 74%

£105

Tel 0579 342001

HR

St Keyne Liskeard Cornwall PL14 4RN

Map 12 C3

From the church in St Keyne take the left fork to St Keyne Well to find this tranquil spot set in small landscaped gardens that include an enchanting duck pond. Owner Nick Wainford and his charming staff are unfailingly helpful and discreet, guaranteeing that a stay here really is a tonic. Off the tiled hall are a relaxing drawing room and an inviting little bar; across the hall, the dining room has magnificent bay windows overlooking the sun terrace and lawns. Individually designed bedrooms and well-equipped bathrooms are immaculately kept. First-rate breakfasts. ***Rooms** 7. Garden, outdoor swimming pool, tennis.* AMERICAN EXPRESS *Access, Visa.*

Restaurant

£65

Daily menus at fixed prices offer four or five choices for each course, featuring what's best and freshest from the local markets. Typical items on the dinner menu (choose 2, 3 or 4 courses) run from Cornish fish soup and confit of duck leg with braised lentils and port to seared monkfish on a pasta rösti, breast of mallard with celeriac purée and millefeuille of calf's kidneys and sweetbreads with basil-flavoured mashed potato. Hot prune and armagnac soufflé is a dessert worth waiting for, and there's a fine

See over

selection of West Country cheeses. Lighter lunches, or a three-course set menu. Decent wine list with standard 'names' and a good selection of half bottles. ***Seats** 32. L 12.30-2 D 7.30-9. Set L £21 Set D from £18.95.*

Liskeard — Place of Interest

Thorburn Museum and Gallery Tel 0579 20325/21129 *Audio-visual gallery.*

Liverpool — Atlantic Tower — 65% — £103

Tel 051-227 4444 Fax 051-236 3973 — **H**

Chapel Street Liverpool Merseyside L3 9RE — **Map 6 A2**

A high-rise city-centre hotel, resembling a great liner's bow in outline, whose various public areas include a bar inspired by Nelson's *Victory* in addition to a smart cocktail bar. Well-equipped bedrooms make good-sized singles but rather compact doubles and twins, with no space between beds in the latter. Corner rooms are larger and there are eight full suites. There's free garage parking just behind the hotel. Conference/banqueting facilities for 140/120. Mount Charlotte Thistle. ***Rooms** 226. Garage.* AMERICAN EXPRESS *Access, Diners, Visa.*

Liverpool — Britannia Adelphi Hotel — 68% — £105

Tel 051-709 7200 Fax 051-708 8326 — **H**

Ranelagh Place Liverpool Merseyside L3 5UL — **Map 6 A2**

Leisure facilities and a health club, conferences for up to 900 delegates, six bars and a night club are among the amenities of a large hotel with many grand original Edwardian features. Bedrooms range from singles to suites and jacuzzi rooms. Children up to 16 stay free in parents' room. The hotel is next door to Lime Street station. ***Rooms** 391. Indoor swimming pool, sauna, spa bath, squash, hairdressing & beauty salon, snooker, coffee shop (11am-2am Mon-Sat).* AMERICAN EXPRESS *Access, Diners, Visa.*

Liverpool — Campanile Hotel — £44

Tel 051-709 8104 Fax 051-709 8725 — **L**

Chaloner Street Queen's Dock Liverpool Merseyside L3 4AJ — **Map 6 A2**

Just outside the city centre. ***Rooms** 82.* AMERICAN EXPRESS *Access, Diners, Visa.*

Liverpool — Gladstone Hotel — 58% — £90

Tel 051-709 7050 Fax 051-709 2193 — **H**

Lord Nelson Street Liverpool Merseyside L3 5QB — **Map 6 A2**

Grey-brick hotel immediately behind Lime Street station, with ample car parking, a vast range of conference and meeting rooms (handling up to 600 delegates) and reduced-price membership of a local sports club. 24hr room food service, a lounge bar serving light meals and a choice of bars. Formerly the *Forte Crest*; still under Forte's ownership. Children up to 16 stay free in parents' room. ***Rooms** 154.* AMERICAN EXPRESS *Access, Diners, Visa.*

Liverpool — La Grande Bouffe — £50

Tel 051-236 3375 — **R**

48a Castle Street Liverpool Merseyside L2 9TL — **Map 6 A2**

Informal basement restaurant, mainly self-service at lunchtime. Evening table service brings the likes of home-made black pudding, feta cheese salad, pot-roast of lamb with haricot beans and steamed monkfish à la niçoise. ***Seats** 60. Parties 30. Private Room 20. Meals noon-10.30pm. Closed L Sat & Sun, all Tues & Bank Holidays.* AMERICAN EXPRESS *Access, Visa.*

Liverpool — Moat House — 67% — £116

Tel 051-709 0181 Fax 051-709 2706 — H

Paradise Street Liverpool Merseyside L1 8JD — Map 6 A2

Spacious bedrooms, large beds, smart public areas and a leisure centre with swimming pool. Conference/banqueting for 450/300. Children up to 16 stay free in parents' room. Nearly half the bedrooms are designated non-smoking. Follow road signs for Albert Dock and Paradise Street car park. ***Rooms** 251. Indoor swimming pool, gymnasium, sauna, spa bath, solarium, coffee shop (10.30am-midnight).* AMERICAN EXPRESS® *Access, Diners, Visa.*

Liverpool — St George's Hotel — 60% — £70

Tel 051-709 7090 Fax 051-709 0137 — H

St John's Precinct Lime Street Liverpool Merseyside L1 1NQ — Map 6 A2

Modern hotel in a central location opposite Lime Street station. Banquets/conferences up to 300. Free overnight parking in adjacent NCP. Forte Heritage. ***Rooms** 155.* AMERICAN EXPRESS® *Access, Diners, Visa.*

Liverpool — Places of Interest

Tourist Information Tel 051-709 3631.
Croxteth Hall & Country Park Tel 051-228 5311.
Speke Hall (NT) Tel 051-427 7231.
Liverpool Cathedral Tel 051-709 6271.
Metropolitan Cathedral of Christ the King Tel 051-709 9222.
Aigburth Cricket Ground Tel 051-427 2930.
Everton Football Ground Goodison Park Tel 051-521 2020.
Liverpool Football Ground Anfield Park Tel 051-263 2361.
Aintree Racecourse Tel 051-523 2600.
Liverpool Aquarium Tel 051-207 0001.
Knowsley Safari Park Prescot Tel 051-430 9009.
Mersey Ferries Tel 051-630 1030.
Beatles Story Albert Dock Tel 051-709 1963.

Theatres and Concert Halls

Empire Theatre Tel 051 709 1555.
Everyman Theatre Tel 051 709 4776.
Liverpool Playhouse Tel 051 709 8478/9.
Neptune Theatre Tel 051 709 7844.

Museums and Art Galleries

Liverpool Museum and Planetarium Tel 051-207 0001.
Merseyside Maritime Museum Tel 051-207 0001.
Walker Art Gallery Tel 051-207 0001.
Tate Gallery Liverpool Tel 051-709 3223.
Pilkington Glass Museum St. Helens Tel 0744 692014.

Lockington — Hilton National E Midlands Airport — 69% — £113

Tel 0509 674000 Fax 0509 672412 — H

Derby Road Lockington Leicestershire DE7 2RH — Map 7 D3

Near junction 24 of the M1 and just 1½ miles from the airport; Donington Park race track is also nearby. A modern low-rise hotel with conference facilities for up to 220. Children up to 14 stay free in parents' room. ***Rooms** 151. Indoor swimming pool, sauna, spa bath, solarium, gymnasium, beauty salon, coffee shop (10am-6pm).* AMERICAN EXPRESS® *Access, Diners, Visa.*

Lolworth — Forte Travelodge — £42

Tel 0954 781335 — L

Huntingdon Road Lolworth Bar Hill Cambridgeshire CB3 8DR — Map 15 F1

On the A604 northbound, 3 miles north of Junction 14 on the M11, 5 miles north of Cambridge. ***Rooms** 20.* AMERICAN EXPRESS® *Access, Visa.*

Long Melford — Black Lion — 65% — £65

Tel 0787 312356 Fax 0787 74557 — **H**

The Green Long Melford Sudbury Suffolk CO10 9DN — **Map 10 C3**

Count the Toby jugs and admire the maps and copper collection or relax in deep sofas in the charming lounge. Bedrooms are bright and comfortable, attractive fabrics complementing neutral walls and carpets. Each room has antique pine furniture and an easy chair or sofa. ***Rooms** 9. Garden. Closed 23 Dec-2 Jan. Access, Visa.*

Long Melford — Bull Hotel — 65% — £102

Tel 0787 378494 Fax 0787 880307 — **H**

Hall Street Long Melford Suffolk CO10 9JG — **Map 10 C3**

Built by a wealthy wool merchant in the 15th century, becoming a posting house with the arrival of the coaching era, the real-Tudor Bull is now a Forte Heritage Hotel combining character with comfort. 10 bedrooms are designated non-smoking. 60-seat conference room. ***Rooms** 25.*

AMERICAN EXPRESS *Access, Diners, Visa.*

Long Melford — Chimneys — £75

Tel 0787 379806 — **R**

Hall Street Long Melford Sudbury Suffolk CO10 9JR — **Map 10 C3**

Sam Chalmers' delightful beamed restaurant offers cooking which combines classical and modern elements. The lunchtime menu changes weekly, with choices which range from white onion soup and filo parcels of smoked haddock and cream cheese to grilled skate wing, chicken curry and roast leg of lamb. The dinner list (fortnightly changing) is a little more elaborate, with dishes such as grilled monkfish with peppers served on a crisp walnut salad, oven-baked quail with a herb stuffing, and fillet of Scottish beef pan-fried with a crisp potato pancake. Youngest vintages appear first on a carefully chosen wine list with a good New World section. ***Seats** 40. Private Room 50. L 12-2 D 7-9. Closed D Sun. Set L £13.95 Set D £27.50. Access, Visa.*

Long Melford — Places of Interest

Kentwell Hall (House, Garden & Maze) Long Melford Tel 0787 310207.

Melford Hall (NT) House & Garden Long Melford Tel 0787 880286.

Longham — Bridge House — 61% — £60

Tel 0202 578828 Fax 0202 572620 — **H**

2 Ringwood Road Ferndown Longham Dorset BH22 9AN — **Map 14 C4**

Anna Joannides is Greek Cypriot and her riverfront hotel on the A348 has a distinctly Mediterranean air; the sunny reception and lounge have white walls with tiles depicting Greek goddesses and the large bar opens on to a terrace overlooking the water. Bedrooms have plain white walls and pink draylon headboards; some large rooms have canopied or four-poster beds. Several conference suites are available for up to 70 delegates. No dogs. ***Rooms** 37. Garden, coarse fishing, children's play area.*

AMERICAN EXPRESS *Access, Visa.*

Longhorsley — Linden Hall — 74% — £115

Tel 0670 516611 Fax 0670 88544 — **H**

Longhorsley nr Morpeth Northumberland NE65 8XF — **Map 5 D2**

Four miles from the A1, through the village on the A697, a long tree-lined drive runs up to a Georgian country house. Elegant and restful public rooms include a lofty inner hall with a splendid sweeping staircase, an antique-furnished drawing room and two bars, one the Linden Pub

in the old converted granary. Bedrooms are of a reasonable size and individual in style; they range from singles to doubles, twins, four-posters and family rooms. A new extension has recently been built housing bedrooms, a good-size swimming pool and further leisure facilities.
***Rooms** 52. Garden, tennis, putting, sauna, solarium, beautician & hair salon, snooker, coarse fishing, mountain bikes, cricket pitch.* American Express *Access, Diners, Visa.*

Longridge — Paul Heathcote's Restaurant ★↑ — £90

Tel 0772 784969 — R

104-106 Higher Road Longridge nr Preston Lancashire PR3 3SY — **Map 6 B1**

Chef-proprietor Paul Heathcote and head chef Andrew Barnes have, in the relatively short space of three years, not only put Longridge on the map, but also demonstrated that when it comes to good cooking and serious restaurants, the north of England does not lag behind any other region. For many years, the likes of *Sharrow Bay* (where Paul cooked for a while) in Ullswater, *Pool Court* in Pool-in-Wharfedale, *McCoys* in Staddle Bridge, and latterly *21 Queen Street* in Newcastle and the *Old Vicarage* in Ridgeway have led the way. Joining them now, and unquestionably a shooting star on its own is this pretty, extended whitewashed cottage, half a mile past the White Bull pub (follow signs for Longridge Golf Club and Jeffery Hill). Since last year, much has changed – there's a new kitchen (visible through the glass frontage), an additional dining room and a reception lounge, all complementing the existing decor of beams, exposed stone walls and immaculate candle-lit table settings, further enhanced by delightful flower arrangements. Committed and friendly staff provide just the right emphasis on service, being well-trained and ultra-professional, and you'll find no better sommelier than Paul Wiltshire anywhere in the country. British chefs are now much in demand, so it's to his credit that Paul decided to return to his native Lancashire to cook with good local produce (such as Goosnargh chickens and ducklings) and the finest-quality ingredients from around the rest of the country. Both the lunch and à la carte menus change quite frequently, reflecting the availability of seasonal raw materials. The result is innovative cooking with flair and great skill in a style best described as 'modern British' – exemplified by dishes such as ham hock, leek and foie gras terrine served with beetroot and caraway chutney and truffle dressing to start, followed by a main course of roast cutlets of lamb served with baked Lancashire hotpot garnish, braised red cabbage and rosemary-scented juices, and perhaps bread-and-butter pudding served with a sauce anglaise, apricot coulis and clotted cream. A gourmet menu (a snip at £32.50) offers six set courses: black pudding served on crushed potatoes with haricot beans and thyme, ravioli of smoked duck with deep-fried vegetables and miller mushrooms, young courgettes with their flowers filled with lobster mousse, mussels and dill sauce, lemon grass sorbet, casserole of oxtail, tongue and shin cooked in red wine with a purée of potatoes and root vegetables, finally ending with poached peach inside a crisp tuile basket with almond ice cream, sugared almonds and a raspberry coulis or a selection of British cheeses in fine condition. After all that you deserve a rest and will probably want to stay the night – ask the restaurant for its recommended b&b down the road, where both excellent accommodation and a taxi service are provided. The carefully compiled wine list, albeit with some gaps, includes some interesting New World wines. No smoking in the dining rooms, but it is allowed in the new lounge. Our Chef of the Year (see page 22). ***Seats** 50. Parties 18. L (Fri & Sun only) 12-2 D 7-9.30. Closed Mon, plus a few days in Jan. Set L £20 Set D £32.50/£38.* American Express *Access, Visa.*

We endeavour to be as up-to-the-minute as possible, but inevitably some changes to key personnel may occur at restaurants and hotels after the Guide goes to press.

Looe **Talland Bay Hotel** **67%** **£107**

Tel 0503 72667 Fax 0503 72940 **H**

Talland Bay nr Looe Cornwall PL13 2JB **Map 12 C3**

The hotel, in a picturesque setting with fine gardens and sea views, is found by taking the Polperro Road out of Looe for two miles and turning left at a crossways with a hotel sign pointing the way. Two lounges (one non-smoking) have a traditional, cosy feel. The small bar, which is decorated with Gurkha memorabilia, has a selection of Scotch whiskies and opens on to the garden and heated outdoor swimming pool. Bedrooms, some with sea views, continue this traditional style with quality darkwood furniture, displays of fresh flowers and a good homely atmosphere. The bathrooms, generally compact but functional, have thoughtful touches such as large bottles of bubble bath. Same owners now for over twenty years. ***Rooms** 24. Garden, outdoor swimming pool, keep-fit equipment, sauna, solarium, games room. Closed Jan.* AMERICAN EXPRESS *Access, Diners, Visa.*

Loughborough **King's Head** **58%** **£96**

Tel 0509 233222 Fax 0509 262911 **H**

High Street Loughborough Leicestershire LE11 2QL **Map 7 D3**

Neat and comfortable hotel in the Jarvis group, built round a courtyard with fountain. Children up to 12 stay free in parents' room. ***Rooms** 78. Pool table.* AMERICAN EXPRESS *Access, Diners, Visa.*

Loughborough **Place of Interest**

The Bell Foundry Museum Tel 0509 233414.

Lower Beeding **Cisswood House** **67%** **£97**

Tel 0403 891216 Fax 0403 891621 **HR**

Sandygate Lane Lower Beeding nr Horsham West Sussex RH13 6NF **Map 11 A6**

A mock-Tudor mansion built in the 1920s for the then chairman of Harrods, using many Harrods craftsmen. The reception area features ornamental pargeting and timbers of oak, the same wood that panels a smart lounge. Bedrooms, except for a few singles, are spacious and bright, with breakfast tables and writing surfaces. Three bedrooms have spa baths; a couple have four-poster beds. The Courtyard Suite of conference and banqueting rooms caters for up to 200. No children under 12. No dogs. Eight miles from Gatwick Airport. ***Rooms** 34. Garden, indoor swimmimg pool. Closed Christmas/New Year.* AMERICAN EXPRESS *Access, Diners, Visa.*

Restaurant **£50**

Chef-patron Othmar Illes's menus are based on French classical traditions with nothing very elaborate and everything prepared with skill and assurance; a few fancy-ingredient dishes bear a small supplement. The choice encompasses grilled sardines with garlic butter, melon with crab and prawns, smoked haddock feuilleté with fresh quail's eggs, Sussex game (pheasant and venison), baked fillet of lamb with pistachio mousse and sage jus, plus a particularly good choice of fish dishes. The dining room setting is plush, with peaceful garden views through the leaded windows. Othmar's son Carl and his wife run *The Willows* in Ashington (see entry)). ***Seats** 60. Private Room 150. L 12.15-2 D 7-9 (Sat to 10). Closed Sun. Set L £14.75/£16.75 Set D £16.50/£18.75*

Lower Beeding **South Lodge** **76%** **£130**

Tel 0403 891711 Fax 0403 891766 **HR**

Brighton Road Lower Beeding West Sussex RH13 6PS **Map 11 A6**

Solicitous staff provide a refreshing welcome at this grand, wisteria-clad Victorian country house set in 90 acres of gardens and parkland with fine views of the South Downs. An abundance of fresh flowers from the gardens adorns the day rooms, which include an inviting lounge with heavily-carved wood panelling, ornate ribbed ceiling, chandeliers and glass-fronted cabinets filled with porcelain and silver objets d'art. Individually designed bedrooms are furnished with a variety of reproduction and original antiques and have luxurious Italian marble bathrooms with a host of extras from bathrobes to cotton buds. 14 large rooms with beamed ceilings are in a converted stable block that surrounds an indoor garden. Guests using the conference facilities (up to 80 delegates) are kept apart from individual guests. ***Rooms** 39.* AMERICAN EXPRESS *Access, Diners, Visa.*

Restaurant

£92

A decorative Victorian dining room is the classic setting for the skilled execution of an interesting à la carte and signature menus from Anthony Tobin. Salad of chargrilled peppers with pasta, rich lobster bisque, pan-fried salmon with a chive cream sauce and lamb cutlets topped with a basil mousse typify the mix of traditional and modern ideas. The signature menu is of three or five courses, with no choice. Hot soufflé of plum pudding with rum and raisin ice cream is one of several alluring desserts. An erratic and expensive wine list – just three clarets under £20. ***Seats** 40. Parties 8. Private Room 8. L 12-2.30 D 7.30-10. Set L £15 (Sun £17.50). Set D £25/£32.*

Lower Beeding — Places of Interest

Leonardslee Gardens Tel 0403 891212.
The High Beeches Gardens Nr Handcross Tel 0444 400589.
Nymans Garden (NT) Handcross Tel 0444 400321 or 400002.

Lower Slaughter — Lower Slaughter Manor 77%

£200*

Tel 0451 820456 Fax 0451 822150

HR

Lower Slaughter nr Bourton-on-the-Water Gloucestershire GL54 2HP

Map 14 C1

Formerly owners of *Rookery Hall* at Nantwich, the Marks family have returned to hotelkeeping at this peaceful manor house next to the village church deep in the Cotswolds. Several comfortably elegant day rooms including some with fine moulded ceilings, furnished in traditional country-house style and with lots of fresh flowers, invite one to relax and while away an hour or three. Bedrooms vary somewhat in appeal and quality of furniture and bathroom – those in the main house are generally the best – but all benefit from all sorts of little extras from sherry and home-made shortbread to magazines, mineral water and, in the bathrooms, towelling robes and huge bath sheets. Room service is offered throughout the day and evening and beds are turned down at night. No children under 10. *Half-board terms only. No dogs. ***Rooms** 19. Garden, indoor swimming pool, sauna, tennis.* AMERICAN EXPRESS *Access, Visa.*

Restaurant ↑

£78

The recently refurbished dining room provides a suitably elegant setting for Julian Ehlers' refined offerings. Never less than skilful cooking includes some star-worthy dishes such as his outstanding parsley and shallot ravioli and the desserts always include a properly made hot soufflé (a rarity in restaurants these days). Pan-fried marinated quail with vegetable terrine; breast of duck with its confit, green pepper sauce and "sautéed spatzeles"; scallops with crusty leaves of pastry on a grain mustard sauce and tarte tatin with vanilla ice cream show the range. The amuse-gueule and petits fours are notably moreish. A carefully compiled wine list offers an excellent choice, especially from France and California, the latter earning the award of California Cellar of the Year (see page 36). No children under 10. No smoking. ***Seats** 35. Private Room 26. L 12-2 (Sun 12.30-2.30) D 7-9 (Fri & Sat til 9.45). Set L £15.95 Set D £28.50.*

We publish annually, so make sure you use the current edition.
It's worth it!

Lower Swell — Old Farmhouse

£60

Tel 0451 830232 Fax 0451 870962

I

Lower Swell Stow-on-the-Wold Gloucestershire GL54 1LF — **Map 14 C1**

A very relaxed and unpretentious place with everything under the personal supervision of Dutch owner Erik Burger. The premises were a working farm until the 1960s, and the original 16th-century farmhouse contains the bar-lounge and restaurant. Above are neat country-style bedrooms, two of which share a bathroom. Further bedrooms are in former stables opening on to the car park; best rooms are in the old coach house, where there's also a quiet residents' lounge with TV, magazines and board games. Lower Swell is one mile west of Stow on the B4068. ***Rooms** 14. Garden. Closed 2 weeks Jan. Access, Visa.*

Ludlow — Dinham Hall 66%

£90

Tel 0584 876464 Fax 0584 876019

H

By the Castle Ludlow Shropshire SY8 1EJ — **Map 6 A4**

A pale-stone Georgian town house, dating from 1792, adjacent to the castle and lovingly restored. Public areas include a cosy drawing room and comfortable lounge with an extravagant, carved-wood fireplace and deep-cushioned sofas. The bedrooms vary in size and are comfortably appointed with matching floral fabrics; two have four-poster beds. Well-lit, fully tiled bathrooms complete the picture. Children up to 12 stay free in parents' room; families can eat informally in *de Ludlows'* brasserie. Polished service with a human touch. ***Rooms** 13. Garden, sauna, keep-fit equipment.* AMERICAN EXPRESS *Access, Visa.*

Ludlow — Feathers Hotel 69%

£104

Tel 0584 875261 Fax 0584 876030

H

Bull Ring Ludlow Shropshire SY8 1AA — **Map 6 A4**

The magnificent timbered and gabled facade of this historic hotel makes a fine first impression. Dating from 1603 and described by Pevsner as 'that prodigy of timber-framed houses', it is near the old Corvegate, one of seven gates that used to protect Ludlow. Inside, the bedrooms (some of which have four-posters) are decorated in bright floral fabrics. A notable Jacobean lounge has wood panelling, intricate plaster ceiling and a large, carved wood mantelpiece above the fireplace. ***Rooms** 40. Snooker.* AMERICAN EXPRESS *Access, Diners, Visa.*

Ludlow — Forte Travelodge

£42

Tel 058 472 695

L

Woofferton Ludlow Shropshire SY8 4AL — **Map 6 A4**

On the A49, 4 miles south of Ludlow at the junction of the A456 and the B4362. 8 miles north of Leominster. ***Rooms** 32.* AMERICAN EXPRESS *Access, Visa.*

Ludlow — Place of Interest

Ludlow Racecourse Tel 0584 77221.

Luton — Forte Crest 60%

£90

Tel 0582 575911 Fax 0582 581859

H

Waller Avenue Luton Bedfordshire LU4 9RU — **Map 15 E1**

Halfway between the M1 (junction 11) and Luton town centre. Caters well for families; also popular for functions and conferences (up to 250). Long-hours brasserie, 24hr room service. ***Rooms** 91.* AMERICAN EXPRESS *Access, Diners, Visa.*

Luton **Forte Posthouse** **57%** **£68**

Tel 0582 575955 Fax 0582 490065 **H**

641 Dunstable Road Luton Bedfordshire LU4 8RQ **Map 15 E1**

Practical accommodation (75% single rooms) in a modern building at Junction 11 of the M1. Family oriented at weekends, when a playroom is available. ***Rooms** 117.* AMERICAN EXPRESS *Access, Diners, Visa.*

Luton **Hotel Ibis** **60%** **£40**

Tel 0582 424488 Fax 0582 455511 **H**

Spittlesea Road Luton Bedfordshire LU2 9NZ **Map 15 E1**

Purpose-built, redbrick hotel opposite Luton airport's main runway. No frills, clean accommodation at a budget price, with many rooms suitable for family use. Children up to 16 stay free in parents' room. ***Rooms** 98. Coffee shop (11am-1am).* AMERICAN EXPRESS *Access, Diners, Visa.*

Luton **Leaside Hotel** **55%** **£55**

Tel 0582 417643 Fax 0582 34961 **H**

72 New Bedford Road Luton Bedfordshire LU3 1BT **Map 15 E1**

Near the town centre but a touch tricky to find, Leaside is a modest but very agreeable little hotel run since 1980 by Carole and Martin Gillies. The building is Victorian, and a certain period charm survives in the panelled bar. In the club room guests can relax over a frame of snooker. Many bedrooms are smallish singles, but the basic needs are supplied and housekeeping is good. Access to the car park at the back is via Old Bedford Road and Villa Road. ***Rooms** 13. Closed 26 Dec, 1 Jan.* AMERICAN EXPRESS *Access, Diners, Visa.*

Luton **Strathmore Thistle** **63%** **£106**

Tel 0582 34199 Fax 0582 402528 **H**

Arndale Centre Luton Bedfordshire LU1 2TR **Map 15 E1**

High-rise hotel next to town-centre shopping and railway station. Banqueting facilities for up to 250, conferences to 300. ***Rooms** 150. Coffee shop (11am-11pm exc Sun).* AMERICAN EXPRESS *Access, Diners, Visa.*

Luton **Places of Interest**

Tourist Information Tel 0582 401579.
St. Georges Theatre Tel 0582 21628.
Luton Hoo Tel 0582 22955.
Luton Museum and Art Gallery Tel 0582 36941.
Stockwood Craft Museum and Gardens Tel 0582 38714.
Luton Town Football Ground Tel 0582 411622.

Lutterworth **Denbigh Arms** **66%** **£65**

Tel 0455 553537 Fax 0455 556627 **H**

High Street Lutterworth Leicestershire LE17 5AD **Map 7 D4**

An extended Georgian coaching inn right on the high street just over a mile from Junction 20 and the M1. Three meeting rooms with a total capacity of 60 (banquets up to 50). Good housekeeping and pleasant, friendly staff. Resort hotels. ***Rooms** 34.* AMERICAN EXPRESS *Access, Diners, Visa.*

Lutterworth **Place of Interest**

Stanford Hall Tel 0788 860250.

Lyme Regis — Alexandra Hotel — 58% — £90

Tel 0297 442010 Fax 0297 443229 — H

Pound Street Lyme Regis Dorset DT7 3HZ — **Map 13 E2**

Built in 1735 as a dower house and converted to a hotel at the beginning of this century, the Alexandra occupies a fine hillside position with a pathway to the beach. Most of the individually-decorated bedrooms overlook Lyme Bay and Cobb Harbour. ***Rooms*** *26. Garden. Closed Christmas-early Feb.* AMERICAN EXPRESS *Access, Diners, Visa.*

Lymington — Gordleton Mill — 65% — £70

Tel 0590 682219 Fax 0590 683073 — HR

Silver Street Hordle nr Lymington Hampshire SO41 6DJ — **Map 14 C4**

A 17th-century mill set in 5½ acres of idyllic gardens with the mill stream running alongside a delightful terrace, Gordleton was beautifully restored, and slightly extended in 1991. It now offers seven charming bedrooms all similarly decorated and furnished with matching fabrics and light polished wood furniture. Fresh flowers, mineral water and a bowl of fruit add the personal touch and beds are turned down in the evening. Good bathrooms all boast whirlpool tubs. A small reception room doubles up as the residents' lounge but there are two further lounges (one for non-smokers) where some of the original mill workings can be seen, that are also used by diners. The ambience here is more that of a restaurant with rooms than a hotel. ***Rooms*** *7. Closed 1-3 Jan.* AMERICAN EXPRESS *Access, Diners, Visa.*

Provence Restaurant

Star chef Jean-Christophe Novelli has now moved on and his successor Didier Haile (formerly sous chef at *Hartwell House*, Aylesbury) arrived just too late in the summer of 1993 for us to inspect for this year's Guide. ***Seats*** *45. Parties 14. Private Room 30. L 12.30-2.30 (Sun to 3) D 7.30-10 (Sat to 10.30). Closed D Sun, all Tue.*

Lymington — Passford House — 70% — £101

Tel 0590 682398 Fax 0590 683494 — H

Mount Pleasant Lane Lymington Hampshire SO41 8LS — **Map 14 C4**

On the edge of the New Forest between Lymington (2 miles) and Sway, this elegant white house was originally the home of Lord Arthur Cecil. Two bedroom wings and a leisure centre have since been added, but the traditional look survives in the lounges – one oak-panelled with an open fire, another with French windows opening on to a patio and ornamental pool. Upstairs there are bright and airy bedrooms with mostly white furniture; carpeted bathrooms have showers and useful toiletries. There are eight 'de luxe' rooms. The purpose-built Dolphin leisure centre has a good range of facilities. Children are catered for admirably, with cots, high-chairs, a separate play area and separate meal times; first child under 12 sharing parents' room is accommodated free. ***Rooms*** *56. Garden, indoor & outdoor swimming pools, sauna, solarium, spa bath, keep-fit equipment, tennis, putting, games room.* AMERICAN EXPRESS *Access, Visa.*

Lymington — Stanwell House — 65% — £98

Tel 0590 677123 Fax 0590 677756 — H

High Street Lymington Hampshire SO41 9AA — **Map 14 C4**

The hotel dates from the 18th century, but careful modernisation has extended its scope. Attractive day rooms include a smart cocktail bar and a chintzy lounge. Behind the restaurant is a paved garden which opens on to a small function/conference suite. Well-equipped bedrooms (including one with a four-poster) are named after Bordeaux wine chateaux. No dogs. ***Rooms*** *35. Garden. Access, Visa.*

Lymington Place of Interest

Spinners Garden Tel 0590 673347.

Lympsham Batch Farm Country Hotel 56% £56

Tel 0934 750371 H

Lympsham nr Weston-super-Mare Somerset BS24 0EX Map 13 E1

Mr and Mrs Brown's hotel, with its 50-acre grounds, stands in open farmland through which the river Axe flows. Origins of the former farmhouse are evident in the beams which adorn the bar and residents' lounges, while the neat, practical bedrooms in an extension enjoy views of either the Mendip or Quantock hills. The adjoining Somerset Suite is a popular venue for functions up to 70. Lympsham is about 3 miles from junction 22 of the M5. No dogs. ***Rooms** 8. Garden, coarse fishing.* AMERICAN EXPRESS *Access, Diners, Visa.*

Lympsham Place of Interest

Taunton Vale Polo Club Southlands, Berrow Road, Burnham on Sea Tel 0278 782266.

Lympstone River House £70

Tel 0395 265147 RR

The Strand Lympstone Devon EX8 5EY Map 13 E3

There are lovely views over the river Exe to Powderham Castle from both the ground-floor bar and restaurant above at Michael and Shirley Wilkes' restaurant with rooms. Dinner is the main attraction, offering two to five courses at various fixed prices: perhaps crab pancakes, smoked ham salad with prawns and grapefruit or lovage, cheese and cream tart to start, followed by terrine of lemon sole and smoked salmon, halibut steak or paupiette of beef casserole in Guinness and port. Fish dishes are always particularly good. At least five different vegetables, prepared in an interesting and varied manner, accompany main courses. Vegetarians are well catered for (£19.50/£23 for 2/3 courses). Puddings offer a good choice, and home-made fudge, praline and chocolates are a treat with coffee. Sunday lunch is a popular affair, with a choice of four dishes per course (always including a roast); weekday lunches are simpler. ***Seats** 34. Private Room 14. L 12-1.30 D 7-9.30 (Sat to 10.30). Closed D Sun, all Mon, Bank Holidays. Set L Sun £16/£20 Set D from £19.50.* AMERICAN EXPRESS *Access, Visa.*

Rooms £74

Pretty bedrooms have en-suite bathrooms and many thoughtful extras. No children under six. *No dogs. Sea fishing.*

Lyndhurst The Crown 65% £97

Tel 0703 282922 Fax 0703 282751 H

High Street Lyndhurst New Forest Hampshire SO43 7NF Map 14 C4

A solid gabled building in the high street opposite the church (follow the one-way traffic signs). Ample lounge areas provide space to relax with pleasant views of the gardens; the bar is a fine period piece with library-style wood panelling. Decent-sized bedrooms have stylish repro and antique furniture and good bathrooms. Children under 16 are accommodated free when they share a room with a parent. ***Rooms** 40. Garden.* AMERICAN EXPRESS *Access, Diners, Visa.*

> Changes in data sometimes occur in establishments after the Guide goes to press. Prices should be taken as indications rather than firm quotes.

Lyndhurst — Lyndhurst Park — 61% — £70

Tel 0703 283923 Fax 0703 283019 — H

High Street Lyndhurst Hampshire SO43 7NL — Map 14 C4

The Forestdale Group's much-extended Georgian mansion set in spacious grounds has a popular conference facility accommodating up to 400, with banqueting for up to 300. Bedrooms have freestanding furniture and small tiled bathrooms. Day rooms include a cocktail bar and little lounge. Summer activity for families centres round the pool and playground. Children up to 15 stay free of charge when sharing parents' room. ***Rooms** 59. Garden, outdoor swimming pool, sauna, tennis, games room, playroom & playground.* AMERICAN EXPRESS *Access, Diners, Visa.*

Lyndhurst — Parkhill Hotel — 67% — £94

Tel 0703 282944 Fax 0703 283268 — H

Beaulieu Road Lyndhurst Hampshire SO4 7FZ — Map 14 C4

Secluded in parkland on the edge of the New Forest, Parkhill was built in 1740 as the country home of the Duke of Clarence. Restored in 1850, it retains a civilised, peaceful atmosphere, with antiques, ornaments, oil paintings and flowers. Spacious and comfortable bedrooms are furnished with solid period-style pieces; the best rooms have views across the lawns to the forest. A self-contained bungalow comprises double/twin bedroom, dressing room, lounge and bathroom, plus a walled garden. Families are well catered for. ***Rooms** 20. Garden, outdoor swimming pool, tennis.* AMERICAN EXPRESS *Access, Diners, Visa.*

Lyndhurst — Places of Interest

Furzey Gardens Minstead Tel 0703 812464.
New Forest Museum and Visitor Centre Lyndhurst Tel 0703 283914.
Rhinefield (New Forest) Polo Club Manor Farm Cottage, Minstead Tel 0703 813678.
New Park Showground Brockenhurst Tel 0590 22400.

Lynmouth — Rising Sun Inn — £79

Tel 0598 53223 Fax 0598 53480 — I

Harbourside Lynmouth Devon EX35 6EQ — Map 13 D1

Medieval character in the form of oak panelling, uneven floors and crooked ceilings survives in a 14th-century thatched inn on the harbour (leave the M5 at junction 23 signposted to Minehead and follow the A39 to Lynmouth). Bedrooms are in keeping, being snug and cottagey. Shelley's cottage, where the poet spent his honeymoon, consists of a double bedroom with four-poster bed, a sitting room and a private garden. There's another literary connection: RS Blackmore wrote part of *Lorna Doone* here. The inn owns a stretch of river for salmon fishing. No children under five. ***Rooms** 16. Garden, fishing.* AMERICAN EXPRESS *Access, Diners, Visa.*

Lynton — Lynton Cottage — 65% — £70

Tel 0598 52342 Fax 0598 52597 — H

North Walk Lynton Devon EX35 6ED — Map 13 D1

Spectacular sea views are enjoyed from the day rooms (and all but three bedrooms) at a family-run hotel on the cliff 500 feet above Lynmouth Bay. Well modernised and smartly kept, it's a warm, friendly place, particularly the bar, with comfortable, old-fashioned seats and Victorian pine panelling. Bedrooms are individually decorated and range from cosy and small to airy and spacious. Well-appointed bathrooms. No children under ten, except babes in arms. ***Rooms** 17. Garden, bar billiards. Closed Jan.* AMERICAN EXPRESS *Access, Diners, Visa.*

Lytham **Clifton Arms** 63% £87

Tel 0253 739898 Fax 0253 730657 **H**

West Beach Lytham Lancashire FY8 5QJ **Map 6 A1**

Best bedrooms at this redbrick Victorian building are the 'Executives' at the front, overlooking the Ribble Estuary; standard rooms are smaller. Winged armchairs and settees fill the lounge. Children can share their parents' room at no charge. Conference/banqueting facilities for 300/200. Lansbury Hotels. ***Rooms** 41. Sauna, solarium, spa bath, keep-fit equipment.*
AMERICAN EXPRESS *Access, Diners, Visa.*

Lytham St Annes **Dalmeny Hotel** 60% £68

Tel 0253 712236 **HR**

19 South Promenade St Annes Lytham St Annes Lancashire FY8 1LX **Map 6 A1**

From modest beginnings nearly 50 years ago the Dalmeny has grown into a large family hotel with squash court, indoor pool, games room and no less than three restaurants. For much of the year there are daily events and amusements laid on for children and a well-equipped playroom becomes an all-day crèche. Pine or lightwood fitted furniture with tiled tops, features in the large, simply-decorated bedrooms, many with extra beds (some are family suites with several bedrooms) and most with kitchenette. Staff are smart, friendly and helpful. The hotel is still growing, with a gymnasium and new conference rooms planned. ***Rooms** 90. Indoor swimming pool, squash, sauna, beauty & hair salon, children's playroom, crèche (supervised, 9-3 high season and holidays), coffee shop (9am-10pm).*
Access, Visa.

C'est La Vie Restaurant £65

The hotel's posh eaterie (there's also a Carvery and a Barbecue restaurant) in a vaulted basement with flagstoned floor. Chef Barry Smith can be seen in his small kitchen giving individual care and attention to each dish from the sensibly limited, French-inspired evening à la carte menu. Lunchtimes, there's a short, keenly-priced table d'hote. No smoking.
***Seats** 45.L 12.30-2.30 D 7-9 Closed Sun, Mon 24, 25, 26 Dec.*
Set L £11.50/£13.50.

Lytham St. Anne's **Place of Interest**

Church Road Cricket Ground Tel 0253 733422.

Macclesfield **Sutton Hall** £85

Tel 0260 253211 Fax 0260 252538 **I**

Bullocks Lane Sutton Macclesfield Cheshire SK11 0HE **Map 6 B2**

First a 16th-century baronial residence, then a nunnery until 30 years ago, Sutton Hall is now a hotel, public house and restaurant full of old-world atmosphere. Black oak beams, flagstones and open log fires characterise the day rooms, and bedrooms feature four-posters, Gothic windows and sturdy English furniture. Traditional bar food, plus restaurant menu. ***Rooms** 10. Garden. Access, Visa.*

Macclesfield **Places of Interest**

Tourist Information Tel 0625 21955.
Macclesfield Silk Museum and Heritage Centre Tel 0625 613210.
Paradise Mill Silk Museum Tel 0625 618228.
Historic Houses, Castles and Gardens
Capesthorne Hall and Gardens Tel 0625 861221.
Gawsworth Hall Tel 0260 223456.
Hare Hill Garden (NT) Hare Hill, Over Alderley Tel 0625 828981.
Jodrell Bank Arboretum Tel 0477 71339.

Madingley **Three Horseshoes** £65

Tel 0954 210221 **R**

High Street Madingley Cambridge Cambridgeshire CB3 8AB **Map 15 F1**

A neat thatched country pub owned by Poste Hotels but run by young chef/manager Richard Stokes whose modern, Mediterranean approach to cooking can be enjoyed either from an extensive bar snack menu or in the comfort of a smart restaurant with large conservatory exterior. Chargrilled scallops with wilted radicchio, chicory and balsamic vinegar; spinach and sage gnocchi with pesto butter and Parmesan; steamed sea bass with a compote of onions, tomatoes and saffron, and rabbit with prosciutto, spinach, mashed potato and Meaux mustard are typical of dishes from the à la carte restaurant menu. Afters include lemon tart, sticky toffee pudding, chocolate pithiviers and a selection of unpasteurised British cheeses from Neal's Yard Dairy. (East of England British Cheeseboard of the Year) An interesting list of 100 wines includes plenty of half bottles anda good choice by the glass. ***Seats*** *55. L 12-2 D 7-10. Closed D Sun. Set L £16.95.* AMERICAN EXPRESS® *Access, Visa, Diners.*

Maiden Newton **Maiden Newton House** 73% £90

Tel 0300 20336 Fax 0300 21021 **HR**

Maiden Newton nr Dorchester Dorset DT2 0AA **Map 13 F2**

Right in the centre of the village, next to the war memorial, the manor house of Maiden Newton is set in 21 acres of parkland with a stream running through the gardens. The experience is one of staying with friends. Wooden floors in the entrance hall gleam by dint of good housekeeping and the drawing room is a model of informal English country comfort. Next door is a charming little library. Roomy, individually decorated bedrooms are very comfortable and come with a battery of cosseting extras. Two rooms have four-posters, another a hand-painted half-tester. No children under 12. ***Rooms*** *6. Garden, game fishing. Closed 1st 3 weeks Dec. Access, Visa.*

Restaurant £70

Dinner is an elegant affair, taken *en famille* with Elizabeth and Brian Ferriss at a polished mahogany dining table. There is no choice. A typical meal could comprise salmon mousseline, roast fillet of pork with garlic and ginger, bread-and-butter pudding and West Country cheeses. Excellent wines by the glass are served with each course. Booking essential. ***Seats*** *16. D only at 8. Set D £25.*

Maiden Newton **Le Petit Canard** £50

Tel 0300 20536 **R**

Dorchester Road Maiden Newton Dorset DT2 OBE **Map 13 F2**

West Coast Canadians Lin and Geoff Chapman bring the influences of France and the Orient to their little former fish café in the centre of the village. Monthly menus have a modern ring, with dishes such as teriyaki salmon and tiger prawn brochette, cashew-stuffed pork tenderloin on a honey and five-spice fumet, chargrilled venison with béarnaise, and a terrine of chocolate and raspberries. An imaginative and keenly-priced wine list is updated almost daily; useful notes. ***Seats*** *28. D only 7-9. Closed Sun & Mon. Set D £18.95. Access, Visa.*

Maidenhead **Fredrick's** 75% £155

Tel 0628 35934 Fax 0628 771054 **HR**

Shoppenhangers Road Maidenhead Berkshire SL6 2PZ **Map 15 E2**

In a quiet residential road, yet only minutes from Junction 8/9 of the M4, Frederick Losel's attractive redbrick hotel offers luxury and high quality service to a predominantly senior executive clientele. The reception area with strikingly modern chandeliers, marble waterfall and complimentary glass of champagne on check-in, sets the tone of public rooms that include a verdant winter garden looking out over a patio with huge parasols and well-established gardens beyond, and sumptuous cocktail bar. A novel feature of the decoratively more restrained bedrooms is that beds are set upon solid plinths. Standard rooms have a pair of easy chairs around a breakfast table while the five larger rooms have settees in separate sitting areas. All have mini-bars, satellite TV and well-appointed bathrooms – most with bidets. Three single rooms have shower and WC only. Rooms are properly serviced in the evenings and staff are notably smart. No dogs. ***Rooms** 37. Garden. Closed 24-30 Dec.* AMERICAN EXPRESS *Access, Diners, Visa.*

Restaurant

£100

An overtly luxurious room – gilt and crystal chandeliers, painted wall panels, monogrammed china and glassware – is matched by formal service under the eye of long-serving maitre d' Tony Guttilla and Brian Cutler's highly professional cooking. Top quality produce is the starting point for stylishly presented dishes like millefeuille of fresh crab, spinach and potatoes; baby squid filled with lobster mousseline on a lime butter sauce; escalope of wild salmon with a horseradish crust; roast duckling with Bramley apples and free-range chicken with fresh morels and asparagus. The same à la carte and table d'hote are available at lunch and dinner (the table d'hote reduced in price at lunchtime). Concise yet broadly based wine list. ***Seats** 60. Parties 15. Private Room 14. L 12-2 D 7-9.45. Closed L Sat, 25 (eve)-30 Dec. Set L £19.50 Set D £28.50.*

Maidenhead — Holiday Inn — 66% — £147

Tel 0628 23444 Fax 0628 770035 — **H**

Manor Lane Maidenhead Berkshire SL6 2RA — **Map 15 E2**

Set in 18 acres of grounds close to junction 8/9 of the M4 and junction 4 of the M40. Top-notch, large conference and banqueting facilities include the characterful, reconstructed Elizabethan Shoppenhangers Manor house in the grounds. Straightforward accommodation, but good leisure facilities, including a children's pool. Playroom provided for children at weekends; families can eat informally in the poolside café. Vast tariff reductions at weekends. ***Rooms** 189. Garden, indoor swimming pool, spa bath, sauna, solarium, squash, gymnasium, snooker, coffee shop (7am-11pm).* AMERICAN EXPRESS *Access, Diners, Visa.*

Maidenhead — Places of Interest

Cliveden (NT) Taplow, Nr Burnham Tel 0628 605069.
Stanley Spencer Gallery King's Hall, Cookham-on-Thames Tel 062 85 20890/20043.
Courage Shire Horse Centre Maidenhead Thicket Tel 0628 824848.

Maidstone — Larkfield Priory — 62% — £72

Tel 0732 846858 Fax 0732 846786 — **H**

812 London Road Maidstone Kent ME20 6HJ — **Map 11 C5**

Leave the M20 at Junction 4 taking the A228 Tonbridge road, then the Maidstone road from the first roundabout, to find a Forte Heritage hotel centred around a Victorian priory. A popular conference venue with facilities for up to 80 delegates. The well-equipped Larkfield Leisure Centre is half a mile away. ***Rooms** 52. Garden.* AMERICAN EXPRESS *Access, Diners, Visa.*

Maidstone — Mandarin Chef — £35

Tel 0622 755917 — **R**

35 Lower Stone Street Maidstone Kent — **Map 11 C5**

Friendly service and sound Chinese cooking by chef Ken Lai make this a popular place with a regular clientele. Peking and Cantonese regions are well represented with dishes such as braised beef fillet, sweet and sour pork, hot and sour soup, pickled cabbage, diced chicken with cashew nuts in yellow bean sauce and baked crab in ginger and spring onion sauce.

See over

Town-centre site with modern decor in assorted blues. Ring ahead for an off-the-menu feast of specials. ***Seats** 75. Parties 14. L 12-2.15 D 5.30-11.30 (Sun to 11.15). Closed 3 days Christmas. Set L from £7 Set D from £13.50.* AMERICAN EXPRESS *Access, Diners, Visa.*

Maidstone — Stakis Country Court Hotel 67% — £93

Tel 0622 734322 Fax 0622 734600 — H

Bearsted Weavering Maidstone Kent ME14 5AA — **Map 11 C5**

Next to the M20 at Junction 7, this hotel is a popular venue for the traveller and businessman alike. Spacious bedrooms have double beds, modern furnishings, smart tiled bathrooms and good showers. Leisure club and extensive high-tech meeting and conference facilities. ***Rooms** 139. Garden, indoor swimming pool, gymnasium, sauna, spa bath, solarium, beauty salon.* AMERICAN EXPRESS *Access, Diners, Visa.*

Maidstone — Places of Interest

Tourist Information Tel 0622 673581.
Hazlitt Theatre Tel 0622 58611.
Boughton Monchelsea Place Boughton Monchelsea Tel 0622 743120.
Leeds Castle and Culpeper Gardens Tel 0622 765400.
Tyrwhitt-Drake Museum of Carriages Tel 0622 54497.
The Moat Cricket Ground Tel 0622 54545.
Kent County Showgrounds Tel 0622 30975.
Leeds Castle Aviary and Culpeper Garden Tel 0622 65400.
Mereworth Parrot Park Seven Mile Lane, Mereworth Tel 0622 812045.

Maldon — Blue Boar 59% — £97

Tel 0621 852681 Fax 0621 856202 — H

3 Silver Street Maldon Essex CM9 7QE — **Map 11 C4**

An ancient inn (parts go back to the 14th century) located just off the High Street, notable for its elegant Georgian facade, heavy oak beams, open fires and timbered wings overlooking a stable yard. Conference and banqueting facilities for up to 300. Forte Heritage. ***Rooms** 28. Garden.* AMERICAN EXPRESS *Access, Diners, Visa.*

Maldon — Francine's — £50

Tel 0621 856605 — R

1a High Street Maldon Essex CM9 7PB — **Map 11 C4**

An unpretentious restaurant, sited in one of Maldon's oldest buildings. The minuteness of John Brotherton's kitchen is not something he lets constrain him. Care is taken over the preparation of distinctly modern, unfussy dishes using the freshest of produce. At front of house John's wife Sara reaps the benefit when customers compliment their menu (which changes on the first Tuesday of each month); Sara also cooks a set Thai menu twice a month. Typical dishes might include tartlets of quail's eggs with cottage cheese and smoked salmon or casserole of snails with Pernod, followed by sautéed fillet of veal with pink grapefruit or baked fillet of brill with a mushroom and herb crust and a white wine sauce, out of four choices at each course. Short wine list with sensible prices. Car parking to the rear. ***Seats** 24. Parties 10. D only 7.30-9.15. Closed Sun & Mon, Bank Holidays, 2 weeks Feb, 2 weeks Aug. Access, Visa.*

Maldon — Places of Interest

Tourist Information Tel 0621 856503.
Oakwood Arts Centre Tel 0621 56503.

Malmesbury Old Bell Hotel 64% £98

Tel 0666 822344 Fax 0666 825145 **H**

Abbey Row Malmesbury Wiltshire SN16 0BW **Map 14 B2**

Hard by the abbey, the Old Bell dates back to 1210 when it was established by the Abbot as a place to refresh his guests. Its wisteria-clad facade is more than a match for its spiritual neighbour. Public rooms comprise two oak-beamed bars and two lounge areas, one with a famous 800-year-old chimney. Bedrooms in the main building come in all shapes and sizes, while those in the converted stables are more uniformly modern. Families are well catered for; children up to 10 stay free in parents' room. No dogs. Clipper Hotels. ***Rooms*** *37. Garden. Access, Visa.*

Malvern Abbey Hotel 62% £70

Tel 0684 892332 Fax 0684 892662 **H**

Abbey Road Malvern Hereford & Worcester WR14 3ET **Map 14 B1**

A mix of impressive, ivy-clad exterior and modern bedrooms in an extension block. Conference/banqueting facilities for up to 350/200. Children under 14 accommodated free in parents' room. De Vere Hotels. ***Rooms*** *107.* AMERICAN EXPRESS *Access, Diners, Visa.*

Malvern Anupam £40

Tel 0684 573814 Fax 0684 893945 **R**

85 Church Street Malvern Hereford & Worcester WR14 2AE **Map 14 B1**

Indian cooking of a dependable quality, plus efficient service and a list of complementary wines compiled by the nearby *Croque-en-Bouche.* The standard menu is supplemented by interesting chef's specials such as patra leaf fried in batter, tandoori mushroom masala, and chicken cooked with pineapple, prunes and rice Kashmir style. ***Seats*** *50. L 12-2.30 D 6-12. Closed 25 Dec. Set meals from £12.* AMERICAN EXPRESS *Access, Diners, Visa.*

Malvern Colwall Park Hotel 62% £77

Tel 0684 40206 Fax 0684 40847 **H**

Colwall Malvern Hereford & Worcester WR13 6QG **Map 14 B1**

In the centre of Colwall village, on the B4218 between Malvern and Ledbury, this mock-Tudor hotel offers simple, well-kept accommodation. Public rooms include a street-facing lounge bar with comfortable chairs and sofas, and a quiet, traditionally furnished lounge. Bedrooms are light and spacious, with quality furniture and functional bathrooms without frills. Families are well catered for. Special interest breaks are regularly organised. ***Rooms*** *20. Garden.* AMERICAN EXPRESS *Access, Visa.*

Malvern Cottage in the Wood 65% £93

Tel 0684 573487 Fax 0684 560662 **HR**

Holywell Road Malvern Wells Hereford & Worcester WR14 4LG **Map 14 B1**

A family-owned and operated hotel with arguably "the best view in England" looking out over the Severn Plain from high on the steep wooded slopes of the Malvern Hills. It comprises three distinct buildings; the public rooms and eight cottagey bedrooms are in a fine Georgian dower house, with further accommodation in the nearby Coach House and Beech Cottage. Private conference room for up to 14 boardroom style. No dogs in the main house. ***Rooms*** *20. Garden.* AMERICAN EXPRESS *Access, Visa.*

Restaurant £65

Kathryn Young's unusual menus offer both 'light' (bacon-wrapped baked banana topped with curry mayonnaise, cod and cockle pie) and 'mega' (steaks, kidneys with bacon, ratatouille) bites at lunchtime and à la carte dinners. Chicken liver éclairs and salmon with kiwi and mint relish are

See over

among the unusual offerings tempered by other more straightforward dishes. Good English cheeses. Traditional three-course Sunday lunches. 15 local English bottles and a couple of unusual Chinese wines are included on the varied wine list. No smoking. ***Seats** 50. Parties 20. Private Room 14. L 12.30-2 D 7-9 (Sun to 8.30). Set L £9.95.*

Malvern — Croque-en-Bouche ★ — £86

Tel 0684 565612 — **R**

221 Wells Road Malvern Wells Hereford & Worcester WR14 4HF — **Map 14 B1**

The seriousness of Robin and Marion Jones's restaurant, here since 1978, is evident in the magnificent wine list (perhaps the law should insist that wine lists are displayed outside the establishment as well as the menu?). Marion's cooking, once influenced mainly by French country cuisine, now expands to take in, for example, some Japanese and exotic touches. Dinner is a five-course affair and might commence with a soup of smoked haddock, tomato and celery, followed by a Japanese selection of sushi, omelette and *hijiki* salad or Cornish skate with beurre noir; main courses might include a ragout of venison braised with root vegetables and port, then served with a parsnip purée, or perhaps guinea fowl roasted with coriander leaves under its skin and accompanied by brown rice, apricot and almond pilaf and a lightly curried sauce. A salad dish, British cheeses and fine desserts like 'The Grand Dessert' (a selection of six tastes), frozen ginger meringue, toffee rice pudding or two Italian desserts (*tiramisu* and *semifreddo*) complete the starry picture. The dozen or so dessert wines and digestifs served by the glass include both Somerset and Herefordhsire apple brandies. Twice winner of our overall Cellar of the Year (as well as winning our California Cellar of the Year), the stupendous wine list is perhaps the only one in the country that would walk off with all the prizes every year – if allowed to do so! Scrutinise it carefully, admire the selection of 76 Californian wines, wonder at the amazingly generous prices and seek Robin's masterly advice (and suggestions, if offered). Two miles south of Great Malvern on the A449. ***Seats** 24. Parties 8. Private Room 8. D only 7.30-9.15. Closed Sun-Tue, Christmas/New Year. Set D from £32.50. Access, Visa.*

Malvern — Foley Arms — 61% — £88

Tel 0684 573397 Fax 0684 569665 — **H**

14 Worcester Road Great Malvern Hereford & Worcester WR14 4QS — **Map 14 B1**

Said to be the town's oldest hotel (built as a coaching inn in 1810), the Foley Arms, under new ownership, stands at the top of the town, commanding magnificent views over the Severn valley. Public areas include two homely lounges (one non-smoking), a pubby bar and a summer dining terrace. Good-sized bedrooms, the best with fine views, are comfortable and unfussy, with duvets and freestanding units. Under-16s stay free in parents' room. ***Rooms** 28. Garden, giant chess.* AMERICAN EXPRESS *Access, Diners, Visa.*

Malvern — Places of Interest

Tourist Information Tel 0684 892289.
Little Malvern Court Nr Great Malvern Tel 0684 892988.

Manchester — Britannia Hotel — 66% — £123

Tel 061-228 2288 Fax 061-236 9154 — **H**

Portland Street Manchester Greater Manchester M1 3LA — **Map 6 B2**

Converted from a cotton warehouse and resplendent with its over-the-top furnishings, the Britannia, a hotel since 1982, is a peculiar mix of showy public rooms (note the fine cantilever staircase) and simply decorated bedrooms. Fancier suites are split-level and bedecked in floral prints. Two discos, together with numerous bars and restaurants, keep up the lively pace. ***Rooms** 362. Indoor swimming pool, keep-fit equipment, sauna, solarium, beauty & hair salons, coffee shop (11am-2am).* AMERICAN EXPRESS *Access, Diners, Visa.*

Manchester **Charterhouse Hotel** **72%** **£114**

Tel 061-236 9999 Fax 061-236 0674 **H**

Oxford Street Manchester Greater Manchester M60 7HA **Map 6 B2**

Formerly the distinctive Refuge Assurance building, adjacent to the BBC and Palace Theatre, two minutes from Oxford Road railway station. Much of the original Victorian architecture – ornate plasterwork, intricate cornicing, lofty columns and stained-glass windows – has been retained, especially in the vast open-plan public areas, which feature contemporary seating, heavy drapes and much greenery in modern country house style. Bedrooms vary in size and are individually decorated with tastefully co-ordinated fabrics; there are thirteen suites. Fully carpeted bathrooms have gold taps, low basins, good-quality toiletries and a telephone. Children up to 12 stay free in their parents' room; cots and extra beds provided. Conference and banqueting facilities. ***Rooms** 58. Coffee shop (10am-11pm).* AMERICAN EXPRESS *Access, Diners, Visa.*

Manchester **Copthorne Hotel** **70%** **£121**

Tel 061-873 7321 Fax 061-873 7318 **H**

Clippers Quay Salford Quays Manchester Greater Manchester M5 3DL **Map 6 B2**

Standing next to the quays in the Salford Docks redevelopment area (just a mile from the city centre) is a modern redbrick hotel. A high ceiling, exposed brickwork and polished tile floor combine to give an up-to-date feel to the foyer, with other day rooms continuing the contemporary theme. The Clippers Bar has tinted mirror walls and is a genuinely comfortable place to relax. The most popular bedrooms overlook the quay and have large bay windows, allowing in plenty of natural light; coloured-wood furniture and bathrooms tiled in two colours continue the bright theme. Superior 'Connoisseur' rooms on the top floor have recently been updated and two suites added. Six bedrooms are specifically adapted for use by wheelchair-bound guests. 24hr room service. Conference and function facilities for up to 150. ***Rooms** 166. Terrace, indoor swimming pool, sauna, solarium, spa bath, keep-fit equipment.* AMERICAN EXPRESS *Access, Diners, Visa.*

Manchester **Forte Posthouse** **60%** **£68**

Tel 061-998 7090 Fax 061-946 0139 **H**

Palatine Road Northenden Manchester Greater Manchester M22 4EH **Map 6 B2**

Mid-70s, high-rise hotel, 3 miles from the airport, 7 miles from the city centre, close to junction 9 of M63. Cosy day rooms and comfortable bedrooms. Banqueting/conference facilities for 100/150. ***Rooms** 190. Garden.* AMERICAN EXPRESS *Access, Diners, Visa.*

Manchester **Gaylord** **£35**

Tel 061-832 6037 **R**

Amethyst House Spring Gardens Manchester Greater Manchester M2 1EA **Map 6 B2**

Tandoori, Mughlai and Kashmiri cuisines find an authentic home in Manchester's best Indian restaurant. Outstanding dishes include home-made cottage cheese (in kebabs, in pakoras, with spinach, with peas or in kulcha (leavened bread)), lamb korma badami, and a splendidly rich chicken tikka masala. Lotus roots are an unusual item in the vegetable section. In the city centre by the main post office, but not too easy to find (approach via King Street if coming by car, as it's half a block from the Market Street precinct). ***Seats** 85. L 12-3 D 6-11.30. Set L £5.95 Set D from £10.95.* AMERICAN EXPRESS *Access, Diners, Visa.*

Manchester — Granada Lodge — £45

Tel 061-410 0076 Fax 061-655 3358 — **L**

M62 Junction 18/19 Birch Manchester Greater Manchester OL10 2QH — **Map 6 B2**

Rooms 37. American Express *Access, Diners, Visa.*

Manchester — Holiday Inn Crowne Plaza — 73% — £124

Tel 061-236 3333 Fax 061-228 2241 — **H**

Peter Street Manchester Greater Manchester M60 2DS — **Map 6 B2**

A grand town-centre hotel (adjacent to the G-Mex centre) restored at great expense to its past glory with ornate ceilings, arches and pillars. The foyer area is vast, with a glass roof and hanging plants crowning white columns. Cane chairs and comfortable couches adorn the adjoining terrace lounge. The high-ceilinged Octagon, one of three bars, is decorated in similar style; there are also three restaurants. Corridors that lead to the bedrooms are wide and reminiscent of a former age of spacious and luxurious hotels. Bedrooms are generously sized and have a high standard of decor, with tiled bathrooms throughout. Extensive conference and banqueting (including kosher) facilities for up to 500. ***Rooms** 303. Indoor swimming pool, sauna, solarium, spa bath, keep-fit equipment, squash, news kiosk.* American Express *Access, Diners, Visa.*

Manchester — Market Restaurant — £50

Tel 061-834 3743 — **R**

104 High Street Smithfield City Centre Manchester Greater Manchester M4 1HQ — **Map 6 B2**

A homely restaurant situated in the back streets of Manchester, close to Smithfield Market and Manchester Craft Village. An authentic 1940s' ambience is evoked by period music, slightly faded decor, sewing-machine tables, oddments of antique crockery and 30s' milk bottles used for serving the house wine. Menus with Middle-and Far-Eastern inspiration change monthly and offer something for everyone – perhaps potted smoked haddock with toast, scallops in filo pastry with chive and red pepper butter sauce or an unusual ethnic dish to start, followed by main courses like Stilton-stuffed fillet of beef wrapped in bacon with a red wine sauce, lemon sole fillets with a turmeric, nut and lemon grass sauce or noisettes of lamb with a little leek pie and rosemary gravy. Vegetarian options are always interesting. As one might expect from a home to the Pudding Club (held six times a year on Tuesday evenings – ideal for all those who read menus from the bottom upwards), desserts are a major attraction with the likes of passion fruit pavlova, caramel custard with caramelised orange salad, 'fruditées' (a plate of fresh fruit with crème fraiche dip) and a rich chocolate and praline terrine with raspberry sauce. First-course addicts now have their own club as well – the Starters Society – gimmicky, perhaps, but obviously satisfying a serious demand. Well-known English farmhouse cheeses and reasonably-priced wines plus 30 or so unusual bottled beers. ***Seats** 40. D only 6-9.30 (Sat from 7). Closed Sun & Mon, 1 week Christmas, 1 week Easter, Aug.* American Express *Access, Visa.*

Manchester — Novotel — 62% — £80

Tel 061-799 3535 Fax 061-703 8207 — **H**

Worsley Brow Worsley Manchester Greater Manchester M28 4YA — **Map 6 B2**

Modern hotel in its own grounds by Junction 13 of the M62. Ample free parking. Banqueting/conferences for up to 160/220. Novotel policy is that two children under 16 are accommodated free, with breakfast included, when sharing their parents' room. ***Rooms** 119. Garden, outdoor swimming pool.* American Express *Access, Diners, Visa.*

Manchester **Penang Village** **£45**

Tel 061-236 2650 **R**

56 Faulkner Street Manchester Greater Manchester **Map 6 B2**

Hot, rich and spicy dishes run the gamut of Malaysian cuisine in a first-floor restaurant on the south corner of Chinatown, near the Chinese Arch. Chicken satay or one of the splendid soups is a popular prelude to a wide range of main courses including, as specialities, grilled king prawns or fish fillets topped with sambal sauce, sizzling chili beef or a squid curry. Buffet lunch Tues, Wed, Thur. Plenty of vegetarian options. Charming service from sarong-clad waitresses. ***Seats 70.*** *Parties 80. L 12-2 D 5.30-12 (Sat & Sun 12-12). Closed 25 & 26 Dec, 1 Jan. Set meals from £15.* AMERICAN EXPRESS *Access, Diners, Visa.*

Manchester **Hotel Piccadilly** **73%** **£138**

Tel 061-236 8414 Fax 061-236 2533 **H**

Piccadilly Plaza Manchester Greater Manchester M60 1QR **Map 6 B2**

In the heart of the city opposite Piccadilly Gardens, a high-rise hotel that is considerably smarter inside than the surroundings would suggest. Fast lifts lead up to an elegant reception area on the second floor, with an expanse of sparkling, coloured-marble flooring, and the Club Bar, both of which set the standard for decor throughout. A Verandah restaurant on the open-plan third floor has good views over Piccadilly Gardens; the Belvedere lounge bar is open until the wee small hours. On the lower ground floor there's a well-equipped leisure club centred around a good-sized pool. Bedrooms are also generously sized with darkwood furniture contrasting against lighter, contemporary colour schemes and well-lit bathrooms. The top, Ambassador floor, has eight suites, its own check-in and a butler. Children up to 14 free in their parents' room. Conference and banqueting facilities for up to 800 in 30 rooms. Jarvis Hotels. ***Rooms*** *271. Indoor swimming pool, gymnasium, spa bath, sauna, solarium, steam room, beauty salon, coffee shop (9am-6pm).* AMERICAN EXPRESS *Access, Diners, Visa.*

Manchester **Portland Thistle** **69%** **£120**

Tel 061-228 3400 Fax 061-228 6347 **H**

Portland Street Manchester Greater Manchester M1 6DP **Map 6 B2**

In the heart of the city overlooking Piccadilly Gardens, the Portman is within easy reach of most of the city's amenities. Parlour plants decorate a sometimes chaotic foyer, but one can always retire to the bars, one of which features a wall of whisky, or to the leisure spa. The Executives are the best of the bedrooms. Conference rooms hold up to 300. Valet parking. 24hr room service. Children up to 16 stay free in parents' room. ***Rooms*** *205. Indoor swimming pool, keep-fit equipment, sauna, solarium.* AMERICAN EXPRESS *Access, Diners, Visa.*

Manchester **Quan Ju De** **£60**

Tel 061-236 5236 **R**

44 Princess Street Manchester Greater Manchester M1 6DE **Map 6 B2**

Authentic Peking restaurant whose chef (Jian Ping Ma) and team came from the parent restaurant in Peking. Despite the bright, simple decor and trendy modern artwork, the menu has plenty of traditional dishes, with roasted duck in an 'authentic Beijing-style' and crispy aromatic duck as the specialities. Grilled dumplings, hot and sour seafood clear soup, a speciality of plaice fillet in rice wine sauce, and teppan beef served on a sizzling platter also feature on a balanced menu of commendable brevity. Good spicing and competent handling of raw materials are the hallmarks. Tempting banquets for two or more include a vegetarian version. Pianist Tues-Sat eves. ***Seats*** *120. Parties 80. Private Room 48. L 12-2.30 D 6-11.30 (Sun 12-11.30). Closed Bank Holidays. Set L from £4.80 Set D from £16.* AMERICAN EXPRESS *Access, Visa.*

Manchester Rajdoot £40

Tel 061-834 2176 **R**

Carlton House 18 Albert Square Manchester Greater Manchester M2 5PR **Map 6 B2**

Rajdoot is a small chain of restaurants serving well-prepared Indian food in comfortable surroundings. Tandoori dishes are a speciality, with mackerel, quail and kidneys joining more familiar variations on lamb, chicken and prawns. Other branches are in Birmingham, Bristol, Manchester and Dublin. ***Seats** 67. Parties 70. L 12-2.30 D 6.30-11.30. Closed L Sun & Bank Holidays, 25 & 26 Dec. Set L £8 Set D £15.50.* AMERICAN EXPRESS *Access, Diners, Visa.*

Manchester Ramada Hotel 73% £115

Tel 061-835 2555 Fax 061-835 0731 **H**

Blackfriars Street Manchester Greater Manchester M3 2EQ **Map 6 B2**

The foyer of this tall hotel (formerly the *Ramada Renaissance*) looks good in marble, and off it the large and sumptuous lounge provides a haven from the bustle of city life. The muted, pastel-shaded bedrooms are all spacious (mini-suite size), with seating areas, desk space, all the expected modern accessories and bright, well-equipped bathrooms. Children up to 16 stay free in parents' room. There are extensive conference and banqueting facilities (maximum capacity 400). ***Rooms** 200. Gift shop.* AMERICAN EXPRESS *Access, Diners, Visa.*

Manchester Sachas Hotel 64% £110

Tel 061-228 1234 Fax 061-236 9202 **H**

Tib Street Piccadilly Manchester Greater Manchester M4 1PQ **Map 6 B2**

Formerly a C&A store, now a brash hotel with a stuffed polar bear in the entrance hall. Bedrooms vary from inner ones with neither windows nor natural light to superior versions with whirlpool baths and four-poster beds. There are lively eating and drinking spots in the basement (the pizzeria is open 6pm-2am) and a variety of conference and banqueting suites catering for up to 650 delegates. Sister hotel to the *Britannia*. ***Rooms** 223. Indoor swimming pool, keep-fit equipment, sauna, solarium, beauty & hair salons, night club.* AMERICAN EXPRESS *Access, Diners, Visa.*

Manchester Siam Orchid £56

Tel 061-236 1388 **R**

54 Portland Street Manchester Greater Manchester M1 4QU **Map 6 B2**

A friendly Thai restaurant on the edge of Manchester's Chinatown, a few steps from both the *Britannia* and *Piccadilly* hotels. A long menu covers the whole Thai range from soups and satay to fish cakes, spicy salads, curries of several hues, noodle platters, rice platters and many variations on pork, chicken, beef, crab, fish, prawns, lobster, squid and eggs. There's plenty of choice, too, for vegetarians, plus a business lunch menu and other set menus for four or more. Sister to *Royal Orchid*. ***Seats** 60. L 11.30-2.30 D 6.30-11.30 (Fri & Sat from 6, Sun 5-11). Closed Bank Holidays. Set L from £5 Set D £16-£26.* AMERICAN EXPRESS *Access, Visa.*

Manchester Sonarga £45

Tel 061-861 0334 **R**

269 Barlow Moor Road Chorlton-cum-Hardy Manchester Greater Manchester **Map 6 B2**

On the edge of south Manchester's residential fringe at Chorlton-cum-Hardy, the broad-fronted Sonarga is more Armani that original Veeraswamy, presenting much more than the oft-seen good shopfitting job. A well-judged modern style of Bangladeshi cooking and service is offered and the kitchen appears eager to offer new ideas without forsaking traditional values. Good thalis, unusually excellent dhal and six hours' notice required for house specialities like Pashoree beef or lobster Lahare. Undoubtedly one of the best Indian restaurants in the area. Fried chicken and chips appears in a short section of the menu wittily labelled "exotic dishes". ***Seats** 62. D 5.30-12 (Fri 5.30-12.30, Sat 3.30-12.30, Sun 3.30-11). Closed L Mon-Fri. Access, Visa.*

Manchester That Café £42

Tel 061-432 4672 **R**

1031 Stockport Road Levenshulme Manchester Greater Manchester M19 2TB **Map 6 B2**

Home cooking comes in generously sized portions at an unpretentious restaurant alongside the A6, to the south of the city. The carte and short set-price menu offer such dishes as smoked haddock tart, chicken and apricot en croute, beef goulash and hot fudge sundae. Vegetarian main courses are always available. ***Seats** 90. Private Room 36. L Sun 12.30-2.30 other days by arrangement D 7-10.30. Closed D Sun. Set L £10.95 Set D £12.95 (Mon-Thurs).* AMERICAN EXPRESS *Access, Visa.*

Manchester Victoria & Albert Hotel 73% NEW £136

Tel 061-832 1188 Fax 061-834 2484 **HR**

Water Street Manchester Greater Manchester M60 9EA **Map 6 B2**

Between their TV studios and the river Irwell, Granada's new flagship hotel is a cleverly converted mid-19th-century warehouse. Original oak-timbered ceilings and cast-iron pillars feature in the smart galleried reception area, 'Watsons' bar/lounge with its comfortable Victorian drawing room atmosphere and conservatory overlooking the river, and in the all-day French-style café/bistro. Bedrooms, which vary in size and shape, also boast timbered ceilings and some exposed brickwork; each is named after, and subtly themed with stills from, a different Granada TV drama or series. King-or queen-sized beds and a high level of equipment – the TV offers account review, quick check-out and breakfast ordering facilities – make for a comfortable stay aided by keen staff offering an above average level of service. Children under 16 years free in parents' room. No dogs. ***Rooms** 132. Garden, keep-fit equipment, sauna, solarium, coffee shop (10am-midnight), news kiosk.* AMERICAN EXPRESS *Access, Diners, Visa.*

Sherlock Holmes Restaurant £65

John Benson-Smith seems to like to amuse – a tiny mouthful of cottage pie as complimentary starter for example – and surprise diners with dishes like suet pudding of monkfish, baby chicken with carrot cake stuffing, three soups in one bowl (magically remaining separate) and tea cup trifle. A slight tendency towards gimmickry (often more in the names than in the actual dishes) is more than compensated for by skilled, careful execution. More recognisably English dishes such as toad-in-the-hole with onion gravy, roast beef and Yorkshire pudding and braised beef with dumplings also make an appearance, especially at lunchtime. Wide choice of excellent home-baked breads. ***Seats** 130. Parties 40. Private Room 16. L 12-2 D 7-10.30. Set L £9.95/£14.95/£20 Set D £19.95/£25/£40.*

Manchester Woodlands £55

Tel 061-336 4241 **R**

33 Shepley Road Audenshaw Manchester Greater Manchester M34 5DJ **Map 6 B2**

A solid Victorian house alongside B6169 is the setting for the Crank family's popular restaurant. Based on sound, classical French traditions, son-in-law and chef Mark Jackson's menus offer a good choice – five or six on the table d'hote, eight or so on the carte at each stage. The style is straightforward – deep-fried whitebait, avocado, smoked duck and *See over* mango salad, lobster soup, followed by medallions of lamb with a light cream mint sauce and dark port sauce (saucing is a strong point) or perhaps plaited salmon and brill served with creamed oyster mushrooms. Lesley Jackson runs front of house with friendliness and efficiency. Descriptive, mainly French wine list. ***Seats** 40. Parties 17. Private Room 24. L 12-2 D 7-9.30 (Sat to 10). Closed L Sat, all Sun & Mon, Christmas/New Year, 1 week Easter, 2 weeks Aug. Set L & D £15.65. Access, Visa.*

Manchester — Yang Sing ★ — £50

Tel 061-236 2200 Fax 061-236 5934 — **R**

34 Princes Street Manchester Greater Manchester M1 4JY — **Map 6 B2**

Still the best 'Chinese' in town with an enormous Cantonese menu that includes such exotic offerings as stewed duck's web and fish lips and several varieties of bird's nest soups along with more familiar dishes. Tanks of live carp, eels and lobsters testify to the importance chef/proprietor Harry Yeung places on freshness and quality of ingredients. Some 40 different dim sum (even more on Sundays) can be chosen from trolleys parked in the middle of the restaurant (sadly the authorities will no longer allow them to ply around the tables) or ordered from the waiting staff lest as the menu puts it, 'you have difficulty making yourself understood in Cantonese to the trolley girls'. Unusually the dim sum are also available throughout the evening – coming direct from the kitchen after 4.30pm. A selection of pastries (all from their own kitchen) or fresh fruit for afters. Recently opened on the ground floor is a Chinese Fondue Restaurant where dishes are cooked in a stock (rather than oil) that is drunk as a soup after the main ingredients of the dish have been eaten. Banquets for up to 200 guests can be held in the largest of several private rooms. ***Seats** 140. Parties 40. Private Room 200. Meals 12-11.30. Closed 25 Dec. Set meals from £26.50 for two.* AMERICAN EXPRESS *Access, Visa.*

Manchester — Places of Interest

Tourist Information Tel 061-234 3157/3158.
Manchester Cathedral Tel 061-773 2959.
Heaton Hall Tel 061-236 9422.
Granada Studios Tour Water Street Tel 061-833 0880.
Old Trafford Cricket Ground Warwick Road Tel 061-848 7021.
Oldham Ski Centre Tel 061-678 4055.

Theatres and Concert Halls

Contact Theatre Tel 061-274 4400.
Library Theatre Tel 061-236 7110.
Manchester Opera House Tel 061-831 7766.
Palace Theatre Tel 061-236 9922.
Royal Exchange Tel 061-833 9833.

Museums and Art Galleries

City Art Gallery Tel 061-236 5244.
Gallery of English Costume Tel 061-224 5217.
The Museum of Science and Industry Tel 061-832 2244.
Manchester Museum Tel 061-275 2634.
Whitworth Art Gallery Tel 061-273 4865.
Art Gallery Oldham Leisure Services Tel 061-678 4651.

Football Grounds

Manchester City Tel 061-226 1191.
Manchester United Tel 061-872 1661.
Oldham Athletic Tel 061-624 4972.

Manchester Airport — Etrop Grange — 67% — £110

Tel 061-499 0500 Fax 061-499 0790 — **HR**

Etrop Green Manchester Greater Manchester M22 5NR — **Map 6 B2**

Unusually for an airport hotel, this privately-owned extended 18th-century Georgian house is set in landscaped gardens. Public areas are comfortably and traditionally furnished, though the conservatory has contemporary decor. Bedrooms (some with no shower over the bath), are mostly on the small side, but offer adequate facilities, though despite double-glazing some rooms suffer from traffic noise; two suites. Leave the M56 at Junction 5. ***Rooms** 41. Conservatory coffee shop (10-6).* AMERICAN EXPRESS *Access, Diners, Visa.*

Restaurant

£70

Diners will discover that Raymond Sharp's cooking, English in character, is rather better than the unnecessarily flowery and fruity menu descriptions indicate. The number of courses you eat determines the price that you pay, and there are sufficient choices in each section to satisfy all tastes, say, a chilled melon soup, timbale of seafood, loin of lamb and rice pudding. Good British farmhouse cheeses, keenly served in chi-chi surroundings, where candles are lit in broad daylight. ***Seats** 65. Parties 10. Private Room 50. L 12-2 D 7-10. Set L £12.95/14.95 Set D from £21.50. Closed L Sat.*

Manchester Airport — Forte Crest — 65%

£107

Tel 061-437 5811 Fax 061-436 2340

H

Ringway Road Wythenshawe Greater Manchester M22 5NS

Map 6 B2

Formerly the Excelsior. Between terminals A & B, 8 miles from the city centre. Most of the bedrooms have recently been refurbished. Banqueting and conference facilities for 200, plus a leisure centre. 24hr room service. ***Rooms** 292. Garden, indoor swimming pool, gymnasium, sauna, café (6.30am-11pm).* AMERICAN EXPRESS *Access, Diners, Visa.*

Manchester Airport — Four Seasons Hotel — 68%

£102

Tel 061-904 0301 Fax 061-980 1787

H

Hale Road Hale Barns nr Altrincham Greater Manchester WA15 8XW

Map 6 B2

A privately owned hotel two miles from the airport (at junction 6 of the M56). Smart modern bedrooms overlook central courtyard gardens. Well geared up for business people with up-to-date conference facilities (maximum 160) and secretarial support services available. There's a good choice of spots in which to relax, including the Lobby Bar, Vivaldi's cocktail bar, Mulligans snug and Mollenski's conservatory. Children up to 14 stay free in parents' room. ***Rooms** 94. Business centre, car hire desk.* AMERICAN EXPRESS *Access, Diners, Visa.*

Manchester Airport — Hilton International — 71%

£159

Tel 061-436 4404 Fax 061-436 1521

H

Outwood Lane Ringway Manchester Airport Greater Manchester M22 5WP

Map 6 B2

Convenient for both the airport and the motorway network, this modern hotel caters admirably for travellers and general businessmen alike with its good business and meeting facilities (for up to 200). Through the new entrance, a fountain leads into a lounge area with a fish-filled pond in one corner. Plaza bedrooms are larger and more impressive than the standard rooms, but all are smartly furnished with contemporary fabrics and have surprisingly spacious bathrooms; all rooms have been refurbished within the last three years and the air-conditioning improved. Double-glazing features throughout, so noise is not a problem, despite the location. Small leisure pool. ***Rooms** 223. Garden, indoor swimming pool, children's pool, keep-fit equipment, spa bath, sauna, steam bath, coffee shop (8am-midnight).* AMERICAN EXPRESS *Access, Diners, Visa.*

Many hotels offer reduced rates for weekend or out-of-season bookings. Always ask about special deals.

Manchester Airport — Moss Nook

£80

Tel 061-437 4778

RR

Ringway Road Moss Nook Manchester Greater Manchester M22 5NA — **Map 6 B2**

Well signed from the airport (one mile away). Red suede walls, heavy drapes, stained glass, silver plate, heavy crystal glassware, and lace slips over the tablecloths lend an air of opulence. The French-style à la carte menu is supplemented by a *menu surprise* (five small courses at lunchtime, seven in the evening). Grand ingredients and an outsize menu typify the style. ***Seats** 60. Parties 10. L 12-1.30 D 7-9.30 Closed L Sat, all Sun & Mon, Bank Holidays, 2 weeks Christmas. Set L £16.50 Set D £28.* AMERICAN EXPRESS *Access, Diners, Visa.*

Room

£140*

An adjacent, self-contained cottage has one double bedroom with two en-suite bathrooms and a lounge. The makings of a Continental breakfast are provided. No children under 12. Accommodation closed for 2 weeks from Christmas Eve. *Price for two including dinner.

Market Drayton — Corbet Arms

£55

Tel 0630 652037 Fax 0630 652961

I

High Street Market Drayton Shropshire TF9 1PY — **Map 6 B3**

A creeper-clad 16th-century coaching inn retaining exposed timbers (and creaky floorboards) in smartly decorated bedrooms. Period ballroom for up to 140 revellers, and smaller private conference rooms. Cheerful staff. No credit cards. ***Rooms** 11.*

Market Drayton — Goldstone Hall 60%

£75

Tel 063 086 202 Fax 063 086 585

H

Goldstone Market Drayton Shropshire TF9 2NA — **Map 6 B3**

South of Market Drayton, follow brown and white signposts from the A459 for Goldstone Hall Gardens. Set in five acres of mature gardens, the proprietor-run hall is an accumulation of centuries of building, with possible Anglo-Saxon origins, and is furnished with the family collection of antiques. Bedrooms are individually designed, with period furniture, and several have large Victorian brass bedsteads. Separate conference and banqueting rooms. ***Rooms** 8. Garden, snooker. Closed 26 Dec.* AMERICAN EXPRESS *Access, Visa.*

Market Drayton — Place of Interest

Market Drayton Pool Tel 0630 2619.

Market Harborough — Three Swans Hotel 65%

£72

Tel 0858 466644 Fax 0858 433101

H

21 High Street Market Harborough Leicestershire LE16 7NJ — **Map 7 D4**

Charles I slaked his thirst here in 1645, by when this splendid coaching inn was already more than 200 years old. Several bars ensure that today's visitors don't go thirsty, and there's an attractive conservatory/lounge and a patio. Bedrooms are in the main building or a block across the courtyard. All are of a good size, decorated in restful pastels and furnished with smart modern units; all have private bathrooms with tubs, shower and toiletries. Friendly staff. Banquets (for up to 95) and conferences (up to 75) catered for. No dogs. ***Rooms** 37.* AMERICAN EXPRESS *Access, Diners, Visa.*

> Never leave money, credit cards or valuables lying around in your hotel room. Use the hotel safe or the mini-safe in your room.

Market Harborough — Places of Interest

Deene Park House and Gardens Nr Corby Tel 078085 278 or 361.
Kirby Hall Nr Corby Tel 0536 203230.
Rockingham Castle Corby Tel 0536 770240.
Rutland Polo Club Barnsdale House, Great Easton Tel 0536 770238.

Markington — Hob Green — 70% — £80

Tel 0423 770031 Fax 0423 771589 — **H**

Markington nr Harrogate North Yorkshire HG3 3PJ — **Map 6 C1**

A long winding drive leads to a mellow stone-built hotel set in over 800 acres of farm and woodland. The gardens are regular winners of local awards, and there are pleasant views of the rolling Yorkshire countryside. The garden room is bright and summery, while the hall and drawing room have a traditional appeal that's helped along by antiques and log fires. Books, magazines and games are available for relaxation. Bedrooms are individually appointed in homely style and furniture is an agreeable mix of period and modern. Most have a little sitting area. ***Rooms** 12. Garden.* AMERICAN EXPRESS *Access, Diners, Visa.*

Markyate — Hertfordshire Moat House — 57% — NEW — £94

Tel 0582 840840 Fax 0582 842282 — **H**

London Road Markyate AL3 8HH — **Map 15 E1**

Only one mile from the M1 (Junction 9) alongside the A5, a recently upgraded hotel with adequate bedrooms and bathrooms, a very good modern gymnasium and a thriving conference trade. ***Rooms** 89. Gymnasium, solarium.* AMERICAN EXPRESS *Access, Diners, Visa.*

Marlborough — Ivy House — 61% — £55

Tel 0672 515333 Fax 0672 515338 — **H**

High Street Marlborough Wiltshire SN8 1HJ — **Map 14 C2**

The Grade II Georgian house faces St Peter's Church, where Charles Wesley was ordained. Once a boarding school for boys, it is now a privately owned hotel comprising a dozen bedrooms in the main house and others in a modern conference centre to the rear; both are interlinked by a cobbled courtyard to the restaurants and sun terrace. Some bedrooms have separate sitting areas. Six further bedrooms (known as The Vines) in country cottage style are in an annexe across the High Street. Banqueting/conferences for 70. Under-10s stay free in parents' room. ***Rooms** 32. Closed 2 weeks Christmas/New Year.* AMERICAN EXPRESS *Access, Visa.*

Marlow — Compleat Angler Hotel — 73% — £164

Tel 0628 484444 Fax 0628 486388 — **HR**

Marlow Bridge Marlow Buckinghamshire SL7 1RG — **Map 15 E2**

A famous Marlow landmark in a glorious riverside setting by the weir. Said to be where Izaak Walton wrote his definitive angling work (after which the hotel is named), it dates in part back to the 16th century, but has been extended over the years. The latest extension houses eighteen bedrooms, twelve of which overlook the river. Creaking floorboards feature in the original rooms, which include riverside rooms at a supplement to already high tariffs. On the ground floor the marble-floored foyer leads to a panelled bar with a conservatory, opening on to a small balcony that also overlooks the river. Children up to 15 stay free in parents' room. Forte Grand. ***Rooms** 64. Tennis, fishing.* AMERICAN EXPRESS *Access, Diners, Visa.*

Valaisan Restaurant — £115

Adequate cooking in the classic mould, good cheeses and decent wine list. Superb views and professional service from an able team. ***Seats** 96.*

See over

Parties 20. L 12.30-2.30 (Sun to 3) D 7-10. Set L from £16.50 (Sun £27.50) Set D from £25.

Marlow **Place of Interest**

Bisham Abbey Sports Centre Tel 0627 476911.

Marston **Forte Travelodge** **£42**

Tel 0234 766755 **L**

Beancroft Road Marston Moretaine Bedfordshire MK43 0PZ **Map 15 E1**

On the A421, 3 miles from Junction 13 of the M1, 6 miles south west of Bedford. ***Rooms** 32.* AMERICAN EXPRESS *Access, Visa.*

Marston Moreteyne **Moreteyne Manor NEW** **£85**

Tel 0234 767003 Fax 0234 765382 **R**

Woburn Road Marston Moreteyne Bedfordshire MK43 0NG **Map 15 E1**

A timbered Tudor manor house is Jeremy Blake O'Connor's latest venture, with new beginnings after a recent fire. Dishes featured on his menus are involved and don't stint on flavours. Leave the choice to him and he will produce a well-balanced, enjoyable repast. ***Seats** 32. Parties 12. Private Room 85. L 12.15-2 D 7.15-10. Closed D Sun, all Mon & 4 days Jan. Set L £12/£18.50 Set D from £22.50.* AMERICAN EXPRESS *Access, Visa.*

Matlock **Riber Hall** **71%** **£107**

Tel 0629 582795 Fax 0629 580475 **HR**

Matlock Derbyshire DE4 5JU **Map 6 C2**

Twenty minutes from junction 28 of the M1, a dark stone Elizabethan manor house which sports antiques, beams, fresh flowers and good housekeeping; there's also a lovely conservatory and walled garden – a wonderfully peaceful location. Bedrooms are located in converted stables across a courtyard where the original beams and rough stone walls remain; all are filled with thoughtful extras, centrally heated and have period four-poster or half-tester beds. Best rooms face south and east and overlook the large garden. Bathrooms are well equipped, neat and warm. A tennis trainer ball machine is available on the all-weather tennis court. No children under 10. No dogs. ***Rooms** 11. Tennis.* AMERICAN EXPRESS *Access, Diners, Visa.*

Restaurant **£66**

An interesting selection of dishes (on both an extensive dinner carte and fixed-price lunch menus) is well served in two elegant dining rooms. Space is limited, so booking is essential. Game terrine with Cumberland jelly, toasted brioche with sautéed calf's liver, shallots, rosemary and port jus, trio of grilled fish with a prawn and baby vegetable charlotte and a Riesling sauce, medallions of venison with a glazed apple and orange tart and red wine sauce. There's also usually a good choice on the pudding and separate vegetarian menus. Good ingredients and presentation throughout. ***Seats** 45. Private Room 34. L 12-1.30 D 7-9.30. Set L £14.50.*

Matlock **Place of Interest**

Gullivers Kingdom Matlock Bath Tel 0629 580540.

Matlock Bath **New Bath Hotel** **63%** **£118**

Tel 0629 583275 Fax 0629 580268 **H**

New Bath Road Matlock Bath Derbyshire DE4 3PX **Map 6 C3**

10 miles from junction 28 of the M1, tucked away down a narrow, twisting gorge, the New Bath is set in five acres of landscaped gardens overlooking the river Derwent. Good leisure facilities include an outdoor

swimming pool fed by a thermal spring. Conference/banqueting and family facilities. Forte Heritage. ***Rooms** 55. Garden, indoor & outdoor swimming pools, sauna, solarium, tennis, putting.* AMERICAN EXPRESS *Access, Diners, Visa.*

Mawnan Smith — Budock Vean Hotel — 65% — £144

Tel 0326 250288 Fax 0326 250892 — **H**

Mawnan Smith nr Falmouth Cornwall TR11 5LG — **Map 12 B4**

65 acres of sub-tropical gardens surround this fine sporting hotel, whose attractions include a private foreshore to the Helford River. The active guest will find plenty to do both inside and out, while relaxing hours can be passed in the cane-furnished conservatory, the cocktail bar (jackets and ties after 7pm) and the various lounges. Spacious bedrooms include some with sitting rooms. ***Rooms** 58. Garden, indoor swimming pool, tennis, golf (9), putting, table tennis, coarse fishing, snooker. Closed 3 Jan-Feb.* AMERICAN EXPRESS *Access, Diners, Visa.*

Mawnan Smith — Meudon Hotel — 69% — £120

Tel 0326 250541 Fax 0326 250543 — **H**

Mawnan Smith nr Falmouth Cornwall TR11 5HT — **Map 12 B4**

The Pilgrim family, owners since 1966, put the accent on peace, quiet and personal service, with no conference or even large parties to intrude. 8½ acres of sub-tropical gardens, laid out by 'Capability' Brown, are a major attraction of staying here and are at their flowering best between March and June; the gardens lead down to a private beach. The house itself was built at the turn of the century, and the new wing, connected at first-floor level, is in matching stone. The main lounge is very comfortable and appealing, with paintings, photographs, fresh flowers and antiques. Bedrooms are individually appointed in elegant style, with furnishings and fittings of a uniformly high standard; all overlook the gardens. Two balcony suites have their own sitting rooms. Residents can enjoy free golf at the Falmouth Golf Club (two miles away) and both sea and river fishing are available. No children under 5. ***Rooms** 32. Garden. Closed Jan & Feb. Access, Diners, Visa.*

Mawnan Smith — Nansidwell — 70% — £140*

Tel 0326 250340 Fax 0326 250440 — **HR**

Mawnan Smith Nr Falmouth Cornwall TR11 5HU — **Map 12 B4**

With wellies (and roller skates and an outboard motor) in the porch and a friendly puppy dog by the log fire, Nansidwell is a real 'country house hotel'. Built at the turn of the century, although the wisteria clad exterior looks older, it has a wonderfully peaceful location in five acres of gardens surrounded by National Trust land between Helford River and the sea. Day rooms have a comfortably lived-in feel with family photos creating a genuinely homely atmosphere. Individually decorated bedrooms with 'country' and near-antique furniture vary considerably in size but all boast fresh flowers and generous quantities of books and magazines. No room service. *Half-board terms only. ***Rooms** 12. Garden, tennis, boules. Closed Jan. Access, Visa.*

Restaurant — £66

An appealing dining room with decorative plates adorning yellow rag-painted walls and views over the terraced gardens. Equally appealing are Tony Alcott's well-executed dishes from a fairly sophisticated menu that might include hot pigeon salad with smoked ham, oyster mushrooms and sherry dressing; steamed salmon with local scallops and garden sorrel; loin of lamb on a leek and port confit with light mustard sauce; praline and plum yeast cake glazed with mint and white wine (puds are a particular strength) and hot apple and almond tart with apricot and ginger sauce. The

See over

à la carte light lunch menu (£12.50 minimum charge for non-residents) is equally interesting. Short but well-chosen wine list. ***Seats** 30. Parties 10. L 12.30-1.45 D 7-9 (booking advisable).*

Mawnan Smith   Places of Interest

Glendurgan Garden (NT) Helford River Tel 0208 74281.
Trebah Garden Tel 0326 250448.

Medmenham   Danesfield House   78%   £150

Tel 0628 891010 Fax 0628 890408   **HR**

Medmenham Marlow Buckinghamshire SL7 3ES   **Map 15 D2**

An impressive Tudor-style, white stone mansion built in the late 19th century complete with clock tower, crenellations and twisted redbrick Elizabethan chimney stacks. A large stone terrace and formal parterre gardens take full advantage of the hotel's elevated position high above a bend in the river Thames. The tapestry-hung Grand Hall is baronial in scale with hammerbeam roof and minstrel's gallery (now a snooker room); other day rooms include a wicker-furnished atrium and bar with leather seating and loggia from which to enjoy the views. Bedrooms come in one of three colours – apricot, blue or pink – with everything from the drag-painted furniture, bathroom tiling and glass drops of the mini-chandeliers in the same colour. All have three phones (with two separate lines) including one in the bathroom, which also offers good toiletries and bathrobes. Friendly staff offer good levels of service with rooms properly serviced in the evenings and a 24hr room service menu. ***Rooms** 93. Garden, outdoor swimming pool, squash, tennis, snooker, helipad.* AMERICAN EXPRESS *Access, Diners, Visa.*

Oak Room   £95

From having four separate restaurants when the hotel opened there is now just a single menu served in the panelled Oak Room, which has a fine ribbed plaster ceiling and a loggia extension where breakfast is served. The short but reasonably well-balanced à la carte includes the likes of potted Devon crab with lemon grass and coriander that also comes with pink grapefruit and avocado; quail filled with duck liver mousse garnished with wine-soaked grapes; and fillet of beef topped with bone marrow and garnished with baby onions braised in grenadine. Good ingredients, including wild mushrooms from the hotel's own grounds, are soundly cooked. Vegetables are generally limited to a garnish with the main dish. ***Seats** 35. Private Room 20. L 12-2.30 D 7-10. Set L £15.50/£19.50 Set D £29.50.*

Melbourn   Pink Geranium   £100

Tel 0763 260215   **R**

Station Road Melbourn nr Royston Hertfordshire SG8 6DX   **Map 15 F1**

Steven Saunders' delightful 16th-century thatched cottage in the village centre is all a country restaurant ought to be. Low, black-beamed ceilings characterise the cosy, intimate ground-floor rooms (there's a lofty upstairs private dining room which has a wide brick chimney breast at its heart). Decor is of palest pink plaster walls, with curtains and upholstery in geranium pink. The pretty floral theme extends throughout, from the comfortable bar which comprises several small interconnecting rooms, to the split-level dining room with its sunny conservatory overlooking an attractive, well-tended garden. David Whiffen brings his considerable previous experience with the *Connaught* and *Inverlochy Castle* to this charming setting, offering carefully researched and well-executed dishes that are firmly in the mould of haute cuisine. Flavours are true, a result of meticulous attention to detail. Only a rouille that accompanied a superb red mullet soup has recently failed to live up to expectations – there was none of the aïoli or fiery chili flavours. Innovative touches are to be found in the use of Japanese shiitake mushrooms which appear in a well-risen

NEW CHEF

soufflé, the mushrooms coming as part of a wonderfully rich and creamy Marsala sauce. Main courses include a crispy duck for two served with a poached pear in red wine and citrus sauce and a beautifully trimmed and cooked Dover sole served off the bone and stuffed with thinly sliced tender scallops then topped with butterflied tiger prawns. The dish is finished off with a gratinated champagne sauce of great flavour and perfect balance. Equally mouthwatering desserts and excellent sweetmeats to finish.
***Seats** 72. Private Room 16. L 12-2 D 7-10 (Sat to 10.30). Closed L Sat, D Sun, all Mon. Set L £13.95/£16.95 Set D £24.95.* AMERICAN EXPRESS *Access, Visa.*

Melbourn — Place of Interest

Bassingbourn Ski Club Royston Tel 0462 34107.

Melksham — King's Arms Hotel

£59

Tel 0225 707272 Fax 0225 702085

I

Market Place Melksham Wiltshire SN12 6EX

Map 14 B3

A cobbled courtyard lit by coaching lamps brighten up the front of a traditional inn built from Bath stone, situated in the town's market place. Heavy carved-oak furniture and a beamed ceiling decorate the residents' lounge and a lounge bar is warmed by an open fire. Bedrooms are bright, pleasant and simply furnished; four singles share two bathrooms. Children up to 10 stay free in parents' room. ***Rooms** 14.* AMERICAN EXPRESS *Access, Diners, Visa.*

Melksham — Toxique — NEW

£65

Tel 0225 702129

R

187 Woodrow Road Melksham Wiltshire SN12 7AY

Map 14 B3

Take the Calne road from the town-centre mini roundabout, turn left after ½ mile into Forest Road and continue for nearly a mile – eventually you'll find Toxique. However, you must book in advance as it's 'famine or feast round these parts', meaning it's closed when not busy and very busy when booked up. Nevertheless, Peter Jewkes and chef-partner Helen Bartlett's slightly eccentric restaurant with its farmhouse look and unusual decor (cheap chairs and tables disguised with loose covers, an abstract mural) is worth a visit. A fixed-price-only menu offers 6 or 7 dishes at each stage: perhaps a crumbly terrine of duck with spiced oranges, a rich filo parcel of chicken livers and thyme with a thick port sauce, or antipasto to start, followed by loin of venison with red wine sauce, poussin with garlic and tarragon, or pan-fried trio of fish (brill, monkfish and salmon) with lime and sweet pepper oil. Saucing is a strong point, as is service from the busy owner. No smoking at the table (but it's allowed in the bar area). Accommodation is also offered (£108 half-board for two) in four rooms. A promising place in an area poorly served by decent restaurants. ***Seats** 36. Parties 20. Private Room 24. L 12.30-2 D 7-10. Closed L Tue-Sat, D Sun, all Mon, 2 weeks Jan/Feb. Set L (Sun only) £13.50/£16.50 Set D £24.* AMERICAN EXPRESS *Access, Diners, Visa.*

Melksham — Place of Interest

Devizes Tourist Information Tel 0380 729408.

Mellor — Millstone Hotel

£84

Tel 0254 813333 Fax 0254 812628

I

Church Lane Mellor nr Blackburn Lancashire BB2 7JR

Map 6 B1

10 minutes from junction 31 of the M6, next to St Mary's church in a quiet village off the A59, this small, friendly hotel effectively mixes modern conveniences with the charm of a traditional roadside inn. One of the two bars also acts as the village local. The well-designed bedrooms are better than one might expect from an inn and are furnished in soft

See over

contemporary colours; some have neat, carpeted bathrooms, while six have shower/WC only. Children up to the age of 16 are free in parents' room. Shire Inns. ***Rooms** 21.* AMERICAN EXPRESS *Access, Diners, Visa.*

Melmerby — Village Bakery

£30

Tel 0768 881515 Fax 0768 881848

R

Melmerby Penrith Cumbria CA10 1HE

Map 4 C3

A converted barn with a bright, airy conservatory and pine furniture, run for 15 years by Andrew and Lis Whitley, and overlooking the green of a beautiful fellside village, ten miles east of Penrith on the A686 Alston road. The owners are committed to providing food produced by organic methods. Breakfast (including a vegetarian fried version with aduki bean pattie) is served until 11am; lunch (12-2) dishes (seafood gratin, grilled Cumberland sausage, brown lentil and red wine moussaka), and marvellous afternoon teas with bread and cakes from their own brick-built oven. A tea garden is planned. Children's portions. No smoking. ***Seats** 45.*
Private Room 25. Meals 8.30-5 (Sun from 9.30). Closed 25 & 26 Dec. Access, Diners, Visa.

Melton Mowbray — George Hotel — 57%

£58

Tel 0664 62112 Fax 0664 410457

H

High Street Melton Mowbray Leicestershire LE13 0TR

Map 7 D3

The entrance hall at this very old former coaching inn was once the archway through which the stage coaches drove. The arrival and departure clock still stands on display, and another traditional touch is provided by four-posters in some of the bedrooms. Children up to 10 stay free in parents' room. There are two bars, one with beams and hunting prints, and a patio. ***Rooms** 22.* AMERICAN EXPRESS *Access, Diners, Visa.*

Mere — Old Ship Hotel

£52

Tel 0747 860258 Fax 0747 860501

I

Castle Street Mere Wiltshire BA12 6JE

Map 14 B3

A splendid 17th-century inn with flagstones, exposed brick and stonework, log fires, panelling and beamed ceilings. Period oak furniture in the three characterful bars (good Badger's beers) and the quiet residents' lounge complements the ancient fabric of the building. Bedrooms in the main house have traditional furnishings (one features a four-poster) while ten in the annexe are more compact and modern; eight bedrooms not en suite share three bathrooms. Characterful gabled and beamed restaurant. This is a popular base for touring, walking and riding. Families are well catered for. ***Rooms** 23.* AMERICAN EXPRESS *Access, Visa.*

Mere — Places of Interest

Stourhead (NT) Stourton Tel 0747 840348.
Stourton House Garden Stourton Tel 0747 840417.

Meriden — Forest of Arden Hotel — 70%

£110

Tel 0676 22335 Fax 0676 23711

H

Maxstoke Lane Meriden West Midlands CV7 7HR

Map 6 C4

Just over a mile off the A45 (west of Coventry), near the M6/M42 intersection, this purpose-built resort-style hotel, golf and country club stands at the end of a country lane in 400 acres of rolling countryside. A Mediterranean feel to the interior is achieved by using archways, tapered white columns, rough-plastered white walls and terracotta tiles throughout the lounge and reception areas. Bedrooms are not large, but are comfortable and furnished with taste in contemporary fashion; bathrooms are carpeted and have good-quality showers. Leisure facilities are housed in an impressive Country Club and include a large pool. A supervised

crèche can be provided by arrangement (as can baby-sitting); families may eat informally in the poolside grill and bar. Country Club Hotels.
***Rooms** 152. 2 golf courses, fishing, indoor swimming pool, sauna, steam room, spa bath, solarium, squash, tennis, snooker, fitness studio, beauty salon, dance studio.* AMERICAN EXPRESS® *Access, Diners, Visa.*

Meriden **Manor Hotel** **64%** **£85**

Tel 0676 22735 Fax 0676 22186 **H**

Main Road Meriden West Midlands CV7 7NH **Map 6 C4**

Impressive, extended Georgian-style building with comfortable bedrooms in a smart modern wing. Popular for conferences and banquets, but no leisure facilities. Children up to 12 free in parents' room. De Vere.
***Rooms** 74.* AMERICAN EXPRESS® *Access, Diners, Visa.*

Mickleton **Three Ways Hotel** **59%** **£68**

Tel 0386 438429 Fax 0386 438118 **H**

Mickleton nr Chipping Campden Gloucestershire GL55 6SB **Map 14 C1**

Standing at the heart of a Cotswold village by the B4632 (formerly the A46) Stratford to Broadway road, a privately-run hotel built from mellow, local stone. Bedrooms are practical rather than luxurious with modest en-suite facilities. Although the decor is dated, cleanliness is a strong point. Friendly and relaxing atmosphere; family facilities (children up to 16 stay free in parents' room). Three conference/function suites, one opening onto a patio. ***Rooms** 40. Garden.* AMERICAN EXPRESS® *Access, Diners, Visa.*

Middle Wallop **Fifehead Manor** **61%** **£85**

Tel 0264 781565 Fax 0264 781400 **H**

Middle Wallop nr Stockbridge Hampshire SO20 8EG **Map 14 C3**

On the A343 in the centre of the village, the manor house stands in 3½ acres of land and has origins going back to the Middle Ages. Central to the house is the medieval dining hall with its mullioned windows and there is a small bar plus a lounge. Large bedrooms in the main house have good-size bathrooms; smaller singles (with showers only) are in an annexe, but have the attraction of leading out on to the rear lawn. Subdued fabrics and colour schemes are used throughout, and the furniture is mostly modern, although a few antiques help contribute to the friendly and informal atmosphere. Fine cooked breakfasts and a restaurant when that tempts more than it delivers. ***Rooms** 16. Garden. Closed 2 weeks Christmas/New Year.* AMERICAN EXPRESS® *Access, Diners, Visa.*

Middlecombe **Periton Park** **66%** **£88**

Tel 0643 706885 Fax 0643 706885 **H**

Periton Road Middlecombe nr Minehead Somerset TA24 8SW **Map 13 D1**

Time stands still at Periton Park, a handsome late-Victorian country residence nestling in its own woodland and gardens on the northern edge of Exmoor National Park. For total relaxation, guests feel quite at home in the stylish drawing room warmed by a log fire in winter; more energetic pursuits include fly-fishing, shooting (parties a speciality) and riding from stables adjacent to the hotel. Each bedroom (all en suite) has its own character and all enjoy splendid views; two are for non-smokers, and one ground-floor room, with French windows opening on to the garden, allows dogs. No children under 12. ***Rooms** 8. Garden, shooting, riding, fishing.* AMERICAN EXPRESS® *Access, Visa.*

See the Conference and Banqueting section for lists of hotels arranged by county.

Middlesbrough — Hotel Baltimore — 62% — £80

Tel 0642 224111 Fax 0642 226156 — **H**

250 Marton Road Middlesbrough Cleveland TS4 2EZ — **Map 5 E3**

Popular executive hotel south of the town centre on the A172. Bedrooms are double-glazed. Children up to 12 stay free in parents' room. Free secured parking. ***Rooms** 31. Solarium.* AMERICAN EXPRESS *Access, Diners, Visa.*

Middlesbrough — Hospitality Inn — 59% — £92

Tel 0642 232000 Fax 0642 232655 — **H**

Fry Street Middlesbrough Cleveland TS1 1JH — **Map 5 E3**

High-rise hotel in the town centre. Five banqueting and conference suites have a maximum capacity of 400. Mount Charlotte Thistle. ***Rooms** 180.* AMERICAN EXPRESS *Access, Diners, Visa.*

Middlesbrough — Places of Interest

Tourist Information Tel 0642 243425.
Ormesby Hall (NT) Tel 0642 324188.
Middlesbrough Football Ground Ayresome Park Tel 0642 819659.
Redcar Racecourse Redcar Tel 0642 484068.
Theatres and Concert Halls
Little Theatre Tel 0642 818971.
Redcar Bowl Tel 0642 231212.
Town Hall Crypt Tel 0642 221866.
Museums and Art Galleries
Captain Cook Birthplace Museum Tel 0642 311211.
Cleveland Crafts Centre Tel 0642 226351.
Cleveland Gallery Tel 0642 225408.
Guisborough Priory Guisborough Tel 0287 38301.
Middlesbrough Art Gallery Linthorpe Road Tel 0642 247445.

Middleton Stoney — Jersey Arms — £70

Tel 086 989 234 Fax 086 989 565 — **I**

Middleton Stoney nr Bicester Oxfordshire OX6 8SE — **Map 15 D1**

A 17th-century Cotswold-stone inn alongside the B430 (between Junctions 9 & 10 of the M40) offering comfortable accommodation in cottagey style. Bedrooms are divided between the main house (where wooden beams and creaking floors abound) and the courtyard, where they are a little more up-to-date; the Lily Langtry Suite has a four-poster bed and sitting room. Day rooms include a low-ceilinged bar warmed by an open fire and a new lounge with half panelling and comfortable seating. ***Rooms** 16.* AMERICAN EXPRESS *Access, Diners, Visa.*

Middleton-in-Teesdale — Teesdale Hotel — 58% — £61

Tel 0833 40264 — **H**

Middleton-in-Teesdale Durham DL12 0QG — **Map 5 D3**

In the centre of a Pennine village, the Teesdale is a carefully modernised 17th-century coaching inn with a lot of charm and welcoming hosts in Dieter and Audrey Streit. Day rooms and bedrooms are traditional in style; holiday cottages are available to let in the courtyard at the rear of the hotel. ***Rooms** 14. Access, Visa.*

Midhurst — Angel Hotel — £55

Tel 0730 812421 — **IR**

North Street Midhurst West Sussex GU29 9DN — **Map 11 A6**

Once a coaching inn dating back to the 16th century, the Angel is virtually plumb in the town centre. The plain white-painted Georgian facade gives no real indication of the warmth and welcome waiting within. Public rooms are largely centred around the two bars and restaurants with a relatively quiet residents' lounge at the front. Furnishings throughout are a mix of well-maintained polished antiques, deep relaxing armchairs and settees with paintings and prints on the walls – the usual traditional trappings that befit a well-cared for establishment such as this. Bedrooms, all on upper floors, are in either the original building or a purpose-built modern block to the rear. All are of a good size and comfortably appointed possessing all the expected extras. Bathrooms too are up to date and kept in good order. ***Rooms** 17. Garden.* AMERICAN EXPRESS *Access, Diners, Visa.*

Restaurant

£60

Diners have a choice of two eating places, both offering the same food. The brasserie, adjacent to the bar, is rustic in style and hence informal in character and the dining room, in contrast, is spacious and classically elegant with large, well-spaced tables. Prices are, naturally, lower in the brasserie. Peter Crawford-Rolt supervises and cooks producing dishes as diverse as terrine of goose liver and Sauternes, oysters with crab and mayonnaise, rump steak and Guinness pie and brill on a bed of asparagus with lime and ginger butter. The fish is particularly good here. The style of cooking is eclectic and the execution of the dishes first-rate. A banana tart flamed with rum is a pyrotechnical then epicurean delight just one of the desserts confirming the restaurant as South of England Dessert of the Year winner. ***Seats** 45. Private Room 40. L 12-2.15 D 7-9.30 (Fri & Sat to 10). Set L from £12.50.*

Midhurst — Spread Eagle — 69% — £78

Tel 0730 816911 Fax 0730 815668 — **H**

South Street Midhurst West Sussex GU29 9NH — **Map 11 A6**

The characterful 15th-and 17th-century buildings combine here with friendly staff and pleasing decor to form a most appealing hotel. The lounge bar with log fire, polished ship's timbers and fresh flowers has great charm, as do the other public areas, including the residents' lounge with its high beamed ceiling. Bedrooms are individually decorated with quiet good taste and are furnished with a mixture of reproduction and antique pieces. Many, including the five four-poster rooms, have old exposed timbers or mellow wood panelling. Two family suites are available in the adjoining Market House; baby-sitting and baby-listening can be arranged. Children up to 10 stay free in parents' room. Smart bathrooms offer huge towels and good toiletries. The 17th-century Jacobean Hall is a characterful setting for banquets and meetings (for around 100). ***Rooms** 41. Garden.*
AMERICAN EXPRESS *Access, Diners, Visa.*

Midhurst — Places of Interest

Petworth House (NT) Petworth Tel 0798 42207.
Cowdray Park Polo Club Cowdray Estate Office Tel 0730 812423.

Milford-on-Sea — Rocher's — £60

Tel 0590 642340 — **R**

69-71 High Street Milford-on-Sea Hampshire SO41 0QG — **Map 14 C4**

Chef-patron Alain Rocher spent two years just down the road at *Chewton Glen* before opening his own restaurant in 1988. Recent refurbishment has made the dining area less cottagey, but have not changed the level of comfort and the adult atmosphere. Alain's style is classical with modern touches and his cooking is characterised by full flavours and excellent saucing. Daily tables d'hote at both lunch (except Sat) and dinner offer a small choice: from gaspacho and *feuilleté de champignons à la crème d'ail* to pan-fried guinea fowl with Meaux mustard sauce and escalope of salmon with fresh herb sauce; perhaps tarte au citron or crème brulée to finish. A la carte extends to include more involved dishes like filo-wrapped asparagus, duck, leek and bacon in a port sauce, and serious saucing with smooth textures, fine seasoning and first-rate consistencies, complementing main courses like fillet of veal with a grapefruit sauce and fillet of halibut with a sorrel sauce. Friendly service is headed by Alain's wife Rebecca.

See over

Exclusively French wine list with helpful notes. No children under 10 (13 at dinner). ***Seats** 26. L (Sun only) 12.15-1.30 D 7-9.30.*
Closed D Sun (except Sun before Bank Holidays), all Mon & Tue, 2 weeks Jun, 2 weeks winter. Set L £13.50 Set D £16.50 (except Sat) & £18.40/£21.90.
AMERICAN EXPRESS *Access, Visa.*

Milford-on-Sea — South Lawn 66% — £84

Tel 0590 643911 Fax 0590 644820 — H

Lymington Road Milford-on-Sea nr Lymington Hampshire SO41 0RF — Map 14 C4

The high proportion of repeat business here says much for the standards of maintenance, service and hospitality provided by Ernst and Jennifer Barten, owners since 1971 of this rambling black-and-white former dower house. Fresh flowers make a colourful show both outside and in the roomy lounge, and the bedrooms (all on the first floor) have views over paddocks and garden. No children under seven. No dogs. ***Rooms** 24. Garden.*
Closed Christmas/New Year. Access, Visa.

Milton Keynes — Forte Crest 68% — £107

Tel 0908 667722 Fax 0908 674714 — H

500 Saxon Gate Milton Keynes Buckinghamshire MK9 2HQ — Map 15 E1

Modern hotel in the centre of town. Banqueting facilities for up to 110, conferences to 150. Part of a catering pilot scheme called Mondiale, with café and brasserie. ***Rooms** 151. Indoor swimming pool, gymnasium, sauna, solarium.* AMERICAN EXPRESS *Access, Diners, Visa.*

Milton Keynes — Friendly Hotel 57% NEW — £79

Tel 0908 561666 Fax 0908 568303 — H

Monksway Two Mile Ash Milton Keynes Buckinghamshire MK8 8LY — Map 15 E1

Practical, modern low-rise hotel at the junction of the A5 and A422. Twelve Premier Plus suites with small kitchenette and fax machine in a small lounge are favoured by both business people and families. Children stay free in parents' room. ***Rooms** 88. Indoor swimming pool, gymnasium, sauna, spa bath, steam room, solarium.*
AMERICAN EXPRESS *Access, Diners, Visa.*

Milton Keynes — Places of Interest

Tourist Information Tel 0908 691995.
Chicheley Hall 023065 252.
The Stables Theatre Tel 0908 314466.
Stowe Landscape Gardens (NT) Nr. Buckingham Tel 0280 822850.
Bladerunner Ice Arena Childs Way Tel 0908 692660.

Minster Lovell — Old Swan 67% — £90

Tel 0993 774441 Fax 0993 702002 — H

Minster Lovell nr Witney Oxfordshire OX8 5RN — Map 14 C2

A half-timbered Cotswold inn close to the Windrush river retaining many of its original pub features. There are three lounges with polished flagstone floors and open log fires, and a beamed restaurant opening on to a picturesque rear garden. Sixteen superior bedrooms offer a comfortable and relaxing stay, while the smaller bedrooms of the adjacent conference centre are offered at a lower rate when not in use by resident delegates. No dogs. ***Rooms** 57. Garden, putting, tennis, fishing, punting.*
AMERICAN EXPRESS *Access, Diners, Visa.*

[bottle symbol] is our symbol for an outstanding wine list.

Monk Fryston — Monk Fryston Hall — 65% — £90

Tel 0977 682369 Fax 0977 683544 — **H**

Monk Fryston nr Leeds North Yorkshire LS25 5DU — **Map 7 D1**

The hall is an imposing greystone building, sturdy and quintessentially English, with formal gardens that include an ornamental lake. Dark oak panelling and fine oil paintings grace the public rooms, along with antique furnishings and carved fireplaces. An oak staircase leads up to bright, traditionally furnished bedrooms, all of which have tiled and carpeted bathrooms. ***Rooms** 28. Garden.* AMERICAN EXPRESS *Access, Visa.*

Monkton Combe — Combe Grove Manor — 71% — £168

Tel 0225 834644 Fax 0225 834961 — **H**

Brassknocker Hill Monkton Combe Bath Avon BA2 7HS — **Map 13 F1**

Perched high up above the Limpley Stoke valley and set within its own 68 acres of wooded grounds, the manor has extensive leisure facilities belonging to the associated country club. Elegant day rooms and the best of the bedrooms – individually decorated in some style with reproduction period-style furniture – are in the original Georgian house beneath which, in the old cellars reached via some external steps, is an informal bar and bistro decorated in ancient Roman style. The majority of more standardised bedrooms are some 50 yards away in the Garden Lodge, designed to take full advantage of the splendid view (just four rooms are rear-facing) with most having a private patio or balcony. Beds are turned down at night. 24hr room service. ***Rooms** 41. Garden, outdoor swimming pool, gymnasium, sauna, spa baths, steam room, solarium, beauty salon, tennis, golf (5-hole), putting, golf driving range.* AMERICAN EXPRESS *Access, Diners, Visa.*

Montacute — King's Arms Inn — £64

Tel 0935 822513 Fax 0935 826549 — **I**

Montacute Somerset TA15 6UU — **Map 13 F2**

A 16th-century hamstone inn, standing opposite the church in a picturesque and unspoilt village, that was once an ale-house owned by the abbey; today's comfortable little inn offers characterful accommodation in 11 en-suite rooms, one with a four-poster bed. The Windsor room is a relaxing lounge; the Pickwick Bar remains the centre of village life, with real ales and bar snacks. Follow a relaxing night with a decent buffet-style breakfast and a walk on the National Trust's wooded St Michael's Hill behind the hotel. No dogs. ***Rooms** 11. Garden. Closed 25 & 26 Dec.* AMERICAN EXPRESS *Access, Diners, Visa.*

Montacute — Place of Interest

Montacute House (NT) Tel 0935 823289.

Morden — Forte Travelodge — £42

Tel 081-640 8227 — **L**

Epsom Road Morden Surrey SM4 5PH — **Map 15 E2**

On A24 Epsom Road, 8 miles south of central London. ***Rooms** 32.* AMERICAN EXPRESS *Access, Visa.*

Moreton-in-Marsh — Annie's — £60

Tel 0608 651981 — **R**

3 Oxford Street Moreton-in-Marsh Gloucestershire GL56 0LA — **Map 14 C1**

In a side street running parallel to the main Oxford road. A romantic, cottagey setting of candle-light and soft music, framed by flagstone floors and exposed Cotswold stonework. David Ellis's self-styled English and French country cooking is without pretension: duck confit, smoked haddock or pigeon breast feuilleté; corn-fed poussin with lemony rosemary

See over

sauce and pistachio nuts; pan-fried lamb with pink peppercorns, leek sauce and mixed pepper garnish; daily fish dishes. Traditional toffee pudding, treacle tart and iced ratafia might feature among the desserts. Fixed-price Sunday lunch offers a small choice and always a roast. Annie herself fronts the house, supervising super-friendly service. Families welcome; high-chair provided. ***Seats** 28. Private Room 10. L (Sun only) 12-2 D 7-10 Set D (Mon-Fri) £19. Closed D Sun, last 2 weeks Jan. Set Sun L £16.* AMERICAN EXPRESS *Access, Diners, Visa.*

Moreton-in-Marsh — Manor House — 66% — £83

Tel 0608 50501 Fax 0608 51481 — **H**

High Street Moreton-in-Marsh Gloucestershire GL56 0LJ — **Map 14 C1**

Parts of this roadside, Cotswold-stone manor house date back to 1545, but others are nearly new. The hall and lounges both have a period feel, while the bar is more modern. Even in the bedrooms there's a choice between traditional and modern. Recent refurbishment covered the restaurant, bar and lounges. ***Rooms** 39. Garden, indoor swimming pool, sauna, spa bath, putting.* AMERICAN EXPRESS *Access, Diners, Visa.*

Moreton-in-Marsh — Marsh Goose — £60

Tel 0608 52111 — **R**

High Street Moreton-in-Marsh Gloucestershire GL56 0AX — **Map 14 C1**

Bare stonework contrasts happily with elegant Villeroy and Boch china in this welcoming Cotswolds restaurant. Chef Sonya Kidney offers a realistically-priced lunch menu that includes a choice of starters that can also be ordered as light meal dishes (warm fillets of red mullet with aubergine, tarragon and tomato or a tartlet with smoked haddock, mussels, parsley and spinach), but also extends to à la carte main courses (supreme of salmon with ginger, sultanas and spring onions). Sonya's style is in a modern mode, but never leaves classic concepts far behind; thus one is as likely to find curried parsnip soup or breast of guinea fowl with lentils and prunes wrapped in bacon on the dinner menu as roast best end of lamb served with basil and mixed mushrooms or grilled scallops with tomatoes and smoked goose breast. The fixed-price-only 3-course dinner menu changes daily, so a dish such as roast partridge with roast pear and red wine sauce can appear in season. There is always a good choice (seven or so dishes at each course) and a few dishes attract a supplement (fillet of sea bass with red pepper coulis and braised fennel). It all excites – right through to the desserts: iced strawberry and ginger terrine with fruit sauce and ginger shortbread biscuit, plum and almond tart with custard sauce are typical. Good Sunday lunch. Smoking in the bar area only. Short, but diverse wine list; a good choice of dessert wines is offered by the glass. ***Seats** 60. Parties 22. Private Room 14. L 12.15-2.30 D 7.30-9.45. Closed D Sun, all Mon. Set L £16 Set D £21. Access, Visa.*

Moretonhampstead — White Hart Inn — £63

Tel 0647 40406 Fax 0647 40565 — **I**

The Square Moretonhampstead Devon TQ13 8NF — **Map 13 D2**

Formerly a Georgian posting house, the White Hart offers traditional hospitality under the proud ownership of Peter Morgan, here since 1976. The oak-beamed bar, which gleams with polished wood, copper and brass, is a popular locals' meeting place, while the lounge is a cosy setting for residents' afternoon tea. Bulging walls add character to the bedrooms, which are comfortably furnished in old-fashioned style. New-fashioned additions in the bathrooms are power showers and telephone extensions. There are 15 golf courses within 30 miles, plus fishing on the Teign and marvellous walks in Dartmoor National Park. No children under ten. ***Rooms** 20. Garden.* AMERICAN EXPRESS *Access, Diners, Visa.*

Moretonhamptstead Place of Interest

Castle Drogo (NT) Chagford Tel 064743 3306.

Morley Breadsall Priory 69% £108

Tel 0332 832235 Fax 0332 833509 H

Moor Road Morley nr Derby Derbyshire DE7 6DL Map 6 C3

A large stone mansion house hotel (just off the A38 to the north of Derby), which is aimed squarely at the conference and leisure markets. A new hospitality suite for up to 120 has its own bar and changing rooms. A parquet-floored foyer with stone columns and archways has a period feel, but there is little period atmosphere elsewhere. Both the main building and modern extension bedrooms are uniform in design, and comfortable. No dogs. Country Club Hotels. ***Rooms** 91. Garden, indoor swimming pool, gymnasium, squash, sauna, spa bath, steam room, solarium, beauty salon, tennis, two golf courses (18), putting green, golf driving range, snooker, helipad.*
AMERICAN EXPRESS *Access, Diners, Visa.*

Morley Place of Interest

American Adventure Theme Park Nr Ilkeston Tel 0773 531521.

Morston Morston Hall 73% £120*

Tel & Fax 0263 741041 H

Morston Holt Norfolk NR25 7AA Map 10 C1

Dating back to the 17th century, Morston Hall is a substantial flint house with well-tended grounds to the front and side including a tranquil walled garden with ancient ice-house in one corner. It stands on the A149 close to Morston's tidal quay from where pleasure boats visit Blakeney Point, which is due north. Galton Blackiston, his wife Tracy and partner Justin Fraser have combined their experience and talents to create a hotel offering country hospitality at its best. The welcome is apparent as soon as you enter the rug-strewn flagstone-floored hall. Fresh flowers and smiles greet you and there is genuine warmth in the welcome. To one side of this entrance hall is a comfortable, relaxing and homely lounge with more flowers, most from the garden. Upstairs all the bedrooms are huge. More are planned, the only small bedroom becoming a connecting hallway to the new rooms. The present bedrooms, some with dual-aspect windows, are sunny and bright, overlooking the gardens and rolling farmland beyond. Each room is equipped with almost every conceivable amenity even a back-scratcher! Furnishings are traditional, even a little old-fashioned. Just as you have cuisine grand-mère this is decor grand-mère. Good bathrooms and in the morning excellent fruit among the breakfast offerings. The set-price dinner menu reads well (Galton was with John Tovey at *Miller Howe*) but results on the plate can disappoint. *Half-board terms only. ***Rooms** 4.*
AMERICAN EXPRESS *Access, Visa.*

Mottram St Andrew Mottram Hall 70% £140

Tel 0625 828135 Fax 0625 829284 H

Mottram St Andrew Prestbury Cheshire SK10 4QT Map 6 B2

De Vere Hotels' impressive Georgian mansion, adjacent to the A538, stands in 270 acres of mature parkland. Extensive leisure facilities include a championship golf course and clubhouse. The leisure club's Terrace Restaurant is open 10am-10pm. Spacious day rooms in the original Mottram Hall feature restored Adam ceilings and fine panelling. Most of the bedrooms are in newer extensions. ***Rooms** 133. Garden, indoor swimming pool, gymnasium, squash, sauna, spa bath, solarium, beauty salon, snooker, tennis, golf (18), games room.* AMERICAN EXPRESS *Access, Diners, Visa.*

Moulsford-on-Thames **Beetle & Wedge** 69% £95

Tel 0491 651381 Fax 0491 651376 **HR**

Moulsford-on-Thames Oxfordshire OX10 9JF **Map 15 D2**

Once the home of Jerome K Jerome (who wrote *Three Men in a Boat*), Richard and Kate Smith's picturesque Thameside Victorian hotel (known affectionately as 'The Beetle') is on the stretch of river immortalsied in *The Wind in the Willows.* Guests, who are treated very much as personal friends, can relax in comfortable surroundings – in front of a real fire in the cosy lounge, or wallowing in old-fashioned cast-iron bath tubs, perhaps with a glass of champagne. The bedrooms, most overlooking the river, have been tastefully designed with excellent fabrics and furniture and many personal touches from Kate – note the wall stencilling and indulgent bathroom extras; one of the rooms is a suite and a cot or extra bed can be provided at a small cost. The old beamed Boat House, with its own terrace, serves as the informal bar, and the Watergarden (complete with lily pond) is the perfect summer setting for afternoon tea or salad lunches on fine days. Terrific English breakfasts. ***Rooms*** *10. Garden, fishing.* AMERICAN EXPRESS *Access, Diners, Visa.*

Dining Room ↑ £80

An elegant and tranquil setting, perfectly matching the understated yet sophisticated cooking of Richard Smith. The freshest of produce is a prerequisite in typical dishes of home-made noodles with scallops, clams, mussels and squid, sautéed calf's sweetbreads with wild mushrooms, avocado salad with Cornish crab, steamed fillet of turbot with spinach and mussels, or roast best end of spring lamb with herb crust and braised endive. There's always an interesting choice of fish dishes and the style is cleverly modern without offending those who like straightforward food: grilled fillets of Dover sole with seared scallops, squid, garlic and ginger may sit happily alongside supreme of duck with apples and Calvados, and fillet of hare with foie gras and wild mushrooms. Desserts could include lemon soufflé pudding, chocolate rum truffle cake with home-made coffee and Tia Maria ice cream or bananas baked in rum with passion fruit ice cream. A selection of good cheeses is always offered. Three-course Sunday lunches always include a traditional roast and fine fish alternatives. Kate oversees the first-class service, and is responsible for a mainly French wine list which features several mature clarets and burgundies, as well as some interesting lesser-known wines. ***Seats*** *35. Private Room 65. L 12.30-2 D 7.30-10. Closed D Sun, all Mon, 25 Dec. Set Sun L £24.50*

Boathouse Brasserie £60

The beamed-roofed, riverside brasserie is more informal than the hotel restaurant, with lower prices on the long, long menu to match the setting. The same emphasis is put on quality ingredients and the open chargrill fire is put to good use in dishes like calf's liver and bacon, kidneys and black pudding with green herb mustard sauce, whole sea bream with fennel and pastis sauce, and wild sea trout with langoustines and béarnaise. Some dishes are priced as both starter and main: avocado with smoked chicken and prawn salad, crispy duck and salad frisée. Seafood and shellfish are always a strong point, alongside "interesting and unusual" cheeses and superior salady selections. Puddings are distinctly a high point: hot rhubarb crumble and cream, meringues and Guernsey cream with red fruits, lime cheesecake with crème fraiche and apricot sauce were among eleven or so on a spring menu. On fine summer days a few tables are set on the riverside terrace. Real ale is served, as is a Somerset cider brandy by the glass. Three high-chairs are provided for junior gourmets. ***Seats*** *50. Parties 20. L 12.30-2 D 7.30-10. Closed 25 Dec.*

See the Conference and Banqueting section for lists of hotels arranged by county.

Moulton **Black Bull** **£56**

Tel 0325 377289 **R**

Moulton nr Richmond North Yorkshire DL10 6QJ **Map 5 E3**

Just east of the A1, a mile south of Scotch Corner. Good fresh fish is the foundation of the Black Bull pub and restaurant's reputation, nurtured by the Pagendam family for nearly 30 years, that extends far beyond North Yorkshire. Grilled Dover sole, poached salmon with hollandaise sauce, and pan-fried scallops on spinach with a chive butter sauce typify the generally straightforward style. For meat-eaters there are fine Aberdeen Angus steaks and the likes of rack of lamb with Provençal herbs. A number of different eating areas include a seafood bar (no booking), a conservatory (complete with huge grapevine) and one of the original Pullman carriages, vintage 1932, from the *Brighton Belle*; no children under 7. Good-value fixed-price lunch (not Saturdays). No food on Sundays. Decent wines at favourable prices. ***Seats** 100. Parties 8. Private Room 36. L 12-2 D 7-10.15. Closed Sun (except bar), 24-26 Dec. Set L (Mon-Fri) £11.75.* AMERICAN EXPRESS *Access, Visa.*

Moulton **Places of Interest**

North Yorkshire County Showground East Cowton Tel 0609 773429.
Catterick Bridge Racecourse Tel 0748 811478.

Mousehole **Lobster Pot** **57%** **£76**

Tel 0736 731251 Fax 0736 731140 **H**

Mousehole nr Penzance Cornwall TR19 6QX **Map 12 A4**

Perched over the small, bustling harbour, the Lobster Pot scores on character if not on size. Four cottages on either side of a street just one car wide provide neat, snug accommodation. The lounge, cocktail bar, restaurant and several bedrooms enjoy views over the bustling harbour. Family facilities include rooms with an adjoining bunk bedroom, high tea and baby listening. Mousehole lies three miles west of Penzance. ***Rooms** 25. Closed 2-31 Jan & Mon-Wed in Feb. Access, Visa.*

Much Birch **Pilgrim Hotel** **64%** **£60**

Tel 0981 540742 Fax 0981 540620 **H**

Much Birch nr Hereford Hereford & Worcester HR2 8HJ **Map 14 A1**

Set back from the A49, this much-extended former rectory stands in four acres of grounds with views over Golden Valley and the Black Mountains. Stone walls, oak furniture and a long stove give character to the bar, and the bedrooms have good-quality furnishings, armchairs and useful desk space. Children under 10 accommodated free in parents' room. ***Rooms** 20. Garden, 3-hole pitch & putt.* AMERICAN EXPRESS *Access, Diners, Visa.*

Mudeford **Avonmouth Hotel** **59%** **£99**

Tel 0202 483434 Fax 0202 479004 **H**

95 Mudeford Christchurch Dorset BH23 3NT **Map 14 C4**

Forte Heritage hotel with a private jetty, slipway and moorings at the end of lawns leading down to Christchurch Harbour. Best bedrooms (with a small supplement) have balconies and/or sea views. ***Rooms** 41. Garden, outdoor swimming pool, games room.* AMERICAN EXPRESS *Access, Diners, Visa.*

Mullion **Polurrian Hotel** **66%** **£164***

Tel 0326 240421 Fax 0326 240083 **H**

Mullion Helston Cornwall TR12 7EN **Map 12 B4**

Large, white clifftop hotel from which a path winds down past tennis court and cricket practice net – there's a keenly contested game between staff and guests each week in high season – to a sheltered sandy cove 300

See over

feet below. It's the epitome of a traditional English holiday hotel with friendly staff and children well catered for with their own high tea, special events arranged during school holidays and plenty to do in the area. Flambards theme park is nearby and the Cornish Seal Sanctuary just a short trip away at Gweek. Comfortable lounges take full advantage of the view and excellent breakfasts include locally caught mackerel with horseradish butter and honey from breakfast chef David's own hives. Bedrooms are comfortable rather than luxurious with well-kept bathrooms. Children under 14 stay free in parents' room with meals 'as taken' charged for those over 6 years. *Half-board terms only. ***Rooms** 40. Garden, indoor & outdoor swimming pools, keep-fit equipment, squash, badminton, sauna, spa bath, solarium, tennis, badminton, putting, sea fishing, boating, snooker, coffee shop (7.30am-8.30pm). Closed Nov-Mar..* AMERICAN EXPRESS *Access, Diners, Visa.*

Nantwich — Rookery Hall — 79% — £115

Tel 0270 610016 Fax 0270 626027 — **HR**

Worleston nr Nantwich Cheshire CW5 6DQ — **Map 6 B3**

The hotel gained its schloss-style outline in mid-Victorian times, having been built fifty years earlier as a country house. Surrounded by extensive grounds, with some lovely walks by the river, the old Hall retains the spacious reception rooms with character highlighted by moulded ceilings, fine antiques and panelling. Stylish additions of recent years are the Coach House, a self-contained conference centre (for up to 80 delegates) converted from Georgian stables with bedrooms built around the courtyard, and the west wing. All bedrooms are luxuriously furnished and some offer fresh flowers; fruit and sherry greet guests on arrival and well-designed bathrooms have excellent overhead showers and good toiletries. Not particularly easy to find – it's on the B5074. ***Rooms** 45. Garden, tennis, putting, coarse fishing, helipad.* AMERICAN EXPRESS *Access, Diners, Visa.*

Restaurant — £85

Several equally elegant dining rooms here – one has old oak panelling, another fine polished mahogany and a third (which is also the breakfast room) is in pretty country house style – in which to enjoy David Alton's intelligently constructed menus. Dishes like roast halibut with lentils, smoked bacon and herb spaghetti; fillet of beef topped with spinach mousseline and garnished with roasted shallots, chestnuts and new potatoes and Gressingham duck on a potato galette with fresh fig and sherry vinegar sauce demonstrate inventiveness without gimmickry. A particularly talented patissier, Dominique Schickele, produces desserts that are as pleasing to the eye as they are to the palate. Local and British cheeses are always well represented on a varied cheeseboard. ***Seats** 60. Parties 8. Private Room 65. L 12-1.45 D 7-9.30 (Sat to 10). Set L £16.50 Set D £25.*

Nantwich — Places of Interest

Crewe Tourist Information Centre Tel 0270 583191
Lyceum Theatre Heath Street, Crewe Tel 0270 211149.

Neasham — Newbus Arms — 62% — £80

Tel 0325 721071 Fax 0325 721770 — **H**

Neasham Road Neasham Darlington Co Durham DL2 1PE — **Map 5 E3**

Chef/patron John Evans is taking the bull by the horns and placing a stronger emphasis on food in this informal and very friendly creeper-clad establishment dating from the 1780s. Day rooms include a panelled lounge and an attractive bar. Bedrooms are modest with no frills, but are well kept and comfortable; decor is light and unfussy with solid traditional furniture and mainly floral fabrics. Bathrooms are equally simple. Children up to 14 stay free in parents' room and are well catered for; bistro and restaurant dining areas. Greatly reduced 'Hopex' rates if payment made three weeks before arrival. ***Rooms** 15. Garden, squash.* AMERICAN EXPRESS *Access, Diners, Visa.*

Needham Market **Pipps Ford** 60% £59

Tel 044 979 208 Fax 044 979 561 **H**

Needham Market nr Ipswich Suffolk IP6 8LJ **Map 10 C3**

Mrs Hackett-Jones welcomes guests personally to her 16th-century farmhouse in a delightful garden just off the A45/A140 roundabout. Winter log fires burn in huge inglenooks, and a fine breakfast featuring home-produced honey, eggs and bread is served in the plant-filled conservatory. Bedrooms are split between the house and adjacent Stables Cottage, where two small singles share a shower room. No phones or TV in the bedrooms. No children under 5. No dogs. No smoking. Note that credit cards are no longer accepted. ***Rooms*** *6. Garden, outdoor swimming pool, tennis, coarse fishing. Closed mid Dec-mid Jan.*

New Alresford **Hunters** £52

Tel 0962 732468 **RR**

32 Broad Street New Alresford Hampshire SO24 9AQ **Map 15 D3**

Wine bar/brasserie with two distinctive bow-fronted windows, awnings and candle-light within, run by the Birmingham family. A dozen or so light dishes at lunchtime range from pan-fried quail breast with watercress salad to bacon-wrapped fillet of pork with pesto and basil cream sauce. Dinner dishes are more involved: black pudding and chicken livers with creamed potatoes and Madeira sauce, cassoulet, grilled halibut with leeks, tomatoes and chives. Local watercress makes regular appearances, as above or in a dish of grilled fillet of salmon on a bed of watercress with pesto cream sauce. Hot apple tart with caramel citrus sauce, and hot chocolate soufflé with warm orange cream sauce complete the picture. Friendly, laid-back service and good-value wines. Children are made welcome with high-chairs and smaller portions; convenient for the nearby Watercress Line preserved steam railway. ***Seats*** *30. Parties 15. Private Room 80. L 12-2 D 7-10. Closed D Sun, 24-27 Dec. Set L £7.95/£9.95 Set D £9.95/£11.75.* AMERICAN EXPRESS *Access, Diners, Visa..*

Rooms £48

Three rooms in an old Georgian building, all with shower and WC en suite. Children under 5 free in room with parents; extra bed £10.

New Barnet **Mims Restaurant** £58

Tel 081-449 2974 **R**

63 East Barnet Road New Barnet Hertfordshire EN4 8RN **Map 15 F2**

Given an unpromising location, next to a petrol station in a rather dowdy street, and modest interior decoration, chef Ismail Al-Sersy's refined, skilful cooking comes as a most agreeable surprise and has attracted a loyal following – some regulars travelling from quite far afield to dine here. The minimum price is fixed (for two courses) at both lunch and dinner, the former being half the price of the latter. Menus lack nothing in interest, with the likes of spinach and ricotta in open ravioli, sauté of calf's brains with grilled herbed bread, roast hake with saffron risotto and Barbary duck casserole. No children under 6 in the evening. ***Seats*** *45. Parties 8. Private Room 50. L 12-3 D 6.30-11 (Sun 12-10.30). Closed L Sat, all Mon, 25-30 Dec. Set L from £8.50 Set D from £17. Access, Visa.*

New Milton **Chewton Glen** 89% £206

Tel 0425 275341 Fax 0425 272310 **HR**

Christchurch Road New Milton Hampshire BH25 6QS **Map 14 C4**

Half way between Bournemouth and Lymington, Martin and Brigitte Skan's magnificent hotel justly enjoys a worldwide reputation not only for what it offers today, but for consistently maintaining the highest standards since 1966. Great hotels rely on the quality of their staff and here they are unquestionably professional, courteous and efficient, superbly directed

See over

by the Skans and managing director Robin Hutson. Set in 70 acres of grounds, including a superlative croquet lawn, the hotel has evolved over the years into one of the country's finest, pioneering styles and setting standards that others have followed; the most recent example is the stunningly-designed leisure and health club whose centrepiece swimming pool of magnificent proportions epitomises the quality to be found throughout. It is hard to imagine that the leisure facilities here can be bettered anywhere else in the UK; hotel guests share the facilities with non-resident club members. The newest garden bedrooms with balconies and terraces are equally luxurious, complementing those that guests have relaxed in for many years, with high-quality fabrics, beautiful colour schemes, period furniture and bathrooms, complete with fresh flowers, that positively pamper; it goes without saying that fruit, sherry, mineral water and home-made biscuits are provided. Such elegance is also apparent in the public areas where the tastefully decorated rooms with their exquisite antiques, fine paintings and memorabilia still provide the atmosphere of a large, modern private house. No children under seven; child-sitting by arrangement; families can eat informally in the balcony lounge of the health club or formally (at a price – hamburger, chips and peas £16!) in the restaurant between 6 and 7. Breakfast, as befits an establishment of this calibre, is fit for a king, ranging from freshly-baked pastries to stewed prunes, kedgeree and kippers. No dogs. Minimum two nights' weekend stay at certain times of year. ***Rooms** 58. Garden, indoor & outdoor swimming pools, solarium, sauna, steam room, spa bath, gymnasium, 9-hole golf course, indoor & outdoor tennis, putting, snooker, valeting, boutique, helipad.* AMERICAN EXPRESS *Access, Diners, Visa.*

Marryat Room Restaurant ★ £100

Chef Pierre Chevillard handles first-rate ingredients with admirable assurance and produces sauces with subtle flavours and perfect textures. Both lunch and dinner see fixed-price and à la carte menus offered, but lighter dishes feature at the former; all menus are refreshingly written in unpretentious English. A three-course table d'hote in spring might offer cream of Cornish crab soup or a salad of king prawns with grilled vegetables, followed by grilled fillet of duck with a marinated grilled pear and red wine sauce or panaché of John Dory, red mullet, sole and turbot accompanied by a bouillon thickened with garlic mayonnaise; home-made sorbets, ice creams, vanilla and pistachio-flavoured crème brulée with almond tuiles or hot raspberry soufflé to finish. The carte shows off Chevillard's prowess at combining complementary flavours: scallops with coconut milk, pheasant and pistachio terrine with onion jam and plum chutney, Stilton and hazelnut soufflé, roast lobster with thyme butter sauce. Dishes can be as simple as grilled Dover sole or as varied as fillet of roe deer with black pepper and brandy sauce, pear, chestnuts and spätzle. The variety is exciting and results on the plate invariably well executed. Vegetarian options are equally good: consommé of cep and shiitake mushrooms, pan-fried potato galette topped with Munster cheese and cumin. Interesting cheeses, both English and French. Desserts are tempting to the point of indulgence: apple and quince tart with Calvados ice cream, caramelised lemon tart with poached honeyed pear, hot caramel soufflé with armagnac and prune ice cream... Lovely petits fours served with coffee show that attention is really paid to detail. Summer eating here is delightful, both on an outdoor terrace area where nine tables are laid out overlooking the gardens (and swimming pool) and in the delightful conservatory dining room. The stupendous wine list presented by Gérard Basset, *chef sommelier*, is generally expensive, but does offer some choice wines at fair prices. ***Seats** 120. Parties 80. Private Room 120. L 12.30-2 (Sun to 2.30) D 7.30-9.30. Set L £23.50 Set D £41.*

Newark — Forte Travelodge £42

Tel 0636 703635 **L**

North Muskham Newark Nottinghamshire NG23 6HT **Map 7 D3**

Situated on the A1 southbound. ***Rooms** 30.* AMERICAN EXPRESS *Access, Visa.*

Newark — Gannets Café-Bistrot — £40

Tel 0636 702066 — **R**

35 Castlegate Newark Nottinghamshire NG24 1AZ — **Map 7 D3**

On the main road through Newark, Gannets comprises a ground-floor café serving an all-day menu of light dishes, and a bistro upstairs where mirrors and pictures share the wall space with blackboards announcing specials. There are candles on the tables and subdued background music. Typical bistro dishes run from vegetable croustade and not-so-spare ribs to seafood pancakes, liver and bacon with a gin and lime sauce and spinach, hazelnut and aubergine bake. To finish, perhaps cherry and almond tart, jam roly poly or home-made ice cream. No smoking. ***Seats** 40. L 12-2 D 6.30-9.30. Closed all Sun, Mon & Tue, 25 & 26 Dec. Set L £7.95. Access, Visa.*

Newark — Grange Hotel — 58% — £53

Tel 0636 703399 Fax 0636 702328 — **H**

73 London Road Newark Nottinghamshire NG24 1RZ — **Map 7 D3**

An unassuming, family-run Victorian hotel on the edge of town. Accommodation runs from singles to family rooms and a four-poster room. No dogs. ***Rooms** 15. Garden. Closed Christmas/New Year. Access, Visa.*

Newbury — Chequers Hotel — 66% — £113

Tel 0635 38000 Fax 0635 37170 — **H**

Oxford Street Newbury Berkshire RG13 1JB — **Map 15 D2**

A handsome Georgian facade conceals an even older town-centre coaching inn. Today's travellers can be sure of up-to-date standards of comfort and modern amenities. Forte Heritage. ***Rooms** 56. Garden.* AMERICAN EXPRESS *Access, Diners, Visa.*

Newbury — Foley Lodge — 71% — £125

Tel 0635 528770 Fax 0635 528398 — **H**

Stockcross Newbury Berkshire RG16 8JU — **Map 15 D2**

Just over a mile from Newbury, off the A4 to Hungerford (take M4 J13), this former Victorian hunting lodge is approached via a winding, tree-lined drive. The entrance is through a glass conservatory with black-and-white tiled floor and wicker chairs, overlooking the landscaped gardens. A "modern Victorian" ambience is cleverly created in both the public rooms and bedrooms by using fringed floral drapes and smart reproduction antiques. There is a high standard of accommodation throughout, with rooms in a new block being equally comfortable. A bright and airy octagonal pagoda is an unusual setting for the bubbling, circular swimming pool. Meeting rooms for up to 250 persons. Children up to the age of 14 free in parents' room; cots, baby-sitting and baby-listening available. ***Rooms** 69. Garden, indoor swimming pool, coffee shop (7am-11pm).* AMERICAN EXPRESS *Access, Diners, Visa.*

Newbury — Hilton National — 69% — £85

Tel 0635 529000 Fax 0635 529337 — **H**

Pinchington Lane Newbury Berkshire RG14 7HL — **Map 15 D2**

Modern low-rise hotel one mile south of Newbury with a variety of conference rooms (catering for up to 200) and a leisure complex. Best of the bedrooms are the Plaza rooms, with bigger beds and more accessories than the others; non-smoking rooms available. Children up to 12 stay free in parents' room. ***Rooms** 104. Indoor swimming pool, keep-fit facilities, sauna, steam room.* AMERICAN EXPRESS *Access, Diners, Visa.*

See over

Newbury — Millwaters — 67% — £75

Tel 0635 528838 Fax 0635 523406 — **H**

London Road Newbury Berkshire RG13 2BY — **Map 15 D2**

The rivers Kennet and Lambourn meet in the 8 acres of grounds of this charming hotel on the A4. The Georgian house has rustic extensions containing public rooms and bedrooms that offer homely touches like scatter cushions, fresh fruit and plants. Some bathrooms feature corner or whirlpool baths and one tub is big enough for a whole family. ***Rooms** 32. Garden, fishing.* AMERICAN EXPRESS® *Access, Diners, Visa.*

Newbury — Regency Park Hotel — 70% — £103

Tel 0635 871555 Fax 0635 871571 — **H**

Bowling Green Road Thatcham Newbury Berkshire RG13 3RP — **Map 15 D2**

Five minutes from Newbury (signposted off the A4 Reading road), and standing in 5 acres of grounds, the original Edwardian house is now rather lost within more modern extensions. Spacious bedrooms offer guests comfortable, carefully planned accommodation in rooms that are light and well appointed. Picture windows in the sun lounge overlook the patio and an ornamental fountain. A separate purpose-built conference centre has rooms for up to 65 people. Keen, helpful management and a variety of special weekend themes and special rates throughout the year. ***Rooms** 50. Garden.* AMERICAN EXPRESS® *Access, Diners, Visa.*

Newbury — Stakis Newbury Hotel — 67% — £108

Tel 0635 247010 Fax 0635 247077 — **H**

Oxford Road Newbury Berkshire RG16 8XY — **Map 15 D2**

Just off Junction 13 of the M4, the Stakis Newbury is well designed for business people. Bedrooms feature good desk/work space, and there are four conference/seminar rooms with up-to-date equipment. ***Rooms** 112. Indoor swimming pool, gymnasium, sauna, spa bath, steam room, solarium.* AMERICAN EXPRESS® *Access, Diners, Visa.*

Newbury — Places of Interest

Tourist Information The Wharf Tel 0635 30267.
Watermill Theatre Bagnor Tel 0635 45834.
Westridge Open Centre Tel 0635 253322.
Highclere Castle Tel 0635 253210 *Home of the Earl and Countess of Carnarvon.*
Sandham Memorial Chapel (NT) Burghclere, Nr Newbury Tel 0635 27 394/292.
Newbury Racecourse Tel 0635 40015.
Chieveley Showground Tel 0635 247111.

Newby Bridge — The Swan — 61% — £86

Tel 053 95 31681 Fax 053 95 31917 — **H**

Newby Bridge nr Ulverston Cumbria LA12 8NB — **Map 4 C4**

Attractively situated opposite the five-arched stone bridge over the River Leven by Windermere's southern shore, the Swan is a comfortable family hotel and fisherman's haunt. In addition to one suite and four de luxe bedrooms with balconies, there are some spacious family rooms and bright, neatly-kept bathrooms throughout. Facilities for conferences of up to 65 delegates. No dogs. ***Rooms** 36. Garden, coarse fishing, mooring, helipad. Closed 2-12 Jan.* AMERICAN EXPRESS® *Access, Diners, Visa.*

> If we recommend meals in a hotel or inn a separate entry is made for its restaurant.

Newby Wiske — Solberge Hall 69% — £60

Tel 0609 779191 Fax 0609 780472 — H

Newby Wiske nr Northallerton North Yorkshire DL7 9ER — **Map 5 E4**

Leisure and business visitors are both well looked after at the Hall, a country mansion dating from 1824 and set in 16 acres of gardens and woodland. The views are impressive and inside there's a delightful wood-panelled foyer with a blue-and-white-tiled fireplace, a homely lounge and a comfortable bar. Bedrooms are good-sized, some having four-posters, with plenty of thoughtful extras. Children under 14 stay free in parents' room. ***Rooms** 25. Garden, clay-pigeon shooting.* AMERICAN EXPRESS *Access, Diners, Visa.*

Newby Wiske — Place of Interest

Thirsk Racecourse Tel 0845 522276.

Newcastle-under-Lyme — Clayton Lodge 60% — £84

Tel 0782 613093 Fax 0782 711893 — H

Clayton Road Newcastle-under-Lyme Staffordshire ST5 4AF — **Map 6 B3**

Jarvis-owned conference and meeting hotel with views over the Lyme Valley. The largest of the several conference rooms can accommodate 270. Well-equipped bedrooms, where children up to 16 stay free with parents. On the A519, a mile from the M6 (J15). ***Rooms 50.*** AMERICAN EXPRESS *Access, Diners, Visa.*

Newcastle-under-Lyme — Forte Posthouse 60% — £68

Tel 0782 717171 Fax 0782 717138 — H

Clayton Road Newcastle-under-Lyme Staffordshire ST5 4DL — **Map 6 B3**

100 yards from junction 15 of the M6, this Posthouse provides decent modern accommodation, keep-fit amenities and conference facilities for up to 70. ***Rooms** 119. Indoor swimming pool, keep-fit equipment, sauna, coffee shop (10am-6pm).* AMERICAN EXPRESS *Access, Diners, Visa.*

Newcastle-under-Lyme — Places of Interest

Tourist Information Tel 0782 711964.
New Victoria Theatre Tel 0782 717954.

Newcastle-upon-Tyne — Copthorne Hotel 73% NEW — £116

Tel 091 222 0333 Fax 091 230 1111 — H

The Close Quayside Newcastle-upon-Tyne Tyne and Wear NE1 3RT — **Map 5 E2**

To the west of the Tyne Bridge and built straight alongside the Tyne the hotel makes the most of its riverside location. All the bedrooms are at the front, some with balconies. Stylishly modern in design with an impressive marble-floored five-floor atrium at its heart, space and high standards of comfort are its hallmarks. Here, in what is also a lounge, there are tan leather seats and burr-walnut tables while in Claspers bar, named after the rower, the ambience is a little more clubby. Classic bedrooms are well-equipped but Connoisseur bedrooms have the edge on comfort with king-size beds, bathrobes and more in the way of little extras. All rooms are fully air-conditioned and have satellite TVs though the movies are not free. Excellent power showers in the bathrooms. Free overnight parking in the multi-storey car park which occupies the rear of the hotel. ***Rooms** 156. Gymnasium, sauna, spa bath, steam room, solarium, news kiosk, shop.* AMERICAN EXPRESS *Access, Diners, Visa.*

Newcastle-upon-Tyne — County Thistle — 68% — £104

Tel 091-232 2471 Fax 091-232 1285 — H

Neville Street Newcastle-upon-Tyne Tyne & Wear NE99 1AH — Map 5 E2

A handsome Victorian building opposite Central station. Popular for conferences (up to 200). Choice of restaurants and bars. Decent bedrooms, studios being the best equipped. ***Rooms** 115. American Express Access, Diners, Visa.*

Newcastle-upon-Tyne — Fisherman's Lodge — £82

Tel 091-281 3281 Fax 091-281 6410 — R

7 Jesmond Dene Jesmond Newcastle-upon-Tyne Tyne & Wear NE7 7BQ — Map 5 E2

In a deep wooded valley two miles from Newcastle city centre, Fisherman's Lodge has been among the best known of north-eastern restaurants for many years (it opened in 1979). Variety is allied to fine cooking throughout the various menus, which include one for vegetarians. 'Chef's classics' put the emphasis on seafood with dishes such as lemon sole meunière, turbot with fennel and mushrooms or roasted monkfish topped with mussels served with a mustard and tarragon sauce. There are meat options, too, typified by duck liver paté among the starters and a main-course medley of Northumbrian lamb (en croute, ragout and fillet). Specialities, which change daily, increase the choice, and desserts include home-made ice creams. No children under 10. No smoking in the dining room (it's permitted with coffee in the lounge). ***Seats** 65. Parties 14. Private Room 40. L 12-2 D 7-11. Closed L Sat, all Sun, Bank Holidays. Set L £16. American Express Access, Diners, Visa.*

Newcastle-upon-Tyne — Forte Crest — 61% — £93

Tel 091-232 6191 Fax 091-261 8529 — H

New Bridge Street Newcastle-upon-Tyne Tyne & Wear NE1 8BS — Map 5 E2

City-centre hotel with a business centre and many meeting/conference rooms (for up to 400). Free overnight (only) parking in the adjacent council car park. ***Rooms** 166. American Express Access, Diners, Visa.*

Newcastle-upon-Tyne — Holiday Inn — 70% — £120

Tel 091-236 5432 Fax 091-236 8091 — H

Great North Road Seaton Burn Newcastle-upon-Tyne Tyne & Wear NE13 6BP — Map 5 E2

One of the earliest Holiday Inns, off a roundabout on the A1 north of the city, six miles from the Metrocentre (five from the airport). The lobby, with its polished stone floor, is imposing and other day rooms include a bar that overlooks the indoor pool. Bedrooms offer modern extras, compact bathrooms with superb showers and a good supply of thick towels. Conference facilities for up to 400; ample parking. Children up to 19 share their parents' room free of charge. ***Rooms** 150. Garden, indoor swimming pool, sauna, solarium, spa bath, keep-fit equipment, kiosk. American Express Access, Diners, Visa.*

Newcastle-upon-Tyne — King Neptune — £45

Tel 091-261 6657 — R

34 Stowell Street Newcastle-upon-Tyne Tyne & Wear NE1 4XB — Map 5 E2

The Mak brothers are first-generation Geordie Chinese and take great pride in their Peking and Szechuan cooking. Seafood is a particularly strong point, from queen scallops and North Sea lobster to abalone and squid. The King Neptune banquets, rising in complexity from "Jade" through "Pearl" to "Diamond", encompass sizzling steak in black pepper Peking sauce, baked lobster with Szechuan sea-spiced chili and deep-fried duck slices with champagne hot and sour sauce. Ask about the fire pot fondue – when we last heard it was in abeyance due to the fire risks! Booking is usually essential, even on Sundays. The restaurant is in the heart of Newcastle's Chinatown. ***Seats** 110. Private Room 55. L 12-1.30 (Sun 12.15-1.45) D 6.30-10.30 (Sat 6-11.15, Sun 6.30-10.15). Closed 25 & 26 Dec, 1 Jan. Set L from £6.50.* AMERICAN EXPRESS *Access, Diners, Visa.*

Newcastle-upon-Tyne — Moat House 59% — £68

Tel 091-262 8989 Fax 091-263 4172 — **H**

Coast Road Wallsend Newcastle-upon-Tyne Tyne & Wear NE28 1HP — **Map 5 E2**

Modern low-riser set in its own grounds on the Silverlink Business Park, by the A19 just north of the Tyne Tunnel. Plenty of free car parking, numerous large conference rooms and a health complex. Good tariff reductions at weekends; children under 14 stay free in parents' room. ***Rooms** 147. Keep-fit equipment, spa bath, sauna, plunge pool, steam room, solarium, games room.* AMERICAN EXPRESS *Access, Diners, Visa.*

Newcastle-upon-Tyne — Novotel 63% — £81

Tel 091-214 0303 Fax 091-214 0633 — **H**

Ponteland Road Kenton Newcastle-upon-Tyne Tyne & Wear NE3 3HZ — **Map 5 E2**

Very modern Novotel just off the A1 on the western by-pass. Children up to 15 stay free in parents' room. Ample free car parking. ***Rooms** 126. Indoor swimming pool, sauna, restaurant (6am-midnight).* AMERICAN EXPRESS *Access, Diners, Visa.*

Newcastle-upon-Tyne — Swallow Gosforth Park 73% — £120

Tel 091-236 4111 Fax 091-236 8192 — **H**

High Gosforth Park Newcastle-upon-Tyne Tyne & Wear NE3 5HN — **Map 5 E2**

A splendid modern hotel in 12 acres of wooded parkland next to Newcastle racecourse and just off the A1. Neat, well-tended grounds form a good first impression. Stylish day rooms include an elegant foyer/lounge and several bars, and there are good conference (up to 600 delegates) and leisure facilities. The Conservatory brasserie is open 7am to 11pm. Accommodation includes luxury suites, studios and spacious Executive rooms. The standard bedrooms are not large, but nevertheless attractive with modern lightwood furniture and an armchair, their bathrooms tidy and well equipped. ***Rooms** 178. Garden, indoor swimming pool, gymnasium, squash, sauna, spa bath, solarium, hairdressing, tennis, helipad, courtesy car.* AMERICAN EXPRESS *Access, Diners, Visa.*

Newcastle-upon-Tyne — Swallow Hotel 63% — £88

Tel 091-232 5025 Fax 091-232 8428 — **H**

2 Newgate Arcade Newcastle-upon-Tyne Tyne & Wear NE1 5SX — **Map 5 E2**

City-centre hotel with large car park and panoramic bar. Children up to 14 stay free in parents' room. Guests have free membership of an adjacent fitness centre. Ample parking. ***Rooms** 94.* AMERICAN EXPRESS *Access, Diners, Visa.*

Newcastle-upon-Tyne — 21 Queen Street ★↑ — £95

Tel 091-222 0755 Fax 091-230 5875 — **R**

21 Queen St Princes Wharf Quayside Newcastle-upon-Tyne Tyne & Wear NE1 3UG — **Map 5 E2**

Now well-established but in an area that is undergoing rapid and much needed redevelopment, 21 Queen Street stands as a beacon signalling that even in such a depressed area as the North East there is hope for those willing to put the achievement of quality uppermost. Located not far from the waterside, and approached from the city centre down a steep twisting street, the sombre, hard stone Victorian exterior belies the interior which

See over

has a decor of modern, delicate pastel tones. There's a comfortable bar in which to contemplate the menu over an aperitif, the front of house being very well orchestrated by the youthful and exuberant Nicholas Shottel. Terry Laybourne the chef/proprietor with his excellent sous-chef Tom Sleigh produces dishes that reflect a classical background but which have been brought bang up to date with innovative touches. Influences from the Mediterranean and Far East create magical sensations on the palate. All is very carefully thought-out, combinations marrying perfectly. Saucing is faultless and presentation quite simply exquisite. A shellfish bisque with a subtle, creamy delicacy is served with tiny, hot, very crisp prawn rolls. A terrine of ham knuckle and foie gras is chunks of meaty ham combined with contrastingly smooth, soft pieces of foie gras and accompanied by a delicious quenelle of pease pudding. Embellishments and garnishes aren't always required as typified by sea-fresh halibut, simply grilled and served with lemon – the superb quality of the fish obviating the need for anything additional. More complex dishes are most certainly present as in medallions of Kielder venison with sour cherries, grapes and walnuts, a sauce Grand Veneur and pasta or the classic tournedos Rossini and roast pigeon with young broad beans and polenta with a heart and liver sauce. To finish, perhaps bitter chocolate tart with white chocolate mousse, hot raspberry gratin with kirsch sabayon or a stunning tarte tatin of mango served with a passion fruit syrup and mango sorbet. (Dessert of the Year North of England regional winner.) Lunchtime also sees a three course fixed-price menu that is every bit as exciting as the à la carte even if a fraction simpler.
Seats *50. L 12-2 D 7-10.45. Closed L Sat, all Sun, Bank Holidays. Set L £16.* AMERICAN EXPRESS *Access, Diners, Visa.*

Newcastle-upon-Tyne Places of Interest

Tourist Information Tel 091-261 0691.
Gulbenkian Studio Theatre Tel 091-232 9974.
Theatre Royal Tel 091-232 2061.
Tyne Theatre Tel 091-232 1551.
Seaton Delaval Hall and Gardens Whitley Bay Tel 091-237 3040/1493.
Newcastle Cathedral Tel 091-232 1939.
Newcastle United Football Ground St. James' Park Tel 091-232 8361.
Newcastle Racecourse Tel 091-236 2020.
Whitley Bay Ice Rink Tel 091-252 6240.
Cullercoats Beach *7 Miles.*
Museums and Art Galleries
Trinity Maritime Centre Tel 091-261 4691.
Laing Art Gallery Tel 091-232 7734.
Hancock Museum Tel 091-222 7418.
Hunday National Tractor and Farm Museum Newton Tel 0661 842553.
Cherryburn, Berwick Museum Mickley, Nr Stocksfield Tel 0661 843276 *Thomas Berwick Birthplace Trust.*

Newcastle-upon-Tyne Airport Moat House 62% £79

Tel 0661 24911 Fax 0661 860157 **H**

Woolsington Newcastle-upon-Tyne Tyne & Wear NE13 8DJ **Map 5 E2**

Low-riser just north of the Tyne Tunnel. Conference/banqueting facilities for 400/350. Children up to the age of 12 are accommodated free in parents' room. 22 rooms are reserved for non-smokers. ***Rooms 100.*** AMERICAN EXPRESS *Access, Diners, Visa.*

Newlyn Higher Faugan Country House Hotel 62% £84

Tel 0736 62076 Fax 0736 51648 **H**

Newlyn nr Penzance Cornwall TR18 5NS **Map 12 A4**

Built by Stanhope Forbes at the turn of the century, this sturdy greystone house stands at the end of a winding drive in 10 acres of lawns and woodland. Day rooms are peaceful and traditional, and the best bedrooms feature Victorian or Edwardian furnishings. Children under 12 sharing parents' room stay free. Possible winter closing – ring to confirm. ***Rooms** 12. Garden, outdoor swimming pool, tennis, putting, solarium, snooker.*

AMERICAN EXPRESS *Access, Diners, Visa.*

Newmarket Moat House 62% £78

Tel 0638 667171 Fax 0638 666533 **H**

Moulton Road Newmarket Suffolk CB8 8DY **Map 10 B3**

Modern Moat House behind the town clock tower, with well-appointed bedrooms and versatile function rooms (up to 150 for conferences). Children up to 14 stay free in parents' room. ***Rooms** 47. Kiosk.*

AMERICAN EXPRESS *Access, Diners, Visa.*

Newmarket White Hart 60% £49

Tel 0638 663051 Fax 0638 667284 **H**

High Street Newmarket Suffolk CB8 8JP **Map 10 B3**

A redbrick hotel in the High Street opposite the Jockey Club. The lounge bar with its cane furniture, mirrors, plants and muted lights, complements the robust public bar, which has stained-glass panels, deep sofas, a panelled serving area and racing pictures. Comfortable bedrooms have either an art deco or a country look. Conferences for up to 120 delegates. ***Rooms** 23.*

AMERICAN EXPRESS *Access, Visa.*

Newmarket Places of Interest

The National Horseracing Museum Tel 0638 667333.
Newmarket Racecourse Tel 0638 663482.

Newquay Hotel Bristol 64% £90

Tel 0637 875181 Fax 0637 879347 **H**

Narrowcliff Newquay Cornwall TR7 2PQ **Map 12 B3**

The Young family, at the helm since the hotel opened 60 years ago, put courtesy and comfort high on their list of priorities. The redbrick Bristol enjoys a fine situation overlooking the sea and the beach (some distance below the cliff), and there are splendid views from many of the bedrooms; these come in various styles, some traditional, others more modern. There are also some self-catering houses. Day rooms provide ample space to relax over a drink, a chat or one of the board games available from reception. Conferences (for up to 180 delegates) and banquets (up to 265) are catered for. Car parking and lock-up garages available behind the hotel. ***Rooms** 76. Indoor swimming pool, sauna, solarium, beauty & hair salon, games room.*

AMERICAN EXPRESS *Access, Diners, Visa.*

Newquay Hotel Riviera 63% £78

Tel 0637 874251 Fax 0637 850823 **H**

Lusty Glaze Road Newquay Cornwall TR7 3AA **Map 12 B3**

Popular for family holidays, functions and conferences (for around 150), this well-appointed modern hotel overlooks a lovely stretch of coastline. Three bars, a lounge and a garden provide plenty of space to relax, and in summer there's evening entertainment. Most of the bedrooms enjoy sea views. ***Rooms** 50. Outdoor swimming pool, squash, sauna, games room, snooker, racquetball, children's playroom and play area. Closed few days Christmas.*

AMERICAN EXPRESS *Access, Visa.*

Newquay Place of Interest

Trerice (NT) Tel 0637 875404.

Newton Abbot — Passage House 65% — £75

Tel 0626 55515 Fax 0626 63336 — **H**

Hackney Lane Kingsteignton Newton Abbot Devon TQ12 3QH — **Map 13 D3**

Follow the racecourse signs from the A380 to find this modern hotel, which enjoys fine views along the Teign estuary. Contemporary decor, spacious bedrooms, friendly staff and purpose-built spa and conference facilities. ***Rooms** 40. Garden, indoor swimming pool, keep-fit equipment, sauna, spa bath, steam room, solarium, coarse fishing.* AMERICAN EXPRESS *Access, Diners, Visa.*

Newton Abbot — Places of Interest

Ugbrooke House Chudleigh Tel 0626 852179.
Outdoor Seasonal Pool Tel 0626 61101.
Newton Abbot Racecourse Tel 0626 53235.
Shaldon Wildlife Trust Shaldon Tel 0626 872234 *7 miles.*
Teignmouth and Meadfoot Beaches.

Newton Solney — Newton Park 67% — £111

Tel 0283 703568 Fax 0283 703214 — **H**

Newton Solney Burton-on-Trent Derbyshire DE15 0SS — **Map 6 C3**

Three miles from the centre of Burton-on-Trent, the 17th-century, creeper-clad Newton Park enjoys a peaceful setting in landscaped grounds overlooking the river. Conference facilities for up to 140 delegates. Jarvis Hotels. ***Rooms** 51. Garden.* AMERICAN EXPRESS *Access, Diners, Visa.*

Nidd — Nidd Hall 77% — £120

Tel 0423 771598 Fax 0423 770931 — **H**

Nidd nr Harrogate North Yorkshire HG3 3BN — **Map 6 C1**

A solid stone Georgian mansion set in 45 acres of grounds 5 miles north of Harrogate (on the B6165, off the A61 Ripon Road), whose true splendour lies in its public areas. An octagonal entrance hall with exquisite plasterwork, statuary and glass cupola high above leads on to the even more impressive galleried inner hall which includes red marble columns and some very fine, intricate wrought-iron work on the stairs amongst many notable features. A large, elegant drawing room boasts an ornate plaster ceiling and pair of splendid matching fireplaces. There is also a mahogany panelled library. Bedrooms are individually decorated in some style and furnished with a mixture of antique and reproduction pieces plus comfortable sofas and armchairs. Good bathrooms all have bidets and separate shower cubicles. Main-house rooms are to be preferred to the 'courtyard' bedrooms. An ongoing programme of refurbishment should see many of the bedrooms and the conference facilities (for up to 250) upgraded for 1994. Children under 12 stay free in parents' room. No dogs. Exclusive Hotels. ***Rooms** 59. Garden, indoor swimming pool, gymnasium, sauna, solarium, beauty salon, squash, tennis, snooker, boating.* AMERICAN EXPRESS *Access, Diners, Visa..*

North Petherton — Walnut Tree Inn 65% — £68

Tel 0278 662255 Fax 0278 663946 — **H**

Fore Street North Petherton nr Bridgwater Somerset TA6 6QA — **Map 13 E2**

A carefully-modernised, 18th-century coaching inn on the A38 (one mile from J25 M5), with conference and function facilities. Business people will appreciate the good work space in both standard and larger Executive bedrooms, while more romantically-inclined weekenders may plump for one of the spacious four-poster suites. Friendly service from resident proprietors. Children under 12 stay free in parents' room. ***Rooms** 28. Garden, solarium. Closed 25 & 26 Dec.* AMERICAN EXPRESS *Access, Diners, Visa.*

North Stifford — Moat House — 61% — £103

Tel 0375 390909 Fax 0375 390426 — **H**

High Road North Stifford nr Grays Essex RM16 1UE — **Map 11 B4**

On the A13 one mile east of the M25 (junction 30/31), this is a well-equipped hotel catering for both business and leisure visitors. Originally a Georgian country house, it stands in 6½ acres of grounds. Children up to 16 stay free in parents' room. ***Rooms** 96. Garden, tennis, pétanque. Closed 27-30 Dec.* AMERICAN EXPRESS *Access, Diners, Visa.*

North Stoke — Springs Hotel — 70% — £100

Tel 0491 36687 Fax 0491 36877 — **H**

Wallingford Road North Stoke Oxfordshire OX9 6BE — **Map 15 D2**

The Springs is midway between the M4 (leave at junction 8/9) and the M40 (exit 6), between Goring and Crowmarsh on B4009. The extended, mock-Tudor half-timbered building dates in parts from 1874, and stands imposingly in 30 acres of grounds with large lawns and a spring-fed lake. Public areas include a panelled lounge of old-world appeal and a small cosy bar. Three separate meeting rooms. Bedrooms generally are spacious and pleasantly appointed with quality fabrics, smart furniture and subtle colours: best are those with private balconies. No dogs. ***Rooms** 37. Garden, outdoor swimming pool, sauna, tennis, putting.* AMERICAN EXPRESS *Access, Diners, Visa.*

Northampton — Courtyard by Marriott — 65% — £77

Tel 0604 22777 Fax 0604 35454 — **H**

Bedford Road Northampton Northamptonshire NN4 0YF — **Map 15 D1**

Five minutes from junction 15 of the M1, just off the A45 alongside the A428, one mile from the town centre. Large bedrooms, competitively priced. Children free in parents' room. Modern meeting rooms for up to 30. Plenty of free parking. Previously the *Holiday Inn Garden Court*. ***Rooms** 104. Keep-fit equipment, restaurant (7am-10.30pm).* AMERICAN EXPRESS *Access, Diners, Visa.*

Northampton — Forte Travelodge — £42

Tel 0604 758395 — **L**

Upton Way Northampton Northamptonshire NN5 6EG — **Map 15 D1**

On the western outskirts of Northampton, on the ring road off the A45. One mile from Junction 15A on the M1. ***Rooms** 40.* AMERICAN EXPRESS *Access, Visa.*

Northampton — Moat House — 63% — £93

Tel 0604 22441 Fax 0604 230614 — **H**

Silver Street Northampton Northamptonshire NN1 2TA — **Map 15 D1**

A tall and distinctive blue and white building in the town centre. Numerous function and meeting rooms (the largest for up to 600) make it a popular conference venue. Children up to 11 stay free in parents' room. ***Rooms** 138. Sauna, spa bath, solarium, beauty salon, hairdressing.* AMERICAN EXPRESS *Access, Diners, Visa.*

Northampton — Stakis Country Court — 68% — £107

Tel 0604 700666 Fax 0604 702850 — **H**

100 Watering Lane Collingtree Northampton Northamptonshire NN4 0XW — **Map 15 D1**

Just a few hundred yards from Junction 15 of the M1, this very modern business-oriented hotel is built around a central courtyard with a fountain. Large bedrooms, all with king-size beds, are bright and summery with

See over

floral fabrics; each has a spacious work desk in addition to the usual unit furniture. The Business Court area has been expanded and a new conference suite brings the delegate capacity to 320. ***Rooms** 139. Garden, indoor swimming pool, sauna, spa bath, solarium, beautician.* AMERICAN EXPRESS *Access, Diners, Visa.*

Northampton **Swallow Hotel** **72%** **£99**

Tel 0604 768700 Fax 0604 769011 **H**

Eagle Drive Northampton Northamptonshire NN4 0HN **Map 15 D1**

A purpose-built, low-rise modern exterior combined with a smart interior that employs black leather, white marble and a distinct Japanese influence. Most of the seating areas are open-plan, but there's also a small lounge that serves mainly as a quiet reading or writing room. Bedrooms are equally modern and all offer a couple of smartly upholstered armchairs and all the usual modern extras. Half the bathrooms have bidets and all are provided with a selection of toiletries. Children up to 14 free if sharing parents' room; families can eat informally in one of the two restaurants. The small but sunny pool has tall windows overlooking a lake. A purpose-built management development centre is attached to the hotel. ***Rooms** 122. Garden, indoor swimming pool, sauna, solarium, spa bath, keep-fit equipment, coffee shop (7am-10.30pm).* AMERICAN EXPRESS *Access, Diners, Visa.*

Northampton **Travel Inn** **£43**

Tel 0604 832340 Fax 0604 831807 **L**

Harpole Turn Weedon Road Northampton Northamptonshire NN7 4DD **Map 15 D1**

Meeting rooms available, 2 miles off Junction 16 of the M1. ***Rooms** 51.* AMERICAN EXPRESS *Access, Diners, Visa.*

Northampton **Westone Moat House** **59%** **£79**

Tel 0604 406262 Fax 0604 415023 **H**

Ashley Way Weston Favell Northampton Northamptonshire NN3 3EA **Map 15 D1**

Built in 1914 by the founder of Trueform shoes, the Westone is a warm, honey-coloured stone mansion set in its own grounds off the A4500 to the east of town. Public rooms have some interesting architectural features and bedrooms are well-equipped with modern comforts. Children up to 12 stay free in parents' room. ***Rooms** 66. Garden, keep-fit equipment, sauna, solarium, putting. Closed Christmas/New Year.* AMERICAN EXPRESS *Access, Diners, Visa.*

Northampton **Places of Interest**

Tourist Information Tel 0604 22677.
Central Museum and Art Gallery Guildhall Road Tel 0604 39415.
The Canal Museum Stoke Bruerne, Nr Northampton Tel 0604 862229.
Wantage Road Cricket Ground Tel 0604 32917.
Towcester Racecourse Tel 0327 50969.
Skew Bridge Ski School Rushden, Nr Wellingborough Tel 0933 59939/53808.
CLA Game Fair Showground Castle Ashby Tel 071 235 0511.

Northleach **Old Woolhouse** * **£85**

Tel 0451 860366 **R**

Market Place Northleach Gloucestershire GL54 3EE **Map 14 C2**

After 20 years little has changed here, but make sure you've booked in the small homely dining room of Jacques and Jenny Astic's restaurant (single diners not encouraged). Thick Cotswold-stone walls, low ceiling and exposed beams make a comfortable setting, enhanced by the open fireplace. Highly polished dark wood tables are set with spotless silver and family china. The short menu ensures fresh ingredients and an honest cuisine bourgeoise with some highlights, like a light entrée of hot foie gras mousse with wild mushrooms. Main courses might offer the likes of *porc à l'armagnac* or *poulet au vinaigre*; desserts, shortbread gateau with strawberries or chocolate cake. Some fine wines are particularly keenly priced. ***Seats** 18. D only 8.15-9.30. Closed Sun & Mon, 1 week Christmas. Set D £30. No credit cards.*

Northleach Wickens £55

Tel 0451 860421 **R**

Market Place Northleach Gloucestershire GL54 3EJ **Map 14 C2**

On one side of the square in this very English village stands Chris and Joanna Wickens' very English restaurant. Exposed Cotswold-stone walls, low ceilings and subtle lighting create an intimate setting for unfussy, English cooking with a traditional base and some modern influences: steamed Evesham asparagus with a herb butter sauce; North Atlantic prawns with a zingy garlic dip; pork steak marinated in soya and ginger, chargrilled and served with spiced oranges; shin of beef braised in real ale topped with horseradish dumplings. Joanna both produces the puddings (perhaps chocolate marquise with an orange cream sauce or sticky toffee pudding) and handles front of house in an admirably homely fashion. Well-kept British farmhouse cheeses are served with fruit and celery. Dinner is a fixed-price, 3- or 4-course affair offering a good choice; menus change weekly. Alongside a splendid New World wine list, France rates only a brief mention. Fair prices, good tasting notes. No smoking. No credit cards. ***Seats** 38. Parties 20. Private Room 20. L 12.15-1.45 D 7.20-8.45. Closed Sun & Mon, Bank Holidays.*

Northleach Place of Interest

Cotswold Countryside Collection Fossewa Tel 0451 60715.

Northwich Hartford Hall 63% £70

Tel 0606 75711 Fax 0606 782285 **H**

School Lane Hartford Northwich Cheshire CW8 1PW **Map 6 B2**

Mock-Victorian is the style of the day rooms at this 16th-century gabled house just off the A556 (M56 junction 7, M6 junction 19). Good desk space in the bedrooms. Beamed conference room for up to 30. Owned by Pennine Inns (Scottish & Newcastle). ***Rooms** 20. Garden.* AMERICAN EXPRESS *Access, Diners, Visa.*

Northwich Place of Interest

Arley Hall and Gardens Arley Tel 0565 777353.

Norwich Adlard's ★ £85

Tel 0603 633522 **R**

79 Upper St Giles Street Norwich Norfolk NR2 1AB **Map 10 C1**

Now in its tenth year, Adlard's is still the best restaurant in Norwich and the surrounding area; it is a classic example of a restaurant run by a thoroughly dedicated chef-patron and his wife. The decor is a sombre affair but quite stylish with a dark green scheme, tables on various levels and oil paintings adorning the walls. Crisp white linen tablecloths add a classic touch and a cosy and welcoming air pervades the whole restaurant. David Adlard's cooking is highly capable, producing accomplished dishes that make the most of seasonal produce; in fact, his professorial look gives a clue to his passionate zeal in sourcing and synergising ingredients. Cheeses, for example, are astutely purchased with a fine understanding of the product, carefully kept and served in prime condition. Cleverly thought-out, fixed-price-only lunchtime menus offer superb value, perhaps starting with softly-boiled quail's egg on a brioche with spinach and brunoise of smoked salmon or confit of duck with beetroot, spring onions and cinnamon sauce, followed by spiced venison sausage with red wine sauce and red cabbage or fillet of cod with pesto, rocket salad and fresh

See over

vermicelli; tulip of rhubarb fool, chocolate marquise with orange syrup or pear sorbet with redcurrant and lime coulis to finish. Cheese straws with aperitifs and buttery shortbread served with coffee are nice star touches. Fixed-price-only, 3- and 4-course dinner menus see the use of more expensive ingredients such as monkfish (served as a starter with red pepper coulis), Morston oysters (poached and served with lentils, spinach and curry butter sauce), turbot and Lunedale duck; puff pillow of local wild mushrooms à la crème, seafood with lobster fumet and chives, rack of English lamb with ratatouille and gratin dauphinois, and hot brioche with compote of armagnac-and orange-flavoured prunes and pistachio ice cream are typical dishes. All menus change daily, with variations in saucing and garnishes where needed. Mary Adlard's service stands up even when under pressure. New World wines are pre-eminent on a fine list that has a good choice of bin beginnings rather than ends! Plenty under £20. ***Seats** 40. L 12.30-1.45 D7.30-10.30. Closed L Sat, all Sun & Mon, 25 Dec. Set L £10/£13 Set D £25/£29. Access, Diners, Visa.*

Norwich — Brasted's — £60

Tel 0603 625949 — **R**

8-10 St Andrew's Hill Norwich Norfolk NR2 1DS — **Map 10 C1**

Chef Adrian Clarke, previously at *Clarke's* in Easton and the *Fox & Goose* in Fressingfield, has recently joined this cosy little restaurant tucked away in the old part of the city, a short walk from both the Cathedral and Castle. Candy-striped fabrics cover the ceiling and walls to create an intimate effect. Carefully-planned menus testify to thoughtful shopping and classic combinations. Hot cheese parcels on an apple and thyme jelly, oeuf en cocotte, terrine of fishes, boeuf en croute, navarin of lamb, grilled fillets of lemon sole Parmesan with a cream and cheese sauce, chocolate marquise and ginger-scented orange baked custard. ***Seats** 22. Parties 18. L 12-2 D 7-10. Closed Sun, Bank Holidays. Set L £9.50/£12.50.* AMERICAN EXPRESS *Access, Diners, Visa.*

Norwich — Forte Posthouse — 63% — £68

Tel 0603 56431 Fax 0603 506400 — **H**

Ipswich Road Norwich Norfolk NR4 6EP — **Map 10 C1**

In secluded grounds just off the A140 to the south of town. The largest of several conference rooms can hold up to 100 delegates theatre-style. ***Rooms** 113. Garden, indoor swimming pool, gymnasium, sauna, spa bath, solarium.* AMERICAN EXPRESS *Access, Diners, Visa.*

Norwich — Friendly Hotel — 60% — £94

Tel 0603 741161 Fax 0603 741500 — **H**

2 Barnard Road Bowthorpe Norwich Norfolk NR5 9JB — **Map 10 C1**

Modern, purpose-built, low-rise hotel 4 miles west of the city centre, on the A1047, offering straightforward accommodation. Fully-equipped leisure centre; conference and banqueting facilities for up to 200. Healthy adults' and children's options on the restaurant menus. ***Rooms** 80. Indoor swimming pool, gymnasium, spa bath, sauna, steam room, solarium.* AMERICAN EXPRESS *Access, Diners, Visa.*

Norwich — Greens Seafood Restaurant — £60

Tel 0603 623733 Fax 0603 615268 — **R**

82 Upper St Giles Street Norwich Norfolk NR2 1LT — **Map 10 C1**

Local supplies of fresh fish form the basis of the menu at Dennis Crompton's popular restaurant with appropriate nautical decor. A bar menu has recently been introduced, adding to the options. Avocado and Cromer crab, tomato and gruyère tart or a selection of shellfish could precede salmon, skate, plaice, sea bass, cod or Dover sole, grilled, steamed or deep-fried and served with herb butter, garlic butter or a sauce. Simple sweets; well-chosen, fairly-priced wines. ***Seats** 48. L 12.15-2.15 D 7-10.45. Closed L Sat & Mon, all Sun, Bank Holidays, 1 week Christmas. Set L £13 Set D from £21. Access, Visa.*

Norwich **Marco's** £80

Tel 0603 624044 **R**

17 Pottergate Norwich Norfolk NR2 1DS **Map 10 C1**

Here since 1970, Marco Vessalio still greets diners from the door of his kitchen, the master of all he surveys; his is quintessential provincial Italian food, steadfastly untrendy, with wonderful ingredients unfailingly well cooked. Besides the à la carte choice there's a set menu of Tuscan dishes such as pasta with a sauce of walnuts, basil and pecorino, lamb baked with garlic and wine, and an opulent vegetable risotto. Helpful notes on an interesting Italian wine list well worth exploring. No smoking. ***Seats** 20. Parties 10. L 12.30-2 D 7.30-10. Closed Sun & Mon, Bank Holidays. Set L & D £19.* AMERICAN EXPRESS *Access, Diners, Visa.*

Norwich **Hotel Nelson** 65% £83

Tel 0603 760260 Fax 0603 620008 **H**

Prince of Wales Road Norwich Norfolk NR1 1DX **Map 10 C1**

A modern red-brick hotel opposite the railway station and alongside the river Wensum. Picture windows in the spacious lounge overlook the water and one of the two bars displays memorabilia of Nelson's flagship *Victory*. Best bedrooms include a sitting area and some have private balconies. The largest of five conference rooms can accommodate up to 90 delegates. ***Rooms** 121. Garden.* AMERICAN EXPRESS *Access, Diners, Visa.*

Norwich **Hotel Norwich** 62% £62

Tel 0603 787260 Fax 0603 400466 **H**

121 Boundary Road Norwich Norfolk NR3 2BA **Map 10 C1**

Modern, privately-run redbrick hotel on the outer ring road (A47) north-east of the city. Roomy, well-equipped bedrooms with ample writing surfaces. Popular for functions, with facilities for around 300. Children under 14 stay free in parents' room. Sister establishment to the *Hotel Nelson* (see entry). ***Rooms** 108. Indoor swimming pool, spa bath, sauna, solarium, keep-fit equipment, coffee shop (10.30am-6.30pm).* AMERICAN EXPRESS *Access, Diners, Visa.*

Norwich **Norwich Sport Village Hotel** 63% £65

Tel 0603 788898 Fax 0603 406845 **H**

Drayton High Road Hellesdon Norwich Norfolk NR6 5DU **Map 10 C1**

Practical, roomy bedrooms are at the centre of a very extensive sports complex situated just off the outer Norwich ring road on the A1067 to Fakenham. All the rooms have en-suite facilities, half showers, half tubs. Children up to 14 share parents' room free. Sporting facilities are the most impressive feature. They include seven squash courts and no less than a dozen tennis courts, seven of them indoors. Hotel guests share the lively open-plan bar, bistro and restaurant with the other users of the complex. No dogs. Conference facilities for thousands. ***Rooms** 55. Garden, indoor swimming pool, gymnasium, squash, sauna, steam baths, solarium, whirlpool bath, multi-sports hall, aerobics, beauty & hair salon, tennis, badminton, snooker, coffee shop (7am-10.30pm).* AMERICAN EXPRESS *Access, Diners, Visa.*

Our inspectors *never* book in the name of Egon Ronay's Guides. They disclose their identity only if they are considering an establishment for inclusion in the next edition of the Guide.

Norwich — Sprowston Manor — 69% — £88

Tel 0603 410871 Fax 0603 423911 — H

Wroxham Road Sprowston nr Norwich Norfolk NR7 8RP — **Map 10 C1**

Built around a 16th-century manor house, once the home of the Gurney banking family, this extended hotel by the A1151 contains a wealth of up-to-date facilities. A leisure club is at the heart of the most recent development, resplendent with palms and stone balustrades. Meeting and conference rooms are kept discreetly apart from the main hotel day rooms, with a separate entrance to the ballroom. Bedrooms benefit from views of the surrounding parkland, home to the adjacent Sprowston Golf Club; they also combine stylish fitted furniture and floral fabrics with up-to-date accessories including mini-bars and wall safes. Older manor house bedrooms are currently being restyled to a similar standard. Children under 16 stay free in parents' room. ***Rooms** 97. Garden, indoor swimming pool, spa bath, sauna, solarium, beauty salon, gymnasium, outdoor chess, coffee shop (7am-9pm).* AMERICAN EXPRESS *Access, Diners, Visa.*

Norwich — Places of Interest

Tourist Information Tel 0603 666071.
Norwich Cathedral Tel 0603 626290
Norwich City Football Ground Carrow Road Tel 0603 612131.
Fakenham Racecourse Nr Norwich Tel 0328 862388.
Norfolk Ski Club Tel 0692 650442.
Royal Norfolk Showground New Costessey Tel 0603 748931.

Theatres and concert halls

Norwich Puppet Theatre Tel 0603 615564.
Theatre Royal Tel 0603 623562.
Little Theatre Sheringham Tel 0263 822347.

Historic Houses, Castles and Gardens

Blickling Hall (NT) Aylsham Tel 0263 733084.
The Fairhaven Garden Trust South Walsham Tel 060549 449.
Felbrigg Hall (NT) Cromer Tel 026 375 444.
Mannington Hall Saxthorpe Tel 026 387 4175.
Norwich Castle Tel 0603 222222.
Raveningham Hall Gardens Raveningham Tel 050846 206.

Museums and Art Galleries

Colman's Mustard Museum Tel 0603 627889.
Norwich Castle Museum Tel 0603 223624.
Sainsbury Centre for Visual Arts University of East Anglia Tel 0603 592470.

Norwich Airport — Ambassador Hotel — 65% — £76

Tel 0603 410544 Fax 0603 789935 — H

Cromer Road Norwich Airport Norwich Norfolk NR6 6JA — **Map 10 C1**

Modern redbrick hotel whose aeronautical associations include the Concorde Bar and a replica Spitfire in the garden. Practical accommodation in decent-sized bedrooms; the honeymoon suites feature four-poster beds and jacuzzis. Purpose-built facility for conferences and banquets (up to 350/500). ***Rooms** 108. Indoor swimming pool, gymnasium, sauna, steam room, whirlpool bath.* AMERICAN EXPRESS *Access, Diners, Visa.*

Nottingham — Forte Crest — 70% — £92

Tel 0602 470131 Fax 0602 484366 — H

St James's Street Nottingham Nottinghamshire NG1 6BN — **Map 7 D3**

Large city-centre hotel whose bedrooms employ bold, up-to-date fabrics, smart, freestanding furniture and restful colour schemes; higher-floor rooms have good views. Bathrooms are fully tiled and well lit, with showers as well as tubs. Public areas include a striking foyer with white floor tiles and contrasting black woodwork. Large conference and function rooms. Family facilities. Overnight NCP parking. ***Rooms** 130.* AMERICAN EXPRESS *Access, Diners, Visa.*

Nottingham **Forte Posthouse** **61%** **£68**

Tel 0602 397800 Fax 0602 490469 **H**

Bostocks Lane Sandiacre Nottingham Nottinghamshire NG10 5NJ **Map 7 D3**

One of the original Posthouses, in a residential area close to Junction 25 of the M1. Practical accommodation plus conference/meeting rooms. ***Rooms** 91. Garden.* AMERICAN EXPRESS *Access, Diners, Visa.*

Nottingham **Higoi** **£50**

Tel 0602 423379 **R**

57 Lenton Boulevard Nottingham Nottinghamshire NG7 2FQ **Map 7 D3**

Japanese chef Mr Kato, assisted by his English wife, continues to educate customers in the delights of his native cooking. Helpful and informative staff will guide you through the complete range of specialities and menus, including good-value vegetarian, children's (£3.99) and *dombure* one-pot lunches and a bento box dinner. Teriyaki, shogoyaki and tempura dinners are preceded by selected hors d'oeuvre; special set meals for four or more include up to five main dishes. On the Nottingham-Derby road (turn left at the Savoy cinema). ***Seats** 35. L 12-2 D 6.30-10.30. Closed L Sun-Tue, all Bank Holidays. Set L from £5.90 Set D from £15.95.* AMERICAN EXPRESS *Access, Diners, Visa.*

Nottingham **Holiday Inn Garden Court** **65%** **£70**

Tel 0602 500600 Fax 0602 500433 **H**

Castle Marina Park Nottingham Nottinghamshire NG7 1GX **Map 7 D3**

Spacious rooms with large beds are a big plus at this bright modern hotel off the A6005, near the marina; good value, too – particularly for families, as the room price covers up to four occupants. Significant tariff reductions at weekends; informal eating in the bright restaurant. ***Rooms** 100.* AMERICAN EXPRESS *Access, Diners, Visa.*

Nottingham **Loch Fyne Oyster Bar** **£25**

Tel 0602 508481 **R**

17 King Street Nottingham Nottinghamshire **Map 7 D3**

Produce from its illustrious Scottish progenitor (see under Cairndow, Scotland) appears not to suffer unduly from its overnight journey south. Loch Fyne oysters and shellfish take their place alongside more humble offerings of mussel stew and Arbroath smokies, with Cheddar, Bonnet and Dunsyre Blue to follow. See also under Elton. ***Seats** 45. Parties 20. Meals 9-8.30 (Thurs to Sat to 10.30). Closed Sun, Bank Holidays.* AMERICAN EXPRESS *Access, Visa.*

Nottingham **Moat House** **59%** **£88**

Tel 0602 602621 Fax 0602 691506 **H**

Mansfield Road Nottingham Nottinghamshire NG5 2BT **Map 7 D3**

A modern block hotel to the north of the city centre. The 40 recently refurbished Executive bedrooms are the ones to ask for. Choice of three restaurants and three bars. Conferences/banqueting for up to 180/160; parking for 300. Not to be confused with the Royal Moat House nearer the heart of the city (see entry below). ***Rooms** 172. Closed 25 & 26 Dec.* AMERICAN EXPRESS *Access, Diners, Visa.*

Nottingham — Noble House — £60

Tel 0602 501105 — R

31 Greyfriar Gate Nottingham Nottinghamshire NG9 1EF — **Map 7 D3**

Friendly and helpful service complemented by stylish, swish black and pink decor all add to the ambience of this sophisticated Peking-style restaurant opposite Broad Marsh Centre. An extensive menu (including some sixteen 'sizzling' dishes) is based on good raw materials that are well handled in choices like sweet and sour fish, fried beef with pickled cabbage, peppered salted scallops or squid, and lamb with yellow bean sauce. High-chairs and booster seats for adventurous junior diners. ***Seats** 80. L 12-2 D 6-11.30 (Sun 12-11.30). Closed 3 days Christmas. Set L from £6 Set D from £14.* AMERICAN EXPRESS *Access, Diners, Visa.*

Nottingham — Novotel 62% — £70

Tel 0602 720106 Fax 0602 465900 — H

Bostock Lane Long Eaton Nottingham Nottinghamshire NG10 4EP — **Map 7 D3**

Practical, modern accommodation just off junction 25 of the M1. Up to two children under 16 stay free of charge (inc breakfast) when sharing their parents' room. 30 rooms are reserved for non-smokers. The hotel restaurant is open for à la carte service from 6am-midnight. Conference facilities for up to 200. ***Rooms** 108. Garden, outdoor swimming pool.* AMERICAN EXPRESS *Access, Diners, Visa.*

Nottingham — Ocean City — £40

Tel 0602 410041 Fax 0602 240369 — R

100-104 Derby Road Nottingham Nottinghamshire NG1 5FB — **Map 7 D3**

A cavernous restaurant just out of the city centre; highly popular with the local Chinese community. The long Cantonese menu is strong on sizzling dishes and assorted seafood that includes lobster, crab and monkfish; these are well complemented by some more unusual and rarely seen dishes on the freshly cooked lunchtime dim sum selection. ***Seats** 250. Parties 12. L 12-2.30 (Mon & Tue to 4) D 6-12 (Mon-Fri), Sat 12-12, Sun 12-10.30. Closed 25 Dec. Set L from £5.90 Set D from £12.* AMERICAN EXPRESS *Access, Diners, Visa.*

Nottingham — Royal Moat House 70% — £101

Tel 0602 414444 Fax 0602 475667 — H

Wollaton Street Nottingham Nottinghamshire NG1 5RH — **Map 7 D3**

An internal arcade planted with tropical trees and plants is a major attraction at this strikingly modern city-centre hotel next to the Theatre Royal. Several bars and restaurants fringe this unique feature, and there's also a sunken lounge off the black marble foyer; the Penthouse Bar offers panoramic views over the city. Bedroom size varies from roomy doubles and twins to rather more compact singles. Decor is light and contemporary in style and all rooms have a mini-bar and the usual modern comforts. Conference facilities for up to 600 delegates. Free multi-storey car parking. No dogs. ***Rooms** 201. Squash, hairdressing, kiosk, coffee shop (10am-6pm).* AMERICAN EXPRESS *Access, Diners, Visa.*

Nottingham — Rutland Square Hotel 72% — £72

Tel 0602 411114 Fax 0602 410014 — H

St James Street Nottingham Nottinghamshire NG1 6FJ — **Map 7 D3**

The impressive, city-centre Rutland Square hotel was, unusually, converted from a warehouse into a quality hotel. Its day rooms have an elegant, contemporary feel. The bright, impressive foyer features a marble-tiled floor and a clubby bar; what was a lounge area is now a glass-roofed, all-day brasserie. Bedrooms are quite small but are tastefully and stylishly appointed with limed oak units and harmonious fabrics. The white marble-tiled bathrooms are also well equipped, with powerful showers and well-lit mirrors. Prices are considerably lower than last year and further tariff reductions apply at weekends. ***Rooms** 104.* AMERICAN EXPRESS *Access, Diners, Visa.*

Nottingham Sonny's £50

Tel 0602 473041 **R**

3 Carlton Street Hockley Nottingham Nottinghamshire NG1 1NL **Map 7 D3**

Sonny's has changed its style and is now open all day Sunday and also offers a café menu (bageuttes, focaccia, salads, pasta, soups and puddings) as well as the set menu (including a three-course Sunday lunch) and à la carte. Warm duck salad with coriander and cloud ear mushrooms, Thai fish cakes, charcuterie with shaved Parmesan and rocket, prawn and chorizo gumbo with sweetcorn and Cheddar hush puppies, rib of beef (for two), sticky toffee pudding and chocolate polenta cake typify the style. As we went to press, a supervised children's play area (advance booking required) was being introduced at Sunday lunchtimes. Smart, informal atmosphere; friendly service. ***Seats** 65. Parties 30. L 12-2.30 D 7-10.30 (Fri & Sat to 11). Closed Bank Holidays. Set L £9.95/£12.95 Set D £12.95.* AMERICAN EXPRESS *Access, Visa.*

Nottingham Stakis Victoria Hotel 62% £72

Tel 0602 419561 Fax 0602 484736 **H**

Milton Street Nottingham Nottinghamshire NG1 3PZ **Map 7 D3**

19th-century Edwardian building in a central position. Accommodation ranges from singles to family rooms and suites. Nine conference rooms handle from 6 to 200 delegates. ***Rooms** 166.* AMERICAN EXPRESS *Access, Diners, Visa.*

Nottingham Strathdon Thistle 66% £106

Tel 0602 418501 Fax 0602 483725 **H**

44 Derby Road Nottingham Nottinghamshire NG1 5FT **Map 7 D3**

Neat, practical bedrooms and stylish day rooms in a modern hotel on the edge of the city centre, directly opposite the Albert Hall conference and exhibition centre and Playhouse theatre. Choice of bars and 24hr room service. Children up to 14 free in their parents' room. Guests have free use of the leisure facilities at the sister hotel the *Donington Thistle* at Castle Donington (see entry). ***Rooms** 69.* AMERICAN EXPRESS *Access, Diners, Visa.*

Nottingham Places of Interest

Tourist Information Tel 0602 470661.
Nottingham Playhouse Tel 0602 419419.
Theatre Royal Tel 0602 482626.
Newstead Abbey Tel 0623 793557 *Home of the poet Byron.*
Wollaton Hall Tel 0602 281333/281130.
Nottingham Forest Football Ground City Ground Tel 0602 822202.
Notts County Football Ground Meadow Lane Tel 0602 861155.
Holme Pierrepoint National Water Sports Centre Adbolton Lane Tel 0602 821212.
Nottingham Racecourse Tel 0602 580620.
Nottingham Ice Stadium Tel 0602 484526.
Nottingham Sutton Centre Ice Rink Sutton-in-Ashfield, Nr Nottingham. Tel 0623 554554.
Carlton Forum Ski Slope Tel 0602 872333.
Museums and Art Galleries
D H Lawrence Birthplace Museum Tel 0773 763312.
The Lace Centre Nottingham Tel 0602 413539.
Museum of Costume and Textiles Tel 0602 483504.
Nottingham Castle Museum Tel 0602 483504.

Nuneaton **Forte Travelodge** **£42**

Tel 0203 382541 **L**

Bedworth Nuneaton Coventry Warwickshire CV12 0BN **Map 6 C4**

On the A444 in close proximity to Junction 3 of the M6 and NEC. No restaurant facilities nearby. ***Rooms** 40.* American Express *Access, Visa.*

Nuneaton **Travel Inn** **£43**

Tel 0203 343584 Fax 0203 327156 **L**

Coventry Road Nuneaton Warwickshire CV10 7PJ **Map 6 C4**

20 minutes' drive from Birmingham International Airport; conference facilities available. ***Rooms** 30.* American Express *Access, Diners, Visa.*

Nutfield **Nutfield Priory** **70%** **£114**

Tel 0737 822066 Fax 0737 823321 **H**

Nutfield Redhill Surrey RH1 4EN **Map 11 B5**

Ten minutes' drive from Junctions 6 and 8 of the M25 (8 miles from Gatwick Airport), built in high Victorian Gothic style by an MP in 1872, the Priory stands on a ridge enjoying panoramic views across gently undulating countryside. Roomy public areas boast fine architectural features including a stone-vaulted cloister restaurant, high stained-glass windows, a panelled library and even an old pipe organ in the galleried grand hall. Bedrooms (nine of which are a recent addition) are decorated in some style with matching fabrics, often with elaborate bedhead drapes, and freestanding furniture varying from oak or yew to rattan; smart bathrooms match their bedrooms. Conferences are an important part of the business, as is the Fredericks sports complex (open to non-residents). No dogs. ***Rooms** 52. Garden, indoor swimming pool, sauna, solarium, spa bath, steam room, gymnasium, beauty salon, badminton, squash, snooker.* American Express *Access, Diners, Visa.*

Oakham **Barnsdale Lodge** **65%** **£70**

Tel 0572 724678 Fax 0572 724961 **H**

The Avenue Rutland Water nr Oakham Leicestershire LE15 8AH **Map 7 E3**

Converted from a 16th-century farmhouse and outbuildings, furnished with practical antiques and period touches from the Edwardian age, like quilted eiderdowns. A flagstone-floored bar has pastel yellow walls and solid oak furniture, while a small lounge has more prints and ornaments from the era. Some of the bedrooms enjoy views over Rutland Water; one has a half tester bed. Three conference rooms cater for up to 80. The hotel stands alongside the A606, two miles east of Oakham. ***Rooms** 17.* American Express *Access, Diners, Visa.*

Oakham **Hambleton Hall** **84%** **£120**

Tel 0572 756991 Fax 0572 724721 **HR**

Hambleton nr Oakham Leicestershire LE15 8TH **Map 7 E3**

At the forefront of country house hotels since its creation in 1979, Tim and Stefa Hart's elegant and imposing Victorian house is a haven of quiet luxury, but at the same time with the feel of a private home where customers are welcomed and treated as old friends. One mile east of Oakham on the A606, signposted Hambleton village, the setting is spectacular, atop mature and terraced grounds that lead down to Rutland Water. The lovely gardens provide many of the blooms that Anne Taylor blends into magnificent flower arrangements throughout the hotel with the grandest of all occupying pride of place in the entrance hall below the fine oak staircase. Elegant day rooms include the drawing room with beautiful views, fine drapes, an ornately plastered ceiling, antiques, pictures, an open fire, and the refurbished bar with its fine inglenook fireplace. Nina

Campbell, the celebrated interior designer, masterminded the decoration of the house at the outset and continues to lend her ideas, illustrated by the luxurious bedrooms furnished with antiques and quality fabrics with an acute eye for detail. Guests want for nothing – remote-control TV, portable radio, home-made biscuits, mineral water, books and magazines, and sumptuous bathrooms, each with a large deep bath, jet shower, bidet, Molton Brown toiletries and huge towels and bathrobes that pamper to the full. Beds are turned down at night, linen and towels changed – an example of caring and efficient service carried out by enthusiastic staff under the watchful eye of general manager Jeffrey Crockett. Meeting room facilities for up to 30. ***Rooms** 15. Garden, outdoor swimming pool, tennis. Access, Visa.*

Restaurant ★↑ £110

Young chef Aaron Patterson continues to uphold the Hambleton tradition of outstanding cooking, leading an equally young and committed kitchen brigade that really does achieve what it sets out to. Two dining rooms, beautifully done out in shades of cream, offer sensational food, polished service, comfort, refinement and superb views. The à la carte menu is beautifully designed and concentrates on just four or five dishes at each course: perhaps starting with a salad of mango and limes served with crispy potatoes, pan-fried foie gras and jasmine tea sauce or pressed layers of Roma tomatoes and fresh crab encircled by Mediterranean vegetables and a saffron vinaigrette, followed by a fish course of red mullet fillets with a farce of langoustines, aubergine pancake, tomatoes and olives or fillet of sea bass with roasted scallops, a light lobster mousse and fennel purée. Main courses might include braised pig's trotter with offal and Chartreuse sauce, roast pigeon with its own ravioli and a light Gewurztraminer sauce or poached lobster with a salad of truffles, green beans, fried shallots and lemon vinaigrette. Pistachio soufflé, caramelised lemon tart with pears and red wine sauce, millefeuille of white and dark chocolate with caramelised hazelnuts are among the desserts. As an alternative to the daily carte, there's a gourmet menu of seasonal specialities and a three-course set menu, typically offering a terrine of red cabbage, beetroot and pigeon, fillet of salmon with fennel purée and lemon sauce, and hot chocolate soufflé with banana ice cream to finish. British, French and Irish cheeses from Neal's Yard are served with home-made walnut bread and biscuits. Three or so tables are set on the terrace in good weather. 'Wines of the moment' – three pages of 30 wines that are drinking particularly well categorised by price – is a novel way of introducing a fine list. ***Seats** 50. L 12-2 D 7-9.30. Set L from £19.50 Set D £26.50/£45.*

Oakham Whipper-In Hotel 70% £80

Tel 0572 756971 Fax 0572 757759 **H**

Market Place Oakham Rutland Leicestershire LE15 6DT **Map 7 E3**

Standing in the market square of Rutland's old county town, this relaxed, rural hotel dates back to the 17th century. A flagstone-floored foyer leads through to a low-beamed bar-lounge that is popular with the locals. Bedrooms, two of which boast four-poster beds, are neat and individually decorated with comfortable seating areas and a few antiques. Children up to 12 free in parents' room. Room service available for all meals. Sister hotel to the *Royal Oak* in Sevenoaks, Kent. ***Rooms** 25. Access, Visa.*

Odiham George Hotel £68

Tel 0256 702081 Fax 0256 704213 **I**

High Street Odiham nr Basingstoke Hampshire RG25 1LP **Map 15 D3**

First granted a licence in 1540, the privately-owned George has kept a good deal of its period character. Timber framing can be seen throughout, and in the Oak Room – a popular place for afternoon tea or private parties –the wattle and daub walls are exposed. The oak-panelled, flagstone-floored restaurant was at one time an assize court. Main-house bedrooms have creaking floors, beams and antiques, while rooms in the converted barn and

See over

coach house are modern behind original exteriors; four-poster rooms attract a small supplement. One mile from the M3 (junction 5). ***Rooms*** *18. Garden.* AMERICAN EXPRESS *Access, Diners, Visa.*

Okehampton — Forte Travelodge — £42

Tel 0837 52124 — **L**

Sourton Cross nr Okehampton Devon EX20 4LY — **Map 13 D2**

On the A30, 4 miles west of Okehampton. ***Rooms*** *32.* AMERICAN EXPRESS *Access, Visa.*

Old Burghclere — Dew Pond — £70

Tel 0635 278408 — **R**

Old Burghclere Newbury Berkshire RG15 9LH — **Map 15 D3**

Surrounded by fields at the foot of Watership Down there's a homely feel to the twin dining rooms of this family-run restaurant set in a creeper-clad 16th-century house. The cooking is down to Keith Marshall whose well-balanced fixed-price menu (the same lunchtime and evening but differently priced) changes every 6-8 weeks. Good clear flavours are evident in dishes like griddled scallops in a puff pastry case with a coriander and ginger sauce; risotto of saffron and pimento with sun-dried tomatoes and sautéed chicken livers; Stilton and leek soup; steamed brill with Thai spices and soy sauce; best end of lamb with minted hollandaise and a tartlet of curried aubergines. If you can't choose between puds like strawberry shortcake, iced nougat, chocolate torte and crème brulée, go for the Grand Plated Selection and get a miniature serving of each. Alternatively there's always a good selection of British farmhouse cheeses. Quite a concise wine list with some good house wines under £15, and fair prices elsewhere. ***Seats*** *40. Private Room 25. L 12-2 D 7-10. Closed L Sat, all Sun & Mon, 2 weeks Jan, 2 weeks Aug. Set L £16/£19.50 Set D £23. Access, Visa.*

Old Harlow — Travel Inn — £43

Tel 0279 442545 Fax 0279 452169 — **L**

Cambridge Road Old Harlow Essex CM20 2EP — **Map 11 B4**

Riverside location, 15 miles from Stanstead Airport. ***Rooms*** *38.* AMERICAN EXPRESS *Access, Diners, Visa.*

Oldbury — Forte Travelodge — £42

Tel 021-552 2967 — **L**

Wolverhampton Road Oldbury Warly West Midlands B69 2BH — **Map 6 C4**

On the A4123 northbound off Junction 2 of the M5, on the outskirts of Birmingham. ***Rooms*** *33.* AMERICAN EXPRESS *Access, Visa.*

Ormesby St Margaret — Ormesby Lodge — 58% — £46

Tel 0493 730910 Fax 0493 733103 — **H**

Decoy Road Ormesby St Margaret nr Great Yarmouth Norfolk NR29 3LG — **Map 10 D1**

A small family-run hotel five miles north of Great Yarmouth and within a mile or so of several beaches. The building is Victorian, and some of the original feel survives in the bar/lounge. Bedrooms vary in their decor and furnishings but all are in good order and all have private bathroom facilities. ***Rooms*** *9. Garden.* AMERICAN EXPRESS *Access, Diners, Visa.*

Oswestry — Forte Travelodge — £42

Tel 0691 658178 — **L**

Oswestry Shropshire SY11 4JA — **Map 8 D2**

At the Mile End service area on the A5/A483 roundabout outside Oswestry. ***Rooms*** *40.* AMERICAN EXPRESS *Access, Visa.*

Oswestry — Wynnstay Hotel — 68% — £83

Tel 0691 655261 Fax 0691 670606 — **H**

Church Street Oswestry Shropshire SY11 2SZ — **Map 8 D2**

In the town centre opposite St Oswalds church, this is a typical Georgian building with stylish day rooms. Besides the restaurant and lounge there are conference facilities for up to 180, plus a 200-year-old crown bowling green as an unusual leisure offering. Best of the bedrooms have whirlpool baths. Children up to ten free in parents' room. ***Rooms** 27. Garden, bowling, coffee shop (9.30am-10pm).* AMERICAN EXPRESS *Access, Diners, Visa.*

Otley — Chevin Lodge — 64% — £87

Tel 0943 467818 Fax 0943 850335 — **H**

York Gate Otley West Yorkshire LS21 3NU — **Map 6 C1**

Set in fifty acres of birchwoods by a private lake and built of Finnish pine, the Lodge is the largest log construction in the country. Bedrooms are in either the main building or smaller log lodges scattered amongst the trees. Despite the rusticity, rooms have all the usual modern conveniences. Executive lodges have separate lounges. The well-equipped Woodlands Suite has facilities for up to 120 conference delegates. Guests have free membership of a private leisure club 5 minutes drive away. ***Rooms** 52. Garden, sauna, solarium, tennis, fishing, games room.* AMERICAN EXPRESS *Access, Visa.*

Oundle — Talbot Hotel — 62% — £96

Tel 0832 273621 Fax 0832 274545 — **H**

New Street Oundle Northamptonshire PE8 4EA — **Map 7 E4**

Built as a monks' hostel, and rebuilt in the 17th century with stones from nearby Fotheringhay Castle, the Talbot is quite splendid with its transom windows and bell-capped gables. Inside is the very staircase descended by Mary Queen of Scots on the day of her execution. Most bedrooms have recently been refurbished. Conference/banqueting facilities for up to 100. Forte Heritage. ***Rooms** 40. Garden.* AMERICAN EXPRESS *Access, Diners, Visa.*

Oxford — Al-Shami — £30

Tel 0865 310066 Fax 0865 311241 — **R**

25 Walton Crescent Oxford Oxfordshire OX1 2JH — **Map 15 D2**

Between Somerville and Worcester Colleges, a Lebanese restaurant open long hours serving authentic dishes including charcoal grills of lamb, chicken and minced meat and the usual wide range of hot and cold hors d'oeuvre. The wine list includes a dozen Lebanese varieties plus arak. ***Seats** 50. Meals 12-12. No credit cards.*

Oxford — Bath Place — £65

Tel 0865 791812 Fax 0865 791834 — **RR**

4 & 5 Bath Place Holywell Street Oxford Oxfordshire OX1 3SU — **Map 15 D2**

Down a cobbled courtyard, off Holywell Street, in the oldest part of Oxford, is this cosy clutter of 17th-century cottages run by the Fawsitt family. The style of cooking is light with modern touches, competitively priced and served in an unpretentious manner. Three-course Sunday lunches are popular and offer a choice of five or so dishes at each course; a smaller choice is offered at weekday lunches. Dinners see a short à la carte or fixed-price, three-choice-per-course menus. Desserts are expensive but can be involved – like a roast conference pear in a lime sorbet-lined feuilleté case accompanied by a ginger-scented crème anglaise. No smoking. Inexpensive wines on a list of 80 bottles offer good drinking under £20. ***Seats** 35. L 12-2 D 7-10 (Fri & Sat to 10.30). Closed L Tue, D Sun, all Mon. Set L £14.50 (Sun £19.50) Set D £21.95/£24.50.* AMERICAN EXPRESS *Access, Visa.*

See over

Rooms £100

More a restaurant with rooms than a hotel, because facilities are lacking. Ten small bedrooms, but neat and smartly furnished with useful accessories to justify the price; day rooms are almost non-existent, with both the tiny residents' lounge and bar doubling up for use by the restaurant's patrons.

Oxford Browns £30

Tel 0865 511995 Fax 0865 52347 **R**

5-11 Woodstock Road Oxford Oxfordshire OX2 6HA **Map 15 D2**

All-day value-for-money eating in one of Oxford's most popular restaurants. Spaghetti, salads, savoury pies, steaks, burgers and hot sandwiches are the basis of the menu, the last including double egg and bacon, club and vegetarian. Lots of puddings, late-morning breakfasts and traditional teas. Families are very welcome, and there's a children's menu and mothers' room. Browns is almost next door to the Radcliffe Infirmary. ***Seats** 250. Parties 30. Private Room 50. Meals 11am-11.30pm (Sun from 12). Access, Visa.*

Oxford Cherwell Boathouse £44

Tel 0865 52746 Fax 0865 391459 **R**

Bardwell Road Oxford Oxfordshire OX2 6SR **Map 15 D2**

Park your car or moor your punt, and enjoy a leisurely meal in the friendly surroundings of a converted boathouse on the river Cherwell. The three-course, short-choice menu changes weekly and the starters and mains always include a dish for vegetarians. Typical starters might be pasta with red onions and toasted walnuts, skewered scallops on yellow pepper sauce or split pea and celeriac soup; main courses always feature good fish (perhaps stuffed grey mullet in wine or fish and shellfish terrine with crab sauce) alongside fillet of hare with vinegar and shallots or breast of pigeon with bacon and lemon. Sticky toffee pudding is a regular favourite dessert, alongside the likes of Spotted Dick, rhubarb and ginger fool, three interesting British cheeses and home-made ice creams. The food may be good, but the wine list is even better, offering an excellent all-round selection, keenly priced, with a particularly fine range of white burgundies. A paved roof terrace allows open-air eating in good weather. ***Seats** 50. L 12-2 D 7-10 (Sat to 10.30). Closed L in winter, D Sun & Mon, Bank Holidays, Christmas. Set L from £7 Set D from £15.* AMERICAN EXPRESS *Access, Diners, Visa.*

Oxford Eastgate Hotel 61% £123

Tel 0865 248244 Fax 0865 791681 **H**

High Street Oxford Oxfordshire OX1 4BE **Map 15 D2**

Comfortably refurbished behind its 18th-century facade, the Eastgate stands at the Magdalen College end of the High (reception entrance is in Merton Street). Pick of the accommodation is the four-poster suite. Forte Heritage. ***Rooms** 43.* AMERICAN EXPRESS *Access, Diners, Visa.*

Oxford Restaurant Elizabeth ↑ £75

Tel 0865 242230 **R**

82 St Aldate's Oxford Oxfordshire OX1 1RA **Map 15 D2**

If there were an Oxford degree in classical cuisine, here's where most of the students would come for their practicals. Dating from the 15th century, the dining areas are very traditional and intimate, a most appropriate setting for the classical dishes that are the cornerstone of Salvador Rodriguez's cooking. Pipérade, paté de foie de volaille and prawns with rice and aïoli; salmon in a white wine sauce, duck à l'orange and rack of lamb with gratin dauphinois – these are typical of the dishes which have been keeping the customers happy from the start. The crème brulée is one of the best you'll find anywhere, and another major attraction is the superb wine list that includes many classic burgundies and clarets, exceptional dessert wines and a good selection from Germany and Spain. Owner Antonio Lopez has been smoothly in charge for more than 35 years. ***Seats** 40. L 12.30-2.30 D 6.30-11 (Sun 7-10.30). Closed Mon, Good Friday, 24-31 Dec. Set L £15.* AMERICAN EXPRESS *Access, Diners, Visa.*

Oxford **15 North Parade** **£65**

Tel 0865 513773 **R**

15 North Parade Avenue Oxford Oxfordshire OX9 1JH **Map 15 D2**

More 'gown' than 'town', Georgina Wood's welcoming restaurant in a narrow street to the north of the city centre is particularly popular with university dons. Becushioned rattan chairs around crisply-clothed tables and a changing collection of art work (for sale) on the walls make for an attractive setting for new chef Colin Gilbert's equally attractive cooking. Colin's recent sojourn in the south of France inspires the weekly-changing menu (about six choices at each stage), which might include roast fillet of salmon with spinach and a fresh tomato, basil and olive oil sauce; lamb cutlets topped with tapénade and served with a thyme-scented jus, and breast of maize-fed chicken with a wild mushroom sauce amongst the main dishes; and starters such as parfait of duck livers with pickled kumquats or seafood mousse with langoustines and a basil butter sauce. Priced à la carte during the week it comes at a fixed price on Saturdays with the addition of a soup course. Short but globe-trotting wine list. ***Seats** 55. L 12-2 D 7-10.30. Closed D Sun, some Bank Holidays, last 2 weeks Aug. Set L £15.75 Set D from £19.50. Access, Diners, Visa.*

Oxford **Forte Travelodge** **£42**

Tel 0865 875705 75705 **L**

London Road Wheatley nr Oxford Oxfordshire OX9 1JH **Map 15 D2**

On the outskirts of Wheatley on the A418, Junction 8 of the M40. 5 miles east of Oxford City Centre. ***Rooms** 24.* AMERICAN EXPRESS *Access, Visa.*

Oxford **Moat House** **62%** **£105**

Tel 0865 59933 Fax 0865 310259 **H**

Wolvercote Roundabout Oxford Oxfordshire OX2 8AL **Map 15 D2**

Modern business hotel two miles north of the city centre at the junction of A34 and A40. Good leisure centre, conference facilities for up to 150, banqueting to 110. Extensive free car parking. ***Rooms** 155. Indoor swimming pool, gymnasium, squash, sauna, spa bath, solarium, putting, snooker, coffee shop (7am-10.30pm). Closed New Year.* AMERICAN EXPRESS *Access, Diners, Visa.*

Oxford **Old Parsonage** **70%** **£125**

Tel 0865 310210 Fax 0865 311262 **H**

1 Banbury Road Oxford Oxfordshire OX2 6NN **Map 15 D2**

At the city end of Banbury Road, the extended Old Parsonage dates from 1660 and underwent a major transformation in order to open as a quality hotel early in 1991. Great style and taste have been employed in its refurbishment, creating an effect that's very easy on the eye. Bedrooms, though not large, are stylishly appointed with striking soft furnishings, muted colours and harmonious fittings. Accessories include mini-bars, hairdryers and remote-control radio and TVs including satellite stations. Stunning marble-fitted bathrooms have two showers, soft towels, fine toiletries and telephone extensions. A clubby bar has walls hung with hundreds of pictures and there's a small lounge. Young, efficient staff. No dining room as such, but light meals are served in the bar, open long hours for such dishes as houmus with ciabàtta and salad, grilled king prawns with spicy mayonnaise, bacon and goat's cheese salad and fillet steak *See over* with French fries. A good selection of wine is available by bottle, half bottle and glass. *Browns* restaurant (under the same ownership as the hotel) is two minutes away. ***Rooms** 30. Garden, punting. Closed 24-26 Dec.* AMERICAN EXPRESS® *Access, Diners, Visa.*

Oxford **Randolph Hotel** 68% £161

Tel 0865 247481 Fax 0865 791678 **H**

Beaumont Street Oxford Oxfordshire OX1 2LN **Map 15 D2**

With a neo-Gothic facade facing the Ashmolean museum, the Randolph is Oxford's best-known hotel. The grand, oak-panelled foyer with high vaulted ceiling and sweeping staircase sets the tone for the day rooms, which include an elegant, chandeliered lounge, clubby bar with red leather armchairs, and Spires restaurant where good breakfasts are served under a splendid plasterwork ceiling. Bedrooms vary in size from small to spacious and include a number of suites. A fairly extensive room-service menu is available throughout the day and evening. Wine bar in the vaults open 11-11 (except Sun). Guaranteed free parking for residents. Forte Grand. ***Rooms** 109. Kiosk, coffee shop (10-8).* AMERICAN EXPRESS® *Access, Diners, Visa.*

Oxford **Places of Interest**

Tourist Information Tel 0865 726871.
Oxford United Football Ground Manor Ground Tel 0865 61503.
Kirtlington Park Polo Club Bicester Tel 0869 50777.
Oxford University Polo Club c/o Wolfson College Tel 0865 274100.
Oxford Ice Rink Tel 0865 248076.
Oxford Cathedral Tel 0865 276155.

Theatres and Concert Halls

Apollo Theatre Tel 0865 244554.
Pegasus Theatre Tel 0865 722851.
Oxford Playhouse Tel 0865 247134.

Historic Houses, Castles and Gardens

Waterperry Gardens Nr Wheatley Tel 0844 339226.
Kingston House Kingston Bagpuiz, Nr Abingdon Tel 0865 820259.

Museums and Art Galleries

The Ashmolean Museum of Art and Archaeology Tel 0865 278000.
Museum of Modern Art Tel 0865 722733.
Museum of Oxford Tel 0865 815559.
The Oxford Story Tel 0865 728822.
The Pitt Rivers Museum Tel 0865 270927.

Padstow **Seafood Restaurant** ★↑ £76

Tel 0841 532485 Fax 0841 533344 **RR**

Riverside Padstow Cornwall PL28 8BY **Map 12 B3**

For eighteen years the Seafood Restaurant has reigned supreme in Cornwall if not the UK for fresh fish. Chef-patron Rick Stein, a quietly unassuming and modest character, has an understanding of his craft and raw materials that helps produce food of quality to make a meal here an experience to both savour and admire. Drinks taken in the conservatory come served with a simple jar of Greek black and green olives, freshly baked baguettes and brown bread – all quality hallmarks showing attention to details. Menus range from a simpler lunch choice where just one dish can be had to an evening menu that could include seafood risotto or grilled sea bass with salsa verde; these illustrate a more Mediterranean influence against a French style classic of a 'fruits de mer' that provides as much theatre as does the plainly decorated but bustling restaurant. Desserts (West Country Dessert of the Year regional winner) might range from traditional bread-and-butter pudding to lemon tart, sticky toffee pudding or outstanding light and dark chocolate parfait with mint sauce. Don't expect service to be as attentive as in a more formal restaurant – it is not their style. There's a very fairly priced wine list with lost of good drinking under £20. Diverse house selection, and note the few bin ends at almost giveaway prices. ***Seats** 70. Parties 12. L 12.30-2.15 D 7-9.30. Closed Sun, late Dec-end Feb. Set L £19.25 Set D £26.50.* AMERICAN EXPRESS *Access, Visa.*

Rooms **£73**

Ten individually decorated bedrooms above the restaurant provide some very comfortable accommodation; light and airy colour schemes plus televisions, mini-bar and tea/coffee making facilities are standard features. Two rooms have private balconies with views of the harbour. All rooms have stylish bathrooms en suite, most with good shower baths. Breakfast taken in the restaurant includes English, kippers or Continental, the nearby delicatessen providing many of the items consumed.

Padstow Place of Interest

Polzeath Beach.

Paignton Palace Hotel 60% £100

Tel 0803 555121 Fax 0803 527974 **H**

Esplanade Road Paignton Devon TQ4 6BJ **Map 13 D3**

Traditional seaside hotel overlooking the pier and Torbay beyond. Good leisure amenities and conference facilities for up to 50. Forte Heritage. ***Rooms** 52. Garden, outdoor swimming pool, keep-fit equipment, sauna, spa bath, solarium, beautician, hair salon, tennis, pool table.* AMERICAN EXPRESS *Access, Diners, Visa.*

Paignton Redcliffe Hotel 60% £90

Tel 0803 526397 Fax 0803 528030 **H**

Marine Drive Paignton Devon TQ3 2NL **Map 13 D3**

A round tower is the central feature of this distinctive turn-of-the-century hotel on Paignton seafront dividing Paignton and Preston beaches. Day rooms enjoy the view, as do some of the bedrooms, which include seven low-ceilinged rooms of character in the tower. A private tunnel leading to the beach is of particular appeal to children. ***Rooms** 59. Outdoor swimming pool, hairdressing, putting, games room. Access, Visa.*

Paignton Places of Interest

Tourist Information Tel 0803 558383.
Compton Castle Tel 0803 872112.
Paignton Zoo Tel 0803 557479.
Paignton Sands Beach.

Painswick Painswick Hotel 70% £95

Tel 0452 812160 Fax 0452 812059 **H**

Kemps Lane Painswick Gloucestershire GL6 6YB **Map 14 B2**

Tucked away down the narrow streets behind the church in one of the most architecturally interesting Cotswold villages, the Painswick Hotel is a grand Palladian mansion. Numerous intriguing features include an Italianate loggia overlooking the croquet lawn in gardens that also enclose a 'grotto' built by a vicar (this was once the Rectory) to amplify his sermons and an elaborate ribbed ceiling in the former chapel, now the bar. Elegant day rooms – some occasionally used for meetings – boast some fine antiques and paintings. It's run in relaxed style by the Moore family and any lack of polish in the service is compensated for by the friendly atmosphere. Accommodation varies from spacious rooms with some notable antiques, objets d'art and stylish fabrics in the original building to smaller rooms with more modest pieces and some modern furniture in a newer wing but all have extras like magazines, mineral water and

See over

bathrobes. Breakfasts with freshly squeezed orange juice and some lovely smoky bacon is the best meal of the day here. ***Rooms** 19. Garden.* American Express *Access, Visa.*

Parkgate Ship Hotel 58% £60

Tel 051-336 3931 Fax 051-353 0051 **H**

The Parade Parkgate The Wirral Cheshire L64 6SA **Map 6 A2**

A small stone-fronted Forte hotel overlooking the Dee estuary; the Birdwatchers bar (serving real ale) has picture windows from which to observe the wildlife on the salt marshes. The two front bedrooms have four-poster beds and the best views. ***Rooms** 26.* American Express *Access, Diners, Visa.*

Parkham Penhaven Country House 64% £98

Tel 0237 451388 Fax 0237 451878 **H**

Parkham nr Bideford Devon EX39 5PL **Map 12 C2**

Maxine and Alan Wade are the friendly hosts at a small 19th-century hotel whose setting in the Devon countryside includes 11 acres of gardens and a nature trail. Inside, all is spick and span, from the bar with its log fire to the bedrooms – these range from standard to 'super-de-luxe' and six cottage suites. All rooms have both bath and shower. No smoking in the restaurant. No children under ten. Turn left at Horns Cross on the A39; 1½ miles into Parkham village then first left. ***Rooms** 12. Garden.* American Express *Access, Diners, Visa.*

Paulerspury Vine House £55

Tel 032 733 267 Fax 032 733 309 **RR**

High Street Paulerspury Northamptonshire NN12 7NA **Map 15 D1**

A 300-year-old village-centre limestone cottage a few miles south of Towcester and a mile off the A5 is now a restaurant with rooms that exudes charm and hospitality. A tiny, cosy bar serves for pre-dinner drinks while the dining room is spacious, bright and, though modernised, still retains much of its original charm. Marcus Springett offers a short, daily-changing menu of excellent seasonal produce. Although the dishes can appear complex and involved, resulting combinations demonstrate a high level of expertise in the kitchen. This is very much bourgeois cooking that is rich, with cream and butter much in evidence. Two crisp rice and prawn croquettes coloured with saffron stigmas arrive with a deliciously creamy leek sauce. Calf's liver is served with buttered marrowfat peas and a smoked bacon sauce and two large pan-fried mackerel fillets are accompanied by a wonderfully crispy bubble and squeak cake and a stunning caper and mustard sauce. Pleasing wine list with lots of bottles under £20, and New World wines particularly keenly priced. Polite, discreet service by Julie Springett. ***Seats** 45. Parties 25. Private Room 12. L 12-2.30 D 7-10. Closed L Mon & Sat, D Sun (except for residents). Set L £13.95 Set D £19.50. Access, Visa.*

Rooms £62

There's a quiet lounge for residents, who have the pleasure of sleeping in one of the 6 prettily decorated bedrooms. Though not large they are well equipped and each has neat en-suite facilities.

Penkridge William Harding's House £45

Tel 078 571 2955 **R**

Mill Street Penkridge Stafford Staffordshire ST19 5AY **Map 6 B3**

Leave the M6 at Junction 12 or 13 and take the A449. Built as a stable in 1693 and occupied by Cromwell's men during the Civil War, this is a small, cottagey restaurant run by Fiona and Eric Bickley. Eric's frequently-changing fixed-price menu can be both classic and enterprising:

rhubarb soufflé served cold with a sliced breast of chicken dressed with sesame seed oil, Cornish crab soup with a hint of sherry, roast brace of boned quail on fresh pineapple and blackcurrants with kirsch, paupiettes of Dover sole with a salmon mousseline. Sunday lunch offers a choice of four dishes for each course. Puddings and British cheeses are served from a sideboard. ***Seats** 24. Parties 18. Private Room 20. L (First & last Sun in month only) 12.30-1.45 D 7.30-9.30. Closed D Sun & Mon, Bank Holidays. Set D £18.45. Access, Visa.*

Penrith — Forte Travelodge

£42

Tel 0768 66958

L

Redhills Penrith Cumbria CA11 0DT

Map 4 C3

¼ mile west of Junction 40 of the M6, 15 miles east of Keswick on the A66. ***Rooms** 32. AMERICAN EXPRESS Access, Visa.*

Penrith — North Lakes Hotel — 71%

£108

Tel 0768 68111 Fax 0768 68291

H

Ullswater Road Penrith Cumbria CA11 8QT

Map 4 C3

A stern-looking hotel, by Junction 40 of the M6, which comfortably divides its time between mid-week conferences and a weekend base for Lakeland visitors. Facilities for both categories are purpose-built around a central lodge of local stone and massive railway-sleeper beams, which houses bar, lounges and coffee shop. Newest Executive-style bedrooms have raised work areas with fold-away beds, while interconnecting syndicate rooms convert handily for family use at holiday times. Children up to 12 free in parents' room. Conference and banqueting facilities for 200. Shire Inns. ***Rooms** 85. Garden, indoor swimming pool, sauna, spa bath, solarium, gymnasium, squash, snooker, coffee shop (9am-11pm). AMERICAN EXPRESS Access, Diners, Visa.*

Penrith — Places of Interest

Acorn Bank Garden (NT) Temple Sowerby Tel 07683 61893.
Dalemain Dacre Tel 07684 86450.

Penzance — Abbey Hotel — 67%

£75

Tel 0736 66906 Fax 0736 51163

HR

Abbey Street Penzance Cornwall TR18 4AR

Map 12 A4

The truly delightful Abbey Hotel is perched above and overlooks the quay in a quiet backwater of town. Jean and Michael Cox describe themselves as the decorators, but this understates the case: their house is a model of good taste, replete with their collections of antiques and fine art, deep armchairs and abundant reading material. Stylish bedrooms retain the building's uniqueness and charm, using colour and light to great advantage where space is limited. "Not a family hotel." ***Rooms** 7. Garden. AMERICAN EXPRESS Access, Visa.*

Restaurant

£58

Do book as, with only six tables, non-residents are only welcomed as space allows, but don't expect any great sense of occasion. A table d'hote offers three choices per course nightly, with vegetarian alternatives always available. Thus a starter may be grilled sardines with mustard mayonnaise or aubergine and red pepper cream soup followed by a seafood gratin of sole, monkfish and prawns or roast quail or pheasant. ***Seats** 18. Parties 6. D only 7.30-8.30. Set D £21.50.*

Set menu prices may not always include service or wine.

Penzance — Berkeley Restaurant — £50

Tel 0736 62541 — R

Abbey Street Penzance Cornwall TR18 4AW — Map 12 A4

On a hillside above the harbour, this tiny first-floor restaurant run by Ian and Denise Morris is part of the Club Zero night club. The food is straightforward, well prepared and cooked to order – from home-made soup and hot garlic mushrooms topped with crab to Dover sole, steaks, chicken and pork dishes. Pasta is always popular (try the home-made tagliatelle with cream and mushroom sauce or tortelloni filled with meat, mortadella and herbs and served with a cream and Parmesan cheese sauce). There's never a rush as a table is allocated for the whole evening, and diners may dance in the club until 1am. ***Seats** 34. D 7.30-10.30. Closed D Sun & Mon in summer (also Tue & Wed in winter), 25 & 26 Dec.* AMERICAN EXPRESS *Access, Visa.*

Penzance — Harris's — £70

Tel 0736 64408 — R

46 New Street Penzance Cornwall TR18 2LZ — Map 12 A4

Owner Roger Harris buys fresh fish from Newlyn Harbour for his friendly little restaurant opposite the Sir Humphrey Davy statue. John Dory and Dover sole (grilled or meunière) are among the favourites. The menu is balanced by meat items such as roast partridge, rack of lamb and fillet steak with a green peppercorn sauce. Vegetarians should give notice on the morning of their visit. Additional lighter lunchtime menu. ***Seats** 30. Private Room 24. L 12-2 D 7-10. Closed Sun, Mon, 25 & 26 Dec, 1 Jan.* AMERICAN EXPRESS *Access, Diners, Visa.*

Penzance — Places of Interest

Tourist Information Tel 0736 62207.
The Acorn Theatre Tel 0736 65520.
St. Michael's Mount (NT) Marazion Tel 0736 710507.
Trengwainton Garden (NT) Tel 0736 63021.
Penzance and District Museum and Art Gallery Tel 0736 63625.
Porthmeor Beach *5 miles NW Penzance.*

Peterborough — Butterfly Hotel — 63% — £70

Tel 0733 64240 Fax 0733 65538 — H

Thorpe Meadows Longthorpe Parkway Peterborough Cambridgeshire PE3 6GA — Map 7 E4

One of a small chain of modern, low-rise brick-built East Anglian hotels (the others are in Bury St Edmunds, Colchester and King's Lynn). Peterborough's Butterfly sits at the water's edge, overlooking Thorpe Meadows rowing lake. Neat, practical accommodation ranges from studio singles to four suites. Children up to eight stay free in parents' room. ***Rooms** 70.* AMERICAN EXPRESS *Access, Diners, Visa.*

Peterborough — Forte Posthouse — 60% — £68

Tel 0733 240209 Fax 0733 244455 — H

Great North Road Norman Cross Peterborough Cambridgeshire PE7 3TB — Map 7 E4

Business hotel at the Norman Cross roundabout on the A1. Good leisure facilities and the usual good Forte value. Meeting rooms for up to 45. Children up to 16 stay free in parents' room. ***Rooms** 90. Indoor swimming pool, gymnasium, sauna, spa bath, solarium, beauty salon, baby listening.* AMERICAN EXPRESS *Access, Diners, Visa.*

Peterborough **Forte Travelodge** **£42**

Tel 0733 231109 **L**

Alwalton Village Nr Peterborough Cambridgeshire PE7 3UR **Map 7 E4**

On the A1 Great North Road southbound, 3 miles from the centre of Peterborough. ***Rooms** 32.* AMERICAN EXPRESS *Access, Visa.*

Peterborough **Moat House** **64%** **£92**

Tel 0733 260000 Fax 0733 262737 **H**

Thorpe Wood Peterborough Cambridgeshire PE3 6SG **Map 7 E4**

Two miles west of the city centre by the Thorpe Wood golf course, a modern redbrick hotel offering extensive leisure and air-conditioned conference facilities; the largest room can take up to 400 delegates. 45 of the bedrooms are reserved for non-smokers. ***Rooms** 125. Indoor swimming pool, gymnasium, sauna, spa baths, solarium.* AMERICAN EXPRESS *Access, Diners, Visa.*

Peterborough **Swallow Hotel** **69%** **£99**

Tel 0733 371111 Fax 0733 236725 **H**

Lynch Road Peterborough Cambridgeshire PE2 0GB **Map 7 E4**

Modern, low-rise hotel by the A605, two minutes from the A1 (take Alwalton-Chesterton-Business Park & Showground sign). Spacious public areas are bright and airy. Extensive leisure and conference facilities. ***Rooms** 163. Garden, indoor swimming pool, keep-fit equipment, sauna, spa bath, steam room, solarium, beauty & hair salon.* AMERICAN EXPRESS *Access, Diners, Visa.*

Peterborough **Places of Interest**

Tourist Information Tel 0733 317336.
Key Theatre Tel 0733 52439.
Lady Lodge Arts Centre Tel 0733 237073.
Peterborough Cathedral Tel 0733 43342.
Peterborough Museum and Art Gallery Tel 0733 43329.
East of England Ice Rink Tel 0733 260222.
East of England Showground Tel 0733 234451.
Peakirk Wildfowl Trust Tel 0733 252271.

Petersfield **Langrish House** **63%** **£63**

Tel 0730 66941 Fax 0730 60543 **H**

Langrish Petersfield Hampshire GU32 1RN **Map 15 D3**

Built around the heart of a 16th-century farmhouse, the house stands in rolling countryside three miles out of Petersfield off the A272. Bedrooms have peaceful pastoral views, traditional furnishings and a few homely extras. The basement bar was reputedly excavated by Royalist prisoners taken at the Civil War's Battle of Cheriton after which they ended up in their own prison! ***Rooms** 18. Garden. Closed 25 Dec-1 Jan.* AMERICAN EXPRESS *Access, Diners, Visa.*

Pingewood **Kirtons Farm Hotel & Country Club** **60%** **NEW** **£100**

Tel 0734 500885 Fax 0734 391996 **H**

Pingewood Reading Berkshire RG3 3UN **Map 15 D2**

Unexceptional standardised bedrooms (those in the new wing are best) except that each has a balcony overlooking the lake where the European water-ski champsionships are sometimes held. Residential conferences are the main business during the week but at weekends it's the extensive leisure facilities of the adjacent country club (also available to hotel

See over

guests) that are the big attraction. 24 hr room service. Near junction 11 of the M4 but ask for detailed directions when booking. Resort Hotels. ***Rooms** 81. Indoor swimming pool, gymnasium, squash, spa baths, sauna, steam room, solarium, beauty & hair salon, snooker, tennis, water-skiing.* AMERICAN EXPRESS *Access, Diners, Visa.*

Pitton **Silver Plough** £55

Tel 0722 72266 **R**

Pitton nr Salisbury Wiltshire SP5 1DZ **Map 14 C3**

An object lesson in good pub-keeping, where a young and professional team are dedicated to quality food, wines and beers. Talented chef Joanne Docherty sets out a blackboard menu featuring fresh dishes in addition to a fixed-price 2-or 3-course printed menu (with a separate vegetarian menu as an option). Dishes show eclectic influences cleverly mixed together in unusual ways: brandade of peppered mackerel in puff pastry, scaloppine of lemon chicken with spinach and beetroot, spiced red mullet fillets with fried aubergine and cucumber raita. Bar snacks range from *soupe au pistou* to tossed Greek salad with feta cheese and olives, and spicy Thai fish curry. Good British cheeses for ploughman's lunches and a choice of roasts at Sunday lunchtime. Several good wines at bargain prices. The main restaurant is in a lower level extension of the original farmhouse, though part of the bar has attractively clothed tables, cosily clustered around the open fire in winter; families with well-behaved children should head for the snug bar and skittle alley. Tables out in the garden in summer. ***Seats** 40. L 12-2 D 7-10. Closed D Sun, 25 Dec, Jan & Feb. Set L £11.95/£13.95 Set D £12.95/£15.95.* AMERICAN EXPRESS *Access, Visa.*

Plumtree **Perkins Bar Bistro** £50

Tel 0602 373695 **R**

Old Railway Station, Station Road Plumtree
Nottinghamshire NG12 5NA **Map 7 D3**

Tony and Wendy Perkins bought an old railway station in 1982, and their conversion work has added a delightful conservatory. France is the main influence on the decor and in the kitchen, which includes wood pigeon St Germain, moules marinière, poached salmon véronique and steak béarnaise in its varied repertoire. Traditional values (properly made stocks and sauces) ally with modern presentation and the place has a very happy, relaxed atmosphere. ***Seats** 75. Private Room 30. L 12-2 D 7-9.45. Closed Sun & Mon, 25 & 26 Dec, 1 Jan, Tues after Easter.* AMERICAN EXPRESS *Access, Diners, Visa*

Plymouth **Boringdon Hall** 70% £65

Tel 0752 344455 Fax 0752 346578 **H**

Colebrook Plympton Plymouth Devon PL7 4DP **Map 12 C3**

1587 saw the transformation of older buildings (originally a monastery) into today's handsome and stately manor house, and Sir Francis Drake was guest of honour at the inaugural grand banquet. A spectacular bar in the Great Hall provides a focal point, overlooked by both restaurant and minstrel's gallery. Above, tower bedrooms feature carved four-posters and matching period furniture. Extensions, externally clad in original stone, stand around a courtyard alongside the leisure club (the latter is not the only modern feature, for Boringdon also boasts extensive conference facilities). Children up to the age of 16 free in parents' room. ***Rooms** 40. Garden, indoor swimming pool, gymnasium, sauna, tennis, pitch & putt.* AMERICAN EXPRESS *Access, Diners, Visa.*

Our inspectors are full-time employees; they are professionally trained by us.

Plymouth — Campanile Hotel — £44

Tel 0752 601087 Fax 0752 223213 — **L**

Marsh Mills Longbridge Road Plymouth Devon PL6 8LD — **Map 12 C3**

Off a roundabout junction on the A38, heading towards Cornwall. ***Rooms** 50.* AMERICAN EXPRESS *Access, Diners, Visa.*

Plymouth — Chez Nous ★ — £94

Tel 0752 266793 — **R**

13 Frankfort Gate Plymouth Devon PL1 1QA — **Map 12 C3**

For the past dozen or so years the charming Marchals have put their personal stamp on a tiny piece of France in a modest, tree-lined shopping precinct. Although the atmosphere within is that of a bistro, the cooking is stylish and rewarding – a nice surprise for first-time diners, although the menu prices give the game away! Jacques' "Cuisine Spontanée" is truly of the moment, relying entirely on the best local produce in its season, and his specialities from the blackboard menu (admirably translated by Suzanne) are models of consistency. *Cassolette d'escargots aux champignons, asperges tièdes aux truffes, filet de boeuf à la moelle et porto,* and *le retour de peche au safran* are representative dishes. Fine desserts and exclusively French cheeses, plus a well-balanced list of mainly French wines with decent house selections and good half bottles. Convenient local parking. ***Seats** 28. L 12.30-2 D 7-10.30. Closed Sun & Mon, Bank Holidays, 3 weeks Feb, 3 weeks Sep. Set meals £26.50.* AMERICAN EXPRESS *Access, Diners, Visa.*

Plymouth — Copthorne Hotel — 70% — £118

Tel 0752 224161 Fax 0752 670688 — **H**

Armada Way Plymouth Devon PL1 1AR — **Map 12 C3**

Follow the signs for the city centre, then signs for the ferry port. The Copthorne is at North Cross roundabout, opposite Plymouth University. It's an attractive hotel, with the light and elegant decor in the foyer setting the overall tone; other public areas include a restaurant, brasserie (open 10-10), Gallery cocktail bar and lounge. Bedrooms include Classic (singles), Connoisseur and suites all with contemporary fitted furniture and plenty of writing space; there are rooms for non-smokers and one for disabled guests; tiled bathrooms have good counter space and large, well-lit mirrors. Children up to 16 stay free in parents' room. Ample free parking. Greatly reduced weekend rates (Fri-Sun). Facilities for banquets and conferences (up to 50). ***Rooms** 135. Indoor swimming pool, gymnasium, sauna, solarium, kiosk.* AMERICAN EXPRESS *Access, Diners, Visa.*

Plymouth — Forte Posthouse — 65% — £68

Tel 0752 662828 Fax 0752 660974 — **H**

Cliff Road The Hoe Plymouth Devon PL1 3DL — **Map 12 C3**

High-riser with fine views from its prime position on the Hoe. Formerly the *Forte Crest*. Conferences for up to 100, banqueting to 80. ***Rooms** 106. Garden, outdoor swimming pool.* AMERICAN EXPRESS *Access, Diners, Visa.*

Plymouth — Moat House — 70% — £118

Tel 0752 662866 Fax 0752 673816 — **H**

Armada Way Plymouth Devon PL1 2HJ — **Map 12 C3**

Day rooms at this high-rise hotel, in particular the penthouse restaurant and bar, command spectacular views of the Hoe and Plymouth Sound. So do many of the good-sized, picture-windowed bedrooms, which have double beds (twins have two double beds), seating areas and plenty of writing space. On the ground floor the large, bright reception area includes the relaxing International Bar. Conference and banqueting

See over

facilities for up to 400. Children under 16 are accommodated free if sharing their parents' room. ***Rooms** 212. Indoor swimming pool, gymnasium, sauna, steam room, solarium, games room.* AMERICAN EXPRESS *Access, Diners, Visa.*

Plymouth — Novotel — 62% — £70

Tel & Fax 0752 221422 — H

Marsh Mills Roundabout Plymouth Devon PL6 8NH — **Map 12 C3**

Practical modern accommodation and conference/banqueting facilities (for up to 240 delegates) on the A38 two miles from the town centre. ***Rooms** 100. Garden.* AMERICAN EXPRESS *Access, Diners, Visa.*

Plymouth — Places of Interest

Tourist Information Tel 0752 264849.
Athenaeum Theatre Tel 0752 266079.
Theatre Royal Tel 0752 668.
City Museum and Art Gallery Tel 0752 264878.
Plymouth Argyle Football Ground Home Park Tel 0752 562561.
Dartmoor Wildlife Park Sparkwell Tel 0755 37209.
Historic Houses, Castles and Gardens
Saltram House (NT) Tel 0752 336546.
Antony House, Woodland Garden and Natural Woods(NT) Torpoint Tel 0752 812191.
Mount Edgcumbe House & Country Park Tel 0752 822236.

Pocklington — Feathers Hotel — £48

Tel 0759 303155 Fax 0759 304382 — I

Market Place Pocklington Humberside YO4 2UN — **Map 7 D1**

A friendly market-town inn, 15 minutes drive from York, useful to know in an area with a dearth of decent accommodation. Main-house rooms include a conservatory and a bridal suite with a four-poster bed. Six rooms with bow-fronted windows are in the stone-clad annexe. Two conference rooms. Free parking for up to 60 cars. No dogs. ***Rooms** 12. Garden.* AMERICAN EXPRESS *Access, Diners, Visa.*

Podimore — Forte Travelodge — £42

Tel 0935 840074 — L

Podimore nr Yeovil Somerset BA22 8JG — **Map 13 F2**

On the A303, 6 miles north of Yeovil and adjacent to the junction with the A37. ***Rooms** 31.* AMERICAN EXPRESS *Access, Visa.*

Polperro — Kitchen at Polperro — £55

Tel 0503 72780 — R

The Coombs Polperro Cornwall PL13 2RQ — **Map 12 C3**

Park in the village car park and walk down to Ian and Vanessa Bateson's lovely little restaurant. The cooking is enjoyable and unpretentious, the menus interesting and varied and always with seafood at centre stage: lobster, crab, mussels baked with lemon, garlic and herb butter, prawns and ginger baked in filo pastry. Meaty dishes, too, plus a good selection of vegetarian main courses such as spinach roulade or parsnip croquettes. ***Seats** 24. Parties 6. D only 7-9.30. Closed Tue in summer, Sun-Thu in winter, 25 & 26 Dec, Jan.* AMERICAN EXPRESS *Access, Visa.*

Pool-in-Wharfedale — Pool Court ★ — £90

Tel 0532 842288 Fax 0532 843115 — RR

Pool Bank Pool-in-Wharfedale Otley West Yorkshire LS21 1EH — **Map 6 C1**

While others around it have come and gone or else change too suddenly and unpredictably for any degree of consistency, Pool Court soldiers on serenely, continuing to offer truly exemplary standards of comfort, service and food. The fine Georgian mansion is run with style and panache by Michael Gill, his wife Hanni, and a long-serving dedicated team headed by manager Steve Ridealgh. No detail is overlooked and the whole place, even the exterior, is beautifully maintained. This almost obsessive quest for perfection has drawn criticisms of blandness, even sobermindedness. The decor can certainly be described as 'safe' with its pale greys, creams, oatmeals and caramels but there's nothing intrinsically wrong with a soothing and relaxing enviroment such as is to be found here. David Watson's range of menus includes healthy eating options. The set 'signature' menu offers carefully balanced courses and includes three glasses of well-chosen complementary wines. The traditional menu is of two, three or four courses while the à la carte is relatively short, with four starters and main dishes – all simpler in style than the rest; for example, fish cakes with a sweetcorn and tartare sauce, roast sirloin salad with new potatoes and horseradish mustard and chargrilled chicken with saffron mashed potato and *pistou*. Choices are made in the bar after a small appetiser of, say, chargrilled salmon with a Mediterranean salad. At the table each place setting has an individual printed card showing the diner's choice. There is no lack of imagination and flair in the cooking with well-conceived combinations as queen scallops and smoked salmon with sour cream and caviar on brioche or a salad of Scarborough woof with lobster, baby leeks and shallots. Main dishes such as Cantonese-style duck – the leg steamed in ginger and garlic, the breast roasted with five spice and served with noodles or best end of lamb with artichoke, foie gras, sweetbread ravioli and sherry sauce, show that current modish culinary trends are selectively pursued and with exceedingly good results. The attention to detail extends to delicious sweets such as a hot raspberry soufflé or a chocolate tart served with white chocolate ice cream. Not one, but two house selections on a wine list that offers plenty of good and interesting wines under £25, some under £9! Now open on Mondays. ***Seats** 65. Private Room 36. D only 7-9.30. Closed Sun, Bank Holidays, 2 weeks Christmas. Set D £24.50/£28.50/£32.50 & £37.50.* American Express *Access, Diners, Visa.*

Rooms £95

The six bedrooms mirror the painstaking attention to detail given to the rest of the place. Monogrammed fine cotton sheets, be-ribboned baskets of all manner of fruits, indeed almost every conceivable pampering extra ensure a supremely comfortable and civilised night's sleep. Well-lit bathrooms are immaculate with the likes of body lotions, excellent soaps, thick cosseting towels and bathrobes provided in each. Super breakfasts are served only in the bedrooms.

Poole Haven Hotel 69% £145

Tel 0202 707333 Fax 0202 708796 **HR**

Banks Road Sandbanks Poole Dorset BH13 7QL **Map 14 C4**

Follow signs to the Swanage ferry to find the Haven, right by the water's edge at the entrance to the world's second largest natural harbour giving most of the bedrooms (many with balconies) fine views either of Brownsea Island and the Purbeck hills or across the Solent to the Isle of Wight. Comfortable rather than luxurious, with lightwood furniture and matching bedcovers and curtains, the rooms are immaculately well kept, as in the whole hotel. Inviting public areas include the beamed Marconi lounge (he made the first wireless telegraph broadcast from here) with leather chesterfields, and a splendid conservatory with comfortably upholstered 'garden' furniture and waterside terrace beyond. The exceptionally comprehensive leisure centre includes both indoor and outdoor pools, just a few steps beyond which is a sandy beach. Possibly the most luxurious gents loos of any hotel in the country are the latest addition to this constantly improving hotel. There's also a fine, purpose-built business centre adjacent to the hotel. No children under 5, but 5-12 year olds stay free in parents' room. ***Rooms** 95. Indoor & outdoor swimming pools,*

See over

gymnasium, squash, sauna, spa bath, steam room, solarium, beauty salon, hairdressing, tennis. AMERICAN EXPRESS *Access, Diners, Visa.*

Restaurant £55

Large, 20s-style dining room with short but well-balanced table d'hote dinner menu: roulade of chicken and asparagus; roast sirloin of Scottish beef with roast garlic, shallots and Brouilly sauce; poached salmon with noodles and basil-scented sauce; warm tart of poached pear; iced banana parfait – supplemented by a varied grill menu. Well-thought-out dishes are reliably cooked and swiftly served. Lunch is a buffet/carvery affair. No children after 7pm. Light lunches are also available in the conservatory. ***Seats** 150. Parties 24. L 12.30-2 D 7-9.30. Set L £13.50 Set D £20.*

La Roche £80

The more intimate à la carte restaurant where chef Karl Heinz Nagler is able to give full rein to his undoubted skills. The sophisticated black-edged decor is a suitable foil to equally sophisticated dishes such as a terrine of chicken and lobster in tarragon jelly; millefeuille of scallops on a bed of spinach with cumin fondue; venison with endives and forest mushrooms in a game jus with bitter chocolate; papillote of sea bass and, to finish, hot banana soufflé or flambé of fresh strawberries with green peppercorns and home-made ice cream. A carefully chosen wine list includes several fine wines by the glass – kept in good condition by the 'Chambrair' system. No children under 10 years. ***Seats** 30. Parties 8. D only 7-10.30. Closed Sun, Mon, 25 & 26 Dec.*

Poole Hospitality Inn 63% £78

Tel 0202 666800 Fax 0202 684470 **H**

The Quay Poole Dorset BH15 1HD **Map 14 C4**

Many rooms overlook the harbour at this modern two-storey, red-brick hotel on the quay (signposted from the town centre). Neat practical bedrooms include 20 reserved for non-smokers. Children under 14 stay free in parents' room. Mount Charlotte Thistle. ***Rooms** 68.* AMERICAN EXPRESS *Access, Diners, Visa.*

Poole Mansion House 74% £110

Tel 0202 685666 Fax 0202 665709 **HR**

11 Thames Street Poole Dorset BH15 1JN **Map 14 C4**

Facing St James Church across a tiny square, the marble-pillared portico and tall, arched windows of the Mansion House epitomise Georgian elegance. It is only a stone's throw from bustling Poole quay, yet it affords an oasis of calm within. The best bedrooms are generously proportioned and airy, although some others are rather less so. Each is decorated in individual style and furnished with fine antiques, to which today's more modern necessities have been sympathetically added. More thoughtful, homely extras extend to mineral water, fresh fruit and boiled sweets in the rooms plus complimentary early morning tea tray and choice of newspaper. Children up to 12 stay free in parents' room. No dogs. ***Rooms** 28.* AMERICAN EXPRESS *Access, Diners, Visa.*

Restaurant £62

A smart dining club, also open to the public, where hotel residents receive the same generous discounts as club members on the well-balanced table d'hote menu. Local seafood is well represented alongside such dishes as boiled beef with herb and horseradish dumplings; chicken, mushroom and tarragon pudding; good vegetarian options and traditional puddings. Sunday lunch sees an unusually wide choice. The clubby atmosphere successfully avoids stuffiness and service is good. ***Seats** 95. Parties 14. Private Room 40. L 12.30-2.15 D 7.30-9.30 (Sun to 9). Closed L Sat, 1 Jan, Easter Monday. Set L £13.45-£18.95 Set D from £21.*

Poole — Sandbanks Hotel — 59% — £110

Tel 0202 707377 Fax 0202 708885 — **H**

15 Banks Road Sandbanks Poole Dorset BH13 3PS — **Map 14 C4**

Ideal for families, with an attractive patio and garden leading on to the surprisingly clean sandy beach, and complete holiday services that include organised activities, a children's restaurant and a nursery. Four tiers of balconied bedrooms look either out to sea or across Poole Bay and the open-plan bar, vast sun lounge and dining rooms also enjoy panoramic views over the sea. 20 larger rooms in the original hotel building are designated as family rooms. Adult guests may use the leisure facilities at the *Haven Hotel* (see entry). No dogs. ***Rooms** 105. Garden, indoor swimming pool, sauna, steam room, solarium, spa bath, gymnasium, crèche (daily in summer), children's outdoor play area.* AMERICAN EXPRESS *Access, Diners, Visa.*

Poole — Places of Interest

Tourist Information Tel 0202 673322.
Poole Arts Centre Tel 0202 685222.
Guildhall Museum Tel 0202 675151.
Waterfront Poole Tel 0202 675151/683138.
Icetrax Ice Rink Tel 0202 716000.
Sandbanks Beach.

Porlock — Oaks Hotel — 65% — £75

Tel 0643 862265 — **HR**

Porlock Somerset TA24 8ES — **Map 13 D1**

A fine elevated position gives Tim and Anne Riley's Edwardian house great views over Porlock sweeping down to the beach and sea. It's a friendly, homely spot, with a lounge full of flowers, books and magazines and an even more intimate bar. Bedrooms are light and pretty with a mix of pine and some nice old-fashioned bedroom pieces. Service is a strong point and the whole place is kept crisp and fresh. ***Rooms** 10. Garden. No credit cards.*

Restaurant — £44

Anne's daily-changing menus are unpretentious and offer fine value. Start with soup (carrot and orange or cream of mushroom) or salmon and avocado roulade, follow with a no-choice fish course (perhaps hot smoked haddock mousse or poached salmon); main courses might include breast of duck with peppercorn sauce, leg of lamb with garlic and rosemary or grilled fillet of Exmoor venison with lemon and redcurrant sauce. Simple puddings: apple pie, rhubarb fool, ice creams, sorbets and local cheeses. Fair prices on a concise wine list. ***Seats** 24. Parties 10. D only 7-8.30. Set D £18.50.*

Portloe — Lugger Hotel — 59% — £98

Tel 0872 501322 Fax 0872 501691 — **H**

Portloe Truro Cornwall TR2 5RD — **Map 12 B3**

At Tregony, take the A3078 and two miles on fork left for Portloe. The hotel, a 17th-century inn and a smugglers' haunt in its early days, is situated on the beach. The Powell family, here since 1950, extend a very warm welcome, and there's a snug, cosy feeling in the bar and older bedrooms. Roomiest accommodation is in a modern building. No children under 12. ***Rooms** 19. Closed Dec & Jan.* AMERICAN EXPRESS *Access, Diners, Visa.*

Portsmouth — Forte Posthouse 65% — £68

Tel 0705 827651 Fax 0705 756715 — H

Pembroke Road Southsea Portsmouth Hampshire PO1 2TA — **Map 15 D4**

Near the Hovercraft terminal at Southsea, a modern hotel with leisure and business centres (conferences for up to 220, banqueting up to 180). Formerly called *Forte Crest*. ***Rooms** 163. Indoor swimming pool, gymnasium, sauna, spa bath, steam room, solarium.* AMERICAN EXPRESS *Access, Diners, Visa.*

Portsmouth — Hilton National 66% — £93

Tel 0705 219111 Fax 0705 210762 — H

Eastern Road Farlington Portsmouth Hampshire PO6 1UN — **Map 15 D4**

Modern low-rise hotel alongside M27 just off the A2050 to Southsea, and ten minutes from Portsmouth city centre. ***Rooms** 122. Indoor swimming pool, keep-fit facilities, sauna, spa bath, floodlit tennis.* AMERICAN EXPRESS *Access, Diners, Visa.*

Portsmouth — Hospitality Inn 61% — £79

Tel 0705 731281 Fax 0705 817572 — H

South Parade Southsea Portsmouth Hampshire PO4 0RN — **Map 15 D4**

Seafront with some Victorian features, but mainly modern bedrooms. Popular for conferences and functions for up to 280 people. ***Rooms** 115.* AMERICAN EXPRESS *Access, Diners, Visa.*

Portsmouth — Pendragon Hotel 59% — £87

Tel 0705 823201 Fax 0705 750283 — H

Clarence Parade Southsea Portsmouth Hampshire PO5 2HY — **Map 15 D4**

A sunny, south-facing position overlooking the Solent for a Forte hotel with a private car park (limited spaces) and free parking at the front. ***Rooms** 49. Patio.* AMERICAN EXPRESS *Access, Diners, Visa.*

Portsmouth — Portsmouth Marriott Hotel 73% — £129

Tel 0705 383151 Fax 0705 388701 — H

North Harbour Cosham Portsmouth Hampshire PO6 4SH — **Map 15 D4**

Previously the *Holiday Inn*, the hotel stands alongside the junction of the A3 and M27, a short drive from the ferry terminals and the town centre. Public areas in atrium-style include swimming pool, lounge, bar and split-level restaurant. Bedrooms on seven floors are roomy, with high standards of housekeeping, stylish wooden furniture, modern fabrics and good sized beds – all doubles and many king sized. Compact bathrooms have good showers (but smallish baths) and plenty of toiletries. Leisure facilities include a snooker room and well-kept secluded garden with barbecue. Banqueting and conference facilities up to 300. ***Rooms** 170. Garden, indoor swimming pool, keep-fit equipment, squash, sauna, spa bath, solarium, snooker, children's playroom & playground.* AMERICAN EXPRESS *Access, Diners, Visa.*

Portsmouth — Places of Interest

Tourist Information Tel 0705 832464.
Kings Theatre Tel 0705 820527.
New Theatre Royal Tel 0705 864611.
Portsmouth Cathedral Tel 0705 823300.
Portsmouth Football Ground Fratton Park Tel 0705 731204.

Museums and Art Galleries

Charles Dickens' Birthplace Museum Tel 0705 827261.
Portsmouth Naval Heritage Trust Tel 0705 861533.
HMS Victory HM Naval Base Tel 0705 819604.
Mary Rose Ship Hall and Exhibition HM Naval Base Tel 0705 750521.
The Royal Naval Museum HM Naval Base Tel 0705 733060.

D-Day Museum Tel 0705 827261.
HMS Warrior 1860 HM Naval Base Tel 0705 291379.

Powburn **Breamish House** 67% £65

Tel 066 578 266 Fax 066 578 500 **H**

Powburn Alnwick Northumberland NE66 4LL **Map 5 D1**

Originally a 17th-century farmhouse, converted to hunting lodge in the 1800s. Breamish House is an elegant Georgian-style building standing in five acres of colourful gardens just off the A697. Each bedroom is individually decorated and named after a tree from the surrounding woodland. Abundant peace and quiet are among the amenities promised by resident owners Doreen and Alan Johnson. Under-12s by arrangement only. ***Rooms*** *11. Garden. Closed Jan-1st week Feb. No credit cards.*

Powerstock **Three Horseshoes Inn** £50

Tel 0308 85328 **RR**

Powerstock Bridport Dorset DT6 3TF **Map 13 F2**

The Three Horseshoes is a stone and thatch country inn with simple country furnishings and open fires, reached by narrow winding lanes. Its restaurant comprises two pine-panelled rooms, one small and cosy, the other more roomy and airy. Fish is what chef-licensee Pat Ferguson is best known for, and the blackboard menu can include anything from freshly boiled crab or grilled lobster to fish pie, bourride and sea bass cooked in a paper bag. Meat and game dishes, too: garlic-studded rack of lamb, kidneys turbigo, venison pie; plus traditional British puddings. Must book for busy Sunday lunches in winter. Tables in the garden for summer eating. ***Seats*** *60. L 12-2 D 7-10 (to 9 Sun). Set L £10.50 (Sun £12.50).*
AMERICAN EXPRESS *Access, Visa.*

Rooms £45

Four large, traditionally-styled rooms have central heating, en-suite bathrooms and lovely views. Delightful garden. Families with children are welcome; cots available.

Prestbury **Bridge Hotel** 63% £84

Tel 0625 829326 Fax 0625 827557 **H**

New Road Prestbury nr Macclesfield Cheshire SK10 4DQ **Map 6 B2**

Old-world charm and modern convenience meet in a privately owned hotel next to the church in the centre of a pretty village. Day rooms retain some feel of the 17th-century origins, while most of the bedrooms are in a modern redbrick extension overlooking the River Bollin. ***Rooms*** *23. Garden.* AMERICAN EXPRESS *Access, Diners, Visa.*

Prestbury **The White House Manor** NEW £115

Tel 0625 829376 Fax 0625 828627 **PH**

The Village Prestbury Cheshire SK10 4HP **Map 6 B2**

Style and luxury combine in the individually themed bedrooms here; the masculine 'Trafalgar' with canopied campaign bed, rich burgundy decor and collection of naval artefacts, 'Glyndebourne' furnished with antiques and including a music centre with library of classical and modern music, or the more feminine 'Campion' with Laura Ashley fabrics and views of the garden. The likes of TV, bar and beverage facilities (there is also room service throughout the day and evening) are all neatly hidden away. Five of the bathrooms have powerful 'body jet' showers rather than tubs and one even combines with a mini Turkish steam room. Public areas are limited to a small conservatory lounge with honesty bar where breakfast is also served. ***Rooms*** *9. Garden.* AMERICAN EXPRESS *Access, Diners, Visa.*

See over

Prestbury — The White House Restaurant NEW — £65

Tel 0625 829376 Fax 0625 828627 — **R**

The Village Prestbury Cheshire SK10 4HP — **Map 6 B2**

Several hundred yards from the hotel, in the centre of the village, the restaurant shares the same sense of style and comfort as its parent. In the kitchen proprietor Ryland Wakeham and his team produce and interestingly varied menu – fricassee of Dublin Bay prawns with ginger and spring onions, bruschetta rossa, half a crispy duckling (a speciality) with cinnamon and caramelised pears, roast fillet of turbot with green salsa, fettuccine carbonara with pancetta and egg, fillet of beef with Stilton tart and Szechuan sauce. Asterisked items on the menu denote those with a minimum of oil, cream and butter for health-conscious diners. Save room for the spiced fruit sponge with custard and hot punch sauce amongst the puds. ***Seats** 60. Private Room 40. L 12-2 D 7-10 Closed D Sun, L Mon, 25 Dec & 1st wk Jan. Set L £10.95 Set D £16.95.* AMERICAN EXPRESS *Access, Diners, Visa.*

Preston — Forte Posthouse — 63% — £68

Tel 0772 259411 Fax 0772 201923 — **H**

The Ringway Preston Lancashire PR1 3AU — **Map 6 B1**

Tall redbrick hotel (formerly the *Forte Crest*) with neatly designed bedrooms, and conference facilities for up to 120. Free parking for guests' cars in an adjacent multi-storey. ***Rooms** 126.* AMERICAN EXPRESS *Access, Diners, Visa.*

Preston — Novotel — 62% — £69

Tel 0772 313331 Fax 0772 627868 — **H**

Reedfield Place Walton Summit Preston Lancashire PR5 6AB — **Map 6 B1**

Practical modern accommodation (half the rooms designated non-smoking) and conference facilities for 240. Children up to 16 stay free in parents' room. Situated on the A6, and handy for the M6 (J29) and M61 (J9). ***Rooms** 100. Outdoor swimming pool.* AMERICAN EXPRESS *Access, Diners, Visa.*

Preston — Travel Inn — £43

Tel 0772 720476 Fax 0772 729971 — **L**

Blackpool Road Lea Preston Lancashire PR4 0XL — **Map 6 B1**

***Rooms** 40.* AMERICAN EXPRESS *Access, Diners, Visa.*

Preston — Places of Interest

Tourist Information Tel 0772 53731.
Hoghton Tower Tel 025 485 2986.
Harris Museum and Art Gallery Tel 0772 58248.
Camelot Theme Park Chorley Tel 0257 455044.

Puckrup — Puckrup Hall Hotel & Golf Club — £78

Tel 0684 296200 Fax 0684 850788 — **HR**

Puckrup Tewkesbury Gloucestershire GL20 6EL — **Map 14 B1**

2 miles north of Tewkesbury on the A38, close to Junction 1 of the M50, Puckrup Hall is a Regency building standing in 140 acres of parkland that include a new 18-hole golf course. The house retains a period elegance, best displayed in the lounge, with its soft decor, comfortable sofas and fine plasterwork. The bar overlooks the croquet lawn and has a clubby atmosphere. Bedrooms, named after months and seasons, have decor and soft furnishings inspired by their names. Carpeted bathrooms, with shower fittings, have copious towels and Taylor's "green" toiletries. Informal eating in The Orangery. A major new development is on course to open soon after we go to press, with 68 further bedrooms, leisure facilities (swimming

pool, gym, aerobics studio, creche, steam room and sauna) and two more restaurants and bars. Graded at 70% in last year's Guide. Owned by Country Mansion Hotels who also run *Wood Hall* and *Moore Place* (see entries under Linton and Aspley Guise). ***Rooms** 16. Garden, golf, putting, fishing.* AMERICAN EXPRESS *Access, Diners, Visa.*

Restaurant **£85**

An elegant dining room with fine plasterwork is the setting for chef Geoff Balharrie's balanced and structured cooking. His menu offers dishes in a number of styles, including many classical main courses, plus inventive vegetarian dishes (wild mushroom and shallot sausage with creamed spinach and nutmeg fondue) and more modern offerings such as mussel and bacon brochettes with sun-dried tomatoes and shallots. The more modern style shines brightly, but traditionalists are unlikely to be disappointed (try the dish of pork 'n' bacon with pease pudding and mustard sauce), with natural flavours carefully enhanced by distinctive saucing. Good sweets and British cheeses. ***Seats** 34. Parties 10. L 12.30-2 D 7-9.30 (Fri & Sat to 10). Set L £13.50 Set D £18.50.*

Puddington Craxton Wood 70% £95

Tel 051-339 4717 Fax 051-339 1740 **HR**

Parkgate Road Puddington South Wirral Cheshire L66 9PB **Map 6 A2**

Old-fashioned standards of service and comfort hold sway at Craxton Wood, where owner/manager Mr Petranca has been greeeting guests since 1967. Extensive wooded grounds, lawns and rose gardens provide a peaceful setting and the spacious bedrooms are reassuringly traditional, with reproduction furniture, conservative decor and neat, bright bathrooms. By contrast, the bar is done out in modern greys, pinks and pastel blues, though the main feature here is the splendid view that can be had of the gardens. The lounge is more traditional in style and very formal, with the highly polished furniture that characterises the bedrooms. Children under 6 stay free in parents' room. No dogs. 6 miles from Chester, 2 miles from both the M56 and M53. ***Rooms** 14. Garden. Closed first week Jan, last 2 weeks Aug, Bank Holidays, Sun.* AMERICAN EXPRESS *Access, Diners, Visa.*

Restaurant **£70**

French menu with English translations, bright Continental service and competent cooking of fresh ingredients. Lobster and salmon soufflé, pastry-topped game consommé, scallops with chive sauce, mushroom-stuffed pheasant breast with dumplings, and steamed halibut wrapped in leeks demonstrate the à la carte style. Fixed-price menus include a six-course *menu dégustation* served for complete table parties. ***Seats** 85. Parties 50. L 12-2 D 7.30-10. Set L (inc wine) & D £19.85/£29.85.*

Puddington Place of Interest

Ness Gardens Liverpool Botanic Gardens Between Neston and Burton Tel 051 336 7769.

Pulborough Chequers Hotel 61% £69

Tel 0798 872486 Fax 0798 872715 **H**

Church Place Pulborough West Sussex RH20 1AD **Map 11 A6**

An intimate hotel, formed from a charming little Queen Anne house and adjacent stone building, which has been run, and lovingly cared for, by the Searancke family for over 30 years. A domestic scale lounge with draylon sofas and armchairs, warmed by a real fire in winter, is the main day room; there is no separate bar. Individually decorated bedrooms vary in size and furniture – one features original panelling and another a four-poster bed. Good modern bathrooms, four with shower and WC only. A splendid magnolia dominates the small garden. ***Rooms** 11. Garden, coffee shop (9.30am-5.30pm).* AMERICAN EXPRESS *Access, Diners, Visa.*

Pulborough **Stane Street Hollow** £56

Tel 0798 872819 **R**

Codmore Hill Pulborough West Sussex RH20 1BG **Map 11 A6**

Converted from two 16th-century cottages, René and Ann Kaiser's long-established, charming restaurant is built of solid Sussex stone. René's cooking is as reliably solid and resilient as the setting, with a menu that changes in its entirety every four weeks. Even after over 17 years Swiss influences are still in evidence (perhaps a *Schwarzwalder Kirsch torte* – chocolate truffle-topped chocolate sponge with cherries and kirsch), but the main theme is French, from *bouchée à l'argenteuil* (vol-au-vent filled with chicken, mushrooms and asparagus in cream sauce), roast loin of lamb with shallots and red wine sauce and casseroled guinea fowl, to curried fish dumplings, pheasant and chicken liver mousse terrine and roast breast of duck with orange sauce. There's a choice of seven dishes at each course including *assiette René* which offers a taster in miniature of four of the desserts. Lunch is a simpler, fixed-price 2-course affair with no choice (boned, stuffed leg of chicken cooked in Madeira, mint parfait with hot chocolate sauce), except on Sundays. Plenty of half bottles on the exceptionally keenly-priced wine list. ***Seats** 34. Private Rooms 14 & 24. L 12.30-1.15 (Sun to 1.30) D 7.30-9.15. Closed L Sat, D Sun, all Mon & Tue, 1 week Christmas, 1 week May, 2 weeks Oct. Set L £8.25 (£12.50/£15.50 Sun). No credit cards.*

Pulborough **Place of Interest**

Parham Elizabethan House & Gardens Parham Park Tel 0903 742021.

Purton **Pear Tree** 74% £92

Tel 0793 772100 Fax 0793 772369 **HR**

Church End Purton nr Swindon Wiltshire SN5 9ED **Map 14 C2**

400 years old but here for only 80! The solution is that this lovely old former vicarage was actually moved, stone by stone, from beside the church to its present site on the outskirts of the village in 1910. Now carefully extended – a charming, galleried atrium joins old and new – the Pear Tree is an immaculately kept and well-run hotel. Pink is the predominant colour scheme for the day rooms which, as yet, have few antiques to complement the mellow exterior. Bedrooms favour pastel hues and come with all sorts of extras from fresh flowers, sherry and mineral water to teletext on the TV and towelling robes and quality toiletries – which vary according to the gender of the guest – in the otherwise fairly standard bathrooms. ***Rooms** 18. Garden.* AMERICAN EXPRESS *Access, Diners, Visa.*

Restaurant £65

Two matching conservatories make a delightful setting in which to enjoy the lively cooking of Janet Pichel-Juan. Typical dishes on the set-price dinner menu run from skewered diced pigeon breast and mushrooms on a coarse-grain mustard sauce to strawberry and vanilla mousse on a peppermint sauce by way of lobster-sauced brill, bacon-wrapped chicken filled with goose liver (watercress sauce) and, for vegetarians, asparagus, chicory and tomato tarts with a parsley and poppy seed sauce. Good cooking, good value, good service, and good wines by the glass on a good list with personal notes on each wine. ***Seats** 60. L 12-2 D 7-9.30. Closed L Sat. Set L £17.50 Set D £27.50.*

We endeavour to be as up-to-the-minute as possible, but inevitably some changes to key personnel may occur at restaurants and hotels after the Guide goes to press.

Quorn — Quorn Grange — 67% — £94

Tel 0509 412167 Fax 0509 415621 — **HR**

Wood Lane Quorn Leicestershire LE12 8DB — **Map 7 D3**

A short drive off the A6 brings you to this extended, ivy-clad Victorian house. The addition of new rooms and self-contained function facilities has lifted it to hotel status. Twelve stylish bedrooms offer garden views and are tastefully appointed using contemporary fabrics offset against plain walls. Impressive, brightly lit bathrooms have huge mirrors, marble surrounds and powerful showers. Original bedrooms are more individual, but with simpler bathrooms. A bar-lounge is housed in a bright, plant-filled conservatory. ***Rooms*** *17. Garden.* American Express *Access, Diners, Visa.*

Restaurant — £60

Dining room windows are hung with Austrian blinds – a quietly elegant setting for chef Gordon Lang's serious cooking. Fixed-price menus are along traditional British lines (cream of vegetable soup with saffron and coriander, medallion of pork with a parsley crust and white wine sauce, treacle sponge) and there's also a short carte that covers a range from spicy coleslaw of crab and lobster with green lentils and pine nuts, to roast rabbit with creamed mustard sauce; vegetarians are usually offered a good choice of dishes. ***Seats*** *50. Parties 12. Private Room 30. L 12-2.30 D 7-9.30 (Sat to 10, Sun to 9). Closed L Sat. Set meals £13 & £16.*

Quorn — The Quorn — 72% — £102

Tel 0509 415050 Fax 0509 415557 — **H**

66 Leicester Road Quorn Leicestershire LE12 8BB — **Map 7 D3**

With gardens reaching down to the river Soar, the Quorn offers ease of access with a touch of the country thrown in. The mahogany-panelled entrance hall with its flagstones, Oriental rugs and carved stone fireplace, has a very welcoming look, and a splendid wooden staircase featuring oil paintings and a brass chandelier heightens the country house feel. Bedrooms in a modern purpose-built part are prettily decorated and tastefully furnished; appointments include air-conditioning, two armchairs and remote-control TV (some with teletext). Staff are very jolly and friendly. The hotel is in the centre of Quorn, a village which is now by-passed by the A6. ***Rooms*** *19. Garden, coarse fishing.* American Express *Access, Diners, Visa.*

Ramsbottom — Village Restaurant — £80

Tel 0706 825070 — **R**

16 Market Place Ramsbottom nr Bury Greater Manchester BL0 9HT — **Map 6 B1**

A six-course, no-choice dinner is cooked by Ros Hunter and served by Chris Johnson on Saturday nights in a style they describe as "extended dinner party"; as we went to press midweek diners in parties of less than eight were being diverted to the supper room (see below). Every care is taken in shopping and preparation of fresh fish, locally picked garden produce and fine unpasteurised British cheeses. A typical menu might offer red pepper salad with anchovy sauce, followed by Scotch broth and then brill with tomato sauce; tournedos Rossini with organic vegetables as a main course, plus cheese and a choice of four desserts – perhaps including crème brulée and banana toffee pie. Over 700 wines are available from their shop next door to which a fixed corkage charge is added. Chris, a teetotaller, also offers a nightly "by the glass" selection to complement Ros's menu. No smoking. Next door also is a coffee shop and supper room where inexpensive bistro-style lunches (Tue-Sat) and 3-course suppers (£9.50 Tue-Fri 6.30 & 9) are now served. ***Seats*** *20. Private Room 30. L 12-2.30 D 8 for 8.30. Closed Sun & Mon, 25 & 26 Dec, 1 Jan. Set D £29.50. Access, Visa.*

Ravenstonedale — Black Swan Inn — £62

Tel 053 96 23204 — I

Ravenstonedale nr Kirkby Stephen Cumbria CA17 4NG — Map 5 D3

Run by the Stuarts as a 'home-from-home', the Black Swan is a pubby, turn-of-the-century, Lakeland-stone inn, six minutes from the M6 (Junction 38) and a mere half an hour from Ullswater, useful as a base for walking and fishing. Main bedrooms in traditional style are supplemented by more modern additions in the old stables, where ramps and wide doorways offer good access for disabled guests; residents have a choice of sitting rooms. Relax in the quaint stone-walled bars with the locals or in the sheltered garden by the village beck. ***Rooms** 16. Garden, lake and river fishing, tennis.* AMERICAN EXPRESS *Access, Diners, Visa.*

Reading — Forte Posthouse — 64% — £68

Tel 0734 875485 Fax 0734 311958 — H

500 Basingstoke Road Reading Berkshire RG2 0SL — Map 15 D2

Near Junction 11 of the M4. Good leisure amenities. Banqueting and conference facilities for 100. ***Rooms** 138. Indoor swimming pool, gymnasium, spa bath, solarium.* AMERICAN EXPRESS *Access, Diners, Visa.*

Reading — Forte Travelodge — £42

Tel 0734 750618 — L

Basingstoke Road Reading Berkshire RG2 0JE — Map 15 D2

On the A33 southbound, close to Reading town centre. 1 mile north of Junction 11 of the M4. ***Rooms** 36.* AMERICAN EXPRESS *Access, Visa.*

Reading — Holiday Inn — 71% — £119

Tel 0734 391818 Fax 0734 391665 — H

Richfield Avenue Caversham Bridge Reading Berkshire RG1 8BD — Map 15 D2

Right on the edge of the river Thames, by the side of Caversham Bridge, this three-storey hotel is ultra-modern in design with a mixture of red brick and sloping roofs. Large, open-plan public rooms include a cocktail bar in the sunken lounge, and a spotless white marble foyer. Limed lightwood furniture graces the uniformly decorated bedrooms. Eight suites have private balconies with river views, good-sized sitting rooms and better quality furnishings. Centrepiece of the hotel is a restaurant with a glass pyramid roof and doors that open on to a riverside verandah. One bar is done out as the *Three Men in a Boat* tavern. Uniformed staff show an admirable willingness to help when required. Fortnightly dinner dances. Run by Queens Moat Houses; previously known as the *Caversham Hotel.* ***Rooms** 112. Indoor swimming pool, sauna, solarium, keep-fit equipment.* AMERICAN EXPRESS *Access, Diners, Visa.*

Reading — Ramada Hotel — 68% — £109

Tel 0734 586222 Fax 0734 597842 — H

Oxford Road Reading Berkshire RG1 7RH — Map 15 D2

A large modern redbrick hotel in the central area of town offering well-equipped bedrooms (all have individually controllable air-conditioning), the best of which are the Executives (worth the £5 premium) with better-quality lightwood furniture giving plenty of work space and a second telephone at the desk. Public areas were due to be refurbished in the summer of 1993 although the sunken lounge with open gas log fire and *Froggies*, an informal café/bar, are to be retained. Free parking is available in a supervised reserved section of a nearby multi-storey car park. Children under 18 stay free in parents' room. ***Rooms** 194. Indoor swimming pool, gymnasium, sauna, spa bath, sun beds, beauty salon.* AMERICAN EXPRESS *Access, Diners, Visa.*

Reading Places of Interest

Tourist Information Tel 0734 566226.
Bulmershe College Dry Ski Slope Tel 0734 663387.
Carters Ski Centre Tel 0734 55589
Historic Houses, Castles and Gardens
The Old Rectory Burghfield Tel 073529 2206.
Englefield House and Garden Theale Tel 0734 302221.
Stratfield Saye House Tel 0256 882882.
Mapledurham House Tel 0734 723350.

Redditch Campanile Hotel £44

Tel 0527 510710 Fax 0527 517269 **L**

Far Moor Lane Winyates Green Redditch Hereford & Worcester B98 0SD **Map 14 C1**

Near A435/A4032 intersection, off M42 Junction 3. ***Rooms** 50.*
AMERICAN EXPRESS *Access, Diners, Visa.*

Reeth Burgoyne Hotel 65% £60

Tel 0748 84292 Fax 0748 84619 **H**

The Green Reeth Richmond North Yorkshire DLII 6SN **Map 5 D3**

Enthusiastic owners Derek Hickson and Peter Carwardine run a small hotel overlooking the village green with a friendly atmosphere and just eight bedrooms. It has been restyled with considerable taste, and an eminently relaxing and civilised air has been created. Comfortable bedrooms are named after local villages and employ plain, but rich fabrics, freestanding furniture and homely extras such as easy chairs and magazines. Bathrooms (three of which are not en suite but have private facilities) are neatly up-to-date. Downstairs a refined air prevails in the two lounges, which have plump-cushioned sofas; one of the rooms is non-smoking as are all the bedrooms. ***Rooms** 8. Garden. Access, Visa.*

Reigate La Barbe £60

Tel 0737 241966 **R**

71 Bell Street Reigate Surrey RH2 7AN **Map 11 A5**

An informal, bistro-like setting with high-backed settles and pine fittings, on the edge of the town centre. Set-price menus change every two months or so and offer a fair choice of freshly prepared dishes. Snails in garlic butter and noisettes of lamb with garlic cloves cooked in goose fat are among the many old favourites, while monkfish terrine in aspic with a tarragon sauce, rabbit and coarse mustard casserole and pan-fried salmon steak with sorrel sauce typify the style. Main courses are served with seasonal vegetables and gratin dauphinois, although boiled potatoes are available on request. A good-value, 2-course *menu du jour* is noted on a blackboard at lunchtime. Vegetarians should notify their requirements in advance. Pear mousse with raspberry purée, dark chocolate charlotte and parfait nougatine might appear on the dessert menu. French cheeses are served from a trolley. Dishes are helpfully (and interestingly) cross-referenced with wines on the well-described list. Car parking immediately opposite. See also entry in Cranleigh (*La Barbe Encore*). ***Seats** 70. Private Room 30. L 12-2 D 7-10. Closed L Sat, all Sun, Bank Holidays (open Good Friday), 25-27 Dec. Set L £9.90/£15.45/£16.95 Set D £18.45/£19.95.* AMERICAN EXPRESS *Access, Visa.*

Reigate Bridge House 61% £83

Tel 0737 246801 Fax 0737 223756 **H**

Reigate Hill Reigate Surrey RH2 9RP **Map 11 A5**

On the A217, just off Junction 8 of the M25, 15 minutes from Gatwick Airport. From its position high on Reigate Hill, this modern hotel enjoys impressive views across the valley. Bedrooms are of a good size, with smart *See over* darkwood units; the best rooms have south-facing balconies and good views, while rear rooms have poor outlooks but are very quiet. No dogs. ***Rooms** 37.* AMERICAN EXPRESS *Access, Diners, Visa.*

Renishaw **Sitwell Arms** 61% £60

Tel 0246 435226 Fax 0246 433915 **H**

39 Station Road Renishaw nr Eckington Derbyshire S31 9WE **Map 7 D2**

18th-century inn (owned by Toby Restaurants) with many extensions and a purpose-built bedroom block. One mile from the M1 (junction 30). ***Rooms** 30. Garden.* AMERICAN EXPRESS *Access, Diners, Visa.*

Retford **Forte Travelodge** £42

Tel 0777 838091 **L**

Markham Moor Nr Retford Nottinghamshire DN22 0QU **Map 7 D2**

On the A1 northbound, 14 miles north of Newark-on-Trent, with access from both north and southbound carriageways. ***Rooms** 40.* AMERICAN EXPRESS *Access, Visa.*

Richmond **Petersham Hotel** 64% £120

Tel 081-940 7471 Fax 081-940 9998 **HR**

Nightingale Lane Richmond Surrey TW10 6UZ **Map 15 E2**

A distinctive mid-Victorian confection in French Gothic style overlooking the Thames, a short walk from the 2500 acres of Royal Richmond Park. The hotel's grand staircase (the longest unsupported Portland stone flight in England) winds through five floors to bedrooms in a variety of styles and sizes. The best have reproduction furniture, spacious bathrooms and stunning river views; singles are cramped by comparison. Receptions and conferences for up to 50 people. No dogs. ***Rooms** 54.* AMERICAN EXPRESS *Access, Diners, Visa.*

Nightingales £65

Decorated in attractive pale pink tones, with glorious river views from a few tables, Nightingales derives its name from the nearby grassy carriageway of Victorian times. Chef Tim Richardson's thoughtful carte includes a few English traditional dishes like steak and kidney pie, calf's liver with bubble and squeak and onion gravy, mixed grill, kedgeree, fish cakes and omelette Arnold Bennett, but also has its sights set on more modern dishes such as crab and guacamole gateau, spinach and pumpkin soufflé with an anchovy sauce, and magret of duck glazed with honey, coriander and cumin and served with kumquats. A dark chocolate soufflé with hazelnut ice cream and a lemon tart with red cherry sauce are listed as specialities among the desserts. Good choice on the separate Sunday menu, served both lunchtime and evening. Unusual private dining room (for up to 20) in the Cellars claret room. ***Seats** 60. **Parties** 14.*
Private Room 20. L 12.15-2.15 D 7-9.45. Closed 25 & 26 Dec.
Set L & D (Sun) £20.

Richmond **Richmond Gate Hotel** 65% £105

Tel 081-940 0061 Fax 081-332 0354 **H**

Richmond Hill Richmond Surrey TW10 6RP **Map 15 E2**

High up on Richmond Hill (opposite the Royal Star and Garter Home), almost overlooking the Thames, the hotel was originally a collection of four 18th-century buildings. The original, Morshead House, contains intimate public rooms and eight luxury double rooms of grand proportions. In a newer extension, to the rear, bedrooms are equally attractive and comfortable, though more uniform in design. Under-7s stay free in parents' room; children can let off steam in either of the two gardens. Adaptable function rooms for up to 70. Eleven extra rooms, in a variety of styles and including three with four-poster beds, were just being completed in renovated Georgian cottages as we went to press. No dogs. ***Rooms** 64. Garden, squash.* AMERICAN EXPRESS *Access, Diners, Visa.*

Richmond River Terrace NEW

£35

Tel 081-332 2524 Fax 081-332 6136 **R**

The Tower Bridge Street Richmond Surrey TW9 1TQ **Map 15 E2**

Great location in a Georgian building right on Richmond Bridge. Eat inside or out on the terrace from a short menu offering corn chips with guacamole; potato tortilla with caponata; salmon with a light, creamy curry sauce; strawberry cheesecake with raspberry coulis. ***Seats** 200. Private Room 60. Meals 12-11 (winter 12-3 & 7-11). Closed D Sun & all Mon (both winter only), 26 Dec-1 Jan.* AMERICAN EXPRESS *Access, Diners, Visa.*

Ridgeway Old Vicarage ★↑

£80

Tel 0742 475814 **R**

Ridgeway Moor Ridgeway nr Sheffield Derbyshire S12 3XW **Map 10 D2**

Tessa Bramley has tried to move up a gear this year in terms of cooking skills, service and all-round value for money; less butter is now used in sauces, and the use of olive oil and nut oils follows the contemporary culinary styles set elsewhere; similarly, expensive ingredients are used less and the kitchen skills themselves made more of a feature. Certainly, the lower-priced set meals are more instantaneous in concept (cannelloni of spinach, leeks and pine kernels with spring herb soufflé, honey-roast duckling with caramelised apple tart, baked chocolate pudding with hot fudge sauce and English custard), but not to the detriment of the overall quality of the dishes produced. Imagination is much in evidence and her food *is* exciting (as well as technically sound), as she wants it to be. The full-price menu includes amuse-gueule and a light intermediate course as well as a starter, perhaps a combination of beef satay, Thai-spiced fish cakes and filo packets of monkfish and lemon balm, followed by roast local duckling on a bed of cabbage with garlic and juniper plus the legs served as Peking duck pancakes with hoi sin sauce – both evolved and involved dishes. Front of house is now run by owner Tessa's son Andrew and his fiancée. The wine list is well thought out and well chosen, with some classic gems at reasonable prices; ask for advice and you'll get it. A separate new bistro dining room opened last year offering "gutsy food" on a fixed-price (£17.50), three-course menu with the likes of mussel tagliatelle with smoked salmon and pepper sauce, pot-roasted lamb shank on a rosemary and garlic-flavoured bean casserole, braised oxtail with mashed potatoes and roast parsnips, filo parcels of ratatouille and pissaladière on a bed of polenta, good farmhouse cheeses and treacle pudding with custard; budget wine prices. ***Seats** 50. Private Room 45. L 12.30-3 D 7-11. Closed D Sun, all Mon, 27-30 Dec. Set meals £18.50 & £27.50.* AMERICAN EXPRESS *Access, Visa.*

Ripley Michels' ★

£88

Tel 0483 224777 **R**

13 High Street Ripley Surrey GU23 6AQ **Map 15 E3**

Occupying a prominent position in the village centre, the Clock House, with its striking redbrick classical Georgian facade, sets the tone for the interior, which has an elegant ground floor dining room with a small sunken bar area at its heart. Arrangements of fresh flowers, large Chinese ornaments and walls studded with modern and classical artwork create a stylish country house ambience. This is all a perfect showcase for Erik Michel's sometimes extraordinarily complex and highly sophisticated cooking. The style is modern with clever juxtaposing of ingredients creating dishes that read well on the menu and are equally successful on the plate. He combines beautiful presentation with good balance and excellent saucing, a vital component. To begin various amuse-gueule are offered –

See over

a soft rock oyster coated in a cheese sauce or fresh sardine mousse with samphire. Starters range from a stunning hot Shropshire blue cheese soufflé turned out on to a light smooth cream cheese sauce surrounded by frisée dressed in an elderberry vinaigrette to a dish of trimmed langoustine tails arranged on a delicate cream of coconut butter sauce subtly flavoured with coriander and mint, and in the centre of the plate paper-thin rounds of pastry with a filling of roasted peppers. For a main course a grilled John Dory is served on a potato/spring onion-stuffed pancake. To one side is a small cabbage stuffed with a dice of vegetables. A sea urchin sauce sprinkled with flying-fish caviar completes an attractive presentation. Guinea fowl is pot-roasted in an infusion of raisin juice, green tea and Malmsey wine and served with a compote of apples, orange and walnuts. An order for sweets is preceded by a plate of English cheeses which are served with mint, dark date and walnut bread and home-made oat biscuits. Sweets (Dessert of the Year, Home Counties regional winner) show the same intense dedication to detail with a moist light savarin ring sitting on a vanilla pastry cream and topped with almost transparent slices of fruit and crisp caramel. Pools of apricot sauce complete the pretty picture. Other sweets include a hot pastry with apples, apple sorbet and toffee sauce. Service, while efficient, can at times be a little serious with only Karen Michel occasionally lightening the proceedings. ***Seats** 50. Private Room 12. L 12.30-1.45 D 7.30-9 (Sat 7-9.30). Closed L Sat, D Sun, all Mon, 25 & 26 Dec, 1 Jan. Set L £20 Set D £22.* AMERICAN EXPRESS *Access, Visa.*

Ripon — Ripon Spa Hotel — 62% — £70

Tel 0765 602172 Fax 0765 690770 — H

Park Street Ripon North Yorkshire HG4 2BU — **Map 5 E4**

A comfortable hotel dating from 1909, with good staff and commendably high standards of housekeeping. The prize-winning gardens, which extend to seven acres, are a major plus, and the setting is secluded considering its proximity to the city centre. Another asset comes in the shape of the high-ceilinged bedrooms. Rooms are individually decorated and furnished, and two have four-posters. Two de luxe rooms have whirlpool baths. Children up to 14 stay free in parents' room. ***Rooms** 40. Garden.* AMERICAN EXPRESS *Access, Diners, Visa.*

Ripon — Places of Interest

Fountains Abbey & Studley Royal Gardens (NT) Tel 0765 86333.
Newby Hall & Gardens Nr Ripon Tel 0423 322583.
Ripon Cathedral Tel 0765 2072.
Ripon Racecourse Tel 0765 602165.
Lightwater Valley Action Park Tel 0765 85321.

Roade — Roadhouse — £55

Tel 0604 863372 — R

16 High Street Roade Northamptonshire NN7 2NW — **Map 15 D1**

Chris Kewley runs a leisurely village restaurant. He cooks a short menu with about six choices per course in a sound, ungimmicky style. A typical menu might include gratin of salmon, brill, scallops and mushrooms, locally-smoked game and poultry, sautéed calf's liver on a bed of sweetcorn and pulses with sherry vinegar and walnut oil sauce, and a roast breast of duck served with its leg confit and a ginger and kumquat sauce. Good-value set-price lunch offers simpler, but equally well-executed dishes (moules marinière, crab fish cakes, oxtail stew). Informal service suits the surroundings; all prices include service. Short, varied wine list with a good selection of half bottles. ***Seats** 45. Parties 20. L 12.30-1.45 D 7-10. Closed L Sat & Mon, Bank Holidays, 2 weeks Jul/Aug. Set L £14.* AMERICAN EXPRESS *Access, Visa.*

Rochester Bridgewood Manor Hotel 68% NEW £84

Tel 0634 201333 Fax 0634 201330 **H**

Bridgewood Roundabout Maidstone Road Rochester Kent ME5 9AX **Map 11 B5**

Virtually beside Junction 3 of the M2 this modern brick-built hotel offers up-to-date meeting and conference facilities as well as a good base for the local tourist attractions. General manager Gail Callaway and her staff provide friendly and helpful service. Public areas including a spacious reception lounge and bar have an ecclesiastical decorative inspiration. Bedrooms are basic with all the expected features, remote TV, trouser presses and compact, clean, functional bathrooms. A central courtyard area provides a sheltered al fresco area in the summer months. There's a wide range of facilities in the self-contained leisure club. Marston Hotels. ***Rooms** 100. Patio, indoor swimming pool, gymnasium, sauna, spa bath, solarium, hair & beauty salon, tennis, snooker.* AMERICAN EXPRESS *Access, Diners, Visa.*

Rochester Forte Posthouse 62% £68

Tel 0634 687111 Fax 0634 684512 **H**

Maidstone Road Rochester Airport Rochester Kent ME5 9SF **Map 11 B5**

Up-to-date comfort in a Posthouse (formerly *Forte Crest*) near Junction 3 of the M2 and Junction 6 of the M20. Children stay free in parents' bedrooms, and many family facilities are offered. ***Rooms** 105. Indoor swimming pool, gymnasium, sauna, spa bath, solarium, beauty salon, coffee shop (7am-10.30pm).* AMERICAN EXPRESS *Access, Diners, Visa.*

Rochester Places of Interest

Tourist Information Tel 0634 843666.
Cobham Hall Cobham Tel 0472 823371.
Rochester Castle (EH) Tel 0634 402276.
Rochester Cathedral Tel 0634 43366.
Charles Dickens Centre Tel 0634 844176.
Alpine Ski Centre Chatham Tel 0634 827979.
Sheerness Beach 22 miles.
Oast House Theatre Gillingham Tel 0634 372121.
Doddington Place Gardens Sittingbourne Tel 079586 385.
The Ice Bowl Gillingham Tel 0634 388477.

Rolleston-on-Dove Brookhouse Hotel 62% £85

Tel 0283 814188 Fax 0283 813644 **H**

Brookside Rolleston-on-Dove nr Burton-on-Trent Staffordshire DE13 9AA **Map 6 C3**

Standing by the village brook, the William and Mary listed brick building dates from around 1690 and was converted to a hotel in 1976. Bedrooms are all individually styled, featuring antique furniture, and many have four-posters, half-testers or Victorian brass beds; several are in an adjacent converted barn. No children under 12. ***Rooms** 19. Garden.* AMERICAN EXPRESS *Access, Diners, Visa.*

Romaldkirk Rose & Crown £74

Tel 0833 50213 Fax 0833 50828 **IR**

Romaldkirk Co Durham DL12 9EB **Map 5 D3**

An imposing 18th-century coaching inn in a most picturesque village setting. The main bar has a fine stone fireplace, wood panelling, old black and white photos of the village, a grandfather clock and some alarming-looking traps. Wrought iron-legged tables are surrounded by roundback chairs or bench seating, and on the dining side of the room there are exposed stone walls, beams and old farm implements. A residents' lounge, heavily endowed with more stripped stone and beams, features wing chairs

See over

and period furniture, books, magazines and board games. Everywhere there are local watercolours. Creaking floorboards, beams, stripped stone walls, well-chosen antique furniture and contemporary fabrics feature in the refurbished and improved bedrooms; duvets can be swapped for sheets and blankets. Front views overlook the village green. Five further rooms, in an outside annexe, are more uniform in size and design, with modern furniture and fittings. Excellent snacks and real ales served in the bar and Crown Room; six tables are outside in front of the hotel. Children under 5 stay free in parents' room. Service is friendly and smiling throughout. Popular with shooting parties. ***Rooms*** *12. Closed 25 & 26 Dec. Access, Visa.*

Restaurant

£65

In the part-panelled restaurant there is a civilised air enhanced by elegantly clothed tables. Chef Christopher Davy's fixed-price, four-course dinners have a local produce bias, using game and black puddings, fowl and cheeses. Dishes are artistically presented, carefully prepared with obvious knowledge and enthusiasm. A typical meal might commence with a parfait of duck livers with walnuts and smoked bacon, continue with carrot and orange soup (served with honey rolls), then a gratin of whiting and prawns glazed with hollandaise, finishing with lemon and hazelnut meringue. ***Seats*** *24. Parties 20. L (Sun only) 12-1.30 D 7.30-9. Set L (Sun) £10.75 Set D £22.*

Romsey — Old Manor House ↑

£90

Tel 0794 517353 — **R**

21 Palmerston Street Romsey Hampshire SO51 8GF — **Map 14 C3**

In cottagey surroundings that are staunchly and traditionally old English, Mauro Bregoli has made his mark with the cuisine of both his native Italy and France. He tracks down wild mushrooms, shoots a lot of game, smokes his own meat, makes his own foie gras, salami, bresaola and pasta. Table settings are impeccable and amuse-gueule interesting – a taste of promising things to follow. Suckling pig and lobster are seasonal favourites and a recent menu offered the likes of risotto with a cream of mushrooms and truffles, *cotechino con lenticchie*, sea bass grilled with thyme and fennel, monkfish with a port and pink peppercorn sauce, fillet of beef with a light Roquefort sauce and escalope of marinated venison with onion confit and spiced fruit. Good breads, cheeşes (a fine French selection), petits fours and coffee complete the picture in the evening. Lunchtime sees a choice of particularly good-value menus with an established repertoire of dishes like smoked salmon mousse, fettuccine with tomato and basil, confit of duck, knuckle of pork with rosemary and garlic, gravad lax, roulade of salmon with mussels and a saffron sauce. An extraordinary selection of clarets stars on a meticulously chosen list that is forty pages long and has depth everywhere you look. Prices are generally high, though the house choices provide good value. ***Seats*** *42. Parties 10. Private Room. L 12-2 D 7-9.30. Closed D Sun, all Mon, 1 week Christmas. Set L £14.50, £17.50 & £25 Set D £35.* AMERICAN EXPRESS *Access, Visa.*

Romsey — White Horse Hotel — 63%

£101

Tel 0794 512431 Fax 0794 517485 — **H**

Market Place Romsey Hampshire SO51 8ZJ — **Map 14 C3**

Georgian facade, oak beams, bedrooms (both period and modern) in a Forte Heritage hotel right on the market place. Courtyard seating. Banqueting facilities for 90, conferences up to 40. ***Rooms*** *33.* AMERICAN EXPRESS *Access, Diners, Visa.*

Many establishments are currently on the market, so ownership could change after we go to press.

Romsey — Places of Interest

Paultons Romany and Village Life Museums and Theme Park Paultons Park, Ower Tel 0703 814442.
Rapids of Romsey Tel 0794 830333.
Wellow Vineyards Tel 0794 830880.
Historic Houses, Castles and Gardens
Broadlands Tel 0794 516878 *Home of Lord Mountbatten.*
Hillier Gardens and Arboretum Ampfield Tel 0794 68787.
Mottisfont Abbey Garden (NT) Mottisfont Tel 0794 41220/40757.

Rosedale Abbey — Milburn Arms — 60% — £70

Tel & Fax 07515 312 — **H**

Rosedale Abbey nr Pickering North Yorkshire YO18 8RA — **Map 5 E3**

Tranquil surroundings in the beautiful North Yorks moors are the big attraction of Terry and Joan Bentley's delightful country hotel which has parts dating back to the 1700s. Plants, ornaments, books and games make the lounge a nice place to spend an hour or two, and the bar is also the village local (tasty bar meals). Individually-decorated bedrooms have good bathrooms and some also have fine views; dogs in ground-floor annexe rooms only. A favoured spot in summer is the peaceful garden, opposite the village green, with tables set out under a splendid 150-year-old cedar. ***Rooms** 11. Garden. Closed 2 days Christmas. Access, Diners, Visa.*

Ross-on-Wye — Chase Hotel — 64% — £80

Tel 0989 763161 Fax 0989 768330 — **H**

Gloucester Road Ross-on-Wye Hereford & Worcester HR9 5LH — **Map 14 B1**

Old-world charm almost blends with the modern decor at this restored Georgian mansion standing in 11 acres of manicured grounds only a short walk from the town centre. Comfortable furniture and appealing fabrics impart a certain country house appeal to the bedrooms, whose up-to-date amenities are practical and unobtrusive. Conference and banquets for up to 300. No dogs. ***Rooms** 39. Garden.* AMERICAN EXPRESS *Access, Visa.*

Ross-on-Wye — Pengethley Manor — 67% — £114

Tel 0989 87211 Fax 0989 87238 — **H**

Pengethley Park nr Ross-on-Wye Hereford & Worcester HR9 6LL — **Map 14 B1**

Fifteen acres of estate with a par 3 golf course, trout lake, vineyard and landscaped gardens enhance Pengethley's tranquil country setting. There is also plenty of activity for sportsmen. Banqueting for up to 90 and conference rooms accommodating 75 kept discreetly separate. Purpose-built bedrooms for disabled guests; children up to 16 stay free in parents' room. ***Rooms** 24. Garden, outdoor swimming pool, golf (9), fishing, snooker, outdoor chess.* AMERICAN EXPRESS *Access, Diners, Visa.*

Ross-on-Wye — Pheasants — £55

Tel 0989 65751 — **RR**

52 Edde Cross Street Ross-on-Wye Hereford & Worcester HR9 7BZ — **Map 14 B1**

Ten neatly spaced tables occupy the front rooms of this former pub alongside a tiny bar-lounge comprising two easy chairs, window seat and open fire. Eileen Brunnarius has created an informal, home-from-home atmosphere, which is reflected in the studied simplicity of her best dishes: roasted hazelnut soup, potted hare with an orange and juniper relish, freshwater bream baked with ginger, soy and garlic, salt-cured braised duck leg, sliced rare fillet of beef with a rye whisky sauce. Desserts are just as interesting, typified by pineapple soup with snow eggs, chocolate paradise (moscatel sauce) and always bread-and-butter pudding. There's also a good selection of British farmhouse cheeses. An unusual wine list, presented by style, with many wines available by the glass, offered on a "try

See over

before you buy" basis. Very fair prices, excellent tasting notes. ***Seats** 22. L 12.30-2 D 7-10. Closed Sun & Mon, Bank Holidays, 1 week Christmas, L between Nov-Mar. Set L £10.£13.50.* AMERICAN EXPRESS *Access, Diners, Visa.*

Rooms **£36**

Guests occupying the two cottagey bedrooms (one double, one twin) share a bathroom with Eileen, her cheese plant and a china hippopotamus. Splendid country breakfasts.

Ross-on-Wye Places of Interest

Tourist Information Tel 0989 62768.
Goodrich Castle Tel 0600 890538.
Hill Court Gardens Hom Green Tel 0989 763123.

Rotherham Campanile Hotel £44

Tel 0709 700255 Fax 0709 545169 **L**

Lowton Way off Denby Way Hellaby Industrial Estate Rotherham South Yorkshire S66 8RY **Map 7 D2**

Off M18 Junction 1, past M1 Junction 32. ***Rooms** 50.* AMERICAN EXPRESS *Access, Diners, Visa.*

Rotherham Moat House 69% £68

Tel 0709 364902 Fax 0709 368960 **H**

Moorgate Road Rotherham South Yorkshire S60 2BG **Map 7 D2**

By the A618, south of town, close to Rotherham General Hospital. Leisure facilities (no pool) and conference suites (for up to 250). 21 rooms reserved for non-smokers. ***Rooms** 83. Spa bath, sauna, solarium, keep-fit equipment.* AMERICAN EXPRESS *Access, Diners, Visa.*

Rotherham Travel Inn £43

Tel 0709 543216 Fax 0709 531546 **L**

Bawtry Road Rotherham South Yorkshire S65 3JB **Map 7 D2**

3 miles off Junction 33 of the M1, 10 minutes from Sheffield and Doncaster. ***Rooms** 37.* AMERICAN EXPRESS *Access, Diners, Visa.*

Rotherham Places of Interest

Tourist Information Tel 0709 823611.
Rotherham Arts Centre Tel 0709 373866.

Rotherwick Tylney Hall 77% £114

Tel 0256 764881 Fax 0256 768141 **HR**

Rotherwick nr Hook Hampshire RG27 9AJ **Map 15 D3**

Well signed from the B3349, just off junction 5 of the M3, this imposing mansion is of palatial proportions. A boarding school until 1984, it stands in 66 acres of mature grounds with lakes and formal gardens. The original carved oak panelling and high, moulded ceilings indicate that no expense was spared when the house was built in Victorian times. Day rooms are large and quite smart, but the bedrooms remain a mix of varying sizes and styles. Although all is grand and comfortable (with appropriate service to match), it doesn't quite achieve luxury status. Children up to 14 stay free in parents' room. ***Rooms** 91. Garden, indoor & outdoor swimming pools, keep-fit equipment, spa bath, sauna, tennis, snooker.* AMERICAN EXPRESS *Access, Diners, Visa.*

Oak Room Restaurant **£85**

An adventurous, wide-ranging carte is complemented by a fixed-price menu of 'traditional English fayre' and both try hard to match the grand, candle-lit setting. Admirably attentive and friendly service and an early-evening children's meal is served on request in the banqueting room. Predictable wine list with some especially hefty mark-ups among the classic clarets. ***Seats** 100. Parties 10. Private Room 100. L 12.30-2 D 7.30-9.30. Set L £19 Set D £27.*

Rothley — Rothley Court — 67% — £100

Tel 0533 374141 Fax 0533 374483 — **H**

Westfield Lane Rothley Leicestershire LE7 7LG — **Map 7 D3**

By the B5328 west of Rothley (six miles outside Leicester), this imposing 13th-century manor stands in six acres of grounds, surrounded by lawns and open farmland. Much historical character is retained, including an 11th-century chapel built by the Holy Order of the Knights Templar. Day rooms feature some fine oak panelling, buttoned-leather chairs, exposed floorboards and stone fireplaces, while the main staircase boasts two fine stained-glass windows. Manor bedrooms vary in size with antique furniture and subdued colour schemes, while annexe rooms are more uniform; feature rooms, like the King Henry III suite in a separate cottage, attract a justifiable 20% supplementary charge. Characterful meeting rooms for up to 100. Forte Heritage. ***Rooms** 36. Garden.* AMERICAN EXPRESS *Access, Diners, Visa.*

Rowde — George & Dragon — £30

Tel 0380 723053 — **R**

High Street Rowde Wiltshire SN10 2PN — **Map 14 B3**

Inspired, inventive and realistically-priced cooking emanates from the kitchen of Tim and Helen Withers' village pub leased from Wadworth's brewery. Dishes run from crab pancakes or moules marinière to aubergine caponata, Provençal fish soup and warm salad of duck breast dressed with Chinese plum sauce, plus the freshest fish from Newlyn marked up on a blackboard (steamed skate with tomato and chili salsa, grilled fillet of red mullet with orange and anchovy). Interesting British-only cheeses, beers and mineral waters. A typical set lunch menu offers alternatives only at each course, perhaps curried parsnip soup or brandade salad, then salmon fish cakes with hollandaise or lamb's kidneys with mushrooms and Madeira, ending with brown sugar meringues and Jersey cream or rhubarb and honey saffron custard. Remarkably, any one of over 40 wines on the list is available by the glass, winning the George & Dragon our Wine Pub of the Year award last year. Booking is always advised, at least one week in advance for tables at weekends, when good Sunday lunches offer a choice of four dishes at each course; fudge served with coffee. Tables in the walled garden during good weather. ***Seats** 35. Private Room 35. L 12-2 D 7-10. Closed D Sun, all Mon, 2 weeks Christmas & New Year. Set L £10 (Sun £12.50). Access, Visa.*

Rowsley — Peacock Hotel — 64% — £116

Tel 0629 733518 Fax 0629 732671 — **H**

Rowsley Matlock Derbyshire DE4 2EB — **Map 6 C2**

Trout and grayling fishing on the river Derwent that runs along the bottom of the garden and an additional 12 rods on the Wye make this 17th-century hotel a popular fisherman's haunt. Mellow, antique-filled public rooms include a beamed bar with rough stone walls, while individually decorated bedrooms offer all the usual modern comforts. Children up to 16 stay free in parents' room. This Jarvis hotel stands on the A6 five miles north of Matlock and three miles south of Bakewell. ***Rooms** 14. Garden, fishing.* AMERICAN EXPRESS *Access, Diners, Visa.*

We do not accept free meals or hospitality – our inspectors pay their own bills.

Ruckhall **Ancient Camp Inn** **£58**

Tel 0981 250449 **I**

Ruckhall nr Eaton Bishop Hereford & Worcester HR2 9QX **Map 14 A1**

On the site of a former Iron Age fort, the inn stands atop an escarpment overlooking a wide bend in the river Wye. Ruckhall (not on many maps) is signposted on the main A465 leaving Hereford towards Abergavenny. Conversion by owners David and Nova Hague retains original stonework and flagstone floor to create an intimate atmosphere, cheered in winter by huge log fires. Nova's home-made pub lunches and informal dinners make this a popular haunt. Three neat bedrooms to the rear have showers/WC only; of two at the front one has a private sitting room, the other an en-suite bath elevated to maximise its river view. No children under 8. No dogs. ***Rooms*** *5. Garden, fishing. Access, Visa.*

Rugeley **Forte Travelodge** **£42**

Tel 0889 570096 **L**

Western Springs Road Rugeley Staffordshire WS15 2AS **Map 6 C3**

On the A51/B5013, 6 miles east of Stafford in the centre of the town, next to the bus station. Take Junctions 13/14 from the M6. ***Rooms*** *32.* AMERICAN EXPRESS *Access, Visa.*

Runcorn **Campanile Hotel** **£44**

Tel 0928 581771 Fax 0928 581730 **L**

Lowlands Road Runcorn Cheshire WA7 5TP **Map 6 A2**

Take Junction 12 off the M56 to the A557 ring road. Close to the station. ***Rooms*** *53.* AMERICAN EXPRESS *Access, Diners, Visa.*

Runcorn **Forte Posthouse** **62%** **£70**

Tel 0928 714000 Fax 0928 714611 **H**

Wood Lane Beechwood Runcorn Cheshire WA7 3HA **Map 6 A2**

A modern hotel not far from the M56 (junction 12), with ample free car parking, a leisure club and a very extensive conference facilities (a choice of 19 rooms holding up to 500 delegates theatre-style). Formerly the Forte Crest. ***Rooms*** *136. Indoor swimming pool, gymnasium, sauna, spa bath, steam room, solarium, beauty & hair salon.* AMERICAN EXPRESS *Access, Diners, Visa.*

Rushden **Forte Travelodge** **£42**

Tel 0933 57008 **L**

Saunders Lodge Rushden Northamptonshire **Map 15 E1**

Located on the A45 near Rushden, 14 miles east of Northampton and 10 miles south of Kettering. ***Rooms*** *40.* AMERICAN EXPRESS *Access, Visa.*

Rusper **Ghyll Manor** **68%** **£80**

Tel 0293 871571 Fax 0293 871419 **H**

High Street Rusper nr Horsham West Sussex RH12 4PX **Map 11 A5**

Surrounded by 40 acres of gardens on the main road to Rusper, two miles east of the A24 from Dorking. Bedrooms are split between the main, original house, two cottages and a converted stable mews set around a cobbled courtyard and high-beamed function room. Those in the extensions are modern and larger than those in the house, which have a few antiques and period detail. A cramped library acts as a sitting room and features an open fire; there is also an adjacent, tiny bar. Children up to 16 accommodated free in parents' room; cots and baby-listening available. Forte Heritage. ***Rooms*** *22. Garden, tennis court.* AMERICAN EXPRESS *Access, Diners, Visa.*

Ryde Hotel Ryde Castle 61% £79

Tel 0983 563755 Fax 0983 568925 **H**

Esplanade Ryde Isle of Wight PO33 1JA **Map 15 D4**

On the esplanade, adjoining the Solent conference and exhibition centre, this is indeed a castle, complete with crenellations and towers. Ribbed ceilings in the foyer and lounge (plus a suit of armour in the red plush bar) are interior period reminders, along with a friendly ghost. Bedrooms mostly have four-poster or half-tester beds with duvets and cream-coloured unit furniture; the best have views overlooking the Solent. Executive rooms claim to have the world's largest bath towels. ***Rooms** 17. Garden. Access, Diners, Visa.*

Ryde Places of Interest

Tourist Information Tel 0983 62905.
Nunwell House and Gardens Coach Lane, Brading Tel 0983 407240.
Osborne House East Cowes Tel 0983 200022.
Carisbrooke Castle Newport Tel 0983 522107.

Rye George Hotel 62% £97

Tel 0797 222114 Fax 0797 224065 **H**

High Street Rye East Sussex TN31 7JP **Map 11 C6**

High-street former coaching inn dating in parts back to 1575. Day rooms are comfortably traditional, and most of the bedrooms have old beams. The Georgian ballroom is a popular choice for banqueting functions (up to 100) and conferences (up to 80). Forte Heritage. ***Rooms** 22.* AMERICAN EXPRESS® *Access, Diners, Visa.*

Rye Landgate Bistro £60

Tel 0797 222829 **R**

5/6 Landgate Rye East Sussex TN31 7LH **Map 11 C6**

Unpretentious restaurant in a picturesque tourist town. Plastic tablecloths, painted brick walls and simple vases of fresh flowers set the scene for some skilful quality cooking. Chef/patron Toni Ferguson-Lees puts together a well-balanced menu of local supplies of fish to cheese. Fish is very much a speciality, from local squid braised in a white wine and tomato garlic sauce to a crab terrine continuing through to cod, Dover sole, turbot, John Dory, monkfish or wild salmon. Balance to this is provided by a selection of meat dishes such as pink-cooked calf's liver, pigeon breasts or local Romney Marsh lamb in various forms. Garnish is kept simple and a high point are salads provided by Frances Smith of Appledore with well-made dressings. A three-course fixed-price menu is on offer from Tuesday to Thursday including many dishes found on the main menu. Especially good is the aptly named 'very fishy stew', a masterpiece of excellent freshness and flavour. ***Seats** 30. D only 7-9.30 (Sat to 10).*
Closed Sun & Mon, 1 week Christmas, 1 week Jun, 1 week Oct.
Set D £14.50. Access, Visa.

Rye Mermaid Inn 60% £98

Tel 0797 223065 Fax 0797 226995 **H**

Mermaid Street Rye East Sussex TN31 7EU **Map 11 C6**

Rebuilt in 1420, the Mermaid stands among the cobbled streets of ancient Rye. Once famous for its smuggling associations, it remains strong on romantic, old-world appeal, with antique furnishings, Elizabethan illustrations and linenfold panelling. Three of the bedrooms have four-posters. No children under 8. No dogs. Free parking at the rear of the inn. ***Rooms** 30.* AMERICAN EXPRESS® *Access, Diners, Visa.*

Rye Places of Interest

Tourist Information Tel 0797 226696.
Lamb House Tel 0797 226696 *Home of Henry James.*
Camber Sands Beach *3 miles E of Rye.*

Saffron Walden Saffron Hotel 57% £55

Tel 0799 522676 Fax 0799 513979 H

10-18 High Street Saffron Walden Essex CB10 1AY **Map 10 B3**

A family-run hotel in the centre of town. There's an old-fashioned panelled bar with exposed brickwork and timbers. Bedrooms, a few with four-posters, vary in size and style, but their decor and appointments are generally quite modest. Some rooms are reached by winding passages with head-threatening beams. It's best to discuss your room requirements when booking. ***Rooms** 24. Garden.* AMERICAN EXPRESS *Access, Diners, Visa.*

Saffron Walden Places of Interest

Audley End House and Park (EH) Tel 0799 22399.
Mole Hall Wildlife Park Widdington, Newport Tel 0799 40400.

St Albans Noke Thistle 68% £107

Tel 0727 854252 Fax 0727 841906 H

Watford Road St Albans Hertfordshire AL2 3DS **Map 15 E2**

Practical accommodation in what was once the farm of Burston Manor. Set in its own grounds near M1, M10 and M25. Banqueting for up to 50, conferences to 55. Residents have free membership of the vast St Albans Health & Racquet Club. ***Rooms** 111. Garden.* AMERICAN EXPRESS *Access, Diners, Visa.*

St Albans St Michael's Manor 63% £80

Tel 0727 864444 Fax 0727 848909 H

Fishpool Street St Albans Hertfordshire AL3 4RY **Map 5 E2**

The manor house, which dates from the 16th century, overlooks beautiful gardens and a lake. Well-proportioned day rooms have a traditional feel, particularly the Oak Lounge, part of the original Tudor structure, with fine plastered ceilings dated 1586. The restaurant has a bright conservatory (Victorian in style but dating from 1987) that's popular for private parties. The grounds contain many specimen trees, after which all the bedrooms are named. Best of the rooms are doubles with four-posters and garden views. ***Rooms** 22. Garden. Closed 3 days between Christmas & New Year.* AMERICAN EXPRESS *Access, Diners, Visa.*

Changes in data sometimes occur in establishments after the Guide goes to press. Prices should be taken as indications rather than firm quotes.

St Albans Sopwell House Hotel & Country Club 65% £108

Tel 0727 864477 Fax 0727 844741 H

Cottonmill Lane Sopwell St Albans Hertfordshire AL1 2HQ **Map 15 E2**

An 18th-century house much added to with extensive leisure facilities and surrounded by expansive lawns. The grand, marble entrance hall sets a good impression and the new country club is a major attraction for residential conference delegates. Informal eating in Bejerano's Brasserie from 7am to 10pm. ***Rooms** 92. Garden, gymnasium, indoor swimming pool, sauna, solarium, spa bath, steam room, beautician, hairdressing, snooker.* AMERICAN EXPRESS *Access, Diners, Visa.*

St. Albans — Places of Interest

Tourist Information Tel 0727 864511.
Abbey Theatre Tel 0727 57861.
The Gardens of the Rose Chiswell Green Tel 0727 50461.
St. Albans Cathedral Tel 0727 60780.
Dunstable Road Showground Redbourne Tel 0582 792626.
Museums and Art Galleries
St. Albans Organ Museum Tel 0727 51557/73896.
The Verulamium Museum St. Michael's Tel 0727 54659 or 866100 Ext 2912.
The Mosquito Aircraft Museum Salisbury Hall, London Colney Tel 0727 22051.

St Austell — Boscundle Manor — 65% — £110

Tel 0726 813557 Fax 0726 814997 — H

Tregrehan St Austell Cornwall PL25 3RL — **Map 12 B3**

Secluded grounds make a peaceful setting for this lovely little 18th-century manor house, whose owners Andrew and Mary Flint have been in residence since 1978, opening for the summer season only. Seven bedrooms are in the main house, one in the Garden Room above the swimming pool and two in a cottage at the top of the garden; all the doubles (8) have spa baths. A new practice golf area has a golf net, two greens, several teeing positions, a lake, a pond and a grassed area for practising shots. Although more suited to residents wanting a quiet holiday, self-entertaining families might find this a pleasant home-from-home, run like a private house. No functions, no lunches for non-residents, just good old peace and quiet. A changed tariff this year offers good-value terms for half-board and longer stays. ***Rooms** 10. Garden, golf practice area, outdoor swimming pool, helipad, keep-fit equipment. Closed mid Oct-Easter. Access, Visa.*

St Austell — White Hart — £63

Tel 0726 72100 Fax 0726 74705 — I

Church Street St Austell Cornwall PL25 4AT — **Map 12 B3**

Dating back to 1735, the White Hart stands in the centre of town. The facade is of grey stone, with a third storey added by the brewers who owned it in the 1920s. Bedrooms sport smart darkwood furniture, pink and plum decor and modern carpeted bathrooms. The saloon bar is the focal point of the day rooms. ***Rooms** 18.* AMERICAN EXPRESS *Access, Diners, Visa.*

St Ives (Cornwall) — Garrack Hotel — 62% — £91

Tel 0736 796199 Fax 0736 798955 — H

Burthallan Lane St Ives Cornwall TR26 3AA — **Map 12 A3**

The Kilby family have been running this creeper-clad hotel since 1965. The main lounge is a busy, family room with games and books, and there are two other more formal lounges plus a pleasant cocktail bar. Bedrooms in the main house are traditionally furnished and vary in size; those in the extension are more modern and roomy with panoramic views over the Porthmeor surf beach and sweeping bay in the distance. A leisure centre (being rebuilt as we went to press) in the two acres of well-tended gardens has a small pool and coffee bar. Facilities for the disabled and a small conference facility (for up to 30) were added in 1993. ***Rooms** 18. Garden, indoor swimming pool, sauna, solarium, spa bath, coffee shop (11am-10.30pm).* AMERICAN EXPRESS *Access, Diners, Visa.*

> 🍾 is our symbol for an outstanding wine list.

St Ives (Cornwall) Pig 'n' Fish NEW £45

Tel 0736 794204 **R**

Norway Lane St Ives Cornwall TR26 1LZ **Map 12 A3**

Chef-patron Paul Sellars spent seven years as understudy at the *Seafood Restaurant* in Padstow. He cooks very much in the Padstow style, but at prices much lower and in an atmosphere of even greater informality. Fish dishes are well-handled, very fresh and in the Mediterranean vogue. Cod with basil crust and pot-roasted pork fillet with pancetta are just two typical dishes in which artistry and understanding of the raw materials are very evident. The restaurant, simple in decor and style, is located above a craft market in a back street; a worthy addition to the local Cornish scene. ***Seats** 28. Parties 20. D only 7-9.30. Closed Sun & Mon, Christmas to mid-Feb. Access, Visa.*

St Ives Places of Interest

Tourist Information Tel 0736 796297.
The Barbara Hepworth Museum (The Tate Gallery) Tel 0736 796226.
Paradise Park Hayle Tel 0736 753365.
Porthmeor Beach *10 miles.*

St Ives (Cambs) Slepe Hall 61% £60

Tel 0480 463122 Fax 0480 300706 **H**

Ramsey Road St Ives Cambridgeshire PE17 4RB **Map 10 B2**

A Grade II listed building dating from 1848 and originally a private boarding school for girls. Now a small, comfortable hotel, it's kept in excellent order by Jan and Colin Stapleton. Several bedrooms feature four-poster or half-tester beds, and among the public areas is the Brunel Suite, which can cater for 220 conference delegates or banqueters. ***Rooms** 16. Closed 25 & 26 Dec. AMERICAN EXPRESS® Access, Diners, Visa.*

St Margaret's Wallett's Court 60% £45

Tel 0304 852424 **H**

West Cliffe St Margaret's Dover Kent CT15 6EW **Map 11 D5**

Chef/patron Chris and Lea Oakley run a small, personal hotel based around their 17th-century family home. Exposed brickwork and beams in the foyer set the old-world rural tone and the comfortable lounge has beams, a brick fireplace, antique furniture and a polished black Steinway upright piano standing proudly at one end. Three spacious rooms in the main house (carrying a supplementary charge) have freestanding furniture, simple fabrics and tiled bathrooms; those in the converted barn on the other side of the car park are smaller but just as comfortable. No dogs. ***Rooms** 7. Garden, tennis. Closed Xmas, 1 week Jan, 1 week Nov. Access, Visa.*

St Martin's St Martin's Hotel 69% £178*

Tel 0720 22092 Fax 0720 22298 **HR**

St Martin's Isles of Scilly TR25 OQW **Map 12 A2**

Hotel launch and Land Rover provide transport for arrivals, so make your travel arrangements when booking. St Martin's, 28 miles out in the Atlantic, provides the ultimate escape for solitude seekers; an equally novel activity centre for families (under-14s stay free in parents' room); and the last word in privacy for a conference (max 100) or private dinner (up to 80). Public rooms include the first-floor sunset lounge which affords wonderful views westward towards Tresco. *Half-board terms only. ***Rooms** 24. Garden, indoor swimming pool, fishing, snooker, sailing and scuba-diving instruction. Closed Nov-Mar. AMERICAN EXPRESS® Access, Diners, Visa.*

Restaurant

£55

Table d'hote dinners make good use of fish and shellfish, game and home-grown vegetables. Typical items on a high-summer menu range from prawn and lobster salad and grilled skate on a bed of steamed courgettes to broccoli soufflé and pan-fried strips of pork in a brandy sauce, garnished with pears. No smoking. Lighter bar lunches. ***Seats** 80. Private Room 14. L in bar only D 7.15-9. Set D £25.*

St Mary's — Hotel Godolphin — 58%

£92*

Tel 0720 22316 Fax 0720 22252

H

Church Street St Mary's Isles of Scilly TR21 0JR

Map 12 A2

Surrounded by a delightful town-house garden filled with sub-tropical plants, the hotel has a welcoming, homely appearance and is just a minute from the harbour beach. The friendly feel continues inside, where a panelled entrance hall leads to a comfortable lounge area with gold velour seating around a marble fireplace. There is also a cosy bar. Most of the simply furnished bedrooms have functional bathrooms without showers; three are not en suite and four are suitable for family use. No dogs. *Half-board terms; B&B rates on application. The Mumford family have been here since 1967. ***Rooms** 31. Garden, sauna. Closed mid Oct-mid Mar. Access, Visa.*

St Mary's — Tregarthen's Hotel — 60%

£110*

Tel 0720 22540 Fax 0720 22089

H

St Mary's Isles of Scilly TR21 0PP

Map 12 A2

Founded in 1840 by a Captain Tregarthen, the hotel stands in terraced gardens overlooking the harbour. Day rooms include the Little Western bar serving good snacks at lunchtime and a roast on Sunday. Bedrooms, some looking out to sea, are neat and comfortable. One bathroom boasts a Victorian cast-iron tub. *Half-board terms. No dogs. ***Rooms** 29. Garden. Closed Nov-end Mar.* AMERICAN EXPRESS *Access, Diners, Visa.*

St Mawes — Idle Rocks Hotel — 64%

£108

Tel 0326 270771 Fax 0326 270062

HR

Tredenham Road St Mawes Cornwall TR2 5AN

Map 12 B4

Privately owned, but not personally run, the Idle Rocks has been comprehensively refurbished over the last several years. A water's-edge terrace running the length of the hotel is a grand spot in summer and public rooms – including a panelled bar and armchair-filled lounge – share the harbour views. Pretty bedrooms in the main building – bedhead drapes, ribbon-hung pictures, antique and reproduction furniture – are not large but have good carpeted bathrooms with darkwood panelled tubs; three, including two tiny singles, have shower and WC only. More spacious bedrooms, with equally good facilities, are in a nearby annexe. Twice a week, weather permitting, trips are available on the hotel's own 55-foot ketch. ***Rooms** 24. Access, Visa.*

Waters Edge Restaurant

£65

Picture windows give views across the bay whilst enjoying Alan Vickops' sound cooking from an à la carte that changes regularly or the day's table d'hote. Marinated salmon and sole with sweet mustard and dill sauce, home-made duck paté on toasted brioche with poached grapes and Cumberland sauce, grilled lemon sole on a tomato and herb dressing, and baked breast of duck in a filo basket with a caramelised orange zest sauce give the style. Bar lunches. ***Seats** 65. Parties 20. D only 7-9.15. Set D £18.95.*

St Mawes — Rising Sun — 62% — £90

Tel 0326 270233 — H

The Square St Mawes Truro Cornwall TR2 5DJ — **Map 12 B4**

A popular and lively place on the waterfront in the centre of the village. The small conservatory frontage houses a lounge bar, and there's a public bar that's a favourite with the locals. Residents can retreat to their own little lounge at the back (six seats, with TV). Bedrooms are smart and simple, with pine furniture and neat, practical bathrooms. Children up to 14 stay free with parents in the family room. ***Rooms** 12.* American Express *Access, Visa.*

St Mawes — Hotel Tresanton — 69% — £70

Tel 0326 270544 Fax 0326 270002 — H

Lower Castle Road St Mawes Cornwall TR2 5DR — **Map 12 B4**

In a charming setting overlooking the Fal estuary, with a sun terrace making the most of the views and a garden that features some exotic plants and trees, the Tresanton is a comfortable hotel, run for over ten years by Graham and Maureen Brockton. When the weather closes in, the drawing room, with its open fire and inviting sofas, is definitely the place to be. Bedrooms all have sea views and private bathrooms, most of which are across a corridor. Four rooms have little balconies. Room price includes Cornish afternoon tea. No children under ten. ***Rooms** 21. Garden. Closed Nov-Feb (open 10 days Xmas).* American Express *Access, Diners, Visa.*

Salcombe — Marine Hotel — 68% — £142

Tel 0548 844444 Fax 0548 843109 — H

Cliff Road Salcombe Devon TQ8 8JH — **Map 13 D3**

Part of town, but with a splendid site alongside the Salcombe estuary, the Marine boasts notably spacious and comfortable, open-plan public areas with picture windows from which to enjoy the panoramic view. Additionally there are plenty of loungers out on the roomy sun deck. Best bedrooms are those on the patio floor – prettily decorated in pink with pink-washed furniture. Others tend to have more functional fitted furniture, often white-painted, and some are overdue a little refurbishment – but not yet seriously so. A decanter of sherry and bottles of mineral water are now standard in every room. All but six rooms have estuary views and all but two of these have usable, furnished balconies. Good leisure facilities include a full-size indoor pool. ***Rooms** 51. Garden, indoor swimming pool, keep-fit equipment, sauna, spa bath, solarium, beauty & hair salon, sea fishing, mooring, games room.* American Express *Access, Diners, Visa.*

Salcombe — Soar Mill Cove — 66% — £128

Tel 0548 561566 Fax 0548 561223 — H

Soar Mill Cove nr Salcombe Devon TQ7 3DS — **Map 13 D3**

Spectacular coastal location and unrivalled sea views make for a memorable holiday hotel. The closeness of 14 bedrooms, all at ground level with neighbouring patios, readily engenders a house party atmosphere, much in keeping with the Makepeace family's philosophy, and to which the staff contribute willingly. Thoroughly comfortable bedrooms, close-carpeted through to equally adequate bathrooms (some new bathrooms have recently been built), provide essential ingredients for a peaceful stay. The National Trust sandy beach and cliff walks prove highly popular daytime activities. Families with young children are admirably catered for (ages 1-6 charged 20% of tariff, 6-15 30%); high tea at 5pm is designed to leave adult residents in peace in the dining room during dinner. An ongoing upgrading programme has recently seen a new entrance hall, and enhanced bedroom and restaurant decorations. Breakfast includes the option of Salcombe smokies (kippered mackerel). ***Rooms** 14. Garden, indoor & outdoor swimming pools, tennis, putting, games room, laundry room. Closed Nov-early or mid-Feb.* AMERICAN EXPRESS *Access, Visa.*

Salcombe South Sands 60% £136*

Tel 0548 843741 Fax 0548 842112 **H**

Cliff Road Salcombe Devon TQ8 8LL **Map 13 D3**

Under the same ownership as the *Tides Reach* (see below) but even closer to the shore with the sandy beach reaching right up to the terrace walk, the South Sands caters more for younger children with ten family suites and a special high tea for youngsters served in the terrace bar/coffee shop anytime up to 7.30pm. Main public room is a spacious, comfortably leather-furnished bar/lounge with splendid views over the bay. Generally good-sized bedrooms, half with freestanding pine and half with white melamine fitted furniture, are uncluttered, with carpeted, fully tiled bathrooms. Friendly staff. No room service. *Half-board terms only, but B&B in early and late season. ***Rooms** 30. Indoor swimming pool, spa bath, steam room, solarium, moorings, children's playroom, coffee shop (noon-8.30 high season only). Access, Visa.*

Salcombe Spinnakers £50

Tel 0548 843408 **R**

Fore Street Salcombe Devon TQ8 8JG **Map 13 D3**

A picturesque waterside location (downstairs in the Salcombe Apartment building) where most of the tables have views of the estuary. David and Sandra May serve up informal bar and patio meals at lunchtime, with a more formal service in the evenings. There's always an unpretentious atmosphere, good fresh fish and a few vegetarian options. ***Seats** 60. Private Room 30. L 12-2 D 7-9.30. Closed D Sun, also all Mon & Tue in winter, all Dec & Jan. Set D £12.95. Access, Visa.*

Changes in data sometimes occur in establishments after the Guide goes to press. Prices should be taken as indications rather than firm quotes.

Salcombe Tides Reach 71% £162*

Tel 0548 843466 Fax 0548 843954 **H**

South Sands Salcombe Devon TQ8 8LJ **Map 13 D3**

The Edwards family maintain consistently high standards at the Tides Reach, a popular holiday hotel for over 25 years; it nestles snugly in the valley immediately behind South Sands beach, with clear views over the estuary and the Bolt Head. All the elegant public areas – the marble-floored conservatory-style entrance, the lounge in restful blue, the stylish Aquarium Bar – enjoy sea views, as do all but three bedrooms. These range from five singles with small double beds to junior and family suites, penthouse rooms with balconies and extra large Premier rooms. The sunbathing deck next to the pool and a grass area around an ornamental pond are both glorious suntraps. Very friendly and willing staff. A small public ferry chugs its way from South Sands beach into the town and there are spectacular coastal walks straight from the hotel. No children under 8. *Half-board terms only in high season. ***Rooms** 38. Garden, indoor swimming pool, sauna, solarium, keep-fit equipment, beauty and hairdressing salons, snooker, squash, sailing, windsurfing (with tuition), water skiing, moorings, boat house & dinghy park. Closed Nov-Feb.* AMERICAN EXPRESS *Access, Diners, Visa.*

Salcombe Place of Interest

Overbecks Museum and Garden (NT) Tel 0548 842893.

Salisbury **Rose & Crown** 56% £98

Tel 0722 327908 Fax 0722 339816 **H**

Harnham Road Harnham Salisbury Wiltshire SP2 8QJ **Map 14 C3**

A 13th-century, half-timbered inn whose gardens border the river Avon. Public areas and five characterful bedrooms are in the original building; other rooms, including family rooms, are in a modern extension. Queens Moat Houses. ***Rooms** 28. Garden.* AMERICAN EXPRESS *Access, Diners, Visa.*

Salisbury **White Hart** 63% £106

Tel 0722 327476 Fax 0722 412761 **H**

1 St John Street Salisbury Wiltshire SP1 2SD **Map 14 C3**

City-centre hotel with an impressive pillared portico and elegant Georgian facade, but modest bedrooms. Forte Heritage. ***Rooms** 68.* AMERICAN EXPRESS *Access, Diners, Visa.*

Salisbury **Places of Interest**

Tourist Information Tel 0722 334956.

Theatres and Concert Halls

Medieval Hall Tel 0980 610304.
Salisbury Arts Centre Tel 0722 21744.
Salisbury Playhouse Tel 0722 20333.

Historic Houses, Castles and Gardens

Fitz House Garden Tel 0722 716257.
Heale Gardens and Plant Centre Tel 0722 73504.
The King's House Tel 0722 332151.
Old Sarum Tel 0722 335398.
Wilton House Wilton Tel 0722 743115.
Stonehenge Nr Amesbury.
Salisbury Cathedral Tel 0722 22457.
Salisbury and South Wiltshire Museum and Stonehenge Gallery Tel 0722 332151.
Salisbury Racecourse Tel 0722 326461.

Saltash **Granada Lodge** £45

Tel 0752 848408 Fax 0752 848346 **L**

A38 bypass Saltash Cornwall PL12 6LF **Map 12 C3**

***Rooms** 31.* AMERICAN EXPRESS *Access, Diners, Visa.*

Samlesbury **Swallow Trafalgar** 60% £72

Tel 0772 877351 Fax 0772 877424 **H**

Preston New Road Samlesbury Lancashire PR5 0UL **Map 6 B1**

Heading east from Junction 31 of the M6 and alongside the A59 at its intersection with the A677 Blackburn road is a practical business-orientated hotel with good leisure facilities and conference capacities of up to 250. ***Rooms** 78. Garden, indoor swimming pool, spa bath, sauna, steam room, solarium, keep-fit equipment, squash.* AMERICAN EXPRESS *Access, Diners, Visa.*

Samlesbury **Tickled Trout** 63% £85

Tel 0772 877671 Fax 0772 847463 **H**

Preston New Road Samlesbury nr Preston Lancashire PR5 OUJ **Map 6 B1**

A modern hotel on the banks of the Ribble, west of junction 31 of the M6. Good accommodation, a comfortable lounge bar with Victorian artefacts and a decent leisure area are among the attractions. Quiet bedrooms (most overlook the river) have fitted furniture, modern fabrics and the usual accessories. Small tiled bathrooms have baths plus showers and hairdryers.

Children up to 14 stay free in parents' room. Conference facilities for up to 100. Rank Hotels. ***Rooms** 72. Indoor swimming pool, fishing.* AMERICAN EXPRESS *Access, Diners, Visa.*

Sandbach **Chimney House** 62% £81

Tel 0270 764141 Fax 0270 768916 **H**

Congleton Road Sandbach Cheshire CW11 0ST **Map 6 B2**

Although only moments from the M6 (Junction 17), the mock-Tudor Chimney House has a remarkably peaceful rural setting within eight acres of wooded grounds. Open-plan public areas focus on a back-to-back pair of original fireplaces; day rooms and half the bedrooms have recently been refurbished. Conference facilities for up to 100 theatre-style. No dogs. ***Rooms** 48. Garden, sauna, solarium.* AMERICAN EXPRESS *Access, Diners, Visa.*

Sandiway **Nunsmere Hall** 77% £120

Tel 0606 889100 Fax 0606 889055 **HR**

Tarporley Road Sandiway Cheshire CW8 2ES **Map 6 B2**

Almost surrounded by a 60-acre lake the Victorian, now extended, Nunsmere Hall enjoys a delightfully secluded woodland setting despite being only just off the A49. A fine galleried entrance hall sets the tone for appealing day rooms which include a comfortable, oak-panelled bar, leather-furnished library and a lounge with a huge floral centrepieces. Notably large, antique-furnished bedrooms are individually decorated and quite harmonious with comfortable sitting area. Sybaritic bathrooms, many with separate shower cubicle, in addition to a large tub, all have bidets, generous towelling and attractive basins sunk into marble-topped wash stands. Rooms are properly serviced in the evenings and there is 24hr room service. No dogs. ***Rooms** 32. Garden, golf practice net, archery, helipad.* AMERICAN EXPRESS *Access, Diners, Visa.*

Garden Room Restaurant £70

The restaurant has been stylishly refurbished with brass chandeliers hanging from the moulded plaster ceiling and floor-length undercloths on tables which boast pretty, high-quality tableware. Chef Paul Kitching's attractively presented offerings tend to be modern in style with the likes of steamed salmon with ragout of saffron pasta and spring vegetables in a light herb and cream sauce; terrine of Continental meats, lentils and wild mushrooms with balsamic vinegar dressing and breast of Gressingham duck with a beetroot and chive-scented game sauce and grilled black pudding. Afters might include a rich chocolate cheese cake and warm rice pudding with honey and coconut beignets or go for a selection of British farmhouse cheeses with home-made date and walnut bread. Particularly good *amuse gueule* arrive with the menu. A lighter menu is served in the lounge or on the terrace throughout the day. ***Seats** 48. Private Room 42. L 12.30-2 (Sun 11.30-2.30) D 7.30-10 (Sat to 10.30). Set L £12.95/£15.50 Set D from £22.50.*

Saunton **Saunton Sands** 67% £120

Tel 0271 890212 Fax 0271 890145 **H**

Saunton nr Braunton Devon EX33 1LQ **Map 12 C1**

An ideal, family-oriented resort hotel, where you may park your car for a week and never need to use it; Saunton Sands commands panoramic views over the North Devon coastline. Five miles of golden sands stretch past the door; within, the leisure facilities are as abundant as the sporting and aquatic activities without. Bedrooms are neat, light and airy, with Laura Ashley-style fabrics. Children's facilities include a crèche, play areas, plenty of cots, baby-sitting, baby-listening and high teas. Three conference suites accommodate 20-200. No dogs. ***Rooms** 96. Garden, tennis, squash, indoor & outdoor swimming pools, spa bath, sauna, solarium, snooker, hairdressing.* AMERICAN EXPRESS *Access, Diners, Visa.*

Sawbridgeworth **Manor of Groves** 74% £90

Tel 0279 600777 Fax 0279 600374 **H**

High Wych Sawbridgeworth Hertfordshire CM21 OLA **Map 11 B4**

Off Junction 7 of the M11 (following the signs to Harlow and then Bishops Stortford) this is a country manor and golf and country club converted and extended by Stuart and Wendy Sharer from a Georgian manor house. It's surrounded by landscaped gardens and the original kitchen walled garden, with a further 150 acres transformed into an 18-hole golf course. Day rooms have restful colours and rich fabrics, including plump-cushioned seating in the drawing room. Most impressive, though, is the long, glazed and colonnaded loggia with check-tiled flooring, wicker furniture and parlour plants; snacks are served here. Bedrooms are tastefully gracious and stylish with soft, carefully co-ordinated fabrics and furnishings; the Coach House has duplex suites. Wonderful bathrooms have marble tiling, bright lighting and splendid, deep baths. Conference/banqueting facilities for 150. Families can eat informally in the Clubhouse, and a children's menu is served in the Loggia at 6pm. ***Rooms** 39. Garden, outdoor swimming pool, gymnasium, sauna, solarium, golf, tennis, snooker, coffee shop (8am-late evening).* AMERICAN EXPRESS *Access, Diners, Visa.*

Scalby **Wrea Head** 65% £90

Tel 0723 378211 Fax 0723 371780 **H**

Scalby nr Scarborough North Yorkshire YO13 0PB **Map 5 F3**

Built in 1881, Wrea Head stands in 14 acres of wooded and landscaped gounds. It's signposted off the A171 and reached by a narrow driveway. A fine panelled hall features a wall-long stained-glass window, while the bar is notable for an unusual terracotta frieze. Bedrooms are generally neat and comfortable, with delightful views. Free use of leisure facilities at *Hackness Grange* (see entry under Hackness), 3 miles away. No dogs. ***Rooms** 21. Garden. Closed 4 days Xmas.* AMERICAN EXPRESS *Access, Visa.*

Consult page 16 for a full list of starred restaurants

Scarborough **The Crown** 63% £97

Tel 0723 373491 Fax 0723 362271 **H**

Esplanade Scarborough North Yorkshire YO11 2AG **Map 5 F3**

A splendid setting on the cliffs above South Bay for a Forte Heritage hotel with an in-house conference facility for up to 200 delegates. ***Rooms** 78. Snooker, hair & beauty salon.* AMERICAN EXPRESS *Access, Diners, Visa.*

Scarborough **Lanterna** £45

Tel 0723 363616 **R**

33 Queen Street Scarborough North Yorkshire YO11 1HQ **Map 5 F3**

Run for 20 years by the Arecco family, a straightforward Italian with a selection of chicken, veal and steak dishes as well as snails, spaghetti, minestrone and scampi. ***Seats** 36. D only 7-9.30. Closed Sun & Mon. Access, Visa.*

Scarborough **Places of Interest**

Tourist Information Tel 0723 373333.
Royal Opera House Tel 0723 36999.
St. Joseph Theatre in the Round Tel 0723 370541.
Whitby Abbey Whitby Tel 0947 603568.
Filey Bay Beach *7 miles from Scarborough.*

Scole Scole Inn £60

Tel 0379 740481 Fax 0379 740762 **I**

Norwich Road Scole nr Diss Norfolk IP21 4DR **Map 10 C2**

A redbrick inn dating from 1655 and listed as of architectural interest. That interest includes splendid brick gables of Dutch inspiration. Bedrooms are divided between the Georgian stable block and the main building, the latter featuring carved oak beams. Four-poster rooms carry a supplement. The bar also abounds in beams and atmosphere. Scole stands on the Norfolk/Suffolk border 2 miles from Diss. ***Rooms** 23. Garden.*
AMERICAN EXPRESS *Access, Diners, Visa.*

Scotch Corner Forte Travelodge £42

Tel 0748 823768 **L**

Scotch Corner Skeeby nr Richmond North Yorkshire DL10 5EQ **Map 5 D3**

On the A1 northbound, ½ mile south of Scotch Corner. ***Rooms** 40.*
AMERICAN EXPRESS *Access, Visa.*

Seahouses Olde Ship Hotel £64

Tel 0665 720200 Fax 0665 721383 **I**

9 Main Street Seahouses Northumberland NE68 7RD **Map 5 D1**

Alan and Jean Glen have emphasised the nautical charm of their characterful old inn overlooking the picturesque harbour and Farne Islands. The tiny cabin bar and handsome saloon bar house marine antiques, while the long gallery lounge has a collection of model ships. It's very much a traditional pub, a social centre for regulars and locals. A small function room with its own bar can accommodate up to 40. Homely bedrooms; two have four-poster beds. No children under 10. No dogs. ***Rooms** 15. Garden, spa bath, putting. Closed Dec & Jan. Access, Visa.*

Seahouses Place of Interest

Beadnell Bay Beach *4 miles South.*

Seale Hog's Back Hotel 64% £108

Tel 0252 782345 Fax 0252 783113 **H**

Seale nr Farnham Surrey GU10 1EX **Map 15 E3**

A tile-hung, gable-fronted hotel on the A31, with day rooms smart in pastel and pale wood, a leisure centre and conference facilities for up to 140 in the Summit Conference Centre. Children up to 14 stay free in parents' room. Jarvis Hotels. ***Rooms** 75. Garden, indoor swimming pool, keep-fit equipment, sauna, spa bath, solarium.* AMERICAN EXPRESS *Access, Diners, Visa.*

Seaview Seaview Hotel 62% £73

Tel 0983 612711 Fax 0983 613729 **HR**

High Street Seaview Isle of Wight PO34 5EX **Map 15 D4**

The epitome of a small, family-run seaside hotel. Nicholas and Nicola Hayward run this charming little hotel-cum-local inn set just back from the sea front with a most appealing hands-on efficiency. A small patio with pub-style white iron tables and chairs at the front of the hotel is a delightful sun trap from which one can watch the world (and his wife) go by; it leads into a narrow hallway, either side of which are a busy bar and a restaurant. To the rear are two snug lounges (one for non-smokers), another popular nautically-themed bar with bare boards and an open-air yard. Public rooms buzz in season, yet are snug in winter. Upstairs, the bedrooms (some with views over the Solent) are all individually decorated with predominantly blue and yellow colour schemes and feature interesting pictures, objets d'art and spotless bathrooms. ***Rooms** 16. Sea fishing, family apartment. Closed 25 Dec.* AMERICAN EXPRESS *Access, Visa.*

See over

Restaurant £50

An intimate dining room with close-set tables, candle-lit in the evenings. Local crab might feature in a creamy soup or a hot ramekin with tarragon, and oak-smoked Island garlic is used in garlic bread and to season a salad of mussels and mushrooms. Main courses are safe, standard fare. Two sittings in high season and on Saturday nights. Good snacks are served in the adjacent bar or out on the terrace (including Sunday nights). Short, realistically-priced wine list. ***Seats** 32. L 12-2 D 7.30-9.30. Closed D Sun.*

Seavington St Mary — The Pheasant — 69% — £70

Tel 0460 40502 Fax 0460 42388 — **H**

Water Street Seavington St Mary nr Ilminster Somerset TA19 0QH — **Map 13 F2**

A setting of landscaped gardens with abundant trees and shrubs imbues the Paolonis' former 17th-century farmhouse with distinctive charm and character. Look for signs for Seavington St Michael from the South Petherton end of the A303 Ilminster bypass. Hand-crafted reproductions of 18th-and 19th-century fine wood furniture feature in all the individually styled bedrooms: two in the main house with beams galore, the rest in cottages across the garden. No dogs. ***Rooms** 10. Garden. Closed 26 Dec-5 Jan.* AMERICAN EXPRESS *Access, Visa.*

Sedgemoor — Forte Travelodge — £42

Tel 0934 750831 — **L**

Welcome Break Sedgemoor Weston-super-Mare Avon BS24 0JL — **Map 13 E1**

Situated on the M5 northbound, 6 miles south of Weston-super-Mare. Access to the southbound carriageway is at Junction 22. ***Rooms** 40.* AMERICAN EXPRESS *Access, Visa.*

Sedlescombe — Brickwall Hotel — 56% — £54

Tel 042 4870 253 Fax 042 4870 785 — **H**

Sedlescombe nr Battle East Sussex TN33 0QA — **Map 11 C6**

A Tudor mansion overlooking the village green. Deep-red velour fireside chairs, oak panelling, exposed beams, willow-pattern plates on the walls and a log fire give character to the bar, and the residents' lounge is equally friendly. Some bedrooms boast four-posters and black beams. ***Rooms** 23. Garden, outdoor swimming pool.* AMERICAN EXPRESS *Access, Diners, Visa.*

Sevenoaks — Royal Oak — 66% — £99

Tel 0732 451109 Fax 0732 740187 — **HR**

High Street Sevenoaks Kent TN13 1HY — **Map 11 B5**

A former coaching inn with abundant atmosphere and character. Rich, bold colours perfectly complement the fabric of the building. Traditional or antique furniture is used in the bedrooms, which are decorated in individual, often striking style. Neat, bright bathrooms. Among the day rooms are a cosy pub-like bar (where imaginative bar snacks are served in a candle-lit section with scrubbed pine tables and comfortable, well-upholstered seats), a beautifully furnished drawing room and a conservatory. ***Rooms** 39. Tennis.* AMERICAN EXPRESS *Access, Diners, Visa.*

Restaurant £65

A charming and comfortable restaurant comprising several rooms that are partially panelled and cleverly lit, creating a relaxing atmosphere. Chef James Butterfill manages to include something for everyone on his à la carte, and the three-course fixed-price menus offer particularly good value. Outdoor eating in good weather on a creeper-clad patio. ***Seats** 60. Parties 24. L 12.30-2 D 7.30-10.30. Closed L Sat. Set L £11.50 Set D £18.50.*

Sevenoaks Places of Interest

Tourist Information Tel 0732 450305.
Lullingstone Castle Eynsford Tel 0322 862114.
Historic Houses, Castles and Gardens
Emmetts Garden Tel 0732 75429.
Great Comp Borough Green Tel 0732 882669.
Ightham Mote (NT) Ivy Hatch, Ightham Tel 0732 810378.
Knole (NT) Tel 0732 450608.
Chartwell (NT) Tel 0732 866368 *Home of Winston Churchill.*
Squerryes Court Westerham Tel 0959 62345.

Shaftesbury Grosvenor Hotel 62% £87

Tel 0747 52282 Fax 0747 54755 **H**

The Commons Shaftesbury Dorset SP7 8JA **Map 14 B3**

Centrally located former coaching inn based around a cobbled courtyard. Homely, traditional feel. Conference/banqueting facilities for 150/120. Forte Heritage. ***Rooms** 35.* AMERICAN EXPRESS *Access, Diners, Visa.*

Shaftesbury Royal Chase Hotel 60% £84

Tel 0747 53355 Fax 0747 51969 **H**

Shaftesbury Dorset SP7 8DB **Map 14 B3**

This former monastery, owned by George and Rosemary Hunt for 21 years, is set back from the A30/A350 roundabout on the eastern side of Shaftesbury. Families are well catered for, particularly in holiday periods, and children up to 16 stay free in their parents' room. Purpose-built conference facilities. ***Rooms** 35. Garden, indoor swimming pool, steam room, solarium.* AMERICAN EXPRESS *Access, Diners, Visa.*

Shaftesbury Place of Interest

Wincanton Racecourse Tel 0963 32344.

Shanklin Cliff Tops Hotel 64% £99

Tel 0983 863262 Fax 0983 867139 **H**

Park Road Shanklin Isle of Wight PO37 6BB **Map 15 D4**

One of the Isle of Wight's largest hotels enjoys panoramic views from its position on the cliff 300 feet above Sandown Bay (a public lift down to the seafront is right alongside). There's a choice of bars, a leisure club, conference rooms for up to 250 delegates and plenty of facilities for children. Most of the bedrooms have balconies. Children up to 14 stay free in parents' room (50% discount in their own room). ***Rooms** 88. Garden, indoor swimming pool, gymnasium, sauna, spa bath, steam room, solarium, beauty & hair salon, snooker, children's play area.* AMERICAN EXPRESS *Access, Diners, Visa.*

Shanklin Old Village The Cottage £50

Tel 0983 862504 **R**

8 Eastcliff Road Shanklin Old Village Isle of Wight PO37 6AA **Map 15 D4**

Three old cottages in a cul de sac on the town side of Shanklin's old village but visible from the main road. Trained to cook the French way, Neil Graham, in the kitchen here for 20 years (with partner Alan Priddle running front of house), draws influences from both sides of the channel: mushroom and garlic pancakes, prawns Thermidor, duckling in a sauce of honey and orange, and fillet steak Shakespeare (grilled "As You Like It"). There's a pretty courtyard garden for summer eating. ***Seats** 32. L 12-2 D 7.30-9.45. Closed D Sun, all Mon, 26 Dec, 4 weeks Feb/Mar and Oct. Set L £7.50. Access, Visa.*

Shanklin — Places of Interest

Sandown Tourist Information Tel 0983 403886.
Pavillion Theatre Tel 0983 402295.
Shanklin Theatre Tel 0983 862739.
Morton Manor Gardens Brading Tel 0983 4061-68.
Nunwell House Gardens Brading Tel 0983 407240.

Sheffield — Charnwood Hotel — 67% — £90

Tel 0742 589411 Fax 0742 555107 — H

10 Sharrow Lane Sheffield South Yorkshire S11 8AA — Map 6 C2

Built in 1786 and once the home of master cutler John Henfrey, this listed building has been restored and converted by Val and Chris King, owners since 1985. Comfort and relaxation are keynotes throughout, from the restaurant, brasserie and conservatory lounge to the quiet period-style drawing rooms and the thoughtfully equipped bedrooms. In addition to the hotel's accommodation there are one, two and three-bedroomed apartments. ***Rooms 22.*** *American Express Access, Diners, Visa.*

Sheffield — Forte Crest — 65% — £93

Tel 0742 670067 Fax 0742 682620 — H

Manchester Road Sheffield South Yorkshire S10 5DX — Map 6 C2

A modern, stilted tower-block building recently upgraded. Half the rooms are non-smoking. Good leisure facilities and conference/banqueting amenities supported by secretarial services; ample free car parking. Children up to 16 free in parents' room; facilities for families. 24hr room service. 5 miles from M1 junction 33, on the A57. ***Rooms 136.*** *Indoor swimming pool, spa bath, sauna, solarium, keep-fit equipment.* *American Express Access, Diners, Visa.*

Sheffield — Grosvenor House — 67% — £77

Tel 0742 720041 Fax 0742 757199 — H

Charter Square Sheffield South Yorkshire S1 3EH — Map 6 C2

Prominent tower-block hotel with direct access from its own car park. Rooms on the higher floors have good views over the city. Large conference/banqueting facilities; two boardrooms seat up to 20. ***Rooms 103.*** *American Express Access, Diners, Visa.*

Sheffield — Holiday Inn Royal Victoria — 67% — £107

Tel 0742 768822 Fax 0742 724519 — H

Station Approach Sheffield South Yorkshire S4 7XE — Map 6 C2

Large redbrick Victorian building with well-proportioned, high-ceilinged day rooms. Conference and banqueting facilities for up to 300. Ample free car parking. ***Rooms 100.*** *American Express Access, Diners, Visa.*

Sheffield — Moat House — 71% — £100

Tel 0742 375376 Fax 0742 378140 — H

Chesterfield Road South Sheffield South Yorkshire S8 8BW — Map 6 C2

A modern redbrick hotel situated alongside the A61, just south of the ring road, offering a range of facilities for both business and leisure visitors. The largest of the function rooms can accommodate 500 delegates, while other rooms hold from 10 upwards. There's also a well-equipped leisure centre, with instructors on hand in the gym. Its day rooms are tastefully styled with an impressive foyer that has polished marble floors and good space. The adjoining lounge area is fashionably and comfortably furnished but the main bar lacks atmosphere. Bedrooms are uniform in both size and design with lightwood units, contemporary fabrics and plenty of work space. ***Rooms** 95. Garden, indoor swimming pool, keep-fit equipment, sauna, spa bath, solarium, beauty salon.* AMERICAN EXPRESS *Access, Diners, Visa.*

Sheffield — Nirmal's

£40

Tel 0742 724054

R

193 Glossop Road Sheffield South Yorkshire S10 2GW

Map 6 C2

Superior North Indian cooking, refreshingly restrained in the use of oil and ghee, shines in Nirmal's exclusive dishes from the specials board, in the well-spiced daily-changing dals and in the splendid home-made paneer. Good-value set lunch, ambitious feasts for two or more and two days notice required for the lamb masallam for six people. ***Seats** 80. Parties 50. L 12-2.30 D 6-12 (Fri & Sat to 1). Closed L Sun, all 25 & 26 Dec. Set L £8/£12 Set D £12/£15.* AMERICAN EXPRESS *Access, Diners, Visa.*

Sheffield — St George Swallow Hotel — 64%

£96

Tel 0742 583811 Fax 0742 500138

H

Kenwood Road Sheffield South Yorkshire S7 1NQ

Map 6 C2

Up-to-date accommodation, conference facilities (for up to 250) and a smart leisure club in a much-extended country house. Set in 11 acres of landscaped gardens (including an ornamental lake), two miles from the city centre. ***Rooms** 141. Garden, indoor swimming pool, keep-fit equipment, sauna, spa bath, steam room, solarium, coffee shop (10am-10pm).* AMERICAN EXPRESS *Access, Diners, Visa.*

Sheffield — Places of Interest

Tourist Information Tel 0742 734671/734672.
Sheffield Cathedral Tel 0742 753434.
Theatres and Concert Halls
Crucible Theatre Tel 0742 79922.
Leadmill Tel 0742 754500.
Merlin Theatre Tel 0742 551638.
Museums and Art Galleries
Graves Art Gallery Tel 0742 734781.
Kelham Island Industrial Museum Tel 0742 722106.
Mappin Art Gallery Tel 0742 726281.
Ruskin Gallery Tel 0742 734781.
Sheffield United FC Bramhall Lane Tel 0742 738955.
Sheffield Wednesday FC Hillsborough Tel 0742 343122.
Sheffield Eagles RLFC Tel 0742 610326.
Sheffield Ski Village Tel 0742 769459.
Don Valley Stadium Tel 0742 560607.

Shepperton — Moat House — 61%

£103

Tel 0932 241404 Fax 0932 245231

H

Felix Lane Shepperton Middlesex TW17 8NP

Map 15 E2

A peaceful location by the Thames is a big plus at this modern hotel with conference facilities for up to 300 delegates. 24hr room service. ***Rooms** 180. Sauna, solarium, keep-fit equipment, snooker, putting, mooring, 9-hole pitch & putt. Closed 1 week Christmas.* AMERICAN EXPRESS *Access, Diners, Visa.*

Shepperton — Warren Lodge

£72

Tel 0932 242972 Fax 0932 253883

I

Church Square Shepperton Middlesex TW17 9JZ

Map 15 E2

In the corner of a pretty village square, this 18th-century inn offers clean, basic accommodation in a picturesque setting. There are views of the river not only from the wood-beamed bar but also from six rooms in a new wing which lead on to a courtyard, motel-style. Bedrooms are modestly

See over

decorated and kept in good order. A handsome old walnut tree dominates the cool and shady garden that leads down to the banks of the Thames. ***Rooms** 52.* AMERICAN EXPRESS *Access, Diners, Visa.*

Shepton Mallet — Blostin's Restaurant — £45

Tel 0749 343648 — R

29 Waterloo Road Shepton Mallet Somerset BA4 5HH — Map 13 F1

Dark and candle-lit bistro where Nick Reed produces consistently well-cooked meals with 2- or 3-course fixed-price menus supplemented by an additional list of à la carte seasonal specialities. Fish soup, salmon mousse wrapped in smoked salmon with watercress sauce, grilled goat's cheese with toasted brioche, loin of venison with wild mushrooms, treacle and walnut tart and home-made ice creams show the style. Vegetarian options. ***Seats** 32. Parties 28. D only 7-9.30. Closed Sun & Mon, 2 weeks Jan, 1 week Jun, 1 week Nov. Set D £13.95/£14.95. Access, Visa.*

Shepton Mallet — Places of Interest

Tourist Information Tel 0749 345258.
Wookey Hole Caves and Mill Wookey Hole Nr Shepton Mallet.
Royal Bath & West Showground Tel 0749 823211.

Sherborne — Eastbury Hotel — 67% — £98

Tel 0935 813131 Fax 0935 817296 — H

Long Street Sherborne Dorset DT9 3BY — Map 13 F2

Built in 1740, the Eastbury is a fine Georgian town house with well-proportioned rooms. Public areas comprise an elegant entrance hall, a comfortably furnished lounge, a library and an intimate cocktail bar with an ornately carved counter. Bedrooms, named after English flowers, have smart polished-wood furniture and pretty fabrics. Bathrooms offer showers and tubs, plus good soaps and toiletries. No dogs. Families are well catered for – children up to 10 stay free in parents' room. Clipper Hotels. ***Rooms** 15. Garden. Access, Visa.*

Sherborne — Forte Posthouse — 58% — £68

Tel 0935 813191 Fax 0935 816493 — H

Horsecastles Lane Sherborne Dorset DT9 6BB — Map 13 F2

Low-rise hotel set in its own grounds on the A30 just outside Sherborne. ***Rooms** 59. Golf driving net, children's playroom, playground.* AMERICAN EXPRESS *Access, Diners, Visa.*

Shifnal — Park House — 71% — £85

Tel 0952 460128 Fax 0952 461658 — H

Park Street Shifnal nr Telford Shropshire TF11 9BA — Map 6 B4

Originally two adjacent country houses of completely different architectural styles, Park House has nevertheless managed to retain much of the atmosphere of a private house. An elegant garden suite and individually stylish private rooms accommodate conferences and catering from 20 to 250. Bedrooms use quality furniture and fabrics, and plentiful extras include decanters of sherry and baskets of fresh fruit. Children under eight stay free in parents' room. Near Junction 4 of the M54. ***Rooms** 54. Garden, indoor swimming pool, spa bath, sauna, solarium, fishing.* AMERICAN EXPRESS *Access, Diners, Visa.*

Shifnal — Places of Interest

Boscobel House Tel 0902 850244.
Weston Park Weston-under-Lizard Tel 095276 207.

Shinfield L'Ortolan ★★★ £140

Tel 0734 883783 Fax 0734 885391 **R**

Old Vicarage Church Lane Shinfield nr Reading Berkshire RG2 9BY **Map 15 D2**

For Londoners, the restaurant is only about an hour's drive from town (a few minutes from Junction 11 of the M4), and certainly worth the journey, since this is undoubtedly one of the finest restaurants in the country. John Burton-Race's creative flair, coupled with his intense enthusiasm, ranks him one of the best, and the extraordinary high standards he demands from his team in the kitchen, and that wife Christine asks from the staff at front of house are all to the benefit of the customer. John, previously in the kitchens at the old *Quaglino's, Chewton Glen, La Sorbonne, Les Quat' Saisons* and *Le Petit Blanc* in Oxford, opened the restaurant with his wife some seven years ago, and in the intervening period they have greatly improved both the inside of the old vicarage, and the beautifully maintained gardens. The drawing-room conservatory has certainly relieved pre-meal seating pressure, so that the best *amuse-gueule* anywhere can be savoured in comfortable surroundings. There are two dining rooms and a further conservatory, overlooking the terrace and the lawn, which is obviously popular in fine weather. There's always a wide variety of exciting dishes available, though the less expensive set meals are not served on Saturday evening. Be that as it may, the cooking is never less than of exceptional quality, and the intricacy that goes into the preparation of dishes has to be experienced to be believed. Burton-Race's signature dishes include *lasagne de langoustines à l'huile de truffe,* layers of langoustines bound with its mousse, scented with tarragon, between leaves of fresh pasta, steamed and masked with a delicate truffle oil, and wondrous desserts – fully deserving the award of Dessert of the Year – *assiette chocolatière,* a taste of various chocolate desserts, and *dome de mousse caramel brulée,* a delicate caramel mousse served in a dome of toffee, all enjoyed on a recent visit, as was a guinea fowl consommé spiked with a julienne of vegetables, garnished with a ravioli of its meat, and wild pigeon breast filled with foie gras, rolled in breadcrumbs and pan-fried, served with onion cream rice. As with all great restaurants, little is left to chance – the superb French cheeseboard, always knowledgeably described, the impeccable service, the china, the decor, all of which add up to some sort of expectation that will not disappoint. The New World (California especially) does get a look-in on the splendid and mostly French wine list, which includes a good selection of half bottles. ***Seats** 60. Private Room 25. L 12.15-2.30 D 7.15-10. Closed D Sun, all Mon, last 2 weeks Aug, last 2 weeks Feb. Set L & D (Tues-Fri) £21.50/£29.50 Set D £44/£52.* AMERICAN EXPRESS *Access, Diners, Visa.*

Shipdham Shipdham Place 64% £60

Tel 0362 820303 **H**

Shipdham nr Thetford Norfolk IP25 7LX **Map 10 C1**

On the A1075, half way between East Dereham and Watton. Although Georgian at first sight, parts of this old rectory date back to 1630 and there's a Victorian addition, too. Day rooms include an elegant morning room, and a TV lounge in the old part has stripped pine panelling. Good breakfasts are served in the delightful old kitchen. More old pine, antiques and rattan easy chairs characterise the pretty bedrooms. ***Rooms** 8. Garden.* AMERICAN EXPRESS *Access, Diners, Visa.*

Shorne Inn on the Lake 61% £70

Tel 0474 823333 Fax 0474 823175 **H**

Shorne nr Gravesend Kent DA12 3HB **Map 11 B5**

A modern stopover set in landscaped grounds with ornamental lakes. Two lounge bars open off the reception area, one quieter with settees, the other with conference chairs and often occupied for that purpose. Of the pleasant

See over

and practical bedrooms, a few on the first floor overlook the lakes and have balconies. No dogs. Banqueting/conference facilities for 500/700. ***Rooms** 78. Garden.* AMERICAN EXPRESS *Access, Diners, Visa.*

Shrewsbury — Lion Hotel — 62% — £92

Tel 0743 353107 Fax 0743 352744 — **H**

Wyle Cop Shrewsbury Shropshire SY1 1UY — **Map 6 A3**

A town-centre Forte Heritage hotel with characterful, beamed bedrooms and other period features amid the modern day rooms and conference facilities. ***Rooms** 59.* AMERICAN EXPRESS *Access, Diners, Visa.*

Shrewsbury — Prince Rupert Hotel — 64% — £85

Tel 0743 236000 Fax 0743 357306 — **H**

Butcher Row Shrewsbury Shropshire SY1 1UQ — **Map 6 A3**

Queens Moat Houses hotel in the medieval city centre (access from Fish Street or Church Street). Bedrooms include two four-poster suites. Children up to 16 stay free in parents' room. Valet parking. ***Rooms** 65.* AMERICAN EXPRESS *Access, Diners, Visa.*

Shrewsbury — Places of Interest

Tourist Information Tel 0743 50761.
The Music Hall The Square Tel 0743 50671.
Quarry Swimming Centre Tel 0743 236583.
Historic Houses, Castles and Gardens
Attingham Park (NT) Attingham Tel 0743 77 203.
Hodnet Hall Gardens Hodnet Tel 063 084 202.
Pitchford Hall Condover Tel 06944 205.
Shipton Hall Much Wenlock Tel 074 636 225.

Sidmouth — Belmont Hotel — 63% — £106

Tel 0395 512555 Fax 0395 579154 — **H**

The Esplanade Sidmouth Devon EX10 8RX — **Map 13 E2**

Standing in substantial grounds on the seafront, the Belmont was built as a private residence in 1820 and enjoys views over the bay from its roomy lounges and from many of its bedrooms. Some rooms have private balconies, and de luxe rooms offer numerous cosseting extras. Guests have free use of the leisure facilities of the sister hotel next door, the *Victoria* (see entry). Popular with families in the summer season. No dogs. ***Rooms** 54. Garden, putting.* AMERICAN EXPRESS *Access, Diners, Visa.*

Sidmouth — Fortfield Hotel — 59% — £91

Tel & Fax 0395 512403 — **H**

Sidmouth Devon EX10 8NU — **Map 13 E2**

Andrew and Annabel Torjussen own and run an Edwardian redbrick hotel overlooking a cricket ground and the sea beyond. A light, sunny lounge makes the most of the location, and a number of bedrooms have balconies. ***Rooms** 55. Garden, indoor swimming pool, sauna, solarium, putting.* AMERICAN EXPRESS *Access, Diners, Visa.*

Sidmouth — Hotel Riviera — 65% — £112

Tel 0395 515201 Fax 0395 577775 — **H**

The Esplanade Sidmouth Devon EX10 8AY — **Map 13 E2**

A handsome Regency facade fronts a terrace of three-storey houses in the middle of the esplanade overlooking Lyme Bay. The Regency Bar is a relaxing spot for a drink, while cream teas can be enjoyed in the lounge or out on the patio. A programme of refurbishment has improved the bedrooms and bathrooms. Most rooms have bay views. ***Rooms** 29.* AMERICAN EXPRESS® *Access, Diners, Visa.*

Sidmouth **Victoria Hotel** **67%** **£120**

Tel 0395 512651 Fax 0395 579154 **H**

The Esplanade Sidmouth Devon EX10 8RY **Map 13 E2**

Named after Queen Victoria, a frequent visitor to her neighbouring residence, the hotel was actually opened early in the reign of Edward VII. Lounges are roomy and relaxing, and most of the well-appointed bedrooms face the sea (many have French windows leading to private balconies). Families are well catered for with good leisure facilities, baby-sitting and considerations for children in the dining room. Room service is available at any hour. No dogs. ***Rooms** 65. Garden, indoor & outdoor swimming pools, keep-fit equipment, squash, sauna, spa bath, solarium, hairdressing, tennis, putting, snooker & games room, lock-up garages.* AMERICAN EXPRESS® *Access, Diners, Visa.*

Sidmouth **Place of Interest**

Jacobs Ladder Beach.

Silchester **Romans Hotel** **64%** **£80**

Tel 0734 700421 Fax 0734 700691 **H**

Little London Road Silchester nr Basingstoke Hampshire RG7 2PN **Map 15 D3**

Built in the early years of this century, this handsome Lutyens house stands amid trim lawns and mature grounds with two hard tennis courts. Inside, polished floors, oak panelling and ornate mouldings take the eye in the day rooms, while bedrooms in the main house have space, comfort and mainly period furniture. Extension rooms are smaller. Not far from the M3 (leave at junction 6) and the M4 (junction 11). Children up to 15 stay free in parents' room. ***Rooms** 23. Garden, outdoor swimming pool, tennis. Closed Christmas/New Year.* AMERICAN EXPRESS® *Access, Diners, Visa.*

Silloth-on-Solway **Skinburness Hotel** **67%** **£55**

Tel 069 73 32332 Fax 069 73 32549 **H**

Silloth-on-Solway nr Carlisle Cumbria CA5 4QT **Map 4 B3**

Somewhat off the beaten track, a recent (1988) Victorian-style restoration featuring brass lamps and ceiling fans, cane furniture and a picturesque conservatory – creating a harmonious interior to what might otherwise be considered as a rather solid redbrick period piece. Accommodation is divided between plainly decorated Green Rooms and generally more comfortable Red Rooms which provide the extra space required by vacationing families. 200 yards from the beach from where there are views across the Solway Firth to Scotland. Special terms for golfers who wish to play at the local championship course. ***Rooms** 25. Garden, keep-fit equipment, sauna, solarium, snooker.* AMERICAN EXPRESS® *Access, Diners, Visa.*

Silverton **Silverton Restaurant** **NEW** **£48**

Tel 0392 860196 **R**

Silverton Devon BX5 4HP **Map 13 D2**

On the first floor of the Silverton Inn on the main street, this informal restaurant – paper cloths, some dark blue banquettes, a few old beams, candles and lots of fresh flowers – is only open for dinner three nights a week plus a Sunday brunch. Mathew Mason (who spent several years with Shaun Hill at Gidleigh Park) presents a short blackboard menu (just five starters and five main dishes) which might include pigeon breasts with basil potato purée, rack of lamb with petit ratatouille, salmon hollandaise

See over

and always rump steak. Particularly good puds like cassis parfait, chocolate marquise and individual caramelised apple tart. ***Seats** 40. L Sun only 12-3 D 7-10.30. Closed L Thur-Sat, D Sun, all Mon-Wed. Access, Visa.*

Simonsbath — Simonsbath House — 64% — £90

Tel 064 383 259 — **H**

Simonsbath Somerset TA24 7SH — **Map 13 D1**

Owned and run by the Burns family, Simonsbath dates from 1654. Right in the centre of the forest of Exmoor, its location is tranquil; inside you'll find oak panelling and velvet drapes, log fires, fresh flowers, comfortable sofas and plenty of books. Individually decorated bedrooms contain a mixture of modern pieces and some four-posters. Self-catering cottages. No children under 10. No dogs. ***Rooms** 7. Garden. Closed Dec & Jan (restaurant closed Nov-Feb).* AMERICAN EXPRESS *Access, Diners, Visa.*

Sindlesham — Reading Moat House — 70% — £132

Tel 0734 351035 Fax 0734 666530 — **H**

Mill Lane Sindlesham nr Wokingham Berkshire RG11 5DF — **Map 15 D2**

Standing in its own grounds near the M4 (junction 10 is closest), a late-80s' hotel built in sympathy with the next door 19th-century mill house that now houses the hotel's own free-house pub (*Poachers*) and night club. Features include a stylish, pine-panelled, marble-floored foyer, a roomy lounge bar and smartly appointed bedrooms and bathrooms. ***Rooms** 96. Garden, gymnasium, sauna, solarium, steam room.* AMERICAN EXPRESS *Access, Diners, Visa.*

Sissinghurst — Rankins — £65

Tel 0580 713964 — **R**

The Street Sissinghurst Kent TN17 2JH — **Map 11 C5**

A charming, white clapboard cottage is the setting for Hugh Rankin to produce enjoyable, varied and interesting dishes such as rich crab soup decorated with spicy white meat, tagliatelle with mushroom sauce, roast duck legs with cranberry and ginger sauce, and pan-fried cuts of best end and loin of lamb with a timbale of Provençal-style courgettes. Desserts are equally hard to resist: coffee and rum charlotte, English toffee ice cream with orange-zested caramel sauce. ***Seats** 30. Parties 20. L (Sun only) 12.30-1.30 D 7.30-9. Closed D Sun-Tue, Bank Holidays, 1 week Oct, 1 week May. Set L £15.50/£19.50 Set D £17/£21. Access, Visa.*

Many hotels offer reduced rates for weekend or out-of-season bookings. Always ask about special deals.

Six Mile Bottom — Swynford Paddocks — 74% — £107

Tel 063 870 234 Fax 063 870 283 — **H**

Six Mile Bottom nr Newmarket Cambridgeshire CB8 0UE — **Map 10 B3**

Previous owners of this country mansion standing in a 60-acre stud farm (six miles south-west of Newmarket on the A1304) include Augusta Leigh (Lord Byron's half sister) and Lord and Lady Halifax. It was converted into a luxurious hotel in 1976. The dado-panelled and galleried hall/reception sets the period tone and from there you can progress to a large bar/lounge with stylishly draped curtains, comfortable easy chairs and a grand piano. The bedrooms have attractive matching bedcovers and curtains and many extras, including books and mini-bars; four 'superior' rooms are particularly spacious with bigger bathrooms and showers as well as tubs. ***Rooms** 15. Garden, all-weather tennis, putting, giant chess. Closed Christmas to New Year.* AMERICAN EXPRESS *Access, Diners, Visa.*

Skipton **Forte Travelodge** **£42**

Tel 0756 798091 **L**

Gargrave Road Skipton North Yorkshire BD23 1UD **Map 6 C1**

At the roundabout junction of the A65 and A59. ***Rooms 32.*** AMERICAN EXPRESS *Access, Visa.*

Skipton **Randell's Hotel** **65%** **£78**

Tel 0756 700100 Fax 0756 700107 **H**

Keighley Road Snaygill Skipton North Yorkshire BD23 2TA **Map 6 C1**

A purpose-built hotel, just south of the town centre, standing by the Trans-Pennine Waterway. Spacious bedrooms are light and contemporary with fully-tiled private facilities. Day rooms include an open-plan lobby and a first-floor bar. There's also a well-equipped leisure centre, conference/banqueting facilities for 400/350 and a terrace overlooking the canal. Splendid facilities for youngsters, including the Playzone supervised nursery with trips on Thomas the Tank Engine. Children up to 16 stay free in parents' room. ***Rooms 61.*** *Indoor swimming pool, gymnasium, squash, sauna, spa bath, solarium, hair & beauty salon, coffee shop (7am-10pm).* AMERICAN EXPRESS *Access, Diners, Visa.*

Slaidburn **Hark to Bounty Inn** **£45**

Tel 0200 446246 **I**

Slaidburn nr Clitheroe Lancashire BB7 3EP **Map 6 B1**

Set in the heart of the Forest of Bowland, Slaidburn's stone-built village inn is an ideal touring base. Dating in parts from the 14th century, it contains a remarkable courtroom which kept that function until 1937. Nowadays, still keeping its old jury benches and witness box (now a bar counter), it's used for banquets (up to 70) or conferences (up to 100 theatre-style). Bedrooms are modest and cottagey in style; one has WC/shower only. To the rear, a sheltered garden runs down to a little river. ***Rooms 8.*** *Garden.* AMERICAN EXPRESS *Access, Diners, Visa.*

Sleaford **Forte Travelodge** **£42**

Tel 0529 414752 **L**

Holdingham Sleaford Lincolnshire NG34 8PN **Map 7 E3**

On the roundabout at the junction of the A17/A15, one mile north of Sleaford on the bypass. ***Rooms 40.*** AMERICAN EXPRESS *Access, Visa.*

Slough **Copthorne Hotel Slough/Windsor** **71%** **£135**

Tel 0753 516222 Fax 0753 516237 **H**

Cippenham Lane Slough Berkshire SL1 2YE **Map 15 E2**

Conveniently situated next to junction 6 of the M4 and a 15-minute drive from Heathrow, the Copthorne owes 80% of its trade to corporate business. All the elegant public areas – the polished granite-floored reception area, the comfortable, spacious lounge and relaxing bar – are Art Deco in style; so, too, the variously sized conference rooms. All bedrooms are decorated to the same high standard with lightwood units and co-ordinating fabrics. Tiled bathrooms offer showers and tubs, plus good soaps and toiletries. First-rate leisure club. Plenty of free parking. ***Rooms 219.*** *Indoor swimming pool, gymnasium, sauna, spa bath, steam bath, solarium, snooker.* AMERICAN EXPRESS *Access, Diners, Visa.*

Slough **Courtyard by Marriott** **60%** **NEW** **£70**

Tel 0753 551551 Fax 0753 553333 **H**

Church Street Chalvey Slough Berkshire SL1 2NH **Map 15 E2**

At the first roundabout towards Slough from junction 6 of the M4, this was the first of Marriott's new (to England) hotels aimed specifically

See over

at the business traveller. There's no porterage or room service but food and drink may be taken to rooms from the cheerful all-day bar/brasserie or 24hr vending machines. Uncluttered bedrooms are well equipped and good bathrooms have both under-floor heating and heated mirrors (to prevent misting). ***Rooms** 148. Keep-fit facilities, brasserie (7am-10pm).* AMERICAN EXPRESS *Access, Diners, Visa.*

Slough — Heathrow/Slough Marriott Hotel — 73% — £135

Tel 0753 544244 Fax 0753 540272 — **H**

Ditton Road Langley Slough Berkshire SL3 8PT — **Map 15 E2**

Next to Junction 5 of the M4, a purpose-built hotel with good modern leisure and conference (for up to 400) facilities plus stylish day rooms. Bedrooms have at least one double bed and are decorated in soft shades with lightwood units. All have tiled, if rather small, bathrooms. Children up to 18 stay free in parents' room. Staff are civil and smart. ***Rooms** 352. Indoor swimming pool, gymnasium, sauna, spa bath, steam room, solarium, beauty & hair salons, all-weather floodlit tennis, games room, coffee shop (11am-11pm), courtesy airport coach.* AMERICAN EXPRESS *Access, Diners, Visa.*

Slough — Place of Interest

Ice Arena Montem Lane Tel 0753 821555.

Solihull — George Hotel — 66% — £116

Tel 021-711 2121 Fax 021-711 3374 — **H**

The Square Solihull West Midlands B91 3RF — **Map 6 C4**

The hotel has purchased some houses to the rear of the bowling green and converted them into new bedrooms, thus forming a quadrangle. The former masonic chapel is now a meeting room and the front bar is comfortable and up-market. Edge-of-town site (take junction 5 from the M42), closer to the National Exhibition Centre than the town centre. Children up to 12 free in parents' room. Conference/banqueting facilities for 200. Jarvis Hotels. ***Rooms** 130.* AMERICAN EXPRESS *Access, Diners, Visa.*

Solihull — Moat House — 69% — £108

Tel 021-711 4700 Fax 021-711 2696 — **H**

Homer Road Solihull West Midlands B91 3QD — **Map 6 C4**

Purpose-built in 1990, this large hotel stands just out of the town centre. A marble-floored entrance hall leads to the reception, main lounge and a raised bar area. Light decor throughout, with seating comfortable and contemporary in both design and colour. Bedrooms are equally stylish, using co-ordinating fabrics and mainly darkwood freestanding furniture. Modern health and fitness club. Conference and banqueting facilities for up to 200. ***Rooms** 115. Indoor swimming pool, gymnasium, sauna, spa bath, solarium.* AMERICAN EXPRESS *Access, Diners, Visa.*

Solihull — Regency Hotel — 64% — £90

Tel 021-745 6119 Fax 021-733 3801 — **H**

Stratford Road Shirley Solihull West Midlands B90 4EB — **Map 6 C4**

The luxurious leisure club is a major feature at this Regency-style building on the A34, half a mile from Junction 4 of the M42. Baby-sitting and baby-listening services available. Conference/banqueting facilities for up to 180. ***Rooms** 112. Garden, indoor swimming pool, gymnasium, sauna, spa bath, solarium, coffee shop (10am-10pm).* AMERICAN EXPRESS *Access, Visa.*

Solihull **St John's Swallow Hotel** **63%** **£108**

Tel 021-711 3000 Fax 021-705 6629 **H**

651 Warwick Road Solihull West Midlands B91 1AT **Map 6 C4**

Comfortable, well-appointed hotel with a distinctive gabled facade, massive conference and good leisure facilities. Children up to 14 accommodated free in parents' room; six family rooms and two rooms equipped for disabled guests. Parking for 400 cars. ***Rooms*** *177. Indoor swimming pool, spa bath, sauna, solarium, steam room, keep-fit equipment.* AMERICAN EXPRESS *Access, Diners, Visa.*

Solihull **Travel Inn** **£43**

Tel 021-744 2942 **L**

Stratford Road Shirley Solihull West Midlands B90 4PT **Map 6 C4**

Rooms *40.* AMERICAN EXPRESS *Access, Diners, Visa.*

Solihull **Places of Interest**

Baddesley Clinton (NT) Tel 0564 783294.
Solihull Ice Rink Tel 021-742 5561.

Somerton **Lynch Country House Hotel** **69%** **£45**

Tel 0458 72316 **H**

4 Behind Berry Somerton Somerset TA11 7PD **Map 13 F2**

Set in the heart of lush Somerset countryside, the Grade II listed house is surrounded by ten acres with 2800 trees, a small lake and formal gardens. Bedrooms contain books, magazines and tourist maps; from Victorian bedsteads to a Georgian four-poster, each possesses its own individual character. A bed and breakfast hotel only, with the breakfast room overlooking the grounds and lake. Self-catering cottages also available. ***Rooms*** *6. Garden. Closed 25 & 26 Dec. Access, Visa.*

Never leave money, credit cards or valuables lying around in your hotel room. Use the hotel safe or the mini-safe in your room.

Sourton **Collaven Manor** **65%** **£79**

Tel 083786 522 Fax 083786 570 **HR**

Sourton nr Okehampton Devon EX20 4HH **Map 13 D2**

On the edge of Dartmoor this small, yet fine, 15th-century, creeper-clad building houses a wealth of exposed beams and stonework, with real fires extending a homely welcome in winter. Kati Chapple and her ladies' touches are everywhere, and concern for her guests' comforts is paramount. Nowhere is this more evident than in the bedrooms, which are prepared with bright flowers, fruit and sherry; fresh milk and water flask are provided at the nightly turn-down and the electric blanket set if you so wish. Dogs and children now welcome. ***Rooms*** *7. Garden, pitch & putt. Access, Visa.*

Restaurant **£45**

Nightly-changing dinner menus and lighter lunches: the former might offer smoked chicken and quail's egg salad followed by an optional fish course (at a supplement), loin of pork with grainy mustard sauce and a selection of home-made sweets to finish. The style is straightforward, epitomised at lunchtimes by dishes such as melon and kiwi fruit, venison casserole and Irish stew. ***Seats*** *35. Parties 25. L 12-1.30 D 7.30-9 (Fri & Sat to 9.30). Set L £10.95 (£11.95 Sun) Set D £16.50/£21.*

South Cave — Forte Travelodge

£42

Tel 0430 424455 — **L**

Beacon service area South Cave Hull Humberside — **Map 7 E1**

Located at the Beacon service area on the eastbound carriageway of the A63, 12 miles west of Kingston-upon-Hull and 1½ miles east of Junction 38 of the M62. ***Rooms** 40. AMERICAN EXPRESS Access, Visa.*

See the Conference and Banqueting section for lists of hotels arranged by county.

South Godstone — La Bonne Auberge

£75

Tel 0342 893184 Fax 0342 893435 — **R**

Tilburstow Hill South Godstone Surrey RH9 8JY — **Map 11 B5**

Set in a large Victorian house just off the A22, south of Godstone village, overlooking a circular lawn and two-acre lake. Many of the attractively presented dishes have a French regional or modern ring, ranging from pastry-encased hare paté with Madeira jelly or lobster-filled ravioli to grilled rib eye of beef carved at the table (accompanied by a gratin dauphinois) and an involved dish of red mullet, salmon and monkfish cooked three ways and served with lime butter sauce. One's meal price is determined by choice of main course on any of the three menus offered (small choice set menus and à la carte); it takes quite some concentration to comprehend the options available. Cheeses are exclusively French; desserts are chosen and served from a trolley. A six-course *menu surprise* is a further option for complete table parties, except sometimes on Saturdays. Three-course, fixed-price dinner menus are for two or more diners and can include a bottle of house wine. Six tables on a patio in good weather; separate banqueting facilities in converted stables. The all-French wine list has some keenly priced bottles. Children welcome, high-chairs provided. 10 minutes from M25, junction 7. ***Seats** 60. Private Room 100. L 12-2 D 7-10. Closed D Sun, all Mon, Bank Holidays. Set L £13.90 & £22.50 Set D £15-£38.50. AMERICAN EXPRESS Access, Diners, Visa.*

South Milford — Forte Posthouse Leeds/Selby 65%

£68

Tel 0977 682711 Fax 0977 685462 — **H**

South Milford nr Leeds North Yorkshire LS25 5LF — **Map 7 D1**

At the junction of the A1 and A63, between York and Leeds. Modern hotel with good conference facilities. Children up to 16 stay free in parents' room. ***Rooms** 105. Indoor swimming pool, sauna, 9-hole pitch & putt. AMERICAN EXPRESS Access, Diners, Visa.*

South Mimms — Forte Posthouse 60%

£68

Tel 0707 643311 Fax 0707 646728 — **H**

Bignells Corner South Mimms nr Potters Bar Hertfordshire EN6 3NH — **Map 15 E2**

Up-to-date accommodation just off to the left of the South Mimms service area on the M25. A room is set aside for children at weekends and there's also a playground. ***Rooms** 120. Gymnasium, sauna, spa bath, solarium, pool table. AMERICAN EXPRESS Access, Diners, Visa.*

South Mimms — Forte Travelodge

£42

Tel 0707 665440 — **L**

Bignells Corner South Mimms nr Potters Bar Hertfordshire EN6 3QQ — **Map 15 E2**

Located at Junction 23 of the M25 at the Welcome Break service area. Central London 15 miles. ***Rooms** 52. AMERICAN EXPRESS Access, Visa.*

South Molton — Whitechapel Manor — 76% — £130

Tel 0769 573377 Fax 0769 573797 — **HR**

South Molton Devon EX36 3EG — **Map 13 D2**

John and Patricia Shapland's peaceful Elizabethan country manor house is set above 14 acres of terraced garden, surrounded by wooded valleys, rolling pasture and arable land. Only five minutes from the A361: take Junction 27 of the M5, signposted to Barnstaple, then the last turning off the second roundabout, signposted to Whitechapel. A magnificent Jacobean oak screen separates the entrance hall from the Great Hall drawing room – one of the comfortable day rooms that feature handsome, early 18th-century panelling and warming log fires. The style is carefully low-key – colours are gentle, and several bedrooms have old paintings above their fireplaces, as well as chintzy curtains and antique pieces. Some rooms are large, others intimate, and thoughtful touches extend to the splendid bathrooms. ***Rooms** 10. Garden, stabling.* AMERICAN EXPRESS *Access, Diners, Visa.*

Restaurant ★↑ — £75

The dining room is simple and discreet, the cooking serious and correct. Thierry Lepretre-Granet's cooking is top-notch, with interesting menus based on prime seasonal produce. 3- or 4-course, fixed-price menus offer an interesting choice with the likes of terrine of duck leg confit with celeriac and walnut oil dressing, cream of crab soup with anise or sautéed Cornish scallops with spinach and an orange and Grand Marnier sauce among the starters; braised shoulder of lamb with rosemary and garlic, sautéed calf's liver with mustard seed sauce, fillet of sea bass with sweet and sour sauce to follow, plus West Country cheeses and classic desserts (warm apple tart with caramel ice cream, strawberry millefeuille with strawberry coulis). Enjoy good petits fours with coffee in the drawing room. No smoking. Reasonable prices on a concise wine list. Service is quietly efficient and friendly. ***Seats** 24. L 12.30-2 D 7-8.45. Set L £16/£26 Set D £16/£26.*

South Normanton — Swallow Hotel — 69% — £96

Tel 0773 812000 Fax 0773 580032 — **H**

Carter Lane East South Normanton Derbyshire DE55 2EH — **Map 7 D3**

Modern, low-rise hotel near Junction 28 of the M1 with spacious public areas and large, up-to-date conference facilities for a maximum of 220 delegates. Two of the bedrooms have been specially designed for disabled guests. ***Rooms** 161. Indoor swimming pool, keep-fit equipment, sauna, spa bath, steam room, solarium.* AMERICAN EXPRESS *Access, Diners, Visa.*

South Normanton — Place of Interest

Sherwood Forest Visitor Centre Tel 0623 824490.

South Witham — Forte Travelodge — £42

Tel 057 283 586 — **L**

New Fox South Witham Colsterworth Lincolnshire LE15 8AU — **Map 7 E3**

Northbound on the A1, 9 miles south of Grantham. ***Rooms** 32.* AMERICAN EXPRESS *Access, Visa.*

South Wootton — Knights Hill Hotel — 64% — £94

Tel 0553 675566 Fax 0553 675568 — **H**

Knights Hill Village South Wootton King's Lynn Norfolk PE30 3HQ — **Map 10 B1**

At the junction of the A148 and A149, Knights Hill stands in 11 acres overlooking King's Lynn and the Wash. Sympathetic conversion of a collection of 17th-century farm buildings has produced a village complex of hotel, pub, leisure club and conference/banqueting centre (up to 300/200) in the spectacular Knights Barn. Accommodation is in up-to-

See over

date bedrooms in a stylish extension or in more modest (and older) courtyard apartments with private entrances. Children up to 15 stay free in parents' room. ***Rooms** 52. Indoor swimming pool, gymnasium, sauna, spa bath, steam room, solarium, tennis, snooker, helipad.* AMERICAN EXPRESS *Access, Diners, Visa.*

Southall **Asian Tandoori Centre** **£15**

Tel 081-574 2597 **R**

114 The Green Southall Middlesex UB2 4BQ **Map 15 E2**

Simple Indian canteen serving hearty, unsophisticated food throughout the day. Particularly good peshwari stuffed nan. Unlicensed; non-smoking area. ***Seats** 80. Meals 9am-10.30pm (Fri & Sat to 11pm).*
Also at:
157 The Broadway, Southall. Tel 081-574 3476. **Map 15 E2**

Southampton **Browns Brasserie** **£70**

Tel 0703 332615 **R**

Frobisher House Nelson Gate Commercial Road Southampton Hampshire SO1 0GX **Map 15 D4**

In a neighbourhood of unfashionable eating houses close to the Mayflower Theatre, there's an air of enthusiasm here that extends beyond the menu prose. An adventurous menu includes the likes of marinated loin of rabbit with rum and prunes encased in pastry, lobster soufflé, shellfish stew, home-smoked brill with Muscadet cream sauce, pot-roast squab, stuffed and sliced pig's trotter (*zampone*), lemon and lime tart, honey millefeuille and a 'naughty but nice' chocolate surprise. British and French cheeses served with walnut bread. No children under 10. ***Seats** 24. L 12-2.30 D 7-11 (Sat to 11.30). Closed Sun, 25 & 26 Dec, 1 Jan. Set L £10.50/£13.50 Set D £10.50/£14.95.* AMERICAN EXPRESS *Access, Diners, Visa.*

Southampton **Dolphin Hotel** **60%** **£82**

Tel 0703 339955 Fax 0703 333650 **H**

High Street Southampton Hampshire SO9 2DS **Map 15 D4**

Modernised high-street coaching inn with conference facilities for 100. Free use of nearby Posthouse health and fitness club. Children up to 15 stay free in parents' room. Forte. ***Rooms** 71.* AMERICAN EXPRESS *Access, Diners, Visa.*

Southampton **Forte Posthouse** **58%** **£68**

Tel 0703 330777 Fax 0703 332510 **H**

Herbert Walker Avenue Southampton Hampshire SO1 0HJ **Map 15 D4**

Ten-storey tower-block hotel with views of the liners' berths from some rooms. Bedrooms, all refurbished in the last couple of years, spacious nautical bar, children's playroom and playground. ***Rooms** 128. Indoor swimming pool, gymnasium, sauna, spa bath, solarium.* AMERICAN EXPRESS *Access, Diners, Visa.*

Southampton **Hilton National** **68%** **£94**

Tel 0703 702700 Fax 0703 767233 **H**

Bracken Place Chilworth Southampton Hampshire SO2 4HB **Map 15 D4**

Up-to-date leisure and business facilities in a Hilton hotel by the A33 and M27 (approach from Junction 5). ***Rooms** 135. Indoor swimming pool, gymnasium, sauna, spa bath, steam room, beauty salon.* AMERICAN EXPRESS *Access, Diners, Visa.*

Southampton — Kuti's

£45

Tel 0703 221585 — **R**

70 London Road Southampton Hampshire SO1 2AJ — **Map 15 D4**

Plush and pristine Indian restaurant off the Avenue by the new Law Courts. Low lit, with comfortable seating and friendly staff. The kitchen puts good raw materials to excellent use in a range of lamb, chicken and prawn dishes that include house specialities cooked in the cast-iron karahi and served with pilau rice and nan bread. Sally lamb is a Parsi wedding dish of lamb with dried apricots in a spicy red masala sauce. Good-value thalis, buffet lunches and fixed-price dinners. ***Seats** 66. Parties 30. L 12-2.15 D 6-11.30. Closed 25 & 26 Dec. Set L from £7.50 Set D from £10.95.* AMERICAN EXPRESS *Access, Visa.*

Southampton — Novotel 62%

£85

Tel 0703 330550 Fax 0703 222158 — **H**

1 West Quay Road Southampton Hampshire SO1 0RA — **Map 15 D4**

Very modern hotel convenient for railway station, ferries and Ocean Village. Geared to business use in the week (with conference facilities for up to 450, banqueting up to 350), families at weekends (children up to 16 stay free in parents' room). ***Rooms** 121. Indoor swimming pool, keep-fit facilities, sauna.* AMERICAN EXPRESS *Access, Diners, Visa.*

Southampton — Polygon Hotel 65%

£77

Tel 0703 330055 Fax 0703 332435 — **H**

Cumberland Place Southampton Hampshire SO9 4GD — **Map 15 D4**

Close by the civic centre, an Edwardian structure in red brick overlooking Watts Park. Banqueting/conference facilities for 400/500. Free use of *Forte Posthouse* health and fitness club in Herbert Walker Avenue. Forte. ***Rooms** 119.* AMERICAN EXPRESS *Access, Diners, Visa.*

Southampton — Southampton Park Hotel 64%

£66

Tel 0703 223467 Fax 0703 332538 — **H**

12 Cumberland Place Southampton Hampshire SO9 4NY — **Map 15 D4**

Functional modern building overlooking Watts Park. Well-equipped bedrooms (front ones have balconies), roomy lounge areas, two restaurants, a cocktail bar, conference rooms (up to 200 delegates) and a leisure club. ***Rooms** 72. Indoor swimming pool, keep-fit equipment, sauna, spa bath, steam room, solarium.* AMERICAN EXPRESS *Access, Diners, Visa.*

Southampton — Places of Interest

Tourist Information Tel 0703 221106.
Maritime Museum Seafront Tel 0703 223941.
Exbury Gardens Exbury Tel 0703 891203.
Lepe Country Park Exbury Tel 0703 899108.
New Forest Butterfly Farm Ashurst Tel 0703 293367.
Southampton City Art Gallery Tel 0703 231375.
Northlands Road Cricket Ground Tel 0703 333788.
Southampton Football Ground The Dell Tel 0703 220505.
Calshort Activities Centre Fawley Tel 0703 891380/892077.
Southampton Ski Centre Bassett Tel 0703 760604.

Theatres and Concert Halls

Mayflower Theatre Tel 0703 330083.
Mountbatten Theatre Tel 0703 832453.
Nuffield Theatre Tel 0705 581576.

Southport New Bold Hotel 58% £51

Tel 0704 532578 Fax 0704 532528 **H**

Lord Street Southport Merseyside PR9 0BE **Map 6 A1**

Family-owned and family-run, the Bold stands on the town's leafy main boulevard. Modernised bedrooms include two for family use and a bridal suite with sunken bath; back rooms are the quietest. A public bar serves traditional beers and Raphael's bar/café has long-hours opening and live entertainment. Reception is upstairs, and the front door leads straight into the bar. ***Rooms** 23. Access, Diners, Visa.*

Southport Prince of Wales Hotel 65% £74

Tel 0704 536688 Fax 0704 543488 **H**

Lord Street Southport Merseyside PR8 1JS **Map 6 A1**

On Southport's tree-lined main street, with modern amenities and some of Southport's Victorian atmosphere remaining both inside and out. Conferences are well catered for, with a maximum capacity of 450 theatre-style. Children up to 16 stay free in parents' room. Forte. ***Rooms** 104. Garden, 24hr lounge service.* AMERICAN EXPRESS *Access, Diners, Visa.*

Southport Places of Interest

Tourist Information Tel 0704 533333.
Atkinson Art Gallery Tel 0704 533133.
Rufford Old Hall (NT) Rufford Tel 0704 821254.
Martin Mere Wildfowl Trust Tel 0704 895181 *6 miles.*
Royal Birkdale Golf Tel 0704 67920.
Trafalgar Road Cricket Ground Birkdale Tel 0704 69951.
Southport Zoo Tel 0704 538102.

Southsea Bistro Montparnasse £55

Tel 0705 816754 **R**

103 Palmerston Road Southsea Hampshire PO5 3PS **Map 15 D4**

Careful cooking and attractive presentation bring the regulars back to Peter and Gillian Scott's warm and welcoming French bistro close to Southsea's main shopping area. Gillian offers a well-thought-out and often inventive choice on fixed-price menus, which change monthly. Risotto of spring vegetables with lemon and Parmesan, terrine of venison and guinea fowl marinated in Madeira with pistachios, strudel of smoked haddock with rice and parsley and chive sauce, osso buco, turbot with basil and champagne sauce, salmon with courgette mousse and lemon beurre blanc, and a bitter sweet chocolate cup filled with white chocolate mousse are typical dishes. A special set menu at £12.50 is also offered on weekdays. ***Seats** 38. D only 7-10. Closed Sun & Mon, Bank Holidays, 3 weeks Jan. Set D £17.50/£19.90.* AMERICAN EXPRESS *Access, Visa.*

Southsea Places of Interest

Southsea Castle Portsmouth Tel 0705 827261.
D Day Museum Clarence Parade Tel 0705 827261.
Pyramids Complex *Fun pools* Tel 0705 294444.
Sea Life Centre Tel 0705 734461.

Southwell Saracen's Head 62% £80

Tel 0636 812701 Fax 0636 815408 **H**

Market Place Southwell Nottinghamshire NG25 0HE **Map 7 D3**

The 16th-century half-timbered inn still shows many original features, including a fine wall painting. Most notable among the guests down the years is Charles I, who stayed in 1646 just before surrendering to the Scottish Commissioners. Today's guests can enjoy the characterful public areas before retiring to bedrooms that offer all the usual modern comforts and conveniences. Forte Heritage. ***Rooms*** *27.* AMERICAN EXPRESS *Access, Diners, Visa.*

Southwell — Place of Interest

Southwell Minster Tel 0636 812649.

Southwold — The Crown — £63

Tel 0502 722275 Fax 0502 724805 — **IR**

90 High Street Southwold Suffolk IP18 6DP — **Map 10 D2**

Southwold brewers, Adnams, take credit for the restoration of their town-centre Georgian inn: to the front, facing the High Street, the Parlour serves as half lounge, half dining area, while the front bar and attendant restaurant exude refinement. Bedrooms are well equipped, with antique or decent reproduction pieces and bright fabrics and furnishings: all have private bathrooms though three are not strictly en suite (the bathroom is across a corridor); one family room has a double and two single beds. Families welcome; informal eating in the bar. ***Rooms*** *12. Closed 1 week Jan.* AMERICAN EXPRESS *Access, Visa.*

Restaurant — £48

Menus are produced daily with an accent on fresh fish, and simpler dishes are the best bet. For starters, perhaps cream of broccoli and nutmeg soup or cornets of smoked halibut filled with trout mousse. Main courses offer the likes of magret of Suffolk-reared duck with juniper berries and red wine and steamed fillet of turbot with lime and olive oil dressing. Also excellent bar meals and vegetarian alternatives. The wine list, as you would expect from a wine merchant, is fabulous. Great depth, keen prices (plenty of exceptional drinking under £20) and authoritative tasting notes. Super selection of wines by the glass changed monthly. ***Seats*** *40. Parties 8. Private Room 24. L 12.30-1.45 D 7.30-9.30. Set L £12.75/£14.75 Set D £17.25/£19.25.*

Southwold — The Swan — 65% — £88

Tel 0502 722186 Fax 0502 724800 — **HR**

Market Place Southwold Suffolk IP18 6EG — **Map 10 D2**

The ancient Swan (*re*built in 1660 and remodelled in the 1820s) faces the market place of a most charming seaside town. An old long-case clock and fresh flowers grace the flagstoned foyer and an abundance of sofas the period drawing room. Main-house bedrooms are traditional in style with freestanding furniture, including the odd antique, while simpler chalet-style rooms surround a garden to the rear. An adjacent brewery can occasionally disturb the peace during the day. Banquets/conferences for up to 50. Good bar snacks. ***Rooms*** *45.* AMERICAN EXPRESS *Access, Visa.*

Restaurant — £65

An elegant, pink dining room and a choice of fixed-price only menus. Chef David Goode offers an interesting mix ranging from salmon and lemon sole mousse cake with saffron mayonnaise to braised Norfolk duck breast with an apple and ginger compote; leave room for puds: lemon meringue pie, praline millefeuille with chocolate sauce and poached pears in a mulled wine syrup are typical. Good British cheeses. Sunday lunch offers a wide choice including vegetarian options. Wines from Adnams, who also own the hotel. ***Seats*** *50. Parties 10. Private Room 20. L 12.15-1.45 (Sun to 1.30) D 7-9.30 (Sun to 9). Closed D 3rd Sun in Jan. Set L £12.50/£16.95 Set D £17.50-£30.50.*

Southwold — Place of Interest

Southwold Beach.

Spark Bridge **Bridgefield House** 60% £70

Tel 0229 885239 Fax 0229 885379 **HR**

Spark Bridge Ulverston Cumbria LA12 8DA **Map 4 C4**

To describe Bridgefield House as modest is to decry neither its homeliness nor the warmth of the proprietors' welcome. A decade of steady improvements has established a hotel of some charm in a superb location overlooking the Crake valley (on the back lane from Lowick Bridge to Spark Bridge). Bedrooms, though spacious, are modestly appointed with mostly freestanding furniture, telephones and clock radios; TVs there are not. "Well-disciplined dogs are welcome." Facilities for families are limited but the Glisters' accommodating attitude promises a relaxing stay; junior gourmets will be over the moon, sports freaks less so. ***Rooms** 5. Garden. Access, Visa.*

Restaurant £70

Dinner at candle-lit dark mahogany tables is courteously overseen by David Glister. His wife Rosemary's daily-changing six-course, fixed-price-only menus are a labour of love and offer a small choice only at starter and pudding stages. A typical menu might commence with smoked sea trout and pasta shells in a vodka and cream sauce then tomato and basil soup with Cheddar bannocks, followed by boned pigeon breasts in a red wine sauce with puréed damson tartlets and four vegetables (including red cabbage with juniper berries, glazed onions with pumpkin seeds and kohlrabi with coriander). Date and butterscotch pudding, whisky syllabub or baked banana, orange and almonds in Southern Comfort with Cointreau cream among the puddings with perhaps sautéed lamb sweetbreads in Madeira on toast or pear with blue Stilton and walnuts as a savoury conclusion. Good cheeses, coffee and truffles. An excellent wine list has a fine selection of half bottles; some of the more expensive clarets and burgundies are erratically priced. No smoking. Booking essential. ***Seats** 30. Parties 24. D only 7.30 for 8. Set D £24.*

Staddle Bridge **McCoy's** 70% £99

Tel 060 982 671 Fax 060 982 660 **HR**

The Cleveland Tontine Staddle Bridge nr Northallerton
North Yorkshire DL6 3JB **Map 5 E3**

Eugene, Peter and Tom McCoy's tontine could almost be called an island paradise, located as it is on a large plot of land surrounded by major roads. The interior has a decadently exotic decor of beautiful but loud multihued cushions scattered over ancient, worn sofas and armchairs. There's now a brilliant green carpet in the bar, which retains its laid-back 30s' ambience. The decor won't please everyone, but there's no doubting its originality. Bedrooms are best described as cosy, with Givenchy wall coverings and double-glazing to keep out traffic noise. The overall informal style is suitably enhanced by chatty yet efficient young staff. The day starts with a memorable breakfast. ***Rooms** 6. Garden. Closed 25 & 26 Dec, 1 Jan.* AMERICAN EXPRESS *Access, Diners, Visa.*

Restaurant ★ £80

Gone are the gigantic Japanese paper parasols and the foil wallpaper. Now the walls are dark and glossy, painted a rich burgundy. Mirrors play an important part, reflecting lights, adding sparkle. The current menu has been adapted to conform with the harsh economic climate that is gripping the North East – the luxury items such as foie gras and truffles persist in such dishes as warm foie gras and grapes stewed in Madeira with toasted brioche and langoustine pasta with truffle, lemon and shellfish sauce but now in addition are more modest offerings, treated no less carefully, such as fresh watercress or spring vegetable soup or wild French mushroom tart with a Muscadet sauce. Main dishes largely retain the magical McCoy stamp: chicken Jo Jo – a breast of chicken with crème fraiche, vermouth and mushrooms; pigeon off the bone with lentils and Lyonnaise sausage;

monkfish with truffle sauce and sea bass with lemon sauce and brown rice. Added to this imaginative repertoire are fillet or sirloin steak with chips and salad bringing the menu firmly down to earth and dispelling any accusation of elitism. There is something for all tastes and pockets. The bistro in the basement offers a simple but many-choiced blackboard menu of dishes prepared with the same care and attention to detail. The wine list has been slimmed down, but still offers shining examples from around the world. ***Seats** 60. Parties 40. Private Room 25. D only 7-10 (Bistro: 12-2, 7-10.30). Closed Sun & Mon.*

Stafford — Tillington Hall — 63% — £80

Tel 0785 53531 Fax 0785 59223 — **H**

Eccleshall Road Stafford Staffordshire ST16 1JJ — **Map 6 B3**

Half a mile from the M6 (J14), this modern De Vere hotel adds good leisure and conference facilities (200 maximum) to decent bedrooms that range from singles to four-poster rooms. Children up to 14 share adult accommodation free, with free breakfast. ***Rooms** 90. Garden, indoor swimming pool, gymnasium, sauna, spa bath, solarium, beauty salon, tennis, snooker, coffee shop (10am-10pm). Closed 28 & 29 Dec.* AMERICAN EXPRESS *Access, Diners, Visa.*

Stafford — Places of Interest

Tourist Information Tel 0785 40204.
Shugborough (NT) House & Garden & Staffordshire County Museum & Park Farm Tel 0889 881388.
Wolseley Garden Park Wolseley Bridge Tel 0889 574888.
County Showground Weston Road Tel 0785 58060.

Stamford — The George of Stamford — 72% — £100

Tel 0780 55171 Fax 0780 57070 — **HR**

71 St Martins Stamford Lincolnshire PE9 2LB — **Map 7 E3**

A gallows sign above the high street announces the George, in a position where a hostelry has stood for over 900 years. Rugs cover a long, flagstoned entrance hallway, either side of which are the dark-panelled London Room and York Bar where travellers used to wait for highway coaches. Comfortable day rooms include a beamed cocktail bar, a cosy lounge with easy couches and armchairs, an open fire and fine exposed stone walls and a bright, covered Garden Lounge filled with wrought-iron garden furniture and plants, where families can eat informally and theme evenings take place throughout the year. The age of the building dictates that sizes and shapes of the bedrooms are varied, but most are well proportioned; several rooms feature four-poster beds. Ivy surrounds the windows of the quietest rooms overlooking a cobbled courtyard (another informal dining area). A converted livery stable houses a business centre that caters for conferences of up to 50 delegates. The bar is popular with locals who enjoy a pint of Adnams. Children up to 10 free in parents' room. Poste Hotels. ***Rooms** 47. Garden, beautician, hair salon, bookshop, coffee shop (7am-midnight).* AMERICAN EXPRESS *Access, Diners, Visa.*

Restaurant — £85

An elegant setting with polished tables, gleaming silverware and oak panelling; a jacket and tie are 'respectfully' requested for gentlemen. The à la carte dinner menu is essentially traditional, with adventurous touches such as terrine of crab and mussels wrapped in spinach with samphire, in contrast to the silver-domed carving wagons offering roast sirloin of Scotch beef and a further daily roast. Trolleys, trolleys, everywhere: smoked salmon is sliced at the table; even the cheese is trundled to your table, as are the desserts. Quick, fixed-price lunch menu offers a good choice of any two from a list of starter-style dishes (chicken and beef satay, cannelloni bolognese), plus dessert or cheese. The super wine list (as with the others in the excellent Poste Hotels group) should serve

See over

as an example to everyone in the restaurant business – keenly priced, expertly compiled and simple to use. East of England Cellar of the Year. Private dining rooms at no extra charge. ***Seats** 80. Private Room 35. L 12.30-2.30 D 7-10.30 (Garden Lounge 8am-11pm). Set L £15.50 (Mon-Sat).*

Stamford — Places of Interest

Tourist Information Tel 0780 55611.
Burghley House Tel 0780 52451.
Stamford Brewery Museum Tel 0780 52186.
Tallington Dry Ski Slope Tel 0788 344990.

Standish — Almond Brook Moat House — 63% — £95

Tel 0257 425588 Fax 0257 427327 — **H**

Almond Brook Road Standish nr Wigan Greater Manchester WN6 0SR — **Map 6 B1**

Two hundred yards from Junction 27 of the M6, this Moat House includes conference rooms (for up to 150) and a leisure centre among its facilities. Bedrooms are smallish but adequate. Families are well catered for; under-14s sharing with parents are free. ***Rooms** 126. Garden, indoor swimming pool, keep-fit equipment, sauna, solarium. Closed 24-30 Dec.* AMERICAN EXPRESS *Access, Diners, Visa.*

Standish — Places of Interest

Wigan Pier Wigan Tel 0942 323666 *4 miles.*
Wigan International Pool Wigan Tel 0942 43345.

Stanstead Abbots — Briggens House — 70% — £106

Tel 0279 792416 Fax 0279 793685 — **H**

Stanstead Road Stanstead Abbots nr Ware Hertfordshire SG12 8LD — **Map 15 F2**

A large, stately home-from-home, a few miles off the M11, set in 45 acres of grounds with its own 9-hole golf course. High standards of service are typified by the smart, uniformed doormen. A magnificent carved wood staircase leads up from the entrance hall with its glass chandelier to 22 bedrooms in the main house; 32 more are in the converted coach house and have lower ceilings, but all are equally tastefully decorated with a good range of extras included as standard. Swagged drapes and stylish reproduction antiques give an elegant air. In summer, tables are set on the expansive lawns outside the French windows leading off the lounge. Function facilities for 100. Children under 12 free in parents' room. Queens Moat Houses. ***Rooms** 54. Garden, outdoor swimming pool, tennis, 9-hole golf course, bowls, fishing. Closed 1 week Christmas.* AMERICAN EXPRESS *Access, Diners, Visa.*

Stanstead Abbots — Places of Interest

Hill House Ware Tel 0920 870013.
Trading Places Gallery New Road, Ware Tel 0920 469620.

Stanton St Quintin — Stanton Manor — 64% — £82

Tel 0666 837552 Fax 0666 837022 — **HR**

Stanton St Quintin nr Chippenham Wiltshire SN14 6DQ — **Map 14 B2**

This 19th-century stone manor house inherits some 900 years of continuous habitation; the oldest surviving building is a unique 14th-century dovecote standing in the five acres of grounds. Just two minutes from the M4 (at Junction 17), it's the home of enthusiastic young proprietors Philip and Elizabeth Bullock, who go out of their way to make guests welcome. Children up to 18 stay free in parents' room. ***Rooms** 10. Garden. Closed 26 Dec-2 Jan, 1st 2 weeks Aug.* AMERICAN EXPRESS *Access, Visa.*

Restaurant £50

Simple dishes appeal on a short à la carte, to which the manor's own kitchen garden contributes seasonal fruit and vegetables. Pancakes bolognaise, king prawns in a sweet and sour sauce, grilled fillets of plaice and roast rack of lamb show the range. Informal service is relaxed and friendly. No smoking while others are eating. ***Seats** 30. Parties 10. Private Room 50. L 12-2 D 7-9. Closed all Sun (dinner residents only).*

> is our symbol for an outstanding wine list.

Stapleford — Stapleford Park 86% £142

Tel 057 284 522 Fax 057 284 651 **HR**

Stapleford nr Melton Mowbray Leicestershire LE14 2EF **Map 7 E3**

"19th-century hospitality backed up by 21st-century technology" is the stated aim at *Chicago Pizza Pie* entrepreneur Bob Payton's sumptuous country house hotel; set in a majestic stately home surrounded by 500 acres of mature parkland, they bet that "the former (hospitality) is easier to deliver than the latter (technology)". Its welcomimg air of freshness and spontaneity owes much to its creator, who with his carefully chosen young staff idiosyncratically cuts out the snobbery. The result is casual luxury at its best, evident throughout day rooms that exude quality and style and in bedrooms individually designed by such eminent names as David Hicks and Turnbull & Asser. The splendid library, lounge and galleried salon abound with beautiful fabrics, oil paintings and ornaments; each bedroom shares this comfortable style with wonderful marble-tiled bathrooms and numerous thoughtful extras. Conference, meeting and private function rooms are equally superb, accommodating up to 200 guests in luxurious yet informal surroundings. Children up to 10 stay free in parents' room. ***Rooms** 35. Garden, fishing, tennis, pitch & putt, basketball.* AMERICAN EXPRESS *Access, Diners, Visa.*

Restaurant £70

Stapleford's restaurant style is light-hearted and isn't afraid to serve French fries when appropriate. Lunch menus might feature Caesar salad, grilled chicken (with French fries) and cheeseburgers. At dinnertime the menu extends to incorporate popular Mediterranean flavours. There's usually a transatlantic twist to the dessert menu and, not unsurprisingly, a marvellous choice of Californian bottles on the wine list which is arranged by taste, with fair prices and lots of good drinking under £20. Twelve tables are set on a terrace for alfresco dining in good weather. A 'casual menu' is also served all day. In certain respects the hotel and restaurant may be laid back, however "ties are not required in the evening but men are requested to wear a jacket". ***Seats** 70. Parties 10. L 12-3 (Sun to 3.30) D 7-10 (Sat to 10.30, Sun to 9.30). Set D £19.92.*

Steeple Aston — Hopcrofts Holt Hotel 63% £80

Tel 0869 40259 Fax 0869 40865 **H**

Steeple Aston Oxfordshire OX6 3QQ **Map 15 D1**

Once a coaching inn, the hotel has now expanded its role with Executive accommodation and purpose-built conference rooms. Just off the A4260 between Banbury and Oxford. Mount Charlotte Thistle. ***Rooms** 88.* AMERICAN EXPRESS *Access, Diners, Visa.*

Stevenage — Novotel 60% £80

Tel 0438 742299 Fax 0438 723872 **H**

Knebworth Park Stevenage Hertfordshire SG1 2AX **Map 15 E1**

Modern, open-plan hotel at Junction 7 of the A1(M). Banqueting facilities for up to 110, conferences up to 150. ***Rooms** 100. Outdoor swimming pool.* AMERICAN EXPRESS *Access, Diners, Visa.*

Stevenage — Places of Interest

Tourist Information Tel 0438 369441.
Gordon Craig Theatre Tel 0438 316291.
Benington Lordship Gardens Tel 0438 85668.
Shaw's Corner (NT) Ayot St. Lawrence Tel 0438 820307 *Home of George Bernard Shaw.*
Welwyn Roman Baths Tel 0707 271362.
Knebworth House Knebworth Tel 0438 812661.
Stevenage Ice Rink Tel 0438 740750.
Welwyn Garden City Ski Centre Tel 0707 331056/330780.
Silver Leys Polo Club Troopers Drivers End. Codicote Tel 0438 820414.

Stilton — Bell Inn — £62

Tel 0733 241066 Fax 0733 245173 — **IR**

Great North Road Stilton nr Peterborough Cambridgeshire PE7 3RA — **Map 6 A2**

Reputedly the oldest coaching inn on the Great North Road, the Bell boasts a Roman well in the courtyard and an impressive 15th-century stone frontage. Modern additions include hotel reception glassed in under the original archway and two rear wings of bedrooms with today's trappings, tokens of antiquity sadly confined to the odd four-poster bed. Separate conference/banqueting in the Marlborough Suite. No dogs. ***Rooms** 19. Garden.* AMERICAN EXPRESS *Access, Diners, Visa.*

Restaurant — £45

The galleried restaurant with vaulted ceiling and exposed rafters is more in character with the original Old Bell. Weekly table d'hote menus and à la carte conclude with good Stilton cheese, plum bread and vintage port. Snacks at lunchtime in the stone-flagged bar. ***Seats** 40. Parties 20. Private Room 12. L (2nd week Dec-1st week Jan only) 12-2 (Sun from 12.30) D 7-9.30 (Sun to 9). Set D £14.50.*

Stockbridge — Grosvenor Hotel — 57% — £77

Tel 0264 810606 Fax 0264 810747 — **H**

High Street Stockbridge Hampshire SO20 6EU — **Map 14 C3**

On the A30 in the village centre, the Grosvenor (in the Lansbury group) has kept many of its original Georgian features, including a colonnaded porch. The bar lacks period appeal, but is one of the focal points of Stockbridge life. Bedrooms in the original house are larger than those in the converted stables. No dogs. Banqueting and conference facilities for around 70. ***Rooms** 25. Garden, sauna, snooker.* AMERICAN EXPRESS *Access, Diners, Visa.*

Stockbridge — Places of Interest

Houghton Lodge House and Gardens Tel 0264 810177.
Museum of Army Flying Middle Wallop Tel 0264 384421.

Stockport — Alma Lodge — 61% — £94

Tel 061-483 4431 Fax 061-483 1983 — **H**

149 Buxton Road Stockport Greater Manchester SK2 6EL — **Map 6 B2**

Two miles from the M6 (junction 12) on the A6 to the south of Stockport, an early Victorian house has been greatly extended to create this business-oriented hotel. Some original features of the old house – wood panelling and open fires – survive in the public rooms. Function facilities for up to 250. Children up to 16 accommodated free in parents' room. Free membership of local bowling club and complimentary tickets at the local cinema. Jarvis Hotels. ***Rooms** 56.* AMERICAN EXPRESS *Access, Diners, Visa.*

Stockport — Forte Travelodge — £42

Tel 0625 875292 — L

London Road South Adlington Stockport Cheshire SK12 4NA — **Map 6 B2**

On the A523, 5 miles south of Stockport and 5 miles north of Macclesfield. *Rooms 32.* AMERICAN EXPRESS *Access, Visa.*

Stockport — Travel Inn — £43

Tel 061-499 1944 Fax 061-437 4910 — L

Finney Lane Heald Green Stockport Cheshire SK8 2QH — **Map 6 B2**

1 mile from Manchester Airport. *Rooms 41.* AMERICAN EXPRESS *Access, Diners, Visa.*

Stockport — Places of Interest

Tourist Information Tel 061-474 3320/3321.
Bramhall Hall Bramhall Tel 061-485 3708.
Stockport Art Gallery War Memorial Building Tel 061-474 4453.

Stockton-on-Tees — Swallow Hotel — 67% — £92

Tel 0642 679721 Fax 0642 601714 — H

10 John Walker Square Stockton-on-Tees Cleveland TS18 1AQ — **Map 5 E3**

Practical town-centre business hotel with an Egyptian-themed leisure centre and an all-day brasserie – Matchmakers – named after John Walker, the man who invented the match and who came from Stockton. Banqueting/conference facilities for 250/300. Head for Stockton town centre and follow signs to the multi-storey car park, whose 6th floor is for hotel residents. ***Rooms** 124. Indoor swimming pool, keep-fit equipment, sauna, spa bath, steam room, sunbeach, coffee shop (7am-10.30pm).* AMERICAN EXPRESS *Access, Diners, Visa.*

Stockton-on-Tees — Places of Interest

Preston Park Museum Tel 0642 781184.
Sedgefield Racecourse Tel 0642 557081.
Billingham Ice Rink Billingham Tel 0642 554449.

Stoke-on-Trent — Haydon House Hotel — 65% — £62

Tel 0782 711311 Fax 0782 717470 — H

Haydon Street Basford Stoke-on-Trent Staffordshire ST4 6JD — **Map 6 B3**

A family-owned Victorian hotel with friendly atmosphere, dependable accommodation and six deluxe suites in adjacent Glebe Mews. Classy Victorian-style day rooms with antique clock collection. Take the A500 from M6 (J15 or 16) to the A53 turn-off. The hotel stands on the A53 at Basford. ***Rooms** 30.* AMERICAN EXPRESS *Access, Diners, Visa.*

Stoke-on-Trent — North Stafford Hotel — 61% — £90

Tel 0782 744477 Fax 0782 744580 — H

Station Road Stoke-on-Trent Staffordshire ST4 2AE — **Map 6 B3**

Red-brick Victorian hotel with cheerful, generally good-sized bedrooms and a ballroom which can hold up to 450 for a conference. 20 of the bedrooms have recently been refurbished. Children up to 14 stay free in parents' room. ***Rooms** 69.* AMERICAN EXPRESS *Access, Diners, Visa.*

Stoke-on-Trent — Stakis Grand Hotel — 68% — £96

Tel 0782 202361 Fax 0782 286464 — **H**

Trinity Street Hanley Stoke-on-Trent Staffordshire ST1 5NB — **Map 6 B3**

Situated at Hanley town centre and close to Stoke Festival Park, the Grand combines a busy conference trade (max 300) with good family facilities and a leisure club. Children up to 15 stay free in parents' room. ***Rooms** 128. Indoor swimming pool, keep-fit equipment, sauna, spa bath, steam room, solarium.* AMERICAN EXPRESS *Access, Diners, Visa.*

Stoke-on-Trent — Stoke-on-Trent Moat House — 70% — £99

Tel 0782 219000 Fax 0782 284500 — **H**

Etruria Hall Festival Way Etruria Stoke-on-Trent Staffordshire ST1 5BQ — **Map 6 B3**

Ten minutes drive from the M6, and equidistant from Junctions 15 and 16, the hotel stands by the A53 at the heart of the 1986 Garden Festival park. Day rooms, leisure club and smart up-to-date bedrooms are in a sympathetically designed stone-clad complex which reflects within it many of the original hall's features. There are no fewer than 23 conference rooms, which can handle 500+ delegates. Free car parking for 350 cars. Children up to 16 stay free in parents' room. ***Rooms** 147. Indoor swimming pool, gymnasium, sauna, spa bath, solarium, beauty salon, snooker, coffee shop (8am-10pm).* AMERICAN EXPRESS *Access, Diners, Visa.*

Stoke-on-Trent — Places of Interest

Tourist Information Tel 0782 411222.
Biddulph Grange Garden (NT) Biddulph Tel 0782 517999.
Stoke City Football Club Victoria Ground Tel 0782 413511.
Port Vale Football Ground Vale Park, Burslem Tel 0782 814134.
North Staffordshire Ski Club Kidsgrove Tel 0782 784908.
Alton Towers Alton Tel 0538 702200.
Festival Park Leisure Complex Tel 0782 283838.

Museums and Art Galleries

Chatterley Whitfield Mining Museum Tel 0782 813337.
City Museum and Art Gallery Tel 0782 202173.
Wedgwood Museum Josiah Wedgwood and Sons Ltd Tel 0782 204218/204141.
Gladstone Pottery Museum Tel 0782 319232.
Minton Museum Tel 0782 744766.
Sir Henry Doulton Gallery Tel 0782 575454.

Stokesley — Chapters — 65% — £59

Tel 0642 711888 Fax ext 223 — **HR**

27 High Street Stokesley North Yorkshire TS9 5AD — **Map 5 E3**

Alan Thompson relocated Chapters restaurant in the former Golden Lion hotel three years ago and embarked on a total transformation. Red-tiled floors and light, bright furnishings lend the ground floor a contemporary feel, with a popular bistro at the front. Refurbishment of the bedrooms is completed. ***Rooms** 13. Garden, bistro (12-11pm).* AMERICAN EXPRESS *Access, Diners, Visa.*

Restaurant — £40

20 or so seats have been lost in this bright, summery restaurant to create a new lounge area and to add to the atmosphere. The menus have an up-to-date ring, especially among the starters, typified by mushrooms filled with crabmeat baked in filo on a Malibu sauce, a hot, thin tart of artichokes, mushrooms and rosemary with dolcelatte and a salad of salmon teriyaki, king prawn spring roll, smoked salmon parcel and shrimps. Main courses run from monkfish with shellfish "in the style of bouillabaisse" to medallions of Lakeland venison with wine-poached pear on a sauce poivrade. The popular sticky toffee pudding on a butterscotch sauce puts

in a frequent appearance on the dessert list. A daily-changing chalked-up menu offers informal eating in the 50-cover bistro. ***Seats** 40.*
L by arrangement D 7-9.30 (Sat to 10). Closed Sun.

Ston Easton — Ston Easton Park 88% — £152

Tel 0761 241631 Fax 0761 241377 — **HR**

Ston Easton nr Bath Avon BA3 4DF — **Map 13 F1**

Equidistant from Bath and Bristol, the magnificent Palladian house was built in 1740 and contains some exceptional architectural features. Extensively restored and refurbished, the mansion is set in the only remaining Humphrey Repton landscape in Somerset – the hotel's gardens, including wells, a ruin and bridges spanning the river Norr, and an 18th-century ice house, are not to be missed. Abutting the Gardener's Cottage (air-conditioned suites with underfloor heating, fine furnishings and antiques) is a castle folly. The magnificence of the gardens is reflected in the wonderful floral displays you'll find in the salon – note the ornate plasterwork and trompe l'oeil murals – and in the library, which contains listed mahogany bookcases. Tastefully-decorated bedrooms, some with four-posters of the Chippendale and Hepplewhite periods, have luxurious bathrooms, boasting fine fittings (Rudge & Co, Czech & Speake) and Crabtree & Evelyn toiletries. Impeccable staff provide excellent service (beds turned down and towels changed when guests are dining), and a real English country house-style breakfast will not disappoint. Children of seven years onwards and babes in arms welcome, and kennelling for dogs is available (free of charge) though dogs are not allowed in bedrooms or public rooms. Ask to see 'downstairs' which has a kitchen museum, 18th-century linen room, servants' hall, billiard room and wine cellars, all in use today. Period meeting rooms (36 theatre-style) and banqueting (the house's original dining room, now called the Yellow Room) for 24. ***Rooms** 21.*
Garden, snooker, tennis, bicycle hire, helipad. AMERICAN EXPRESS *Access, Diners, Visa.*

Restaurant ↑ — £95

The main dining room, with fine wood panelling painted in soft colours and bamboo-style furniture, was the old parlour. Relying on the best and freshest produce, including vegetables, herbs and fruit from the walled kitchen garden, chef Mark Harrington cooks with style, imagination and consistency. His four-course dinner menu, always with a vegetarian dish, combines traditional and modern choices, say, poached quenelles of pink trout with roasted scallops and fried leeks or open ravioli of wild mushrooms and grilled asparagus dressed in balsamic vinaigrette, followed by pot-roasted guinea fowl set on a bed of braised butter beans or breast of Gressingham duckling with caramelised apple and sage stuffing. The hot dessert might be poached pear and chocolate in filo pastry on a red wine sabayon, or a cold offering, perhaps a platter of home-made ice creams or sorbets. Fine British cheeses, and an easy-to-use, well-balanced wine list with a fine New World section, many bin ends and an extensive half bottle selection. Lunch can be taken on the terrace in fine weather. ***Seats** 40.*
Parties 8. Private Room 24. L 12.30-2 D 7.30-9.30 (Fri & Sat to 10).
Set L £26 Set D £38.

Stonehouse — Stonehouse Court 68% — £98

Tel 0453 825155 Fax 0453 824611 — **H**

Bristol Road Stonehouse Gloucestershire GL10 3RA — **Map 14 B2**

Conveniently situated about a mile from Junction 13 of the M5, Stonehouse Court is an imposing 17th-century building set in six acres of secluded gardens. Accommodation is split between spacious rooms with mullioned windows in the main house and more uniform ones in redbrick extensions. Day rooms include a large panelled lounge with fine carved stone fireplace, abundant seating and a bar with green leather chesterfield

See over

sofas. Conference/banqueting facilities for up to 120. Friendly management. Clipper Hotels. ***Rooms** 37. Garden, putting, snooker, fishing, helipad. Access, Visa.*

Stonehouse Place of Interest

Slimbridge Wildfowl Trust Tel 0453 890333.

Stonham Mr Underhill's ★ £70

Tel 0449 711206 **R**

Stonham nr Stowmarket Suffolk IP14 5DW **Map 10 C3**

Chris and Judy Bradley's delightful restaurant, which they've run since 1981, stands north of Ipswich on the A140. Much like the decor, Chris's French-influenced cooking is in the modern idiom, with carefully chosen, balanced ingredients and imaginative combinations that are neither fussy nor fanciful. Evening menus offer three or four courses at fixed prices: warm salad of smoked haddock preceding fillet of beef with wild mushroom essence, or escalope of salmon with chive beurre blanc followed by Barbary duck with Provence herbs. Choose then perhaps between classic pecan and apple tart, Creole coffee parfait, sticky toffee pudding and the superb cheeseboard. True value, too, for 2- or 3-course Sunday lunches. There are helpful guidance notes on the world-wide wine list that includes many interesting bottles and plenty of half bottles. ***Seats** 24. Parties 16. L by arrangement D 7.30-9. Closed D Sun, all Mon, Bank Holidays (open 25 & 26 Dec). Set L £15/£19.95 Set D from £18.95.* AMERICAN EXPRESS *Access, Visa.*

Stonor Stonor Arms £75

Tel 0491 638345 Fax 0491 638863 **RR**

Stonor nr Henley-on-Thames Oxfordshire RG9 6HE **Map 15 D2**

Two levels of food in an attractively converted, 18th-century village pub: informal, lunchtime snacking in Blades Brasserie and more formal (but not over-ambitious) menus in the elegant restaurant proper and conservatory room. Aperitifs and canapés are served in a spacious drawing room graced with antiques and comfortable sofas. Stephen Frost uses fresh produce from local sources, fish from Cornwall and some meats and vegetables from their own farm or estates in Scotland. Red pepper and tomato soup, scallops and mussels in saffron and cream sauce or terrine of rabbit and juniper could precede chargrilled monkfish, grilled breast of Barbary duckling or roast fillet of pork with a black pudding mousse, with perhaps a hot apricot soufflé to finish. Super and fairly-priced wine list (Midlands/Heart of England Cellar of the Year) featuring Olivier Leflaive burgundies, several French country wines and good house recommendations. Plenty of half bottles. ***Seats** 40. Private Room 24. Bar: L & D 7 days, Restaurant: L by arrangement D 7-9.30. Closed D Sun. Set D £29.50.* AMERICAN EXPRESS *Access, Visa.*

Rooms £93

A wing of bedrooms, numbering nine (including two suites), is furnished to a high standard with some antiques. Cots and Z-beds for children are additional charges. No dogs.

Storrington Abingworth Hall 71% £96

Tel 0798 813636 Fax 0798 813914 **HR**

Thakeham Road Storrington West Sussex RH20 3EF **Map 11 A6**

2 miles north of Storrington on the B2139. There's a pretty lake within the eight acres of grounds surrounding Abingworth Hall, which has had a succession of colourful owners, including Sir Oswald Mosley. Built in the 1930s, the white-painted house has been extended to include 20 bedrooms, all with immaculate en-suite bathrooms and decorated with a range of furnishings from antique to cane. An oak-panelled drawing room and rattan-furnished conservatory look out on to the lawned garden and are

peaceful and tranquil, as is the whole setting. Housekeeping standards and repair are maintained at a high level throughout by the considerate owners Mr and Mrs Bulman. No children under ten. No dogs. ***Rooms** 20. Outdoor swimming pool, helipad, garden, tennis, putting, coarse fishing. Closed 2 weeks Jan. Access, Visa.*

Restaurant

£65

Tasteful decor, large, well-spaced tables with crisp linen and high-quality cooking from Peter Cannon guarantee an enjoyable meal. His style is modern but with a conservative streak, offering both à la carte and table d'hote menus for lunch (3-course) and dinner (4-course). Prices have been considerably reduced since last year. Gentlemen are requested to wear a jacket and tie for dinner. ***Seats** 50. Parties 20. Private Room 54. L 12.30-1.45 D 7.15-9. Set L £12.50 (Sun) Set D £20.*

Storrington Little Thakeham 78%

£150

Tel 0903 744416 Fax 0903 745022

HR

Merrywood Lane Storrington West Sussex RH20 3HE

Map 11 A6

A fine example of a Sir Edward Lutyens manor house standing in delightful gardens designed in the style of Gertrude Jekyll. Tim and Pauline Ractliff have furnished their beautiful house in a style sympathetic to its architectural features; the minstrel's gallery, mullioned windows, polished stone floors and oak doors are complemented by period furniture in leather and oak, arts and crafts-designed chairs and sideboards, and pictures, flowers and ornaments. The bedrooms are spacious (although not always furnished in keeping with the country house style), with garden views, period Liberty prints, some lovely oak furniture and personal touches such as pot-pourri, books and magazines. No dogs. Children by arrangement. ***Rooms** 9. Garden, outdoor swimming pool, tennis, helipad. Closed 2 weeks Christmas/New Year.* AMERICAN EXPRESS *Access, Diners, Visa.*

Restaurant

£90

An elegant dining room and a short, four-course, fixed-price dinner menu offering a safe choice of uncomplicated cooking, but at a fairly hefty price. A typical lunch menu might start with carrot and coriander soup, smoked trout and quail's eggs, duck liver parfait with Cumberland sauce, Italian tomato salad or salmon and spinach wrapped in filo pastry with lemon butter sauce to start, followed by fillet of beef with brandy and green peppercorn sauce, breast of Sussex chicken with oyster mushrooms and Madeira, rack of Southdown lamb and redcurrant sauce, calf's liver and bacon or fillet of brill with prawn sauce. Several classics on the wine list at more reasonable prices than elsewhere. ***Seats** 30. Private Room 120. L 12.30-2 D 7.30-9.30. Closed D Sun. Set L £16.50/£21.50 Set D £32.50.*

Storrington Manley's

£90

Tel 0903 742331

RR

Manleys Hill Storrington West Sussex RH20 4BT

Map 11 A6

A sharp appetite is a must when visiting this attractive, low-beamed Sussex-stone restaurant, where Karl Löderer cooks hearty Continental dishes with care and presents them with flair. Sole fillet filled with crab, scallops and ginger then topped with a soufflé and served with a beurre blanc is typical of the effort that goes into each dish (and that's just to start); follow with strips of veal with cream sauce, Gruyère and spinach spätzle or three medallions of fillet steak coated with duxelles, tomato concassé and hollandaise. Locally grown vegetables are always good, as are details like bread, canapés and amuse-gueule; pretty, involved desserts like *la cage défendue* – a spun basket filled with home-made sorbets and marinated fruits – or *Salzburger nockerln* (a lemon and orange-flavoured soufflé cooked in honey and rum, for two), reflect Löderer's Austrian background. The carte is a set price for two dishes, but the table d'hote also offers a good

See over

choice of dishes at both sessions. Some fairly-priced lesser wines, though classics are quite pricy, and entry price for champagne is a whopping £41. Friendly, efficient service and delightful fresh flower arrangements add to the enjoyment. Sunday lunches are popular. No service charge is added to the bill – what you see is what you pay. ***Seats** 48. Parties 34. Private Room 20. L 12-2 D 7-9.30. Closed D Sun, D 25 & 26 Dec, all Mon, Bank Holidays except Good Friday, 1st 2 weeks Jan. Set L £18.60 (£22.50 Sun) Set D £26.* AMERICAN EXPRESS *Access, Diners, Visa.*

Room **£87**

A handsome suite overlooking the downs is available for restaurant guests who wish to stay overnight. No children or dogs.

Storrington — Old Forge — £55

Tel 0903 743402 — R

6a Church Street Storrington West Sussex RH20 4LA — **Map 11 A6**

A converted beamed forge is the relaxing setting for adventurous cooking from chef-patron Clive Roberts, who offers monthly-changing menus. Inspiration for dishes is varied: start, perhaps, with lamb's sweetbreads braised with sherry and ginger, layered in puff pastry and served with a yoghurt sauce, or rosemary-scented chicken and avocado mousseline with a cucumber vinaigrette, followed by freshly-grilled 'shrimp' set around a steamed scallop pudding on a coriander sauce, or baked salami, orange and walnut-stuffed magret of duck with a vermouth sauce. An ever-changing board of eight 'artisan-produced' farmhouse cheeses is offered and ice creams and sorbets are home-made. Banana and lime charlotte with a hint of rum and a mango and lime coulis might be among the desserts, ably complemented by a varied selection of sweet wines and eaux de vie by the glass. Coffee and petits fours are complimentary. Special food and wine evenings are held six times a year. ***Seats** 22. Parties 18. Private Room 12. L 12.30-1.30 D 7.30-9. Closed L Sat & Tues, D Sun, all Mon, Bank Holidays, 3 weeks Oct. Set L £11/£13 Set D £16/£18.50.* AMERICAN EXPRESS *Access, Diners, Visa.*

Storrington — Place of Interest

St. Mary's House and Gardens Bramber Tel 0903 816205.

Stourbridge — Talbot Hotel — 59% — £50

Tel 0384 394350 Fax 0384 371318 — H

High Street Stourbridge West Midlands DY8 1DW — **Map 6 B4**

A charming town-centre inn with many reminders of its coaching-days origins. These include the heavy doors to the coach entrance and some handsome timbers in the day rooms. A marvellous old staircase winds up to bedrooms, which vary in their size and furnishings. ***Rooms** 25. Coffee shop (9am-11pm).* AMERICAN EXPRESS *Access, Visa.*

Stourbridge — Places of Interest

Hagley Hall Nr Stourbridge Tel 0562 882408.
Broadfield House Glass Museum Barnett Lane, Kingswinford Tel 0384 252401.

Stourport-on-Severn — Moat House — 62% — £49

Tel 0299 827733 Fax 0299 878520 — H

Hartlebury Road Stourport-on-Severn Hereford & Worcester DY13 9LT — **Map 6 B4**

Well set up for business or pleasure, the Moat House stands in a wooded 23-acre site. Conferences up to 450 delegates. Children up to 14 stay free in parents' room. Take the Hartlebury Road out of Stourport; the hotel is half a mile along on the left. ***Rooms** 68. Garden, outdoor swimming pool, keep-fit equipment, squash, sauna, tennis, snooker.* AMERICAN EXPRESS *Access, Diners, Visa.*

Stourport Place of Interest

Eastgrove Cottage Garden Nursery Sankyns Green, Nr Shrawley
Tel 0299 896389.

Stow Bardolph Hare Arms £50

Tel 0366 382229 **R**

Stow Bardolph nr Downham Market Norfolk PE34 3HT **Map 10 B2**

A picturesque country pub in a delightful Norfolk village nine miles south of King's Lynn. There are two menus: a regularly changing table d'hote (Mon-Thur) with dishes like mushroom tartlet, roast turkey and beef bourguignon, and a seasonal à la carte with a wider choice typified by seafood pasta, chicken liver pancakes, sea bream with a fennel and lime sauce and lamb steak with rosemary and garlic. Also bar snacks lunch and evening. No children under ten. ***Seats** 35. Parties 24. Private Room 45. D only 7.30-9.30. Closed Sun, 25 Dec, Bank Holiday Mons. Set D £15.50 (Mon-Thurs). No credit cards.*

Stow-on-the-Wold Fosse Manor 60% £95

Tel 0451 30354 Fax 0451 32486 **H**

Fosse Way Stow-on-the-Wold Gloucestershire GL54 1JX **Map 14 C1**

Resident proprietors Bob and Yvonne Johnston (21 years at the helm) and their loyal staff run a family haven that attracts many repeat visits. Built in the style of a Cotswold manor house, it stands in its ivy coat in grounds set back from the A429 (originally the Fosse Way). Bedrooms (including ten equipped for family use) overlook colourful gardens and the bright look of the day rooms is enhanced throughout by potted plants, fresh flowers and spotless housekeeping. Family facilities include supervised play times for children in a playroom and playground on high days and holidays. ***Rooms** 20. Garden, sauna, spa bath, solarium, beauty salon. Closed 22-30 Dec.* AMERICAN EXPRESS *Access, Diners, Visa.*

Stow-on-the-Wold Grapevine Hotel 67% £98

Tel 0451 830344 Fax 0451 832278 **H**

Sheep Street Stow-on-the-Wold Gloucestershire GL54 1AU **Map 14 C1**

Friendly town-centre hotel, dating back to the 1600s, with considerable charm. Winnie the parrot presides in the cosy reception/lounge (a further sitting room, sometimes used for small meetings, is for smokers), there's a convivial beamed bar, and a 100-year-old grapevine provides a living canopy in the conservatory restaurant, where breakfast is taken. Beams and exposed stonework give character to the main-house rooms, which are generally more modest (three have shower/WC only) than the six stylish Garden rooms – the only ones with remote control for the TV for example. In between are the pine-furnished Rafters' rooms, All are equally well kept and offer a welcoming glass of sherry. No dogs. ***Rooms** 23. Patio. Closed Dec 24-Jan 9.* AMERICAN EXPRESS *Access, Diners, Visa.*

Stow-on-the-Wold Unicorn Hotel 59% £100

Tel 0451 830257 Fax 0451 832243 **H**

Sheep Street Stow-on-the-Wold Gloucestershire GL54 1HQ **Map 14 C1**

17th-century origins with some period appeal (steep tiled roof, dormer windows and original beams). Forte. ***Rooms** 20.* AMERICAN EXPRESS *Access, Diners, Visa.*

Stow-on-the-Wold Wyck Hill House 74% £90

Tel 0451 831936 Fax 0451 832243 **HR**

Burford Road Stow-on-the-Wold Gloucestershire GL54 1HY **Map 14 C1**

Two miles south of Stow off the A424 this early 18th-century Cotswold stone manor stands in 100 acres of its own grounds and gardens commanding fine views across the Windrush Valley. Day rooms combine comfort with a carefully created lived-in feel; rugs over time-worn floorboards in the cedar-panelled library and inner hall with its fine galleried staircase, leather armchairs in the clubby bar and dark oil portraits and various items of porcelain that look deceptively as if they have always been part of the house. Generally spacious bedrooms are either in the main house (traditionally furnished with antique and reproduction pieces and floral fabrics), the Orangery some 100 yards away (bright summery rooms with rattan furniture and orange patterned soft furnishings, each with French windows opening on to a patio) or, at a similar distance from the main building, in the coach house where pine-furnished rooms open directly on to a central courtyard. Rooms are all of a similar standard except that de luxe rooms get the better views and a couple of little extras like sherry, sweets and shortbread. Attentive, friendly staff. ***Rooms** 30. Garden, riding.* AMERICAN EXPRESS *Access, Diners, Visa.*

Restaurant £95

A contrast in styles here between the richly opulent inner dining room with red damask fabric covered walls and huge central flower display and a large conservatory which takes full advantage of the panoramic views. Plenty of choice too on Ian Smith's confidently handled, modish à la carte: deep-fried squid and king prawns on an artichoke, sun-dried tomato and basil salad with pesto dressing; coulibiac of salmon in brioche pastry with sour cream and caviar; fillets of brill with scampi mousse and seafood sausage on champagne and lobster sauces; medallions of beef on red onion and mushroom confit with burgundy sauce. Yet more choice for afters with a good selection of puds, home-made sorbets, farmhouse cheeses and even an example of that much neglected item – the savoury. At lunchtime there's an individually priced light menu in addition to the table d'hote. ***Seats** 60. Parties 9. Private Room 40. L 12.30-2 D 7.30-9.30. Set L £16.95.*

Stowmarket Forte Travelodge £42

Tel 0449 615347 **L**

Stowmarket Suffolk IP14 3PY **Map 10 C3**

On the A45 westbound, 12 miles north of Ipswich with Bury St Edmunds also within easy reach. ***Rooms** 40.* AMERICAN EXPRESS *Access, Visa.*

Stratfield Turgis Wellington Arms £68

Tel 0256 882214 Fax 0256 882934 **I**

Stratfield Turgis Basingstoke Hampshire RG27 0AS **Map 15 D3**

Hard by the A33 between Basingstoke and Reading, behind a handsome white Georgian facade, a charming old inn with a mix of the old and new. The polished flagstone floor of the small and pubby L-shaped bar leads directly round into a friendly drawing room in country-house style with tall, draped windows, open fire, sunken-cushioned sofas, gilt-framed oil portraits and glass-cased stuffed birds. Fifteen bedrooms in the original building include two "luxury doubles" (one a suite with a heavily-carved four-poster and spa bath); while the other 20 are in a two-storey modern extension to the rear, uniformly decorated with Laura Ashley pastel blues and yellows plus modern light oak furniture suites, and overlooking a grassed area. A couple of modern suites serve as both small meeting rooms and family rooms with pull-down additional beds. Beef Wellington is, of course, served in the traditionally-furnished restaurant; good light meals and snacks in the bar/lounge. Next door to the Duke of Wellington's estate (Stratfield Saye House, where river fishing can be arranged) and close to

Wellington Country Park (ideal for family outings). The Long Room, converted from original stabling, caters for banquet-style functions of up to 70. Busy Mon-Thurs with business travellers but more restful at weekends, when greatly reduced rates apply. Badger Inns. ***Rooms** 35. Garden, fishing.* Access, Diners, Visa.

Stratford-upon-Avon — Alveston Manor — 65% — £115

Tel 0789 204581 Fax 0789 414095 — H

Clopton Bridge Stratford-upon-Avon Warwickshire CV37 7HP — Map 14 C1

A Midsummer Night's Dream was first performed in the seven acres of gardens of this manor house, behind whose gabled exterior there remains a good deal of period charm in the day rooms. Bedrooms, though, are mainly modern; children under 16 stay free in parents' room. Forte Grand. ***Rooms** 108. Garden, pitch & putt.* Access, Diners, Visa.

Stratford-upon-Avon — Billesley Manor — 76% — £135

Tel 0789 400888 Fax 0789 764145 — HR

Billesley Alcester nr Stratford-upon-Avon Warwickshire B49 6NF — Map 14 C1

A centuries-old stone manor house standing in 11 acres of typically English gardens, three miles from Stratford-upon-Avon on the A46. Within, its public rooms are impressive, with oak panelling, leather seating and open log fires in the cocktail bar, plus polished mahogany tables and fine garden views through stone-mullioned windows in the restaurant. More panelling, period furniture and some four-poster beds imbue main-house bedrooms with the most character; the remainder are housed in two modern wings with a high degree of comfort. Housekeeping throughout is good, staff are polite and efficient. Conference and banqueting facilities for up to 100. No dogs. Queens Moat Houses. ***Rooms** 41. Garden, tennis, pitch & putt, indoor swimming pool.* Access, Diners, Visa.

Restaurant — £90

Chef Mark Naylor produces a confident combination of balanced textures and well-defined flavours. Salad of John Dory, figs and hazelnuts with a port dressing; marinated duck breast with an orange juniper gin sauce; and warm mango tart with lime and ginger sauce show the style of his à la carte menus. ***Seats** 40. Parties 9. L 12.30-2 D 7.30-9.30. Set L £17 Set D £26.*

Stratford-upon-Avon — Dukes Hotel — 65% — £65

Tel 0789 269300 Fax 0789 414700 — H

Payton Street Stratford-upon-Avon Warwickshire CV37 6UA — Map 14 C1

Two Georgian town houses dating from 1820 make up a civilised hotel not far from the centre, the shops and the theatres. Well-worn armchairs, antique furniture and ornaments make a homely, lived-in lounge, and there's a small bar. Bedrooms are neat and comfortable, with period pieces; there are four-poster rooms and suites. No children under 12. No dogs. ***Rooms** 22. Garden. Closed 10 days Christmas/New Year.* *Access, Diners, Visa.*

Stratford-upon-Avon — Ettington Park — 76% — £140

Tel 0789 450123 Fax 0789 450472 — H

Alderminster Stratford-upon-Avon Warwickshire CV37 8BS — Map 14 C1

An imposing neo-Gothic stately home with a Grade 1 preservation listing. It stands five miles south of Stratford on the A34 to Oxford, in mature parkland by the Stour. The interior of the house fully lives up to the promise of the setting and is being refurbished this year. Notable features include a lovely plant-filled conservatory entrance, a fine Victorian drawing room, a richly panelled library bar and a very elegant and

See over

relaxing lounge. Bedrooms are no less impressive, with plenty of space, well-chosen antiques, light, restful colour schemes and all sorts of little personal touches. The majority of rooms enjoy fine country views. The Long Gallery is one of the most characterful meeting rooms in the country, with book-lined walls and a high, wood-panelled vaulted ceiling; it holds up to 60 delegates. Similarly, there are other interesting rooms like the 14th-century chapel with stained-glass windows, suitable for private dining and board meetings. Children up to 12 stay free in parents' room. No dogs. ***Rooms** 48. Garden, tennis, helipad, indoor swimming pool, sauna, solarium, spa bath, coarse fishing, riding, clay-pigeon shooting.* AMERICAN EXPRESS *Access, Diners, Visa.*

Stratford-upon-Avon — Falcon Hotel — 63% — £94

Tel 0789 205777 Fax 0789 414260 — **H**

Chapel Street Stratford-upon-Avon Warwickshire CV37 6HA — **Map 14 C1**

Behind a classic timbered facade there's a blend of old and new. The beamed and panelled Oak Bar is as old as the building (1640), while the conference rooms (for up to 200) are thoroughly up-to-date. 20 bedrooms, including a four-poster suite, are in the original part, the rest in a modern section. Ample car parking. Children up to 14 stay free in parents' room. 27 rooms are designated non-smoking. Queens Moat Houses. ***Rooms** 73. Garden.* AMERICAN EXPRESS *Access, Diners, Visa.*

Stratford-upon-Avon — Forte Posthouse — 59% — £68

Tel 0789 266761 Fax 0789 414547 — **H**

Bridgefoot Stratford-upon-Avon Warwickshire CV37 7LT — **Map 14 C1**

Popular tourist, family and business base overlooking the river Avon, opposite the theatre. ***Rooms** 60. Children's playground.* AMERICAN EXPRESS *Access, Diners, Visa.*

Stratford-upon-Avon — Moat House International — 71% — £125

Tel 0789 414411 Fax 0789 298589 — **H**

Bridgefoot Stratford-upon-Avon Warwickshire CV37 6YR — **Map 14 C1**

A purpose-built, modern hotel close to the centre of town (on the A34) with a wealth of facilities to keep the conference trade happy. Spacious public rooms include a simply furnished residents' lounge and another that overlooks the River Avon. The Tavern Bar is pub-like and The Actors night club opens six nights a week. Bedrooms have the usual uniformity of chain hotels but are of a good size and comfortable, with smart dark furniture. Some of the rooms have views of the Royal Shakespeare Theatre and river; 64 on the third floor are reserved for non-smokers; eight are triple rooms for families (children up to 15 stay free in their parents' room). The Warwick Grill opens only for dinner and Sunday lunch; a Carvery also overlooks the river. Superb Metropolitan health and fitness centre. Conference and banqueting facilities for up to 450. ***Rooms** 247. Garden, gymnasium, indoor swimming pool, spa bath, sauna, steam room, solarium, beautician, hairdressing, mooring, helipad, disco, shopping arcade, news kiosk.* AMERICAN EXPRESS *Access, Diners, Visa.*

Stratford-upon-Avon — The Opposition — £50

Tel 0789 269980 — **R**

13 Sheep Street Stratford-upon-Avon Warwickshire CV37 9EF — **Map 14 C1**

Nigel Lambert's busy bistro restores the fun to eating out: good food at fair prices, of which Stratford's opposition should take note. Handy for the High Street and the Royal Shakespeare (for pre-theatre suppers booking is advised). A light snack may take the form of spinach and ricotta cannelloni and deep-pan pizzas alongside, perhaps, tomato, mozzarella and basil salad and spaghetti with spicy meatballs from the daily blackboard menu. Diners by night may equally be tempted by the croissant of seafood mornay and

Scotch beef medallions with mushroom, tomato and red wine sauce. Most leave room for the crème brulée, banoffi pie or tiramisu. A lively, musically-humming place is this, where even when the buzz borders on the frenetic, service excels. ***Seats** 50. Parties 12. L 11-2 (Sun 1-3) D 5.30-11 (Sun till 10). Closed 25, 26 Dec, 2 wks Jan & Sun in winter. Access, Visa.*

Stratford-upon-Avon — Shakespeare Hotel — 69% — £127

Tel 0789 294771 Fax 0789 415111 — **H**

Chapel Street Stratford-upon-Avon Warwickshire CV37 6ER — **Map 14 C1**

A Forte Heritage hotel with a central location (next to the town hall) and a long history. The gabled and timbered facade is typical of its 17th-century origins, and inside are beams and flagstones, open fires and period furnishings. Floral fabrics and smart darkwood furniture are used in the bedrooms, which include suites and four-posters. Function facilities for up to 120. ***Rooms** 63. Garden.* American Express *Access, Diners, Visa.*

Stratford-upon-Avon — Stratford House — 62% — £82

Tel 0789 268288 Fax 0789 295580 — **H**

18 Sheep Street Stratford-upon-Avon Warwickshire CV37 6EF — **Map 14 C1**

Approximately one hundred yards from the Royal Shakespeare Theatre and the river Avon, this quiet little hotel in a Georgian house is a comfortable, friendly home from home. An open fire warms the lounge, and there's a bright conservatory restaurant and bar. In warm weather the walled garden comes into its own. Neat bedrooms use floral fabrics and darkwood units. Families are welcome, with most facilities provided. Charged parking in a nearby car park. ***Rooms** 11. Garden. Closed 4 days Christmas.* American Express *Access, Diners, Visa.*

> Our inspectors are full-time employees; they are professionally trained by us.

Stratford-upon-Avon — Welcombe Hotel — 74% — £140

Tel 0789 295252 Fax 0789 414666 — **H**

Warwick Road Stratford-upon-Avon Warwickshire CV37 0NR — **Map 14 C1**

The parkland surrounding this extensive, handsome Jacobean-style mansion includes two lakes and an 18-hole, par 70 golf course, whose clubhouse is a popular spot for a drink or a snack. There's an Italian garden, a rose garden, a winter garden and a water garden. In the main building is the oak-panelled bar, named after sometime owner Sir George Trevelyan. In the lounge, deep sofas and armchairs provide abundant comfort, and a log fire burns in the ornate black marble fireplace. Individually furnished bedrooms in the main house have antiques and period pieces, plus marble bathrooms with separate showers. Some of the suites are most impressive – the Lady Caroline (Trevelyan) comprises four-poster bedroom, drawing room, study and luxurious bathroom. Rooms in a garden wing are smaller but equally comfortable. Owners are Orient Express Hotels. ***Rooms** 76. Garden, tennis, golf course. Closed 28 Dec-3 Jan.* American Express *Access, Diners, Visa.*

Stratford-upon-Avon — White Swan — 62% — £112

Tel 0789 297022 Fax 0789 268773 — **H**

Rother Street Stratford-upon-Avon Warwickshire CV37 6NH — **Map 14 C1**

The gabled, medieval front of this Forte Heritage hotel has changed little down the years, and inside oak beams and 16th-century wall paintings keep the character. Best of the accommodation are four-poster/half-tester bedrooms. ***Rooms** 37.* American Express *Access, Diners, Visa.*

Stratford-upon-Avon — Windmill Park — 64% — £98

Tel 0789 731173 Fax 0789 731131 — **H**

Warwick Road Stratford-upon-Avon Warwickshire CV37 0PY — **Map 14 C1**

Four linked blocks provide practical accommodation in a modern redbrick hotel on the A439 (leave the M40 at Junction 15). Fully-equipped leisure centre; conference facilities for up to 360; many large family and interconnecting bedrooms, with under-12s staying free in parents' room. ***Rooms** 100. Indoor swimming pool, gymnasium, sauna, spa bath, steam room.* American Express *Access, Diners, Visa.*

Stratford-upon-Avon — Places of Interest

Tourist Information Tel 0789 293127.
The Teddy Bear Museum Tel 0789 293160.
The Shakespeare Birthplace Trust's Properties The Shakespeare Centre Tel 0789 204016.
Stratford-upon-Avon Racecourse Tel 0789 267949.
Theatres and Concert Halls
Royal Shakespeare Theatre Tel 0789 295623.
Swan Theatre Tel 0789 295623.
The Other Place Tel 0789 292565.

Streatley-on-Thames — Swan Diplomat — 72% — £134

Tel 0491 873737 Fax 0491 872554 — **HR**

High Street Streatley-on-Thames Berkshire RG8 9HR — **Map 15 D2**

In a delightful setting on the banks of the Thames, an attractive, efficiently run hotel owned by a Swedish family. Bedrooms are spacious and elegantly furnished with traditionally styled mahogany pieces; decor is light, restful and modern. Over half the rooms have balconies and river views, and day rooms like the panelled bar and comfortable lounge also enjoy the views. The old Magdalen College barge, fully restored to its 19th-century splendour, is an unusual venue for drinks or meetings. *Reflexions* leisure club offers many diversions for the active; a riverside terrace off the lounge provides less exhausting (but equally satisfying) attractions for the more sedate – many guests put both to good use. A 12-seater Edwardian saloon launch is moored in front of the hotel and is available by prior arrangement for river trips and picnics. 9 miles from Junction 12 of the M4. ***Rooms** 46. Garden, indoor 'fit' pool, sauna, solarium, keep-fit equipment, beautician, rowing boats, moorings.* American Express *Access, Diners, Visa.*

Riverside Restaurant — £80

Something of a garden house feel here with trellis ceiling and faux-rattan chairs, but it's the riverside setting that's still the main attraction. Executive chef Christopher Cleveland is a consummate professional and under his guidance the kitchen reliably produces both a well-crafted à la carte and a table d'hote. The former covers a popular range (oysters, terrine of duck, potted shrimps, scampi with curried sauce, lobster Thermidor, Barnsley chop, crepes Suzette) with vegetarian options; the latter includes less involved but equally well-executed dishes – perhaps green pea soup with garlic croutons, lime-marinated tuna steak, desserts from a trolley. Some good names on the wine list, though pricing appears inconsistent. Breakfast, light lunches and afternoon tea are served in the Duck Room, which also has river views. Summer barbecues. ***Seats** 75. Private Room 100. L 12.30-2 D 7.30-9.30 (Sat from7, Sun to 9). Closed L Sat. Set L £15.50/£19.25 Set D £24.*

Any person using our name to obtain free hospitality is a fraud.
Proprietors, please inform the police and us.

Street — Bear Hotel — 63% — £60

Tel 0458 42021 Fax 0458 840007 — **H**

53 High Street Street Somerset BA16 0EF — **Map 13 F1**

On the edge of town, just off the A39, the late-Victorian stone-built Bear retains its intimate air in the small fire-lit residents' lounge and livelier bar and patio. There's a sturdy, old-fashioned feel to the main-house bedrooms; seven in the Rose Cottage annexe are more modern. Well-equipped conference and function facilities. No dogs. ***Rooms** 17. Closed 7 days Christmas.* AMERICAN EXPRESS *Access, Visa.*

Stretton — Ram Jam Inn — £59

Tel 0780 410776 Fax 0780 410361 — **IR**

Great North Road Stretton nr Oakham Leicestershire LE15 7QX — **Map 7 E3**

Hard by a service station nine miles north of Stamford on the northbound lane of the A1 (southbound drivers take the B668 exit to Oakham and follow signs), the Ram Jam Inn is a very pleasing alternative to the mass of commercial hotels and eating places along the A1. Public rooms are devoted completely to informal, yet smartly furnished eating areas (bar, snack, outdoor terrace and restaurant). All the bedrooms overlooking the garden and orchard are individually and tastefully decorated with limed pine furniture, and surprisingly quiet considering the proximity to the road. ***Rooms** 10. Garden, coffee shop (7am-10pm). Closed 25 Dec.* AMERICAN EXPRESS *Access, Visa.*

Restaurant — £35

Served in a pleasingly light dining room overlooking the orchard, an interesting range of dishes runs from prawns with mayonnaise and spiced confit of duck leg with green lentils, bitter lettuce and sherry vinegar to Cajun-style lamb steak and a vegetarian Mediterranean platter. Breakfast is served from 7-10.30, and snacks are available throughout the day. ***Seats** 40. Private Room 25. L 12-2.30 D 7-10 (light meals 7am-10pm).*

Stroud — Oakes ★ — £80

Tel 0453 759950 — **R**

169 Slad Road Stroud Gloucestershire GL5 1RG — **Map 14 B2**

On the B4070 just out of town, Oakes is an early 19th-century Cotswold stone house that was once a school for young ladies. It is now a restaurant of renown, with Chris Oakes preparing memorable meals from the finest fresh produce. Many of his suppliers are local, and the menu gives them generous individual credit. His technique is sure and sound throughout menus where the choice is short but alluring: terrine of dab and gurnard served on a bed of leeks with a balsamic vinegar dressing; Gloucestershire pork sausage with mixed lettuces, poached egg, bacon and shallot vinaigrette; poached strips of lemon sole with braised wild rice; fillet of beef topped with horseradish, accompanied by a red wine sauce. Don't miss out on superb desserts like warm sultana and almond brioche served with a chocolate sauce and vanilla ice cream. Lots of half bottles on the wine list. ***Seats** 35. L 12.30-1.45 D 7.30-9.30. Closed D Sun, all Mon, Bank Holidays. Set L £18 Tue-Sat, Sun L £22 Set D £35.* AMERICAN EXPRESS *Access, Visa.*

Stroud — Places of Interest

Tourist Information Tel 0453 765768.
Misarden Park Gardens Tel 028582 309.
Painswick Rococo Garden Painswick Tel 0452 813204.

Stuckton The Three Lions £60

Tel 0425 652489 Fax 0425 656144 **R**

Stuckton nr Fordingbridge Hampshire SP6 2HF **Map 14 C4**

The long-standing reputation for good, confident, down-to-earth cooking remains high in this converted pub with a relaxed, informal ambience. Locals and visitors from further afield crowd round the blackboard menus, a feature of the dining room along with pine tables, copper and brass ornaments, pewter plates and corn dollies. The choice, which changes daily and varies between lunch and dinner, is long and interesting, covering New Forest game soup, trilogy of Swedish marinated herrings, mussels from Poole Bay, grilled mackerel fillets with warm sun-dried tomato and olive oil dressing, wiener schnitzel, skate wings with black butter and capers, and beef stroganoff with rice. All pasta, bread, sorbets and petits fours are made by chef/proprietor Karl Wadsack himself. An excellent all-round wine list (South of England Cellar of the Year) includes an especially comprehensive selection of Alsace, Australian and German wines. No children under 14. ***Seats** 55. Parties 40. L 12.15-1.30 D 7.15-9 (Sat to 9.30). Closed Sun, Mon & Bank Holidays. Access, Visa.*

Stuckton Place of Interest

Rockbourne Roman Villa Nr Fordingbridge Tel 072 53 541.

Studland Bay Knoll House 63% £165*

Tel 092 944 251 Fax 092 944 423 **H**

Studland Bay nr Swanage Dorset BH19 3AH **Map 14 C4**

100 acres of land near Studland Beach provide the setting for this friendly hotel, run since 1959 by the Ferguson family with families very much in mind. There's an adventure playground with a pirate ship, indoor play rooms, family suites with interconnecting rooms and even a children's dining room with a separate kitchen to keep the little ones happy, while the health spa is designed for adults. Wooded grounds, a nearby bird sanctuary and a safe, sandy beach provide other diversions. There's plenty of comfortable lounge space, and bedrooms – neither large nor small – are plain and practical. TVs may be hired. *Half-board terms. ***Rooms** 80. Garden, outdoor swimming pool, keep-fit equipment, sauna, steam room, solarium, whirlpool bath, tennis, golf (9), boutique. Closed Nov-Easter. No credit cards.*

Studland Bay Place of Interest

Swanage Beach.

Sturminster Newton Plumber Manor £52

Tel 0258 72507 Fax 0258 73370 **RR**

Hazelbury Bryan Road Sturminster Newton Dorset DT10 2AF **Map 14 B4**

The Prideaux-Brune family has been here since the Manor was built in 1665. The location is ideal for exploring Hardy country. Dinner might start with an oyster mushroom millefeuille with brandy, basil and cream or grilled goat's cheese with blackcurrant and cassis, followed by a set fish course (lemon sole with mushrooms and white wine) and a small choice of main courses – perhaps medallions of beef with green peppercorns, supreme of chicken with ham and Brie mousse or a vegetarian option. Sweets and cheeses from a trolley. Good wines. A good spot for a weekend touring Hardy country. ***Seats** 60. Private Room 40. L (Sun only) 12.30-1.30 D 7-9.30. Closed Feb. Set L (Sun only) £17.50 Set D £20/£25.*

AMERICAN EXPRESS *Access, Diners, Visa.*

Rooms £80

The 16 rooms are spacious and well appointed, most having antique furniture. Six are in the main house; stable-block rooms are more modern and even larger. Full English breakfast plus fresh fish. *Tennis.*

Sudbury Mabey's Brasserie £55

Tel 0787 374298 **R**

47 Gainsborough Street Sudbury Suffolk CO10 7SS **Map 10 C2**

More bistro than brasserie (it's only open at usual meal times) with pine and pews and a new blue colour scheme, there is also now a separate dining room for smokers. The menu, written on blackboards above the open kitchen, is varied, if a little less eclectic that it used to be, with deep-fried parcels of Cambazola cheese, gravad lax with dill sauce, chicken and vegetable terrine and warm salad of crispy Chinese-style duck among the starters; various chargrilled dishes included in the mains: chicken breast with noodles and sesame sauce, calf's liver and bacon with black pudding, chump of lamb with tarragon sauce; plus cod baked with a herb crust and salmon on salad with basil vinaigrette and new potatoes. Vegetables, like the bread, are extras. Puds range from summer pudding and vanilla crème brulée to Earl Grey tea and lemon sorbet. Air-conditioned. ***Seats** 36. Parties 8. Private Room 25. L 12-2 D 7-10. Closed Sun & Mon, Bank Holidays.* AMERICAN EXPRESS *Access, Visa.*

> Many establishments are currently on the market, so ownership could change after we go to press.

Sudbury Mill Hotel 58% £89

Tel 0787 375544 Fax 0787 373027 **H**

Walnut Tree Lane Sudbury Suffolk CO10 6BD **Map 10 C3**

The old mill overlooks the river Stour and a large mill pond. Bedrooms are either old-fashioned or extension-modern. Note the old millwheel in the bar-lounge. ***Rooms** 50. Coarse fishing.* AMERICAN EXPRESS *Access, Diners, Visa.*

Sudbury Places of Interest

Tourist Information Tel 0787 881320.
Gainsborough's House Gainsborough Street Tel 0787 72958.
Colne Valley Railway Castle Hedingham Tel 0787 61174.
Historic Houses, Castles and Gardens
Hedingham Castle Castle Hedingham Tel 0787 60261.

Sunderland Swallow Hotel 70% NEW £95

Tel 091-529 2041 Fax 091-529 4227 **H**

Queen's Parade Seaburn Sunderland Tyne & Wear SR6 8DB **Map 5 E2**

A smart, modern hotel sited north of Sunderland right on the seafront overlooking a long stretch of good sand with amusement arcades a little further along. The Swallow, transformed in 1991 from the simpler *Seaburn* hotel, now seems almost out of place because of its high standards of decor and service. A uniformed bell boy greets you at the entrance and carries your luggage to your room. Reception is in a part of a spacious lounge area done out, as is the whole place, in a smart, colourful, contemporary style. The Mariner bar, as its name implies, has a nautical theme. Best of the bedrooms overlook the sea. These are spacious and have sitting areas; all rooms are well equipped with, in addition to the usual facilities, an iron and board, mini-bar and satellite TV. Reasonable breakfasts are taken in the sunny restaurant. 24hr room service and guarded parking. ***Rooms** 66. Indoor swimming pool, keep-fit equipment, sauna, spa bath, solarium.* AMERICAN EXPRESS *Access, Diners, Visa.*

Sunderland Places of Interest

Tourist Information Tel 091-565 0960/0990.
Sunderland Empire Theatre Tel 091-514 2517.
Hylton Castle Tel 091-548 0152.
Washington Old Hall (NT) Washington Tel 091-416 6879.
Sunderland Football Ground Roker Park Tel 091-514 0332.
Sunderland Ice Rink and Leisure Centre Tel 091-514 2511.
Silksworth Dry Ski Slope Tel 091-522 9119.
Washington Waterfowl Park Washington Tel 091-416 5454.

Surbiton Chez Max £65

Tel 081-399 2365 **R**

85 Maple Road Surbiton Surrey KT6 4AW **Map 15 E2**

Chef-patron Max Markarian's conservatory-roofed suburban restaurant is a haven for francophiles; well-conceived dishes of meat, fish and fowl come across with clear, positive flavours. Menus are fixed price, with plats du jour at lunchtime and some supplements in the evening. Some typical choices: egg and cheese soufflé with spinach and cream sauce, spicy duck in filo pastry with apricot sauce, rack of lamb with white wine and shallots, fillet steak with mustard and horseradish sauce. Home-made sorbets are a popular dessert. Few half bottles on an otherwise easy-to-use wine list. ***Seats*** *40. L 12.30-2 D 7.30-10. Closed L Sat, all Sun & Mon (open Mothering Sunday), Bank Holidays. Set L £15.95 Set D £15.95 (Sat £16.50).* AMERICAN EXPRESS *Access, Diners, Visa.*

Sutton Holiday Inn 70% £129

Tel 081-770 1311 Fax 081-770 1539 **H**

Gibson Road Sutton Surrey SM1 2RF **Map 15 E3**

A new, redbrick town-centre hotel (overshadowing the Secombe Centre next door) with ample free parking. Practical and convenient accommodation rather than luxurious; well laid-out bedrooms have the usual Holiday Inn virtues of large beds, plenty of well-lit work space and good easy chairs around a substantial breakfast table. Bathrooms are user-friendly, too, with thermostatically-controlled showers over tubs, good shelf space and large towels. Executive rooms have various extras and include seven Study Rooms equipped with fax machines. Six rooms are specially designed for guests in wheelchairs. Public areas are fairly plain although the colourful waistcoats or braces of the keen young staff brighten things up. Good breakfasts; light snacks in the Balcony Lounge overlooking the health and leisure club where there's a separate children's splash pool. Modern conference facilities for up to 200. Children under 19 can share their parents' room at no charge; vast tariff reductions at weekends. Ask for a map showing directions from M25. ***Rooms 116.*** *Indoor swimming pool, spa bath, sauna, solarium, steam room, beautician, keep-fit equipment, snooker, coffee shop (9am-6pm).* AMERICAN EXPRESS *Access, Diners, Visa.*

Sutton Partners Brasserie £55

Tel 081-644 7743 **R**

23 Stonecot Hill Sutton Surrey SM3 9HB **Map 15 E3**

In a shopping parade on the busy A24, Partners is not like a brasserie to look at with its pale-green rag-painted walls. Well-prepared dishes include baked eggs with smoked haddock fillet, brioche bun with prawns, mussels and spring vegetables, fish casserole, cassoulet, steamed salmon with wilted greens and chargrilled steaks. British cheeses and sensibly-priced wines. Separate Sunday Brunch menu covers a range from croissant BLT to a traditional roast with Yorkshire pudding.

Sister restaurant to *Partners West Street* (see entry under Dorking) ***Seats*** *32. L 12-2 D 7-9.30. Closed L Sat, D Sun, all Mon, Bank Holidays. Set L & D £9.95/£12.95.* AMERICAN EXPRESS *Access, Diners, Visa.*

Sutton — Places of Interest

Epsom Polo Club Tel 0372 362593.
Epsom Racecourse Tel 0372 726311.

Sutton Coldfield — Forte Travelodge — £42

Tel 021-355 0017 — **L**

Boldmere Road Sutton Coldfield West Midlands B72 5UP — **Map 6 C4**

5 miles from both Junctions 5 and 6 of the M6. Situated on Boldmere Road (B4142), off the A452. 2 miles from Sutton Coldfield and 6 miles from Birmingham. ***Rooms*** *32.* AMERICAN EXPRESS *Access, Visa.*

Sutton Coldfield — Moor Hall — 62% — £90

Tel 021-308 3751 Fax 021-308 8974 — **H**

Moor Hall Drive Four Oaks Sutton Coldfield West Midlands B75 6LN — **Map 6 C4**

In a rural setting, but handy for the motorway network, the extended Edwardian building is surrounded by a golf course. It has its own leisure centre, plus facilities for up to 200 delegates. There are two bars, and the bedrooms include suites and Executive rooms. ***Rooms*** *75. Garden, indoor swimming pool, gymnasium, sauna, solarium, beauty salon.* AMERICAN EXPRESS *Access, Diners, Visa.*

Sutton Coldfield — New Hall — 78% — £129

Tel 021-378 2442 Fax 021-378 4637 — **HR**

Walmley Road Sutton Coldfield West Midlands B76 8QX — **Map 6 C4**

Twenty-six acres of beautiful grounds surround New Hall, said to be the country's oldest moated building. Dating from the 13th century, the sympathetically restored house is now a luxury hotel of some note. Though owned corporately by Mount Charlotte Thistle, it is run along personal lines by Ian and Caroline Parkes who have an obvious love of the house. Day rooms include an elegantly furnished lounge and feature panelling, ornate ceilings and latticed windows. Bedrooms in the main house are largest and most are sumptuously appointed, but the majority of rooms are in an unobtrusive modern wing built around a courtyard. There is generally a high standard of decor and furnishing; all the bathrooms are luxuriously fitted out. Immaculately turned-out, professional staff. No children under eight. A choice of sumptuous meeting rooms can accommodate up to 40 delegates. No dogs. Seven miles from Birmingham city centre; 10 miles from the National Exhibition Centre. Guests can play golf, by arrangement, at the Belfry. ***Rooms*** *60. Garden, golf driving net, putting, helipad.* AMERICAN EXPRESS *Access, Diners, Visa.*

Restaurant — £90

The elegant, panelled dining room is in the oldest part of the house. Chef Glenn Purcell cooks in an "unmistakably English" style, with innovation and attractive presentation enhancing many classic dishes. Both fixed-price and à la carte menus are offered, the former maybe offering "feuillette" of queenie scallops and mussels bound in leek cream followed by roast saddle of lamb stuffed with apricot and black pudding and a choice of dessert. A la carte extends to equally interesting and more involved dishes like mussel and curry broth glazed with Pernod sabayon, crab tortellini with crispy leeks, and cutlets of lamb garnished with sweet pea mousse and grilled pleurottes on a tarragon sauce. Prime produce is meticulously handled and desserts like praline soufflé (with Bailey's ice cream), millefeuille of hot caramelised bananas or the chocolate feast are truly wonderful. A serious wine list, with comments where necessary, spans

See over

the world; note the house selection, and the number of wines served by the glass. ***Seats** 60. Parties 12. Private Room 8. L 12.30-2 (Sun to 2.15) D 7-10 (Sun to 9.30). Closed L Sat. Set D £24.95.*

Sutton Coldfield — Penns Hall — 66% — £132

Tel 021-351 3111 Fax 021-313 1297 — H

Penns Lane Walmley Sutton Coldfield West Midlands B76 8LH — **Map 6 C4**

Originally a 17th-century house but now extended with modern additions to create a large conference venue. A covered walkway across the large, picturesque lake leads to the Sebastian Coe Health Park, complete with running track. Special event facilities in a variety of rooms holding up to 650. Easy access from Junction 9 of the M42 (4 miles), linking to the M6 (J6) and M40 (J4). Jarvis. ***Rooms** 114. Garden, indoor swimming pool, squash, gymnasium, spa bath, sauna, solarium, beauty salon, steam room, snooker, children's playground.* AMERICAN EXPRESS® *Access, Diners, Visa.*

Sutton Scotney North — Forte Travelodge — £42

Tel 0962 761016 — L

Sutton Scotney North nr Winchester Hampshire S021 3JY — **Map 15 D3**

At the Northside Welcome Break service area on the A34 northbound, 8 miles north of Winchester city centre. Easy access to M3 and M4. ***Rooms** 31.* AMERICAN EXPRESS® *Access, Visa.*

Sutton Scotney South — Forte Travelodge — £42

Tel 0962 760779 — L

Sutton Scotney South nr Winchester Hampshire SO21 3JY — **Map 15 D3**

At the Southside Welcome Break service area on the A34 southbound, 8 miles north of Winchester city centre. ***Rooms** 40.* AMERICAN EXPRESS® *Access, Visa.*

Swavesey — Forte Travelodge — £42

Tel 0954 789113 — L

Cambridge Road Swavesey nr Cambridge Cambridgeshire — **Map 15 F1**

8 miles north-west of Cambridge on the eastbound carriageway of the A604. ***Rooms** 36.* AMERICAN EXPRESS® *Access, Visa.*

Swindon — Blunsdon House — 69% — £93

Tel 0793 721701 Fax 0793 721056 — H

Blunsdon Swindon Wiltshire SN2 4AD — **Map 14 C2**

A farm guest house in 1958, a country club in 1960, and a fully licensed hotel since 1962 – and the Clifford family have been here from the beginning. It's a popular conference rendezvous (up to 300 delegates) with extensive leisure club facilities. Guests are provided with a good standard of comfort in the form of gardens, formal and casual bars, a residents' lounge, two restaurants and porterage. All the bedrooms are reasonably roomy and many have pleasant views. Decoration and appointments are of smart modern business standard, and bathrooms all have shower attachments and ample toiletries; some have spa baths. A nine-hole golf course opened in 1993. Families are well catered for; children up to 16 stay free in parents' room. No dogs. From Junction 15 of the M4 take the A419 Cirencester road. After about 7 miles turn right to Broad Blunsdon. ***Rooms** 88. Garden, indoor swimming pool, gymnasium, squash, sauna, spa bath, solarium, beauty & hair salon, tennis, golf (9), putting, games room, snooker, crèche.* AMERICAN EXPRESS® *Access, Diners, Visa.*

Swindon — De Vere Hotel — 69% — £100

Tel 0793 878785 Fax 0793 877822 — **H**

Shaw Ridge Leisure Park Whitehill Way Swindon Wiltshire SN5 7DW — **Map 14 C2**

Follow the signs to Shaw Ridge Leisure Park, some 2½ miles from the M4 (junction 16), or Link Centre. Brick-built and fronted by a clock tower and futuristic leisure club, it offers extensive and well-equipped conference and banqueting areas. Two floors of bedrooms with Executive-style facilities are built around a central courtyard; half the bedrooms are reserved for non-smokers. Children up to 14 stay free in parents' room. ***Rooms** 154. Indoor swimming pool, gymnasium, sauna, spa bath, solarium, beauty salon, snooker, coffee shop (8am-10pm).* AMERICAN EXPRESS® *Access, Diners, Visa.*

Swindon — Forte Crest — 62% — £100

Tel 0793 831333 Fax 0793 831401 — **H**

Oxford Road Stratton St Margaret Swindon Wiltshire SN3 4TL — **Map 14 C2**

Modern low-rise hotel on the A420, near the A419 roundabout. Very much geared-up to the need of the business traveller with secretarial services, in-house pager facilities, 24hr room service and meeting rooms for up to 50 people theatre-style. ***Rooms** 91. Snooker.* AMERICAN EXPRESS® *Access, Diners, Visa.*

Swindon — Forte Posthouse — 63% — £68

Tel 0793 524601 Fax 0793 512887 — **H**

Marlborough Road Swindon Wiltshire SN3 6AQ — **Map 14 C2**

70s' hotel set in five acres of grounds between Junction 15 of the M4 and the town centre. Conference facilities for 80. Popular with families at weekends. ***Rooms** 100. Garden, indoor swimming pool, keep-fit equipment, sauna, spa bath, solarium.* AMERICAN EXPRESS® *Access, Diners, Visa.*

Swindon — Swindon Marriott — 71% — £123

Tel 0793 512121 Fax 0793 513114 — **H**

Pipers Way Swindon Wiltshire SN3 1SH — **Map 14 C2**

A modern purpose-built hotel standing in mature woodland next to a golf course. It's easily found when approaching from junction 15 of the M4, and only half a mile from the Old Town. Scandinavian-influenced public areas overlook the Leisure Area and are open-plan, with central beams and pine ceilings. Contemporary-style bedrooms have plenty of natural light and individual temperature control; children stay free in parents' room. There are three suites and twelve rooms with king-size beds; 24hr room service is available. Conferences and banqueting for up to 280. ***Rooms** 153. Indoor swimming pool, keep-fit equipment, squash, sauna, spa bath, steam bath, solarium, beauty and hair salon, tennis, shop.* AMERICAN EXPRESS® *Access, Diners, Visa.*

Swindon — Wiltshire Hotel — 62% — £100

Tel 0793 528282 Fax 0793 541283 — **H**

Fleming Way Swindon Wiltshire SN1 1TN — **Map 14 C2**

Swindon's only central hotel, a short walk from bus and railway stations and with ample free parking. Meeting rooms from 22 to 230, with banqueting for up to 200. Mount Charlotte Thistle. ***Rooms** 95.* AMERICAN EXPRESS® *Access, Diners, Visa.*

Swindon — Places of Interest

Tourist Information Tel 0793 530328/526161.
Wyvern Theatre Tel 0793 24481.
Buscot Park (NT) Faringdon Tel 0367 240786.
Great Western Railway Museum Tel 0793 526161.
Swindon Town Football Ground County Ground Tel 0793 430430.
Ice Rink Link Centre Tel 0793 871212.

Swinfen — Swinfen Hall 70% £85

Tel 0543 481494 Fax 0543 480341 — **H**

Swinfen nr Lichfield Staffordshire WS14 9RS — **Map 6 C4**

Set back from the A38 two miles south of Lichfield, the present Hall was completed in 1757, a wing being added in the Edwardian period. The grand entrance hall with its minstrel's gallery, Corinthian columns and stuccoed ceiling carved by Italian craftsmen, makes a good first impression, and other notable day rooms include a handsome banqueting hall and bar. The cocktail bar has French windows opening on to a balustraded terrace, with an ornamental fountain beyond. Spacious bedrooms range from singles to suites; rooms on the second floor are particularly bright and airy, with pastel shades and light oak furniture. Banquets up to 150, conferences to 200 theatre-style. ***Rooms** 19. Garden. Closed 4 days end Dec.*
AMERICAN EXPRESS *Access, Visa.*

Tadworth — Gemini Restaurant NEW £55

Tel 0737 812179 — **R**

Station Approach Tadworth Surrey KT20 5AH — **Map 15 E3**

In a parade of shops near the station there's a pleasantly unsophisticated 1940s feel – wheelback chairs, a couple of black-painted beams – to the decor of this welcoming restaurant. There is nothing unsophisticated about Robert Foster's cooking, however, with the seasonally changing fixed-price menu (choice of about nine main courses supplemented by several dishes of the day) including the likes of fettuccine of mussels and prawns with crème fraiche and fresh coriander, home-smoked duck breast with orange and pine kernel salad, poached salmon and halibut with lobster sauce and timbale of wild rice and breast of chicken in an oyster mushroom *café au lait* sauce with fresh ginger. The list of tempting desserts is recited at the table. From Tuesday to Thursday evenings it's possible to opt for just two courses at £17.50. ***Seats** 40. L 12-2 D 7-9.30. Closed D Sun, Mon, 1 week after Christmas, 2 weeks June. Set L £9.50/£11.50 Set D £17.50 (Tues-Thurs only)/£21. Access, Visa.*

Tamworth — Granada Lodge £45

Tel 0827 260123 Fax 0827 260145 — **L**

M42/A5 Junction 10 Tamworth Staffordshire B77 5PH — **Map 6 C4**

Rooms 63. AMERICAN EXPRESS *Access, Diners, Visa.*

Taplow — Cliveden 91% £210

Tel 0628 668561 Fax 0628 661837 — **HR**

Taplow nr Maidenhead Berkshire SL6 0JF — **Map 15 E2**

Elegance and an unrivalled grandeur are the hallmarks of Britain's finest country house hotel. The former home of a Prince of Wales, several dukes and the Astor family, Cliveden has been at the centre of Britain's social and political life for over three centuries; since 1986 it has also set the highest standards of hotel-keeping, lacking nothing in modern amenities that include superb sport and health facilities. Overlooking the Thames, it is set in 376 acres of National Trust private gardens (a nominal contribution is included with all services provided) and parkland and is Britain's only hotel that is also a stately home. Much of the original mansion remains to this day – witness the terrace, the dominant feature of the south facade overlooking the 17th-century parterre and river Thames way below in the valley, one of the finest hotel views in England, the main staircase, the Great Hall and the library. These are public areas on a grand scale, featuring magnificent antiques, paintings and tapestries (the Orkney tapestries in the Great Hall celebrate the Duke of Marlborough's victory at Blenheim), while the stylish bedrooms are exquisitely and individually decorated to the very highest standard and stunning bathrooms provide for every conceivable need. The Pavilion, situated within the original walled garden, houses a luxurious leisure complex, including a Canadian hot tub and specially designed rooms for massage, health and beauty, while for outdoor enthusiasts the hotel has jogging trails around the estate, its own horses, an Edwardian river launch and an electric canoe. Situated in the privacy of the Garden wing is the state-of-the-art and fully air-conditioned Churchill boardroom that opens directly on to its own terrace. Families with children (and dogs) are admirably catered for, with everything from videos in the rooms to picnics and a playroom provided; however, children from 2 to 12 may only use the facilities in the walled garden and in the Pavilion before noon, while under-2s are not allowed to disturb the adults' pleasure at all. Breakfast is served in the sumptuous French Dining Room – one of the finest private dining rooms in the country; light lunches are also served in the Pavilion. Right from one's initial contact with the tail-coated doorman (who opens your car door almost before it stops – very regal!) through to the waiting staff in both restaurants, the service is usually nothing short of impeccable. ***Rooms** 31. Garden, indoor and outdoor swimming pools, saunas, plunge pool, whirlpool bath, solarium, steam room, hairdressing, gymnasium, indoor and outdoor tennis, squash, badminton, snooker, riding, coarse fishing, boats, valeting, laundry service.* AMERICAN EXPRESS *Access, Diners, Visa.*

Terrace Dining Room — £120

The most majestic of dining rooms (undoubtedly one of the finest settings in England), overlooking extensive formal gardens. Fine Spode china and linen complete the smart table settings and a menu is offered that mixes both classical French and English styles with a modern touch. Dishes range from the straightforward (melon with Parma ham, mixed grill, Dover sole, Welsh rarebit) to the involved (spiced foie gras, tongue and artichokes; chargrilled scallops on saffron and sage linguini with Mediterranean vegetables; pears in puff pastry on a poire William and Kirsch sabayon). Game (grouse, snipe, partridge or woodcock) also features in season. The improved and revised wine list has plenty of half bottles and an Australian Penfolds list all to itself! Ask for tasting notes if needed. No smoking. ***Seats** 70. Parties 12. Private Room 42. L 12.30-2.30 D 7.30-10. Set L from £24.*

Waldo's ↑ — £125

Down a flight of stairs, a lobby full of photographs depicting some of the famous visitors to the house leads to a windowless, clubby, pine-panelled bar beyond which is the 'inner sanctum' of Waldo's itself – exclusively small and intimate, with rich red fabric-covered walls, well-upholstered chairs and button-back benches. With its own separate kitchen, this is where Ron Maxfield is able to give full rein to his inventiveness in dishes like a compilation of rabbit with a Thai and coriander-scented sauce, Pernod and blackcurrant sorbet (refreshingly unsweet for a between-course water ice), a warm tartlet of Camembert matured in Calvados with apples and a rocket salad or deep-fried fresh figs filled with raspberries on a sherry cream sauce. Care in preparation and great attention to the detail of presentation are hallmarks of some highly professional cooking. The outstanding wine list is shared with the Terrace dining room. No smoking. ***Seats** 24. Parties 6. Private Room 12. D only 7.30-9.30. Closed Sun & Mon. Set D £47, £55 & £60.*

Taunton — Castle Hotel — 76% — £102

Tel 0823 272671 Fax 0823 336066 — **HR**

Castle Green Taunton Somerset TA1 1NF — **Map 13 E2**

The Chapman family take great pride in presenting a carefully understated Englishness, and it is this that is the wisteria-clad Castle's greatest strength: look no further than the foyer and staircase to absorb its history echoed by chiselled stonework, wrought iron and English oak, given warmth by rich oils, tapestries and floral displays. Such a building necessarily imposes limitations on modernisation, thus some single rooms are on the small side. A fine hotel, nevertheless, carefully balancing the old and new with a worthy reputation for accommodation and service; nowhere is this more apparent than in the plush garden suites, whose deep sofas, comfortable canopied beds and spacious, well-appointed bathrooms remain as luxurious as ever. Informal lunchtime eating in the Minstrel's Bar (except Sun). Special rates for honeymooners and parents and old boys at local schools! ***Rooms** 35. Garden, lock-up garaging with car-wash service.* American Express *Access, Diners, Visa.*

Restaurant ★↑ — £80

The restaurant at the Castle has been at the forefront of the revival in English culinary traditions for ten years and chef Phil Vickery continues in the same vein. He gives due recognition on his menus to the first-rate suppliers who provide tip-top produce on a daily basis in order to satisfy the daily-changing dishes. A choice of well-balanced menus is offered for both lunch and dinner, one of which is designed for those who want a lighter meal – ideals, perhaps, for residents who are staying for a period; both are written in straightforward English with no sign of pretence or embellishment. A typical lighter lunch might offer a terrine of sweetbreads with tomato compote and toast followed by braised ham hocks with onions and seed mustard, and bread-and-butter pudding to finish; those who wish to push the boat out might opt for steamed lobster sausage with couscous, tournedos Rossini, and a dish of four chocolate desserts. Evening menus see a very similar assortment of dishes – from interesting soups (celery and tarragon or yellow split pea with ham and croutons) to marinated salmon, gravad lax and mussels with parsley pasta and sweet dill dressing, a vegetarian option (baked sweet onion and thyme tart with basil hollandaise) and a handful of more involved meat and fresh fish dishes such as braised duck with lentils and creamed potatoes, braised shoulder of lamb with thyme, garlic and winter vegetables or roast scallops with saffron noodles and braised onions. A special selection of desserts attracts a supplement, but is well worth the ten-minute wait; baked egg custard tart with nutmeg ice cream, almond blancmange (albeit with lemon grass syrup and candied lemon) or steamed chocolate pudding with hot chocolate sauce should bring back a few nursery memories! A fine British cheeseboard (West Country winner of British Cheeseboard of the Year) is offered as an alternative to dessert on all menus. Sunday lunch is a traditional three-course affair, often with roast sirloin of beef in a salt crust and Yorkshire pudding. The very serious wine list is quite reasonably priced; note the super-value house wines, wide range of ports and single malt whiskies. ***Seats** 60. Parties 10. Private Room 90. L 12.30-2 D 7.30-9. Set L £13.50/£14.90 & £25.90/£29.90 (Sun £14.90, children half price) Set D £17.90/£21.90 & £29.90.*

Taunton — County Hotel — 61% — £97

Tel 0823 337651 Fax 0823 334517 — **H**

East Street Taunton Somerset TA1 3LT — **Map 13 E2**

A white-fronted former coaching inn offering comfortable Superior rooms, more functional Standards, a town-centre location and convenient free parking. Extensive conference facilities seating up to 400, and banqueting for up to 350. Forte Heritage. ***Rooms** 66.* American Express *Access, Diners, Visa.*

Taunton — Forte Posthouse — 66% — £68

Tel 0823 332222 Fax 0823 332266 — **H**

Deane Gate Avenue Taunton Somerset TA1 2UA — **Map 13 E2**

Two miles from the town centre, close to Junction 25 of the M5. Modern conference facilties for up to 200. ***Rooms** 97. Keep-fit equipment, sauna.* AMERICAN EXPRESS *Access, Diners, Visa.*

Taunton — Porters Wine Bar — £40

Tel 0823 256688 — **R**

49 East Reach Taunton Somerset TA1 3EX — **Map 13 E2**

The straightforward menu changes daily offering dishes such as spiced apple soup, chicken liver and pork paté, scallops and bacon with a tomato coulis, pan-fried chicken with orange and tarragon and French apple flan. Oven-baked potatoes with interesting fillings, kedgeree with salad and shepherd's pie are typical light lunch options. Three vegetarian dishes (parsnip, leek and Gruyère bake) every day and around a dozen wines available by the glass. Four courtyard tables in good weather and a non-smoking area to the rear of the restaurant. ***Seats** 50. Parties 30. L 12.30-2 D 7.30-10. Closed L Sat, all Sun, Bank Holidays. Access, Visa.*

Taunton — Travel Inn — £43

Tel 0823 321112 Fax 0823 322054 — **L**

81 Bridgwater Road Taunton Somerset TA1 2DU — **Map 13 E2**

Close to Junction 25 of the M5. ***Rooms** 40.* AMERICAN EXPRESS *Access, Diners, Visa.*

Taunton — Places of Interest

Tourist Information Tel 0823 274785.
Brewhouse Theatre Tel 0823 83244.
Forde Abbey and Gardens Nr Chard Tel 0460 20231.
Hestercombe House and Gardens Cheddon Fitzpaine Tel 0823 337222.
Somerset County Museum Tel 0823 255504.
County Cricket Ground Tel 0823 272946.
Royal Naval Equestrian Association Orchard House, Hatch Beauchamp Tel 0823 480223.
Taunton Racecourse Tel 0823 337172.
Wellington Sports Centre Wellington Tel 082 347 3010.
Cricket St. Thomas Wildlife Park Chard Tel 0460 30755.

Teffont Evias — Howard's House — 68% — £90

Tel 0722 716392 Fax 0722 716820 — **HR**

Teffont Evias Dinton nr Salisbury Wiltshire SP3 5RJ — **Map 14 C3**

In a sleepy hamlet of medieval origins the families Firmin and Ford have studiously converted their Tudor stone farmhouse into a very comfortable private house hotel. Downstairs is dominated by the restaurant and smaller lounge; there's no bar but drinks are served at any time. Gracious living is exemplified by top-quality linen in the bedrooms and mushroom tartlets with poached eggs and hollandaise for breakfast. A little gem of a place, high up the value-for-money ladder. ***Rooms** 8. Garden.* AMERICAN EXPRESS *Access, Visa.*

Restaurant — £75

Paul Firmin pays as much attention to detail in his fixed-price dinner menu as to the accommodation. Six or more choices per course include a good selection of game in winter and fish in spring. Typical dishes might include grilled quail with chicken liver crostini, hot salmon mousseline with girolles and Madeira cream sauce or breast of pigeon with foie gras

See over

wrapped in puff pastry to start, followed by fillet of beef with mustard seed and peppercorn jus with turned vegetables, fillet of halibut with baby leeks and red wine sauce or saddle of venison with pomegranate and timbale of celeriac and tarragon. Good desserts and a selection of French cheeses. The wine list is carefully compiled, concise and very fairly priced. Five tables on a terrace for outdoor eating. ***Seats** 34. L (Sun only) 12.30-2 D 7.30-10. Set L £17.50 Set D £25.50/£27.50.*

Teignmouth — Thomas Luny House — £60

Tel 0626 772976 — **PH**

Teign Street Teignmouth Devon TQ14 8EG — **Map 13 D3**

Built by the marine artist Thomas Luny in the late 18th century, this small Georgian town house has been charmingly restored by the Allans, who now run it as a Wolsey Lodge. This means that one is essentially a guest in their home, socialising with them and fellow guests in the well-appointed drawing room that displays family photos, and sharing the evening meal around a large polished dining table. The simple, carefully prepared set dinner (for residents and their guests only) is a joint effort by John and Alison Allan and there is a short, modestly-priced list of wines from which to choose. Four antique-furnished bedrooms have been decorated with great style and quality and have excellent co-ordinating bathrooms (one has shower and WC only). All rooms have direct-dial telephones and remote-control TV. It all adds up to a delightful alternative to a conventional hotel. Follow signs to the quay and turn into Teign Street just before the port entrance. No children under 12. No dogs. ***Rooms** 4. Garden. Closed mid Dec-mid Jan. No credit cards.*

Telford — Forte Travelodge — £42

Tel 0952 251244 — **L**

Admaston Road Shawbirch Telford Shropshire TF1 3QA — **Map 6 B4**

On the A5223 at the junction of the A442 and B5063, 3 miles from Junction 6 of the M54. 6 miles north-west of Telford. ***Rooms** 40.*
AMERICAN EXPRESS *Access, Visa.*

> We do not accept free meals or hospitality – our inspectors pay their own bills.

Telford — Holiday Inn Telford/Ironbridge — 68% — £108

Tel 0952 292500 Fax 0952 291949 — **H**

St Quentin Gate Telford Shropshire TF3 4EH — **Map 6 B4**

With easy access to the M54 (Junction 4) and town centre, this modern low-riser is adjacent to Telford Racquet and Exhibition Centre. Business centre serves conferences (max 290) and banqueting up to 180. Health and leisure club. ***Rooms** 100. Indoor swimming pool, gymnasium, sauna, spa bath, steam room, solarium.* AMERICAN EXPRESS *Access, Diners, Visa.*

Telford — Madeley Court — 67% — £90

Tel 0952 680068 Fax 0952 684275 — **R**

Madeley Telford Shropshire TF7 5DW — **Map 6 B4**

A striking Elizabethan manor house in extensive grounds just off the A442, recently restored to create an attractive hotel of much character and with serious ambitions. The 16th-century mill has now been converted to provide conference and banqueting facilities for up to 200, and 15 bedrooms have been added. The original (13th-century) hall houses the hotel restaurant, and there's a brasserie in the undercroft. ***Rooms** 47.*
AMERICAN EXPRESS *Access, Diners, Visa.*

Telford **Moat House** 67% £95

Tel 0952 291291 Fax 0952 292012 **H**

Forgegate Telford Shropshire TF3 4NA **Map 6 B4**

Modern hotel with good conference (12 rooms catering for up to 400 delegates) and leisure facilities. Comfortable atrium lounge and Forgegate Bar. Children up to 16 free in parents' room. The hotel is visible from the M54 (junction 5). ***Rooms** 148. Indoor swimming pool, sauna, spa bath, solarium.* American Express *Access, Diners, Visa.*

Telford **Telford Hotel Golf & Country Club** 64% £89

Tel 0952 585642 Fax 0952 586602 **H**

Great Hay Sutton Hill Telford Shropshire TF7 4DT **Map 6 B4**

Standing south of the town centre above Ironbridge Gorge, the hotel combines comfortable, modern accommodation with golf and country club facilities and a state-of-the-art conference centre. Unusually, East meets West in the *Kyoto* restaurant, where ethnic menus are offered. Under-16s stay free in parents' room; good family facilities at weekends (the hotel is convenient for the seven Ironbridge museums), plus a children's menu and play area in the Racquets coffee shop. Queens Moat Houses. ***Rooms** 86. Garden, indoor swimming pool, gymnasium, golf course, golf driving range, spa bath, sauna, solarium, steam room, hairdressing, coffee shop (9am-9.30pm).* American Express *Access, Diners, Visa.*

Telford **Places of Interest**

Tourist Information Tel 0952 291370.
Benthall Hall (NT) Broseley Tel 0952 882159.
Ironbridge Gorge Museum Tel 095 245 3522.
Telford Ice Rink Tel 0952 291511.
Telford Ski Slope Tel 0952 586791.

Tetbury **Calcot Manor** 74% £107

Tel 0666 890391 Fax 0666 890394 **HR**

Tetbury Gloucestershire GL8 8YJ **Map 14 B2**

Actually a former farmhouse complex dating back in part to the 14th century, turned into a charming country hotel. Real log fires warm the civilised lounge, where service is friendly yet discreet. Bedrooms vary in size from the Master and de luxe rooms with antique furniture, to standard and 'small' rooms with pine or painted pieces, but all are individually decorated with the same good taste and are equally well appointed, with good bathrooms – the best with separate showers and bidets. The three most characterful rooms, with exposed beams and natural stone features, are in the separate 'courtyard' wing created out of the former stables. Children are now accommodated but not dogs. The hotel stands at the junction of the A46 and A4135. ***Rooms** 16. Garden, outdoor swimming pool, clay-pigeon shooting.* American Express *Access, Diners, Visa.*

Restaurant £65

New chef Ben Davies has brought a slightly less complex, more modern approach to the cooking here which has also resulted in a lowering of prices. Tagliatelle of mussels, squid and fresh herbs, watercress and sorrel soup topped with curried hollandaise, roast fillet of lemon sole on braised cabbage with a tarragon and tomato dressing, loin of lamb on a stew of lentils with beetroot and vegetable sauce give the style of the fixed-price menus. Dishes on an additional light lunch menu are individually priced. Good selection of about a dozen English and Irish cheeses. No smoking. ***Seats** 40. Parties 25. Private Room 50. L 12.30-2 D 7.30-9.30. Set L £13/£17 Set D £26.*

Tetbury — The Close — 72% — £95

Tel 0666 502272 Fax 0666 504401 — **H**

8 Long Street Tetbury Gloucestershire GL8 8AQ — **Map 14 B2**

Built in the 1700s by a wool merchant, the Close offers a relatively modest face to the main street. More impressive is the rear elevation, which forms one side of a delightful walled garden hidden away from the market-town bustle. New owners and management had various plans as we went to press, including catching up a slight maintenance backlog and replacing some of the antiques and paintings that left with the previous owners. Rag, drag and stipple painting take the eye in the day rooms and in the bedrooms, which vary in size and shape; some feature old beams, none lack in comfort, staff are friendly and there's 24 hr room service. Beds are turned down at night. No dogs. ***Rooms** 15. Garden.* AMERICAN EXPRESS *Access, Diners, Visa.*

Tetbury — Snooty Fox Hotel — 69% — £80

Tel 0666 502436 Fax 0666 503479 — **H**

Market Place Tetbury Gloucestershire GL8 8DD — **Map 14 B2**

A mellowed 16th-century building with steep stone gables and original wooden pillars, the Snooty Fox stands in the town centre opposite the old market hall. Lounge space is plentiful and the two rooms (one for non-smokers) are peaceful and traditional in character with deep sofas, magazines, oil paintings and prints of the Beaufort Hunt, with which the hotel has long associations. The bar, with its imposing copper fire hood, is a contrastingly lively spot. Family antiques and portraits continue the period tone in the individually designed bedrooms, all of which are upstairs – where little extras like a basket of fruit and bottles of mineral water are typical thoughtful touches. The bathrooms are carpeted and light, and boast luxurious bathrobes and towels. No dogs. Hatton Hotels. ***Rooms** 12.* AMERICAN EXPRESS *Access, Diners, Visa.*

Tetbury — Places of Interest

Tourist Information Tel 0666 503552.
Chavenage House Tel 0666 502329.
Beauford Polo Club Down Farm, Westonbirt Tel 0666 88214.

Tewkesbury — Royal Hop Pole — 66% — £105

Tel 0684 293236 Fax 0684 296680 — **H**

Church Street Tewkesbury Gloucestershire GL20 5RT — **Map 14 B1**

One of the smaller hotels in the Forte chain, with a charm all its own. Walled rose gardens run down to the Avon and the hotel's own mooring. Sympathetic conversion has provided an elegant drawing room and rear-facing bar. Best of the bedrooms feature a four-poster and executive extras, but many may plump for the oak-beamed character of the older rear bedrooms, where bathroom space is at a premium. ***Rooms** 29. Garden, mooring.* AMERICAN EXPRESS *Access, Diners, Visa.*

Tewkesbury — Tewkesbury Park — 62% — £98

Tel 0684 295405 Fax 0684 292386 — **H**

Lincoln Green Lane Tewkesbury Gloucestershire GL20 7DN — **Map 14 B1**

Built around an 18th-century mansion, but the atmosphere today is more country club than country house and conferences (up to 150 people) are big business. Well-appointed bedrooms afford views of the Malvern Hills. Good facilities for families with a supervised crèche in the leisure club throughout the week. Children's playroom and playground. No dogs. Country Club Hotels. ***Rooms** 78. Garden, indoor swimming pool, keep-fit equipment, squash, sauna, spa bath, solarium, beauty salon, tennis, golf, snooker, coffee shop (10am-10.30pm).* AMERICAN EXPRESS *Access, Diners, Visa.*

Thame **Spread Eagle** 63% £84

Tel 0844 213661 Fax 0844 261380 **H**

Cornmarket Thame Oxfordshire OX9 2BW **Map 15 D2**

Standing square and proud in the town centre, the 16th-century Spread Eagle has a story that includes playing host to Charles II and captor to French prisoners during the Napoleonic wars. It offers period charm and a variety of accommodation that includes suites and family rooms. Children under 15 are accommodated free of charge in parents' room. Also banqueting suites and syndicate rooms. No dogs. ***Rooms** 33.* AMERICAN EXPRESS *Access, Diners, Visa.*

Thetford **The Bell** 62% £97

Tel 0842 754455 Fax 0842 755552 **H**

King Street Thetford Norfolk IP24 2AZ **Map 10 C2**

An old coaching inn overlooking the Ouse with many architectural features dating back to the 15th century. Bedrooms in the old part are beamed, several boasting four-posters; wing rooms are more up to date. The function facility houses banqueting for 75, conferences up to 90. Forte Heritage. ***Rooms** 47.* AMERICAN EXPRESS *Access, Diners, Visa.*

Thetford **Places of Interest**

Euston Hall Thetford Tel 0842 766377.
Kilverstone Wildlife Park Tel 0842 755369.
Snetterton Motor Racing Circuit Snetterton Tel 095 387 303.

Thornaby-on-Tees **Forte Posthouse** 60% £68

Tel 0642 591213 Fax 0642 594989 **H**

Low Lane By Stainton Village nr Thornaby-on-Tees
Cleveland TS17 9LW **Map 5 E3**

An older-style Posthouse in the village of Stainton. All bedrooms were refurbished in 1992. Conferences for up to 120 delegates. ***Rooms** 135.* *Garden, sauna, solarium.* AMERICAN EXPRESS *Access, Diners, Visa.*

Thornbury **Thornbury Castle** 80% £150

Tel 0454 281182 Fax 0454 416188 **H**

Thornbury nr Bristol Avon BS12 1HH **Map 13 F1**

Henry VIII slept with Ann Boleyn at this authentic Tudor castle which today combines atmosphere and history with modern comforts. Bedrooms, some reached via stone spiral staircases, are full of character with many original features. The most recently renovated rooms are the most Tudor in style with embroidered fabrics, solid oak furniture, open (gas log) fires and exposed stone work; others feature pretty co-ordinating colour schemes and antique pieces. All have good bathrooms and little extras like fruit and a decanter of sherry. Baronial public rooms gain even more atmosphere when numerous candles are lit each evening. ***Rooms** 18.* *Garden, helipad.* AMERICAN EXPRESS *Access, Diners, Visa.*

Thornton Heath **Mamma Adele** £50

Tel 081-683 2233 **R**

23 Brigstock Road Thornton Heath Surrey CR7 7JJ **Map 11 B5**

An agreeable little family restaurant with a real taste of Italy. Kam Memon runs front of house with urbane good humour, and Adele is always happy to prepare a full meal or just a plate of pasta (the latter includes not only familiar variations but some one-offs such as vodka and Stilton). Seasonal specials add to the choice, and there's always something for vegetarians. The

See over

wine list includes plenty of decent Italian bottles. ***Seats** 32. L by arrangment with 24 hours notice D 6.30-10.30 (Sat 7-11.30). Closed Sun, Bank Holidays, all Jan. Access, Visa.*

Thornton-le-Fylde — River House — £75

Tel 0253 883497 Fax 0253 892083 — **RR**

Skippool Creek Thornton-le-Fylde nr Blackpool Lancashire FY5 5LF — **Map 6 A1**

The change of category (from Inn to Restaurant with Rooms) does not indicate any changes here but rather an attempt to describe more accurately Bill Scott's most individual establishment. Built for a gentleman farmer in the 1830s the house has a charming setting opposite Skippool Creek –the road outside floods at spring tides – and boasts a pubby bar (for diners and residents only), plant-filled conservatory, antiques, objets d'art, three dogs and various cats but it's the dark green dining room that is at the heart of things. Fresh fish from nearby Fleetwood is always well represented on a menu that might include a soufflé Suissesse, scallops in a creamy wine and herb sauce, gravad lax, rare breast of duck (locally reared by Mrs Sykes) with green peppercorn and orange sauce, bloody young grouse with redcurrant sauce (overcooked meat is an abomination according to Bill, but if you insist …) and salmon teriyaki. The enthusiastic yet unfussy cooking is a combined effort with Bill looking after the meat and fish, wife Carole the starters and sauces and Karen Jones some excellent puds like ticky tacky pudding (hot date and walnut pudding with butterscotch sauce) and individual apple tarts. Everything is home-made from the nibbles with the menu to the chocolates served with some good coffees and a wide range of loose-leaf teas and infusions. Not the easiest wine list to select from, but it's certainly interesting and has many bin ends worth choosing from. ***Seats** 40. Private Room 40. L by arrangement D 7.30-9.30. Closed D Sun, some Bank Holidays. Set L £12.75 Set D £20. Access, Visa.*

Rooms — £100

More antiques and knick-knacks in four bedrooms that combine modern comforts like remote-control TV and direct-dial phone – with an old-fashioned feel. Bathrooms (two en-suite and one across the corridor) offer good toiletries and generous towelling and two have splendid old Victorian hooded tubs. The smallest bedroom has an en-suite shower but its loo is down the hall. *Garden.*

Thrapston — Forte Travelodge — £42

Tel 0801 25199 — **L**

Thrapston Bypass Thrapston Northamptonshire — **Map 7 E4**

On the A14 (the new A1/M1 link road), 8 miles east of Kettering. Corby 8 miles, Wellingborough 10 miles. ***Rooms** 40.* AMERICAN EXPRESS *Access, Visa.*

Thrussington — Forte Travelodge — £42

Tel 0664 424525 — **L**

Thrussington Green Acres filling stations Thrussington Leicestershire LE7 8TF — **Map 7 D3**

On the A46 southbound, 8 miles north of Leicester city centre. ***Rooms** 32.* AMERICAN EXPRESS *Access, Visa.*

Thundridge — Hanbury Manor — 79% — £180

Tel 0920 487722 Fax 0920 487692 — **HR**

Thundridge nr Ware Hertfordshire SG12 0SD — **Map 15 F2**

By the A10, in 200 acres of parkland that include a 30-acre arboretum, Hanbury Manor is a late 19th-century house built in the Jacobean style, converted recently into a fine, modern country house hotel and sporting complex. The style and character of the old building have been greatly enhanced with well-chosen fabrics and furnishings. Wonderful carved panelling and wall tapestries in the Oak Hall give a real taste of the past, while an elegant and comfortable cocktail bar features a hand-painted ceiling. The Library also has a fine marble fireplace and views over the golf course. Sumptuous furnishings, fine-quality fabrics, period furniture and marble bathrooms make the bedrooms exceptional; some rooms are in the Manor house, others in the smart Garden Court annexe, built in sympathetic style. Superb leisure facilities, including a palatial swimming pool and a magnificent 18-hole (par 72) golf course. Conference and banqueting facilities for up to 138 in a selection of ten rooms including the unusual Poles Hall. 25 miles from central London. A Rockresort hotel. ***Rooms** 96. Garden, golf, tennis, squash, putting, indoor swimming pool, spa bath, sauna, solarium, snooker, gymnasium, riding, beautician, crèche, news kiosk, helipad.* AMERICAN EXPRESS *Access, Diners, Visa.*

Zodiac Restaurant and Conservatory ↑ £115

Light snacks may be taken in all-day *Vardon's* above the health club or longer lunches in the light and airy Conservatory restaurant (where breakfast is also served) with views over the golf course. More formal dinners are offered in the elegant Zodiac Restaurant where chef Rory Kennedy (in consultation with Albert Roux) offers a complex à la carte (with more than the odd touch from *Le Gavroche*). Consommé of quail with a paysanne of herb pasta, oysters and foie gras poached with vermouth, roast lobster with garlic, thyme and spring vegetables, lamb cutlets with sweetbreads, garlic and basil, pigeon and cauliflower with star anise, magret of duck with olives and braised shallots give the style. Pleasing, all-round wine list with plenty of half bottles; could be improved with some tasting notes. Sunday brunch in *Vardon's* and a ***menu du jour*** in Zodiac; Conservatory closed in the evenings. ***Seats** 40. Parties 8. L 12-3 D 7-10. Closed D Sun. Set L £19.50 Set D £25.*

Thurlestone — Thurlestone Hotel 69% £160

Tel 0548 560382 Fax 0548 561069 **H**

Thurlestone Kingsbridge Devon TQ7 3NN **Map 13 D3**

The elegance of the 20s combines with the amenities of the 90s in a handsome family-owned hotel in a lovely setting with spectacular sea views. Splendidly geared to family holidays, with an excellent leisure club, it also has an off-peak trade in small conferences (for up to 100). Day rooms make the most of the location, likewise half the smart, well-equipped bedrooms. Children up to 12 can stay free of charge in their parents' room. ***Rooms** 68. Garden, indoor & outdoor swimming pools, keep-fit equipment, squash, sauna, sun bed, beauty salon, hairdressing, tennis, golf (9), putting, badminton, games room, coffee shop (8am-10pm). Access, Visa.*

Thurrock — Granada Lodge £55

Tel 0708 891111 Fax 0708 860971 **L**

M25 Junction 30/31 Dartford Crossing Thurrock Essex RM16 3BG **Map 11 B5**

***Rooms** 35.* AMERICAN EXPRESS *Access, Diners, Visa.*

Tickton — Tickton Grange 62% £56

Tel 0964 543666 Fax 0964 542556 **H**

Tickton nr Beverley Humberside HU17 9SH **Map 7 E1**

A family-owned Georgian house standing just off the A1035 east of Beverley in 3½ acres of rose gardens, where afternoon teas are served in the summer. Day rooms retain a traditional appeal, and bedrooms are decorated in a fresh, light style. There are two suites, one with a Georgian four-poster bed. Tickton truffles are offered as a welcome. The Whymant family run the hotel along friendly and informal lines. ***Rooms** 16. Garden.* AMERICAN EXPRESS *Access, Diners, Visa.*

Tintagel Trebrea Lodge 66% NEW £60

Tel 0840 770410 **HR**

Trenale Tintagel Cornwall PL34 0HR **Map 12 B2**

A little inland from the village on a slight rise, this civilised country hotel dates back to 600 years, although the facade is Georgian. It's furnished throughout with antiques (one of the partners owns an antique shop in London); there's an elegant and sunny first-floor drawing room and cosy 'honesty' bar (the only place in the house where one may smoke) where a log fire burns for most of the year. Appealing bedrooms, all enjoying fine views across fields to the sea in the distance, are individually decorated in 'designer' style with good bathrooms; about half have shower and WC only. No children under 5. ***Rooms*** *7.* AMERICAN EXPRESS *Access, Visa.*

Restaurant £40

Dinner, served at 8pm in the small candle-lit oak panelled dining room, is a simple no-choice affair that allows the excellent, often local, ingredients to speak for themselves. A typical menu might be avocado and bacon salad followed by sea trout with hollandaise sauce and blackberry cream pots and cheese to finish. Just a dozen wines to choose from with no half bottles but good house wine available by the glass. No smoking. No children under 5. ***Seats*** *16. Set D £13.75.*

Tiverton Forte Travelodge £42

Tel 0884 821087 **L**

Sampford Peverell Service Area M5 Junction 27 nr Tiverton Devon EX16 4LY **Map 13 D2**

At Junction 27 of the M5. 7 miles east of Tiverton. ***Rooms 40.*** AMERICAN EXPRESS *Access, Visa.*

> We endeavour to be as up-to-the-minute as possible, but inevitably some changes to key personnel may occur at restaurants and hotels after the Guide goes to press.

Toddington Granada Lodge £45

Tel 0525 875150 Fax 0525 875358 **L**

Toddington service area M1 Southbound nr Dunstable Bedfordshire LU5 6HR **Map 15 E1**

Rooms *43.* AMERICAN EXPRESS *Access, Diners, Visa.*

Tonbridge Goldhill Mill NEW £60

Tel 0732 851626 Fax 0732 851881 **PH**

Golden Green nr Hadlow Tonbridge Kent TN11 0BA **Map 11 B5**

Check directions when booking at this superior bed-and-breakfast hotel with luxurious accommodation. It enjoys an idyllic location beside a river surrounded by twenty acres including mature gardens and freshwater crayfish ponds (a breakfast speciality in summer months). Amiable hosts Shirley and Vernon Cole ensure that you relax in what has been their family home since the late 1930s. The house is stylishly decorated – a kitchen (used for breakfast) resplendent with working mill wheel, a drawing room with wood-burning stove, a small TV/video lounge. Three individually decorated bedrooms beautifully furnished in chintzy soft furnishings offer an abundance of extras, remote-control TVs, fruit bowls and fresh floral displays. One room has a four-poster. Lavishly appointed bathrooms include jacuzzi baths in two rooms and excellent toiletries. ***Rooms*** *3. Garden, tennis. Access, Visa.*

Tonbridge — Rose & Crown — 59% — £97

Tel 0732 357966 Fax 0732 357194 — H

125 High Street Tonbridge Kent TN9 1DD — Map 11 B5

A 16th-century coaching inn with traditionally furnished bedrooms in the old part, modern rooms (non-smoking) in the garden wing. Conference/banqueting facilities for 110/80. Forte Heritage. ***Rooms*** *50. Garden.* AMERICAN EXPRESS *Access, Diners, Visa.*

Torquay — Grand Hotel — 69% — £108

Tel 0803 296677 Fax 0803 213462 — H

Sea Front Torquay Devon TQ2 6NT — Map 13 D3

Commanding a superb position overlooking Torbay, the Grand is an impressive, turreted Edwardian building whose grounds include a lido with heated swimming pool. Most of the bedrooms enjoy sea views and some have balconies. 12 rooms are suitable for family use. As we went to press, a full refurbishment programme was nearing completion. Additions include a gymnasium and snooker room. ***Rooms*** *112. Garden, indoor & outdoor swimming pools, keep-fit equipment, sauna, spa bath, solarium, hair salon, tennis, coffee shop (10-6).* AMERICAN EXPRESS *Access, Visa.*

Torquay — Homers Hotel — 63% — £98

Tel 0803 213456 Fax 0803 213458 — H

Warren Road Torquay Devon TQ2 5TN — Map 13 D3

Pamela and Derek Oatley are former regular guests who bought the hotel in 1989, and have carefully refurbished the interior in an individual comfortable style. Chandeliers and gilt cornices reflect the building's Victorian origins (it was built into the rock face about 150 years ago), and the residents' bar in a recessed alcove adds an intimate atmosphere. Though many bathrooms are a bit small, the bedrooms, one with a fine four-poster, are generally good-sized; best of all are those with splendid views over Torbay. Private conference/dining facilities for up to 50. No children under 12. ***Rooms*** *15. Garden.* AMERICAN EXPRESS *Access, Diners, Visa.*

Torquay — Imperial Hotel — 81% — £160

Tel 0803 294301 Fax 0803 298293 — H

Parkhill Road Torquay Devon TQ1 2DG — Map 13 D3

Opened as a resort hotel in 1866, and much favoured by royalty in the years that followed, the Imperial still operates on a grand scale. From the pink-pillared foyer, through palatial lounges to the Pool Terrace, overlooking the sweep of Torbay, both decor and appointments set out to impress. The hotel attracts many regulars and the Torbay suite is increasingly popular for conferences and banqueting with a capacity of 350. Light, bright bedrooms contain good-quality furniture and fabrics: most have sea views and private balconies. A major refurbishment programme has recently been under way; the restaurant has been completed and public areas were about to receive attention as we went to press. Leisure facilities are extensive, and there's dancing six nights a week in high season (Fri & Sat rest of year) to a resident band. ***Rooms*** *167. Garden, indoor & outdoor swimming pools, sauna, solarium, whirlpool bath, gym, tennis, squash, snooker.* AMERICAN EXPRESS *Access, Diners, Visa.*

We welcome bona fide complaints and recommendations on the tear-out pages at the back of the book for readers' comments. They are followed up by our professional team.

Torquay — Livermead Cliff Hotel — 60% — £80

Tel 0803 299666 Fax 0803 294496 — H

Sea Front Torquay Devon TQ2 6RQ — **Map 13 D3**

Right by the sea, with direct access to the beach and popular for family holidays. From the M5, take the A379 to Torquay, follow the A3022 through town to the seafront. Turn right for Paignton and the hotel is 600 yards along on the seaward side. It's geared up to the conference trade (for up to 70 delegates), so it's quite a busy place all year round. Picture windows in the lounge look out to sea. Parents with offspring are well catered for with cots, baby-sitting, baby-listening and children's high tea available. Good housekeeping, friendly staff. ***Rooms** 64. Garden, outdoor swimming pool, solarium, laundry room.* AMERICAN EXPRESS *Access, Diners, Visa.*

Torquay — Livermead House — 60% — £88

Tel 0803 294361 Fax 0803 200758 — H

Sea Front Torquay Devon TQ2 6QJ — **Map 13 D3**

A popular guest house in the last century, where author Charles Kingsley once stayed. Today's Livermead House, under the personal direction of the Rew family, lives on as a thoroughly modern hotel. Picture windows afford panoramic sea views beyond the pool and tennis court, and there's plenty of activity indoors on rainy days. Conferences (max 100) and banqueting (140) are kept discreetly separate from private guests. No dogs. ***Rooms** 64. Garden, outdoor swimming pool, keep-fit equipment, squash, sauna, solarium, tennis, putting, snooker.* AMERICAN EXPRESS *Access, Diners, Visa.*

Torquay — Osborne Hotel — 65% — £110

Tel 0803 213311 Fax 0803 296788 — H

Hesketh Crescent Meadfoot Beach Torquay Devon TQ1 2LL — **Map 13 D3**

Careful renovation has kept some of the original feel at the Osborne, which stands at the centre of Torquay's best example of Regency architecture (ask for directions when booking). Day rooms include a high-ceilinged lounge bar, a long-hours brasserie/wine bar and a library that's used for meetings. Bedrooms – named not numbered – are smart and spacious, with seating areas and plenty of creature comforts. As well as the bedrooms there are several luxury apartments. No dogs. ***Rooms** 23. Garden, indoor & outdoor swimming pools, keep-fit equipment, sauna, spa bath, solarium, tennis, brasserie (10.30am-11pm). Access, Visa.*

Torquay — Palace Hotel — 68% — £110

Tel 0803 200200 Fax 0803 299899 — H

Babbacombe Road Torquay Devon TQ1 3TG — **Map 13 D3**

Once the home of the Bishops of Exeter, the Palace, set in 25 acres of gardens and woodland stretching to the sea, opened in 1921 as a hotel offering some of the finest sporting facilities in the land. It still provides admirably for the active guest (golf, swimming, tennis and squash professionals on hand), but the roomy and elegant lounges hold equal appeal for moments (or hours!) of quiet relaxation. Music or entertainment is provided nightly, and families are very well catered for. Out of season the hotel is often busy with conferences (handling up to 450 delegates theatre style and offering a full range of services). Six large bedroom suites have splendid views, individual decor and good-quality furniture; other rooms are simpler but comfortable with handsome period bathrooms. No dogs. ***Rooms** 140. Garden, indoor & outdoor swimming pools, squash, sauna, hairdressing, indoor & outdoor tennis, 9-hole golf course, snooker, nanny, children's playroom. Access, Diners, Visa.*

Torquay **Table Restaurant** £73

Tel 0803 324292 **R**

135 Babbacombe Road Babbacombe Torquay Devon TQ1 3SR **Map 13 D3**

A little gem of a restaurant just out of town with Trevor Brooks in the kitchen and the efficient and charming Jane Corrigan out front. So many things are done very well, with the saucing and seasoning of dishes particularly noteworthy, and the vegetables that accompany the main courses perfectly cooked. The menu – fixed-price with five or so choices at each course – offers the likes of rabbit, ham and yellow pea terrine with watercress mayonnaise, sesame seed crepe with home-smoked salmon and horseradish lime fondue to start, followed by saddle of venison with orange and bay leaf sauce and hazelnut spätzle or breast of duck with tarragon jus and fried polenta; finish with a delectable assortment of desserts, perhaps including open apple strudel with Kirsch sabayon or poached pears with saffron ice cream. There is usually a good selection of traditional farmhouse cheeses that varies seasonally. Sweetmeats served with coffee. A variety of half bottles features on the wine list, which lists bottles by character. No children under 10. ***Seats** 20. D only 7.30-10 (Sun to 9.30). Closed Mon, Bank Holidays, 2 weeks Feb, 2 weeks Sept. Set D £26. Access, Visa.*

Torquay **Places of Information**

Tourist Information Tel 0803 297428.
Torre Abbey Tel 0803 293593 *Includes Dame Agatha Christie Memorial Room.*
Wessex Ski Club Tel 0803 313350.
Odicombe, Anstey's Cove and Meadfoot Beaches.

Towcester **Forte Travelodge** £42

Tel 0327 359105 **L**

East Towcester Bypass Towcester Northamptonshire NN12 0DD **Map 15 D1**

Off Junction 15A of the M1 towards Oxford, on the A43, 8 miles south of Northampton. ***Rooms** 33.* AMERICAN EXPRESS *Access, Visa.*

Tresco **Island Hotel** 67% £170*

Tel 0720 22883 Fax 0720 23008 **HR**

Tresco Isles of Scilly TR24 0PU **Map 12 A2**

Tresco, England's "Island of Flowers", is privately owned and maintained, its lanes free of traffic. Guests arriving at the quay or heliport (from Penzance) are transported by tractor-drawn charabanc to the island's only hotel, set in beautifully tended gardens by the shore. Picture windows make the most of this spectacular location and the panoramic sea views: should the mists close in there's a Terrace Bar and a Quiet Room stacked with books, magazines and games. Special holiday packages for gardeners, bird-watchers and others. *Half-board terms only. ***Rooms** 40. Garden, outdoor swimming pool, fishing, boating, bowling green, games room. Closed Nov-Feb.* AMERICAN EXPRESS *Access, Visa.*

Restaurant £60

Table d'hote and à la carte menus place strong emphasis on local seafood (Scillonian scallops, Bryher crab), and there's Devonshire beef from the grill and a cold buffet. Traditional farmhouse cheeses. Luxurious Sunday buffet (including lobster). Children under 12 can eat half-price from the carte. No smoking. ***Seats** 95. Private Room 10. L 12-2 D 7-9.30. Set D £24.*

Tresco **Place of Interest**

Tresco Abbey Gardens Tel 0720 22849.

Tring — Travel Inn — £43

Tel 0442 824819 Fax 0442 890787 — L

Tring Hill Tring Hertfordshire HP23 4LD — **Map 15 E2**

***Rooms** 30.* AMERICAN EXPRESS *Access, Diners, Visa.*

Troutbeck — Mortal Man Inn — £100*

Tel 053 94 33193 Fax 053 94 31261 — I

Troutbeck nr Windermere Cumbria LA23 1PL — **Map 4 C3**

A bright, well-cared-for inn of 17th-century origins, with an established reputation for hospitality (owner Christopher Poulsom has been here since 1974). Join the regulars in the Village bar or relax in the residents' bar and sunny lounge overlooking the Troutbeck Valley. Bedrooms are smart, bathrooms compact and housekeeping praiseworthy. No children under five. * Half-board terms only. ***Rooms** 12. Garden. Closed mid Nov-mid Feb. No credit cards.*

Troutbeck — Place of Interest

Holebird Garden Tel 09662 6238.

Truro — Alverton Manor — 70% — £90

Tel 0872 76633 Fax 0872 222989 — H

Tregolls Road Truro Cornwall TR1 1XQ — **Map 12 B3**

An impressive Victorian Gothic building on the edge of town; part of what was once a convent, the chapel is now a novel function room. Conferences are an important part of the hotel's business. Apart from the restaurant, the only day room is an elegantly proportioned and comfortable lounge that also incorporates the bar, although the soft furnishings are showing signs of wear in places. Excellent, individually decorated bedrooms are the great strength here with stylish fabrics, good-quality reproduction antique furniture and extras like sherry and mineral water. Bathrooms, three with shower and WC only, are equally good, with robes and generous towelling. Service is extensive in that rooms are properly serviced in the evenings and there is a 24hr room service, but it lacks polish and the sense of direction that more professional management would bring. ***Rooms** 25. Garden, games room.* AMERICAN EXPRESS *Access, Diners, Visa.*

Truro — Places of Interest

Tourist Information Tel 0872 74555.
City Hall Tel 0872 76461.
Trelissick Garden (NT) Tel 0872 862090.
Trewithen House and Gardens Probus Tel 0726 882764.
Truro Cathedral Tel 0872 76782.
Flambards Theme Park Culdrose Manor Tel 0326 574549.

Tuckenhay — Floyd's Inn (Sometimes) — £100

Tel 0803 732350 Fax 0803 732651 — RR

Bow Creek Tuckenhay Totnes Devon TQ9 7EQ — **Map 13 D3**

Shaunagh and Keith (of TV fame) Floyd's delightfully rusticated pub dates back to 1550 and enjoys an idyllic location on the quayside of a very pretty wooded creek. The menu in the bar (at road level) divides between 'Canteen Snacks' (where caviar sits rather uneasily alongside egg and chips and beans on toast at 'market price') and 'Floyd's Far Flung Feasts' – a truly eclectic mix covering grilled kipper, iced gaspacho, Asian steamboat, Malaysian beef rendang, Cork-style bacon and cabbage with parsley sauce, and sherry trifle. In the newly opened restaurant an elaborate (and expensive) table d'hote is also offered. Lunchtimes in summer, weather permitting, there's a barbecue with tables down on the quayside. 'We

do not serve half portions' proclaims the menu. Three bedrooms were on line to open as we went to press. The name may be jokey, but the intentions are serious; nevertheless, its popularity can push service and standards to the limits of acceptability – arrive early or expect a long wait! This used to be called the *Maltster's Arms* – one of several in the neighbourhood, causing confusion. ***Seats** 26. Parties 6. L 12-2 D 7-9.*
Closed L Sat, D Sun and all Tue. Set L £25 Set D £42.50. Access, Visa.

Tunbridge Wells — Cheevers — £60

Tel 0892 545524 — **R**

56 High Street Tunbridge Wells Kent TN1 1XF — **Map 11 B5**

Cool decor, crisp white tablecloths, good tableware and quiet, professional service create the ambience, while Tim Cheevers provides the good food to complement it. He sticks to what he knows best and carefully sources ingredients for dishes that are both fresh and imaginative: mussel and fennel broth, mousseline of scallops, John Dory baked with cider, Barbary duck with apple and celeriac, rack of lamb with a mint and almond crust. Typical desserts are lemon tart and hot walnut and ginger pudding. A la carte at lunchtime, fixed-price menu at dinner; both menus offer a choice of around six dishes per course. Short, mixed-up wine list with a first-rate choice of half bottles. Martin Miles runs front of house with a smile for everyone. ***Seats** 32. Parties 12. L 12.30-2 (Sat to 1.45) D 7.30-10.30.*
Closed Sun & Mon, Bank Holidays, 2 weeks Jan. Set D £22.50.
American Express *Access, Visa.*

Tunbridge Wells — Downstairs at Thackeray's — £45

Tel 0892 537559 — **R**

85 London Road Tunbridge Wells Kent TN1 1EA — **Map 11 B5**

Downstairs, with its own courtyard entrance, this delightful little place with cosy, close-set tables and fresh flowers has the friendly relaxed feel of a bistro. Dishes are varied and imaginative, ranging from *zampone* with Puy lentils and haggis with apples and cider sauce to roast grey mullet with garlic butter, and braised ham with prunes in red wine at lunchtime (plus tapas-style 'nibbles'). Dinner sees an extended menu that covers all the above plus Loch Fyne oysters, pigeon breast with blackcurrants, Rye cod with Dijon mustard and breadcrumbs, and good desserts. 15 wines under £15. Booking advised. ***Seats** 30. L 12.30-2.30 D 7.30-9.30.*
Closed Sun & Mon, Bank Holidays, 1 week Christmas. Set L £5.90/£8.75.
Access, Visa.

Tunbridge Wells — Royal Wells Inn — 64% — £80

Tel 0892 511188 Fax 0892 511908 — **H**

Mount Ephraim Tunbridge Wells Kent TN4 8BE — **Map 11 B5**

The royal coat of arms atop the family-run Royal Wells is a proud memento of the days when, during her childhood, Queen Victoria used to stay here. Inside, there's a stylish reception/lounge with columns, marble-effect wallcoverings and matching fabrics as well as a light and attractive bar area. Best bedrooms are on the top floor – these have brass beds, quality pine furniture, Laura Ashley fabrics and up-to-date, tiled bathrooms; two rooms have four-posters. The hotel bus is a 1909 Commer. Conference/banquet facilities for 100/90. ***Rooms** 22.* American Express *Access, Diners, Visa.*

Tunbridge Wells — Spa Hotel — 72% — £84

Tel 0892 520331 Fax 0892 510575 — **HR**

Mount Ephraim Tunbridge Wells Kent TN4 8XJ — **Map 11 B5**

Sister hotel to *The Goring* in London, the Spa stands in 15 acres of gardens and parkland that include two lakes. It was built in 1766 and has been run as a hotel by the same family since 1880. The foyer opens on to a spacious *See over* lounge with Corinthian columns, darkwood panelling and a gas log fire at each end; half is reserved for non-smokers. The Equestrian Bar is a favourite place for a drink or bar food. Bedrooms vary in size and decor, the older ones having woodchip wallpaper, but all feature freestanding furniture (many finished in burr walnut). De luxe rooms have king-sized beds and tend to be larger, with views across several acres of informal parkland gardens. Although conferences (for up to 340) form most of the weekday business, there is an atmosphere of a moderately grand hotel run along traditional lines, with fine leisure facilities and an emphasis on good service from friendly staff. Children up to 14 free in parents' room. ***Rooms*** *76. Garden, indoor swimming pool, gymnasium, sauna, spa bath, solarium, beauty & hair salon, tennis, games room, children's adventure playground.* AMERICAN EXPRESS *Access, Diners, Visa.*

Chandelier Restaurant — £60

Large, high-ceilinged Regency dining room where good-quality produce is best enjoyed in the simpler dishes and lunchtime roasts carved and served formally from a trolley. Lighter, individually-priced dishes are also served at lunchtime in the lounge and bar; more elaborate, but limited, à la carte and table d'hote dinner menus. ***Seats*** *90. L 12.30-2 D 7-9.30. Closed L Sat.*

Tunbridge Wells — Thackeray's House ★ — £90

Tel 0892 511921 — **R**

85 London Road Tunbridge Wells Kent TN11 1EA — **Map 11 B5**

In the green and white clapboard house that was once Thackeray's home, chef Bruce Wass has been presenting carefully prepared versions of classical dishes for ten years. A great deal of care and attention to detail goes into his dishes and there are various price options among the menus. Lightly curried parsnip soup with coriander and orange, soft game paté with toasted brioche or croustade of scallops and skate could get your meal under way, followed perhaps by pigeon breasts with blackcurrants, roast fillet of cod with parsley pesto sauce or stuffed pig's trotters with Puy lentils. Finish in some style with a selection of farmhouse cheeses or a walnut and ginger pudding with toffee sauce. Interesting house and Italian selections on a well-compiled wine list that includes over 50 half bottles. ***Seats*** *36. Private Room 50. L 12.30-2.30 D 7-10 (Downstairs open all day daily). Closed D Sun, all Mon, Bank Holidays, 1 week Christmas. Set L £10/£15 Set D £19.85. Access, Visa.*

Tunbridge Wells — Places of Interest

Tourist Information Tel 0892 515675.
Assembly Hall Tel 0892 30613.
Trinity Arts Centre Tel 0892 44699.
Neville Road Cricket Ground Tel 0892 20846.
Bowles Outdoor Pursuits Centre Tel 0892 64127.

Historic Houses, Castles and Gardens

Scotney Castle Garden (NT) Lamberhurst Tel 0892 890651.
Penshurst Place Penshurst, Tonbridge Tel 0892 870307.
Moorlands Gardens Friars Gate, Nr Crowborough Tel 0892 652474.

Turners Hill — Alexander House — 79% — £165

Tel 0342 714914 Fax 0342 717328 — **HR**

East Street Turners Hill West Sussex RH10 4QD — **Map 11 B5**

A retirement home for the clergy between 1953 and 1984, this imposing country mansion stands in 135 acres on the B2110. Distinguished buildings have occupied the site since the 14th century and the oldest part of the present house dates from the early 17th century. Numerous grand day rooms feature many high-quality antiques, paintings (including *A Jamaica Bay* by Noel Coward) and other decorative features like the painted silk chinoiserie panels in the main salon and a pair of ornate French ormolu lamps in the foyer. Many bedrooms have traditional yew furniture and boast original paintings plus many little extras like fresh flowers, fruit and magazines. Smart, friendly staff. No children under 7. Handy for Gatwick (9 miles). ***Rooms** 14. Garden, hairdressing, tennis, helipad, snooker, limousine service, valeting.* AMERICAN EXPRESS *Access, Diners, Visa.*

Restaurant

£120

An elegant room in a striking shade of pinky orange with a level of service from attentive staff (some in tail-coats) and quality of tableware (fine Royal Worcester china) that one is entitled to expect at this price level. Smoothly professional cooking is accomplished rather than inspired with attractively presented dishes such as a warm asparagus mousse with truffles; fricassee of scallops with tagliatelle; loin of lamb with ravioli of tomatoes, mint and garlic; and a roulade of chicken with a mousse of peppers and a shallot confit. A nicely varied dessert list ranges from pear tart with Poire William sorbet and chocolate and Grand Marnier soufflé to Spotted Dick with hazelnuts and vanilla ice cream. ***Seats** 60. Private Room 55. L 12.30-2 D 7.30-9.30 (Sun to 9). Set L £18.50 (Sun £22.50) Set D £35.*

Tutbury — Ye Olde Dog & Partridge Inn

£70

Tel 0283 813030 Fax 0283 813178

I

High Street Tutbury nr Burton-on-Trent Staffordshire DE13 9LS — **Map 6 C3**

In the middle of the main village street, the inn has kept much of its 15th-century character, and its half-timbered frontage with diamond-leaded windows is a pretty subject for a picture postcard. There are two traditional bars and a restaurant where a busy buffet and carvery operate and a pianist plays nightly. Three bedrooms with black-and-white panelling and creaking floorboards are in the main building, the rest in an adjacent Georgian house with a central spiral staircase. ***Rooms** 17. Garden. Closed 25 & 26 Dec.* AMERICAN EXPRESS *Access, Visa.*

> Our inspectors *never* book in the name of Egon Ronay's Guides. They disclose their identity only if they are considering an establishment for inclusion in the next edition of the Guide.

Twickenham — Cézanne's Restaurant

£50

Tel 081-892 3526

R

68 Richmond Road Twickenham Middlesex TW1 3BE — **Map 15 E2**

Formerly *Café Cézanne*, now with a new chef (ex-*Savoy*) and more up-market menus. From one of his early menus come crab, ginger and sweetcorn-filled samosas with tomato coulis; maize-fed chicken with morilles and Jura wine sauce; and lamb with roast garlic, aubergine and honey. ***Seats** 38. Parties 50. L 12.30-2 D 7-10.30 (Fri & Sat to 11). Closed L Sat, all Sun, Bank Holidays.* AMERICAN EXPRESS *Access, Diners, Visa.*

Twickenham — Hamiltons

£50

Tel 081-892 3949

R

43 Crown Road St Margarets Twickenham Middlesex TW1 3EJ — **Map 15 E2**

Inviting setting with stained-glass windows, painted brick walls and a menu with the likes of salmon and monkfish terrine with gazpacho mayonnaise, poached pear with cheese and herb paté and a tarragon sauce, steak and vegetable or fish pie, wholemeal pancakes filled with wild mushrooms and leeks, and bananas baked with rum and butterscotch sauce. Tuesday to Friday lunchtimes see a fixed-price menu with soup or salad to start followed by just one daily-changing dish. Live jazz during family Sunday lunchtimes. ***Seats** 40. Private Room 8. L 12-2.30 D 7-11. Closed L Sat, D Sun, all Mon, 1 week New Year. Set L £10.95 (£14.50 Sun).* AMERICAN EXPRESS *Access, Visa.*

Twickenham McClements ★ £70

Tel 081-755 0176 Fax 081-890 1372 **R**

12 The Green Twickenham Middlesex TW2 5AA **Map 15 E2**

In his pretty little French restaurant opposite Twickenham Green John McClements produces dishes that look good and taste even better. His velouté of oysters is a well-established favourite among the starters, along with scallops (on our last visit they came grilled with their coral, roast endives and a delicate Sauternes sauce). Fresh crab salad with basil dressing, mixed leaves and artichokes is a dish of deceptive simplicity, while more obviously elaborate is a confit of rabbit leg filled with ham and foie gras. Meticulous preparation and timing are evident in fillet of turbot with lobster and noodles, and in veal shank, braised slowly in white wine to perfect tenderness but before the usual osso buco-style disintegration stage. Artistically arranged little vegetables complete a thoroughly accomplished main course. There's usually a quartet of desserts (soufflé with ice cream or Calvados sauce, pyramid of tiny choux buns with chocolate sauce and zabaglione iced parfait) and a plated assortment of French cheeses. Coffee and beautiful petits fours round off a classy meal served with the right blend of gravity and good humour in what really is a little gem of a restaurant. John McClements was due to open a brasserie at 2 Whitton Road, Twickenham after we went to press; the food will be modish in style. ***Seats*** *14. Parties 8. Private Room 20. L 12-2.30 D 7-10 (Sat to 10.30). Closed L Sat, all Sun. Set L & D £19.50. Access, Visa.*

Uckfield Horsted Place 79% £140

Tel 0825 750581 Fax 0825 750459 **HR**

Little Horsted Uckfield East Sussex TN22 5TS **Map 11 B6**

Off the A26 to the south of Uckfield, Horsted Place is a fine example of high-Victorian architecture with its distinctive chequered brickwork, splendidly exuberant Pugin staircase and grounds laid out by Geoffrey Jellicoe. Day rooms, which are off an elegant central hall running the length of the house, include a library and large lounge, boasting two real fires in winter, just refurbished in rich shades appropriate to the period of the house. Individually decorated in some style, bedrooms vary somewhat in size but all are furnished with good reproduction antiques and offer all sorts of comforts from books and magazines to fruit and mineral water. Guests have access to the adjacent championship golf course (under the same ownership as the hotel and home to the European Open for the next four years) and Glyndebourne is just five minutes down the road. ***Rooms*** *17. Garden, indoor swimming pool, tennis, golf (18).* AMERICAN EXPRESS *Access, Diners, Visa.*

Pugin Dining Room £95

Designed by the eponymous architect (also responsible for the Houses of Parliament) in one of his more restrained moments, this luxuriously appointed dining room is an appropriate setting for Allan Garth's sensibly short menu of dishes that are a well-judged balance between interest, lack of complication and modern trends. Rabbit salad with balsamic vinegar dressing and deep-fried vegetables; ballotine of foie gras with Sauternes jelly and hot brioche toast; roast rib of beef with béarnaise sauce and shallot jus; pigeon with brown lentils, confit of garlic and port sauce, and a gratin of rhubarb with Grand Marnier sauce exemplify the style. ***Seats*** *30. Parties 12. Private Room 22. L 12.30-2 D 7.30-9.30. Set L £18.50 Set D £28.50.*

Uckfield Places of Interest

Sheffield Park Garden (NT) Tel 0825 790655.
Bluebell Railway Sheffield Park Station Tel 082 572 2370 *Talking Timetable 3777.*

Ullswater Leeming House 75% £164

Tel 076 84 86622 Fax 076 84 86443 **HR**

Watermillock Ullswater Cumbria CA11 0JJ **Map 4 C3**

On the northern shore of Ullswater and surrounded by 20 acres of beautifully landscaped gardens, Leeming House, now a Forte Grand Hotel, dates from the early 1800s. Public rooms lead off a long, pillared entrance hall and, in keeping with the character of the building, are classically traditional in decor and furnishings. The library, with book-filled shelves, and the adjoining sitting and drawing rooms have comfortable deep-cushioned settees and armchairs arranged in well-spaced groupings. The bar is dark and clubby with wood-panelled walls. The drawing room and a wide, tiled conservatory which connects a wing of newer bedrooms have good views over the gently sloping grounds, with glimpses of the lake through a fine collection of trees. Best bedrooms, too, have excellent views. Fourteen have balconies and five ground-floor rooms have patios. Possessing a tasteful floral decor with smart darkwood furniture they are all elegantly furnished and comprehensively equipped. Bathrooms have lovely old-fashioned fittings as well as good toiletries and bathrobes. ***Rooms** 40. Garden.* AMERICAN EXPRESS *Access, Diners, Visa.*

Restaurant £77

A long, beautifully proportioned dining room with fine south-facing views over the grounds to the lake. Familiar classics on the menu are interspersed with a few simple innovations. The choice for dinner is three or six courses while lunchtime has a slightly shorter three-course menu. Results on the plate are not lacking in flavour. Friendly service. ***Seats** 80. Parties 20. L 12.30-1.45 D 7.30-8.45. Set L £15.75 (Sun) Set D £27.50/£34.50.*

Ullswater Old Church Hotel 67% £90

Tel 076 84 86204 Fax 076 84 86368 **HR**

Watermillock Ullswater Cumbria CA11 0JN **Map 4 C3**

A stylish water's-edge hotel (on the A592) where residents are greeted very much as Kevin and Maureen Whitemore's house guests. Both lounges are built for relaxation and packed with board games and periodicals. Maureen's bold colour schemes brighten the bedrooms (priced according to the view), with crown canopies and half-testers framing really comfortable beds. By contrast, bathrooms are on the cramped side. Breakfasts deserve to be taken seriously, ranging from Lakeland yoghurts and home-made muesli to Manx kippers, Cumberland sausage and mixed grill with black pudding. No dogs. ***Rooms** 10. Garden, fishing, boating. Closed Nov-Mar. Visa.*

Restaurant £60

The smaller lounge doubles as an aperitif bar where guests gather prior to dinner (availability is limited for outside diners). The short-choice menu (order by 7.30) might start with mushrooms and crispy bacon with garlic butter, or prawns and avocado with salad leaves, and progress via soup to salmon, rack of lamb or sirloin of beef béarnaise. Choice of puds, then cheese, coffee and fudge. Fair prices and helpful tasting notes on a concise wine list. Note that the restaurant is no longer open for lunch. No smoking. ***Seats** 30. D 7.30 for 8. Set D £20.*

Ullswater Rampsbeck Country House Hotel 65% £90

Tel & Fax 076 84 86442 **HR**

Watermillock Ullswater Cumbria CA11 0LP **Map 4 C3**

Rampsbeck's lakeside garden is filled with rhododendron bushes and the backdrops of the fells make for a spectacular location, to which Thomas and Marion Gibb add just the right touch of Lakeland hospitality. The grandfather clocks, open log fire and profusion of flowers bring serenity to the panelled lounge: the bar opens on to a patio and the garden.

See over

Enlarged (and much improved) bedrooms are immaculately kept; those guests lying in can enjoy the luxury of their not-so-early-morning tea tray. The fresh, crisp bed linen is turned down in the evening. Not suitable for young children. Just over 5 miles from Penrith on the shore of Lake Ullswater. ***Rooms** 21. Garden, spa bath, fishing, mooring.*
Closed 6 weeks Jan/Feb. Access, Visa.

Restaurant £55

Andrew McGeorge's modern classical cooking is never dull and abounds with experimental combinations of texture and flavour. The four-course table d'hote dinner menu might offer pan-fried salmon with salad, a cream of Jerusalem artichoke soup (or damson sorbet), ragout of lamb with herb dumplings and lemon tart with a tuile basket of pineapple sorbet and raspberry coulis. A la carte is more involved – from steamed brill lasagne with mussel cream sauce flavoured with lemon grass and ginger to pan-fried loin of venison with wild mushroom and foie gras pithiviers and a game jus flavoured with green Chartreuse; the chef's Symphony of desserts is a fitting climax. Vegetarians are particularly well catered for, with a separate table d'hote dinner menu offering alternatives at each of the four courses. Fixed-price lunch on Sundays; bar lunches every day. Very fairly priced and well-chosen wine list (short on half bottles, though), presented by style. ***Seats** 36. Private Room 20. L 12-1.30 D 7-8.45.*
Set L £21.95 Set D £24 & £32.50.

Ullswater Sharrow Bay 82% £160*

Tel 076 84 86301 Fax 076 84 86349 **HR**

Howtown Ullswater Cumbria CA10 2LZ **Map 4 C3**

Little could Francis Coulson have foreseen back in 1949, when he opened Sharrow, the phenomenal success that this, the first country house hotel, would continue to enjoy into the 90s. He and Brian Sack, here since 1952, have together created the epitome of gracious country living. Not only does the hotel, bordered on three sides by 12 acres of gardens, have an idyllic location on the very edge of Lake Ullswater, but the main house and its equally desirable satellites – the Lodge Gatehouse, Garden Cottage, Bank House (1 mile away) and Thwaite Cottage, Tirril (4 miles distant and with no room service) – offer every conceivable pampering comfort. Success feeds on success and such is the renown of this hotel that there are times, particularly at the peak of the season, when some may be disappointed if only from lack of space. The hotel is in a National Park and petty bureaucrats envious of or blind to the hotel's potential veto the alteration of even a single stone. The erection of a Victorian conservatory was deemed acceptable however, though size was strictly delineated and thus has helped in creating additional seating (though without a lake view). This view is to be had from the main lounge with its picture windows. Here as in the second lounge and conservatory are deep-cushioned settees and armchairs, fresh flowers, fine ornaments and paintings. There is no bar proper, so drinks are served in the lounges. Bedrooms upstairs in the main house do not all have their bathrooms en suite, but all the remainder do. Each and every bedroom is furnished to the highest standards of comfort and luxury with fine embroidered linen sheets on sleep-inducing mattresses. Fine porcelain and tassels (two of Francis' passions) are everywhere, and plants and books adorn the tables. Most have sitting areas and bathrooms have exquisite toiletries and thick cosseting towels. Breakfasts are as much of an institution here as the famed afternoon teas, lunches and dinners. Newly baked croissants, brioches, freshly squeezed orange juice and a cooked breakfast *sans pareil* are all guaranteed to set you up for at least a day's fell walking. Staff under the supervision of manager Nigel Lawrence are long serving and very dedicated, each ensuring that every guest is properly cared for and the hotel kept in absolute gleaming ship-shape order. *Half-board terms only. See also Hosts of the Year, page 42.
***Rooms** 28. Garden. Closed Dec-Feb. No credit cards.*

Restaurant ★

£95

The choice is whether to eat in the lakeside dining room with its splendid views over the water, or next door in the Victorian panelled studio dining room with its genteel ambience and spaciously arranged tables. For both rooms you file past a sample tray of that mealtime's desserts having them described as you go, your order for dinner having previously been taken in one of the lounges. The menu has changed little in its format down the years. There's an almost overwhelming choice of starters on the six-course fixed price dinner list. Lunch is five courses with just as much choice. The menu changes twice daily, the range encompassing the simple such as cream of leek and potato soup or beef consommé with a julienne of herb crepes and the more elaborate such as ravioli of lobster wrapped in lemon pasta with a fried julienne of vegetables and lobster sauce; duck foie gras on a bed of noodles with a pancake of summer vegetables and a champagne and herb sauce or hot chicken liver mousse served with chicken livers and a Madeira, port and butter sauce. Starters are always followed by a single fish course, which could be a fillet of halibut served with a cider and onion confit. A light and delicate cheese suissesse soufflé accompanies every time. A sorbet is served to refresh the palate before the main course. Here there's a choice of several and can include roast breast of Lunesdale duckling, honey glazed, very crisp-skinned and tender, with a confit of duck legs, orange and grapefruit segments and a sauce flavoured with honey and thyme, or roast loin of young English lamb cooked off the bone, served on a potato and leek galette with shaped vegetables and a wild mushroom sauce. These are typical of essentially simple preparation made complex by the elaborate garnishes that accompany each. As if these were not enough, vegetables are plentiful, arriving in the form of a carrot mousse, ratatouille, baby sweetcorn and mange tout as well as chateau and new potatoes. Several choices for sweet include the superb Old English Regency syllabub, lemon tart with vanilla ice cream, very rich and indulgent chocolate and coffee truffle with coffee sauce or crème brulée with a compote of red fruits. Finally, for dinner, cheeses, all British, and in prime condition. The rhetorical style of the menu may not please some but it serves as an indication of the richness of the cooking. From the wonderful selection of breads to begin through to the delightful petits fours at the end eating here is an experience to be relived again and again. An impressive range of New World wines alongside traditional Europe. For a hotel of this class, it's good to see so many wines served by the glass. ***Seats** 65. Parties 10. L 1-1.45 D 8-8.45. Set L £29.50 Set D £39.50.*

Ulverston Bay Horse Inn

£57

Tel 0229 583972 Fax 0229 580502

RR

Canal Foot Ulverston Cumbria LA12 9EL

Map 4 C4

Follow the signs for Canal Foot to find this old pub with a sympathetic conversion that includes an intimate conservatory restaurant with picturesque views over the Leven estuary. Chef Robert Lyons gives full rein to his wide-ranging repertoire; once the protegé of co-owner John Tovey at Miller Howe, he's equally at home with a deceptively simple salad or an Aberdeen Angus steak (hung in the cold room for at least four weeks) as with something more elaborate such as breast of farm chicken stuffed with leeks, mushrooms and sage, wrapped in puff pastry, baked and served with a rich Madeira sauce. Coffee is served with home-made truffles in the lounge. There are two wine lists, though customers choose mainly from the outstanding New World list (80+), which features many gems at keen prices. No children under 12. No smoking. ***Seats** 50. Private Room 30. L 12-2 D 7.30 for 8. Closed L Mon. Set L £13.50. Access, Visa.*

Rooms

£140*

Overnight accommodation is provided in six attractive en-suite bedrooms, five of which open on to a small terrace with a view of the estuary. No children under 12. *Half-board terms.

Ulverston Place of Interest

The Laurel and Hardy Museum Tel 0229 582292.

Upper Slaughter Lords of the Manor 75% £135

Tel 0451 820243 Fax 0451 820696 **HR**

Upper Slaughter nr Bourton-on-the-Water Gloucestershire GL54 2JD **Map 14 C1**

Victorian and later additions to a 17th-century rectory have created a delightful jumble of a building with peaceful walled garden, charming courtyard and fine views of some very English countryside from the front of the house. Also very English are the bedrooms with chintzy fabrics, nice antique pieces and restful watercolours on the walls. Bottles of mineral water, a bowl of fruit and welcoming decanter of sherry add the homely touches. Bathrooms, which match the individually decorated bedrooms, boast high-class toiletries and generously sized robes. Various day rooms – there are three lounges in addition to the bar – have a nice country-house feel with lots of fresh flowers and real log fires in winter. Attentive staff offer good standards of service. No dogs. ***Rooms*** *29. Garden, fishing.*
AMERICAN EXPRESS *Access, Diners, Visa.*

Restaurant £90

A pleasing room, with yellow walls, crisp white napery and quality tableware looking out on to the walled garden, where a patio makes a fine spot for drinks or coffee (or even a meal) when the weather allows, Dishes on new chef Clive Dixon's shortish fixed-price dinner menu are both well conceived and well executed – terrine of salmon and brill with spinach and soft herbs (a notably good dish), pastry tartlet of rabbit confit on spring greens with creamy garlic sauce, sea bass with ratatouille and olive oil on a bed of tagliatelle, sirloin of Aberdeen Angus beef with a celeriac purée and onion sauce, hot rhubarb soufflé with custard ice cream. The slightly longer luncheon menu is individually priced allowing for the smallest, or keenest, of midday appetites. A serious wine list has a good choice of house recommendations and helpful notes. Also some good wines (and nearly a dozen ports) by the glass. The French classic vintages are erratically priced. ***Seats*** *45. Private Room 60. L 12.30-2 D 7.30-9.30. Set D £27/£33.50.*

Uppingham Forte Travelodge £42

Tel 0572 87719 **L**

Glaston Road Morcott nr Uppingham Leicestershire LE15 8SA **Map 7 E4**

On the A47 eastbound, 4 miles east of Uppingham. ***Rooms*** *40.*
AMERICAN EXPRESS *Access, Visa.*

Uppingham The Lake Isle £50

Tel 0572 822951 Fax 0572 822951 **RR**

16 High Street East Uppingham Leicestershire LE15 9PZ **Map 7 E4**

Owned and run personally by David and Claire Whitfield, this charming restaurant in an 18th-century property is reached by way of a flower-decked yard just off the town centre. David gathers the ingredients for his short multi-course menus from near and far with twice-weekly deliveries from the Paris Rungis market, fish from Grimsby and Cornwall, plus herbs from his own walled garden. A sure touch is evident throughout, from 'healthy food choices ' on the lunchtime menu – baked stuffed tomato with goat's cheese and pesto, salmon and smoked haddock fish cakes with tomato and oregano sauce – to equally appealing dishes on the short-choice dinner menu: parsnip and chestnut soup, puff-pastry pillow of Brie and celery, wild boar cooked in Guinness and port with baby turned vegetables. A very serious wine list indeed with many half bottles (including vintage clarets and burgundies) and several bargains – lots of good drinking under £20. ***Seats*** *40. Parties 20. L 12.30-1.45 (Sun to 2) D 7.30-9.30 (Sat 7-10,*

Sun 7.30-8.30). Closed L Mon, D Sun except to residents. Set L from £9.95 Set D from £19.50. AMERICAN EXPRESS *Access, Diners, Visa.*

Rooms **£66**

The twelve bedrooms vary in size and style but all have direct-dial phones, colour TVs and thoughtful extras like fruit, mineral water and a decanter of sherry.

Uttoxeter — Forte Travelodge

£42

Tel 0889 562043 **L**

A50/A5030 Ashbourne Road Uttoxeter Staffordshire ST14 5AA **Map 6 B3**

On the outskirts of Uttoxeter, 5 miles south of Alton Towers Leisure Park. ***Rooms** 32.* AMERICAN EXPRESS *Access, Visa.*

Uttoxeter — White Hart

£43

Tel & Fax 0889 562437 **I**

Carter Street Uttoxeter Staffordshire ST14 8EU **Map 6 B3**

An old town-centre coaching inn owned by Ansells Brewery. Adequate overnight accommodation; 15 of the bedrooms have en-suite facilities. Two meeting rooms for up to 50 people. ***Rooms** 26.* AMERICAN EXPRESS *Access, Diners, Visa.*

Uttoxeter — Place of Interest

Uttoxeter Racecourse Tel 0889 562561.

Ventnor — Royal Hotel 60%

£66

Tel 0983 852186 Fax 0983 855395 **H**

Belgrave Road Ventnor Isle of Wight PO38 1JJ **Map 15 D4**

Neat gardens front a Victorian sandstone hotel owned by Forte. The rattan-furnished conservatory entrance hall and the cosy bar are favourite areas to sit and relax. Bedrooms have lightwood fitted units and colourful floral curtains. ***Rooms** 54. Garden, outdoor swimming pool, games room.* AMERICAN EXPRESS *Access, Diners, Visa.*

Ventnor — Places of Interest

Tourist Information Tel 0983 853625.
The Winter Gardens Tel 0983 855111.
Appuldercombe House (Ruins and Park) Wroxall Tel 0983 852484.

Veryan — Nare Hotel 70%

£124

Tel 0872 501279 Fax 0872 501856 **HR**

Carne Beach Veryan nr Truro Cornwall TR2 5PF **Map 12 B3**

Standing above the mile-long sandy Carne Beach, the Nare has been transformed from a simple, seaside family hotel to a model of good taste and a haven of tranquillity. Lounges and drawing room face extensive patios and garden and have country house appeal with antique furniture pieces. The very best of the bedrooms have easy chairs and sofas, with beautiful views out to sea and over the hotel lawns from picture windows and balconies. Expect fruit and flowers on arrival and join fellow guests for complimentary afternoon tea. Not really a young person's hotel out of season; in season the good sports amenities are a main attraction. A new drying/boot room (useful for walkers) has recently been completed. Concessionary vouchers are given to guests who wish to play golf at Truro Golf Club. Families are well catered for, but at a price – cots are charged at half room tariff! ***Rooms** 39. Garden, outdoor swimming pool, sauna, solarium, tennis, keep-fit equipment, snooker, sports boat, sail boards. Closed 6 weeks Jan/Feb. Access, Visa.*

See over

Restaurant

£70

Appealing sea views through windows with swathed pelmets; standard fare, using good local produce and seafood, is served in healthy-sized portions. Flambé dishes (charged as a supplement to the table d'hote) are popular and hors d'oeuvre, desserts and cheese are served on well-laden trolleys. A light lunch is served in the Gwendra Room and adjacent terrace during the week; traditional Sunday lunch is in the dining room. Jacket and tie preferred in the evening. No children under 7 in the dining room at night; an early children's dinner is served at 5.30pm in the Gwendra Room (£9 children's menu). Minimum à la carte charge £27 per person. ***Seats** 80. L 12.30-2 D 7.15-9.30. Set L (Sun) £12.50 Set D (5-course) £24.*

Wadhurst Spindlewood 60%

£83

Tel 0580 200430 Fax 0580 201132

HR

Wallcrouch Wadhurst East Sussex TN5 7JG

Map 11 B6

Set in five acres of gardens, ponds and woodland, Victorian Spindlewood is an easy drive from several historic castles and stately homes. Public rooms are semi-grand but informal. A half-panelled, parquet-floored lounge doubles as a conference room (capacity 20) and there's a bay-windowed bar overlooking the gardens. Individually decorated bedrooms have mainly period furniture. The hotel, which stands on the B2099 two miles south-east of Wadhurst, has been under the personal care of the Fitzsimmons family since 1979. No dogs. ***Rooms** 9. Garden. Closed 4 days Christmas. Access, Visa.*

Restaurant

£62

In a peaceful and charming French Provincial-style dining room Harvey Lee Aram continues to cook in fine form, as he has done since 1979! Typical choices could include a trio of baked cheese filo pastries on a celery salad with redcurrant and lime dressing, followed by fricassee of liver, kidneys and sweetbreads with a Dijon mustard cream sauce and then a liqueur ice cream or chilled chocolate soufflé with Grand Marnier sauce. Good-quality fresh ingredients, clear flavours and well-made sauces. Light snack lunches now served Mon-Fri (last orders 2pm); three-course Sunday lunches offer a choice of four dishes at each stage. ***Seats** 40. Private Room 24. L 12.15-1.30 D 7.15-9. Closed L Bank Holidays. Set L £14.95 Set D £23.20.*

Wakefield Campanile Hotel

£44

Tel 0924 201054 Fax 0924 201055

L

Monckton Road Wakefield West Yorkshire

Map 6 C1

Canalside location, 15 minutes' drive outside Leeds. Nearest motorway junction is J39 from the M1, taking A636 Denby Dale road. ***Rooms** 77.* AMERICAN EXPRESS *Access, Diners, Visa.*

Wakefield Cedar Court 59%

£90

Tel 0924 276310 Fax 0924 280221

H

Denby Dale Road Calder Grove Wakefield West Yorkshire WF4 3QZ

Map 6 C1

Modern, purpose-built business hotel on the roundabout at junction 39 of the M1, 12 miles south of Leeds. Open-plan day rooms, practical accommodation including several suites and a dozen Executive rooms; phone extensions in bathrooms; some whirlpool baths. Conference/banqueting facilities up to 400. Children stay free in parents' room. No dogs. ***Rooms** 151. Garden.* AMERICAN EXPRESS *Access, Diners, Visa.*

Wakefield Forte Posthouse 64%

£68

Tel 0924 276388 Fax 0924 276437

H

Queen's Drive Ossett Wakefield West Yorkshire WF5 9BE

Map 6 C1

Modern low-rise hotel near Junction 40 of the M1. Facilities for up to 160 delegates in the largest of several conference rooms. 24hr lounge menu. ***Rooms** 99. Garden.* AMERICAN EXPRESS *Access, Diners, Visa.*

Wakefield Granada Lodge £45

Tel 0924 830569 Fax 0924 830609 **L**

M1 Junction 38/39 Woolley Edge Wakefield West Yorkshire WF4 4LQ **Map 6 C1**

Rooms 31. AMERICAN EXPRESS *Access, Diners, Visa.*

Wakefield Swallow Hotel 58% £86

Tel 0924 372111 Fax 0924 383648 **H**

Queen Street Wakefield West Yorkshire WF1 1JU **Map 6 C1**

A tall hotel, with splendid views from bedrooms on the upper floors, near the Cathedral in the city centre. Public rooms are on the first and second floors. The largest of several conference rooms can take up to 250 delegates. Parking for 40 cars. Guests have free membership of a local gym/sauna centre and snooker club. ***Rooms 63.*** AMERICAN EXPRESS *Access, Diners, Visa.*

Wakefield Places of Interest

Theatre Royal and Opera House Drury Lane Tel 0924 366556.
Nostell Priory (NT) Tel 0924 863892.
Wakefield Cathedral Tel 0924 373923.
Museums and Art Galleries
Wakefield Art Gallery Wentworth Terrace Tel 0924 375402 or 295796.
Yorkshire Mining Museum and Underground Tours Caphouse Colliery, New Road, Overton Tel 0924 848806.
Yorkshire Sculpture Park Bretton Hall, West Bretton Tel 0924 830579/830302.
Featherstone Rovers RLFC Tel 0977 702386.
Wakefield Trinity RLFC Tel 0924 372445.

Walberton Avisford Park 66% £106

Tel 0243 551215 Fax 0243 552485 **H**

Yapton Lane Walberton Arundel West Sussex BN18 0LS **Map 11 A6**

From Arundel, follow the A27 towards Chichester and turn left on to the B2132 to find a Georgian manor house set in 62 acres of grounds. The day rooms at this former boys' school are on a big scale and might swamp the individual guest, as might the swarms of conference delegates. The new Garden Lodge Business Centre is linked by an enclosed walkway and comprises a Grand Hall (holding up to 350 conference delegates), 24 Executive bedrooms, two suites and an Italian restaurant. No dogs. ***Rooms 126.*** *Garden, indoor swimming pools, sauna, solarium, snooker, 9-hole golf course, tennis, squash.* AMERICAN EXPRESS *Access, Diners, Visa.*

Walkington Manor House 72% £93

Tel 0482 881645 Fax 0482 866501 **HR**

Northlands Walkington Beverley Humberside HU17 8RT **Map 7 E1**

In a wonderfully peaceful location surrounded by the Yorkshire Wolds, 3 minutes from Beverley on the B1230, is this late-Victorian house run by Derek and Lee Baugh along the lines of a private house with family guests. The bedrooms, all with king-size beds, offer fine country views and are decorated in soft tones. Comfortable seating, flowers, magazines and ornaments add to the homely appeal. Bathrooms squeeze with difficulty into 19th-century rooms, but are well equipped. Day rooms include an elegant drawing room with fine antiques, oil paintings and seating made for relaxation. Friendly staff and notably good housekeeping. No children under 12. ***Rooms 6.*** *Garden.* AMERICAN EXPRESS *Access, Visa.*

Restaurant £75

An elegant blue dining room and adjoining conservatory provide a choice of environments in which to enjoy Derek Baugh's cooking. Fixed-price-only menus are described in refreshingly straightforward English and the

See over

style gives classical dishes a new-wave twist: smoked squab pigeon breasts on a quail and armagnac paté with salad leaves and apple vinaigrette; Cajun-spiced, seared tenderloin of beef and pork with chive and spicy roast garlic aïoli; baby guinea fowl served off the bone on an apple bubble and squeak and tarragon and blackberry sauce. Traditional roast duckling should be ordered 24hrs in advance. Simpler lunches offer an interesting choice – from garlic mussels with parsley sippets to lemon-roasted chicken with apricot demi-glace and traditional puds with custard (Spotted Dick, bread-and-butter pudding). A good-value, nightly table d'hote also keeps things simple. Lee Baugh lends a more-than-capable hand to the patisserie and baking, her forte. New World wines offer best value on an excellent all-round wine list. ***Seats** 50. Parties 24. Private Room 20.*
L (Wed & Fri only) 12.15-1.30 D 7.30-9.15. Closed Sun. Set L £15 Set D from £15.

Wallingford George Hotel 60% £90

Tel 0491 836665 Fax 0491 825359 **H**

High Street Wallingford Oxfordshire OX10 0BS **Map 15 D2**

Dick Turpin took rooms at this historic coaching inn and during the Civil War Royalist troops were billeted here. Now, in a less turbulent phase, the George mixes tradition with basic modern hotel amenity. A self-contained suite can accommodate up to 120 conference delegates. Children up to 12 stay free in parents' room. Mount Charlotte Thistle. ***Rooms** 39.* American Express *Access, Diners, Visa.*

Wallingford Shillingford Bridge Hotel 58% £70

Tel 086 732 8567 Fax 086 732 8636 **H**

Ferry Road Shillingford nr Wallingford Oxfordshire OX10 8LX **Map 15 D2**

Adjacent to Shillingford Bridge, on the A329 one mile and a half north of Wallingford, this riverside hotel comprises several buildings, the oldest dating from the 16th century. The hotel owns a stretch of river frontage, and fishing, moorings and boat hire (nearby) are offered. An 11-bedroom extension opened in May 1993, and almost all rooms have been redecorated within the last three years; five rooms are in a bungalow, others in an annexe. Forestdale Hotels. ***Rooms** 42. Garden, outdoor swimming pool, squash, coarse fishing.* American Express *Access, Diners, Visa.*

Wallingford Place of Interest

Corn Exchange Market Place Tel 0491 39336.

Walsall Forte Posthouse 61% £68

Tel 0922 33555 Fax 0922 612034 **H**

Birmingham Road Walsall West Midlands WS5 3AB **Map 6 C4**

Take Junction 7 of the M6, then A34 to ring road intersection to find a modern block on four floors without many of the usual Posthouse amenities, but with three bars. ***Rooms** 98.* American Express *Access, Diners, Visa.*

Walsall Wood Baron's Court Hotel 62% £55

Tel 0543 452020 Fax 0543 361276 **H**

Walsall Wood Walsall West Midlands WS9 9AH **Map 6 C4**

Tudor-inspired styling and fittings feature throughout the ground-floor areas of this unusual hotel on the A461. Bedrooms employ Queen Anne-style furniture and soft decor. Executive rooms are larger and have whirlpool baths. ***Rooms** 100. Indoor swimming pool, keep-fit equipment, sauna, spa bath, steam room, solarium.* American Express *Access, Diners, Visa.*

Walsall Places of Interest

Museum and Art Gallery and Garman Ryan Collection Tel 0922 653135.
Walsall Leather Centre Museum Tel 0922 721153.

Waltham Abbey Swallow Hotel 66% NEW £110

Tel 0992 717170 Fax 0992 711841 **H**

Old Shire Lane Waltham Abbey Essex EN9 3LX **Map 15 F2**

Just north of Junction 26 of the M25, this is one of Swallow's newest hotels. Public rooms and bedrooms radiate from an impressive lobby bar and lounge area which is dominated by a huge, glittering funnel-shaped fountain. Neat, well-equipped bedrooms offer 24hr room service. Good leisure facilities. ***Rooms** 163. Garden, indoor swimming pool, children's swimming pool, keep-fit equipment, sauna, spa bath, solarium, Fountain Lounge (10am-6pm), courtesy mini-bus.* AMERICAN EXPRESS *Access, Diners, Visa.*

Wansford-in-England Haycock Hotel 70% £90

Tel 0780 782223 Fax 0780 783031 **HR**

Wansford-in-England Peterborough Cambridgeshire PE8 6JA **Map 7 E4**

A lovely 17th-century honey-coloured stone coaching inn in 6 acres of grounds next to the junction of A1 and A47. It has been much extended, in sympathetic style, the most recent additions being a large conference/ballroom and the stone-walled Orchard Room with all-day bar and coffee-shop menu. Other day rooms include a pubby bar and two traditional lounges. Bedrooms in the older parts of the building are full of character, but all have been decorated with great style and flair by Julia Vanocci using high-quality fabrics and furnishings. Bathrooms are equally luxurious. Extensive grounds include award-winning gardens which stretch along the banks of the river Nene and the village cricket pitch. The variety of food on offer in both bar (excellent bar snacks), Orchard Room (7am-10pm) and restaurant caters for all tastes and pockets; outdoor barbecue daily in summer with seating for 100. The ballroom is a lovely setting for functions with its soaring oak beams, enormous fireplace and private garden. Poste Hotels. ***Rooms** 51. Garden, fishing, pétanque.* AMERICAN EXPRESS *Access, Diners, Visa.*

Restaurant £70

Candelabras and highly-polished silver add to the mellow, traditional atmosphere of the twin dining rooms here. Chef Richard Brandrick's menu is pretty traditional too, with the likes of 'cheffy's' steak and kidney pie, jugged hare, and the roast sirloin of prime English beef that always features on the silver trolley. A charge of £3.95 for vegetable and potatoes is somewhat less traditional! Other offerings might include a stir-fry of mangetout, prawns and walnuts, black pudding with fried apple and Calvados sauce, or sautéed fillet of bacon-wrapped beef fillet stuffed with Stilton and served with a claret sauce. Home-made desserts served with double cream from a trolley. The wine list is sensibly priced, clearly laid out and cleverly balanced – bravo! ***Seats** 100. Private Rooms 18-200+. L 12-2.30 D 7-10.30.*

Wantage Bear Hotel 58% £58

Tel 02357 66366 Fax 02357 68826 **H**

Market Square Wantage Oxfordshire OX12 8AB **Map 14 C2**

Since the 16th century the Bear has been a notable feature on the market square of the town where Alfred the Great was born (his statue is another landmark). The cobbled courtyard evokes some of the atmosphere of the past, and a few of the bedrooms are furnished with some older pieces, including brass bedsteads. The Ascot Suite provides conference facilities for up to 80. No dogs. ***Rooms** 34.* AMERICAN EXPRESS *Access, Diners, Visa.*

Wareham Priory Hotel 72% £75

Tel 0929 551666 Fax 0929 554519 **HR**

Church Green Wareham Dorset BH20 4ND **Map 14 B4**

Trim lawns and immaculate gardens reach down to the river Frome (which leads into Poole Harbour), making a lovely setting for the former priory of Lady St Mary, which dates from the early 16th century. Two beautifully decorated lounges overlook the gardens, and there is a small traditional bar. Bedrooms vary in size but all are thoughtfully equipped: each has mineral water, fresh fruit, books and magazines, plus bathrobes, clothes brushes and hairdryers. One room has a four-poster and a whirlpool bath and all feature handsome antique furniture. The Boathouse, converted from a 16th-century clay barn, contains two bedrooms and two luxurious suites. Moorings are available for guests arriving by boat. No dogs. ***Rooms** 19. Garden, croquet, coarse & game fishing.* AMERICAN EXPRESS *Access, Diners, Visa.*

Restaurant £75

Two rooms: ground-floor dining room for breakfast and lunch; Abbots Cellar in vaulted stone cellars for candle-lit dinner. Good traditional English dishes range from hot black pudding on braised lentils with gravy to crisp roast Gressingham duck with ginger and honey. Fine puds and desserts from the trolley and a good selection of English cheeses. The fairly-priced wine list, with some classic bottles, provides interesting notes on the producing areas. *L 12.30-2 D 7.30-10. Set L £11.95/£13.95. Set D £22.50/£26.50.* ***Seats** 44. Private Room 24.*

Wareham Springfield Country Hotel 60% £90

Tel 0929 552177 Fax 0929 551862 **H**

Grange Road Stoborough nr Wareham Dorset BH20 5AL **Map 14 B4**

Set in 6 acres of stylishly landscaped gardens off the A351, a pleasant redbrick hotel with an appealing modern exterior. The spacious foyer is dominated by a splendid stag's head and there are two cosy bars. Agreeable bedrooms, decorated in pink, include doubles, twins and singles, plus a number of family rooms and suites. New for this year is a leisure complex with bars, a restaurant and function facilities (up to 180). ***Rooms** 32. Garden, indoor & outdoor swimming pool, squash, sauna, steam room, solarium, tennis, badminton, games room, snooker,* AMERICAN EXPRESS *Access, Diners, Visa.*

Wareham Place of Interest

Tank Museum Bovington Camp Tel 0929 403329.
Swanage Beach *9 miles SE of Wareham.*

Warminster Bishopstrow House 79% £123

Tel 0985 212312 Fax 0985 216769 **HR**

Boreham Road Warminster Wiltshire BA12 9HH **Map 14 B3**

Built in 1817, Bishopstrow is an elegant house in a lovely setting. The entrance hall, morning room and dining rooms are stylish and formal, with fine oil paintings, French and English antiques, Persian carpets and deep, inviting armchairs. Flower displays add splendid splashes of colour. Spacious bedrooms are in three places: main house, garden rooms and courtyard rooms reached by long corridors. Rooms are either standard or de luxe. Fruit, biscuits, plants and magazines are provided and some of the bedrooms feature spa baths or separate showers. A stunning indoor swimming pool looks out on to the gardens. Conference facilities for up to 60. Sister hotel to *Charingworth Manor* (see entry under Chipping Campden). ***Rooms** 32. Garden, indoor & outdoor swimming pools, indoor & outdoor tennis, game fishing, helipad.* AMERICAN EXPRESS *Access, Diners, Visa.*

Restaurant

£80

Garden views accompany inventive modern cooking by Chris Suter. Typifying his style is a weekly-changing lunch menu offering risotto marinara with saffron or warm salad of wild rabbit with black pudding and creamy vinaigrette to start, followed by wild boar sausages with mashed potatoes and onion gravy or millefeuille of pan-fried salmon with a chervil sauce, finishing with plated farmhouse cheeses, apple-flavoured crème brulée with Granny Smith sorbet or a tulip filled with mango and grape mousse on a passion fruit coulis. Refreshingly straightforward menu descriptions in English belie the effort and invention that go into producing the evening à la carte: terrine of puréed chicken livers wrapped in bacon and served with a grape and kumquat chutney, salad of smoked duck breast with black pudding, steamed medley of fish with chive and caviar sauce, braised lamb shank with potatoes, garlic and rosemary. Steamed chocolate sponge with hot chocolate sauce and white chocolate mousse adds a nursery angle to the puddings. ***Seats** 60. Private Room 22. L 12.30-2 D 7.30-9 (Fri & Sat to 9.30). Set L £10.50 Set D £31.*

Warminster — Granada Lodge

£45

Tel 0985 219639 Fax 0985 214380 — L

A36/A350 Warminster Wiltshire BA12 7RU — Map 14 B3

***Rooms** 31.* AMERICAN EXPRESS *Access, Diners, Visa.*

Warminster — Place of Interest

Longleat House and Wildlife Park Tel 09853 551/328.

Warrington — Holiday Inn Garden Court — 65%

£77

Tel 0925 838779 Fax 0925 838859 — H

Woolston Grange Avenue Woolston Warrington Cheshire WA1 4PX — Map 6 B2

By junction 21 of the M6, one of the 'junior' Holiday Inns offering good bedrooms (half for non-smokers), limited public areas and minimal service. The room price covers up to four occupants and children up to 19 stay free in parents' room. ***Rooms** 100.* AMERICAN EXPRESS *Access, Diners, Visa.*

Warrington — Lord Daresbury Hotel — 67%

£115

Tel 0925 267331 Fax 0925 265615 — H

Chester Road Daresbury Warrington Cheshire WA4 4BB — Map 6 B2

Conveniently located by junction 11 of the M56, this modern, conference-oriented hotel (meeting rooms for up to 400 delegates) also offers extensive leisure amenities. De Vere Hotels. ***Rooms** 141. Garden, indoor swimming pool, gymnasium, sauna, spa bath, steam bath, solarium, beautician, squash, snooker, games room, coffee shop (9.45am-9.45pm).* AMERICAN EXPRESS *Access, Diners, Visa.*

Warrington — Travel Inn

£43

Tel 0925 414417 Fax 0925 414544 — L

Winwick Road Warrington Cheshire — Map 6 B2

Close to Junction 9 of the M62. ***Rooms** 40.* AMERICAN EXPRESS *Access, Diners, Visa.*

Warrington — Places of Interest

Tourist Information Tel 0925 36501.
Museum & Art Gallery Tel 0925 44400/30550.
Warrington RLFC Tel 0925 35338.

Warwick Hilton National 66% £140

Tel 0926 499555 Fax 0926 410020 **H**

Stratford Road Warwick Warwickshire CV34 6RE **Map 14 C1**

Conferences for up to 500 are catered for at this low-rise modern hotel at the junction of the A46 and the M40. ***Rooms** 181. Indoor swimming pool, keep-fit equipment, sauna, steam room, solarium, pool table.* AMERICAN EXPRESS *Access, Diners, Visa.*

Warwick Places of Interest

Tourist Information Tel 0926 492212.
Doll Museum Tel 0926 495546.
Warwickshire Museum Tel 0926 410410 ext 2021.
Warwick Racecourse Tel 0926 491553.
Historic Houses, Castles and Gardens
Charlecote Park (NT) Tel 0789 470277.
Warwick Castle Tel 0926 495421.
Packwood House (NT) Hockley Heath Tel 0564 782024.

Washington Campanile Hotel £44

Tel 091-416 5010 Fax 091-416 5023 **L**

Emerson Road Washington nr Newcastle-upon-Tyne Tyne & Wear NE37 1LE **Map 5 E2**

Off the A1(M) between the A1231 and A195. ***Rooms*** 77. AMERICAN EXPRESS *Access, Diners, Visa.*

Washington Forte Posthouse 59% £68

Tel 091-416 2264 Fax 091-415 3371 **H**

Emerson District 5 Washington Tyne & Wear NE37 1LB **Map 5 E2**

Just south of Washington Services on A1(M), a practical modern hotel that's popular with business visitors, who obviously appreciate good-value rooms and conference facilities. Children under 16 free in parents' room. ***Rooms** 138. 18-hole pitch & putt, children's playroom & playground.* AMERICAN EXPRESS *Access, Diners, Visa.*

Washington Granada Lodge £45

Tel 091-410 0076 Fax 091-410 0057 **L**

A1(M) Washington Tyne & Wear DH3 2SJ **Map 5 E2**

***Rooms** 35.* AMERICAN EXPRESS *Access, Diners, Visa.*

Washington Moat House 66% £93

Tel 091-417 2626 Fax 091-415 1166 **H**

Stone Cellar Road High Usworth District 12 Washington Tyne & Wear NE37 1PH **Map 5 E2**

First-class leisure facilities are the main attraction at a modern Moat House standing by a championship golf course. Large bedrooms have all the usual modern accessories. Popular with business people during the week and sportsmen and families at weekends. Conference/banqueting suites for 200/180. ***Rooms** 106. Garden, indoor swimming pool, 18-hole golf course, pitch & putt, golf driving range, spa bath, sauna, solarium, keep-fit equipment, squash.* AMERICAN EXPRESS *Access, Diners, Visa.*

Waterhouses — Old Beams ★ — £80

Tel 0538 308254 Fax 0538 308157 — RR

Leek Road Waterhouses Staffordshire ST10 3HW — Map 6 C3

A charming restaurant with a conservatory and rooms, on the A523 Leek-Ashbourne road. Inside, oak beams, an open fire, fresh flowers, a grand piano and good-quality place settings are matched by Nigel Wallis' fine cooking and attentive service led by Anne. His no-nonsense dishes are full of flavour and interest and often use luxury ingredients: smoked salmon mousse with a lime and coriander dressing, fresh foie gras with muscat jelly and blinis, turbot poached in Noilly Prat served on a 'real parsley sauce', millefeuilles of chargrilled fillet steak covered with a Madeira sauce, duet of pears with chestnut ice cream. A well balanced wine list, which offers sensible tasting notes, though the entry price for champagne is a bit steep! No smoking. ***Seats** 50. Private Room 12. L 12-2 D 7-10. Closed L Sat, D Sun, all Mon, Bank Holidays, 2 weeks Jan. Set L from £9.95 Set D from £18.50.* AMERICAN EXPRESS *Access, Diners, Visa.*

Rooms — £87

Five of the six bedrooms are in a building across the road and are quite superb in every way, with hand-made beds, Egyptian cotton sheets and most luxurious marble bathrooms. No smoking.

Wateringbury — Wateringbury Hotel 59% — £61

Tel 0622 812632 Fax 0622 812720 — H

Tonbridge Road Wateringbury nr Maidstone Kent ME18 5NS — Map 11 C5

Rooms at this tile-hung roadside inn range from singles to a four-poster suite. There's a cane-furnished conservatory, a cocktail bar and two function rooms (catering for up to 80 delegates). ***Rooms** 40. Garden, sauna.* AMERICAN EXPRESS *Access, Diners, Visa.*

Watford — Hilton National 64% — £109

Tel 0923 235881 Fax 0923 220836 — H

Elton Way Watford Hertfordshire WD2 8HA — Map 15 E2

Practical accommodation, a leisure centre and extensive conference facilities (for up to 350). Children under the age of 14 are accommodated free in parents' room, but their time in the leisure centre is limited. ***Rooms** 198. Indoor swimming pool, gymnasium, sauna, spa bath, steam room, beauty salon.* AMERICAN EXPRESS *Access, Diners, Visa.*

Watford — Places of Interest

Palace Theatre Tel 0923 35455.
Watford Football Ground Vicarage Road Tel 0923 30933.
Watford Ski School Garston Tel 0923 676559.

Wath-in-Nidderdale — Sportsman's Arms — £60

Tel 0423 711306 — RR

Wath-in-Nidderdale Pateley Bridge nr Harrogate North Yorkshire HG3 5PP — Map 6 C1

Ray Carter and Chris Williamson put prime English produce to excellent use in this very cheerful inn dating from the 17th century. Their network of suppliers guarantees the best raw materials for dishes like fillet of Nidderdale trout in a sun-dried tomato sauce, breast of duckling with redcurrants, olives and oranges in a tarragon sauce, and roast best end of lamb with whole roast garlic with leeks and tomato concassé. Summer pudding has for many years been the favourite dessert. Separate cheese list. Super wine list with especially keen prices to match – several bottles under £10. Good New World selection. ***Seats** 50. Private Room 8. L 12-2 D 7-9.30. Closed 25 Dec. Set L £13 Set D £18.75. Access, Visa.*

See over

Rooms £50

Seven rooms (five of which are not en suite) offer comfortable accommodation.

Watlington — Well House £60

RR

Tel 0491 613333

34-40 High Street Watlington Oxfordshire OX9 5PY Map 15 D2

In a quiet village 12 miles south-east of Oxford and two miles from the M40 (J6), five little properties, some dating back to the 15th century, have been carefully altered to produce a delightful restaurant with rooms. Owners Patricia and Alan Crawford are particularly friendly hosts and meals in the beamed dining room, with its exposed brick fireplace and well-spaced tables, are very relaxed affairs. Patricia's cooking is sound and very straightforward, offered on both table d'hote and carte at lunch and dinner: gratin of seafood in a scallop shell, wild mushrooms in a pastry case, stir-fried beef with ginger and spring onions, rack of lamb with port and redcurrant sauce, chicken supreme with prawns and water chestnuts. A vegetarian menu offers four choices at each stage. Simpler snacks at lunchtime in the small bar. Good wine list with plenty of choice under £20. ***Seats** 40. Private Room 15. L 12.30-2 D 7-9.15 (Sat to 9.30). Closed L Sat, D Sun, all Mon, most Bank Holidays except 25 Dec. Set meals £12.90/£16.40.* AMERICAN EXPRESS *Access, Diners, Visa.*

Rooms £76

Ten bedrooms all have their own shape and character; there's a quiet lounge with an open fireplace and a bar with an old well and access to the rear terrace. Cots and high-chairs provided for junior guests.

Weedon — Crossroads Hotel 63% £52

H

Tel 0327 40354 Fax 0327 40849

High Street Weedon Northamptonshire NN7 4PX Map 15 D1

A convenient location at the junction of the A5 and A45, and a quarter-century in the Amos family's ownership are two pluses here. Notable throughout the public rooms is a unique private collection of antique clocks. Accommodation is divided between traditionally furnished bedrooms in the main building (once a tollhouse and lodge) and uniform, double-glazed rooms in the newer Garden House. Under-16s stay free in parents' room. Conferences up to 50; banquets to 120. ***Rooms** 48. Garden, outdoor swimming pool, tennis, brasserie (7am-6pm). Closed 25 & 26 Dec.* AMERICAN EXPRESS *Access, Diners, Visa.*

Wells — Ritcher's £52

R

Tel 0749 679085

5 Sadler Street Wells Somerset BA5 2RR Map 13 F1

Tucked away down an alley between two shops in the town centre, there's a choice of dining at Nick Hart and Kate Ritcher's bistro/restaurant. The pine-furnished bistro on the ground floor (open seven days a week for lunch and dinner) offers a wide selection from steaks and home-made beefburgers to salmon with tarragon hollandaise and Somerset game pie; most main dishes are around £6-8. In the evenings there is also a fixed-price menu written up on a blackboard. Upstairs, the more formal restaurant (dinner Tues-Sat, lunch by arrangement) boasts comfortably upholstered rattan chairs around crisply-clothed tables and a fixed-price menu with the likes of quails stuffed with chicken and asparagus mousse on a citrus julienne with tarragon butter, and fresh salmon with Chablis cream sauce and white crab meat. Tables outside in a small courtyard (Bistro menu only) are about to benefit from a sliding roof to cope with the fickle English summer. Friendly, informal service. Parking can be difficult during the day. No children under 10 in the restaurant. ***Seats** 14. Private Room 18. L 11.30-2.30 D 7-9.30. Closed 26 Dec. Set L £8.75/£10.95 (bistro) Set D £14.50/£17.50. Access, Visa.*

Wells Places of Interest

Tourist Information Tel 0749 72552.
Wells Cathedral Tel 0749 74483.
Historic Houses, Castles and Gardens
The Bishop's Palace Tel 0749 78691.
Milton Cottage and Gardens Tel 0749 72168.
Pear Tree House Litton Tel 076121 220.

Wembley Hilton National 65% £129

Tel 081-902 8839 Fax 081-900 2201 **H**

Empire Way Wembley Middlesex HA9 8DS **Map 15 E2**

Practical modern accommodation, within easy walking distance of Wembley Arena, Stadium and Conference Centre. Carvery-style restaurant and a bar that gets very busy on match and concert dates. 10 conference rooms catering for up to 250 delegates. A leisure centre is due to replace the business centre in early 1994. ***Rooms** 300. News kiosk.* AMERICAN EXPRESS *Access, Diners, Visa.*

Wentbridge Forte Travelodge £42

Tel 0977 620711 **L**

Barnsdale Bar Wentbridge nr Pontefract West Yorkshire WS8 3JB **Map 7 D1**

Located on the A1 southbound at the Barnsdale Bar service area. 6 miles south of Junction 33 of the M62, 8 miles north of Doncaster. ***Rooms** 56.* AMERICAN EXPRESS *Access, Visa.*

Wentbridge Wentbridge House 63% £75

Tel 0977 620444 Fax 0977 620148 **H**

Wentbridge nr Pontefract West Yorkshire WF8 3JJ **Map 7 D1**

Creeper-clad Wentbridge House, now owned by a local businessman, sits in 15 acres of wooded grounds in the beautiful Went Valley, just half a mile from the A1. Built in 1700, it has a period feel reinforced by suits of armour hanging in the main stairwell. Bedrooms, including the four-poster Oak Room, are individually furnished in traditional style. Popular for conferences; the largest of several meeting rooms can take up to 120 people theatre-style. Bedrooms, front hall and restaurant were due to have been refurbished by the end of 1993. No dogs. ***Rooms** 12. Garden.* AMERICAN EXPRESS *Access, Diners, Visa.*

Weobley Ye Olde Salutation Inn NEW £53

Tel 0544 318443 **I**

Market Pitch Weobley Hereford & Worcester HR4 8SJ **Map 14 A1**

Remarkable transformation by dedicated young owners of this 14th-century ale and cider house has created stylish overnight accommodation with a unifying Victorian theme. Three large bedrooms (one with a four-poster) have en-suite WC/shower rooms, while two smaller doubles, which share a vast Victorian bathroom, are let at a realistic economy price. No smoking in bedrooms but it's allowed in the residents' lounge. Commendable breakfasts. No children under 12, except infants (by arrangement). ***Rooms** 5.* AMERICAN EXPRESS *Access, Visa.*

West Bexington — Manor Hotel — 59% — £76

Tel 0308 897785 Fax 0308 897035 — **H**

Beach Road West Bexington nr Bridport Dorset DT2 9DF — **Map 13 F2**

"Where country meets coast", says their literature, and indeed Richard and Jayne Childs' manor house stands in a garden on a gentle slope near the famous Chesil Bank shingle beach. Stone walls and oak panelling are much in evidence. Day rooms include lounge/reading room, cellar bar, restaurant and conservatory. Pretty, cottagey bedrooms, most with sea views, are furnished with old pine and enhanced with books and ornaments. Families are very well catered for. ***Rooms** 13. Garden, children's playground.* AMERICAN EXPRESS *Access, Diners, Visa.*

West Bromwich — Moat House — 59% — £89

Tel 021-553 6111 Fax 021-525 7403 — **H**

Birmingham Road Bromwich West Midlands B70 6RS — **Map 6 C4**

A modern hotel with good-sized bedrooms and conference facilities. M5, junction 1, close to M6 interchange. ***Rooms** 172. Coffee shop (8am-4pm), news kiosk. Access, Diners, Visa.*

West Bromwich — Places of Interest

Art Gallery and Museum Wednesbury Tel 021-556 0683.
West Bromwich Albion Football Ground The Hawthorns Tel 021-525 8888.

West Chiltington — Roundabout Hotel — 61% — £80

Tel 0798 813838 Fax 0798 812962 — **H**

Monkmead Lane West Chiltington nr Pulborough West Sussex RH20 2PF — **Map 11 A6**

"Nowhere near a roundabout", a Tudor-style hotel with leaded windows, whitewashed walls and attractive, cottagey exterior. The cartwheel chandelier in the entrance hall, fairy lights over the bar and armchairs upholstered in tapestry style all characterise the public rooms. Attractive oak furniture neatly offsets the very English, rose-patterned bedcovers and curtains in the bedrooms. More spacious rooms are classified as Executive (although decorated in essentially the same style) and some have four-poster beds. Tiled bathrooms are modest, but well kept. Children up to 12 stay free in parents' room. ***Rooms** 24. Garden.* AMERICAN EXPRESS *Access, Diners, Visa.*

West Runton — The Links Country Park Hotel & Golf Club — 62% — £150*

Tel 0263 838383 Fax 0263 838265 — **H**

Sandy Lane West Runton nr Cromer Norfolk NR27 9QH — **Map 10 C1**

Midway between Sheringham and Cromer on the A149, the privately-owned Links is a large Edwardian mock-Tudor building. Conferences and banquets are a growing part of the business, but private guests are well looked after in comfortable day rooms and decently-equipped bedrooms (satellite TV, 24hr room service). Suitable for sports-orientated families; children under 16 free in parents' room. *Half-board terms only.
***Rooms** 40. Garden, indoor swimming pool, tennis, 9-hole golf course, sauna, solarium. Access, Visa.*

Weston-on-the-Green — Weston Manor — 61% — £100

Tel 0869 50621 Fax 0869 50901 — **H**

Weston-on-the-Green Oxfordshire OX6 8QL — **Map 15 D1**

2 miles from junction 9 of the M40, on the B430 six miles morth of Oxford, a castellated 15th-century manor house standing in 13 acres of gardens and grounds. Accommodation is divided between the main house and smaller, more modern rooms in the former coach house. Most characterful of the day rooms is the Baronial Hall dining room complete with minstrel's gallery. Themed party weekends are a regular feature. ***Rooms*** *37. Garden, outdoor swimming pool, squash.* AMERICAN EXPRESS *Access, Diners, Visa.*

Weston-super-Mare — Grand Atlantic — 64% — £95

Tel 0934 626543 Fax 0934 415048 — **H**

Beach Road Weston-super-Mare Avon BS23 1BA — **Map 13 E1**

Modernised Victorian hotel standing in pleasant gardens across from sandy bay and pleasure beach. Winter conference trade. ***Rooms*** *76. Outdoor swimming pool (Jul & Aug only).* AMERICAN EXPRESS *Access, Diners, Visa.*

Weston-super-Mare — Places of Interest

Clevedon Court (NT) Nr Clevedon.
The Manor House Walton-in-Gordano Tel 0272 872067.
Weston-Super-Mare Beach.
Avon Ski Centre Churchill Tel 0934 852335.

Weston-under-Penyard — Wharton Lodge — 73% — £85

Tel 0989 750795 Fax 0989 750700 — **HR**

Weston-under-Penyard Ross-on-Wye Hereford & Worcester HR9 7JX — **Map 14 B1**

Three miles east of Ross-on-Wye, by the A40, Wharton Lodge stands in 15 acres of mature parkland. From the grand entrance hall a carved oak staircase ends in a minstrel's gallery where antiques and heirlooms abound. Each bedroom is individually named and furnished with fine pieces, bold fabrics and gold-tapped bathrooms. Small private function facilities and a private dining room seating 60. No children under 7; 7-12s free in parents' room. ***Rooms*** *9. Garden, riding, fishing.* AMERICAN EXPRESS *Access, Diners, Visa.*

Restaurant — £75

An elegant setting for light lunches (from croque monsieur with stuffed olives to local game and winter vegetable pie or paella) and candle-lit dinners with a good à la carte choice. ***Seats*** *40. Parties 16. L 12.30-2 D 7-9 (Sun to 8.30). Set L £10.50 Set D £22.50.*

Weston-under-Redcastle — Hawkstone Park — 61% — £75

Tel 0939 200611 Fax 0939 200311 — **H**

Weston-under-Redcastle Shrewsbury Shropshire SY4 5UY — **Map 6 B3**

Sandy Lyle learned his game here, and the golf courses (one 18-hole and a further 9-hole) remain a great attraction; a new golf and social centre opened last year with indoor teaching facilities and other golf amenities plus a new bar and restaurant. Many other sport and leisure facilities are available, both indoors and out, and for après sport there's a pub, a cocktail bar, a lounge and two restaurants. Day rooms and bedrooms (all with fully-tiled bathrooms) are part of an ongoing improvement programme. The splendid monuments and follies in the grounds have been restored and are now open to the public. Conference facilities for up to 200 delegates. Children up to 14 stay free in parents' room. No dogs. ***Rooms*** *59. Garden, outdoor swimming pool, golf, putting, tennis, sauna, solarium.* AMERICAN EXPRESS *Access, Diners, Visa.*

Westonbirt — Hare & Hounds — 59% — £75

Tel 0666 880233 Fax 0666 880241 — H

Westonbirt nr Tetbury Gloucestershire GL8 8QL — Map 14 B2

A former farmhouse built of Cotswold stone and standing in wooded grounds by the A433. Jeremy and Martin Price have run it for 40 years, and its old-fashioned charm and homely atmosphere remain a great appeal. Sturdy oak and leather are used for furnishings, and some of the bedrooms have four-posters. Five rooms are in the garden cottage, with their own adjacent parking. ***Rooms** 30. Garden, squash, tennis, putting, snooker.* AMERICAN EXPRESS *Access, Diners, Visa.*

Wetheral — The Crown — 70% — £106

Tel 0228 561888 Fax 0228 561637 — H

Wetheral nr Carlisle Cumbria CA4 8ES — Map 4 C3

The Crown stands above the river Eden, tucked away from the village itself, yet only minutes from junction 42/43 of the M6 (via the A69/B6263). Despite its somewhat austere, bright white frontage, it's a warm and welcoming hotel and the staff are excellent. *Waltons,* the pubby bar, exudes atmosphere and serves a good pint of Thwaites (who own Shire Inns), while the garden-facing lounge is suitably relaxing. Bedroom accommodation is attractive and well-maintained with bright modern bathrooms. Both the conference facilities (for up to 200) and the smart leisure club (complete with children's splash pool) are purpose-built and discreetly separate. Pleasant conservatory restaurant. Children under 16 stay free in parents' room. Shire Inns. ***Rooms** 49. Garden, indoor swimming pool, sauna, solarium, spa bath, keep-fit equipment, squash, snooker.* AMERICAN EXPRESS *Access, Diners, Visa.*

Wetherby — Sheba — £35

Tel 0937 583694 — R

Swan Cottage 36 North Street Wetherby West Yorkshire LS22 4NN — Map 7 D1

Reliable Bangladeshi restaurant using no animal fats. Speciality home-style pasanda and tikkas. ***Seats** 40. D only 6-11.30 (Fri & Sat to 12). Closed 25 Dec. Access, Visa.*

Weybridge — Casa Romana — £65

Tel 0932 843470 — R

2 Temple Hall Monument Hill Weybridge Surrey KT13 8RH — Map 15 E3

Etchings of old Rome adorn the walls of a comfortable Italian restaurant where diners sit on colourful striped chairs. The menu offers a lengthy selection of hors d'oeuvre, which could precede a fish special, a steak or one of many ways with chicken or veal (veal Casanova is cooked with oysters in a brandy and lobster sauce and topped with melted mozzarella). Set menus include one for vegetarians. Good-value, fixed-price lunches offer a reasonable choice. Popular for Sunday lunch when a choice of roasts is offered plus sweets and cheeses from a trolley. Good Italian wines, though vintages are rarely shown on the list; a dozen or so fine French bottles complete the choice. ***Seats** 90. L 12-3 D 7-10.45 (Sun to 10). Closed L Sat, 25 & 26 Dec. Set L £12.95 (Sun £14.95) Set D £16.50.* AMERICAN EXPRESS *Access, Diners, Visa.*

Weybridge — Oatlands Park — 69% — £128

Tel 0932 847242 Fax 0932 842252 — H

146 Oatlands Drive Weybridge Surrey KT13 9HB — Map 15 E3

A late 18th-century mansion, in 10 acres of parkland, whose porticoed entrance leads into a most impressive galleried lounge with trompe l'oeil marble columns and tapestry hangings under a large glass dome. Bedrooms feature mahogany furniture, but sizes vary considerably. Weekly residential conferences (for up to 300) are the main business. Sister hotel to the *Swiss Cottage Hotel* in London. ***Rooms** 117. Garden, coffee lounge (10am-11pm), tennis.* AMERICAN EXPRESS *Access, Diners, Visa.*

Weybridge Ship Thistle 63% — £116

Tel 0932 848364 Fax 0932 857153 — **H**

5 Monument Green Weybridge Surrey KT13 8BQ — **Map 15 E3**

Originally an 18th-century coaching inn, now much extended with conference/banqueting facilities for up to 140. Open-plan public rooms with a few antiques adding period character. ***Rooms** 39.* AMERICAN EXPRESS *Access, Diners, Visa.*

Weymouth Perry's NEW — £57

Tel 0305 785799 — **R**

The Harbourside 4 Trinity Road Weymouth Dorset DT4 8TJ — **Map 13 F3**

Down by the attractively busy Old Harbour, Perry's offers a good choice of meat dishes – terrine of chicken, rack of lamb, venison with cassis – but the main emphasis is on the blackboard menu of seafood dishes that vary according to the local catch. Simply cooked fresh vegetables accompany. A small covered patio to the rear is popular in summer. ***Seats** 50. Parties 40. Private Room 40. L 12-2 D 7-10. Set L £8.95/£10.95. Closed L Mon & Sat & D Sun in winter. Access, Visa.*

Weymouth Places of Interest

Weymouth Tourist Information Tel 0305 772444.
Weymouth Beach.
Nothe Fort Barrack Road Tel 0305 787243.

Whimple Woodhayes Hotel 75% — £85

Tel 0404 822237 — **HR**

Whimple nr Exeter Devon EX5 2TD — **Map 13 E2**

Katherine Rendle and her family run their delightfully situated Georgian home-from-home just off the A30 Exeter to Honiton Road with great style and panache. Surrounded by park-like gardens, an apple orchard and sheep grazing in the distance, the setting is rural and peaceful, although Exeter is only eight miles away. The guests' wishes come first, and afternoon tea with mouthwatering cakes included in the tariff is a typically personal touch; their policy of no nasty extras on bills (teas, coffees, sandwiches and light laundry are not charged as extra) is "greatly appreciated" by their guests. There are two lounges, one with green, pale blue and apricot decor and soft sofas, the second with a grey scheme, a small library and even deeper sofas. For a peaceful drink, head for the flagstoned bar with its old pine furniture. Spacious bedrooms have solidly traditional furniture. Housekeeping is good and the breakfasts are excellent. An adult, friendly country retreat, with no children under 12 to disturb the peace. No dogs. ***Rooms** 6. Garden, tennis.* AMERICAN EXPRESS *Access, Diners, Visa.*

Restaurant — £62

Katherine discusses her menus with guests and special diets are gladly catered for. Dinners are party occasions in the lovely dining room (where French doors lead out on to a terrace), and the six courses could include such dishes as avocado, apple and smoked salmon salad, crab bisque, steamed turbot with mustard and dill sauce, and saddle of lamb with wild mushroom stuffing. Home-made ice creams and sorbets are offered as an alternative to crème brulée or perhaps prune and armagnac tart to finish. First-rate, unpasteurised mature local Cheddar (or Stilton) is also offered, accompanied by oatcakes, grapes and walnuts. ***Seats** 18. Parties 10. L by arrangement for residents (£15) D 7-9.30. Set D £25.*

Whitewell — Inn at Whitewell — £63

Tel 020 08 222 — **I**

Whitewell Forest of Bowland nr Clitheroe Lancashire BB7 3AT — **Map 6 B1**

Richard Bowman and his staff imbue this ancient stone inn with warmth, personality and a pleasing quirkiness. It's set amid the wild beauty of North Lancashire, overlooking the River Hodder and standing next to the village church. A stone-floored tap room and a library with good books and pictures are both mellow and civilised. Bedrooms feature luxurious fabrics, Bang & Olufsen music systems and video recorders; some have antique furniture, peat fires and Victorian baths. Telephones are available on request. Food in both bar and restaurant; good breakfasts. ***Rooms** 9. Garden, coarse & game fishing, pool table.* AMERICAN EXPRESS *Access, Diners, Visa.*

Whitstable — The Whitstable Oyster Fishery Company — NEW — £45

Tel 0227 276856 Fax 0227 770666 — **R**

The Royal Nature Oyster Stores The Horseridge Whitstable Kent CT5 1BU — **Map 11 C5**

The restaurant is housed in the original oyster store of the company from which it takes its name. It overlooks the sea, and the original tidal tanks hold oysters and other live shellfish. The eating area is simple in decor but manages to be warm and welcoming (especially in the evening when the gingham-clad tables are lit by candles). The blackboard menu is short, straightforward and fishy, and on a typical day you might find oysters, fish soup, deep-fried cuttle fish, grilled plaice, hake, sea bass and lobster. Accompaniments are new potatoes, salads and a simple sauce or mayonnaise. ***Seats** 67. Private Room 30. L 12-2.30 D 7-9.30. Closed Mon (exc. Bank Holidays).* AMERICAN EXPRESS *Access, Diners, Visa.*

Wickham — Old House Hotel — 66% — £85

Tel 0329 833049 Fax 0329 833672 — **HR**

The Square Wickham Hampshire PO17 5JG — **Map 15 D4**

A splendid Georgian town house overlooking the village square at the Junction of the A32 and B2177. It's run with dedication by Richard and Annie Skipwith, who have created a civilised and unpretentious hotel. Polished wood floorboards, rugs and period furniture grace the two lounges, one of which is panelled; solid period pieces are also to be found in the warm, comfortable and prettily decorated bedrooms. No dogs. ***Rooms** 12. Garden. Closed 2 weeks Christmas, 2 weeks Aug.* AMERICAN EXPRESS *Access, Diners, Visa.*

Restaurant — £70

Classical and modern elements meet in the kitchen, and Annie Skipwith's background in Provence is a major influence on chef Nick Harman. The surroundings are relaxed and friendly, and the short menu, which changes weekly, offers dishes such as spicy lentil soup, breast of duck with a warm fresh herb vinaigrette and pork fillet served with a sauce of dark rum and orange. Home-made ices are regulars on the dessert menu. ***Seats** 40. Private Room 14. L 12.30-1.45 D 7.30-9.45. Closed Bank Holidays, L Sat-Mon, D Sun. Set meals £19/£23.*

Willerby — Grange Park — 67% — £87

Tel 0482 656488 Fax 0482 655848 — **H**

Main Street Willerby nr Hull Humberside HU10 6EA — **Map 7 E1**

Adjacent to the A164 and Willerby Shopping Park, Grange Park is a much-extended Victorian house standing in 12 acres of grounds. Besides comfortable modern accommodation it offers extensive purpose-built conference facilities (for up to 550). Families are quite well catered for with a children's playground and (limited) crèche facilities; children up to 10 stay free in parents' room. ***Rooms** 104. Garden, indoor swimming pool, gymnasium, helipad.* AMERICAN EXPRESS *Access, Diners, Visa.*

Willerby **Willerby Manor** **62%** **£97**

Tel 0482 652616 Fax 0482 653901 **H**

Well Lane Willerby nr Hull Humberside HU10 6ER **Map 7 E1**

Part of a local family-owned wine merchant business, this predominantly business hotel is in a Victorian house standing in three acres of landscaped gardens. Everglades Bar is conservatory in style and overlooks the garden; there are two restaurants (French and Italian in style) and a number of rooms for conferences and banquets (catering for up to 500 delegates). Most of the bedrooms are in a modern annexe, and half have king-size beds. ***Rooms** 36. Garden.* AMERICAN EXPRESS *Access, Visa.*

Williton **White House** **£65**

Tel 0984 632306 **RR**

Williton Somerset TA4 4QW **Map 13 E1**

Engaging hosts Dick and Kay Smith have spent more than 25 years entertaining here, and are still gaining new friends. Their nightly-changing dinners are based on the best local produce, with a choice of three courses at a set price. Warm salad of pigeon breast with hot beetroot, black-baked chicken with mango salsa and sweet potato purée and fillet of beef 'Alice Waters' (marinated in red wine, rolled in freshly chopped herbs and roasted) show their delightfully different style derived from England, France and California. Even the Orient gets a look-in with Korean-style pork served with pear salad. Soufflés might appear in a suissesse (cheese) version, or in a crab tartlet or lemon cheesecake. Naturally flavoured soups and local cheeses with home-made oatcakes are optional extras. No smoking. A serious, very personal and mainly French wine list has just a smattering of New World wines. Many half bottles (French only), interesting tasting notes and very fair prices. ***Seats** 36. D only 7.30-8.30. Set D £25. Closed Nov-May. No credit cards (could change).*

Rooms **£68**

Residents may choose between a bedroom in the main house or those in the former stables with individual access. Twelve rooms in all.

Wilmington **Home Farm** **58%** **£56**

Tel 040483 278246 **H**

Wilmington nr Honiton Devon EX14 9JR **Map 13 E2**

A thatched former farmhouse, with a five-acre garden, a cobbled courtyard, a flagstoned bar and a homely lounge with piano, books and board games. Bedrooms are divided between the main house and the Garden and Courtyard wings. Four rooms do not have en-suite facilities. ***Rooms** 13. Garden.* AMERICAN EXPRESS *Access, Visa.*

Wilmslow **Harry's** **£48**

Tel 0625 528799 **R**

70 Grove Street Wilmslow Cheshire **Map 6 B2**

Harry Yeung, chairman, managing director and head chef of Yang Sing Restaurants Ltd (see under Manchester), is the head chef here opposite Barclays Bank. A simple, single doorway leads up to the first-floor location where those in the know enjoy excellent Cantonese-inspired dishes served by friendly, helpful staff. A whole page of the menu is given over to Harry's Suggestions, which could include king prawns with glazed walnuts, scallops with pickled vegetables, chicken with pineapple pieces and

See over

beef and yam casserole in coconut cream sauce. ***Seats** 90. Private Room 40. D only 6-11. Closed Mon, 25 Dec. Set D from £16.* AMERICAN EXPRESS *Access, Visa.*

Wilmslow Moat House 58% £96

Tel 0625 529201 Fax 0625 531876 **H**

Altrincham Road Wilmslow Cheshire SK9 4LR **Map 6 B2**

A modern hotel in Swiss chalet style offering modest accommodation, with good, on-the-spot leisure club facilities, conference facilities for 300 and a nightclub. Courtesy coaches to Manchester Airport, a mile away. Free long-term parking (up to two weeks) for overnight guests on production of flight tickets. Vastly reduced weekend 2-night rates. ***Rooms** 125. Indoor swimming pool, gymnasium, squash, sauna, spa bath, solarium, beautician.* AMERICAN EXPRESS *Access, Diners, Visa.*

Wilmslow Stanneylands 70% £106

Tel 0625 525225 Fax 0625 537282 **HR**

Stanneylands Road Wilmslow Cheshire SK9 4EY **Map 6 B2**

Set in a semi-rural location, hidden in the Bollin Valley, but with easy access from the A34 and close to Manchester Airport (10 minutes away). Two acres of picturesque gardens surround the redbrick house, and the interior is more modern than the Edwardian exterior might suggest, mainly due to modernisation in order to cater for conferences of up to 80. Original day rooms include an oak-panelled lounge and a cosy bar-lounge with an open fire. Individually decorated bedrooms with solid, freestanding furniture benefit from pleasant views. Two characterful private dining rooms hold up to 100. Weekend rates are greatly reduced. ***Rooms** 33. Garden.* AMERICAN EXPRESS *Access, Diners, Visa.*

Restaurant £80

The twin wood-panelled dining rooms are clubby and comfortable with discreet, efficient service from long-serving restaurant manager, Jacques Franke and his team. In the kitchen Steven Kitchen keeps up with modern trends with such dishes as a sun-dried plum tomato bavarois with horseradish surrounded by carpaccio of courgette; roast peppers and lentil salad on olive bread with a beetroot and onion vinaigrette; and seared scallops on finely sliced aromatic vegetables with a warm fino sherry dressing. A seasonally changing à la carte is supplemented by weekly market specials plus a good value fixed-price lunch and, at night, a six-course set menu of interesting tastes and textures. Reliably cooked dishes are attractively presented. An excellent and comprehensive wine list has great depth, with many fairly-priced wines to choose from. ***Seats** 80. Parties 25. Private Room 100. L 12.30-2 D 7-10. Closed 1 Jan, Good Friday, 26 Dec, D Sun (except to residents). Set L £9.50/£12.50 Set D £25.*

Wilmslow Place of Interest

Quarry Bank Mill, Museum of the Cotton Textile Industry Styal Tel 0625 527468.

Wimborne Les Bouviers £60

Tel 0202 889555 **R**

Oakley Hill Merley Wimborne Dorset BH21 1RJ **Map 14 C4**

Chef-patron James Coward presents an enterprising French and English menu in a cottagey and sunny restaurant with ceiling fans, floral drapes and a conservatory. Local produce is used whenever possible, and everything from bread to sorbets and petits fours is made on the premises. Some typical choices: terrine of confit of duck garnished with orange and pear salad, hot cheese soufflé with watercress and horseradish sauce, steamed salmon with lemon grass sauce and scampi tails, noisettes of lamb cooked with turmeric and served on a bed of aubergine with courgette, olive and basil sauce. The carte is full of unnecessarily overlong descriptions (in both English and French). No smoking. ***Seats** 40. Private Room 12. L 12-2.15 D 7-10 (Sat from 6.45). Closed L Sat, all Sun, 1 week Christmas. Set L £8.45/£11.75 Set D £19.95 (5-course).* AMERICAN EXPRESS *Access, Visa.*

Wimborne Places of Interest

Wimborne Minster Tel 0202 884753.

Historic Houses, Castles and Gardens

Cranborne Manor Gardens Cranborne Tel 07254 248.
Edmondsham House and Gardens Cranborne Tel 07254 207.
Kingston Lacey (NT) Tel 0202 883402.

Winchester Forte Crest 69% £68

Tel 0962 861611 Fax 0962 841503 **H**

Paternoster Row Winchester Hampshire SO23 9LQ **Map 15 D3**

A modern hotel just across from the cathedral. Among the day rooms are a coffee shop with lots of light pine, a lounge with dark leather seating and a cocktail bar. Bedrooms boast smart Italian furniture and Executive rooms overlook the cathedral. ***Rooms** 94.* AMERICAN EXPRESS *Access, Diners, Visa.*

Winchester Lainston House 75% £145

Tel 0962 863588 Fax 0962 72672 **H**

Sparsholt Winchester Hampshire SO21 2LJ **Map 15 D3**

63 acres of majestic parkland surround Lainston House, an elegant William and Mary building dating from 1668; 2½ miles from Winchester on the A272. That it's an impressive establishment is clear from the moment you enter the parquet-floored foyer, which is dominated by a large fireplace decorated with fine Delft tiles. Flowers, paintings, books and ornaments make the comfortable lounge homely and relaxing and there's a splendid bar panelled with carved cedar. Main-house bedrooms are of grand proportions, with quality soft furnishings, period furniture and harmonious colour schemes; annexe rooms in Chudleigh Court are smaller. The old stable block was converted last year to provide six smart new bedrooms; these overlook a rose garden. Exclusive Hotels. ***Rooms** 38. Garden, tennis, coarse fishing, helipad.* AMERICAN EXPRESS *Access, Diners, Visa.*

Winchester Royal Hotel 67% £65

Tel 0962 840840 Fax 0962 841582 **H**

St Peter Street Winchester Hampshire SO22 8BS **Map 15 D3**

Hidden away just 100 yards from the High Street, this former Benedictine convent (now owner-run) conceals behind a modest frontage a secluded walled garden overlooked by lounge, bar terrace and a modern extension of smart, up-to-date bedrooms. A striking marble-floored foyer leads to separate function and meeting rooms accommodating up to 120 delegates. The terrace barbecue is a popular summer feature. Under-14s stay free in parents' room. *Garden. **Rooms** 76.* AMERICAN EXPRESS *Access, Diners, Visa.*

Winchester Wykeham Arms £73

Tel 0962 853834 Fax 0962 854411 **IR**

75 Kingsgate Street Winchester Hampshire SO23 9PE **Map 15 D3**

Tucked away down narrow back streets, immediately south of the Cathedral (by Kingsgate on the junction between Canon Street and Kingsgate Street), Graeme and Anne Jameson have turned the 200-year-old 'Wyk' into one of the finest hostelries in the land. The main bar has old-fashioned schoolroom desks with integral seats, some authentically carved with the initials of inattentive pupils from years gone by. Collections of hats, mugs and fascinating old prints and cartoons adorn six other

See over

interconnecting rooms, all set up for eating. Individually decorated bedrooms have stylish matching bedcovers and curtains and mostly honeyed pine furniture. All have mini-bars, television and telephones plus homely extras like fresh flowers, books, magazines and pot-pourri. Modern en-suite bathrooms, all with showers over tubs, boast quality toiletries. First-rate breakfasts begin with freshly-squeezed orange juice and are served in a charming period breakfast room on the first floor. No children under 14 overnight or in restaurant. ***Rooms*** *7. Garden, sauna.* AMERICAN EXPRESS *Access, Visa.*

Restaurant £50

A blackboard menu changes twice daily offering unusual but successful combinations of flavours like parsnip and apple or green pea and thyme soup, coarse country pork and apricot paté, or broccoli, walnut and Roquefort strudel. Lunchtime sees a menu encompassing sandwiches (some toasted), ploughman's, a good choice of starters and popular hot dishes such as Wyk potted haddock smokie and cottage pie with crusty bread. White chocolate and Drambuie mousse with bananas or raspberry and cassis trifle might be among the six or so desserts. 22 of the wines, from a well-chosen list, are also available by the glass. For summer eating and drinking there is a neat walled garden. Booking is absolutely essential. No-smoking area. ***Seats*** *50. Parties 8. L 12-2.30 D 6.30-8.30. Closed Sun, 25 Dec. Set L £10/£14 Set D £13/£16.*

Winchester Places of Interest

Tourist Information Tel 0962 840500/848180.
Theatre Royal Tel 0962 842122.
Avington Park Tel 0962 78202.
Hinton Ampner (NT) Nr New Alresford Tel 0962 771305.
Winchester Cathedral Tel 0962 53137.
Marwell Zoo Colden Common Tel 0962 777406.
Museums and Art Galleries
Museums Peninsula Barracks Tel 0962 864176.
Winchester Cathedral Triforium Gallery NH Museum of the Year Awards 1990 - Winner, Best Fine/Applied Art Museum.
Gurkha, Light Infantry Royal Green Jackets and Royal Hussars.
Winchester City Museum Tel 0962 848269.
Guildhall Gallery Tel 0962 52874.

Windermere Holbeck Ghyll 68% £130*

Tel 053 94 32375 Fax 053 94 34743 **HR**

Holbeck Lane Windermere Cumbria LA23 1LU **Map 4 C3**

If approaching from Windermere on the A591, take the right turning signposted Troutbeck *after* the Brockhole Visitor Centre (coming from Ambleside, it's the first Troutbeck sign to the left). Once the hunting lodge of Lord Lonsdale, the first president of the Automobile Association, and the man who bequeathed the Lonsdale Belt to British boxing champions, the house commands a majestic view over Lake Windermere. There's a wonderful smell of polish in the oak-panelled entrance hall with its inglenook fireplace, and the comfortable lounges and billiard room are traditionally furnished in country-house style. Lots of attention to detail in the individually designed bedrooms includes a decanter of sherry, flowers and home-made biscuits with early morning tea. Good bathrooms with excellent water pressure (from their own spring) provide large bathrobes and Potter & Moore toiletries. Caring service under the watchful eyes of owners Patricia and David Nicholson. Small boardroom seats 16. Free use of indoor leisure facilities within a couple of minutes' drive. Families with young children are well catered for. *Half-board terms only. ***Rooms*** *14. Garden, putting, snooker.* AMERICAN EXPRESS *Access, Visa.*

Restaurant

£55

An oak-panelled restaurant serving a four-or five-course menu of traditional English-style dishes ranging from seafood risotto, duck livers pan-fried with foie gras or asparagus salad to scrambled egg with smoked salmon and then lemon sole fillets with orange and mango or a duo of Herdwick lamb. Dishes involve many flavours (as appears to be the Lake District way!) but not so many as to detract from the main intention. Desserts served from a buffet table. Fairly-priced, diverse wine list and attentive service. No smoking. ***Seats** 30. D only 7-8.45. Set D £26/£29.*

Windermere Merewood Hotel 66%

£75

Tel 053 94 46484 Fax 053 94 42128

H

Ecclerigg Windermere Cumbria LA23 1LH

Map 4 C3

Standing in 25 acres of secluded grounds, almost midway between Windermere and Ambleside on the A591, the hotel is approached up a long, quite steeply inclined twisting drive. From its elevated position there are good views of the lake from public rooms and from the six large front-facing bedrooms. Built in 1812, it was, until very recently, a private residence and still retains many fine original features. The conservatory bar with its mosaic-tiled floor, mahogany panelling and brown leather chesterfields has a smart Edwardian ambience. The drawing room and library, next door to it, are both used as lounges and in keeping with the character of the building have traditional suites of furniture. Bedrooms, some with pine, others with mahogany furniture, are of a good size and have a colourful, homely decor. All are named after poets and authors and have all the expected amenities like tea/coffee-making facilities and remote-control TVs. Simple, neat bathrooms. ***Rooms** 20. Garden.* AMERICAN EXPRESS *Access, Diners, Visa.*

Windermere Miller Howe 70%

£169*

Tel 053 94 42536 Fax 053 94 45664

H

Rayrigg Road Windermere Cumbria LA23 1EY

Map 4 C3

John Tovey's Miller Howe, an impressive Edwardian country house, stands well above Lake Windermere, with probably the grandest and most stunning views of any hotel in the Lake District. Built alongside the A592 it has well-tended grounds which sweep down almost to the water's edge. The hotel's public rooms and best bedrooms all share the panoramic vista with sunsets over the distant Cumbrian mountains particularly glorious. A heavy wooden door leads from the porch into a homely entrance hall lined with numerous past awards. Unusual objets d'art, sculptures ancient and modern and fine antique pieces put together unfussily create a comfortable, welcoming, lived-in feel. Lounges have brown leather chesterfields and are sombrely decorated contrasting with the fairly recently built conservatory that runs along the front of the hotel. Here the bright decor comprises cushioned white garden furniture and windowsills of potted plants. Bedrooms, though not large, have a cosy, rather old-fashioned appeal having changed little down the years. White laminate built-in units are used in even the best rooms, compensated for in the high standards of cleanliness and amenities on offer: books, games, small stereo system with classical music cassettes, trouser press, even umbrellas. The best bedrooms overlook the lake and have balconies with seating at white wrought-iron tables. Binoculars are provided too. Pretty ornaments add to the bedrooms' sense of homeliness. Compact bathrooms have lots of extras, all of good quality – thick towels, classy toiletries and bathrobes. Coming down for breakfast guests are greeted at the foot of the stairs with a complimentary Bucks Fizz which is followed by a very extensive menu that will leave you replete till lunchtime at the earliest. Breakfast apart, the food at this one-time bastion of British cooking seems, judged on recent visits, to have lost its edge (mismatched combinations of flavours and textures). *Half-board only. ***Rooms** 13. Garden. Closed early Dec-early Mar.* AMERICAN EXPRESS *Access, Diners, Visa.*

Windermere — Roger's Restaurant — £55

Tel 053 94 44954 — **R**

4 High Street Windermere Cumbria LA23 1AF — **Map 4 C3**

Roger Pergl-Wilson is the sole cook and his wife Alena the most affable of hostesses at their cosy corner of France in the heart of the English Lakes (located opposite Windermere Information Centre). Local demand for lamb, duck and steaks has partially permeated the à la carte menu, but the French provincial cookery evenings and special fish night menus are not to be missed. Roger's quality cooking and powerful flavour combinations are of undiminished appeal. Wickedly rich sweets, impressive cheeses and a good, short wine list selected with flair. Particularly good-value, 3-course table d'hote includes canapés and coffee with petits fours. ***Seats** 42. Parties 26. Private Room 30. D only 7-9.30. Closed Sun, 1 week Xmas. Set D £12.50.* AMERICAN EXPRESS *Access, Diners, Visa.*

Windermere — Places of Interest

Tourist Information Tel 053 94 46499.
Lake District National Park Centre Brockhole Tel 053 94 46601.
Windermere Steamboat Museum Tel 053 94 45565.

Windsor — Castle Hotel — 67% — £146

Tel 0753 851011 Fax 0753 830244 — **H**

High Street Windsor Berkshire SL4 1LJ — **Map 15 E2**

Period atmosphere and modern facilities behind a Georgian facade. Children up to the age of 16 free in parents' room; baby-sitting and listening. Forte Grand. ***Rooms** 104. Coffee shop (10am-10.30pm).* AMERICAN EXPRESS *Access, Diners, Visa.*

Windsor — Oakley Court — 78% — £168

Tel 0628 74141 Fax 0628 37011 — **HR**

Windsor Road Water Oakley nr Windsor Berkshire SL4 5UR — **Map 15 E2**

Three miles west of Windsor on the A308, this grand Victorian manor house is in 35 acres of landscaped grounds that slope gently down to the banks of the river Thames. Over 200 films were shot here during its uninhabited period of the 60s and 70s, including the St Trinians series, *The Rocky Horror Show* and Hammer's *Dracula.* Nowadays, it's a comfortable hotel with an impressive lounge decorated in pale yellow with chandeliers and an original, ornate plasterwork ceiling, two fireplaces plus an abundance of comfortable chairs and settees. Bedrooms are most appealing, with almost all rooms in separate extensions (the Riverside and Garden Wings) close to the main house; many are particularly spacious and boast splendid red granite bathrooms; the six luxurious suites in the original house have a more traditional, period feel. Five bedrooms are reserved for non-smokers. Informal eating in the 30-seater Boaters Brasserie (closed L Sun). Boats for hire from the hotel's private jetty; weekend summer steam boat service to Windsor. Queens Moat Houses. ***Rooms** 92. Garden, billiards, 9-hole golf, boating, fishing.* AMERICAN EXPRESS *Access, Diners, Visa.*

Oak Leaf Restaurant — £100

Dado-level light oak panelling and candle-light assist the quiet calm of the elegant dining room. Menus range from table d'hote luncheons (ragout of smoked haddock and mushrooms, Chinese-style duck, lemon meringue tart) and dinners to an à la carte which includes traditional favourites and a good choice of vegetarian dishes, as well as more elaborate creations from long-serving chef Murdo MacSween (here since 1983). Good desserts and petits fours. A good wine list offers wines selected by committee and listed both by country and grape variety. 15 tables on the terrace in summer. ***Seats** 120. Parties 20. L 12.30-2 D 7.30-10. Set L 16.50/£18.75 Set D £29/£35.*

Windsor Places of Interest

Tourist Information Tel 0753 852010.

Theatres and Concert Halls

Farrer Theatre Eton College Tel 0753 866278.
Windsor Arts Centre Tel 0753 859336.
Theatre Royal Tel 0753 853888.

Historic Houses, Castles and Gardens

The Savill Garden Wick Lane Englefield Green Tel 0753 860222.
Dorney Court Tel 0628 604638.
The Valley Gardens (Windsor Great Park) Tel 0753 860222.
Windsor Castle Tel 0753 831118.
St George's Chapel Tel 0753 865538.
Royal County of Berkshire Polo Club North Street, Winkfield Tel 0433 886555.
Windsor Racecourse Tel 0753 865234.

Winkleigh Pophams NEW £28

Tel 0837 83767 **R**

Castle Street Winkleigh Devon EX19 8HQ **Map 13 D2**

The most intimate of restaurants with just two tables and a couple of stools at a side shelf squeezed into a tiny village shop premises along with a delicatessen counter and the kitchen where Melvyn Popham creates his daily-changing lunchtime blackboard menu. Although laid out as starters, main dishes and puds they will happily serve just a single dish. Leek and watercress soup, fish terrine with chilled hollandaise, duck breast with plum sauce and vegetable goulash with saffron rice give the style. Round off an excellent meal with some unusual home-made ice cream or a pud like Melvyn's wicked rum, date and stem ginger tart. Partner Dennis Hawkes runs front of room(!) – the close quarters encouraging a chatty relaxed atmosphere. Unlicensed but no corkage charge if you bring your own. No children under 14. ***Seats** 10. Parties 10. L only 11.30-3. Closed Sun, 25 Dec & all Feb. Access, Visa.*

Winkton Fisherman's Haunt Hotel £55

Tel 0202 477283 Fax 0202 478883 **I**

Salisbury Road Winkton Christchurch Dorset BH23 7AS **Map 14 C4**

The river Avon is just across the road from this well-kept hotel, which stands on the B3347 Christchurch–Ringwood road about 2 miles from Bournemouth (Hurn) Airport. The building's 17th-century origins are not all that evident, but the bars, one featuring an old well with spring water, have a certain personality as well as real ale. Bedrooms, furnished in various styles, are spread around the main building (largest rooms), an old coach house and a nearby cottage. ***Rooms** 20. Garden. Closed 25 Dec.*
AMERICAN EXPRESS *Access, Diners, Visa.*

Winsford Royal Oak Inn £90

Tel 064 385 455 Fax 064 385 388 **I**

Winsford Somerset TA24 7JE **Map 13 D2**

At the centre of a sleepy Exmoor village resistant to street lighting and noise, Charles Steven's cosy inn doubles as village inn and celebrated haunt for the hunting and fishing folk who throng the place, especially in winter. The hotel waters run through the village and additional beats, fishing tuition and the hire or purchase of fishing tackle can be arranged. Residents enjoy the privacy of cosy chintz lounges and cottagey main-house

See over

bedrooms which nestle under thatched eaves. Five double bedrooms and a family cottage are in a sympathetically converted annexe around the rear courtyard. Children under 10 stay free in parents' room. ***Rooms** 14. Garden, fishing, garage.* AMERICAN EXPRESS *Access, Diners, Visa.*

Winterbourne **Grange Resort Hotel** **68%** **£100**

Tel 0454 777333 Fax 0454 777447 **H**

Northwoods Winterbourne Avon BS17 1RP **Map 13 F1**

Seven miles from Bristol, but only minutes from M4 (J19); nevertheless, you should obtain directions when booking. The much extended Victorian building stands in mature parkland, just outside the village. Conference facilities (up to 150 delegates) occupy much of the main house with bedrooms and leisure club in attendant modern blocks. Resort Hotels. ***Rooms** 52. Garden, indoor swimming pool, keep-fit equipment, sauna, spa bath, solarium, beauty salon, ballooning, helipad.* AMERICAN EXPRESS *Access, Diners, Visa.*

Winteringham **Winteringham Fields** **↑** **£88**

Tel 0724 733096 Fax 0724 733898 **RR**

Winteringham Humberside DN15 9PF **Map 7 E1**

Dating back to the 16th century and once the property of the Marquis of Lincolnshire, the house now belongs to Annie and Germain Schwab. Germain offers an à la carte menu plus *menu epicurien* (four courses with no choice: typically, consommé of pigeon, brill with beetroot dressing, calf's kidneys on glazed shallots and iced Grand Marnier soufflé) and *menu surprise* (six courses, served to complete table parties only). The former might include such delights as gratin of gnocchi with fresh oysters and smoked duck breast, Savoy cabbage-wrapped turbot with foie gras, sherry and tomato, and even noisette and casserole of goat with a richly-reduced sauce of its juices. Fixed-price lunch menus offer three somewhat simpler choices at each course. Vegetarian dishes always available; cheese served from a trolley. Our North of England Cellar of the Year perhaps does not have that many names on it, but it's both carefully chosen and fairly priced, complementing well the style of cooking. Good depth with several New World wines to choose from. No smoking throughout. 4 miles west of the Humber Bridge, on the south bank. ***Seats 36.** Parties 8. Private Room 10. L 12-1.30 D 7.30-9.30. Closed L Mon & Sat, all Sun, Bank Holidays, 2 weeks Xmas, 1 week Aug. Set L £14.75 Set D £33/£38. Access, Visa.*

Rooms **£95**

Seven en-suite bedrooms, including three in converted stables, are decorated with delightful taste, and fine period furniture complements the exposed beams and creaking floors. Top of the range is the Lord Fitz Hugh room with a four-poster. No children under 8, dogs or smoking.

Winteringham **Places of Interest**

Scunthorpe Tourist Information Tel 0724 282301.
Scunthorpe Civic Theatre Tel 0724 85912.
Normanby Hall and Country Park Normanby Tel 0724 720588.

Wishaw **The Belfry** **73%** **£110**

Tel 0675 470301 Fax 0675 470178 **H**

Lichfield Road Wishaw Warwickshire B76 9PR **Map 6 C4**

This large, ivy-clad hotel in the De Vere group stands amid two international standard golf courses (the Derby & Championship Brabazon) set in 360 acres of grounds. Golf is big business, so too conferences, and the facilities for both are extensive. The largest of the eight bars, with a pubby feel, overlooks one of the courses and has special spike-proof flooring. Also notable among the public areas is a sunken amphitheatre-style lounge with a glass roof and abundant greenery. Smart and stylish bedrooms with solid period furnishings are in four wings and are named after famous golfers. Choice of four restaurants. ***Rooms** 219. Golf centre, floodlit driving range, putting green, gymnasium, indoor swimming pool, spa bath, sauna, steam room, solarium, beautician, squash, tennis, children's playground, night club.* American Express *Access, Diners, Visa.*

Witherslack Old Vicarage 68% £78

Tel 05395 52381 Fax 05395 52373 **HR**

Church Road Witherslack Cumbria LA11 6RS **Map 4 C4**

In Witherslack village, turn up the lane signposted to the church to find this Georgian former vicarage set in five acres of informal gardens in the Lake District National Park. Inside, the hotel retains the charm and character of its Victorian heyday, and personal service from the owners is friendly and caring. There's a choice of accommodation between the up-to-date comforts and quiet seclusion of the Orchard House and the homelier period pieces in the Vicarage. Don't miss the Cumberland breakfast with black pudding, free-range eggs and home-cured bacon. ***Rooms** 15. Garden, tennis. Access, Visa.*

Restaurant £55

The fixed-price set dinner epitomises British country house cooking. A typical menu might comprise salmon mousse followed by soup then a traditional roast with all the trimmings before a choice of puddings (perhaps chocolate and chestnut roulade and a hot rhubarb and ginger Brown Betty) and a splendid selection of British farmhouse cheeses, mostly from the north of England. Coffee comes with Kendal mint cake and chocolates. A fairly priced wine list has plenty from the New World. No children under 10. No smoking. ***Seats** 36. Parties 12. Private Room 18. L Sun only 12.30 for 1 D at 7.30 for 8. Set L £15 Set D £19.50/£27.50*

Witney Witney Lodge 62% £84

Tel 0993 779777 Fax 0993 703467 **H**

Ducklington Lane Witney Oxfordshire OX8 7TJ **Map 14 C2**

Just outside Witney at the junction of the A40 and A415, a modern hotel with an attractive stone frontage. Bright, practical accommodation, rustic-style bar-lounge, purpose-built leisure centre with a decent-size indoor pool. Popular for conferences – the main function room can take up to 150. Family facilities include a children's splash pool alongside the bright, daylight pool. No dogs. ***Rooms** 74. Gymnasium, indoor swimming pool, spa bath, sauna, solarium, snooker.* American Express *Access, Diners, Visa.*

Wiveliscombe Langley House 66% £95

Tel 0984 23318 Fax 0984 24573 **HR**

Langley Marsh Wiveliscombe nr Taunton Somerset TA4 2UF **Map 13 E2**

Peter and Anne Wilson's pale-peach Georgian house nestles in lovely countryside at the foot of the Brendon Hills; drive half a mile north of Wiveliscombe on the road to Langley Marsh. It's a pretty place with award-winning gardens, cobbled courtyard and attractive, lived-in drawing rooms. Bedrooms are particularly stylish and appealing with well-planned colour schemes and lots of little extras. The Wilsons' personal care and attention are of a high order and breakfasts are super. ***Rooms** 8. Garden. Closed Feb.* American Express *Access, Visa.*

Restaurant £63

The beamed, candle-lit restaurant with its silver and crystal table settings enhances the air of well-being to which Peter's dinner menus, changing nightly, do full justice. Produce is first-rate, carefully cooked and (puddings apart) presented without choice; a walled kitchen garden provides the freshest of ingredients. A typical five-course weekend menu might commence with a chilled mangetout soufflé with a tomato coulis, followed

See over

by carrot and orange soup with coriander, then grilled baby turbot with crab crust and pepper sauce and finally pan-fried rosettes of Somerset lamb with onion tartlet and cassis purée. Five or so desserts and West Country cheeses (with walnut and banana bread) are offered for those who want the complete experience! The wine list is strong in red Bordeaux and half bottles. No smoking. ***Seats** 18. Parties 8. Private Room 18. L by arrangement D 7.30-8.30 (Sat at 8.30 only). Set D from £22.50.*

Woburn — Bedford Arms — 63% — £104

Tel 0525 290441 Fax 0525 290432 — **H**

George Street Woburn nr Milton Keynes Bedfordshire MK17 9PX — **Map 15 E1**

Mount Charlotte Thistle-owned former coaching inn with a long Georgian frontage, standing within the grounds of Woburn Abbey two miles from junction 13 of the M1. A refurbishment programme is improving public areas and bedrooms. Children up to the age of 14 stay free in parents' room. ***Rooms** 55. Access, Diners, Visa.*

Woburn — Bell Inn — 57% — £65

Tel 0525 290280 Fax 0525 290017 — **H**

21 Bedford Street Woburn Bedfordshire MK17 9QD — **Map 15 E1**

A privately-owned hotel with a mixture of Tudor, Georgian and Victorian buildings standing on either side of the street. To one side are a beamed bar and restaurant, to the other reception and a residents' lounge. The bar is a popular spot for snacks. A conference room can accommodate up to 35. Bedrooms retain much of the character of the original buildings; all but two singles have en-suite bathrooms. Children up to 16 share family rooms without charge. No dogs. ***Rooms** 27. Access, Diners, Visa.*

Woburn — Paris House — £90

Tel 0525 290692 Fax 0525 290471 — **R**

Woburn Park Woburn Bedfordshire MK17 9QP — **Map 15 E1**

Located off the A4012, Paris House enjoys one of the grandest entrances of any restaurant in this country. Beyond a magnificent stone gateway, the drive sweeps through a deer park curving round and affording a fine view of the splendid half-timbered house fronted by a well-tended garden where, in fine weather, drinks are served. Inside, the ground floor includes a cosy bar decorated with horseracing memorabilia. The dining room has bold ivy-patterned wallpaper and some large abstract paintings. Peter Chandler, now in his 10th year, has a steady and regular following for dishes that mostly follow the mainstream of modernised classical cooking. There are no great surprises, just reliably-prepared and well-presented food. As well as a multiple choice three-course prix-fixe menu there's a daily-changing *menu du jour* – three course at lunchtime, five in the evening. These are well balanced and a good showcase for his talents. A fricassee of snails with quartered wild mushrooms in a creamy sauce contains chopped nuts and caramelised orange zest; paupiette of sole stuffed with a light salmon mousse is accompanied by a saffron sauce and a fine dice of peppers and a crayfish. After a complimentary sorbet such as pink grapefruit come main courses like rack of lamb with tarragon and a selection of sometimes overcooked vegetables. Desserts include a hot Grand Marnier soufflé which on our last visit though well risen had little flavour. ***Seats** 40. Parties 21. Private Room 16. L 12-2 D 7-10. Closed D Sun, all Mon, Bank Holidays. Set L £21.50 (Sun £23) Set D £38. Access, Diners, Visa.*

Woburn — Place of Interest

Woburn Abbey Tel 0525 290666.

Wokingham — Stakis St Anne's Manor — 69% — £130

Tel 0734 772550 Fax 0734 772526 — **H**

London Road Wokingham Berkshire RG11 1ST — **Map 15 D2**

A converted and extended manor house conveniently situated in 25 acres of grounds close to the A329(M). Well-appointed bedrooms (recently refurbished) and comfortable public areas. Good leisure amenities. Banqueting/conference facilities for 300/250. ***Rooms** 130. Garden, indoor swimming pool, sauna, spa bath, steam room, solarium, tennis.* AMERICAN EXPRESS *Access, Diners, Visa.*

Wolverhampton — Goldthorn Hotel — 62% — £65

Tel 0902 29216 Fax 0902 710419 — **H**

Penn Road Wolverhampton West Midlands WV3 0ER — **Map 6 B4**

Intricate plaster ceilings add character to the cocktail bar and lounge at a 19th-century house with large, modern extensions in distinctly contrasting architectural style. One mile south of the town centre on the A449, half a mile from the Wolverhampton ring road. Modest accommodation with a mix of old and modern rooms. Conference facilities for up to 130. ***Rooms** 93. Garden.* AMERICAN EXPRESS *Access, Diners, Visa.*

Wolverhampton — Mount Hotel — 60% — £102

Tel 0902 752055 Fax 0902 745263 — **H**

Mount Road Tettenhall Wood Wolverhampton West Midlands WV6 8HL — **Map 6 B4**

Eight miles from Junction 10 of the M6 and two miles from the centre, a solid, 1870s redbrick building with modern bedroom wings, set in extensive gardens. Banqueting/conference facilities (for 160/200) include the Grand Library complete with Italian rococo-style ceiling and minstrel's gallery. Jarvis Hotels. ***Rooms** 56. Garden.* AMERICAN EXPRESS *Access, Diners, Visa.*

Wolverhampton — Victoria Hotel Periquito — 67% — £73

Tel 0902 29922 Fax 0902 29923 — **H**

Lichfield Street Wolverhampton West Midlands WV1 4DB — **Map 6 B4**

Next to the town's Grand Theatre, opposite the station. Smart, modern hotel with a marble-tiled foyer and lively bar, now run by Periquito Hotels (previously known as the *Victoria Park Hotel*). Bright furnishings are used throughout, trying hard to compensate for some compact single bedrooms and generally small bathrooms. Short on amenities, the hotel aims largely at the conference and function trade, catering for up to 200 and 150 respectively. ***Rooms** 117.* AMERICAN EXPRESS *Access, Diners, Visa.*

Wolverhampton — Places of Interest

Tourist Information Tel 0902 312051.
Grand Theatre Tel 0902 29212/714775.
Civic Hall Tel 0902 312030.
Bantock House Bantock Park, Bradmore Tel 0902 24548.
Central Art Gallery and Museum Tel 0902 312032.
Wolverhampton Wanderers Football Ground Molineux Stadium Tel 0902 712181.
Wolverhampton Racecourse Tel 0902 24481.
Historic Houses, Castles and Gardens
Chillington Hall Tel 0902 850236.
Moseley Old Hall (NT) Tel 0902 782808.
Wightwick Manor (NT) Tel 0902 761108.

Woodbridge — Seckford Hall — 68% — £90

Tel 0394 385678 Fax 0394 380610 — **H**

Woodbridge Suffolk IP13 6NU — Map 10 D3

Look out for the hotel sign on the A12 Woodbridge by-pass (don't turn off into the town) to find this imposing Elizabethan manor house set in extensive gardens which include an ornamental fountain and lawns leading down to a willow-fringed lake. Inside, period features abound with linenfold panelling and heavily beamed ceiling in the Great Hall (lounge), huge stone fireplaces and carved doors. Bedrooms are comfortably furnished more in private house than hotel style, four have four-poster beds (one dates back to 1587) and some are in a courtyard complex that includes an inspired conversion of an old tithe barn into a delightful heated swimming pool. Adjacent 9-hole pay-and-play golf course. ***Rooms** 35. Garden, indoor swimming pool, solarium, spa bath, keep-fit equipment. Closed 25 Dec.* AMERICAN EXPRESS *Access, Diners, Visa.*

> Changes in data sometimes occur in establishments after the Guide goes to press. Prices should be taken as indications rather than firm quotes.

Woodford Bridge — Prince Regent Hotel — 63% — £85

Tel 081-505 9966 Fax 081-506 0807 — **H**

Manor Road Woodford Bridge Essex IG8 8AE — Map 11 B4

The main house is Georgian, although now much extended to include substantial function and conference facilities for up to 300 delegates. Smart, up-to-date bedrooms are in a converted Victorian abbey joined to the original building. ***Rooms** 51. Garden.* AMERICAN EXPRESS *Access, Diners, Visa.*

Woodhall Spa — Dower House — 62% — £60

Tel 0526 52588 — **H**

Manor Estate Woodhall Spa Lincolnshire LN10 6PY — Map 7 E2

In over two acres of grounds on a private road, an Edwardian hotel sheltered from the nearby town centre. Comfortable armchairs around a log fire in the entrance hall give winter visitors a warm welcome, while summer guests will enjoy the garden views from the lounge and bar. Traditional bedrooms (six en suite: one with bathroom down the corridor) are spacious and quiet. ***Rooms** 7. Garden.* AMERICAN EXPRESS *Access, Visa.*

Woodstock — Bear Hotel — 66% — £128

Tel 0993 811511 Fax 0993 813380 — **HR**

Park Street Woodstock Oxfordshire OX7 1SZ — Map 15 D2

Longstanding landmark of local catering, the origins of the creeper-clad coaching inn going back to the 12th century. It stands in a quiet side street before the gates to Blenheim Palace. Bedrooms come in all shapes and sizes with decorations ranging from antique to modern. There is plenty of period charm, including heavy black beams and a Cotswold-stone fireplace with roaring log fire in the downstairs lounge-bar. Forte Heritage. ***Rooms** 45.* AMERICAN EXPRESS *Access, Diners, Visa.*

Restaurant — £60

Darkwood reproduction furniture, white napery and original oak beams make a good contrast in the dining room. The short, seasonal menu offers the likes of terrine of aubergines, sweet peppers and lamb fillet, wild mushroom, truffle and lamb's kidney ravioli, followed by roast monkfish with bananas and chutney, vegetable and walnut soufflé and fillet steak. ***Seats** 75. Parties 65. L 12.30-2.30 (Sun 12-2.30) D 7-10 (Sun to 9.30). Set L from £12.50 (Sun £17.50) Set D £21.50.*

Woodstock — Feathers Hotel — 73% — £105

Tel 0993 812291 Fax 0993 813158 **HR**

Market Street Woodstock Oxfordshire OX7 1SX — **Map 15 D2**

Eight miles north of Oxford, within walking distance of Blenheim Palace. Situated in the heart of a historic village, behind a 17th-century Cotswold-stone frontage, the Feathers offers a comfortable range of accommodation with bedrooms differing in price by size (suites are particularly attractive). All have elaborately draped curtains and a useful range of extras that includes mineral water, chocolates, fresh flowers, magazines and tea on arrival. Some rooms have draped awnings over the beds, while the best have four-posters. Bathrooms are luxuriously fitted in marble throughout, with bathrobes and an abundance of toiletries provided. The upstairs drawing room with a library and open fire is the most inviting of the day rooms and a cosy bar has flagstone flooring and an open fireplace. During warm weather the courtyard garden is a delightful spot for light meals (which are also served in the bar). Service is courteous and efficient.
***Rooms** 17. Garden, mountain bikes.* AMERICAN EXPRESS *Access, Diners, Visa.*

Restaurant — £75

A quiet, sophisticated air pervades the dining room, where à la carte and fixed-price menus provide a choice of interesting options. Spinach mousse with wild mushrooms, chicken liver parfait or oak-smoked wild boar could precede duck confit with red cabbage and spring onions, fillet of Scottish beef or a simple grill. Tempting sweets, British cheeses served with walnut, onion and herb bread. Good selection of house wine and half bottles. Fair choice under £20. Lighter eating in the Whinchat Bar.
***Seats** 60. Private Room 60. L 12.30-2.30 D 7.30-9.30. Set L from £14.50 Set D from £19.50.*

Woodstock — Places of Interest

Tourist Information Tel 0993 811038.
Blenheim Palace Tel 0993 811325.
Oxfordshire County Museum Tel 0993 811456.

Woody Bay — Woody Bay Hotel — 59% — £66

Tel 05983 264 **H**

Woody Bay Barnstaple Devon EX31 4QX — **Map 13 D1**

Martin and Colette Petch can offer guests at their 100-year-old hotel two major attractions: spectacular views from its woody site overlooking the bay and an abundance of peace and quiet. All but two of the rooms enjoy the views and those two are slightly discounted. There are two four-poster rooms and a family suite. Not suitable for children under eight. Leave the A49 at Martinhoe Cross (or go via the Valley of Rocks coastal toll road).
***Rooms** 15. Access, Visa.*

Woolacombe — Woolacombe Bay Hotel — 65% — £172*

Tel 0271 870388 Fax 0271 870613 **H**

South Street Woolacombe Devon EX34 7BN — **Map 12 C1**

Family summer holidays, winter breaks and conferences (for up to 200 delegates) are the main business at this imposing Edwardian hotel, whose lawns and gardens reach down to three miles of golden sands. Public rooms are fairly grand, bedrooms bright and roomy, with mostly modern furnishings. There are self-catering suites, apartments and flats. No dogs. *Half-board terms only. ***Rooms** 61. Garden, indoor & outdoor swimming pools, keep-fit equipment, squash, sauna, spa bath, steam room, solarium, hairdressing, tennis, pitch & putt, bowling, billiards room, children's playroom and organiser in high season. Closed Jan.* AMERICAN EXPRESS *Access, Diners, Visa.*

Woolacombe — Place of Interest

Woolacombe and Porthminster Beaches.

Woolton Hill — Hollington House — 79% — NEW — £110

Tel 0635 255100 Fax 0635 255075 — **HR**

Woolton Hill nr Newbury Berkshire RG15 9XR — **Map 15 D2**

Australians John and Penny Guy have brought an air of homely informality to this fine Edwardian mansion set in 14 acres of woodland gardens to the south of Newbury (follow signs to Hollington Herb Garden from the A343). The several lounges and galleried oak-panelled inner hall are comfortably relaxing with books, magazines, fresh flowers and, in winter, real log fires. Personal touches include John's collection of model ships in glass cases and Penny's splendid appliqué and patchwork cushions. Spacious, individually decorated bedrooms are most appealing, with antique and reproduction pieces and sybaritic bathrooms (most with whirlpool tubs and separate walk-in showers) with huge bath sheets, oversized bath robes and every little extra one can imagine. Good breakfasts. No dogs. ***Rooms** 20. Garden, outdoor swimming pool, tennis, putting.* AMERICAN EXPRESS *Access, Visa.*

Restaurant — £70

NEW CHEF

The setting is formal and traditional – oak panelling, stone mullioned windows, comfortable armed chairs, impeccable table settings – but chef Richard Lovett's short, daily-changing à la carte is rather more adventurous. Along with traditional English dishes like steak and kidney pie and bread and butter pudding come more modern and sophisticated offerings such as a salad of sun-dried tomatoes, roast peppers and quail eggs; turbot roasted with thyme and shallots; crépinette of oxtail and, as the vegetarian choice, Japanese vegetable tempura with dashi. Dishes are well thought out and executed with a perfectionist's care. Australian wines (the owners had a Relais & Chateaux property just outside Melbourne) feature prominently on a fine list with some inexpensive items alongside the classics. ***Seats** 50. Parties 45. Private Room 45. L 12-2.30 D 7-9.30. Set L £12/£15.*

Worcester — Brown's — £75

Tel 0905 26263 — **R**

24 Quay Street Worcester Hereford & Worcester WR1 2JJ — **Map 14 B1**

A spacious, high-ceilinged restaurant converted from a corn mill, with large picture windows overlooking the river. Dinner is a fixed-price (fully inclusive), three-course affair with wholesome dishes such as crab cakes with a mild curry sauce, confit of duck legs with Puy lentils, chargrilled quails with a herb risotto or roast rack of lamb. Also fresh fish of the day, a vegetarian special and home-made water ices among the desserts. Lunch is a simpler meal along the same lines. ***Seats** 95. L 12.30-1.45 D 7.30-9.45 (Sat to 10). Closed L Sat, D Sun, Bank Holidays, 1 week Christmas. Set L £15 Set D £30.* AMERICAN EXPRESS *Access, Diners, Visa.*

Worcester — Fownes Resort Hotel — 70% — £100

Tel 0905 613151 Fax 0905 23742 — **H**

City Walls Road Worcester Hereford & Worcester WR1 2AP — **Map 14 B1**

Standing on the site of a famous glove factory, by an attractive canalside walk just a short distance from the cathedral and city centre, Victorian character is evident in the stylish and spacious interior; public rooms include a large foyer, a smart cocktail bar and an intimate library, where dark green walls and green leather wing chairs allow both the books and the collection of Royal Worcester china to be seen to advantage. Spacious bedrooms, all sited away from the busy main road, are well equipped, with freestanding mahogany furniture and quiet colour schemes. Good desk

space and seating are provided. The John Fownes suite caters for conferences of up to 120. ***Rooms** 61. Keep-fit equipment, sauna.*
AMERICAN EXPRESS *Access, Diners, Visa.*

Worcester — Giffard Hotel — 61% — £62

Tel 0905 726262 Fax 0905 723458 — **H**

High Street Worcester Hereford & Worcester WR1 2QR — **Map 14 B1**

Decent accommodation in concrete 1960s' hotel opposite the cathedral. Conferences and banqueting cater for up to 130. Free garage parking is a major asset. Forte. ***Rooms** 103. Snooker.* AMERICAN EXPRESS *Access, Diners, Visa.*

Worcester — Places of Interest

Tourist Information Tel 0905 726311/723471.
Swan Theatre Tel 0905 27322.
Worcester Arts Workshop Tel 0905 21095.
The Greyfriars (NT) House & Gardens Tel 0905 23571.
Spetchley Park Gardens Tel 090565 224/213.
Worcester Cathedral Tel 0905 28854.
Museums and Art Galleries
City Museum and Art Gallery Tel 0905 763763.
The Dyson Perrins Museum of Worcester Porcelain Worcester Royal Porcelain Works Tel 0905 23221.
The Elgar Birthplace Crown East Lane, Lower Broadheath Tel 0905 333224.
New Road Cricket Ground Tel 0905 787394.
Worcester Racecourse Tel 0905 25364.

Worfield — Old Vicarage — 67% — £85

Tel 074 64 497 Fax 074 64 552 — **HR**

Worfield Bridgnorth Shropshire WV15 5JZ — **Map 6 B4**

Set in two acres of grounds overlooking fields and farmland, Peter and Christine Iles's handsome Edwardian parsonage reflects the peace and quiet of its village setting. Twin conservatories jutting out into the garden house a relaxing lounge with wicker chairs. Individually designed bedrooms, each named after a local village, sport reproduction furniture, pretty soft furnishings and copious extras: the ground-floor Leighton Suite has been specially equipped for disabled guests. Four rooms in the Coach House have superior fittings and open on to a private garden with unspoilt views across the valley to the river Worfe; six of the bedrooms are for non-smokers. Staff are particularly friendly and families with children are welcome – no charge for extra beds or a cot in parents' room; high tea at 6pm. ***Rooms** 14. Garden.* AMERICAN EXPRESS *Access, Diners, Visa.*

Restaurant — £72

Daily set-price lunches and dinners are quite adventurous, offering chilled tomato soup with oregano, basil and garlic alongside a puff-pastry pillow filled with Shropshire asparagus and a sweet and sour dressing, or escalope of smoked codling topped with Welsh rarebit, and grilled black pudding on a potato and grain mustard galette to start. Local meat features strongly in main-course dishes such as rosettes of lamb on creamed lentils and red pepper glaze. The choice is around four dishes at each stage for lunch, extending to six or so at dinner. Don't miss the fine selection of cheeses from around Britain (last year's Cheeseboard of the Year Midlands regional winner), served with biscuits baked in a wood-fired brick oven. There are further delights past the cheeses – perhaps a mango cheesecake with raspberry sauce and almond tuile, a light strawberry-studded apricot mousse or rum and raisin ice cream in meringue with a blackcurrant coulis. A splendid and easy-to-use all-round wine list with an excellent choice

See over

of half bottles. No smoking in the dining rooms. ***Seats** 40. Parties 30. Private Room 14. L 12-2 D 7-9 (Sun at 7). Set L £11.50/£14.50 Set D £15-£22.50.*

Worksop — Forte Travelodge — £42

Tel 0909 501528 — **L**

St Anne's Drive Dunkeries Mill Worksop Nottinghamshire S80 3QD — **Map 7 D2**

At the junction of the A57 and A60, west of Worksop. ***Rooms** 40.*
AMERICAN EXPRESS *Access, Visa.*

Worthing — Beach Hotel — 64% — £82

Tel 0903 234001 Fax 0903 234567 — **H**

Marine Parade Worthing West Sussex BN11 3QJ — **Map 11 A6**

In a prime seafront position, the Beach offers modest comfort behind its long, bland frontage. Public rooms are on a scale large enough to handle conferences of up to 200. Fifty-three of the double-glazed bedrooms are singles; most are generally light and spacious with a traditional look. Some rooms have their own balconies directly overlooking the sea. No children under eight in the restaurant for dinner. No dogs. ***Rooms** 82. Coffee shop (10am-10pm).* AMERICAN EXPRESS *Access, Diners, Visa.*

Worthing — Chatsworth Hotel — 57% — £77

Tel 0903 236103 Fax 0903 823726 — **H**

Steyne Worthing West Sussex BN11 3DU — **Map 11 A6**

A conference-orientated hotel in a one-way system (turn left after the pier) with fine creeper-covered Georgian facade, overlooking Steyne Gardens and the sea. Well-kept bedrooms are not luxurious, but include the extras one now expects as standard. Children under 14 accommodated free in parents' room; cots and baby-listening available. ***Rooms** 105. Games room.* AMERICAN EXPRESS *Access, Diners, Visa.*

Worthing — River Kwai — £50

Tel 0903 211901 — **R**

16 Ambrose Place Worthing West Sussex BN11 1PZ — **Map 11 A6**

Waitresses in traditional Thai dress move gracefully around this stylish restaurant, where authentic music and cushioned bamboo chairs help set the scene for some fine cooking. Careful preparation and subtle flavourings are evident in dishes like hot and sour soup with prawns, beef with oyster sauce and freshly-cooked noodles with prawns, crab and bean sprouts. The restaurant is a short walk from the main shopping street. Note that its only lunch opening is Tuesday and that it's now open Sunday. ***Seats** 38. Parties 20. L (Tues only) 12-2.30 D 6-10.30. Access, Visa.*

Worthing — Places of Interest

Tourist Information Tel 0903 210022.
Connaught Theatre Tel 0903 35333.
Pavilion Theatre Tel 0903 820500.
Highdown Gardens Goring-by-Sea Tel 0903 48067.
Worthing Museum and Art Gallery Chapel Road Tel 0903 39999 Ext 121 *Saturday 204229.*

Worthington — Kilhey Court — 65% — £90

Tel 0257 472100 Fax 0257 422401 — **H**

Chorley Road Worthington Wigan Lancashire WN1 2XN — **Map 6 B1**

Built by a Wigan brewer in 1884, the main building stands in ten acres of woodland alongside the A5106, near Standish. Additions such as the conference and business centres (catering for up to 150), a leisure club with a small pool, a bedroom block and the reception area lack much of the house's original elegance. Bedrooms are provided with a work desk and mini-bar, and finished in white ash and floral fabrics – putting practicality ahead of luxury. Rural tranquillity and proximity to the M61 and M6 are major assets. Now managed by Principal Hotels. ***Rooms** 55. Garden, night club (Fri & Sat), indoor swimming pool, sauna, solarium, keep-fit equipment, spa bath, fishing.* AMERICAN EXPRESS *Access, Diners, Visa.*

Wrotham Heath — Forte Posthouse Maidstone/Sevenoaks 67% — £68

Tel 0732 883311 Fax 0732 885850 — **H**

London Road Wrotham Heath nr Sevenoaks Kent TN15 7RS — **Map 11 B5**

Located on the A20 close to junction 2A of the M26, offering spacious, well-designed public areas and good leisure facilities. The bar and lounge areas are in an open-plan arrangement, one section of the lounge overlooking an inner courtyard with an ornamental pool. Meeting room for 60. ***Rooms** 106. Garden, indoor swimming pool, sauna, solarium, whirlpool bath, gymnasium, children's play area.* AMERICAN EXPRESS *Access, Diners, Visa.*

Wrotham Heath — Travel Inn — £43

Tel 0732 884214 Fax 0732 780368 — **L**

London Road Wrotham Heath Nr Sevenoaks Kent TN15 7RX — **Map 11 B5**

10 minutes drive from Brands Hatch and the town centres of Sevenoaks and Maidstone. ***Rooms** 40.* AMERICAN EXPRESS *Access, Diners, Visa.*

Wroxton St Mary — Wroxton House Hotel 66% — £98

Tel 0295 730482 Fax 0295 730800 — **H**

Wroxton St Mary nr Banbury Oxfordshire OX15 6QB — **Map 14 D1**

On the Stratford side of Banbury (A422), three village houses interlinked with a modern clocktower wing make up this genuinely friendly honey-stone hotel. Reception and a sunken lounge flank the flagstoned foyer, beyond which is a period-style bar. Bedrooms are individually decorated, with original timbers preserved in some of the older rooms; the balance in a newer block use stylish darkwood furniture. Children under 10 free in their parents' room; family facilities provided. ***Rooms** 32. Garden.* AMERICAN EXPRESS *Access, Diners, Visa.*

Wylam — Laburnum House — £50

Tel 0661 852185 — **RR**

Main Street Wylam Northumberland NE41 8AJ — **Map 5 D2**

A house dating from the early 18th century is home for a pleasant little restaurant with comfortable wicker chairs at attractively laid tables. "French and modern cuisine" is Kenn Elliott and Rowan Mahon's description of their cooking. Some typical items on the frequently-changing menu: salmon and asparagus terrine, smoked turkey with Japanese salad, lemon sole with lime butter, braised pheasant with Calvados and cream, fillet of beef *au poivre*. ***Seats** 40. D only 6.30-9.30 (Sat to 10). Closed Sun, Bank Holidays (open Good Friday), 2 weeks Feb.* AMERICAN EXPRESS *Access, Visa.*

Rooms — £50

Four neat bedrooms, all doubles and all quite large, three have private shower rooms and one a bathroom.

Many hotels offer reduced rates for weekend or out-of-season bookings.
Always ask about special deals.

Wymondham Number Twenty Four £45

Tel 0953 607750 **R**

24 Middleton Street Wymondham Norfolk NR18 0BH **Map 10 C2**

The acquisition of adjacent premises has enabled this town-centre restaurant significantly to enlarge its dining potential. This is particularly relevant on a Saturday, when reservations need to be made well in advance. The new dining room is spacious and prettily decorated. The original dining rooms are tiny, almost cottagey. Lunchtime sees a blackboard menu of individually priced dishes as well as a three-course fixed-priced menu of virtually the same dishes. There are a few more choices on the evening three-course menu. Terrine of local pork, apricot and walnuts comes with home-made chutney and toast; white onion, smoked bacon and potato soup is accompanied by tiny cheese and herb scones and mussels are served as a little stew with cream, cucumber and pernod. Main dishes are typically an escalope of salmon baked with a herb and brioche crust with an orange butter sauce; pot-roasted Suffolk chicken in a garlic, mushroom and tarragon cream with poppy seed pasta; or Longshore skate wing braised in beer with tomato and thyme cream. Sweets could be moist Bramley apple spice cake, chocolate truffle torton or a honey parfait with rhubarb sauce – sound, reliable, imaginative cooking without pretensions in friendly, informal surroundings. Also open from 10-3 Mon-Sat for lighter snacks. No smoking before 9.30. ***Seats** 102. Parties 20. Private Room 22. L 12-2.30 (Sun to 2) D 7.30-9.30. Closed D Sun-Tue, 25-30 Dec. Set L £7.95 Set D £14.95. Access, Visa.*

Yattendon Royal Oak £80

Tel 0635 201325 Fax 0635 201926 **IR**

The Square Yattendon nr Newbury Berkshire RG16 0UF **Map 15 D2**

A redbrick wisteria-clad inn in the village square, where Cromwell dined before the battle of Newbury in 1644. Food is still a big attraction here with the characterful beamed bars largely given over to bar meals. The sofa-filled hotel reception/lounge is also used for pre-and post-prandial drinks by restaurant diners. Five pretty bedrooms have all mod cons and all sorts of extras in bathrooms of which two are private (just across the hall) but not en suite. New owners plan some timely refurbishment of lounge and bedrooms but no change in character or style is envisaged. No dogs. ***Rooms** 5. Garden.* AMERICAN EXPRESS *Access, Diners, Visa.*

Restaurant £90

Just six antique tables gleam in the candlelight of a charming dining room decorated in sunny yellow with fresh flowers and tall-stemmed fruit bowls on each table. New chef Graham Newbould (previously starred at *Inverlochy Castle* in Scotland) took over at the end of July, and his new menus are likely to restore the inn's reputation for fine food. There's also a bar menu. No smoking. ***Seats** 25. Private Room 6. L 12-2 D 7-10. Set L £18.50.*

Yelverton Moorland Links 65% £70

Tel 0822 852245 Fax 0822 855004 **H**

Yelverton nr Plymouth Devon PL20 6DA **Map 12 C3**

This well-liked, low-rise hotel is signposted off the A386 between Plymouth and Tavistock, within the Dartmoor National Park. Main day rooms include a lounge, the Gun Room bar and a ballroom giving on to the lawns. Individually decorated bedrooms are spacious and comfortable, with well-equipped, carpeted bathrooms. Conference facilities for up to 120, banqueting up to 200. Children up to 16 stay free in parents' room. Forestdale Hotels. ***Rooms** 30. Garden, tennis, helipad. Closed 1 week Christmas.* AMERICAN EXPRESS *Access, Diners, Visa.*

Yelverton Place of Interest

Buckland Abbey (NT and Plymouth City Council) Tel 0822 853607.

Yeovil Little Barwick House

£55

Tel 0935 23902 Fax 0935 20908

RR

Barwick Village nr Yeovil Somerset BA22 9TD

Map 13 F2

The Colleys' listed Georgian dower house faces west with delightful sloping gardens, just off the A37 two miles south of Yeovil. Veronica's four-course, fixed-price menu offers a small choice of dishes, using top-quality produce and straightforward presentation. Avocado and chicken tikka salad or "Popeye" pancakes of spinach and cream cheese typically precede local rack of lamb, pie of the week, West Bay sole fillets or fillet steaks. Game appears in season – try the game pie or breast of pheasant stuffed with chestnuts, cumin and minced leg meat. Vegetarian options, traditional English puddings and Christopher's chatty informality complete the picture. Smoking is actively discouraged in both dining room and bedrooms. ***Seats 40.*** *Private Room 16. D only 7-9 (Sat to 9.30). Closed Sun (except residents), 2 weeks Jan. Set D £16.90/£22.90.* AMERICAN EXPRESS *Access, Visa.*

Rooms

£72

Six spotlessly kept bedrooms with simple decor and furnishings promise peace and quiet in an abundantly calm rural setting. Exemplary breakfasts are served in the sunlit morning room.

Yeovil The Manor Hotel 63%

£97

Tel 0935 231161 Fax 0935 706607

H

Hendford Yeovil Somerset BA20 1TG

Map 13 F2

Close to the town centre, an old mansion dating from 1735 with converted stables offering modern bedroom facilities. Conferences and private dining for up to 70; attractive conservatory opening to enclosed formal garden. Forte Heritage. ***Rooms 41. Garden.*** AMERICAN EXPRESS *Access, Diners, Visa.*

Yeovil Places of Interest

Tourist Information Tel 0935 71279.
Octagon Theatre Tel 0935 22884.
Fleet Air Arm Museum and Concorde Exhibition Yeovilton Tel 0278 75595.
Yeovil Ski Centre Tel 0935 21702.
Historic Houses, Castles and Gardens
Brympton d'Evercy Tel 0935 862528.
Clapton Court Gardens and Plant Centre Crewkerne Tel 0460 73220/72200.
Lytes Cary Manor (NT) Somerton Tel 045822 3297.

Never leave money, credit cards or valuables lying around in your hotel room. Use the hotel safe or the mini-safe in your room.

York Abbey Park Resort Hotel 57%

£75

Tel 0904 658301 Fax 0904 621224

H

The Mount York North Yorkshire YO2 2BN

Map 7 D1

One mile from the city centre, this hotel offers modern facilities behind a Georgian facade. A programme of bedroom refurbishment is due for completion by April 1994. ***Rooms 85.*** AMERICAN EXPRESS *Access, Diners, Visa.*

York **Dean Court** **63%** **£95**

Tel 0904 625082 Fax 0904 620305 **H**

Duncombe Place York North Yorkshire YO1 2EF **Map 7 D1**

Originally built to provide homes for the clergy of York Minster (opposite the west front of which it stands) Dean Court is now a privately owned hotel. The public areas boast some fine yew-veneered furniture and fittings; the downstairs bar has recently been turned into a function suite. Bedrooms are light and airy, and those at the front have fine views of the Minster and its close. Valet parking (the car park is just three minutes walk away). No dogs. ***Rooms** 42. Coffee shop (9.30am-6.30pm).* AMERICAN EXPRESS *Access, Diners, Visa.*

See the Conference and Banqueting section for lists of hotels arranged by county.

York **Forte Posthouse** **65%** **£68**

Tel 0904 707921 Fax 0904 702804 **H**

Tadcaster Road York North Yorkshire YO2 2QF **Map 7 D1**

Bright and airy day rooms surround a central lawn at a practical modern hotel on the A1036, south of the city. Banqueting for 65 and conferences for up to 120 theatre-style. ***Rooms** 139. Garden.* AMERICAN EXPRESS *Access, Diners, Visa.*

York **Forte Travelodge** **£42**

Tel 0973 531823 **L**

Bilbrough nr York North Yorkshire **Map 7 D1**

On the eastbound carriageway of the A64, 7 miles south-west of York and 5 miles north-east of Tadcaster. ***Rooms** 40.* AMERICAN EXPRESS *Access, Visa.*

York **Grange Hotel** **74%** **£98**

Tel 0904 644744 Fax 0904 612453 **HR**

Clifton York North Yorkshire YO3 6AA **Map 7 D1**

A fine Regency town house, carefully restored from a group of flats, just 400 yards north of the city walls on the A19 road to Thirsk. The relaxed, homely atmosphere is exemplified by the elegant morning room – plump cushions on the couches, a fine open fire, oil paintings hanging on the walls and fresh flowers. The bedrooms may not be large but are individually furnished with fine-quality fabrics, antique furniture and English chintz. The young management and friendly staff have high hotel-keeping standards and help make this a good alternative to uniform, commercial rivals. Baby-sitting can be arranged in advance and there's a high-chair in the Brasserie (easiest access is via the rear car park). Meeting rooms for up to 35. ***Rooms** 29. 24hr lounge service.* AMERICAN EXPRESS *Access, Diners, Visa.*

Ivy Restaurant **£70**

Chef Cara Baird's interesting fixed-price lunch and dinner menus might include salmon and asparagus terrine with dill yoghurt, salad of lamb's kidneys or chicken livers to start, followed by carbonnade of beef, a selection of seafish or roast lamb stuffed with apricots and rosemary. The carte is slightly more involved, with good vegetarian options, and written in a refreshingly unpretentious style, matching the kitchen's intentions. Simpler fare is offered (except Sun) in the brick-vaulted Brasserie converted from the old cellars. ***Seats** 55. Private Room 60. L 12.30-2.30 D 7-10. Set L £12.50 Set D £21.*

York — Judges Lodging — 64% — £110

Tel 0904 638733 Fax 0904 679947 — **H**

9 Lendal York North Yorkshire YO1 2AQ — **Map 7 D1**

Close to York Minster, within the footstreet zone, a fine Georgian town house which was the official residence of the Assize Court judges from 1806. It remained such until 1977, when it was restored and opened as a hotel. Two curved stone stairs lead you from the courtyard to the lovely central door, beyond which is a beautifully proportioned hall with a small lounge area. Arched redbrick ceilings add character to the cellar bar and the bedrooms are delightful, with antiques, fine paintings, prints and lots of extras. Family facilities. Own parking. ***Rooms** 13. Garden.*
AMERICAN EXPRESS *Access, Diners, Visa.*

York — Melton's — £48

Tel 0904 634341 — **R**

7 Scarcroft Road York North Yorkshire YO2 1ND — **Map 7 D1**

Lucy and Michael Hjort continue to work hard and aim to please all-comers with a short menu that mixes the adventurous with more standard fare; thus, braised lamb's hearts with sauce Robert and peppered roast rib of beef with beetroot pasta amd wild mushrooms stand proudly alongside daily fresh fish specials like salad of crab and pink grapefruit, and fillet of brill with lobster sauce. Evening specialities vary by day: seafood on Tuesdays, puddings on Wednesdays and vegetarian on Thursdays. New this year are good-value fixed-price lunches (including Sundays) and early dinners (leave by 7.45pm). Desserts might include a white chocolate parfait with lime syrup or bread-and-butter pudding. Both mineral water and coffee are free to diners and prices are inclusive of service. Short, diverse and sensibly priced wines. ***Seats** 28. Parties 12. Private Room 12. L 12.30-2 D 5.30-10. Closed D Sun, L Mon, 3 weeks from Christmas Eve, 1 week late Aug. Set L & early D £10.50/£12.50. Access, Visa.*

York — Middlethorpe Hall — 79% — £149

Tel 0904 641241 Fax 0904 620176 — **HR**

Bishopthorpe Road York North Yorkshire YO2 1QB — **Map 7 D1**

A fine example of a William and Mary house, magnificently restored by Historic House Hotels. Middlethorpe Hall stands in well-tended grounds alongside York racecourse. Its classical exterior is complemented by a carefully decorated and furnished interior; first impressions as you enter the hall are flagstones, a log fire, fine paintings and a splendid carved oak staircase. A wealth of fine-quality furniture includes some good antiques, and the chandeliered drawing room boasts numerous beautifully upholstered sofas and armchairs. Bedrooms are of a similarly high standard, with plenty of extras; Edwardian-style bathrooms are graced by brass fittings as well as high-class toiletries, generous towels and bathrobes. No children under eight; no dogs. Smart meeting and conference facilities. ***Rooms** 30. Garden.* AMERICAN EXPRESS *Access, Diners, Visa.*

Restaurant — £100

A formal dining room with panelled walls, professional service and choice of menus. The fixed-price lunch and dinner menus offer a good variety with dishes that show a good understanding of classical cooking skills from chef Kevin Francksen: chicken consommé, crab ravioli, panaché of seafood, Dover sole, rack of lamb with turned vegetables, trio of chocolate puddings (parfait, mousse and ice cream with a raspberry coulis) are typical dishes from the carte, which is supplemented by interesting table d'hote at both lunchtimes and in the evening. Grill Room open 7.30-9.45 (Fri & Sat, summer only). No children under 8. ***Seats** 60. Parties 7. Private Room 50. L 12.30-2.30 D 7.30-9.45. Set L £14.90/£16.90 Set D £29.95.*

York Mount Royale 68% £75

Tel 0904 628856 Fax 0904 611171 **H**

119 The Mount York North Yorkshire YO2 2DA **Map 7 D1**

An individual hotel, run since 1965 by the Oxtoby family, that makes a pleasant alternative to the uniformity so often found elsewhere. Two fine William IV houses are joined to make a friendly little hotel on the edge of the city centre. Antiques and gilt-framed oil paintings help create a welcoming atmosphere with an air of restrained elegance. There's a homely feel throughout and the small, oak-panelled cocktail bar is distinctly club-like. Bedrooms each have their own individuality, although floral fabrics predominate; garden rooms open on to the garden by way of a verandah. ***Rooms** 23. Garden, outdoor swimming pool, sauna, steam room, solarium.* AMERICAN EXPRESS® *Access, Diners, Visa.*

York 19 Grape Lane £72

Tel 0904 636366 **R**

19 Grape Lane York North Yorkshire YO1 2HU **Map 7 D1**

Contemporary English cooking takes centre stage at No. 19, located down a narrow lane between Stonegate and Low Petergate. Chef Michael Fraser offers light lunches, maybe of smoked duck salad with raspberry vinaigrette or a trio of salmon terrine, supplemented by daily blackboard specials which offer the best value. Fixed-price dinner (with a choice of three or four dishes per course) might include a cassolette of North Sea fish with avocado, pan-fried lamb's liver with onion marmalade and glazed orange, and chocolate and raspberry roulade. Go à la carte for chicken mousseline with wild mushrooms and pastry-encased guinea fowl breast with lime sauce. There's usually a Colston Bassett Stilton as an alternative to traditional hot puddings like Yorkshire treacle tart, Eve's pudding and Bakewell tart served with custard, or a dish with "a little of everything". One room is non-smoking. ***Seats** 34. Private Room 22. L 12-1.45 D 7.30-10.30 (Sat from 7). Closed Sun & Mon, 3 days Christmas, 3 days New Year, 2 weeks Feb, 2 weeks Sep. Set D £18.95. Access, Visa.*

York Novotel 62% £85

Tel 0904 611660 Fax 0904 610925 **H**

Fishergate York North Yorkshire YO1 4AD **Map 7 D1**

Uniform chain hotel in the city centre (A19 Selby road). Conference/banqueting facilities for 210/150. ***Rooms** 124. Indoor swimming pool.* AMERICAN EXPRESS® *Access, Diners, Visa.*

York Royal York Hotel 65% £100

Tel 0904 653681 Fax 0904 623503 **H**

Station Road York North Yorkshire YO2 2AA **Map 7 D1**

Set in three acres of landscaped garden in the centre of York, this handsome Victorian hotel was one of the first great transport hotels. It's a popular venue for conferences (up to 180 delegates accommodated theatre-style) and a leisure centre has recently been opened. Children up to 14 stay free in parents' room. ***Rooms** 148. Keep-fit equipment, sauna, steam room, putting.* AMERICAN EXPRESS® *Access, Diners, Visa.*

York Stakis York 68% £130

Tel 0904 648111 Fax 0904 610317 **H**

Tower Street York North Yorkshire YO1 1SB **Map 7 D1**

Modern redbrick hotel whose city-centre location overlooking Clifford's Tower is a major asset. Well-appointed bedrooms include Executive Club rooms and suites. Conference facilities for up to 150 delegates. Formerly a *Holiday Inn. **Rooms** 128.* AMERICAN EXPRESS® *Access, Diners, Visa.*

York Swallow Hotel 64%

£105

Tel 0904 701000 Fax 0904 702308

H

Tadcaster Road York North Yorkshire YO2 2QQ

Map 7 D1

A mile from the city centre on the A1036, the Swallow stands in its own grounds overlooking the historic Knavesmire racecourse. A purpose-built management training centre has recently been added to the facilities which include a leisure club and parking for 200+ cars. Children up to 14 free in parents' room. ***Rooms** 113. Garden, indoor swimming pool, steam room, spa bath, sauna, solarium, beautician, keep-fit equipment, pitch & putt, coffee shop (11am-11pm).* AMERICAN EXPRESS® *Access, Diners, Visa.*

York Viking Hotel 69%

£113

Tel 0904 659822 Fax 0904 641793

H

North Street York North Yorkshire YO1 1JF

Map 7 D1

Tall, modern Queens Moat Houses hotel standing in a convenient central location by the river Ouse. Style and comfort are not lacking in the brick-walled reception, the lounge and the bar, the last two with river views. A choice of conference suites can handle up to 300 delegates. Bedrooms are well lit and amply furnished. ***Rooms** 188. Gymnasium, sauna, spa bath, solarium, golf practice net.* AMERICAN EXPRESS® *Access, Diners, Visa.*

York Places of Interest

Tourist Information Tel 0904 621756.
Grand Opera House Tel 0904 628877.
Theatre Royal Tel 0904 23568.
York Minster Tel 0904 623608.
York Racecourse Tel 0904 620911.
Flamingo Land Zoo and Family Fun Park Malton Tel 065 386287.

Historic Houses, Castles and Gardens

Assembly Rooms Tel 0904 61361.
Beningbrough Hall Tel 0904 470666.
Castle Howard Tel 065 384 333.
Merchant Adventurers' Hall Tel 0904 654818.
Treasurer's House (NT) Tel 0904 624247.
Sutton Park Sutton-on-the-Forest Tel 0347 810249.

Museums and Art Galleries

The Arc Archaeological Resource Centre Tel 0904 654324.
Fairfax House Tel 0904 655543.
Jorvik Viking Centre Tel 0904 643211.
National Railway Museum (Science Museum) Tel 0904 621261.
York Castle Museum Tel 0904 653611.
York City Art Gallery Tel 0904 623839.
York Story Tel 0904 628632.

Yoxford Satis House 63%

£65

Tel 072 877 418

H

Yoxford Saxmundham Suffolk IP16 3EX

Map 10 D2

Set in three acres of parkland alongside the A12, the house dates back to 1817. Charles Dickens was a friend of the original owner and mentioned the house in *Great Expectations*. The entrance hall is paved with York stone and leads to public rooms furnished with antiques. Two of the bedrooms are older in style with large, solid wood half-tester double beds and Edwardian baths and fittings, while others are more modern and have been recently refurbished. No children under 14 or dogs. Malaysian food is a speciality in the restaurant (D only, closed Sun & Mon) and their Kenduri feast is always popular. ***Rooms** 7. Garden, sauna, solarium, spa bath, keep-fit equipment.* AMERICAN EXPRESS® *Access, Diners, Visa.*

HEAD

Scotland

Aberdeen Ardoe House 70%

£108

Tel 0224 867355 Fax 0224 861283

H

South Deeside Road Royal Deeside Grampian AB1 5YP

Map 3 D4

Though only a few minutes' drive from the centre of Aberdeen, Ardoe House enjoys a secluded setting at the end of a winding drive. Its style is Scottish Baronial, and day rooms retain all their best original features, with carved oak panelling and handsome ceiling work. The drawing room and cocktail bar are warm and inviting, and there's a choice of rooms available for conferences and banquets (for up to 150/200). Bedrooms are comfortable and well appointed, whether in the main building (some reached by a fine oak staircase past a stained-glass window) or in the sympathetically designed modern section, where the majority are located. Children up to 12 stay free in parents' room. ***Rooms** 71. Garden, putting, pétanque.* AMERICAN EXPRESS *Access, Diners, Visa.*

Aberdeen Atlantis

£62

Tel 0224 591403

R

16 Bon Accord Crescent Aberdeen Grampian AB1 2DE

Map 3 D4

Seafood is bought whenever possible from Aberdeen's renowned fish market, and chef Mark Ronaldson favours a simple approach to preserve the fresh flavours and textures. Orkney oysters and mussels are favourite starters, with sole, salmon and king prawns among the most popular main courses. Dishes come plain or sauced: véronique for king prawns, green peppercorns for monkfish, herb butter to accompany fillets of lemon sole stuffed with a salmon and leek mousse. The cold seafood platter for two is a selection of all the seafood presented with four different dips. A couple of non-fish dishes are available. ***Seats** 36. Parties 20. L 12-2 D 6.30-10. Closed L Sat, all Sun, Bank Holidays. Set L £7.* AMERICAN EXPRESS *Access, Diners, Visa.*

Aberdeen Caledonian Thistle 68%

£125

Tel 0224 640233 Fax 0224 641627

H

Aberdeen Grampian AB9 1HE

Map 3 D4

City-centre hotel with Regency-style day rooms, double-glazed bedrooms and a choice of eating places. ***Rooms** 80. Sauna.* AMERICAN EXPRESS *Access, Diners, Visa.*

Aberdeen Copthorne Hotel 68%

£129

Tel 0224 630404 Fax 0224 640573

H

122 Huntly Street Aberdeen Grampian AB1 1SU

Map 3 D4

City-centre hotel behind a converted warehouse facade. Good standards of accommodation in Classic and Connoisseur rooms and suites. 24hr room service. Conference facilities for 200+. No dogs. ***Rooms** 89.* AMERICAN EXPRESS *Access, Diners, Visa.*

Aberdeen Gerard's

£67

Tel 0224 639500

R

50 Chapel Street Aberdeen Grampian AB1 1SN

Map 3 D4

Reliable, sound cooking – French and international – is the hallmark of Gerard Flecher's city-centre restaurant, off the west end of Union Street. Very good-value business lunches offer an unusually wide choice, while a relaxed evening meal might offer parfait of smoked turkey with avocado and lime dressing, followed by plaice meunière or scallops Thermidor and finish with hot peaches filled with black cherries in a Pernod-flavoured cream on a table d'hote. An à la carte full of French classics – from frogs' legs and onion soup to pastry-wrapped fillet of marinated venison and clafoutis – completes the picture. Predominantly French wine list with twenty or so fine reserve wines. ***Seats** 80. Parties 50. L 12-2.30 D 6-11. Closed Sun, Local Bank Holidays, 2 days Christmas, 2 days New Year. Set L £9.50 & £11.50 Set D £21.50.* American Express, *Access, Diners, Visa.*

Aberdeen — Holiday Inn Crowne Plaza — 69% — £112

Tel 0224 713911 Fax 0224 714020 — **H**

Oldmeldrum Road Bucksburn Aberdeen Grampian AB2 9LN — **Map 3 D4**

Formerly the *Bucksburn Moat House*, this very modern hotel stands between the city and the airport. Well equipped for leisure and for conferences (500+ theatre-style). ***Rooms** 144. Indoor swimming pool, gymnasium, sauna, steam room, solarium.* American Express *Access, Diners, Visa.*

Aberdeen — Silver Darling — £64

Tel 0224 576229 Fax 0224 626558 — **R**

Pocra Quay North Pier Aberdeen Grampian AB2 1DQ — **Map 3 D4**

A French speciality 'barbecued seafood' restaurant overlooking the city and old port from the farthest point of the North Quay. Most of the fish is cooked in full view of diners through a large kitchen window. Starters range from tartare of salmon and turbot marinated in lemon and dill to grilled Orkney oysters and king scallops with mushroom ravioli; main courses are accompanied by good sauces – wild mushroom and herb with Shetland salmon escalope, a trio of sauces with sea trout, rock turbot and monkfish. On a recent menu, duck (cooked in an iron pot and served with shallots, a millet pancake and liver paté on toast) was the alternative to the fishy offerings. Short, carefully annotated all-French wine list. Booking is essential. ***Seats** 35. Parties 30. L 12-2 D 7-10. Closed L Sat & all Sun, 2 weeks Christmas.* American Express *Access, Visa.*

Aberdeen — Stakis Tree Tops — 63% — £127

Tel 0224 313377 Fax 0224 312028 — **H**

161 Springfield Road Aberdeen Grampian AB9 2QH — **Map 3 D4**

In a residential area on the western edge of the city, a hotel offering singles, doubles, twins, Executive rooms, family rooms and a suite, all complete with the expected up-to-date accessories. There's a well-equipped leisure club and large, comprehensive conference facilities catering for up to 620 delegates. Children up to 15 stay free in parents' room. ***Rooms** 110. Indoor swimming pool, gymnasium, spa bath, sauna, tennis.* American Express *Access, Diners, Visa.*

Aberdeen — Travel Inn — £43

Tel 0224 821217 — **L**

Murcar Bridge of Don Aberdeen Grampian AB2 8BP — **Map 3 D4**

Rooms 40. American Express *Access, Diners, Visa.*

Aberdeen — Places of Interest

Tourist Information Tel 0224 632727.
St Andrew's Cathedral Tel 0224 640290.
St Machar's Cathedral Tel 0224 485988.
St Mary's R.C. Cathedral Tel 0224 640160.
Aberdeen F.C. Pittodrie Tel 0224 632328.
Caimhill Ski Slope Tel 0224 311781.
Alford Slope Tel 09755 63024.
Beach Leisure Centre Tel 0224 649930.
Theatres and Concert Halls
Aberdeen Music Hall Tel 0224 641222.
Aberdeen Arts Centre Tel 0224 635208.
Capitol Theatre Tel 0224 583141.
Haddo House Hall Tel 06515 851770 *By Tarves 10 miles.*
His Majesty's Theatre Tel 0224 641122.

Historic Houses, Castles and Gardens
Castle Fraser (NT) Sauchen. Tel 0330 3463.
Cruickshank Botanic Gardens Tel 0224 272704.
Crathes Castle Garden Banchory. Tel 0330 44525.
Drum Castle Tel 0330 811204.
Duthie Park and Winter Gardens Tel 0224 276276.
Kildrummy Castle Gardens Alford Tel 09755 71277.
Seaton Park Don Street. Tel 0224 276276.
Pitmedden Garden (NT) Udny. Tel 065 1842352.
Museums and Art Galleries
Art Gallery/James Dun's House Tel 0224 635208/646333.
Peacock Artspace Tel 0224 639539.
Maritime Museum/Provost Ross's House Tel 0224 585788.
University Marischal Museum Tel 0224 273131.
Grampian Transport Museum Alford. Tel 09755 62292.
Crombie Woollen Mill Woodside Tel 0224 483201.

Aberdeen Airport — Aberdeen Marriott Hotel 70% — £141

Tel 0224 770011 Fax 0224 722347 — H

Riverview Drive Farburn Dyce Aberdeen Grampian AB2 0AZ — Map 3 D4

Low-rise hotel near the airport built around a central leisure area with kidney-shaped pool. Standardised bedrooms are spacious and practical rather than luxurious – poly-cotton sheets, open hanging space – but the 24hr room service menu includes sous-vide dishes from the Roux brothers. Executive rooms get various extras. ***Rooms** 154. Indoor swimming pool, keep-fit equipment, sauna, spa bath, solarium.* AMERICAN EXPRESS *Access, Diners, Visa.*

Aberdeen Airport — Airport Skean Dhu Hotel 65% — £110

Tel 0224 725252 Fax 0224 723745 — H

Argyll Road Dyce Aberdeen Grampian AB2 0DU — Map 3 D4

Conveniently close to the aiport terminal, this Mount Charlotte Thistle hotel combines roomy, well-equipped bedrooms with a busy conference trade. ***Rooms** 148. Garden.* AMERICAN EXPRESS *Access, Diners, Visa.*

Aberfeldy — Farleyer House 70% — £90

Tel 0887 820332 Fax 0887 829430 — HR

Weem Aberfeldy Perthshire Tayside PH15 2JE — Map 3 C4

An original 16th-century croft enlarged in the 1700s to house the Bailiff and transformed again in the 18th century to become Dower House to nearby Menzies Castle, Farleyer House enjoys a fine position overlooking the Tay valley to the west of town on the B846. The elegant drawing room and library bar with inner sanctum are comfortably furnished in country house style with deep armchairs and a relaxed atmosphere. Bedrooms vary somewhat in size and appeal with some built-in furniture plus a good scattering of antiques and individual decor. Rooms are properly serviced in the evenings and breakfasts come with freshly squeezed orange juice. Guests have use of the leisure facilities at the nearby Kenmore Club. Children under 12 stay free in parents' room. Dogs in kennels only. ***Rooms** 11. Garden.* AMERICAN EXPRESS *Access, Diners, Visa.*

Menzies Restaurant — £75

A new name, but the dining room remains unchanged with its polished tables, dark green decor and floral curtains. The fixed-price dinner menu offers no choice, although alternatives can be had from the menu of the hotel's informal Scottish bistro, except for the number of courses taken. Richard Lyth is doing a sterling job with some well-judged dishes such as a warm salad of duck, wood pigeon and oyster mushrooms; a refined soup just bursting with fresh asparagus flavour and a good turbot dish with spinach, courgette and tomato. No smoking. ***Seats** 32. Parties 12. L by arrangement D 7.30-8.30 (Bistro 10-2 & 6-9.30). Set D £23/£26/£29.*

Aberfeldy — Places of Interest

Tourist Information Tel 0887 820276.

Aberfoyle — Braeval Old Mill

£75

Tel 087 72 711

R

Braeval by Aberfoyle Central FK8 3UY

Map 3 B5

An old stone mill, standing on the A81 a mile south of Aberfoyle, with exposed stone walls, pavement slab floor, black polished wood tables and fabric wall hangings. Chef-patron Nick Nairn uses only first-rate ingredients in his four-course, fixed-price dinners beginning with the day's soup and continuing with a starter, main and choice of desserts or cheese (no choice in other courses). Some very good drinking under £20 (note the house selection) on a well-conceived and balanced wine list. ***Seats** 32. L weekdays by arrangement, Sun 12.30-1.30 D 7-9.30. Closed D Sun & Mon, Bank Holidays, 2 weeks Nov. Set L £18.50 Set D £27.50.* AMERICAN EXPRESS *Access, Visa.*

Aberfoyle — Places of Interest

Tourist information Tel 08772 352.

Abington — Forte Travelodge

£42

Tel 08642 782

L

Abington Biggar Strathclyde ML12 6RG

Map 4 B1

At the junction of the A74 with the M74 at the Welcome Break Service Area, Abington. ***Rooms** 54.* AMERICAN EXPRESS *Access, Visa.*

> Our inspectors are full-time employees; they are professionally trained by us.

Achiltibuie — Summer Isles 64%

£73

Tel 085 482 282 Fax 085 482 251

HR

Achiltibuie by Ullapool Highland IV26 2YG

Map 2 B2

A friendly family-run hotel in a particularly beautiful area. Public areas include a sitting room with TV, honesty bar and games, plus a small study with a telephone. There are no TVs or phones in the neat, light bedrooms, three of which are in Norwegian pine-log cabins a few steps from the main building. Owners Mark and Geraldine Irvine will be happy to give advice about fishing, bird-watching and walking. No children under eight.
***Rooms** 11. Garden, coffee shop (10am-8pm in high season). Closed mid Oct-Easter. No credit cards.*

Restaurant

£75

There are spectacular views of the Summer Isles to be had from the dining room. Chris Firth-Bernard makes good use of top-quality produce, almost all of which is of local provenance. The five-course dinner, served at 8 o'clock, offers no choice (except at dessert), but the menu is displayed at reception, so negotiation in advance is possible. A typical dinner might offer spinach soup with garlic croutons and a leek and onion scone to start, followed by fillet of roe deer carpaccio with a tomato, pepper and anchovy relish plus a salad of dandelion and endive; then pan-fried scallops in pastry with a creamy vermouth and dulse (seaweed) sauce, and finally, perhaps, steamed pear and caramel pudding and/or cheeses served from a trolley. The wine list is balanced and fairly priced with plenty of half bottles.
***Seats** 26. Parties 8. D only at 8. Set D £31.*

Advie Tulchan Lodge 77% £350*

Tel 0807 510200 Fax 0807 510234 **H**

Advie nr Grantown-on-Spey Highland PH26 3PW **Map 2 C3**

One of the finest Edwardian shooting lodges in Scotland, Tulchan continues to offer some of the best fishing on 8 miles of the Spey – both banks (each beat has its own ghillie and luxurious fishing cabin where lunch is served) – and shooting on the 25,000-acre estate (grouse, pheasant, duck flighting and roe deer stalking). The atmosphere is much more that of a country house weekend party than a hotel with long-serving butler and general factotum, Joe, tending to guests' needs in immensely civilised surrounding; antiques, important paintings, hunting trophies, an elegant drawing room, button-back leather armchairs in the panelled library and spacious, sumptuously decorated bedrooms with bathrooms designed to pamper with huge bath sheets and top-quality toiletries. Dinner, for residents only, is served butler style at a single large polished table weighed down with silver candelabra and table decorations. The simple no-choice menu leans heavily on Estate produce with saddle of venison or baked salmon providing a typical main dish. *Full-board terms only. Mid-April to September is the summer fishing season, October to January it is open only for shooting parties and February to early April it is closed altogether. Dogs in kennels only. ***Rooms** 11. Garden, game fishing, shooting, snooker, tennis. Closed Oct-Apr except by prior arrangement.* AMERICAN EXPRESS®

Airth Airth Castle 68% £100

Tel 0324 831411 Fax 0324 831419 **H**

Airth by Falkirk Central FK2 8JF **Map 3 C5**

Careful restoration has kept a sense of history at the castle, but some bedrooms and two of the conference rooms (up to 400 delegates) are in a recent extension. Public areas are splendid, with fine proportions, ornate ceilings and elegant traditional furniture. Modern-day facilities are provided in bedrooms that range from spacious Executive-style to romantic four-poster. Leisure amenities are in the country club at the end of the drive. No dogs. ***Rooms** 75. Garden, indoor swimming pool, sauna, solarium, spa bath, keep-fit equipment, children's play areas.* AMERICAN EXPRESS® *Access, Diners, Visa.*

Airth Places of Interest

Bannockburn Museum (NT) Tel 0780 812664 *11 miles.*

Alexandria Cameron House 81% £150

Tel 0389 55565 Fax 0389 59522 **HR**

Loch Lomond Alexandria Strathclyde G83 8QZ **Map 3 B5**

An extended Georgian house turned into an elegant hotel with most impressive leisure facilities. Just off the A82, it enjoys a splendid location by Loch Lomond on a large estate that includes time-share lodges. Peaceful, country house-style day rooms in the original house contrast with the more lively bar that overlooks the leisure club. Spacious bedrooms are individually decorated with stylish fabrics and boast comfortable armchairs; there are huge, soft towels and bathrobes in the bathrooms. Smiling staff offer a warm welcome and high standards of service. Families are well catered for, with a daily crèche (normally to 5pm, but extended to 9pm on Thurs & Fri) and baby-sitting available. No dogs. ***Rooms** 68. Indoor swimming pools, steam room, sauna, solarium, spa bath, squash, badminton, snooker, gymnasium, hairdressing, beauty salon, crèche, kiosk, 9-hole golf course, tennis, watersports centre, marina, fishing, mountain bikes.* AMERICAN EXPRESS® *Access, Diners, Visa.*

Georgian Room

£75

Sparkling chandeliers, rich drapes and quality silverware create a luxurious setting for serious, sophisticated cooking; the short à la carte menu seems to have learned something from the decor. Casserole of langoustines with woodland mushrooms and black, ginger-flavoured noodles and a lobster and lentil sauce; supreme of chicken with leek and truffle ravioli; and geranium and blackcurrant parfait served with a praline basket of fruits are indicative of the involved style. An imaginative, six-course Celebration menu is also offered – for those wishing to become even more involved – plus fixed-price daily menus. ***Seats** 60. L 12-3 D 7-10. Set L £12.95/£15.50 Set D £29.50.*

Alexandria Places of Interest

Balloch Castle Country Park Tel 0389 58216.

Altnaharra Altnaharra Hotel 60%

£112*

Tel & Fax 054 981 222

H

Altnaharra by Lairg Highland IV27 4UE

Map 2 B2

Very much a place for the discerning angler, this remote 19th-century inn keeps fishing records that go back over 100 years. Ghillies can be hired and there's a chalet offering rod racks, deep freeze and drying facilities. Healthy walks in lovely country are another popular option. There are no TVs or telephones in the airy bedrooms, among which are two annexe cottages ideal for anglers' families. *Half-board terms only. ***Rooms** 20. Garden, game fishing. Closed Oct-early Mar. Access, Visa.*

Alyth Drumnacree House

£50

Tel 082 83 2194

RR

St Ninians Road Alyth Perthshire Tayside PH11 8AP

Map 3 C4

A keen amateur cook during his 20 years in the oil industry, chef-patron Allan Cull is never short of enthusiasm and a good deal of skill is evident in his short, fixed-price dinner menu. This might commence with a plate of charcuterie or home-cured gravad lax, followed by supreme of duck au poivre with a brandy and cream sauce or best end of lamb with a walnut crust and Madeira sauce. Steaks are always popular, as are several Cajun specialities – from prawn gumbo to blackened meat dishes served with "dirty" rice. Ellen Cull looks after the front of house with its pretty pink linen and candles. ***Seats** 24. D only 7-10. Closed all Sun & Mon, Jan & Feb. Set D £17.50. Access, Visa.*

Rooms

£60

Five neat, no-smoking bedrooms offer modest comfort with duvets, TVs, tea and coffee kit and en-suite shower rooms. No charge for children under 5. Good breakfasts might offer kedgeree, kippers and home-made black pudding. *Garden.*

Alyth Lands of Loyal Hotel 62%

£65

Tel 082 83 3151 Fax 082 83 3313

H

Alyth by Blairgowrie Perthshire Tayside PH11 8JQ

Map 3 C4

The Howell family's hotel is a sandstone mansion built after the Battle of Waterloo and added to over the years. It stands in 10 acres of rambling gardens on a hillside overlooking the Vale of Strathmore. Most splendid of the day rooms is the galleried main hall with oak panelling and a blazing fire in winter. Bedrooms offer practical accommodation with either white melamine or older traditional-style furniture. Fishing and field sports can be arranged with notice. ***Rooms** 14. Garden.* AMERICAN EXPRESS *Access, Diners, Visa.*

Annan Warmanbie Hotel 59% £74

Tel 0461 204015 **H**

Annan Dumfries & Galloway DG12 5LL **Map 4 C2**

Home of the Duncan family since 1953, this Georgian house by the river Annan was converted to a hotel in 1983. There's still a homely, private house feel about the day rooms, and a traditional look to the bedrooms, which offer easy chairs, books, mini-bars and tea-makers; two rooms have four-poster beds. Mainly modern bathrooms, except the four-poster room which has a Victorian tub. A holiday cottage (Warmanbie Lodge) on the estate sleeps four people in two bedrooms. Under-16s stay free in their parents' room. ***Rooms** 7. Garden, game fishing.* AMERICAN EXPRESS *Access, Visa.*

Anstruther Cellar £70

Tel 0333 310378 **R**

24 East Green Anstruther Fife KY10 3AA **Map 3 D5**

Tucked away behind the harbour, the Cellar is full of character with natural stone walls and, for most of the year, real fires burning in old black grates at each end of the room – a charming setting for Peter Jukes's cooking, which combines simplicity with sophistication. Fish from nearby Pittenweem harbour is the mainstay of the menu and is sympathetically handled in dishes like hot quiche of lobster, langoustines and smoked salmon, grilled halibut with lime juice and butter, and monkfish roasted on the bone with tomato and basil sauce by the side. Some real gems on an exceptional wine list. France to the fore, but a good selection of New World wines too. Booking is essential to save disappointment. ***Seats** 30. L 12.30-1.30 D 7.30-9. Closed L Mon, all Sun, 10 days Christmas. Set D from £15-£27.50.* AMERICAN EXPRESS *Access, Visa.*

Anstruther Places of Interest

Scottish Fisheries Museum Tel 0333 310628.

Appin Invercreran County House Hotel 67% £108

Tel 063 173 414 Fax 063 173 532 **H**

Appin Glen Creran Highland PA38 4BJ **Map 3 B4**

A long, low-level hotel built in the 70s, overlooking the river and Glen Creran. 25 acres of mature gardens and woodland surround the hotel, which lies off the A828 Oban-Fort William road. A semi-circular part at the centre of the building is fronted by balconied terracing and houses lounge and dining areas; drinks service comes from a neat dispense bar. Downstairs are master bedrooms with spacious tiled bathrooms, all with showers and bidets. No children under five; up-to-14s sharing parents' room pay for meals only. Dogs in kennels only. ***Rooms** 9. Garden, sauna. Closed 16 Nov-28 Feb (except 29 Dec-3 Jan). Access, Visa.*

Ardentinny Ardentinny Hotel 59% £78

Tel 036 981 209 Fax 036 981 345 **H**

Loch Long Ardentinny nr Dunoon Strathclyde PA23 8TR **Map 3 B5**

A former droving inn on the A880 by Loch Long, Ardentinny offers comfortable accommodation with the bonus of stunning views of the loch and surrounding forests and mountains. There's a selection of malt whiskies to be had in the Viking and Lauder bars, where yachtsmen and fishermen take their ease. Bedrooms are neat and bright, the best (designated 'Fyne') being slightly larger, with better views and some extras; some have showers only. ***Rooms** 11. Garden, fishing, hotel boat, mountain bikes. Closed Nov-mid Mar.* AMERICAN EXPRESS *Access, Diners, Visa.*

Ardentinny Places of Interest

Younger Botanic Garden Benmore Tel 0369 6261 7 *miles.*

Arduaine Loch Melfort Hotel 63%

£90

Tel 08522 233 Fax 08522 214

H

Arduaine by Oban Argyll Strathclyde PA34 4XG

Map 3 B5

Philip and Rosalind Lewis offer guests a comfortable and relaxing break at their peaceful hotel facing south across Asknish Bay. The scenery is spectacular, and there are superb views from both main-house and Cedar-wing bedrooms. The latter are connected by a covered walkway; rooms have either a patio or a balcony. Day rooms include two lounges, a panelled library and the Chartroom Bar – a favourite with yachtsmen. ***Rooms** 27. Garden, mooring, book & gift shop. Closed Jan & Feb.* AMERICAN EXPRESS *Access, Visa.*

Arisaig Arisaig House 75%

£135

Tel 068 75 622 Fax 068 75 626

HR

Beasdale Arisaig Highland PH39 4NR

Map 3 A4

The spectacualr Road to the Isles also leads to peaceful, civilised Arisaig House. The house itself is of Victorian stone, the grounds abound in redwood and oak, roses and rhododendrons, and the views to the distant hills of Ardnamurchen and Roshven are breathtaking. The broad terrace comes into its own in summer, when guests or casual visitors can enjoy a light lunch or afternoon tea. Inside, the look is of the 1930s, and natural light shows off immaculate housekeeping. Hosts Ruth and John Smithers aim to give guests a comfortable, relaxing and happy stay; there's certainly no shortage of comfort in the morning room, in the vaulted drawing room with its inviting sofas and armchairs or in the bedrooms – large beds and easy chairs, with luxury added by bathrobes, good toiletries and bidets in the bathrooms. No children under 10. No dogs. ***Rooms** 13. Garden, snooker, helipad. Closed end Oct-early Apr. Access, Visa.*

Restaurant

£85

The nightly fixed-price menus make excellent use of locally bought meat or fish, and many of the vegetables and herbs come from the hotel's gardens. Mallaig scallops with red wine and shallot sauce might precede cream of artichoke soup (or mixed salad leaves) and young duck baked with citrus fruits; chocolate nut pie or a selection of good cheeses complete the picture. Alternatives might include calf's sweetbreads with brioche in Madeira sauce, shellfish bisque, saddle of lamb with spinach stuffing, grilled West Coast halibut with sesame seed crust and iced Drambuie soufflé. Good vegetarian options. Lunch is a lighter affair of sandwiches, salads and omelettes. Fine clarets on the almost exclusively French wine list. No smoking in the dining room. ***Seats** 36. Parties 10. L 12.30-2 D 7.30-8.30. Set D £29.50 & £35/£40.*

Auchterarder Auchterarder House 75%

£130

Tel 0764 663646 Fax 0764 662939

HR

Auchterarder Tayside PH3 1DZ

Map 3 C5

A baronial-style mansion originally built in 1832. Nowadays it's a hotel popular with corporate clients and boasting many fine features: carved oak panelling in the central hall, ribbed ceilings and marble fireplace in the day rooms, a characterful billiard room bar, and charming conservatory. The Brown family have added the warm welcome and many homely touches like original paintings, an abundance of fresh flowers and numerous objets d'art. Bedroom decor varies, but all have extras both luxurious (like a cut-glass decanter of good sherry) and practical (iron and ironing board). Many of the bathrooms include bidets and separate showers. No children under 10. $1\frac{1}{2}$ miles north of Auchterarder on the B8062. ***Rooms** 15. Garden, pitch & putt, putting green.* AMERICAN EXPRESS *Access, Diners, Visa.*

See over

Restaurant £90

Jacket and tie are 'de rigueur' for dinner in the gracious, dado-panelled dining room. New chef David Hunt's short, three-course, fixed price dinner changes daily and might offer millefeuille of scallops with ginger sauce, followed by fillet of beef Strathallan with a pickled walnut sauce or poached darne of Tay salmon with a saffron sauce. Steamed syrup pudding with crème anglaise or Grand Marnier soufflé baked in a crepe and served with a tangy orange sauce among the puddings. Canapés and petits fours are included in the fixed prices. Reservations are essential for both lunch and dinner. Many fine clarets on an excellent and fairly-priced wine list. No smoking. ***Seats** 25. Parties 8. Private Room 15. L 12-2.30 D 7-9.30. Set L £15/£18.50 Set D £25/£35.*

Auchterarder Gleneagles Hotel 86% £205

Tel 0764 662231 Fax 0764 662134 **H**

Auchterarder Tayside PH3 1NF **Map 3 C5**

Jack Nicklaus's name has now been added to the famous sportsmen who have given their names to the outstanding sporting facilities at this renowned resort hotel. The latest 18-hole golf course, the Monarch's course, was designed by Nicklaus and opened in May 1993, adding to the famous King's and Queen's and Wee Course facilities; clubs may be hired (even by under-14s) and professional tuition is offered. Gleneagles may be synonymous with golf but it has many further sporting attractions: a Health Spa in the leisure centre, Jackie Stewart's Shooting School, the Mark Phillips Equestrian Centre, the British School of Falconry and an arcade where one can shop (considered an equally professional sporting activity by some) in such famous names as Harvey Nichols, Mappin and Webb, Burberry's and even a branch of the Bank of Scotland. The hotel is grand in every sense of the word with large, high-ceilinged public rooms featuring numerous faux-marble fluted columns and pilasters, and decorative plaster ceilings. The cocktail bar and restaurant boast pianists and there is dancing to a live band in the drawing room each evening. The grading of bedrooms depends largely on size and outlook; all are individually decorated to the same high standards from the smallest single room to the twenty full suites. Good family facilities; informal eating in the Country Club or Equestrian Centre; formal dining has been a disappointment on recent visits. With equal staff to guest ratio, levels of service are kept high. ***Rooms** 236. Garden, indoor swimming pool, sauna, solarium, whirlpool bath, gymnasium, hairdressing, tennis, squash, golf courses, pitch & putt, jogging trails, bowling green, riding, clay-pigeon shooting, coarse and game fishing, mountain bikes, children's playground, snooker, valeting, shopping arcade, bank, post office.* AMERICAN EXPRESS *Access, Diners, Visa.*

Auchterarder Places of Interest

Tourist Information Tel 0764 663450.

Auchterhouse Old Mansion House 68% £95

Tel 082 626 366 Fax 082 626 400 **HR**

Auchterhouse by Dundee Tayside DD3 0QN **Map 3 C5**

Seven miles from Dundee on the B954, a 16th-century, whitewashed Scottish baronial house has been skilfully converted by Nigel and Eva Bell to a charming and relaxed hotel. Some nice architectural features include the vaulted entrance hall, an open Jacobean fireplace and a splendidly ornate 17th-century plasterwork ceiling. Pleasantly furnished bedrooms – two are family suites with separate children's bedrooms – have good bathrooms well stocked with toiletries. Informal eating in the courtyard bar. ***Rooms** 6. Garden, outdoor swimming pool, squash, tennis. Closed Christmas, 1 week Jan.* AMERICAN EXPRESS *Access, Diners, Visa.*

Restaurant

£66

Much local produce is used for the varied carte that is supplemented by a separate vegetarian menu. Cullen skink, smoked Tay salmon, whole prawn tails in a curried apple and cucumber cream sauce, medallions of venison, and raspberry crème brulée with a nut crust are typical dishes. Good-value lunches. No under-10s at night. No smoking. ***Seats 50.*** *Private Room 22. L 12-2 D 7-9.30 (Sun to 9). Set L £11.95/£13.95.*

Aviemore — Aviemore Highlands Hotel — 61%

£70

Tel 0479 810771 Fax 0479 811473

H

Aviemore Centre Aviemore Highland PH22 1PJ

Map 3 C4

On the A9 Perth to Inverness road, a modern hotel popular for both business and pleasure, with banqueting/conference facilities for around 200, and amenities for families (crèche, baby-listening, baby-sitting). Children up to 14 can stay free in their parents' room. ***Rooms 103.*** AMERICAN EXPRESS *Access, Diners, Visa.*

Aviemore — Stakis Aviemore Four Seasons — 70%

£100

Tel 0479 810681 Fax 0479 810534

H

Aviemore Highland PH22 1PF

Map 3 C4

A seven-storey hotel at the heart of the skiing centre, a mile from the A9, with views of the Spey Valley and the Cairngorms. Centrally-heated bedrooms with smart darkwood furniture range from singles to triples. Main day room is a bright, picture-windowed lounge. Half the bedrooms are designated non-smoking. ***Rooms 89.*** *Garden, indoor swimming pool, gymnasium, sauna, spa bath, steam bath, solarium, ski school, coffee shop (10am-6pm).* AMERICAN EXPRESS *Access, Diners, Visa.*

Aviemore — Stakis Coylumbridge Resort Hotel — 62%

£96*

Tel 0479 810661 Fax 0479 811309

H

Aviemore Highland PH22 1QN

Map 3 C4

Skiing is the thing at Aviemore, but this sprawling modern hotel caters admirably for all sorts of activities for both adults and children. New since last year are a sports hall for children, a fun house and an outdoor play area. It's also geared up for large conferences (maximum 750 delegates). Most of the bedrooms are big enough for family use, and baby-sitting, baby-listening and (at busy times) a crèche are provided. A couple of rooms are suitable for disabled guests. *Half-board terms preferred. ***Rooms 175.*** *Two indoor swimming pools, sauna, spa bath, steam bath, solarium, beauty & hair salon, tennis, archery.* AMERICAN EXPRESS *Access, Diners, Visa.*

Aviemore — Places of Interest

Tourist Information Tel 0479 810363.
Strathspey Steam Railway Tel 0479 810725.
Aviemore Mountain Resort Centre Ice Rink Tel 0479 810624.
Caird Sport Dry Ski Slope Tel 0479 810310.
Cairngorm Reindeer Centre Tel 0479 861228.
Cairngorm Chairlift Company Tel 0479 861261.

Ayr — Caledonian Hotel — 64%

£99

Tel 0292 269331 Fax 0292 610722

H

Dalblair Road Ayr Strathclyde KA7 1UG

Map 4 A1

Town-centre hotel with leisure facilities and a conference suite (for up to 175). Many bedrooms suitable for families (children up to 16 stay free in parents' room). Within easy reach of eight golf courses, thus popular for sporting breaks. Jarvis. ***Rooms 114.*** *Indoor swimming pool, gymnasium, sauna, spa bath, solarium, snooker.* AMERICAN EXPRESS *Access, Diners, Visa.*

Ayr — Fouters Bistro

£40

Tel 0292 261391 — **R**

2a Academy Street Ayr Strathclyde KA7 1HS — **Map 4 A1**

Cheerful bistro in vaulted basement premises down a cobbled lane opposite the Town Hall. Scottish produce is cooked in French style with consistently enjoyable results. Good-value bistro menus and plenty of half bottles on the wine list. Non-smoking area. ***Seats** 38. L 12-2 D 6.30-10.30 (Sun 7-10). Closed L Sun, all Mon, 25 & 26 Dec, 1-3 Jan.* AMERICAN EXPRESS *Access, Diners, Visa.*

Ayr — The Stables

£48

Tel 0292 283704 — **R**

Queen's Court 41 Sandgate Ayr Strathclyde KA7 1BD — **Map 4 A1**

Within an appealing shopping area formed out of a group of Georgian and Victorian buildings. Whilst explaining/exploring the menu, owner Edward Baines demonstrates his extensive knowledge of Scottish culinary history and seems to know all his suppliers personally. Pies like The Real McCoy (from an 18th-century recipe with beef, mussels, pickled walnuts and spices), ham and haddie (15th-century with rough cured ham and smoked haddock) and venison (marinated in claret and juniper berries) are a speciality and the family's own smoke-house provides smoked salmon, duck breast, trout and eel. Haggis is not forgotten and there are steaks and roast meats. Scottish farmhouse cheeses on offer always include one made with vegetarian rennet. A wide-ranging wine list has a strong English section and a fascinating selection of traditional country wines. No smoking. ***Seats** 50. Meals 10-5 (Sun from 1). Closed 25 & 26 Dec, 1 & 2 Jan.* AMERICAN EXPRESS

Ayr — Places of Interest

Tourist Information Tel 0292 284196.
Gaiety Theatre Tel 0292 264639.
Ayr Racecourse Tel 0292 264179.
Ayr Ice Rink Tel 0292 263024.
Historic Houses, Castles and Gardens
Burns Cottage Alloway. Tel 0292 441215.
Blairquhan Castle and Gardens Straiton Nr Maybole. Tel 065 57 239.
Culzean Castle Garden and Country Park (NT) Maybole. Tel 065 56 274.

Ballachulish — Ballachulish Hotel — 60%

£75

Tel 085 52 606 Fax 085 52 629 — **H**

Ballachulish Argyll Highland PA39 4JY — **Map 3 B4**

An imposing inn set below rugged mountains which sweep down to Loch Linnhe, on the A828 Fort William-Oban road. Impressive views are shared by restaurant, cocktail bar and baronial residents' lounge. There's a "local" atmosphere in the Ferry Bars. Bedrooms are called Lairds or Chieftains, the latter enjoying the best of the light, space and views. Guests have free use of the leisure centre at the sister hotel *The Isles of Glencoe* about two miles away. Families are well catered for. ***Rooms** 30. Garden, sea fishing. Access, Visa.*

Ballachulish — Isles of Glencoe Hotel — 59%

£79

Tel 085 52 603 Fax 085 52 629 — **H**

Ballachulish Highland PA39 4HL — **Map 3 B4**

"Almost afloat" on the shore of Loch Leven this new, clean-cut purpose-built hotel makes a useful overnight stop with comfortable uncluttered bedrooms, although their narrow sloping windows fail to make the best of the views – the loch and ancient burial island of the Clan McDonald on one side and mountains on the other. Friendly young staff are uniformed in polo shirts displaying the hotel's logo. Men and women share changing facilities for the basic leisure centre; there's also a supervised crèche between 9 and 3. Informal eating in the Lochside bar all day. ***Rooms** 39. Indoor swimming pool, spa bath, sauna, steam room, coffee shop (10am-10pm). Access, Visa.*

Ballachulish — Places of Interest

Tourist Information Tel 085 52 296

Ballater — Craigendarroch Hotel — 74% — £135

Tel 033 97 55858 Fax 033 97 55447 — **H**

Braemar Road Ballater Grampian AB3 5XA — **Map 3 C4**

Seven miles from Balmoral on the banks of the River Dee, this fine hotel in Scottish baronial style offers comfort, peace and a wealth of sports and leisure amenities. Fair-sized bedrooms are bright and modern, with plenty of toiletries in the bathrooms, and views of the Dee valley to wake up to. There are two bars (one with regular live music nights) and three restaurants. No dogs, but excellent facilities for children, including a daily crèche. ***Rooms** 50. Garden, indoor swimming pool, gymnasium, squash, sauna, spa bath, solarium, beauty & hair salon, tennis, dry ski slope, snooker. Closed 5-10 Jan.* AMERICAN EXPRESS *Access, Diners, Visa.*

Ballater — Tullich Lodge — 71% — £160

Tel 033 97 55406 Fax 033 97 55397 — **HR**

Ballater Grampian AB35 5SB — **Map 3 C4**

Hector Macdonald and Neil Bannister have been installed at their delightful pink granite mansion (on the A93 Aberdeen to Braemar road, 1½ miles east of Ballater) since 1968. Crenellations and towers are outward distinguishing features, while inside antiques, pictures and handsome furnishings grace the drawing room and chintzy little sitting room (the perfect place to retire with a book); an old Broadwood piano in the drawing room 'responds kindly to early 19th-century music'. Bedrooms are individually decorated in keeping with the rest of the place, and the Tower Room, on the third floor, provides not only exercise but a splendid Victorian bathroom; televisions are available on request only; however, a wireless is in every room. This is a hotel of real character and atmosphere, and many of the guests return regularly. High tea is served to children in the kitchen and both picnic lunches and packed dinner ('for the train') are provided. ***Rooms** 10. Garden. Closed Dec-Mar.* AMERICAN EXPRESS *Access, Diners, Visa.*

Dining Room — £62

Dinner in the mahogany-panelled room offers no choice, but Neil can be relied upon to provide a good, straightforward meal prepared from the best seasonal produce. A typical menu might include shrimps on a raft, watercress soup, roast rib of beef and warm blackberries and raspberries with glazed cream (or cheeses). A lighter lunch (soup, open sandwich or grilled lamb cutlet, cheese and coffee) is served at 1 o'clock in the bar. No smoking in the dining room. Jacket and tie requested. ***Seats** 26. Parties 12. L at 1 D 7.30-8.30. Set L in the bar £7.50 Set D £23.*

Ballater — Places of Interest

Tourist Information Tel 03397 55306.
Balmoral Castle Tel 03397 42334 Open May to July. *8 miles.*
Braemar Castle Tel 03397 41219.

Banchory Invery House 78% £125

Tel 033 02 4782 Fax 033 02 4712 **H**

Bridge of Feugh Banchory Royal Deeside Grampian AB31 3NJ **Map 3 D4**

CLOSED

Owners Stewart and Sheila Spence bought the house in 1985 and have turned it into a country house hotel of great charm and character. It is a Georgian mansion set on the west bank of the river Feugh in 40 acres of grounds that include a croquet lawn and walled garden. Tasteful decor is pleasantly non-designer with fresh flowers, ormolu vases, tapestry fire screens and the like adding a homely touch to the elegantly proportioned drawing room. Antique-furnished bedrooms (four designated non-smoking) are named after the novels of Sir Walter Scott, a frequent visitor to the house, and offer various extras like a decanter of sherry, fresh fruit and mineral water. Smart, spacious bathrooms often find room for an old washstand or wicker chair, taking them a little out of the ordinary. Bedrooms are properly serviced at night and room service can provide hot food 24 hours a day. Children up to 12 stay free in parents' room. ***Rooms** 14. Garden, tennis, snooker, game fishing, putting, helipad.* AMERICAN EXPRESS *Access, Diners, Visa.*

Banchory Raemoir House 71% £110

Tel 033 02 4884 Fax 033 02 2171 **HR**

Raemoir Banchory Grampian AB31 4ED **Map 3 D4**

2½ miles north of Banchory on the A980. Three generations of the Sabin family have built friendly hospitality into the fabric of their hotel, an 18th-century mansion set in a 3500-acre estate. Rich red brocade chairs, panelled walls and valuable antiques enhance the traditional look of the morning room, and the bar is fashioned from a Tudor four-poster. Bedrooms are all different in size and character, but most have inviting chaises longues, day beds or armchairs. Six rooms are in the historic 16th-century Ha'Hoose immediately behind the mansion. There are five self-catering apartments converted from the original coach-house and stables. Bar and picnic lunches. ***Rooms** 25. Garden, sauna, solarium, keep-fit equipment, tennis, game fishing, 9-hole mini golf, shooting, helipad. Closed 1 week Jan.* AMERICAN EXPRESS *Access, Diners, Visa.*

Restaurant £68

Top-quality produce is cooked without undue elaboration and served in generous portions by friendly staff. Crab paté, cream of lettuce and pea soup or venison consommé, devilled whitebait, honey-roast duckling with a Grand Marnier and kumquat sauce, grilled rack of lamb with a redcurrant tartlet, and poached salmon from the river Dee typify chef Derek Smith's style. Both table d'hote and à la carte are offered, plus a long choice for vegetarians, individually-presented sweets (from a piquant lemon tart to a chocoholic's delight) and a fine Scottish cheese trolley. ***Seats** 64. Private Room 32. L by arrangement on Sun 12.30-2 D 7.30-9. Set L £13.50 (Sun) Set D £23.50.*

Banchory Tor-na-Coille Hotel 66% £85

Tel 033 02 2242 Fax 033 02 4012 **H**

Inchmarlo Road Banchory Grampian AB3 4AB **Map 3 D4**

Built as a private house in 1873 and a hotel since the turn of the century, Tor-na-Coille retains much of its Victorian character. The programme of refurbishment instituted by owner Roxanne Sloan most recently involved the foyer and stairs. The function room can accommodate 90 people for a banquet, 80 for a conference. Bedrooms are furnished with antiques. The hotel copes very well with children (under-10s stay free in parents' room). ***Rooms** 25. Garden, squash, playground, crèche (8-4, Mon-Fri). Closed 25-28 Dec.* AMERICAN EXPRESS *Access, Diners, Visa.*

Banchory **Places of Interest**

Tourist Information Tel 03302 2000.

Bearsden **Fifty Five BC** **NEW** **£50**

Tel 041-942 7272 Fax 041-942 9650 **R**

128 Drymen Road Bearsden Glasgow Strathclyde G61 3RB **Map 3 B6**

Formerly the *October* Restaurant, a new owner has brought a complete change of style to what is now a smart bar with small restaurant area to the rear. The short menu might include warm scallop and potato salad with pine nuts and walnut oil dressing, Tay salmon with lemon butter sauce, piccata of veal with tomato and oregano, and tangy lemon tart – all competently cooked and served by notably friendly staff. The bar menu (Mon to Thur 12-3 & 5-7, Fri and Sat noon-7pm, Sun 12.30-2.30) ranges from crispy potato skins and BLT to home-made burger and pasta of the day. Families are encouraged with a special children's menu. ***Seats** 20/50. L 12-2.30 D 7-11. Access, Visa.*

Bearsden **Place of Interest**

Bearsden Ski Club Tel 041-942 2933.

Beattock **Auchen Castle** **65%** **£70**

Tel 06833 407 Fax 06833 667 **H**

Beattock nr Moffat Dumfries & Galloway DG10 9SH **Map 4 C2**

Signposted from the A74 a mile north of Beattock, a Scottish baronial-style mansion built in 1849, once the home of the Willam Younger family for 70 years. The hillside position offers views over upper Annandale and the Moffat hills and there are terraced gardens running down to a trout lake. A comfortable, traditional air pervades the public rooms, which include a chintzy lounge and a bar with unusual seating brought from Hong Kong. Best bedrooms are in the main house; these are spacious with antique furniture and easy chairs. Other rooms have fitted furniture and there are ten more functional rooms in a separate lodge. ***Rooms** 25. Garden, game fishing. Closed 3 weeks Christmas/New Year.* AMERICAN EXPRESS *Access, Diners, Visa.*

Beattock **Places of Interest**

Dumfries Tourist Information Tel 0387 53862. At Dumfries 25 miles.
Drumlanrig Castle and Country Park Tel 0848 31682.
Museums and Art Galleries
Dumfries Museum Tel 0387 53374.
Gracefield Arts Centre Tel 0387 62084.
Robert Burns Centre Tel 0387 64808.
Burns House Tel 0387 55297.

Blairgowrie **Kinloch House** **70%** **£138***

Tel 0250 884237 Fax 0250 884333 **HR**

Kinloch by Blairgowrie Tayside PH10 6SG **Map 3 C5**

Highland cattle graze in the parkland that surrounds a creeper-clad 19th-century house which has been turned into a relaxing country hotel by David and Sarah Shentall. Public areas include a period drawing room but most guests prefer the convivial atmosphere of the comfortable bar or the charm of the plant-filled conservatory with its Lloyd Loom chairs and tables. All the rooms are now traditionally furnished and boast particularly luxurious bathrooms. Extras include books, magazines, ironing boards and bathrobes. Shooting parties and fishermen appreciate the Sportsman's room, which offers everything from a deep freeze to dog bowls. Room service is limited. *Half-board terms only. ***Rooms** 21. Garden. Closed 2 weeks Dec.* AMERICAN EXPRESS *Access, Diners, Visa.*

See over

Restaurant

£57

A civilised dining room where a daily-changing dinner menu brings a good choice of dishes, both simple and more elaborate – from marinated herrings or spinach and cheese pillows to carpetbagger steak (stuffed with an oyster) and prawns in a Pernod and butter sauce. Also informal lunches. The wine list is well constructed and fairly priced, with plenty of half bottles. No children under 7 at night (a high tea is served at 5.30 in the conservatory). No smoking. ***Seats** 55. Parties 30. L 12.30-2 D 7-9.15. Set L £10.50/£13 Set D £22.90.*

Blairgowrie Places of Interest

Tourist Information Tel 0250 872960.

Bonnyrigg Dalhousie Castle 62%

£130

Tel & Fax 0875 820153

H

Bonnyrigg nr Edinburgh Lothian EH19 3JB

Map 3 D6

Built around 1450 from locally quarried red sandstone, Dalhousie is a real castle complete with tower, crenellations and dungeons. Notable features of the public areas include more fine Gothic-style fan vaulting in the entrance hall and a 'wedding cake' moulded ceiling in the rather over-furnished wood-panelled library that is the main day room. Bedrooms vary considerably in furnishings and decor from woodchip or less than sympathetic patterned papers on the walls to solid oak or elaborate, marble-topped French-style furniture. All have functional en-suite bathrooms. Functions and meetings are a major part of the business here. ***Rooms** 25. Garden.* AMERICAN EXPRESS *Access, Diners, Visa.*

Bonnyrigg Places of Interest

Tourist Information Tel 031 660 6814.

Bridge of Allan Royal Hotel 59%

£66

Tel 0786 832284 Fax 0786 834377

H

Henderson Street Bridge of Allan Central FK9 4HG

Map 3 C5

Built in 1842 in what was then a spa town, the Royal stands half a mile from the railway station and one mile from the M9 (junction 11). Refurbished bedrooms offer all the usual accessories, and all have modern bathrooms. There's a plush bar, an oak-panelled lounge and several conference rooms (maximum capacity 150). ***Rooms** 32. Garden.* AMERICAN EXPRESS *Access, Diners, Visa.*

Cairndow Loch Fyne Oyster Bar

£32

Tel 049 96 264 Fax 049 96 234

R

Clachan Farm Cairndow Strathclyde PA26 8BH

Map 3 B5

Pop in for a few oysters or push the boat out for a feast of shellfish, all of local origin. Their own smokehouse produces a wonderful platter of smoked trout, eel, salmon, mussels, cod's roe and mackerel. Other attractions range from haggis with tatties and neeps to fine langoustines, salads, baked oysters in garlic butter and breadcrumbs, home-made shortbread and fruit loaf. Carefully chosen, short wine list. Situated at the head of Loch Fyne, with seats outside for fine weather. ***Seats** 80. Parties 50. Meals 9-9.* AMERICAN EXPRESS *Access, Visa.*

Callander — Roman Camp — 70% — £80

Tel 0877 30003 Fax 0877 31533 — **H**

off Main Street Callander Tayside FK17 8BG — **Map 3 C5**

Neither town nor country house, the 17th-century Roman Camp enjoys the best of both worlds: a lively shopping town is literally at the top of the 20 acres of gardens, and private fishing on the river Teith is at the bottom. Pink-turreted and rather reminiscent of a small French chateau, it was once a hunting lodge for the Dukes of Perth: grand proportions, ornate ceilings and wood panelling characterise the lounges, which look down to the river. Store your fishing rods in the tiny stone chapel and restore yourselves by the open fire. Heritage enthusiasts seek out the creaky, characterful original bedrooms, while those of lesser mobility will find more modern ground-floor bedrooms a boon. ***Rooms** 14. Garden, game fishing.* AMERICAN EXPRESS *Access, Diners, Visa.*

Callander — Places of Interest

Tourist Information Tel 0877 30342.
Rob Roy and Trossachs Visitor Centre Tel 0877 30342.

Canonbie — Riverside Inn — £55

Tel 038 73 71512 — **RR**

Canonbie Dumfries & Galloway DG14 0UX — **Map 4 C2**

Robert and Susan Phillips' white-painted inn overlooks the river Esk in a picturesque village just off the A7. His sound cooking of fine, often local produce results in an enjoyable five-course dinner: leaf spinach pancake, chicken and bacon terrine, Dover sole in brown butter, vegetarian bread-and-butter pudding with sun-dried tomatoes, roast ribs of beef with mustard pudding and horseradish hollandaise. Lunch and supper menus, written on a blackboard and changed daily, offer lighter choices in a similar vein. Concise wine list with fair prices. No smoking. ***Seats** 28. L 12-2 D 7.30-8.30. Closed L Sun, 2 weeks Nov, 2 days Christmas, 2 days New Year, 2 weeks Feb. Set D £21. Access, Visa.*

Rooms — £62

The residents' lounge is quiet and cosy, and the lounge bar stocks a variety of specialised malt whiskies. Eight bedrooms, with matching fabrics and thoughtful extras, have a homely appeal. All but two have modern en-suite bathrooms. No dogs.

Chapel of Garioch — Pittodrie House — 65% — £110

Tel 0467 681444 Fax 0467 681648 — **H**

Chapel of Garioch nr Inverurie Highland AB51 9HS — **Map 2 D3**

Fishing, stalking, shooting and riding are all available locally, combining with facilities on the premises to make this a fine base for sporting holidays. The house dates largely from the 17th century (rebuilt from 15th-century origins) and the reception rooms are very traditional and homely, with antiques, family portraits and log fires. The wine bar is stocked with more than ninety malt whiskies. Bedrooms are either in the main building (motley fabrics, antiques, some bathrooms not en suite) or in a 1990-built wing, with reproduction furniture and decent modern bathrooms. There are banqueting and conference facilities for up to 130. ***Rooms** 27. Garden, squash, tennis, snooker.* AMERICAN EXPRESS *Access, Diners, Visa.*

Many establishments are currently on the market, so ownership could change after we go to press.

Cleish — Nivingston House — 65% — £90

Tel 0577 850216 Fax 0577 850238 — H

Cleish Kinross Tayside KY13 7LS — Map 3 C5

Formerly a farmhouse, stone-built Nivingston House enjoys a tranquil setting in 12 acres of gardens at the foot of the Cleish Hills (yet only two miles from J5 of the M90). Public rooms include a quiet drawing room and a cosy, plush bar whose attractions include 50 malts. Pretty bedrooms with Laura Ashley fabrics and wallpapers are well kept, like the whole hotel, and there are neat bathrooms, a few of which have shower and WC only. Children up to 13 stay free in parents' room. ***Rooms*** *17. Garden, golf driving net, putting.* AMERICAN EXPRESS® *Access, Visa.*

Colbost — Three Chimneys Restaurant — £60

Tel 047 081 258 — R

Colbost by Dunvegan Isle of Skye Highland IV55 8ZT — Map 2 A3

Take the scenic B884, signposted Glendale, and follow the single-track road until you reach the old crofter's cottage where Shirley and Eddie Spear have created a charming restaurant with some seriously good Scottish cooking. Local produce such as venison, lamb and beef from the Highlands and especially the seafood (lobster, langoustines, oysters, mussels and scallops) which is delivered direct from the fishing boats to the kitchen door is the starting point for Shirley's natural talent and imagination, producing fine dishes such as wild rabbit and hare terrine with chopped walnuts and prunes, chargrilled scallop and monkfish brochette marinated in olive oil, lemon, ginger, garlic and coriander; lobster salad with raspberry dressing and venison collops with chocolate and chestnut sauce. Lunchtime sees a mix-and-match menu that includes a seafood platter, while dinner is now a 4-course, fixed-price affair that changes about every four days or so; there are always vegetarian options. A typical dinner menu may offer a daily soup, then smoked breast of wild pheasant with roast chestnut and apple sauce, followed by poached fillet of brill and fresh scallops with a chive and lemon balm cream, and a choice of irresistible sweets, up to 12 Scottish cheeses, plus home-baked breads. The Grand Seafood Platter menu for two people (£60) offers a real taste of Scotland! Eddie's wine list is both keenly priced and of a sensible length – a fine match to Shirley's cooking. No smoking. Plans are afoot to expand the restaurant to cover the whole of the ground-floor, including a lounge area and small bar. ***Seats*** *30. Parties 21. L 12-2 D 7-9. Closed Sun (open Sun before Bank Holidays), Nov-Easter. Set D £25. Access, Visa.*

Colbost — Places of Interest

Dunvegan Castle Tel 047 022 206.
Skye Silver Tel 047 081 263.
Colbost Folk Museum Tel 047 022 296.

Contin — Craigdarroch Lodge — 56% — £98

Tel 0997 421265 — H

Contin by Strathpeffer Highland IV14 9EH — Map 2 B3

Built as a shooting lodge in the early part of the 19th century, Craigdarroch stands along a tree-lined drive off the A835 at the foot of the mountains. It's a great base for touring, walking and all kinds of outdoor activities – much of its business now revolves around special golfing packages. On site are a bar and lounge, plus a range of leisure pursuits. Bedrooms are modest but provide the basic comforts. ***Rooms*** *13. Garden, indoor swimming pool, sauna, solarium, tennis, snooker. Closed Jan & Feb. No credit cards.*

Craigellachie — Craigellachie Hotel — 68% — £91

Tel 0340 881204 Fax 0340 881253 — **HR**

Craigellachie Grampian AB3 9SS — **Map 2 C3**

A hundred years old and still going strong, this solidly built hotel on the A95 overlooks a stretch of the river Spey. Public areas include an airy lounge with lace-draped grand piano, antique sideboard and plenty of good armchairs and sofas, plus a small library and snug green bar. Floral chintzy fabrics decorate the bedrooms, which have smart modern bathrooms and either antique or contemporary traditional-style furniture. Children under 10 stay free in parents' room. ***Rooms** 30. Garden, sauna, solarium, keep-fit equipment, games room.* AMERICAN EXPRESS *Access, Diners, Visa.*

Restaurant — £66

The Ben Aigan restaurant puts great reliance on local produce for its four-course dinners: asparagus in a timbale of aspic with a caper and red onion dressing; locally smoked salmon set on a honey and Pommery mustard dressing; venison and veal escalopes in a roulade. Cheeses served with warm herb brioche. No smoking. ***Seats** 50. Parties 15. Private Room 20. L 12.30-1.45 D 7.30-9.30. Set L £9.75 Set D £25.50*

Craignure — Isle of Mull Hotel — 56% — £84

Tel 068 02 351 Fax 068 02 462 — **H**

Craignure Isle of Mull Argyll Strathclyde PA65 6BB — **Map 3 A4**

A long, low modern building where all bedrooms look out across the Sound of Mull. Day rooms offer plenty of space to relax, and one of the lounges has access to a patio. Children up to the age of 6 stay free in parents' room. ***Rooms** 60. Garden. Closed Nov-Mar.* AMERICAN EXPRESS *Access, Visa.*

Craignure — Places of Interest

Tourist Information Tel 06802 377.

Crieff — Crieff Hydro — 64% — £104*

Tel 0764 655555 Fax 0764 653087 — **H**

Crieff Tayside PH7 3LQ — **Map 3 C5**

An enormous Victorian building, now a family hotel par excellence with an impressive range of leisure activities to keep everyone busy and fit – from indoor cinema and table tennis room to outdoor riding school and golf course. Apart from singles, most of the bedrooms are of a decent size, furnished with either lightwood units or more traditional or antique pieces; nine two-storey family chalets are in the woods behind. Table licence only, no bar. Banqueting for up to 350 and conference facilities for up to 400 people. *Egon Ronay's Heinz Guide 1993* Family Hotel of the Year: the hotel has just celebrated its 125th anniversary and they know that "happy children mean happy parents". No dogs (a few kennels are provided, but require prior booking). *Half-board terms only. ***Rooms** 199. Garden, indoor swimming pool, whirlpool, spa bath, sauna, steam room, sunbeds, boutique, hairdressing and beauty salon, tennis, squash, badminton, 9-hole golf course, putting, bowling green, snooker, riding school, football pitch, cinema, supervised crèche (7-9pm), playroom, playground.* AMERICAN EXPRESS *Access, Diners, Visa.*

Crieff — Places of Interest

Tourist Information Tel 0764 652578.
Visitors Centre Tel 0764 654014.
Stuart Crystal Tel 0764 654004.
Glen Turret Distillery Tel 0764 652424.
Drummond Castle Gardens Muthill. Tel 0764 681321.

Crinan — Crinan Hotel 69% — £110

Tel 054 683 261 Fax 054 683 292 — **HR**

Crinan by Lochgilphead Strathclyde PA31 8SR — **Map 3 B5**

At the northern end of the canal connecting Loch Fyne with the Atlantic stands a tiny fishing village and the Ryans' hotel which has been constructed in such a way that every window has a view either westwards up the Jura sound or down over the canal's 15th, and final, lock. Interiors by Mrs Ryan (alias Frances MacDonald the well-known artist) add colour to Italian varnished pine bedrooms of which the pick have private balconies. The old public bar was redecorated last year, giving it a more warm and welcoming feel, complete with fire. ***Rooms** 22. Garden, coffee shop (9-5). Closed 3 days Christmas. Access, Visa.*

Lock 16 Restaurant ★ — £75

On the hotel's top floor, this restaurant opens *only* when the local fishing fleet comes in (late afternoon) to unload at the quayside below. Most of the fish is loaded straight into a waiting pantechnicon to be whisked off to Europe, but not before Nick Ryan takes the pick of the catch – to be served that evening at the very peak of freshness. Mussels from Loch Craignish, princess clams from Loch Fyne, jumbo prawns from Loch Crinan, lobster from Jura or locally-smoked salmon may form the basis of a real feast of freshness. Local cheeses with oatcakes and Mount Kenya coffee round off the meal in style. Always an interesting wine list with new additions every year; easy to use, helpful personal notes – we're sure the owners drink here! Booking essential. Gentlemen require jackets and ties. ***Seats** 20. D only at 8. Closed Sun & Mon, Oct-Mar. Set D £35.*

Westward Restaurant — £65

Seafood also features in Crinan's ground-floor restaurant on both lunch and dinner menus; the latter changes nightly, and carnivores may find Aberdeen Angus beef, either roast or charcoal-grilled, alongside some superb shellfish. Victoria plum tartlets, tulip cases with mango cream, Scottish farmhouse cheeses with oatcakes might follow. Light lunches served in the bar at the east end of the hotel. ***Seats** 50. D only 7-9. Closed 3 days Christmas. Set D £25.50.*

Cumbernauld — Travel Inn — £43

Tel 0236 725339 Fax 0236 736380 — **L**

4 South Muirhead Road Cumbernauld Strathclyde G67 1AX — **Map 3 D5**

Just off A80 in town centre. ***Rooms** 37. AMERICAN EXPRESS Access, Diners, Visa.*

Cumbernauld — Westerwood Hotel 73% — £90

Tel 0236 457171 Fax 0236 738478 — **HR**

St Andrews Drive Westerwood Cumbernauld Strathclyde G68 0EW — **Map 3 D5**

Set on a hill above the A80, Westerwood is a modern hotel and country club with a golf course (designed by Dave Thomas and Severiano Ballesteros) that boasts a 40ft waterfall at the 15th green and wonderful views over the Campsie Hills. For après-golf choose between the hotel's luxurious lounge and cocktail bar with fabric-covered walls and indoor garden or the less formal tartan-carpeted country club. Artificial trees are a novel form of decor in good standard bedrooms. Beds are turned down at night and staff are friendly and helpful. Families are well catered for and can eat informally by the pool or in the clubhouse. ***Rooms** 47. Garden, 18-hole golf course, bowling green, pétanque, tennis, indoor swimming pool, snooker, gymnasium, spa bath, steam room, solarium, hairdressing, coffee shop (10am-6pm). AMERICAN EXPRESS Access, Diners, Visa.*

Old Masters Restaurant — £55

An unusual circular dining room with dark-green watered silk-effect walls and tented ceiling from which hangs a large brass chandelier. Sophisticated menus offer River Tay salmon carved on a trolley, filo pastry moneybag filled with crab, leeks and mushrooms and served on a brandy and shellfish sauce, medallions of Scottish venison with an Arran mustard sauce and liquorice and juniper-perfumed sauce, good fish main courses, and tempting desserts. Some interesting New World wines, French bottles more predictable. Service is as smooth and confident as the cooking. ***Seats** 70. Parties 24. D only 7-9.45. Closed Sun & Mon. Set D £16.50/£18.50.*

Cumbernauld Places of Interest

Palacerigg Country Park Tel 0236 720047.

Cupar Ostlers Close

Tel 0334 55574

£60 R

25 Bonnygate Cupar Fife KY15 4BU

Map 3 C5

Wild mushrooms garnered from nearby forests, herbs and salad ingredients from his own garden and other good local produce give Jimmy Graham's careful cooking a head start at an unpretentious restaurant hidden down an alleyway off Bonnygate. Lobster ravioli poached in chicken broth, roast saddle of roe venison served with wild mushrooms in a red wine sauce, and honey, Drambuie and oatmeal ice cream could make up a typical meal. Thoughtful wine list with a fine selection under £20. No children under 6 in the evening. ***Seats** 28. Private Room 20. L 12.15-2 D 7-9.30 (Sat to 10). Closed Sun & Mon, 25 & 26 Dec, 1 & 2 Jan, 1 week Jun. Access, Visa.*

Cupar Places of Interest

Tourist Information Tel 0334 52874.
Douglas Bader Gardens Tel 0334 53722 ext 437.
Scottish Deer Centre Bow-of-Fife Tel 033 781 391.

Dalguise Kinnaird 76%

Tel 0796 482440 Fax 0796 482289

£170 HR

Kinnaird Estate Dalguise by Dunkeld Tayside PH8 0LB

Map 3 C4

On the B898 to the north of Dunkeld, about four miles off the A9, the 18th-century Kinnaird House, surrounded by its 9,000-acre estate, has a splendid position overlooking the river Tay. Extensively, and expensively, renovated over the last few years, it has now become a fine country house hotel. Spacious bedrooms, each with gas log fire, are lavishly decorated in great style and comfort with sybaritic bathrooms. Day rooms, furnished almost entirely with antiques, include the red cedar-panelled drawing room, where fresh flowers and family mementos and pictures create a homely feel, and a clubby snooker room. No children under 12. Dogs in (heated) kennels only. ***Rooms** 9. Garden, tennis, game fishing, shooting, snooker. Closed Feb.* AMERICAN EXPRESS *Access, Visa.*

Restaurant

£88

Exquisite painted panels depicting figures in an Arcadian landscape compete for attention with magnificent, real-life views over the Tay valley from the high windows of this supremely elegant dining room. John Webber's sophisticated, stylish cooking is entirely appropriate to the setting: sautéed scallop salad with a dressing of carrot and Sauternes, filo pastry flan of courgette and tomato, breast of wood pigeon with an essence of wild mushrooms and smoked bacon, noisettes of local lamb set on an onion and coriander tartlet. Cheeses from the trolley, then a serious pudding such as hot banana and Galliano soufflé or brandied prune tart set on a rich custard sauce. There are plenty of half bottles on an excellent list, which includes inexpensive French country wines and a page of house suggestions. No smoking. Gentlemen should wear jackets and ties. ***Seats** 45. Parties 25. L 12.30-1.45 D 7.15-9.30. Set L £19.50/£24 Set D £34.*

Dirleton — Open Arms Hotel — 67% — £110

Tel 0620 85241 Fax 0620 85570 — H

Dirleton nr North Berwick Lothian EH39 5EG — Map 3 D5

A good name for a friendly, characterful hotel in a charming position overlooking the village green and the ruins of 16th-century Dirleton Castle. It's been in the same family for nearly half a century, and there's a relaxed, domestic warmth to the lounge, which has comfortable armchairs and sofas, a log fire, magazines and newspapers; the bar is tiny but full of character. Bedrooms are mostly bright and airy, with floral curtains; each has an easy chair and personal touches such as flowers and fruit. Good light meals in the lounge (Mon-Sat) and Sunday lunches. Children up to 10 stay free in parents' room. ***Rooms** 7. Garden. Closed 1 week Jan. Access, Visa.*

Drumnadrochit — Polmaily House — 63% — £100

Tel 0456 450343 — HR

Drumnadrochit Highland IV3 6XT — Map 2 B3

Uninterrupted peace and relaxation are virtues fostered by owners Alison and Nick Parsons, whose hotel is little changed from its origins as a private house. It's set in 18 acres of unspoilt grounds, on the A831 west of Drumnadrochit. There's a little bar, a drawing room and a library with cards, board games and a TV. TVs are absent from the bright, airy bedrooms (two not en suite), though they have telephones. Children under 18 stay free in parents' room. No dogs. ***Rooms** 9. Garden, tennis, outdoor swimming pool. Access, Visa.*

Restaurant — £56

Nick Parsons affably plays host while Alison, with Barbara Drury, produces small-choice, four-course dinners based on fresh local ingredients. Some typical dishes: roast quail salad, asparagus in filo pastry with sorrel sauce, fried cod with apples and Benedictine, apricot-stuffed fillet of pork, sautéed venison steak bourguignon, lemon and melon tart with ginger ice cream. Good Scottish cheeses. No smoking. ***Seats** 30. Parties 12. D only 7.30-9.30. Set D £23.*

> is our symbol for an outstanding wine list.

Drybridge — Old Monastery Restaurant — £55

Tel 0542 32660 — R

Drybridge Buckie Grampian AB56 2JB — Map 2 C3

The former monastery enjoys lovely views of the sea and the mountains beyond. Maureen Gray offers a warm welcome front of house, while Douglas in the kitchen uses the best of the local larder with fish from the Spey and seasonal game. Popular choices include scampi and salmon Thermidor, Aberdeen Angus steaks and medallions of Highland venison with a sharp raspberry and redcurrant sauce. There are plenty of half bottles on a well-priced wine list. Turn off A98 at Buckie junction on to Drybridge road. Follow road for 2½ miles – do *not* turn right into Drybridge village. ***Seats** 45. L 12-1.45 D 7-9.30 (Sat to 10). Closed Sun & Mon, Bank Holidays, 3 weeks Jan, 2 weeks Nov.* AMERICAN EXPRESS *Access, Visa.*

Drybridge — Places of Interest

Banff Boyndie Bay beach Inverboyndie.
Buckle Maritime Museum Tel 0542 32121.

Dryburgh — Dryburgh Abbey — 58% — £130

Tel 0835 22261 Fax 0835 23945 — **H**

St Boswells Dryburgh Borders TD6 0RQ — **Map 4 C1**

From the A68 at St Boswells follow signs to Dryburgh's ruined abbey; this splendid early-Victorian sandstone house stands adjacent on the banks of the Tweed. It was acquired in 1991 by the Grose family, who also own the *Thurlestone Hotel* in South Devon. It's an ideal venue for salmon or trout fishing and shooting parties, or simply as a base for touring and it also has additional conference facilities accommodating up to 150. Family breaks include free stay in parents' room for under-12s. ***Rooms** 26. Garden, putting, fishing. Access, Visa.*

Dryburgh — Places of Interest

Jedburgh Tourist Information Tel 0835 63435 *8 miles.*
Jedburgh Abbey Tel 0835 63925.
Mary Queen of Scots House Tel 0835 63331.

Drymen — Buchanan Highland Hotel — 62% — £128

Tel 0360 60588 Fax 0360 60943 — **H**

Main Street Drymen by Loch Lomond Central G63 0BQ — **Map 3 B5**

A former coaching inn whose role has gradually expanded: besides its 50 comfortably fitted bedrooms there's an excellent leisure centre (the Buchanan Club) and a versatile range of conference and banqueting suites (up to 200 delegates and 130 for a function). Children up to 12 stay free in parents' room. Baby-sitting and baby-listening are available. ***Rooms** 50. Garden, indoor swimming pool, gymnasium, sauna, spa bath, tennis, golf (9), bowling green, coffee shop (10am-9pm).* AMERICAN EXPRESS *Access, Diners, Visa.*

Drymen — Place of Interest

Ben Lomond Tel 041 552 8391 *11 miles.*

Dulnain Bridge — Auchendean Lodge — 62% — £64

Tel 0479 851 347 — **HR**

Dulnain Bridge Grantown-on-Spey Highland PH26 3LU — **Map 2 C3**

An owner-run country hotel set in spectacular scenery a mile south of Dulnain Bridge on the A95. A range of activities – canoeing on the Spey, skiing in the Cairngorms, shooting, fishing and hiking – is available locally. The hotel is a converted Edwardian hunting lodge, now comfortably enough equipped not to disappoint guests kept in by spells of inclement weather. There's period furniture in two open-fired lounges. Individually-styled bedrooms have electric blankets, radio/alarms and TVs, but no phones. 200 acres of woods and $1\frac{1}{2}$ acres of gardens surround the hotel. ***Rooms** 7. Garden, pitch & putt. Closed 2 weeks Nov.* AMERICAN EXPRESS *Access, Diners, Visa.*

Restaurant — £55

Dinner is a daily-changing, four-course affair making good use of local game, fish, garden vegetables and wild mushrooms – a passion of chef Eric Hart. Typical fare might be black pudding and apple, cep and mushroom soufflé, Scotch broth, baked haddock with chanterelle cream, spicy steak pieces in oatmeal with mushroom cream, and lamb and lemon casserole. The choice usually covers three starters and alternative main and dessert courses. Good Scottish cheeses. Snacks or picnics provided if prior notice given. No smoking. ***Seats** 18. D only 7.30-9. Set D £22.50.*

Dulnain Bridge — Muckrach Lodge — 59% — £78

Tel 047 985 257 Fax 047 985 325 — H

Dulnain Bridge Grantown-on-Spey Highland PH26 3LY — Map 2 C3

Considerably improved by the Watsons over the last couple of years, this former Victorian hunting lodge sits in ten acres of its own grounds with fine views of the Dulnain valley all around. If you stay for more than one night, or have stayed before, you are rewarded with miniatures of malt whisky and fresh fruit in bedrooms furnished with good-quality freestanding furniture and decorated in a variety of soft colour schemes. Carpeted bathrooms offer good towelling and all sort of bits and bobs from cotton wool balls to a nail brush. Magazines and fresh flowers add to the comfort and relaxation in the lounge. The former steading (stables) now houses two full suites, one especially adapted for wheelchair-bound guests. No dogs. Children under five years stay free in parents' room. ***Rooms*** *12. Garden, fishing. Closed 3 weeks Nov.* AMERICAN EXPRESS® *Access, Diners, Visa.*

Dumbarton — Forte Travelodge — £42

Tel 0389 65202 — L

A82 Milton Dumbarton Strathclyde G82 2TY — Map 3 B6

On the A82 westbound, 8 miles west of Glasgow, 1 mile east of Dumbarton centre. ***Rooms*** *32.* AMERICAN EXPRESS® *Access, Visa.*

Dunblane — Cromlix House — 82% — £160

Tel 0786 822125 Fax 0786 825450 — HR

Kinbuck Dunblane Central FK15 9JT — Map 3 C5

Although David and Ailsa Assenti (from *Ballathie House* at Kinclaven by Stanley) have taken over the running of the hotel on a long-term tenancy, the ownership of the estate remains with the family who have been here for 500 years and their collection of fine furniture, paintings and porcelain continues to grace this sturdy Victorian mansion set in glorious countryside to the north of Dunblane. The collection of fishing rods, croquet mallets and wellies in the entrance hall indicates the country house atmosphere to be found within. Day rooms such as the leather-furnished library and morning room with its floral-patterned linen covers on armchairs and settees, combine elegance with comfort. Spacious antique-furnished bedrooms (more than half are full suites) often have period light fittings and other features that give something of an Edwardian feel to which Ailsa is adding her own choice of stylish fabrics. Bathrooms, with fittings from various periods, are all large and boast quality toiletries and towelling. ***Rooms*** *14. Garden, tennis, shooting, fishing. Closed mid Jan-end Feb.* AMERICAN EXPRESS® *Access, Diners, Visa.*

Restaurant — £85

A room of great elegance with fluted pilasters and ornate gilt light fittings matched by fine bone china and rat's-tail silver cutlery with pistol-grip knives. Fixed-price dinners, with just a couple of choices at each stage, might include a warm quail and orange salad with tarragon dressing, Jacob's lamb cutlets with a mint and almond crust with Meaux mustard reduced sauce, sole mousseline with shellfish and a vermouth and grape sauce and hot soufflé beignets rolled in a mixed spice sugar with a pear essence; all carefully prepared and attractively presented. No smoking. ***Seats*** *32. Private Room 40. L 12.30-1.30 D 7-9. Set L £15/£22 Set D £32.*

> We endeavour to be as up-to-the-minute as possible, but inevitably some changes to key personnel may occur at restaurants and hotels after the Guide goes to press.

Dunblane — Stakis Dunblane Hydro — 61% — £131

Tel 0786 822551 Fax 0786 825403 — **H**

Perth Road Dunblane Central FK15 0HG — **Map 3 C5**

Handsome Victorian building set high above the main road to Perth in 44 acres of grounds. The main attraction is the leisure facility, and it's well geared up to family holidays. Conferences are also big business, with room for up to 500 theatre-style. ***Rooms** 214. Garden, indoor swimming pool, keep-fit equipment, sauna, solarium, beauty salon, tennis, putting, playroom.* AMERICAN EXPRESS *Access, Diners, Visa.*

Dunblane — Places of Interest

Tourist Information Tel 0786 824428.
Dunblane Cathedral Tel 0786 824254.
Leighton Library Tel 0786 822850.
Doune Motor Museum Carse of Cambus. Tel 0786 841203.

Dundee — Angus Thistle — 69% — £105

Tel 0382 26874 Fax 0382 22564 — **H**

Marketgait Dundee Tayside DD1 1QU — **Map 3 C5**

A modern, six-storey hotel in the heart of the city offering a good standard of bedroom accommodation (including five suites) and conference facilities for up to 500 delegates; some rooms have views across the Tay Estuary. 24hr room service. ***Rooms** 58.* AMERICAN EXPRESS *Access, Diners, Visa.*

Dundee — Invercarse Hotel — 59% — £80

Tel 0382 69231 Fax 0382 644112 — **H**

371 Perth Road Dundee Tayside DD2 1PG — **Map 3 C5**

Some three miles west of the city centre, the privately owned Invercarse is an extended Victorian house set on a hill affording views across the Tay to the Fife hills beyond. Bedrooms vary in size, and some of the singles have recently been knocked into twins and doubles. There's a lounge bar with views, and a leather-furnished cocktail bar. ***Rooms** 38. Garden.* AMERICAN EXPRESS *Access, Diners, Visa.*

Dundee — Travel Inn — £43

Tel 0382 561115 — **L**

Kingsway West Invergowrie Dundee Tayside DD2 5JU — **Map 3 C5**

***Rooms** 40.* AMERICAN EXPRESS *Access, Diners, Visa.*

Dundee — Places of Interest

Tourist Information Tel 0382 27723.
St Paul's Cathedral Tel 0382 24486.
Camperdown Country Wildlife Park Tel 0382 623555.
University Botanic Garden Tel 0382 66939.
Olympia Leisure Centre Tel 0382 203888.
Shaw's Dundee Sweet Factory Tel 0382 610369.
Tay Road Bridge Observation Platforms.

Theatres and Concert Halls

Dundee Repertory Theatre Tel 0382 23530.
Whitehall Theatre Tel 0382 22684.
Steps Film Theatre Tel 0382 23141/24938.

Museums and Art Galleries

Barrack Street Museum Tel 0382 23141.
Broughty Castle Museum Tel 0382 23141.
McManus Galleries Tel 0382 23141.
Mills Observatory Tel 0382 67138.
Seagate Gallery and Printmakers Workshop Tel 0382 26331.

See over

H.M. Frigate Unicorn Tel 0382 200900.
R.R.S. Discovery Tel 0382 201245.

Dunfermline King Malcolm Thistle 65% £93

Tel 0383 722611 Fax 0383 730865 **H**

Queensferry Road Dunfermline Fife KY11 5DS **Map 3 C5**

Fifteen miles from the centre of Edinburgh and a short drive from junction 2 of the M90. Modern bedrooms have all the expected amenities plus 24hr room service. The Malcolm Suite can accommodate up to 150 delegates theatre-style. Children up to 14 stay free in parents' room. ***Rooms** 48. Garden.* AMERICAN EXPRESS *Access, Diners, Visa.*

Dunfermline Places of Interest

Tourist Information Tel 0383 720999.
Knockhill Motor Racing Circuit Tel 0383 723337.

Dunoon Chatters NEW £50

Tel 0369 6402 **R**

58 John Street Dunoon Strathclyde TA23 8BJ **Map 3 B5**

Dunoon is at last blessed with an establishment of real charm and quality, thanks to Rosemary MacInnes, a young Scot of equal charm and ability who has created a truly welcoming little restaurant that caters throughout the day for those after excellent-value, accomplished cooking. Delicious home baking caters for morning and afternoon teas, as well as supplementing lunch and dinner menus of great finesse and interest. Typical starters could include terrine of guinea fowl and rabbit or a filo basket of baby leeks and asparagus, whilst main courses such as medallions of venison with pickled walnuts or lamb chartreuse are supplemented by simply handled fine-quality fish – either from Loch Fyne in the case of shellfish, or from the nearby fleet. Leave room for some delectable desserts – perhaps coffee and whisky parfait or lemon cream pie. The garden is a lounge in fine weather. ***Seats** 35. Open 10-4. D 6-10. Closed Sun, January. Access, Visa.*

Duror Stewart Hotel 59% £80

Tel 063 174 268 Fax 063 174 328 **H**

Glen Duror Appin Argyll Highland PA38 4BW **Map 3 B4**

The hospitable Lacy family and their young staff offer a friendly welcome at their Victorian house, which stands in five acres of terraced gardens with beautiful views of Loch Linnhe. Drive through Glencoe past the village and follow the signs to Oban to find it. The oldest part was built 120 years ago in the style of a hunting lodge. An open fire warms the simple yet pleasant bar and upstairs there's a quiet and spacious lounge. Bedrooms are in a new wing; they are simple and neat, with views (most), modest modern furniture and tiny bathrooms. Children up to 12 stay free in parents' room. ***Rooms** 19. Garden, riding, sailing. Closed mid Oct-Easter.* AMERICAN EXPRESS *Access, Diners, Visa.*

East Kilbride Bruce Swallow Hotel 59% £75

Tel 03552 29771 Fax 03552 42216 **H**

Cornwall Street East Kilbride Strathclyde G74 1AF **Map 3 C6**

Purpose-built, concrete-and-glass hotel in East Kilbride's centre aimed primarily at the business person. A number of bedrooms have recently been refurbished. ***Rooms** 79. Beauty and hair salon.* AMERICAN EXPRESS *Access, Diners, Visa.*

East Kilbride — Stuart Hotel — 62% — £70

Tel 03552 21161 Fax 03552 64410 — H

Cornwall Way East Kilbride Strathclyde G74 1JR — Map 3 C6

A modern hotel whose day rooms include two bars and a function suite with an unusual brass ceiling. Biggest and best bedrooms are Executives. Informal eating in Archies lounge bar. Conference facilities for up to 200, banqueting for 150. ***Rooms** 39. Closed 25 Dec, 1 Jan.* AMERICAN EXPRESS *Access, Diners, Visa.*

East Kilbride — Westpoint Hotel — 74% NEW — £125

Tel 03552 36300 Fax 03552 33552 — H

Stewartfield Way East Kilbride Strathclyde G74 5LA — Map 3 C6

Part of the Craigendarroch Group – see *Craigendarroch* and *Cameron House* hotels – this modern hotel is unusual in both design and location. Situated on a new industrial estate, it lies close enough to Glasgow to attract the business community, though it appears the hotel's major appeal is in its superb leisure facilities, accessible by a covered walkway. There are nice touches in the public areas such as large floral displays and daily newspapers laid out, and though the decor in the bedrooms could be described as dull, there's nothing lacklustre about their style or quality. Executive bedrooms especially are models of good taste, with spacious sitting areas and splendid bathrooms (separate walk-in power shower), with marble-effect tiling, robes and fine Scottish toiletries. Extractor fans hiss and it's a pity there are no shaving mirrors. Among the thoughtful extras in the bedrooms are a sherry decanter, sweets, pot pourri, fruit and flowers, and a full turn-down service is carried out. The TV cabinet houses a mini-bar (with fresh milk), sliding hospitality tray and swivelling remote-controlled hi-tech set that provides teletext and satellite. Standard breakfast includes a pleasant buffet. ***Rooms** 74. Indoor swimming pool, gymnasium, squash, sauna, spa bath, solarium, beauty salon, snooker, lounge (10-10).* AMERICAN EXPRESS *Access, Diners, Visa.*

East Kilbride — Places of Interest

The Ice Bowl Ice Rink Tel 03552 44065.

Edinburgh — Alp-Horn — £42

Tel 031-225 4787 — R

167 Rose Street Edinburgh Lothian EH2 4LS — Map 3 C6

Just off Charlotte Square, a Swiss restaurant with pine-clad columns and ceiling, alpine landscape scenes and cowbells lending an authentic air. Cheese and beef fondues (for two or more) are well-executed specialities, and air-dried Swiss beef and ham (*assiette de Grisons*), veal sausage (*kalbsbratwurst*), venison with apple and cranberry sauce and spätzli, plus *emincé de veau zurichoise* with rösti potatoes are also faithful to their origins. Apfel strudel is made on the premises. Lunchtimes see an excellent value 'square deal lunch' of two courses and a shortened à la carte. Try the Swiss wines, even though they may seem expensive alongside the rest of the wine list. Separate room for non-smokers. ***Seats** 62. Parties 40. Private Room 24. L 12-2 D 6.30-10. Closed Sun, 25 & 26 Dec, 1st week Jan, local holidays. Set L £5.50. Access, Visa.*

Edinburgh — Atrium ↑ NEW — £60

Tel 031 228 8882 — R

Cambridge Street Edinburgh Lothian EH1 2ED — Map 3 C6

Andrew Radford (ex-*Flying Scotsman*, *Handsel's* and most recently, *Waterloo Place*) has, it seems, at last dealt himself a winning hand. Having been let down by various backers in the past with alarming regularity he and his wife, Lisa, have decided to go it alone, creating, with some

See over

of Edinburgh's most avant-garde designers, a striking post-modernist environment in which to enjoy his considerable culinary talents. Railway-sleeper tables, canvas-enveloped chairs and horn-shaped coloured glass kerosene torches set the scene, whilst at lunchtime glass double doors open on to the towering glass-roofed atrium. The menus change for every lunch and dinner, offering around four choices per course and exceptional value for money. Fish is his strong point – witness a sublime warm escalope of gravad lax with ginger, leeks and Parmesan or meltingly simple steamed haddock with green vegetables and a delicate beurre blanc, but he seems equally at home with the likes of roasted wood pigeon on a bed of lentils with olive oil mash and, a favourite ingredient, leeks. Homely desserts include baked apple and a tart of summer fruit. A small but intelligently chosen wine list includes gems by half bottle (Gewurztraminer 1988 Rolly Gassmann) and glass (late harvest muscat, Willunga Hill 1989). A take-away sandwich bar serving the offices and Traverse Theatre in the same building was due to open as we went to press. ***Seats** 65. L 12-3 D 6-10.30. Closed L Sat, all Sun, 2 weeks Christmas. Access, Diners, Visa.*

Edinburgh L'Auberge £75

Tel 031-556 5888 **R**

56 St Mary Street Edinburgh Lothian EH1 1SX **Map 3 C6**

Daniel Wencker's long-established and comfortable French restaurant is in Edinburgh's 'old town', off the Royal Mile near John Knox House. Although there is a carte of French classics, much emphasis is put on the good-value table d'hote at lunchtime and in the evening (4-course). The latter might commence with Provençal fish soup, then chicken liver paté or duo of salmon terrines, followed by rabbit with mustard, escalope of salmon with tomato coulis, entrecote of beef with red wine sauce or a vegetarian option; grilled goat's cheese with salad, lemon mousse or bitter chocolate terrine to finish. Lots of half bottles on an extensive French wine list, but few bargains among the classics; better value in lesser-known names. ***Seats** 50. Private Room 30. L 12.15-2 D 6.30-9.30 (Sat to 10). Closed 25 & 26 Dec, 1 & 2 Jan. Set L £9/£11 (from £11.45 Sun) Set D £19.85.* AMERICAN EXPRESS *Access, Diners, Visa*

Edinburgh The Balmoral 83% £190

Tel 031-556 2414 Fax 031-557 3747 **HR**

Princes Street Edinburgh Lothian EH2 2EQ **Map 3 C6**

An established landmark with its prominent clock tower next to Waverley Station (at the eastern end of Princes Street), the North British was one of the greatest of all the railway hotels, originally built in 1902. Following a major modernisation and refurbishment programme, much of the Victorian splendour and shape of the building remains, particularly in the public areas. A kilted doorman greets you on arrival at the renamed Balmoral and will arrange to park your car; there's a magnificent and opulent entrance foyer featuring solid marble, ornate columns, glittering chandeliers, plush carpeting and seating and delightful flower arrangements, overlooked by a balustraded gallery. The reception desk is hidden around a corner and the staff carry out their duties efficiently and with a smile. To the rear of the foyer lies the elegant Palm Court Lounge (*the* place for afternoon tea or morning coffee) and there are two bars discreetly away from the entrance. Perrins Wine Bar specialises in real ale. Luxurious bedrooms with splendid decorations and furnishings throughout, including special rooms for non-smokers, disabled and female guests. Linen sheets, a carriage clock and professional hairdryer are pluses, along with phones on the desks as well as by the beds. Bathrooms are also all they should be, with bathrobes and quality toiletries provided, but do not have shaving mirrors. Turn-down service at night, superb and comprehensive leisure complex (there's even a TV in the sauna!), and a business centre. Forte Grand. ***Rooms** 189. Health club.* AMERICAN EXPRESS *Access, Diners, Visa.*

The Grill ↑

£110

You're in for several surprises when entering this grand dining room, with its Oriental lacquered walls, the astonishingly comfortable armchairs (none of your normal restaurant seating here) and impeccable service, which includes synchronised removal of cloches. Only the rolls and rather fussy presentation of vegetables disappointed on our last visit, otherwise cooking by new executive chef Ralph Porciani has settled in well and cooking is of a high standard (with prices to match). Local Scottish produce is used to good effect, from marinade of Tay salmon flavoured with beetroot and apple and spices, or baked torte of Crathie pigeon with spinach and woodland mushrooms, to tranche of smoked sea bass with ratatouille, saffron and basil, or noisettes of Perthshire lamb in its jus with tomato and basil. Plainer dishes are also available from the grill and there's a separate vegetarian menu. For dessert try the apple soufflé, or choose farmhouse cheeses in good condition from the board. The wine list is of sensible length, though there's not much of note under £20. ***Seats** 50. Parties 10. L 12-2.15 D 7-10. Closed L Sat & Sun. Set L £18.50/£21.50 Set D £27.50/£33.*

Bridges Brasserie

£36

A brasserie in the Continental style, with an all-day menu of salads, sandwiches, appetisers (stuffed mushrooms, quiche, paté) and main courses (fish and chips, grilled rib-eye steak). Also a wide selection of cakes and pastries, coffees and teas. ***Seats** 95. Parties 12. Meals 7am-11pm.*

Edinburgh — Barnton Thistle — 63%

£103 **H**

Tel 031-339 1144 Fax 031-339 5521

Queensferry Road Edinburgh Lothian EH4 6AS — **Map 3 C6**

On the A90, handy for airport and city centre, providing modern comfort for both leisure and business visitors. Conference/banqueting facilities for 130/100. ***Rooms** 50.* AMERICAN EXPRESS® *Access, Diners, Visa.*

Edinburgh — Braid Hills Hotel — 61%

£89 **H**

Tel 031-447 8888 Fax 031-452 8477

134 Braid Road Edinburgh Lothian EH10 6JD — **Map 3 C6**

A lofty, baronial hotel whose upper-floor bedrooms afford sweeping views over Edinburgh. A strong group and function clientele enjoys neatly kept, well-equipped rooms serviced by obliging staff. A pub in the grounds is due for major refurbishment. ***Rooms** 69. Garden.* AMERICAN EXPRESS® *Access, Diners, Visa.*

Edinburgh — Caledonian Hotel — 79%

£192 **HR**

Tel 031-225 2433 Fax 031-225 6632

Princes Street Edinburgh Lothian EH1 2AB — **Map 3 C6**

Affectionately known as 'the Caley', the hotel stands on the site of the old Caledonian railway station (demolished in 1965), one mile from the current Waverley station at the end of Princes Street overlooking Edinburgh Castle. The carpeted foyer leads to a grand, gracefully proportioned and elegant lounge, furnished with plush shot-silk sofas. Carriages restaurant and bar retains the redbrick former station entrance as an inside wall. Bedrooms are individually styled, featuring well-chosen furniture and luxurious drapes; 5th-floor rooms are smaller than some of the others; 41 rooms are reserved for non-smokers. De luxe rooms and those with a view of the Castle attract a supplement; there are also 22 suites. Towelling robes are provided in all the bathrooms, which include a TV/radio speaker; elegant antique-style fittings in Executive bathrooms. Plus factors are the number of telephone extensions in the rooms, 24hr lounge service and a turn-down service. Families are particularly well catered for; children up to 12 stay free in parents' room. No dogs. Conference facilities for up to 300; banqueting for 200+. Own free parking. Queens Moat Houses. ***Rooms** 240. News kiosk.* AMERICAN EXPRESS® *Access, Diners, Visa.*

See over

Pompadour Room

£100

The Pompadour is elegant and formal; ornate plasterwork frames large wall paintings of delicate flowers, a pianist plays soothing music and excellent staff provide impeccable service. Chef Tony Binks offers an interesting lunch menu and a long evening carte with modern French dishes – from parfait of quail with watercress and glazed oranges or langoustines wrapped in smoked salmon with vegetable blinis to roast fillet of sea bass with crispy leeks and a caviar butter sauce and grilled fillet of Angus beef with a claret sauce and braised onion hearts. A *menu dégustation* offers five well-balanced light courses. Good French and Scottish cheeses. The wine list is well chosen but offers little choice under £20. ***Seats** 50. Private Room 160. L 12.30-2 D 7.30-10.30. Closed L Sat & Sun, also D Sun Nov-Mar. Set L £27 Set D £35*

Carriages Restaurant

£60

The hotel's second restaurant is open for breakfast, lunch and dinner seven days a week, serving familiar dishes like chicken liver paté, choices from a salad bar, lamb hot pot and pasta shells with seafood and a lobster sauce, along with a few Scottish favourites such as Musselburgh pie and haggis with neeps and tatties. There are also daily-changing table d'hote lunch and dinners, plus traditional Sunday lunches. Exemplary staff and high-chairs for the wee ones. Dinner dance every Saturday night when the band plays until past midnight. ***Seats** 150. B 7-10 (Sun 7.30-10.30) L 12-2.30 (Sat & Sun from 12.30 D 6.30-10. Set L £13.75/£17.25 (Sun £14.75) Set D £23.50.*

Edinburgh — Carlton Highland — 68%

£138

Tel 031-556 7277 Fax 031-556 2691

H

North Bridge Edinburgh Lothian EH16 6XY

Map 3 C6

Besides well-equipped bedrooms and comfortable day rooms the Carlton Highland (located between Princes Street and the Royal Mile) has a fine leisure club, conference facilities for up to 350, two restaurants and a night club (the Minus One) with dancing and live entertainment several nights a week. Children up to 16 stay free in their parents' room (15 rooms suitable for family use). ***Rooms** 199. Indoor swimming pool, gymnasium, sauna, spa bath, steam room, solarium, squash, snooker, hair & beauty salon, coffee shop (7am-10.30pm).* AMERICAN EXPRESS *Access, Diners, Visa.*

Edinburgh — Channings — 64%

£115

Tel 031-315 2226 Fax 031-332 9631

H

South Learmonth Gardens Edinburgh Lothian EH4 1EZ

Map 3 C6

A few minutes' walk from the city centre is a series of fine, adjoining Edwardian town houses run as a comfortable, privately-owned hotel with a country house feel. Traditional features – oak panelling, high moulded ceilings, ornate fireplaces, antique furniture and prints – remain in the peaceful lounges, while the bedrooms (some overlooking old Edinburgh) are individually furnished in a more contemporary manner. Staff are friendly and there's a relaxed ambience throughout. Children up to 14 years can stay free in their parents' rooms. ***Rooms** 48. Terrace.* AMERICAN EXPRESS *Access, Diners, Visa.*

Edinburgh — Denzlers 121 — NEW

£50

Tel 031-554 3268

R

121 Constitution Street Leith Edinburgh Lothian EH6 7AE

Map 3 C6

Sister restaurant to the Alp-Horn and with a similarly Swiss menu but without the chalet-style decor. Externally forbidding former bank premises down amongst the bonded warehouses of Leith, inside is bright and welcoming. Solidly traditional Swiss favourites like veal zurichoise, air-dried beef and cheese fondues (minimum 2 persons) share the menu with the likes of smoked duck breast with Cumberland sauce and salmon tossed in oatmeal with a mild horseradish sauce. Puds include *apfel strudel, coupe Nesselrode* and a rich chocolate mousse. ***Seats** 65. L 12-2 D 6.30-10. Closed L Sat, all Sun, Mon, Bank Holidays, 1st week Jan, 2 weeks July.* AMERICAN EXPRESS *Access, Visa.*

Edinburgh — Forte Posthouse — 62% — £68

Tel 031-334 0390 Fax 031-334 9237 — H

Corstorphine Road Edinburgh Lothian EH12 6UA — Map 3 C6

On the A8 halfway between airport and city centre, with both Murrayfield (for the rugby) and the zoo nearby. Conference facilities for up to 120 delegates. ***Rooms** 200.* AMERICAN EXPRESS *Access, Diners, Visa.*

Edinburgh — Forte Travelodge — £42

Tel 031-441 4296 — L

A720 Dreghorn Link City Bypass Edinburgh Lothian EH13 9QR — Map 3 C6

On the eastbound carriageway of the A720 Edinburgh City bypass at Dreghorn, and 8 miles south of the city centre. ***Rooms** 40.* AMERICAN EXPRESS *Access, Visa.*

Edinburgh — George Inter-Continental Hotel — 74% — £186

Tel 031-225 1251 Fax 031-226 5644 — H

19 George Street Edinburgh Lothian EH2 2PB — Map 3 C6

Very conveniently located for the shopping on Edinburgh's Princes Street. The classical facade conceals a grand entrance lobby complete with elegant, fluted Corinthian columns, polished marble floors and a raised seating area behind a wooden balustrade from where one can observe the busy comings and goings. Other public areas include the clubby Gathering of the Clans bar sporting clan mementoes and curios from the whisky trade. Luxurious bedrooms have comfortable settees or armchairs and quality freestanding furniture (mostly in yew), teletext TVs, in-house movies and beverage facilities neatly hidden away in cabinets. Lobby, lounge and some bedrooms are being refurbished. Conference/banqueting facilities for 220/170. ***Rooms** 195. News kiosk, 24hr lounge service.* AMERICAN EXPRESS *Access, Diners, Visa.*

Edinburgh — Granada Lodge — £45

Tel 031-653 2427 Fax 031-653 6106 — L

A1 Musselburgh Bypass Musselburgh Edinburgh Lothian EH21 8RE — Map 3 C6

***Rooms** 44.* AMERICAN EXPRESS *Access, Diners, Visa.*

Edinburgh — Hilton National — 68% — £130

Tel 031-332 2545 Fax 031-332 3805 — H

69 Belford Road Edinburgh Lothian EH4 3DG — Map 3 C6

A modern hotel just a few minutes walk from Princes Street. Public areas centre on a glitzy, split-level cocktail bar; a more pubby bar is to be found in what was an old flour mill. ***Rooms** 144.* AMERICAN EXPRESS *Access, Diners, Visa.*

Edinburgh — Holiday Inn Garden Court — 65% — £93

Tel 031-332 2442 Fax 031-332 3408 — H

107 Queensferry Road Edinburgh Lothian EH4 3HL — Map 3 C6

Formerly a Crest hotel, located on the A90 a mile from the city centre. Bedrooms are somewhat smaller than the normal Holiday Inn standard and 36 of the single rooms have shower and WC only. More than half the

See over

bedrooms are reserved for non-smokers. Meeting rooms for up to 70. Ample free parking. ***Rooms** 119. Gymnasium.* AMERICAN EXPRESS® *Access, Diners, Visa.*

Edinburgh Howard Hotel 75% £180

Tel 031-557 3500 Fax 031-557 6515 **H**

36 Great King Street Edinburgh Lothian EH3 6QH **Map 3 C6**

A stark exterior designed by James Craig (1766) conceals a wealth of architectural splendour. Three inter-connected town houses now make up the intimate, elegant and friendly Howard, employing the three domed stairwells as a unifying theme. Service lives up to the civilised ambience given splendour by crystal chandeliers, marble fireplaces, Scottish antiques and wall-coverings that evoke the grandeur of the 18th century. Bedrooms have consummate style and comfort, with individual colour schemes making best use of irregular room shapes and available daylight. Bathrooms echo the period without detracting from the comforts provided: twin basins, shower stalls, luxury lighting, toiletries and bathrobes. Children are accommodated free of charge when sharing their parents' room. Special weekend half-board rates (except in August). No dogs. ***Rooms** 16. Garden.* AMERICAN EXPRESS® *Access, Diners, Visa.*

Edinburgh Indian Cavalry Club £42

Tel 031-228 3282 Fax 031-225 1911 **R**

3 Atholl Place Edinburgh Lothian EH3 8HP **Map 3 C6**

Modern Indian cooking with an emphasis on steaming; the menu unusually suggests side dishes as suitable accompaniments for main-course dishes and also suggests wines to match. Stylish setting, with enormous swagged curtains and black-and-white checked floor in the high-ceilinged ground-floor Officers' Mess and a marquee-style Club Tent downstairs; military-uniformed waiters provide attentive service. Buffet-style choice of main courses at lunchtime; interesting seafood banquet for two or more. *Also at:* 8-10 Eyre Place (Tel 031-556 2404). ***Seats** 73. Private Room 50. L 12-2.30 D 5.30-11.30. Set L from £6.95 Set D from £9.95 (vegetarian) & £15.95.* AMERICAN EXPRESS® *Access, Diners, Visa.*

Edinburgh Kalpna £35

Tel 031-667 9890 **R**

2 St Patrick Square Edinburgh Lothian EH8 9EZ **Map 3 C6**

Gujerati vegetarian food has few finer homes than Kalpna, a non-smoking restaurant in the student area. Their elephant logo was designed to show that you can be big, strong and intelligent without eating meat. Here you will feast on bhel poori, dosa masala, wok-fried vegetables with ginger, nuts and a sweet/sour sauce, special rice dishes like basmati with coconut, lentils, lemon and coriander, stuffed paratha bread, carrot-based halva with almonds and cardamom and gulab jaman. The lunchtime buffet starts at £3.50, and there are various price options in the evening with a choice of set thali meals. A sister restaurant, *Spices*, at 110, West Bow Street, Grassmarket, is not exclusively vegetarian. ***Seats** 65. Parties 30. L 12-2 D 5.30-11. Closed L Sat, all Sun, Dec 25 & New Year's Day. Set L from £3.50 Set D from £8. Access, Visa.*

Edinburgh Kelly's £55

Tel 031-668 3847 **R**

46 West Richmond Street Edinburgh Lothian EH8 9DZ **Map 3 C6**

In a former baker's shop in a Georgian block just off the Pleasance (convenient for the theatres), Jeff and Jacquie Kelly run one of Edinburgh's better restaurants. The room is small and L-shaped, with wall lamps, plants, tubular chairs and pink napery. Cooking is modern and British on a short, fixed-price dinner menu typically offering galantine of duck with

Cumberland sauce, turbot parcel with seafood mousse and a leek and lemon timbale with a dill beurre blanc, lemon tart with crème anglaise. No smoking before 9 pm. ***Seats** 36. Private Room 36. D only 6.45-9.45. Closed Sun & Mon, 1st week Jan, 1st 3 weeks Oct. Set D £20.*
AMERICAN EXPRESS *Access, Diners, Visa.*

Edinburgh — King James Thistle — 70% — £126

Tel 031-556 0111 Fax 031-557 5333 — H

St James Centre 107 Leith Street Edinburgh Lothian EH1 3SW — Map 3 C6

Accommodation is first rate at this luxurious hotel in a position that's ideal for both business and tourist visitors. Double-glazing keeps traffic noise at bay, and bedrooms have good writing areas and mini-bars. En-suite bathrooms are well equipped, with powerful showers. 55 bedrooms are set aside for non-smokers and there are several Lady Executive rooms. Children up to 16 stay free in parents' room. Public areas are split between the ground and third floors. The street-level foyer-lounge is elegant, with marble-effect floor, chandelier and comfortable winged armchairs. The American-themed bar, brasseries and cocktail bar are reached by means of a swift and efficient lift. The hotel is linked to a shopping centre. Conference/banqueting facilities for 250. Regular evening entertainment includes a two-hour haggis ceremony. ***Rooms** 147.* AMERICAN EXPRESS *Access, Diners, Visa.*

Edinburgh — Martin's — £75

Tel 031-225 3106 — R

70 Rose Street North Lane Edinburgh Lothian EH2 3DX — Map 3 C6

Martin's restaurant is to be found between Frederick Street and Castle Street in cobbled North Lane. Last year, Martin and Gay Irons celebrated their tenth anniversary of nurturing customers in a charming atmosphere that features clever lighting and lots of fresh flowers. Chef Forbes Stott produces short, daily-changing menus utilising good ingredients (most of the vegetables are organically grown and Martin's father provides the herbs from his own garden) that are simply but carefully cooked in dishes like grilled rabbit saddle with red cabbage and shallots, sautéed langoustines with lentils, leeks and chilis, steamed fillet of turbot with fennel and a carrot and rosemary sauce, or boned roast quail stuffed with wild rice, peppers and apricots. Good-value, fixed-price-only, two-course lunches offer a small choice: perhaps a warm salad of smoked haddock, skate wing and pickled plums followed by roast leg of lamb with garlic. Desserts might range from sautéed banana with butterscotch sauce and a chilled Benedictine soufflé to apple, raisin and cinnamon strudel with vanilla ice cream, with unpasteurised Scottish and Irish cheeses in support. No background music, no smoking and no children under 8. Several lesser-known names on the fairly-priced and concise wine list. ***Seats** 28. Private Room 8. L 12-2 D 7-10. Closed L Sat, all Sun & Mon, 4 weeks Dec/Jan, 1 week end Jun. Set L £10.50.* AMERICAN EXPRESS *Access, Diners, Visa.*

Edinburgh — Ristorante Raffaelli — £40

Tel 031-225 6060 — R

10 Randolph Place Edinburgh Lothian EH3 7TA — Map 3 C6

A sophisticated setting for all-day service of generally mainstream Italian cooking. Good home-made pasta features in a dish like tagliatelle with porcini mushrooms; other choices might include four-cheese or seafood risotto, grilled sea bass with barbecue sauce, medallions of venison with Barolo and polenta or grilled T-bone of veal with garlic and rosemary. Snacks in the wine bar next door. ***Seats** 60. Parties 20. Meals 12.15-9.30 (Sat 6.30-10.30) Closed L Sat, all Sun, 25 & 26 Dec, 1 & 2 Jan.*
AMERICAN EXPRESS *Access, Diners, Visa.*

Edinburgh — Ristorante Tinelli — £35

Tel 031-652 1932 — **R**

139 Easter Road Edinburgh Lothian EH7 5QA — **Map 3 C6**

Unassuming, modestly comfortable restaurant where chef-patron Giancarlo Tinelli's North Italian fare is offered on a short but varied menu. Cheese-topped baked polenta, tortelli with fillings of ricotta, chestnut and pumpkin, lobster gratin and baked rabbit with a cream and rosemary sauce sit beside more familiar dishes such as spaghetti carbonara, saltimbocca and chicken alla cacciatora. The lunchtime choice is a selection from the evening menu. ***Seats** 32. L 12-2.30 D 6.30-11. Closed Sun & Mon, 25-27 Dec, 1-5 Jan. Set L £8.95.* AMERICAN EXPRESS® *Access, Visa.*

> Set menu prices may not always include service or wine.

Edinburgh — Roxburghe Hotel — 64% — £90

Tel 031-225 3921 Fax 031-220 2518 — **H**

38 Charlotte Square Edinburgh Lothian EH2 4HG — **Map 3 C6**

On the corner of elegant Charlotte Square and noisy George Street where buses and taxis run all night; inward-facing rooms also suffer from the noise of air-conditioning units, not all of which belong to the hotel. The smart interior manages to mix both country and town house feels. Decor in the bedrooms varies widely, but a programme of redecoration has kept them all in good order. Children up to 12 stay free in parents' room; families can eat informally in the 'Melrose on the Square' bistro. Conference/banqueting facilities for 180/200. Limited, charged parking. ***Rooms** 75. Coffee shop (7.30am-7pm, till 10pm summer).* AMERICAN EXPRESS® *Access, Diners, Visa.*

Edinburgh — Royal Terrace Hotel — 70% — £151

Tel 031-557 3222 Fax 031-557 5334 — **H**

18 Royal Terrace Edinburgh Lothian EH7 5AQ — **Map 3 C6**

Glittering chandeliers, sumptuous carpets and elaborately draped curtains grace the elegant reception and lounge areas at a hotel consisting of six linked houses in Edinburgh's Royal Terrace, built to commemorate King George IV's visit to the city in 1822. Bedrooms vary in size but all are given an appealing period feel by plaster-panelled walls and many have stylish bedhead drapes. Bathrooms mostly have spa baths but a few boast luxurious impulse showers. Children up to 14 stay free in parents' room. Paved and landscaped gardens to the rear run the length of the hotel. The hotel is ten minutes walk from Princes Street. ***Rooms** 95. Garden, indoor swimming pool, gymnasium, sauna, spa bath, solarium, beauty & hair salon, outdoor chess.* AMERICAN EXPRESS® *Access, Diners, Visa.*

Edinburgh — Scandic Crown Hotel — 68% — £155

Tel 031-557 9797 Fax 031-557 9789 — **H**

80 High Street The Royal Mile Edinburgh Lothian EH1 1TH — **Map 3 C6**

The exterior resembles a 17th-century Scottish turret house, so despite its youth the Scandic Crown blends well into its historic surroundings. Inside, the Scandinavian influence shows in uncluttered public rooms and spacious, well-designed bedrooms, all with a good range of up-to-date accessories. A notable feature among the day rooms is a circular dining area in the turret with views along the Royal Mile. There are several conference and syndicate rooms catering for up to 220 delegates. ***Rooms** 238. Indoor swimming pool, gymnasium, sauna, solarium.* AMERICAN EXPRESS® *Access, Diners, Visa.*

Edinburgh **Shamiana** **£40**

Tel 031-228 2265 **R**

14 Brougham Street Edinburgh Lothian EH3 9JH **Map 3 C6**

Around the corner from the King's Theatre is an Indian restaurant with decidedly untypical black, white and grey-tiled decor. North-West Indian Kashmiri cooking is the speciality with subtle spicing ringing the changes from run-of-the-mill Indian cooking. Shahi jahar kurzi (royal lamb) is a festive dish requiring 24 hours notice. ***Seats** 43. Private Room 14. L 12-2 D 6-11.30. Closed L Sat & Sun, 25 Dec, 1 Jan. Set L from £5.95.* AMERICAN EXPRESS *Access, Diners, Visa.*

Edinburgh **Sheraton Grand Hotel** **79%** **£199**

Tel 031-229 9131 Fax 031-228 4510 **H**

1 Festival Square Edinburgh Lothian EH3 9SR **Map 3 C6**

The inside of the hotel is unrecognisable from last year, following sympathetic refurbishment throughout, transforming it into a modern hotel with classical elegance featuring its own tartan, commissioned from Hunters of Brora, makers of fine Scottish fabrics. Out have gone the escalators and in their place a grand staircase leading to the second level, housing the new bar and lounge area, shopping gallery, boardroom and meeting rooms, two of which have fine views of the castle. Bedrooms (there are three floors of superior Grand/Castle View rooms in country house style offering bathrobes and an evening turn-down service) have tasteful American cherrywood furniture, tartan checks and prints of old Edinburgh, as well as the usual facilities of remote-control satellite TV, mini-bar, and hospitality tray. Bathrooms, it must be said, are on the small side. Excellent service from the committed and attentive staff, also attired in tartan. Conference and banqueting facilities for 485. ***Rooms** 261. Indoor swimming pool, gymnasium, sauna, spa bath, solarium, 24hr lounge service.* AMERICAN EXPRESS *Access, Diners, Visa.*

Edinburgh **Stakis Grosvenor Hotel** **64%** **£115**

Tel 031-226 6001 Fax 031-220 2387 **H**

Grosvenor Street Edinburgh Lothian EH12 5EF **Map 3 C6**

Behind the Victorian facade of this comfortable, centrally situated hotel are sombrely decorated modern rooms. Banqueting facilities for 450 and conference facilities for up to 300 people. No dogs. ***Rooms** 136.* AMERICAN EXPRESS *Access, Diners, Visa.*

Edinburgh **Swallow Royal Scot** **65%** **£120**

Tel 031-334 9191 Fax 031-316 4507 **H**

111 Glasgow Road Edinburgh Lothian EH12 8NF **Map 3 C6**

Five miles west of the city centre, two miles from the airport, a large 70s' hotel with a leisure club and conference/banqueting facilities for 350/250. Children up to 14 stay free in parents' room. ***Rooms** 259. Indoor swimming pool, keep-fit equipment, sauna, spa bath, solarium, hairdressing.* AMERICAN EXPRESS *Access, Diners, Visa.*

Edinburgh **Szechuan House** **£30**

Tel 031-229 4655 **R**

12 Leamington Terrace Edinburgh Lothian EH10 4JN **Map 3 C6**

This unpretentious little restaurant serves authentic Szechuan cooking, with spicy items underlined on the menu. These include bang bang chicken, steamed lamb and steamed beef in the starters, and various seafood, poultry and meat dishes among the mains. New premises since last year.

See over

Seats 50. Parties 25. Private Room 25. L Fri only 12-2 D only 5-12. Closed Mon & 2 days at Chinese New Year. Set D from £10.15-£12.10. Access, Visa.

Edinburgh — Vintners Room, The Vaults — £55

Tel 031-554 6767 — **R**

87 Giles Street Leith Edinburgh Lothian EH6 6BZ — **Map 3 C6**

The old sale room of the Vintners' Guild with its 17th-century Italian plasterwork (smoke-blackened from the candles that provide the only illumination) is home to Tim Cumming's appealingly robust, well-executed cooking. Market-fresh produce gets modern treatment in dishes like scallop and sherry mousse, asparagus cheese tartlets, steamed halibut with sweet pepper sauces and venison noisettes wrapped in bacon, with a lemon and honey sauce. Some of the desserts require (and deserve!) a 15-minute wait: apple and Calvados soufflé, hot pear and almond tart. Informal lunch in the wine bar offers a 2-or 3-course, fixed-price menu with a small choice; the setting is more formal for dinner. No smoking. Fair prices and lots of half bottles on a sound wine list. ***Seats** 65. Private Room 36. L 12-2.30 D 7-10.30. Closed Sun, 2 weeks Christmas. Set L £7.50/£10.* AMERICAN EXPRESS *Access, Visa.*

Edinburgh — Places of Interest

Tourist Information Tel 031-557 1700.
Edinburgh Airport Tourist Information Tel 031 333 2167.
British Rail, Waverley Station Tel 031-556 2451.
Busline LRT Tel 031-554 4494 3858. **FMT** 031-556 84864
St. Giles Cathedral Tel 031-225 4363.
St Mary's R.C. Cathedral Tel 031-556 1798.
Clan Tartan Centre Tel 031-553 5161.
Hearts F.C. Tel 031-337 6132.
Hibs F.C. Tel 031-661 2159.
Meadowbank Sports Centre and Stadium Tel 031-661 5351.
Hillend Ski Centre Tel 031-445 4433.
Central Cycle Hire Tel 031-228 6333.
Portobello Swimming Pool Tel 031-669 4077
Royal Commonwealth Pool Tel 031-667 7211
Murrayfield Ice Rink Tel 031-337 6933.
Edinburgh Zoo Tel 031-334 9171.
Ingliston Motor Racing Circuit Tel 041-641 2553.
Camera Obscura Tel 031-226 3709.
Edinburgh Experience Tel 031-556 4365.

Theatres and Concert Halls

Church Hill Theatre Tel 031-447 7597.
Festival Fringe: Enquiries Tel 031-226 5257.
International Festival Box Office Tel 031-226 4001.
Kings Theatre Tel 031-229 1201.
Netherbow Arts Centre Tel 031-556 9579.
Playhouse Theatre Tel 031-557 2590.
Royal Lyceum Theatre Tel 031-229 7404.
Queens Hall Tel 031-668 2019.
Traverse Theatre Tel 031-226 2633.
Usher Hall Tel 031-228 1155.

Historic Houses, Castles and Gardens

Dalkeith Country Park Tel 031-663 5684.
Edinburgh Castle Tel 031-225 9846.
Edinburgh Dungeon Tel 031-225 1331.
Craigmillar Castle Tel 031-661 4445.
Dalmeny House South Queensferry Tel 031-331 1888.
Edinburgh Butterfly and Insect World Lasswade Tel 031-663 4932.
Hopetoun House South Queensferry Tel 031-331 2451.
The Georgian House Tel 031-225 2160.
Lennoxlove Haddington. Tel 062 082 3720.
Palace of Holyroodhouse Tel 031-556 7371.

Royal Botanic Garden Tel 031-552 7171.
Museums and Art Galleries
The Fruitmarket Gallery Tel 031-225 2383.
Edinburgh Crystal Visitor Centre Penicuik Tel 0968 675128.
Collective Gallery Tel 031-220 1260.
Edinburgh Gallery Tel 031-557 5227.
Royal Scottish Academy Tel 031-225 6671.
Edinburgh University Collection of Historical Instruments Tel 031-447 4791.
Huntly House Museum and Museum of Childhood Tel 031-225 2424.
National Gallery of Scotland Tel 031-556 8921.
Scottish National Portrait Gallery Tel 031-556 8921.
Scottish National Gallery of Modern Art Tel 031-556 8921.
Royal Museum of Scotland Tel 031-225 7534.
Scottish Whisky Heritage Centre Tel 031-220 0441.

Elgin — Mansion House — 67% — £100

Tel 0343 548811 Fax 0343 547916 — **H**

The Haugh Elgin Moray Grampian IV30 1AW — **Map 2 C3**

Set in gardens next to the river Lossie, the turreted mansion built in the mid-19th century is within a stone's throw of the town centre. The chandeliered entrance hall makes a good first impression, and spruce day rooms comprise the piano lounge (a favourite pre-dinner meeting place), the Wee Bar and the still room with its whisky collection. Good-sized bedrooms offer a lot of extras, including a welcoming glass of sherry and a mini-bar. A staircase connects the bedrooms to the Country Club, whose facilities include an all-day snack bar; families can eat informally in the poolside Dip Inn. No dogs. ***Rooms** 22. Garden, indoor swimming pool, sauna, spa bath, gymnasium, snooker.* AMERICAN EXPRESS *Access, Diners, Visa.*

Elgin — Places of Interest

Tourist Information Tel 0343 542666.
The Glenfiddich Distillery Dufftown. Tel 0340 20373.
Elgin Cathedral Tel 0343 547171.

Eriska — Isle of Eriska — 73% — £145

Tel 063 172 371 Fax 063 172 531 — **HR**

Eriska Ledaig by Oban Strathclyde PA37 1SD — **Map 3 B5**

Robin and Sheena Buchanan-Smith invite guests to share in the peace, comfort and relaxation that abound in their baronial mansion on the island sanctuary of Eriska. The island's 247 acres provide splendid walks in majestic scenery (packed lunches can be arranged) and there are many facilities for more formal exercise. Each of the bedrooms has its own character and highly individual furnishings; common to all are immaculate housekeeping and lovely displays of fresh flowers. Complimentary morning coffee and afternoon tea are provided. Children up to 10 stay free in parents' room. ***Rooms** 17. Garden, fishing, riding, tennis, shooting, putting, windsurfing, water-skiing. Closed Dec-Feb.* AMERICAN EXPRESS *Access, Visa.*

Restaurant — £85

Dinner, as befits the setting, is taken at leisure in the panelled, candle-lit restaurant. With canapés in the bar, and coffee and tablet in the main hall, a house party atmosphere is soon engendered. Mrs Buchanan-Smith offers only alternatives on her fixed-price menus that might include deep-fried Brie with spicy tomato sauce or gravad lax with dill to start, followed by cream of leek soup or fillet of plaice with chive butter, then baked cod with a herb cheese crust or roast rib of beef carved at the table, with Yorkshire pudding. Desserts are served from a trolley; Scottish cheeses. The wine list is fairly priced and dips its toes world-wide. ***Seats** 40. Parties 12. D only 7.30-9. Set D from £35.*

Erskine — Forte Posthouse — 62% — £68

Tel 041-812 0123 Fax 041-812 7642 — **H**

by Erskine Bridge Strathclyde PA8 6AN — **Map 3 B6**

Close to the M8 on the south side of Erskine Bridge. Conference facilities for up to 600, banqueting to 450. ***Rooms** 166. Indoor swimming pool, keep-fit equipment, sauna, spa bath, solarium, beauty salon, pitch and putt, children's playground.* AMERICAN EXPRESS *Access, Diners, Visa.*

Ettrickbridge — Ettrickshaws Hotel — 62% — £76

Tel 0750 52229 — **H**

Ettrickbridge Selkirk Borders TD7 5HW — **Map 4 C1**

A turn-of-the-century house standing in spectacular countryside seven miles west of Selkirk on the B7009. The drawing room, bar and restaurant all enjoy the views, and all the public rooms are weather-proofed by log fires. The bedrooms are of a good size, with varying decor and traditional furniture; all overlook the river and hills. No children under nine. ***Rooms** 6. Garden, game fishing. Closed Dec & Jan. Access, Diners, Visa.*

Falkirk — Hotel Cladhan — 60% — £82

Tel 0324 27421 Fax 0324 611436 — **H**

Kemper Avenue Falkirk Central FK1 1UF — **Map 3 C5**

Behind the somewhat unprepossessing modern exterior the Cladhan's interior is stylish and attractive. Public areas are open-plan and designed in a striking modern style with an art deco influence. The bedrooms are light and airy, with good-quality fitted furniture and thermostatically controlled heating. The hotel can cater for banquets and conferences for up to 200. ***Rooms** 37. Garden.* AMERICAN EXPRESS *Access, Diners, Visa.*

Falkirk — Pierre's — £50

Tel 0324 35843 — **R**

140 Graham's Road Falkirk Central FK2 7BQ — **Map 3 C5**

Patron Pierre Renjard obviously imagines himself and his customers to be in a pleasant little corner of France. His menus stick in the main to tried and tested favourites from the French bistro repertoire: oysters (albeit from Loch Fyne), moules à la provençale, soupe de poissons, French onion soup, scampi provençale, contrefilet de veau normande, profiteroles and Gaelic coffee. Good-value business lunch and Taste of France menus in addition to the à la carte. ***Seats** 38. Parties 25. L 12-2 D 6.45-9.30 (Sat from 7). Closed L Sat, all Sun & Mon, 1-10 Jan, 2 weeks mid-July. Set D £11.35 (£9.45 before 7.30pm).* AMERICAN EXPRESS *Access, Diners, Visa.*

Falkirk — Places of Interest

Tourist Information Tel 0324 20244.

Museums and Art Galleries

Kinneil Museum and Roman Fortlet Tel 0506 824318.

Falkirk Museum Tel 0324 24911.

Forfar — Royal Hotel — 57% — £65

Tel & Fax 0307 62691 — **H**

Castle Street Forfar Tayside DD8 3AE — **Map 3 C4**

A modest entrance conceals a thriving, compact, well-kept hotel complete with leisure centre, ballroom and roof garden. A cheerful welcome and real fire greet guests in the tiny tartan reception area with cosy bar and rattan-furnished lounge nearby (changes are planned to the day rooms). Bedrooms, apart from one four-poster room, are small, but neat and

practical. No dogs. Conferences for up to 220. ***Rooms** 19. Indoor swimming pool, sauna, spa bath, solarium, hair salon, coffee shop (10am-11pm).*
AMERICAN EXPRESS *Access, Diners, Visa.*

Forfar Places of Interest

Tourist Information Tel 0307 467876.
Edzell Castle and Gardens Nr Brechin. Tel 031-244 3101 *18 miles.*
Barrie's Birthplace (NT) Kirriemuir. Tel 0575 72646 *6 miles.*

Fort William Crannog Seafood Restaurant £50

Tel 0397 705589 **R**

Town Pier Fort William Highland PH33 7NG **Map 3 B4**

Converted ticket office and bait store in a quayside setting with views down Loch Linnhe. Scrubbed tables and a simple, mainly fish menu (including a vegetarian dish of the day). Local langoustines are a speciality and they smoke salmon, trout and mussels in their own smokehouse. Try cranachan (toasted oats with whisky, whipped cream and raspberries) or vacherin (meringue, whipped cream, ginger and Cointreau) to finish. ***Seats** 60. Private Room 20. L 12-2.30 D 6-10.30. Access, Visa.*

Fort William The Factor's House £60

Tel 0397 705767 Fax 0397 702953 **RR**

Torlundy Fort William Highland PH33 6SN **Map 3 B4**

Dinner at this former manager's house at the foot of Ben Nevis is mostly for residents, but outsiders can join in. Soup is followed by, for example, roast lamb or salmon en croute. Charcoal grilled sirloin is always on the menu. Children's meal served between 6 and 7. ***Seats** 24. Parties 8. D only 7-9. Closed Mon, also mid Nov-mid Mar. Set D £20. Access, Visa.*

Rooms £82

Bedrooms have views of either Ben Nevis or the surrounding hills. Guests have the use of the facilities of Inverlochy Castle. ***Rooms** 7. Garden*

Fort William Inverlochy Castle 90% £240

Tel 0397 702177 Fax 0397 702953 **HR**

Torlundy Fort William Highland PH33 6SN **Map 3 B4**

"I never saw a lovelier or more romantic spot" noted Queen Victoria in her diary after spending a week here in 1873; an observation as true today as it was then. Built just ten years earlier complete with tower and turrets this castle was nevertheless designed for comfort rather than defence. Perhaps the grandest of the five day rooms is the Great Hall with ornate Venetian crystal chandeliers hanging from a frescoed ceiling depicting chubby cherubs cavorting amongst the clouds. Highly polished antiques abound both in the public areas and in the luxurious bedrooms above, each individually decorated, often in summer shades, with proper sofas and armchairs, fresh flowers, books and sybaritic bathrooms (the smallest would be large by most hotel standards) many with bidets and separate showers, the others all having 'power' showers over tubs – and finished with marble. Generous towelling, robes and quality toiletries are standard. What makes Inverlochy special though is the very highest standards of service from staff who evince a genuine interest in the comfort and well-being of guests. Dogs in kennels only. ***Rooms** 16. Garden, tennis, fishing, snooker, valeting. Closed Dec-Feb.* AMERICAN EXPRESS *Access, Diners, Visa.*

Restaurant ↑ £100

Two dining rooms, both equally well appointed, with bone china and elegant tableware on polished wooden tables, make a most civilised setting for Simon Haigh's accomplished offerings. The shortish but well-balanced fixed-price dinner menu lists dishes that are modern in style without being gimmicky – roast monkfish tail with sauce of red peppers and spices;

See over

terrine of duck with pistachio and caramelised apple; loin of red deer with pear and walnuts; grilled Dover sole with lime; hot chocolate tart with orange sauce; caramelised rice pudding with exotic fruits (Scottish winner of Dessert of the Year). A shorter fixed-price lunch is supplemented by an à la carte choice should one wish for just a single dish. No smoking. ***Seats** 28. Private Room 15. L 12.30-1.45 D 7.15-9.30. Set L £24.50/£27.50 Set D £39.95.*

Fort William — Mercury Hotel — 58% — £79

Tel 0397 703117 Fax 0397 700550 — **H**

Achintore Road Fort William Highland PH33 6RW — **Map 3 B4**

Modern hotel with half of its standardised bedrooms enjoying views across Loch Linnhe. Much favoured by coach parties. The very spacious bar/lounge is smart and comfortable having recently been refurbished. Children up to 13 stay free in parents' room. ***Rooms** 86. Sauna, pool table.* American Express *Access, Diners, Visa.*

Fort William — Places of Interest

Tourist Information Tel 0397 703781.
Ben Nevis *5 miles*

Gairloch — Creag Mor — 66% — £77

Tel 0445 2068 Fax 0445 2044 — **H**

Charleston Gairloch Highland IV21 2AH — **Map 2 B3**

Larry and Betty Nieto offer year-round hospitality among the spectacular scenery of Wester Ross. The two-level Gallery Lounge enjoys marvellous views and also houses an exhibition of watercolours. In the bar there's a choice of more than 100 whiskies. Bedrooms are neat, bright and well equipped for a comfortable stay. Informal eating in the Buttery. ***Rooms** 17. Garden, games room, coffee shop (8am-11pm).* American Express *Access, Visa.*

Gairloch — Places of Interest

Tourist Information Tel 0445 2130.
Inverewe Garden Tel 044586 356.

Garve — Inchbae Lodge — 57% — £56

Tel 099 75 269 — **H**

Inchbae by Garve Highland IV23 2PH — **Map 2 B3**

About three miles north of Garve on the A835, this old stone-built (now white-painted) hunting lodge is a very friendly, convenient sort of place. The small, rustic bar is also the 'local' and in the lounge, where a real fire burns most of the year, the modern low-backed settees are arranged so as to encourage conversation amongst guests. There are lots of board games and jigsaw puzzles for the occasional rainy day. Bedrooms, half in the main house and half in an adjacent red cedar chalet, are modestly appointed – no TV, radio or telephone and all but three have shower and WC only – but well-kept and quite attractive with pine furniture and a plum and pale green colour scheme. Breakfast choices include locally smoked haddock. ***Rooms** 12. Garden, fishing. No credit cards.*

Gatehouse of Fleet — Cally Palace — 69% — £89

Tel 0557 814341 Fax 0557 814522 — **H**

Gatehouse of Fleet Dumfries & Galloway DG7 2DL — **Map 4 B2**

A hundred acres of grounds provide a secluded setting for an 18th-century mansion with lofty public rooms decorated in Louis XIV style and a plush cocktail bar. Bedrooms have pleasant decor, good bathrooms and thoughtful extras. Conference facilities (for up to 80) are well patronised, and the hotel is also popular for family holidays and special occasions. An 18-hole golf course will be ready for 1994. ***Rooms** 56. Indoor swimming pool, sauna, solarium, tennis, games room. Closed Jan & Feb. Access, Visa.*

Gatehouse of Fleet **Murray Arms Inn** **£79**

Tel 0557 814207 Fax 0557 814370 **I**

Anne Street Gatehouse of Fleet Dumfries & Galloway DG7 2HY **Map 4 B2**

A warm, friendly old posting inn (established over 300 years) whose hospitable day rooms include the Burns Room, where the poet reputedly wrote *Scots Wha Hae*. There's also a little cocktail bar. Bedrooms, all centrally heated, are by no means grand but lack nothing to provide a good night's rest. These, and the bathrooms, are kept in very good order. Children up to 14 free in parents' room. The inn stands on the A75 Dumfries to Stranraer road. ***Rooms** 13. Garden, coffee shop (noon-9.45pm).* AMERICAN EXPRESS *Access, Diners, Visa.*

Gatehouse of Fleet **Places of Interest**

Tourist Information Tel 0557 814212.

Giffnock **Macdonald Thistle** **64%** **£102**

Tel 041-638 2225 Fax 041-638 6231 **H**

Eastwood Toll Giffnock nr Glasgow Strathclyde G46 6RA **Map 3 B6**

Modern commercial hotel convenient for Glasgow Airport (six miles) and the city centre (five miles). Conference facilities for up to 150, banqueting up to 100. ***Rooms** 56. Sauna, solarium.* AMERICAN EXPRESS *Access, Diners, Visa.*

Glamis **Castleton House** **71%** **£90**

Tel 0307 840340 Fax 0307 840506 **HR**

Glamis by Forfar Angus Tayside DD8 1SJ **Map 3 C4**

On the A94 three miles from Glamis Castle, a Victorian house has been turned by William and Maureen Little into a charming little country hotel with the emphasis on comfort, service and good food. The six bedrooms, all with en-suite facilities, are furnished with high-quality reproduction pieces, and there are showers above the dark-panelled tubs. Children stay free in parents' room. The hotel can arrange fishing, shooting and stalking. Informal eating in the conservatory restaurant from 8am-10pm. No dogs. ***Rooms** 6. Garden, putting.* AMERICAN EXPRESS *Access, Visa.*

Restaurant **£48**

William uses local produce plus fruit and vegetables from his own garden on the varied menu that might include wood pigeon salad, West Coast mussels with bacon, garlic, white wine and cream, venison terrine, cushion of salmon with a potato crust and sorrel beurre blanc, baked loin of pork with red cabbage sauerkraut, sticky toffee pudding, profiteroles with hot chocolate sauce. Good-value, five-course, no-choice 'chef recommends' menu in addition to the carte. No smoking. ***Seats** 28. L 12-2.30 D 7-9.30. Set L £11.75 Set D £19.50.*

Glamis **Places of Interest**

Glamis Castle Tel 030 784 242/3.
Folk Museum Tel 030 784 288.

Glasgow **Amber** **£36**

Tel 041-339 6121 **R**

130 Byres Road Glasgow Strathclyde G12 8TD **Map 3 B6**

One of Glasgow's favourite Chinese restaurants. Under colonial fans and red-tinged lights, menus, music and cutlery may appear Westernised but the cooking is authentic. Lunch choices offer remarkable value without *See over* compromising quality and the chef's specialities include fried wun tun, stuffed green peppers, Peking and aromatic duck, and a fried combination for two of duck, king prawn, meat, chicken, fish ball, squid and Chinese vegetables. ***Seats** 70. L 12-2 D 5-11.30 Meals Sat 12-12. Closed 3 days Chinese New Year. Set L from £4.50 Set D from £13.* AMERICAN EXPRESS *Access, Diners, Visa.*

Glasgow — Ashoka West End — £30

Tel 041-339 0936 — **R**

1284 Argyle Street Glasgow Strathclyde — **Map 3 B6**

Punjabi restaurant on the corner of Glasgow's longest and shortest streets. Dozens of variations on lamb, chicken and prawn; thalis and set meals for 2+. ***Seats** 70. Parties 30. D only 5-12.30 (Fri & Sat to 1). Set D from £16.75.* AMERICAN EXPRESS *Access, Diners, Visa.*

Glasgow — Brasserie on West Regent Street — £45

Tel 041-248 3801 — **R**

176 West Regent Street Glasgow Strathclyde G2 8HF — **Map 3 B6**

Part of the *Rogano* stable, with the familiar tartan carpet and smart, white-aproned staff, the Brasserie places more contemporary reliance on fresh local and seasonal produce. Smoked chicken salad with raspberry and mint vinaigrette, grilled sardines with black butter, rack of lamb with ginger jus and seaweed and saffron pasta with cauliflower and Parmesan butter typify the choice. There are also 'something lighter' and 'post-theatre' menus offering such dishes as sweet pickled herring with apple salad or chicken and mangetout stir-fry. ***Seats** 100. Private Room 55. L Sat 12-3 D Sat 6-12 Meals Mon-Fri 12-11. Closed Sun, Bank Holidays. Set L £12/£15.50 Set D £15.50/£21 (post theatre £9.75).* AMERICAN EXPRESS *Access, Diners, Visa.*

Glasgow — Buttery — £75

Tel 041-221 8188 — **R**

652 Argyle Street Glasgow Strathclyde G3 8UF — **Map 3 B6**

Plush converted Victorian pub serving a tempting selection of dishes, many of them interestingly different: spinach salad with sliced duck and a brown lentil orange yoghurt, cream of cheese, broccoli and sweetcorn soup, steamed supreme of chicken filled with Scottish haggis in a soft mustard seed cream, pan-fried fillet steak on a potato and chive sauce with a carrot cream. ***Seats** 54. Parties 12. Private Room 8. L 12-2.30 D 7-10.30. Closed L Sat, all Sun, Bank Holidays. Set L £14.75.* AMERICAN EXPRESS *Access, Diners, Visa.*

Glasgow — Café Gandolfi — £35

Tel 041-552 6813 — **R**

64 Albion Street Glasgow Strathclyde — **Map 3 B6**

All-day eating in a bistro-style café that was once a Victorian pub. No under-14s after 8pm. ***Seats** 60. Parties 12. Meals 9am-11.30pm. Closed Sun, Bank Holiday Mondays. No credit cards.*

Glasgow — Copthorne Hotel — 64% — £122

Tel 041-332 6711 Fax 041-332 4264 — **H**

George Square Glasgow Strathclyde G2 1DS — **Map 3 B6**

An imposing Victorian landmark with a modern glass colonnade overlooking busy George Square; Queen Street railway station is adjacent. Bedrooms (many recently refurbished) comprise Classic, Connoisseur and suites, and all offer 24hr room service; under-16s stay free in parents' room. Conference and banqueting suites can accommodate up to 100. ***Rooms** 140.* AMERICAN EXPRESS *Access, Diners, Visa.*

Glasgow **D'Arcy's** **£45**

Tel 041-226 4309 **R**

Basement Courtyard Princes Square Glasgow Strathclyde **Map 3 B6**

Granite-topped tables in a covered courtyard setting. Popular dishes from around the world: stuffed mushrooms, deep-fried Camembert, seafood terrine with mustard and dill sauce, veal milanese, moules marinière, steaks. Fixed-price dinner in the Back Room, lunch and dinner in the dining room, all-day snacks, salads, burgers and sandwiches. ***Seats*** *72. Parties 16. Meals 9.30am-12 midnight (Sun 11-6). Closed D Sun, 25 & 26 Dec, 1 & 2 Jan. Set L & D from £6.95.* AMERICAN EXPRESS® *Access, Diners, Visa.*

Glasgow **Devonshire Hotel** **£120**

Tel 041-339 7878 Fax 041-339 3980 **PH**

5 Devonshire Gardens Glasgow Strathclyde G12 0UX **Map 3 B6**

On the corner of a tree-lined Victorian terrace, the Devonshire is an agreeably peaceful retreat behind a classic porticoed entrance and a few stone steps; "excellence without compromise" is their motto. A handsomely restored carved staircase leads past stained-glass windows up to individually appointed, spacious bedrooms, with smart, tasteful fabrics, old pine furniture and stylish bathrooms. The restaurant, with just four tables, is for residents only, as is the civilised drawing room with its subdued lighting and comfortable seating. Children up to 14 stay free in parents' room. A good setting for small meetings. ***Rooms*** *15.* AMERICAN EXPRESS® *Access, Diners, Visa.*

Glasgow **Forte Crest** **74%** **£117**

Tel 041-248 2656 Fax 041-221 8986 **H**

Bothwell Street Glasgow Strathclyde G2 7EN **Map 3 B6**

Classic re-styling in marble and primary colours, customer-conscious staff and strong management all contribute to the former Albany's position among Glasgow's top hotels. Day rooms are stylish and relaxed while in the bedrooms touches of luxury are provided by mini-bars, remote-control TV and comprehensive grooming accessories. Bathrooms are smartly fitted and brightly lit. Informal eating in both the Original Carvery (under-5s eat free, under-16s half price) and Jules' Bar & American Grill (Sunday brunch menu). The hotel has no leisure amenities, but guests are offered some elite services: same-day laundry, valeting, multi-lingual reception staff and valet parking. There are excellent facilities for conferences, with room for up to 800 delegates theatre-style and first-class support services. ***Rooms*** *254.* AMERICAN EXPRESS® *Access, Diners, Visa.*

Glasgow **Glasgow Hilton** **78%** **NEW** **£140**

Tel 041-204 5555 Fax 041-204 5004 **HR**

1 William Street Glasgow Strathclyde G3 8HT **Map 3 B6**

This latest addition to Glasgow's skyline is easily spotted from the urban motorway (exit at Junction 18) on the western edge of the city centre. Bird's-eye maple pillars feature in a vast, galleried lobby off which distinctively themed public rooms include Raffles old colonial bar and Minsky's New York Deli, where an extensive buffet breakfast is laid out. Air-conditioned bedrooms (with sealed windows) have standardised decor and furnishings but an extra £25 on the room-only rate brings Executive status with extras like bathrobe and slippers, and use of the top-floor Executive lounge with complimentary Continental breakfast, afternoon tea and evening drink. One floor caters specifically to Japanese guests with signs and room information in the appropriate language, green tea added to the beverage tray and a yukata (Japanese pyjamas) provided as standard. A traditional Japanese breakfast is also available. Staff are friendly and helpful. Extensive 24hr room service and conference/banqueting facilities. Valet parking. ***Rooms*** *321. Indoor swimming pool, gymnasium, sauna, spa bath, steam room, solarium, hair salon, news kiosk, coffee shop (6.30am-11pm).* AMERICAN EXPRESS® *Access, Diners, Visa.*

See over

Camerons Restaurant

£92

Luxuriously styled to resemble several rooms in a Scottish country house, with a menu featuring good local produce in dishes such as venison consommé with wild mushrooms and tarragon ravioli, Loch Fyne oysters with creamed spinach and Orkney Cheddar, terrine of Perthshire game, and saddle of venison with elderberry jelly and thyme jus. Sound cooking is overseen by executive chef Ferrier Richardson who comes here from his own successful restaurant (*October*) in nearby Bearsden. Wines on a globe-trotting list are, unusually, grouped by grape variety. ***Seats** 52. Parties 12. Private Room 12. L 12-2.30 D 7-11. Closed L Sat & Sun. Set L £16.50/£19. Set D £35.*

Glasgow **Glasgow Marriott** **73%** **£136**

Tel 041-226 5577 Fax 041-221 9202 **H**

Argyle Street Anderston Glasgow Strathclyde G3 8RR **Map 3 B6**

Close to the city centre (by Junction 19 of the M8), extensive public areas (part of which overlook the indoor pool) have recently benefited from a major refurbishment programme. Good-sized bedrooms all offer large beds, breakfast table and ample work space plus mini-bars and individually controllable air-conditioning. A supplement of £15 brings Executive status with extras like bath robe and slippers, fresh fruit, complimentary wine and a turn-down service in the evening. Comprehensive 24hr room service and extensive conference/banqueting facilities. Ample free parking. Formerly the *Holiday Inn*. ***Rooms** 298. Indoor swimming pool, gymnasium, squash, sauna, spa bath, solarium, hair salon, kiosk, coffee shop (10am-6pm).* AMERICAN EXPRESS *Access, Diners, Visa.*

Glasgow **Hospitality Inn** **67%** **£130**

Tel 041-332 3311 Fax 041-332 4050 **H**

36 Cambridge Street Glasgow Strathclyde G2 3HN **Map 3 B6**

Mount Charlotte Thistle hotel with conference suites to hold up to 1500 and a free 250-space car park for residents. Especially roomy de luxe bedrooms and efficient 24hr room service. The Grand Ballroom has recently been refurbished and attention has now turned to the bedrooms. ***Rooms** 307. Coffee shop (7am-11.30pm).* AMERICAN EXPRESS *Access, Diners, Visa.*

Glasgow **Jurys Pond Hotel** **59%** **£78**

Tel 041-334 8161 Fax 041-334 3846 **H**

2 Shelly Road Great Western Road Glasgow Strathclyde G12 0XP **Map 3 B6**

Overlooking the boating pond from which it takes it name, this is the first Scottish outlet for the Irish-based Jurys group (it was previously the Stakis). Good leisure and conference facilities, the latter for up to 150. Well set up for families (under-16s stay free in parents' room). The hotel stands on the Great Western Road three miles west of the city centre (leave the M8 at junction 17 and follow the A82 for $2\frac{1}{2}$ miles). ***Rooms** 137. Indoor swimming pool, children's pool, gymnasium, sauna, spa bath, solarium.* AMERICAN EXPRESS *Access, Diners, Visa.*

Glasgow **Kelvin Park Lorne Hotel** **63%** **£81**

Tel 041-334 4891 Fax 041-334 1659 **H**

923 Sauchiehall Street Glasgow Strathclyde G3 7TE **Map 3 B6**

10 minutes from the city centre, a Queens Moat Houses hotel with a choice of accommodation (standard Executive, superior Executive and suites) and five conference suites. ***Rooms** 99. Coffee shop (11.30-10). Closed 25 & 26 Dec.* AMERICAN EXPRESS *Access, Diners, Visa.*

Glasgow **Loon Fung** **£45**

Tel 041-332 1240 Fax 041-332 3705 **R**

417 Sauchiehall Street Glasgow Strathclyde G2 3JD **Map 3 B6**

Colourful carvings of the dragon and phoenix (Loon Fung) decorate one end of this smart restaurant, which takes pride in its authentic Cantonese cooking. It's open all day, with a set lunch, and dim sum available until 7. Sliced abalone with oyster sauce, crunchy stuffed duck and sizzling platters of Cantonese-style fillet steak take centre stage in the evening. Vegetarian meals available. Special banquets can be ordered by prior arrangement. Recent refurbishment involves a new bar and lounge area and a toilet with access for disabled visitors. ***Seats** 200. Private Room 24. Meals 12-11.30. Closed 3 days Chinese New Year. Set L £5.70 Set D from £10.* AMERICAN EXPRESS *Access, Diners, Visa.*

Glasgow **Mata Hari** **£35**

Tel 041-332 9789 **R**

17 West Princes Street Glasgow Strathclyde **Map 3 B6**

Malaysian cooking in a basement restaurant with a non-smoking section. Dishes to try include chicken, beef and prawn satay (also mushroom for vegetarians), *kari udang* (prawns with green pepper, coconut and spices), *rendang ayam* (chicken with spices and lemon grass), *assam manis ikan* (fish in a sweet and sour sauce) and *acar* (mixed vegetable pickle with sesame in a spiced lemon grass sauce). Desserts include coconut pancakes. ***Seats** 62. Private Room 15. L 12-2 D 6-11 (Fri & Sat to 11.30). Closed L Sat, all Sun, 25 & 26 Dec, 1 Jan. Set L from £5 Set D £17.50.* AMERICAN EXPRESS *Access, Diners, Visa.*

Glasgow **Moat House International** **69%** **£126**

Tel 041-204 0733 Fax 041-221 2022 **H**

Congress Road Glasgow Strathclyde G3 8QT **Map 3 B6**

Adjacent to the Scottish Exhibition Centre (follow signs from J19 of the nearby M8), with fine views across the Clyde. Historical connections with Glasgow's shipbuilding past are recalled by the vast mural which dominates one end of the spacious, glass-walled public areas. On ground and mezzanine floors conference and banqueting suites will hold up to 600, serviced by a self-contained business centre. The chief recreation area is the Waterside health and leisure club. Roomy bedrooms are identically equipped with maple-effect fitted furniture and marble-finish bathrooms; state-of-the-art TV includes a breakfast order facility, bill check and automatic payment service. The latest addition is the Anchorage Suite with double and twin bedrooms, plus separate living and dining rooms. Family facilities; under-13s free when sharing their parents' room; special entertainment on Sundays includes a steamship brunch. ***Rooms** 282. Indoor swimming pool, gymnasium, spa bath, sauna, solarium, coffee shop (7am-11pm).* AMERICAN EXPRESS *Access, Diners, Visa.*

Glasgow **One Devonshire Gardens** **82%** **£155**

Tel 041-339 2001 Fax 041-337 1663 **HR**

1 Devonshire Gardens Glasgow Strathclyde G12 0UX **Map 3 B6**

Our Hotel of the Year (see page 20) is set in a tree-lined Victorian terrace, ten minutes from the city centre. Owned by Ken McCulloch, and superbly run by Beverly Payne, this is a hotel of real style and distinction created from three town houses. Fresh flowers and a myriad of paintings, prints and decorative features abound throughout the public areas, which include a restful lounge and bar, both with deep armchairs and sofas, perhaps best described as 'designer Victorian'. Quality is the keynote in the sumptuous bedrooms with French mahogany furniture and rich fabrics that extend to bedhead drapes and scatter cushions on the sofas and settees. Colour schemes are very masculine in the main with dark reds and blues,

See over

though some lighter rooms are in grey or beige. The latest-technology television and CD player are tucked away in a cabinet along with the mini-bar, and other thoughtful touches include fresh flowers, books, magazines and quality toiletries in the wonderful marble bathrooms that provide generously sized hooded bathrobes and luxurious towels. Friendly and attentive staff offer particularly high levels of service, from the moment one rings the doorbell to gain admittance to the turning-down of beds and cleaning of bathrooms at night. Banquets for up to 32 and conferences up to 50 in either the boardroom, study or private dining room. Children under 14 may stay free in their parents' room. In 1988 Leonard Bernstein found a stay here to be "friendly and pure theatre – truly inspirational"; naturally we concur. ***Rooms** 27. AMERICAN EXPRESS Access, Diners, Visa.*

Restaurant £80

In stylish surroundings – clever lighting, dark drapes, elegant china and glassware – pinafored waitresses serve dishes from a menu that changes with the markets and the seasons. Lunch might comprise smoked haddock ravioli, game casserole and cold baked rice pudding, while dinner might extend to *potage du jour* with home-baked bread, then foie gras terrine or escabeche of red mullet followed by tournedos of Scottish beef fillet with a confit of shallots and sweet garlic or a nage of langoustines, scallops and mussels in a bouillon of baby leeks and tomatoes. Vegetarian options are also offered. Desserts might include lemon tart with sauce anglaise, a chocolate assiette and a trio of passion fruit. Good Scottish cheeses. Many fine wines on the carefully compiled list, plus a good selection of half bottles. Outdoor eating on a patio. ***Seats** 40. Parties 8. L 12.30-2 D 7-10. Closed L Sat. Set L £19 Set D £32.*

Glasgow La Parmigiana £50

Tel 041-334 0686 R

447 Great Western Road Glasgow Strathclyde G12 8HH **Map 3 B6**

An unpretentious family-run trattoria, rather smarter than most. The menu has been recently changed and now pasta and meat main courses (including quail, veal cutlet and guinea fowl) stand out. Popular three-course lunch offers a good choice (considering the almost unbelievably low price); booking advisable. ***Seats** 50. L 12-2.30 D 6-11. Closed L Bank Holidays, all Sun. Set L £6.80. AMERICAN EXPRESS Access, Diners, Visa.*

Glasgow Ristorante Caprese £35

Tel 041-332 3070 R

217 Buchanan Street (basement) Glasgow Strathclyde G1 2JZ **Map 3 B6**

Cheerful, inexpensive and atmospheric basement Italian restaurant close to the Royal Concert Hall. Red check cloths adorn the tables and the walls are covered with photos and postcards from their many regular customers. The menu holds few surprises but cooking is enjoyably robust and homely. House specialities include veal cordon bleu, steak pizzaiola and chicken Kiev. Also daily blackboard dishes. ***Seats** 60. Private Room 25. L 12-2.30 D 5.30-11. Closed L Sat, all Sun, Bank Holidays. Set L from £5.50. AMERICAN EXPRESS Access, Diners, Visa.*

Glasgow Rogano £75

Tel 041-248 4055 R

11 Exchange Place Glasgow Strathclyde G1 3AN **Map 3 B6**

Popular as ever among tourists, business people and the citizens of Glasgow spending their own money, and as firmly traditional as its setting of art deco ocean-liner decor and white-aproned waiters, Rogano is a Glasgow institution. Fish and seafood feature strongly on the menu – from sashimi with pickled ginger and wasabi to grilled sole or steamed John Dory in a tomato and vermouth sauce. Typically, rack of Borders lamb with sweet roast garlic and peppers, malt whisky parfait with prunes and Earl

Grey syrup plus good cheeses complete the picture. Good-value 'theatre dinner' served 5-6.30pm and after 10pm; downstairs, the Café Rogano is more informal. ***Seats** 50. Private Room 16. L 12-2.30 D 6.30-10.30 (Sun to 10) (Café 12-11; to midnight Fri & Sat). Closed L Sun, all Bank Holidays. Set L £15.* AMERICAN EXPRESS *Access, Diners, Visa.*

Glasgow Stakis Grosvenor 66% **£99**

Tel 041-339 8811 Fax 041-334 0710 **H**

Grosvenor Terrace Glasgow Strathclyde G12 0TA **Map 3 B6**

At the west end of the city, just opposite the Botanical Gardens, a Victorian frontage conceals much refurbishment. Conference/banqueting for up to 400, an all-day coffee shop, 50% non-smoking bedrooms and 14 spacious family rooms (under-12s stay free) are among the facilities. ***Rooms** 95. Coffee shop (7.30am-11pm).* AMERICAN EXPRESS *Access, Diners, Visa.*

Glasgow Swallow Hotel 61% **£92**

Tel 041-427 3146 Fax 041-427 4059 **H**

517 Paisley Road West Glasgow Strathclyde G51 1RW **Map 3 B6**

A mile west of the city centre at junction 23 of the M8, near Ibrox Park, a busy modern hotel with conference facilities for up to 380, a leisure club and parking for 150 cars. ***Rooms** 117. Indoor swimming pool, gymnasium, sauna, spa bath, steam room.* AMERICAN EXPRESS *Access, Diners, Visa.*

Glasgow Tinto Firs Hotel 62% **£85**

Tel 041-637 2353 Fax 041-633 1340 **H**

470 Kilmarnock Road Glasgow Strathclyde G43 2BB **Map 3 B6**

A modern, if modest, hotel in the suburbs (three miles from the city centre) with club class bedrooms and two suites. Banqueting for 130, conferences up to 200. Friendly staff create a relaxed atmosphere. Mount Charlotte Thistle. ***Rooms** 30. Garden.* AMERICAN EXPRESS *Access, Diners, Visa.*

Glasgow Town House 69% **£110**

Tel 041-332 3320 Fax 041-332 9756 **H**

54 West George Street Glasgow Strathclyde G2 1NG **Map 3 B6**

Converted from a town house that used to be home to the Royal Scottish Academy of Music and Drama, some fine architectural features have been retained including a vaulted entrance hall and bas-reliefs (honouring famous composers) that grace the cantilevered staircase. The individually decorated bedrooms are its main strength; sufficiently roomy to accommodate a large quilt-covered bed, armchairs or a sofa around a coffee table, a breakfast table and desk. Changes were afoot as we went to press. Parking is virtually impossible without a 5 to 10 minute walk – a serious drawback. ***Rooms** 34. Closed 25 & 26 Dec.* AMERICAN EXPRESS *Access, Diners, Visa.*

Glasgow Two Fat Ladies **£55**

Tel 041-339 1944 **R**

88 Dumbarton Road Glasgow Strathclyde G11 6NX **Map 3 B6**

Generous portions of market-fresh fish are the big attraction at this relaxed restaurant near the City Art Gallery. Choices run from garlicky-spicy fish soup and grilled herring with wasabi and daikon to octopus and surf clam salad, skate wing with black butter and chargrilled gurnard with salsa. The kitchen is in the window. ***Seats** 28. Parties 28. D only 6.30-10.30. Closed Sun & Mon, 2 weeks Christmas/New Year. Access, Visa.*

Glasgow — Ubiquitous Chip

£72

Tel 041-334 5007

R

12 Ashton Lane Glasgow Strathclyde G12 8SJ

Map 3 B6

A former Victorian coach house and stables in a cobbled lane near the university. The main restaurant is in the covered courtyard (with rampant greenery) with an inventive menu that combines a strong Scottish slant with modern touches – Ayr-landed cod on a bed of clapshot (mashed swede and potatoes) with roasted peppers and chili oil; boiled silverside with root vegetables, barley and grain mustard vinaigrette; stuffed Loch Fyne mussels; shortbread layered with strawberries, orange cream and nectarine coulis. Cooking is bistroish rather than refined, with generously-sized portions. 'Upstairs at the Chip' offers a less expensive all-day menu along similar lines. Good selection of Scottish cheeses. A fabulous and keenly priced all-round wine list also features a super selection of wines by the glass, as well as a long list of single Highland malts that will delight whisky drinkers. ***Seats** 120. Parties 45. Private Room 25. L 12-2.30 D 5.30-11. Closed Christmas/New Year. Set L £10.* AMERICAN EXPRESS, *Access, Diners, Visa.*

Glasgow — Places of Interest

Tourist Information Tel 041-204 4400.
Caledonian MacBrayne Ferries Tel 0475 33755.
City Tours Tel 041-332 1607.
ScotRail Tel 041-332 9811.
Glasgow Airport Tel 041-887 1111.
Glasgow Cathedral Tel 041-552 3205.
St Mary the Virgin Cathedral Tel 041-339 6691.
Glasgow Ski Centre Club Tel 041-427 4991.
Kelvin Hall Int. Sports Arena Tel 041-357 2525.
Celtic F.C. Celtic Park Tel 041-556 2611.
Rangers F.C. Ibrox Stadium Tel 041-427 8811.
Calderpark Zoo Tel 041-771 1185.

Theatres and Concert Halls

Citizens Theatre Tel 041-429 0022.
Glasgow Royal Concert Hall Tel 041-332 6633.
Glasgow Film Theatre Tel 041-332 6535.
Greenock Arts Guild Theatre Tel 0475 23038.
Royal Scottish Academy of Music Tel 041-332 5057.
Scottish Exhibition and Conference Centre Tel 041-248 3000.
The Tramway Tel 041-227 5511.
City Halls Tel 041-227 5511 .
Kings Theatre Tel 041-227 5511.
Mitchell Theatre Tel 041-227 5511.
Pavilion Theatre Tel 041-332 1846.
SNO Henry Wood Hall Tel 041-226 3868.
Theatre Royal Tel 041-332 9000.
Third Eye Centre Tel 041-332 7521.
Tron Theatre Tel 041-552 4267.

Historic Houses, Castles and Gardens

Greenbank Garden Tel 041-639 3281.
Botanic Gardens Tel 041-334 2422.
The Hill House Helensburgh. Tel 0436 3900.
Hutcheson's Hall Tel 041-552 8391.
Pollock House & Park (Burrell Collection in Pollock Park) Tel 041-632 0274.
Provands Lordship Tel 041-552 8819.
The Tenement House Tel 041-333 0183.

Museums and Art Galleries

Art Gallery and Museum Tel 041-357 3929.
Burrell Collection Tel 041-649 7151.
Dome of Discovery Tel 041-427 1792.
Hunterian Art Gallery Tel 041-330 5431.
Hunterian Museum Tel 041-330 4221.

McLean Museum and Art Gallery Greenock Tel. 0475 23741.
McLellan Galleries Tel 041-351 1854.
Museum of Tranport Tel 041-357 3929.
Peoples's Palace Tel 041-554 0223.
Paisley Museum and Art Galleries Paisley. Tel 041-889 3151.
Police Museum Tel 041-204 2626.

Glasgow Airport — Forte Crest — 68% — £95

Tel 041-887 1212 Fax 041-887 3738 — **H**

Abbotsinch nr Paisley Strathclyde PA3 2TR — **Map 3 B6**

The only hotel located directly beside Glasgow airport. All the bedrooms are sound-proofed, double-glazed and air-conditioned. Three floors of rooms have recently been refurbished. Banqueting/conference facilities for 300/500. ***Rooms 300.*** AMERICAN EXPRESS *Access, Diners, Visa.*

Glasgow Airport — Stakis Normandy — 61% — £102

Tel 041-886 4100 — **H**

Inchman Road Renfrew Glasgow Airport Strathclyde PA4 5EJ — **Map 3 B6**

A modern hotel on the A8, some five minutes from the airport. Bedrooms offer practical comforts, and nine suites accommodate up to 1000 for conferences. ***Rooms 141.*** *Garden, golf-driving range.* AMERICAN EXPRESS *Access, Diners, Visa.*

Glenborrodale — Glenborrodale Castle — 75% — £173

Tel 097 24 266 Fax 097 24 224 — **HR**

Glenborrodale Ardnamurchan Peninsula Highland PH36 4JP — **Map 3 A4**

One of the most beautifully situated hotels in the UK, Glenborrodale Castle commands spectacular views over Loch Sunart to the Isle of Mull. It's an ideal setting for lovers of the great outdoors, and the mood throughout is one of total relaxation. Antique furniture abounds in the public rooms with ornaments, pictures, books and games spread around. Bedrooms are luxurious, with very pretty co-ordinating fabrics, and many of the smart, carpeted bathrooms have Victorian tubs. Thoughtful touches like decanters of sherry and bowls of fruit add to the appeal. The State Rooms have splendid four-poster beds. Not a conference delegate in sight! ***Rooms 16.*** *Garden, keep-fit equipment, sauna, solarium, beauty salon, tennis, putting, fishing, riding, mooring, hotel boat, snooker. Closed Nov-Easter.* AMERICAN EXPRESS *Access, Visa.*

Restaurant — £85

The dining room is elegant, with a beamed ceiling, panelled walls and heavy drapes. A high proportion of the ingredients used in the kitchen come from the hotel's own land, while Loch Sunart provides fish and shellfish. Dishes on a recent menu included artichoke soup, terrine of game with apple chutney and brioche, steamed fillet of brill coated in a langoustine mousse and served on a caviar sauce, and sautéed strips of beef and lamb with red pepper and pak choi. No smoking. ***Seats 32.*** *L 12-2 D 7-9. Set D from £32.50.*

Glencarse — Newton House Hotel — 58% — £75

Tel 073 886 250 Fax 073 886 717 — **H**

Glencarse nr Perth Tayside PH2 7LX — **Map 3 C5**

Set back in gardens from the A85 just east of Perth, this is a substantial double-fronted dower house dating from 1840. It's well kept throughout, comfortable and genteel. There's a little lounge and a cocktail bar, and bedrooms ranging from small singles to more roomy doubles and twins. ***Rooms 10.*** *Garden.* AMERICAN EXPRESS *Access, Diners, Visa.*

Glenelg Glenelg Inn NEW £120*

Tel 059 982 273 Fax 059 982 373 **IR**

Glenelg by Kyle of Lochalsh Highlands IV40 8JR **Map 3 B4**

It's a spectacular and somewhat precipitous drive to reach this old inn, idyllically set on the shore of Glenelg Bay, that has been sympathetically refurbished by local man Christopher Main. To a convivial, rustic bar has been added, within the original stable block, half-a-dozen spacious bedrooms individually decorated and furnished with antiques. Each has its own smart bathroom. The Morning Room with Victorian paintings and photos, green leather chesterfield, stag's head and various antiques and objets d'art, makes a comfortable retreat where residents socialise after dinner. Stay for two nights and there is a free excursion on the hotel's own boat; seven nights' stay earns a full day's Loch fishing along with other 'extras'. *Half-board terms only. ***Rooms** 6. Garden, fishing, boat trips. No credit cards.*

Restaurant £50

The intimate dining room has a civilised air with candles and fresh flowers on the tables and a real fire on chilly evenings. Local seafood, venison and hill-bred lamb are the mainstays of the fixed-price menu. Typical main dishes might include Loch Hourn monkfish with baby scallops and an orange, ginger and pepper cream sauce, roast breast of duckling with wholegrain mustard and tarragon sauce, and king prawns oriental finished with peppers and black bean sauce. ***Seats** 20. D only 8.30-9. Set D £19. Closed Oct-Easter.*

Glenrothes Balgeddie House 65% £87

Tel 0592 742511 Fax 0592 621702 **H**

Balgeddie Way Glenrothes Fife KY6 3ET **Map 3 C5**

Until recently surrounded by farmland, this 18th-century Georgian house was only converted to a hotel in 1989 and is now part of a suburb of Glenrothes new town. The whole place is well kept, from lounge and oak-panelled bar to the bedrooms; those on the first floor are superior and spacious, with fine modern bathrooms, those on the second floor are twins, with sloping ceilings. Two separate bars with juke box, fruit machine and pool tables set the tone inside; outside there's a lawn the size of a football pitch and eight acres of landscaped gardens. Children stay free in their parents' room. Functions/conferences for up to 70. Tariff reductions for two nights' minimum stay at weekends. ***Rooms** 18. Garden.* AMERICAN EXPRESS *Access, Diners, Visa.*

Glenrothes Places of Interest

Glenrothes Tourist Information Tel 0592 754954.
Kirkcaldy Tourist Information Tel 0592 267775.
Adam Smith Theatre Kirkcaldy Tel 0592 260498.
Falkland Palace & Garden (NT) Tel 0337 57397.
Kirkcaldy Ice Rink Tel 0592 52151.
Crystals Arena Ice Rink Tel 0592 773774.
Museums and Art Galleries
Burntisland Edwardian Fair Tel 0592 260732.
Kirkcaldy Museum and Art Gallery Tel 0592 260732.

Gourock Stakis Gantock Hotel 64% £95

Tel 0475 34671 Fax 0475 32490 **H**

Cloch Road Gourock Strathclyde PA15 1AR **Map 3 B5**

Friendly staff, smart day rooms and well-equipped bedrooms including Executive suites. Fine views across the Clyde. Extensive banqueting and conference facilities, including two new boardrooms. ***Rooms** 99. Indoor swimming pool, keep-fit equipment, sauna, spa bath, solarium, floodlit tennis, children's playground.* AMERICAN EXPRESS *Access, Diners, Visa.*

Gourock Places of Interest

Tourist Information Tel 0475 39467.

Gretna Green Forte Travelodge £42

Tel 0461 37566 **L**

A74 Trunk Road Gretna Green Dumfries & Galloway CA6 5HQ **Map 4 C2**

On the A74 northbound, 8 miles north of Carlisle on the main route to Glasgow, 2 miles north of Gretna. ***Rooms** 41.* AMERICAN EXPRESS *Access, Visa.*

Gullane Greywalls Hotel 76% £150

Tel 0620 842144 Fax 0620 842241 **HR**

Muirfield Gullane Lothian EH31 2EG **Map 3 C5**

Built in 1901, Greywalls is one of the few examples of Lutyens' architecture north of the Border. In a lovely position next to Muirfield Golf Course, the house has a perfect unity of design. The Library is a very fine room with lightwood panelling, grand piano, 'His Master's Voice' gramophone and an open fire; to the north you glimpse the Firth of Forth, to the south Gertrude Jekyll's rose garden. There's a clubby bar and a delightful sun room. Bedrooms are generally of fine proportions and full of light; little personal touches like books and portable radios make the hotel a home from home. Enchanting cottage-style rooms in the lodge. Good breakfast, friendly service. On the A198 at the east end of Gullane village. ***Rooms** 23. Garden, tennis. Closed Nov-Mar.* AMERICAN EXPRESS *Access, Diners, Visa.*

Restaurant £80

A delightful dining room is the setting for Paul Baron's careful cooking. Neat presentation is one of his hallmarks; attention to detail (everything from bread to petits fours is home-made) is another. Hollandaise-topped mussel and leek tartlet, warm chicken mousse with morel mushrooms and foie gras sauce, grilled halibut brushed with herb mustard and brioche crumbs and a dry Vermouth sauce, roast loin of venison on a bed of beetroot purée and juniper sauce, tangy lemon tart, chestnut and cinnamon tart with walnut ice cream and praline sauce may be typical dishes on the fixed-price, four-course menu that changes daily. Booking is essential for dinner. Traditional roast Sunday lunch. There's a very fine selection of clarets on the sound wine list that offers plenty of good drinking under £20. ***Seats** 50. Parties 16. L 12.30-2 D 7.30-9.30. Set L £15 (£20 Sun) Set D £33.*

Gullane La Potinière ★ £65

Tel 0620 843214 **R**

Main Street Gullane Lothian EH31 2AA **Map 3 C5**

David Brown is the most attentive of hosts and Hilary goes from strength to strength in the kitchen. Inside the cottage setting the flowers hit you centre stage, their colour and perfume filling the beamed dining room. Hilary's French-inspired cooking shows a light and sophisticated style: tomato and mint soup, sole mousseline with basil, breast of Barbary duck with a red wine reduction sauce, and apricot parfait typify her style. The superlative wine list (past winner of our Cellar of the Year award and this year's Scotland regional winner) requires careful scrutiny. Wherever you look there are gems and bargains to be found (note the south-west of France section). Superb collection of clarets and burgundies, many half bottles, fair prices – paradise! No smoking. Plan your visit well in advance as the single sitting for dinner is booked months ahead. ***Seats** 30. Parties 16. L at 1 D at 8. Closed L Fri & Sat, D Sun-Thur, all Wed, 25 & 26 Dec, 1 & 2 Jan, 1 week Jun, Oct. Set L £17.50 (£18.50 Sun) Set D £27.50. No credit cards.*

Harray — Loch Merkister Hotel — 57% — £59

Tel 085 677 366 Fax 085 677 515 — H

Harray Loch Orkney KW17 2LF — **Map 2 C1**

First and last a fishing hotel, with great sport on Loch Harray and three other lochs. The brown trout fishing is among the best in the world, and boats, outboards and ghillies can be arranged. Deep-freezing facilities are available, and smoking of the fish can be organised. Seafood features prominently on the menu, along with speciality steaks. Owner Angus MacDonald is a keen fisherman himself, and is always willing to give guidance, and his wife Elma runs the hotel with great charm. Centre of affairs is the bar, and after swapping fishy tales guests settle down for a comfortable night in the modest, well-kept bedrooms. Birdwatchers are also attracted here, and the hotel has a bird hide in the grounds. Ask for a map showing directions from Stromness ferry terminal when booking. ***Rooms** 15. Garden, game fishing. Closed Nov-end Feb.* AMERICAN EXPRESS *Access, Visa.*

Helmsdale — Navidale House — 60% — £60

Tel 043 12 258 — H

Helmsdale Highland KW8 6JS — **Map 2 C2**

Beautifully situated in six acres of woods and gardens running down to the foreshore, this friendly former hunting lodge is on the A9 just north of Helmsdale. The bar is small and cosy; the lounge rather old-fashioned. Bedrooms in the main house are pleasantly furnished, with period pieces and functional tiled bathrooms. Five rooms are in a lodge in the grounds. Children up to the age of 10 stay free in parents' room. ***Rooms** 14. Garden, game fishing. Closed Nov-New Year. Access, Visa.*

Helmsdale — Places of Interest

Tourist Information Tel 043 12 640.
Dunrobin Castle Golspie Tel 0408 633177.

Ingliston — Norton House — 66% — £115

Tel 031-333 1275 Fax 031-333 5305 — H

Ingliston nr Edinburgh Lothian EH28 8LX — **Map 3 C5**

With a secluded parkland setting at the end of a long drive (look for the hotel sign on the A8 between airport and motorway), this Victorian manor does not quite manage to be 'grand' although there are a couple of marble columns in the hall and the dado-panelled lounge has a nice period feel. The Tavern (in converted stables in the grounds) provides a lively alternative to the rather tired cocktail bar. Best rooms in the original house are notably spacious and comfortable with extras like bathrobe, fresh flowers and mineral water but standard rooms in a modern extension are also well equipped and attractively decorated with matching fabrics. Staff are exceptionally friendly. Decent breakfasts are served in a conservatory extension to the dining room. ***Rooms** 47. Garden.* AMERICAN EXPRESS*, Access, Diners, Visa.*

Inverness — Bunchrew House — 70% — £115

Tel 0463 234917 Fax 0463 710620 — H

Bunchrew Inverness Highland IV3 6TA — **Map 2 C3**

From Inverness follow the signs to Beauly/Drywall on the A862. A mile from the outskirts of Inverness you'll find the entrance to 16th-century Bunchrew House (opened as a hotel in 1987), which stands in 15 acres of landscaped gardens and woodland on the shores of Beauly Firth. New owners took over in April 1993 and plan improvements. ***Rooms** 11. Garden, fishing.* AMERICAN EXPRESS *Access, Visa.*

Inverness **Caledonian Hotel** **69%** **£99**

Tel 0463 235181 Fax 0463 711206 **H**

33 Church Street Inverness Highland IV1 1DX **Map 2 C3**

Alongside the river Ness, a smart city-centre hotel with good conference (for up to 300 delegates) and leisure facilities plus modern public rooms. Ample parking. Children free up to the age of 14 in parents' room. Jarvis Hotels. ***Rooms*** *106. Indoor swimming pool, gymnasium, sauna, spa bath, solarium.* AMERICAN EXPRESS *Access, Diners, Visa.*

Inverness **Culloden House** **73%** **£150**

Tel 0463 790461 Fax 0463 792181 **HR**

Culloden Inverness Highland IV1 2NZ **Map 2 C3**

An impressive Adam-style Georgian mansion set in 40 acres of parkland and run by resident owners Marjory and Ian McKenzie. History abounds in the house (Bonnie Prince Charlie once seized it), the 40 acres of parkland and the surrounding countryside. The traditional feel is preserved within the chandeliered hall, and in the grandly proportioned lounge and dining room with their ornate plasterwork, friezes and carved fireplace surrounds. Some bedrooms are grand, while those in the wings tend to be much smaller. Several rooms have spa baths and antique four-posters, with pretty crown canopies and co-ordinated fabrics all adding to the style. Four stylish no-smoking suites are in the imposing Garden Mansion 200 yards from the main building (don't be alarmed if you find a little wild roe deer grazing outside your window in the morning when you wake up). No children under ten. ***Rooms*** *23. Garden, tennis, snooker, sauna, solarium.* AMERICAN EXPRESS *Access, Diners, Visa.*

Restaurant **£80**

Lunch in the elegant Adam Room is à la carte and dinner an inclusive affair of five courses. Michael Simpson applies classical French skills to the best of local produce in dishes like quenelles of smoked mackerel mousse with salmon roe and a lime vinaigrette or medallions of venison coated with honey-flavoured red wine sauce and wild mushrooms; finish with chocolate marquise with hazelnut praline ice cream and caramel sauce. A vegetarian main course is always available. Some big names (with prices to match!) on the fine wine list that also has plenty of good-value wines to offer. ***Seats*** *40. Private Room 34. L 12.30-2 D 7-9. Set D £29.50.*

Inverness **Dunain Park** **69%** **£130**

Tel 0463 230512 Fax 0463 224532 **HR**

Inverness Highland IV3 6JN **Map 2 C3**

Ann and Edward Nicoll's handsome former hunting lodge stands in six acres of garden and woodland a mile from Inverness on the A82 road to Loch Ness. Various styles of accommodation are available, top of the range being six suites in the main building with spacious sitting rooms and Italian marble bathrooms. Two rooms are in cottages in the grounds. ***Rooms*** *14. Garden, indoor swimming pool, sauna. Closed 2 weeks Feb.* AMERICAN EXPRESS *Access, Diners, Visa.*

Restaurant **£62**

The dining room overlooks extensive gardens, where many of the vegetables, fruit and herbs are grown for the kitchen. Ann Nicoll's cooking is Scottish with French influences, based on seasonal local produce: turnip soup, terrine of smoked haddock and whiting, brochette of pigeon and bacon, wild turbot with hollandaise, saddle of venison rolled in oatmeal and served with a claret and crème de cassis sauce. Sweets from the buffet. No smoking in the dining room. A choice of 85 malt whiskies puts the icing on the cake. ***Seats*** *36. Parties 12. D only 7-9.*

Inverness — Kingsmills Hotel — 67% — £110

Tel 0463 237166 Fax 0463 225208 — **H**

Culcabock Road Inverness Highland IV2 3LP — **Map 2 C3**

18th-century house modernised and extended. Conference facilities for up to 70, banqueting up to 40. Swallow Hotels. ***Rooms** 84. Keep-fit equipment, sauna, spa bath, solarium, beauty & hair salon (aromatherapy by appointment), pitch & putt.* AMERICAN EXPRESS *Access, Diners, Visa.*

Inverness — Mercury Hotel — 62% — £85

Tel 0463 239666 Fax 0463 711145 — **H**

Millburn Road Inverness Highland IV2 3TR — **Map 2 C3**

At the foot of the North Kessoch Bridge, which connects Inverness with the Black Isle. Can cater for conferences of up to 250 delegates, although other facilities are limited. Mount Charlotte Thistle. ***Rooms** 118.* AMERICAN EXPRESS *Access, Diners, Visa.*

Inverness — Places of Interest

Tourist Information Tel 0463 234353.
Eden Court Theatre Tel 0463 221718.
Cawdor Castle Tel 066 77 615.
Culloden Battlefield and Museum Tel 0463 790607 *7 miles.*
St Andrew's Cathedral Tel 0463 233535.
Inverness Museum and Art Gallery Tel 0463 237114.
Inverness Ice Centre Tel 0463 235711.
Clan Tartan Centre Holm Woolen Mills Tel 0463 223311.

Irvine — Hospitality Inn — 68% — £86

Tel 0294 74272 Fax 0294 77287 — **H**

46 Annick Road Irvine Strathclyde KA11 4LD — **Map 4 A1**

A Moorish theme pervades the central concourse, lounge and bar. Superior bedrooms are round the atrium and the pool. Children sharing parents' room pay only for meals as taken. Conference facilities for up to 320, banqueting to 220. Mount Charlotte Thistle. ***Rooms** 128. Indoor swimming pool, spa bath, golf (9-hole), putting.* AMERICAN EXPRESS *Access, Diners, Visa.*

Irvine — Places of Interest

The Galleon Ice Rink Kilmarnock. Tel 0563 24014 *10 miles.*

Isle of Raasay — Isle of Raasay Hotel — 57% — £64

Tel 0478 660222 — **H**

Isle of Raasay by Kyle of Lochalsh Highland IV40 8PB — **Map 2 A3**

The Isle of Raasay is a 15-minute trip by ferry from Skye and its only hotel is this Victorian house with a modern accommodation wing. The whole place is light and neat, from the lounge with its lovely views and the pine-ceilinged bar to the bedrooms, which have traditional furnishings, tweedy fabrics and carpeted bathrooms. Motorists should note that there's no petrol on Raasay. ***Rooms** 12. Garden, courtesy transport. Closed Oct-Mar. No credit cards.*

Kelso — Ednam House — 64% — £72

Tel 0573 224168 Fax 0573 226319 — **H**

Bridge Street Kelso Borders TD5 7HT — **Map 5 D1**

A town-centre Georgian house with lawns reaching down to the River Tweed, a homely open fire, sporting paintings, cosy armchairs and waders and waterproofs in the hall. It's a popular fishing hotel, and outside high season the large majority of guests are salmon fishers (Feb/Mar &

Oct/Nov). The bars (where lunches are served Monday to Saturday) are convivial and the lounges are quietly traditional. Well-kept bedrooms match modern comforts with old-fashioned courtesies. ***Rooms** 32. Garden, fishing. Closed 24 Dec-12 Jan. Access, Visa.*

Kelso — Sunlaws House — 72% — £128

Tel 0573 450331 Fax 0573 450611 — **H**

Heiton Kelso Borders TD5 8JZ — **Map 5 D1**

An imposing Scottish country house three miles from Kelso on the A698, at the south end of Heiton village, offering peace, quiet and plenty of sporting activities. Log fires keep things cosy in the entrance hall, the elegantly draped drawing room, the library bar and the central hall with its ornate carved wooded fireplace. The two best bedrooms also have log fires, along with antique furnishings. Other main-house rooms use good-quality darkwood pieces, while those in the converted stable block tend to have fitted units. Bathrooms are decorated to match their individually styled bedrooms where beds are turned down at night. Falconry, hawking, horse trail riding and archery can be arranged for guests. The tennis court was recently resurfaced. ***Rooms** 22. Garden, tennis, putting, game fishing.* AMERICAN EXPRESS *Access, Diners, Visa.*

Kelso — Places of Interest

Tourist Information Tel 0573 23464.
Tait Concert Hall Tel 0450 75991.
Kelso Museum Tel 0573 25470.
Historic Houses, Castles and Gardens
Floors Castle Tel 0573 23333.
Mellerstain Gordon. Tel 057 381 225.

Kenmore — Kenmore Hotel — 62% — £88

Tel 0887 830205 Fax 0887 830262 — **H**

Kenmore Perthshire Tayside PH15 2NU — **Map 3 C5**

Reputedly Scotland's oldest inn (1572), the Kenmore attracts many fishermen (they have 2 miles of private beats on the Tay, which flows past the inn) and golfers. The various cosy public rooms, one called the Poets Parlour to commemorate a visit by Robert Burns, are made even more inviting by real fires. Bedrooms, 14 in a Victorian gatehouse opposite, vary considerably in decor and furnishings with everything from melamine to antiques. Guests have free use of the swimming pool and leisure facilities at the nearby Kenmore Club. The hotel is at the east end of Loch Tay on the A827. ***Rooms** 38. 18-hole golf course, game fishing, tennis.* AMERICAN EXPRESS *Access, Visa.*

Kentallen of Appin — Ardsheal House — 67% — £160*

Tel 063 174 227 Fax 063 174 342 — **HR**

Kentallen of Appin Highland PA38 4BX — **Map 3 B4**

A private drive bordering Loch Linnhe yields stunning views on the approach to Robert and Jane Taylor's stone and granite hotel. The views remain glorious from the hotel itself, which is set in 900 acres of hills, woods, garden and shorefront. It lies four miles south of the Ballachulish bridge between Glencoe and Appin. With leather sofas, parquet floor, scatter rugs and Victorian snooker room, the house has a faintly masculine look but the atmosphere is very much that of a country house party. Bedrooms, all with antiques and each with an individual charm and character, have direct-dial phones but no TVs. Spotless bathrooms have fluffy towels and good toiletries. Excellent breakfasts. *Half-board terms only. ***Rooms** 13. Garden. Closed 3 weeks Jan.* AMERICAN EXPRESS *Access, Visa.*

Restaurant — £80

The conservatory dining room enables the garden (which contributes vegetables and herbs to the kitchen) to be enjoyed along with George

See over

Kelso's sound cooking. The menu changes every day, offering alternatives for each course: tomato soufflé or seafood terrine; green pea and lettuce soup or vegetable consommé; breast of duck with brandy and pink peppercorn sauce or baked brill with a herb crust and a champagne butter sauce; warm carrot and plum cake with ginger crème anglaise or strawberry yoghurt mousse or fresh fruit and cheese. A concise and easy-to-use wine list offers fair prices and quality. Lunches on the lawn. No smoking in the dining room. ***Seats** 40. L 12-2 D at 8.15. Set L £17.50 Set D £32.50.*

Kentallen of Appin — Holly Tree — 65% — £75

Tel 063 174 292 Fax 063 174 345 — **H**

Kentallen of Appin Highland PA38 4BY — **Map 3 B4**

An old railway station which has been cleverly converted into a civilised hotel, the Holly Tree stands on the edge of Loch Linnhe, three miles south of Ballachulish Bridge. The little bar was once the station tea room, and there's a delightful lounge with a central fireplace and comfortable seating. Bedrooms are equally appealing, with floral fabrics and pine furniture; bathrooms are up-to-date and attractively tiled. The restaurant is non-smoking. Children under 5 stay free in parents' room; families are well catered for. ***Rooms** 11. Garden, fishing.* AMERICAN EXPRESS *Access, Visa.*

Kilchrenan — Ardanaiseig — 74% — £210*

Tel 08663 333 Fax 08663 222 — **HR**

Kilchrenan by Taynuilt Strathclyde PA35 1HE — **Map 3 B5**

There's ten miles of winding single-track road (an attractive drive in itself) to negotiate before reaching the noted rhododendron-and azalea-filled woodland gardens that surround this Scottish baronial-style mansion gloriously set on the edge of Loch Awe. Day rooms include a grand, elegantly proportioned drawing room and cosy library bar – both with real log fires when it's chilly. Bedrooms – the most spacious have either loch or garden views – are individually decorated, some more recently than others, and furnished with antiques. Extras include mineral water, fresh fruit and bathrobes. Bathrooms, all with hand showers over plastic tubs, offer good-quality toiletries but smallish towels. In the summer of 1993 the hotel was being run by a triumvirate of the staff pending the arrival of the new owner in 1994 or 1995. *Half-board terms only. No children under eight. ***Rooms** 14. Garden, fishing, hotel boat, snooker, helipad. Closed Nov-Easter.* AMERICAN EXPRESS *Access, Diners, Visa.*

Restaurant — £80

After four years in the kitchen here Mark Taylor has inherited the head chef's hat, producing essentially simple but carefully cooked dishes. A five-course dinner menu, with a choice of two dishes at each stage, might include a salad of smoked venison; seafood timbale; breast of pheasant with bread sauce, game chips and a port jus; and grilled monkfish tail with a mussel stew. A short list of alternative main dishes (at a supplement to the menu price) concentrates on simple grills. Splendid views of the Loch from the dark red dining room. No children under eight. No smoking. ***Seats** 30. L 12.30-2 D 7.30-9. Set D £30.*

Kilchrenan — Taychreggan Hotel — 66% — £72

Tel 08663 211 Fax 08663 244 — **HR**

Kilchrenan by Taynuilt Strathclyde PA35 1HQ — **Map 3 B5**

With a glorious location on the edge of Loch Awe, this former drovers' inn (they spent the night here before swimming their cattle across the Loch) was modestly extended in the 1970s to enclose a charming cobbled courtyard. New owners have made a good start with the installation of central heating and some tasteful refurbishment of the several lounges, and plan a gradual programme to upgrade the bedrooms. No children under six years. ***Rooms** 15. Garden, coarse and game fishing, boating, sail boarding.* AMERICAN EXPRESS® *Access, Visa.*

Restaurant **£66**

The introduction of antique tables, smart new chairs and a collection of modern paintings around the walls has considerably improved the dining room here while the kitchen remains in the safe hands of head chef Hugh Cocker. A daily-changing five-course set menu that might consist of a rabbit terrine followed by a choice of soups or sorbet before a main dish of halibut with a risotto of courgette, tarragon and sun-dried tomatoes with peach-filled brandy snap basket and a selection of cheese for afters, is accompanied by a list of alternative main dishes (at a small supplement) such as sirloin of Angus beef bordelaise and Mull salmon grilled with anchovy butter and sauce vierge. An à la carte lunch menu which includes both snacks and more substantial dishes may be taken in either the bar or the dining room. No children under six. ***Seats** 40. L 12.30-2 D 7.30-9. Set D £24*

Kildrummy — Kildrummy Castle — 70% — £104

Tel 097 55 71288 Fax 097 55 71345 — **H**

Kildrummy Alford Grampian AB3 8RA — **Map 3 C4**

Built in 1900 as a rather grandiose castellated country house, the hotel has a lovely setting overlooking the ruins of a 13th-century castle, and gardens which feature specimen trees, Alpine plants and rare shrubs. (Grampian has more than 70 castles, many just a short drive from the hotel.) The baronial entrance hall contrasts with the Adam elegance of the sunny drawing room. Two carved lions act as sentries on a splendidly ornate staircase which leads to the bedrooms. These are less grand than the day rooms but are comfortable, spacious and warm. Charming attic rooms have sloping ceilings. Children stay free in their parents' room and are offered their own menu in the lounge, plus an outdoor playground. Long-serving owner Thomas Hanna strongly motivates his staff, who are outgoing and friendly. Trout and salmon fishing are available on a 3½-mile stretch of the river Don, and local centres organise shooting, stalking, riding and pony trekking. ***Rooms** 16. Garden, snooker. Closed 3 weeks Jan.* AMERICAN EXPRESS® *Access, Visa.*

Kilfinan — Kilfinan Hotel — £68

Tel 070 082 201 Fax 070 082 205 — **IR**

Kilfinan by Tighnabruaich Strathclyde PA21 2AP — **Map 3 B5**

A delightful Swiss/Scottish couple, Rolf and Lynne Mueller, run this remote white-stoned coaching inn amid magnificent scenery on the east shore of Loch Fyne, reached down a single-track road (B8000, off the A886) between Strachur and Tighnabruaich. The Dunoon ferry is less than an exhilarating hour's hair-raising drive across the moors. Purchased about ten years ago by the Laird of Kilfinan, so that it would not fall into the hands of developers, the inn has exclusive access to beautiful Kilfinan Bay (about 20 minutes walk through the garden and the estate) and is well placed for traditional outdoor pursuits. Two bars, neither of them a lounge, are both cosy and characterful with log fires, and the bedrooms – some antique-furnished – offer all the usual little luxuries, including good-quality toiletries in the carpeted en-suite bathrooms; one room overlooks St Finnan's graveyard, a surprisingly pleasant view. Incidentally, don't be alarmed by the brown peat-coloured water – 'at least it hasn't been filtered seven times by humans!'. Good walking country begins right outside the door. ***Rooms** 11. Garden, fishing.* AMERICAN EXPRESS® *Access, Visa.*

Restaurant **£55**

Crisp table linen, cutlery and glassware gleaming in the candle-light, and a glowing log fire make the twin dining rooms particularly appealing. Rolf brings Swiss precision into his cooking, exemplified in the fixed-price-only dinner menu that offers a small choice at each of the four courses: a recent

See over

menu offered salad of duck breast with orange and pink peppercorn sauce, ragout of wild mushrooms and asparagus or grilled smoked halibut with sherry butter sauce to start, followed by potage valaisanne and then langoustine-stuffed supreme of chicken with a champagne sauce, fondant of lamb in a rosemary jus or steamed fillets of brill in a port and beetroot sauce. Tarte tatin with apple, chocolate marquise with a mint anglaise or a selection of local cheeses to finish, plus good coffee served with petits fours. Lighter lunches are served in the recently refurbished Lamont Room. Outdoor eating in the garden in good weather. ***Seats*** *22. D only 7.30-9.30. Set D £22.*

Killiecrankie — Killiecrankie Hotel — 64% — £92

Tel 0796 473220 Fax 0796 472451 — **H**

Killiecrankie by Pitlochry Tayside PH16 5LG — **Map 3 C4**

Four acres of landscaped gardens overlook the river Garry and the Pass of Killiecrankie (turn off the A9 north of Pitlochry). There's something of the feeling of an inn about the little hotel, which was built as a manse in 1840. The reception hall and small panelled bar (which has a suntrap extension) have displays of stuffed animals and an upstairs lounge offers various board games plus a variety of books as distractions. Pine-furnished bedrooms are fresh and bright. ***Rooms*** *11. Garden, putting. Closed Jan & Feb.* AMERICAN EXPRESS *Access, Visa.*

Killiecrankie — Place of Interest

Blair Castle Tel 079 681 207.

Kilmelford — Cuilfail Hotel — 52% — £56

Tel 085 22 274 Fax 085 22 264 — **H**

Kilmelford Strathclyde PA34 4XA — **Map 3 B5**

Midway between Oban and Lochgilphead, at the head of Loch Melfort, a creeper-covered, stone-built roadside inn. In the mellow hall antiques give a traditional feel which is echoed in the two lounges, one of which has pine panelling and dark green velour chesterfields. Good-sized bedrooms use a variety of period furnishings; a refurbishment programme is ongoing. ***Rooms 12.*** *Garden, keep-fit equipment, sauna, solarium. Access, Visa.*

Kilmore — Glenfeochan House — 70% — £124

Tel 063 177 273 Fax 063 177 624 — **HR**

Kilmore Oban Strathclyde PA34 4QR — **Map 3 B5**

Built in 1875 (though some parts are probably much older), the house stands at the head of Loch Feochan, five miles south of Oban, on a 350-acre estate of hills, lochs, rivers and farmland. The six-acre garden is a source of great pride and is open to the public; there's also a Victorian walled garden. Inside, all is spick and span, from the entrance hall and stairway featuring pitch pine to the drawing room with a fine moulded ceiling and complementary antiques. Bedrooms have plain walls, floral curtains and more antiques. TVs and radios are provided, but no phones; three rooms for non-smokers. The Tulip Room has an en-suite round bathroom in the turret. Self-catering accommodation is available in the farmhouse. No children under ten. No dogs. ***Rooms*** *3. Garden, fishing. Closed Nov-early Mar. Access, Visa.*

Restaurant — £70

Guests gather for dinner at 8 and non-residents can join them by prior arrangement. Patricia Baber is an excellent cook and her short dinner menus (discussed at breakfast time) make as much use as possible of produce from the estate or local sources: wild fresh or home-smoked salmon or trout, Jura venison with rowan jelly, squat lobster, roast guinea fowl with damson and gin sauce. British cheeses served with home-made oatcakes and water biscuits. Packed lunches (£6) are provided. ***Seats** 10. D only at 8. Set D £28.*

Kilwinning Montgreenan Mansion House Hotel 70% £94

Tel 0294 57733 Fax 0294 85397 **H**

Montgreenan Estate Torranyard by Kilwinning Strathclyde KA13 7QZ **Map 3 B6**

18th-century features, including marble and brass fireplaces and decorative plasterwork, have been retained at this impressive Georgian-style mansion, which stands in 45 acres of gardens and grounds four miles north of Irvine on the A736. Day rooms (recently refurbished) are of quite grand proportions, the lounge-library being particularly appealing. There are several conference rooms (maximum capacity 100). Bedrooms, furnished with reproduction pieces or antiques, range from standard singles to suites. Children up to 16 stay free in parents' room. ***Rooms** 21. Garden, tennis, 5 practice golf holes, putting, snooker.* AMERICAN EXPRESS *Access, Diners, Visa.*

Kilwinning Places of Interest

Brodick Castle, Garden and Country Park Isle of Arran. Tel 0770 2202 *via ferry from Ardrossan.*

Kinclaven by Stanley Ballathie House 74% £120

Tel 0250 883268 Fax 0250 883396 **HR**

Kinclaven by Stanley Tayside PH1 4QN **Map 3 C5**

With lawns sloping down to the edge of the river Tay this Victorian baronial-style mansion enjoys a splendid location at the heart of its own 15,000 acre estate. Some fine ceilings and marble fireplaces feature in the numerous, comfortable and stylishly decorated day rooms that include an elegantly proportioned drawing room, clubby leather-furnished bar and spacious inner hall from which a grand oak staircase leads to the bedrooms. These vary considerably in size from large master rooms to a few compact singles amongst the standard rooms but all are individually decorated to the same high standard and all are equally well appointed. Good bathrooms (just two with shower, WC only), a few with original fittings. ***Rooms** 27. Garden, tennis, fishing, putting, shooting. Closed 25 & 26 Dec, 2 weeks Feb.* AMERICAN EXPRESS *Access, Diners, Visa.*

Restaurant £68

An elegant room with fine views across the River Tay from its high windows. The daily-changing set dinner is supplemented by a weekly list of starters and main dishes (about six or seven of each) that often feature local and Scottish ingredients – grilled West Coast scallops with wild garlic butter, Perthshire lamb with walnut and herb crust, Scottish asparagus with hollandaise sauce. Basically sound cooking. Lunch brings a good value à la carte during the week and a fixed-price menu on Sunday. Quite fair prices on a sensible wine list. No smoking. ***Seats** 60. Parties 12. Private Room 32. L 12-2 D 7-9. Set L (Sun only) £14.75 Set D £25.*

Kingussie The Cross £70

Tel 0540 661166 Fax 0540 661080 **RR**

Tweed Mill Brae Ardbroilach Road Kingussie Highland PH21 1HX **Map 3 C4**

Tony and Ruth Hadley have made a splendid job (Tony was his own architect) of converting an old tweed mill by the river Gynack (just a short walk from their former high street address) into The Cross's new home. White-painted rough stone walls and a timbered ceiling contrast with immaculately crisp white linen and luxurious table settings in the cleverly lit dining room where Ruth continues with her sympathetic and refined use of the best of Scottish produce. The limited-choice fixed-price dinner (four courses during the week and seven on Saturday's 'Gastronomic

See over

Menu') might include toasted Gigha goat's cheese with capsicum salad; game sausage; plump tender scallops, prawns and asparagus in a West Coast seafood salad; grilled Shetland salmon with pesto; Ayrshire guinea fowl with rosemary and crème fraiche sauce; and young shoots of garden rhubarb poached in orange juice with a caramel ice cream. For the less sweet-toothed there's always a recherché selection of mostly Scottish cheeses. Past winner of our Cellar of the Year, the current wine list rests happily in the new surroundings, and offers fabulous drinking at very fair prices. Germany and the New World well-represented alongside France – some guidance notes, but ask Tony Hadley for advice. No children under eight. No smoking. ***Seats** 30. L 12.30-2 D 7-9 Closed L Wed, all Tues, Dec-Feb. Set L £12.50/£15 Set D £25 (Sat 7-course £32.50). Access, Visa.*

Rooms **£150***

Upstairs, beyond a resident's lounge that successfully mixes antiques with Scandinavian-style seating, are nine individually styled bedrooms that generally combine pine and antique furniture to good effect. Good bathrooms, mostly with bidet and separate shower cubicle in additon to the tub, boast large towels and good-quality toiletries. No smoking except in the lounge. The waterside terrace makes a good spot for Continental breakfast that comes with lovely home-made jams. *Half-board terms only.

Kingussie — Places of Interest

Tourist Information Tel 0540 661297.
Kincraig Highland Wildlife Park Tel 0540 651270.
Waltzing Waters Newtonmore Tel 0540 673752.

Kinlochbervie — Kinlochbervie Hotel — 64% — £84

Tel 0971 521275 Fax 0971 521438 — **H**

Kinlochbervie by Lairg Highland IV27 4RP — **Map 2 B2**

Built 25 years ago, the hotel sits above Kinlochbervie harbour almost at the northernmost tip of mainland Scotland. Picture windows on two sides of the hotel lounge and dining room overlook loch and ocean from high up on a hill. Six bedrooms (and a first-floor residents' lounge crammed with literature for walkers and fishermen) enjoy these views to the full. All rooms have showers as well as baths. A convivial bar and bistro adjacent are popular with locals. No smoking in the restaurant. 47 miles from Lairg. ***Rooms** 14. Sea fishing and loch fishing. Closed 1 Nov-end April.*
AMERICAN EXPRESS *Access, Diners, Visa.*

Kinross — Granada Lodge — £45

Tel 0577 64646 Fax 0577 64108 — **L**

M90 Junction 6 Kinross Tayside KY13 7NQ — **Map 3 C5**

***Rooms** 35.* AMERICAN EXPRESS *Access, Diners, Visa.*

Kinross — Windlestrae Hotel — 62% — £85

Tel 0577 863217 Fax 0577 864733 — **H**

The Muirs Kinross Tayside KY13 7AS — **Map 3 C5**

There were just four bedrooms here when the Doyles arrived ten years ago; the latest development brings that number up to 45 and includes a new leisure centre, complete with a good-sized swimming pool and bistro for informal eating. Spacious bedrooms are well kept and comfortable with Parker Knoll easy chairs. Smart bathrooms all have thermostatically controlled showers over the tubs and generous towelling. Staff are friendly and helpful and there's a pretty garden with a children's playground. ***Rooms** 45. Garden, indoor swimming pool, sauna, steam room, spa bath, solarium, keep-fit equipment.* AMERICAN EXPRESS *Access, Diners, Visa.*

Kirkmichael — Log Cabin Hotel — 59% — £50

Tel 0250 881288 Fax 0250 881402 — **H**

Kirkmichael Tayside PH10 7NB — **Map 3 C4**

Built of Norwegian pine logs, this unusual hotel stands half a mile from the A924, high in Glen Derby, equidistant from Pitlochry and Blairgowrie. There is a snug bar serving an impressive number of malt whiskies, but this is essentially a relaxing, out-of-doors place, with fishing, shooting and walking heading the list of activities. There are no telephones or TVs in the modest bedrooms, though TVs can be supplied on request. Informal dining in the Viking Bar; formal in the Edelweiss restaurant. ***Rooms** 13. Garden, games room, game fishing, shooting. Closed 25 & 26 Dec.* AMERICAN EXPRESS *Access, Diners, Visa.*

Kirknewton — Dalmahoy Hotel, Golf & Country Club — 78% — £125

Tel 031-333 1845 Fax 031-333 1433 — **HR**

Kirknewton Lothian EH27 8EB — **Map 3 C6**

Seven miles west of Edinburgh just off the A71, surrounded by two mature golf courses and with a well-equipped leisure centre, Dalmahoy is not only conveniently placed but also offers plenty of diversions. The original, grand Georgian mansion contains the reception area with separate concierge desk, two smart lounge-like bars with quality settees and armchairs, and eight high-ceilinged period bedrooms. Standardised rooms and a further informal bar-restaurant are in a new extension; these are good-sized rooms with oak furniture, matching fabrics and all the usual modern comforts. Function facilities for up to 190. Children up to the age of 16 accommodated free in parents' room. Informal eating in the poolside Terrace restaurant. Country Club Hotels. ***Rooms** 115. Garden, 18-hole golf courses, putting, tennis, indoor swimming pool, squash, sauna, solarium, snooker, gymnasium, spa bath, beautician, coffee shop (9.30am-10pm).* AMERICAN EXPRESS *Access, Diners, Visa.*

Pentland Restaurant — £70

A fairly ambitious à la carte menu and generally competent cooking in a stylish setting with views over the golf course. Table d'hote menu available only on request at dinner. ***Seats** 100. Parties 10. L 12-2 D 7-10. Closed L Sat. Set L £12.50/£14.50 Set D £21.*

Kirknewton — Places of Interest

Epsom Polo Club Dalmohay Estate Office. Tel 031-333 1331.

Kyle of Lochalsh — Lochalsh Hotel — 63% — £87

Tel 0599 4202 Fax 0599 4881 — **H**

Ferry Road Kyle of Lochalsh Highland IV40 8AF — **Map 2 B3**

A privately owned, white-painted building opposite the ferry terminal and looking over the sea to Skye. Beauty spots abound locally, and a day's sightseeing can conclude agreeably with a dram or two in the cocktail bar. Bedrooms are fresh, bright and comfortable. ***Rooms** 40. Garden.* AMERICAN EXPRESS *Access, Diners, Visa.*

Kyle of Lochalsh — Places of Interest

Tourist Information Tel 0599 4276.
Eilean Donan Castle Wester Ross. Tel 059 985 202.
Lochalsh Woodland Garden Tel 059981 219.

Langbank — Gleddoch House — 68% — £130

Tel 047 554 711 Fax 047 554 201 — H

Langbank Strathclyde PA14 6YE — Map 3 B5

The large windows of Gleddoch House look out on to beautiful countryside, and inside there's plenty to please the eye too. In the main lounge area there are leather easy chairs in which to relax, and dado panelling and more leather chairs give a period feel to the baize-lined bar, which offers a hundred different brands of whisky. The rooms are all named after Scottish birds, each engraved on the door-plate. Children under 12 stay free in parents' room. A further golf course (9-hole) is due to be available in 1994. ***Rooms** 33. Garden, squash, sauna, golf (18), riding.* AMERICAN EXPRESS *Access, Diners, Visa.*

Lerwick — Shetland Hotel — 62% — £74

Tel 0595 5515 Fax 0595 5828 — H

Holmsgarth Road Lerwick Shetland ZE1 0PW — Map 2 D2

Close to the town centre and overlooking the harbour (where the ferries from Aberdeen dock), the Shetland is a skilfully designed modern hotel that caters well for both the summer tourist and year-round business. Bedrooms are uniformly light and spacious, recently refurbished, and with private bathrooms throughout. There is a bright, comfortable bar, a long-hours coffee shop and impressive function hall. Banqueting facilities available for up to 200 and conferences for 350 delegates. Children up to 11 stay free in parents' room. ***Rooms** 66. Garden, indoor swimming pool, sauna, solarium, coffee shop (11am-9.30pm).* AMERICAN EXPRESS *Access, Diners, Visa.*

Lerwick — Places of Interest

Tourist Information Tel 0595 3434.

Letham — Fernie Castle — 60% — £75

Tel 033 781 381 Fax 033 781 422 — H

Letham by Cupar Fife KY7 7RU — Map 3 C5

On the A914, one mile north of A91 junction, 12 miles south of the Tay Bridge. The castle was first recorded in the mid-14th century, and later additions have not spoilt its charm; the latest owners have instigated a programme of refurbishment. Best of the public rooms is the first-floor drawing room in a Georgian extension and the most atmospheric the medieval Keep Bar with its rough-stone vaulted ceiling. Bedrooms vary from a small single to a few spacious rooms with reproduction antique furniture; most fall somewhere between the two. No dogs. Function facilities for around 150. ***Rooms** 15.* AMERICAN EXPRESS *Access, Visa.*

Linlithgow — Champany Inn — ★ — £100

Tel 050 683 4532 — R

Champany Linlithgow Lothian EH49 7LU — Map 3 C5

2 miles north-east of Linlithgow, by the corner of both the A904 and A803. To buy the best and cook it simply but skilfully is the secret of Clive and Anne Davidson's success at the collection of old buildings (dating back to the 16th century, the time of Mary Queen of Scots who was born two miles away at Linlithgow Palace) that comprise the Champany Inn. Aberdeen Angus beef, their speciality, is hung for a minimum of three weeks in their own chill rooms and comes from the charcoal grill as rib eye, porterhouse, sirloin, carpet bagger (fillet stuffed with a fresh oyster) and chateaubriand among others, having been cut to order by butcher Nigel Best in full view of the customer. The old saying goes: "the nearer the bone the sweeter the meat" – sound advice. Seafood is another strength, with lobster and crayfish coming from the sea-water pool that is also

a decorative feature of the restaurant. Scottish lamb appears in season and their own smokehouse provides smoked salmon and beef. The sweet trolley includes fresh fruits and a selection of home-made ice creams. Past winner of our Cellar of the Year award, the biblical wine list here is extraordinary – 10 own-label house wines, burgundies by the bucketful, an enormous South African selection and a good worldwide choice at fair prices. No children under eight. ***Seats** 50. Parties 14. L 12.30-2 D 7-10. Closed L Sat, all Sun, 1 week Christmas. Set L £13.75 Set D £27.50/£35.* AMERICAN EXPRESS *Access, Diners, Visa.*

Linlithgow — Champany Inn Chop & Ale House — £50

Tel 050 683 4532 — **R**

Champany Linlithgow Lothian EH49 7LU — **Map 3 C5**

The same outstanding Aberdeen Angus steaks (though less expensive and cut a bit smaller) as at its sister restaurant, together with various burgers, deep-fried Scottish prawn tails (scampi), char-grilled grain-fed chicken and a cold buffet with help-yourself salad bar are among the offerings at this much less formal eaterie. For afters go for the home-made, hot malted waffles or Champany's own cheesecake served with apricot purée. Ten tables set in a courtyard for alfresco dining; high-chairs for trainee trencher-persons. ***Seats** 32. Parties 6. L 12-2 (Sun 12.30-2.30) D 6.30-10. Closed 25 & 26 Dec.* AMERICAN EXPRESS *Access, Diners, Visa.*

Linlithgow — Places of Interest

Tourist Information Tel 0506 844600.
Linlithgow Palace Tel 0506 842896.

Lochinver — Inver Lodge Hotel — 70% — £130

Tel 057 14 496 Fax 057 14 395 — **H**

Lochinver Highland IV27 4LU — **Map 2 B2**

Built at the beginning of 1988, the hotel is set high above the village in a scene of exceptional peace and beauty. It's an ideal base for fishing (10 rods on local rivers, 10 more with boats on the lochs), bird-watching and hill walking, and after the day's activity the lounge and cocktail bar offer comfort and conviviality. Generously sized bedrooms – each named after a nearby mountain or loch – feature bold earth tones and colourful fabrics. Two rooms, Suilven and Canisp, have dining tables and sofas. Children up to 15 are accommodated free in parents' room. ***Rooms** 20. Sauna, solarium, fishing, snooker. Closed Nov-Mar.* AMERICAN EXPRESS *Access, Diners, Visa.*

Lochinver — Places of Interest

Tourist Information Tel 05714 330.

Markinch — Balbirnie House — 74% — £125

Tel 0592 610066 Fax 0592 610529 — **H**

Balbirnie Park Markinch by Glenrothes Fife KY7 6NE — **Map 3 C5**

A fine example of the 18th-century classical period of architecture, Balbirnie House sits in the middle of a very pretty 400-acre park overlooking a golf course. It opened as a hotel in late 1989. The splendid public rooms include a gallery with vaulted ceiling, "spider's web" windows and cherubic murals, a book-lined library bar and a well-proportioned drawing room with a marble fireplace, beautiful fabrics, luxurious seating and oil paintings. The Gamekeeper's inn was converted from an 1815 kitchen. Function rooms can accommodate up to 120 for banquets, 150 for conferences. Bedrooms progress in size from two singles to very spacious 'superior' rooms and suites; all have individual, stylish

See over

fabrics and the best boast antiques. Now under the managment of the Russell family, previously at *Chapeltoun House*, Stewarton. ***Rooms** 30. Garden, keep-fit equipment, snooker.* AMERICAN EXPRESS *Access, Diners, Visa.*

Maryculter — Maryculter House — 65% — £73

Tel 0224 732124 Fax 0224 733510 — **H**

South Deeside Road Maryculter Grampian AB1 0BB — **Map 3 D4**

A fine location on the banks of the river Dee makes Maryculter a popular wedding venue, especially with their new function suite for up to 200 people. The oldest room (now a rattan-furnished cocktail bar/lounge) has high stone walls and dates back to the 13th century. The other main public room is the Victorian-styled Poachers Bar which opens on to a riverside patio. Bedrooms, including those in a new extension, feature pine furniture and pretty fabrics with matching curtains and duvet covers. ***Rooms** 24. Garden.* AMERICAN EXPRESS *Access, Diners, Visa.*

Maybole — Ladyburn — 73% — NEW — £140

Tel 06554 585 Fax 06554 580 — **HR**

By Maybole Ayrshire Strathclyde KA19 7SG — **Map 4 A2**

Set in 23 acres (4½ of which are well-kept gardens) near the Kilkerran estate, signposted off the B741 2 miles south of Crosshill. The family home of the Hepburns, it has been a hotel for only 2 years and is run by the chatty Jane Hepburn in country-house style with family photos and pictures in the day rooms (a very pleasant drawing room with pale pink and pale green armchairs and Chinese lacquered pieces and an equally pleasant library for smokers) along with fresh flowers, ornaments and objets d'art that are to be found throughout the hotel. Bedrooms feature plain cream walls setting off antique furniture, more flowers, fruit, books, ornaments and Royal Doulton bone china for tea and coffee-making facilities. Bathrooms (3 with large showers only) have generous bottles of bath oil plus huge bath sheets. Rooms are properly serviced at night. There is no bar, but drinks are served in the drawing room or library. No children under 14. No dogs. ***Rooms** 8. Garden. Closed few weeks in Jan/Feb.* AMERICAN EXPRESS *Access, Visa.*

Dining Room — £58

Dried flowers in the fireplaces, lacy cloths over yellow undercloths, bone china and fresh flowers help create a pleasant dining room. Mrs Hepburn cooks in a simple, homely style, which has proved a great success. Most of the produce is local, including the meat and free-range eggs, and many vegetables come from their own garden. Four-course, fixed-price dinners offer a choice of 3 or 4 dishes at each course: perhaps a home-made soup or Stilton tartlets and creamed mushrooms to start, followed by roast beef with Yorkshire pudding or local wild salmon with hollandaise and lovely apple tart topped with crumble and treacle to finish. The wine list is short but varied with a good sprinkling of half bottles. ***Seats** 25. L by arrangement D 7.30-8.45. Closed L Sun to non-residents. Set D £21.95.*

Melrose — Burts Hotel — £68

Tel 089 682 2285 Fax 089 682 2870 — **I**

Market Square Melrose Borders TD6 9PN — **Map 4 C1**

Graham and Anne Henderson have been the owners for more than 20 years of this 18th-century inn set on the historic market square, 200 yards from the River Tweed – "Scotland's favourite salmon river". It's a friendly place, and the little lounge bar is shared with locals who make it a popular meeting place; upstairs is a separate residents' lounge. Bedrooms are light, contemporary and kept in pristine order and have pleasant matching bedcovers and curtains plus good-quality furniture. Bathrooms, five of which have just shower/WC, feature large fluffy bath sheets. Good family facilities (cots and extra beds in rooms, baby-sitting by arrangement and high-chairs provided); informal snacks in the bar (lunch and supper).

Shooting, fishing and other outdoor pursuits can be arranged. On the A6091, 3 miles from the A7 and 2 miles from the A68. ***Rooms** 21. Garden, snooker. Closed 26 Dec.* AMERICAN EXPRESS *Access, Diners, Visa.*

Melrose — George & Abbotsford Hotel — 56% — £66

Tel 089 682 2308 Fax 089 682 3363 — **H**

High Street Melrose Borders TD6 9PD — **Map 4 C1**

A Victorian look has been restored to this town-centre former coaching inn, once a haunt of Sir Walter Scott. Glass-shaded brass chandeliers, red plush upholstery and dado panelling set the tone in the day rooms; separate conference rooms accommodate up to 160. Neat bedrooms range from standards with shower/WC only to four-poster rooms. Children up to 15 stay free in parents' room. ***Rooms** 30. Garden, game fishing.* AMERICAN EXPRESS *Access, Diners, Visa.*

Melrose — Places of Interest

Tourist Information Tel 089 682 2555.
Teddy Melrose Teddy Bear Museum Tel 089 682 2464.
Historic Houses, Castles and Gardens
Abbotsford House Tel 0896 2043 *Home of Sir Walter Scott.*
Mertoun Gardens St Boswells. Tel 0835 23236.
Priorwood Garden Tel 089 682 2555.
Thirlestane Castle Lauder Tel 05782 430.

Milngavie — Black Bull Thistle — 59% — £70

Tel 041-956 2291 Fax 041-956 1896 — **H**

Main Street Milngavie Strathclyde G62 6BH — **Map 3 B5**

A useful stopover on the A81 six miles north of the centre of Glasgow. Children up to 10 stay free in parents' room. ***Rooms** 27.* AMERICAN EXPRESS *Access, Diners, Visa.*

Muir-of-Ord — Dower House — £64

Tel & Fax 0463 870090 — **RR**

Highfield Muir-of-Ord Highland IV6 7XN — **Map 2 B3**

Personally run by Robyn and Mena Aitchison, the house stands a mile out of Muir-of-Ord on the A862 Dingwall road, in three acres of mature grounds. Dinner in the ornate dining room (no smoking) comprises four courses prepared by Robyn. Sautéed chicken livers with sherry sauce or goat's cheese with sesame salad, cream of Jerusalem artichoke soup, breast of duck with elderberry sauce and caramelised shallots or darne of salmon with green peppercorn mayonnaise show the style; tropical fruit roulade or apple soufflé with sabayon sauce and home-made truffles with coffee complete the picture. Families are welcome, but no children under 5 in the dining room after 7pm (they can have supper from 5.30pm). No smoking. ***Seats** 18. Private Room 26. L by arrangement D 7.30-8.30. Closed 1 week Oct, 2 weeks Feb, Christmas. Set D £27.50. Access, Visa.*

Rooms — £90

The five bedrooms are comfortable and cottagey, and all have Victorian-style bathrooms with cast-iron baths and brass fittings. One has its own sitting room. No dogs.

Nairn — Carnach House — 60% — £80

Tel 0667 52094 — **H**

Delnies Nairn Highland IV12 5NT — **Map 2 C3**

The house stands in eight acres of wooded and lawned grounds overlooking the Moray Firth. It's 14 miles from Inverness, 2 miles from Nairn and close to the A96 and changed hands last year. The new owners

See over

have reduced the number of bedrooms available and were still making changes as we went to press. Built in 1914, the house remained a private residence until 1980, and much of the original decor remains. ***Rooms** 9. Garden. Access, Visa.*

Nairn Clifton Hotel 70% £96

Tel 0667 53119 Fax 0667 52836 **HR**

Viewfield Street Nairn Highland IV12 4HW **Map 2 C3**

A truly civilised town house overlooking the Moray Firth; the beach is a very short walk away, and the Nairn Pottery studio is next door; turn west at the only roundabout on the A96 through town to find it. J. Gordon Macintyre, hotelier and patron of the arts, has been at the helm for half a century and has filled the house with hand-chosen antiques. Public areas include a long red hallway hung with framed prints, the yellow sitting room, the Green Room (no smoking) and a drawing room full of fresh and dried flowers and fragrant with pot-pourri. There are antiques, too, in the bedrooms, where TVs and telephones do not intrude. ***Rooms** 12. Garden. Closed Nov-Mar.* AMERICAN EXPRESS *Access, Diners, Visa.*

Green Room £60

A brief, hand-written menu is presented in French, but the owner is on hand to translate and explain. Typical of Charles Macintyre's dishes are *champignons à la grecque, tarte aux poireaux, aubergine charlotte, filet de boeuf aux champignons sauvages, carré d'agneau à la touraine.* Up to seven vegetarian options. The pudding menu goes British with the likes of caramel custard, sherry trifle and chocolate chestnut cake, and the outstanding Scottish cheeses earn the restaurant Scotland British Cheeseboard of the Year. ***Seats** 40. Parties 24. Private Room 12. L 12.30-1 D 7-9.30.*

Nairn Golf View Hotel 65% £99

Tel 0667 52301 Fax 0667 55267 **H**

Seabank Road Nairn Highland IV12 4HD **Map 2 C3**

Built at the very end of the last century, the hotel stands on the shores of the Moray Firth, overlooking Black Isle. It's a great place for family holidays, with a games room, pool, a children's play area and weekend evening entertainment. A golf course is just around the corner and there's a children's leisure park a short walk away. Nearly half the bedrooms are suitable for family occupation and children are charged according to age (under-4s free). Baby-listening and baby-sitting can be arranged. Day rooms were refurbished in 1993. ***Rooms** 47. Garden, outdoor swimming pool, tennis, putting, games room.* AMERICAN EXPRESS *Access, Diners, Visa.*

Nairn Newton Hotel 65% £90

Tel 0667 53144 Fax 0667 54026 **H**

Inverness Road Nairn Highland IV12 4RX **Map 2 C3**

At the bottom of a winding, tree-lined private road, this imposing building is set in 27 acres with sweeping views overlooking the Nairn golf course and the Moray Firth beyond. The high-ceilinged rooms within the main house are more interesting than the newer, more contemporary ones in the adjacent Newton Court, a converted granary and stables. The peaceful setting, well-chosen antiques and velvet upholstery recall the gracious Victorian era. Families welcome: under-5s share parents' accommodation free, 5s-14s have a 50% reduction. ***Rooms** 44. Garden, sauna, solarium, tennis, games room.* AMERICAN EXPRESS *Access, Diners, Visa.*

Nairn Places of Interest

Tourist Information Tel 0667 52753.
Cawdor Castle Cawdor Tel 06677 615 *6 miles.*

Newburgh Udny Arms Hotel 60% £76

Tel 035 86 89444 Fax 035 86 89012 **H**

Main Street Newburgh Grampian AB41 0BL **Map 2 D3**

The Victorian facade is on the main street but at the back there are pleasant views over a golf course and the Ythan estuary. Day rooms vary: perhaps the most appealing is the mellow cocktail bar with its pine-board banquettes, scrubbed pine tables and Windsor chairs. Bedrooms are furnished mainly in traditional style and are all en suite; the best rooms overlook the picturesque estuary. Children under 12 stay free in parents' room; informal eating in the bistro and café/bar. Theatre-style conferences for up to 125. Parking for 100 cars. ***Rooms** 26. Garden.* AMERICAN EXPRESS *Access, Visa.*

Newburgh Places of Interest

Dundee and Perth Polo Club Newhill Auchtermuchty. Tel 031-557 3313.

Newhouse Travel Inn £43

Tel 0698 860277 Fax 0698 861353 **L**

Glasgow Road Newhouse nr Motherwell Strathclyde ML1 5SY **Map 3 C6**

***Rooms** 40.* AMERICAN EXPRESS *Access, Diners, Visa.*

Newton Stewart Kirroughtree Hotel 75% £116

Tel 0671 2141 Fax 0671 2425 **HR**

Newton Stewart Dumfries & Galloway DG8 6AN **Map 4 A2**

Standing in a high position amid eight acres of landscaped gardens, Kirroughtree dates from 1719. Main day room is an oak-panelled lounge with rococo furnishings and French doors that open on to the terrace and croquet lawn. Bedrooms are decorated in individual style, ornately furnished and very spacious. The vast and splendid Regal Suite has a sitting room with lovely views of Wigtown Bay in the mid-distance. Smartly tiled and carpeted bathrooms boast many extras. New owners took over recently and have started to make 'small changes which will make a huge difference' – like a welcoming glass of sherry and fresh fruit in the rooms. No children under ten in hotel or restaurant. ***Rooms** 22. Garden, tennis, badminton, putting. Closed 2 Jan-early Feb. Access, Visa.*

Restaurant £65

Roux-trained Ian Bennett cooks in fine style, and guests can choose a smoking or non-smoking room (both are plush and comfortable). Four-course dinner menus offer only a small choice, but a typically interesting menu might commence with grilled oysters with laverbread and Stilton, followed by game terrine studded with pistachio and served with onion chutney and brioche, champagne sorbet, panaché of red mullet and brill with fennel fondue and ginger sauce; nougat glacé with grilled hazelnuts and raspberry sauce to finish. Vegetarians should advise in advance. Gentlemen should wear jackets and ties. Lighter lunches might include a salad of West Coast scallops or smoked salmon, fresh asparagus, sautéed veal kidneys, and sticky toffee pudding. Well-balanced wines cater for most tastes – from simple to indulgent! ***Seats** 70. Parties 20. Private Room 20. L 12.30-1.30 D 7-9.30. Set D £22.50.*

Newton Stewart Places of Interest

Tourist Information Tel 0671 2431.

Newtonmore — Ard-na-Coille Hotel — 67% — £120*

Tel 0540 673214 Fax 0540 673453 — **HR**

Kingussie Road Newtonmore Highland PH20 1AY — **Map 3 C4**

On the A86 at the north end of Newtonmore and high in the forest, amongst its two acres of pine woodland, Nancy Ferrier and Barry Cottam's former shooting lodge is today a tranquil and intimate country hotel. Edwardian-style public rooms and sunny terrace have an open outlook towards the Cairngorm mountains. Most of the guest bedrooms have a southerly aspect and all enjoy uninterrupted views of the Spey Valley. Each is different in decor and period furniture; all are immaculately kept. Dogs in two rooms only, by prior arrangement. *Half-board terms only. ***Rooms** 7. Garden. Closed 6 weeks Nov/Dec, 1 week Apr, 1 week Sep. Access, Visa.*

Restaurant — £65

Five-course set dinner, prepared by the proprietors, is served at 7.45pm after much care with cooking and presentation and equal emphasis on local produce. Langoustine ravioli, leek and lime soup, roast Ayrshire guinea fowl breast and stuffed leg with sun-dried tomato sauce typify the balance of ingredients and flavours. A wide selection of cheeses could then precede a little pot of orange-flavoured chocolate custard. A sensational wine list, very generously priced, has an extensive (eg 30+ California) section of New World wines listed by grape variety. ***Seats** 18. Parties 16. Private Room 6. L by arrangement D at 7.45. Set D £25.*

Newtown St Boswells — Le Provençale — £40

Tel 0835 23284 — **R**

Monksford Road Newtown St Boswells Borders TD6 0SB — **Map 4 C1**

Frenchman René Duzelier in the kitchen and his Scottish wife Elizabeth at front of house make a fine team in their spotless little restaurant just off the A68. The daily-changing menu is handwritten with English descriptions in a distinctive French script. Straightforward cooking covers dishes like garlic snails, cream of vegetable soup, Provençal chicken casserole, fillets of haddock in vermouth and, to finish, oranges in Grand Marnier or the 90s revival dish bread-and-butter pudding. Smaller portions of the same dishes for lunch. ***Seats** 46. L 12-2.30 D 6.30-10. Closed Sun & Mon, 2 weeks Jul, 1 week Nov. Set L £5.20/£7.95 Set D £9.80/£12.55. No credit cards.*

North Berwick — Marine Hotel — 64% — £100

Tel 0620 2406 Fax 0620 4480 — **H**

Cromwell Road North Berwick Lothian EH39 4LZ — **Map 3 D5**

Fine coastal views of the Firth of Forth are enjoyed from this imposing Victorian hotel with a long golfing tradition (it overlooks the 16th green of the North Berwick Championship Westlinks Course). Bedrooms are more practical than luxurious, save for those in the turret. Banqueting for 250; conferences up to 350. Various sporting facilities have been added, and there's a baby-listening service and a three-days-a-week crèche. Forte Heritage. ***Rooms** 84. Outdoor swimming pool, sauna, sun bed, tennis, putting, snooker, children's playground. AMERICAN EXPRESS Access, Diners, Visa.*

North Berwick — Places of Interest

Tourist Information Tel 0620 2197.
Malleny Garden (NT) Balerno Tel 031449 2283.

North Middleton — Borthwick Castle — 66% — £95

Tel 0875 20514 Fax 0875 21702 — **H**

North Middleton nr Gorebridge Lothian EH23 4QY — **Map 3 C6**

Hardly altered since being built in 1430 (although Cromwell's cannon left their mark in 1650), historic Borthwick Castle with its tall twin towers once held Mary Queen of Scots as a prisoner. She escaped from a window of the vast stone-vaulted main hall which now serves as the dining room, bar and lounge with leather sofas around the huge fireplace. Spiral staircases within the massive stone walls lead to bedrooms offering more atmosphere than luxury. Top of the range is the Mary Queen of Scots four-poster 'double bedchamber'. Most bathrooms have shower and WC only. Probably the most genuinely atmospheric medieval castle hotel in the country (follow Historic Buildings sign on the A7). ***Rooms** 10. Garden.* AMERICAN EXPRESS *Access, Diners, Visa.*

North Queensferry — Queensferry Lodge — 63% — £68

Tel 0383 410000 Fax 0383 419708 — **H**

St Margaret's Head North Queensferry nr Inverkeithing Fife KY11 1HP — **Map 3 C5**

A modern family-run hotel overlooking the River Forth and its famous bridges. Bedrooms are quite generous on space and accessories, and sparkling bathrooms have good showers over the tubs and ample towelling. A tourist information office is manned from 10 to 6 throughout the year, and in a Scottish crafts shop you can find out all about the area. Conference and banqueting facilities for 150/200. ***Rooms** 32.* AMERICAN EXPRESS *Access, Visa.*

Oban — Alexandra Hotel — 57% — £90

Tel 0631 62381 Fax 0631 64497 — **H**

Corran Esplanade Oban Strathclyde PA54 5AA — **Map 3 B5**

Built in the late 1860s, the hotel stands on the esplanade a short stroll from the town centre. Modest accommodation, two lounges and a cocktail bar. Trips can be arranged on the hotel's motor cruiser, the *Ocean Ranger*. Function facilities for up to 120. A new leisure centre with indoor swimming pool, solarium, spa bath, gym and snooker table was on course to open by autumn 1993. ***Rooms** 60. Garden. Closed Jan.* AMERICAN EXPRESS *Access, Visa.*

Oban — Columba Hotel — 60% — £53

Tel 0631 62183 Fax 0631 64683 — **H**

North Pier Esplanade Oban Strathclyde PA34 5QD — **Map 3 B5**

An Edwardian sandstone building on the North Pier, with views across the bay to the Western Isles. Three bars offer a choice for a relaxing drink, and conference suites can cater for up to 400 delegates. Children up to 10 stay free when sharing parents' room. Some rooms have shower/WC only. ***Rooms** 49. Closed early Jan-early Mar.* AMERICAN EXPRESS *Access, Visa.*

Oban — Knipoch Hotel — 72% — £125

Tel 085 26 251 Fax 085 26 249 — **HR**

by Oban Strathclyde PA34 4QT — **Map 3 B5**

The Craig family's elegant Georgian hotel stands six miles south of Oban on the A816 halfway along the shore of Loch Feochan, an arm of the sea stretching four miles inland. Lounges and bars are filled with family heirlooms, and there are plenty of magazines to read in the leathery comfort of fireside armchairs. Well-proportioned bedrooms have period furniture and particularly well-appointed bathrooms. A purpose-built bedroom extension blends well with the original. Good housekeeping. No dogs. ***Rooms** 17. Garden. Closed mid Nov-mid Feb.* AMERICAN EXPRESS *Access, Diners, Visa.*

See over

Restaurant

£80

Dinner is three or five courses featuring excellent produce from garden, loch and the hotel's own smokery; their salmon is cured, marinated in juniper, rowan, Barbados sugar, herbs and whisky then smoked over oak for three days. Soup and home-baked bread could precede scallops with hollandaise sauce or oysters with champagne sauce and – the centrepiece of the longer meal – fillet of Aberdeen Angus beef. Next comes cheese, then dessert (strawberry in a brandy snap tuile, Cointreau crepes) and coffee with petits fours. The wine list looks impressive, but regrettably too many wines are marked "n/a". ***Seats** 40. L by arrangement D 7.30-9. Set D from £27.50.*

Oban Places of Interest

Tourist Information Tel 0631 63122.
Highland Theatre Tel 0631 62444.
Gateway Leisure Centre Tel 0631 62345.
Easdale Island Folk Museum Tel 08523 370.
Oban Distillery Tel 0631 64262.
Highland Salmon Centre Kilninver Tel 08562 202.
Sealife Centre Barcaldine Tel 063172 386.

Onich Allt-nan-Ros Hotel 63%

£133*

Tel 085 53 250 Fax 085 53 462

HR

Onich nr Fort William Highland PH33 6RY

Map 3 B4

The name means 'Burn of the Roses', a reference to the stream which runs through the garden of this Victorian former shooting lodge and into Lochs Leven and Linnhe. There are exceptional views across the hotel's gardens and mountain scenery beyond from all the public rooms and bedrooms. Superior rooms have large bay windows and two country cottage-style bedrooms are in converted stables. *Half-board terms only. ***Rooms** 21. Garden, putting. Closed mid Nov-mid Dec.* AMERICAN EXPRESS *Access, Diners, Visa.*

Restaurant

£55

Four-course dinners offer a triple choice of starter, main course and sweet, plus a soup. Typical dishes run from ham mousse with radicchio and soured cream to carrot, cauliflower and capsicum soup, roasted whole smoked poussin in a red wine and wholegrain mustard sauce, and roast leg of lamb stuffed with sage and onion in a rosemary sauce. To finish, perhaps hot strawberries glazed with a lemon sabayon. They encourage young children to be fed earlier (evening meal available at 5.30). Coffee is served in the lounge with petits fours. A smaller lunchtime menu is available. Straightforward wine list with useful notes. ***Seats** 50. Parties 25. L 12.30-2 D 7-8.30. Set L £6/£8.50 Set D £17.50.*

Consult page 16 for a full list of starred restaurants

Onich Lodge on the Loch 63%

£131*

Tel 085 53 237 Fax 085 53 463

H

Creag Dhu Onich nr Fort William Highland PH33 6RY

Map 3 B4

Loch and mountain views are a spectacular feature at this friendly little hotel, which stands just off the A82 (five miles north of Glencoe, twelve miles south of Fort William). Plump-cushioned sofas make for easy relaxation in the lounge, and there's a modern bar. Best bedrooms are the Chieftains with loch views. Guests have free membership of "The Isles Club" with a pool, sauna, steam room and turbopool, 3 miles away at sister hotel the *Isles of Glencoe*. *Half-board terms only (children up to 16 sharing parents' room charged only for meals). ***Rooms** 18. Garden. Closed mid Nov-mid Dec, early Jan-early Feb. Access, Visa.*

Onich Onich Hotel 61% £74

Tel 085 53 214 Fax 085 53 484 **H**

Onich nr Fort William Highland PH33 6RY **Map 3 B4**

Fine views of Loch Linnhe, well-maintained gardens and multifarious activities for all ages make the Onich hotel a popular year-round choice. Iain Young has put his personal stamp on the place for over 30 years, developing an atmosphere of friendly informality where guests and locals chat together in the bars. It lies on the A82 two miles north of Ballachulish Bridge and ten miles south of Fort William, making it a splendid base from which to explore the West Highlands and Islands (the hotel can recommend many walks and day tours). The best front bedrooms (a small supplement payable) have lochside balconies. None is denied a fair share of the view, but some suffer slightly from proximity to the road. ***Rooms** 27. Garden, spa bath, solarium, pool table.* AMERICAN EXPRESS *Access, Diners, Visa.*

Peat Inn Peat Inn ★ £78

Tel 033 484 206 Fax 033 484 530 **RR**

Peat Inn by Cupar Fife KY15 5LH **Map 3 C5**

The village which takes its name from this former coaching inn is not much more than a crossroads (B940/B941), but David and Patricia Wilson have really put it on the map. The dining room has the feel of an upmarket French country restaurant, with carved sideboard, high-backed tapestry chairs, red and gold curtains and rough white plaster walls. David's modern cooking makes use of local supplies where possible and in the evening there's a choice of four-course set menu, six-or seven-course tasting menu and à la carte. Many favourites stay on the list – fish soup, lobster salad in a citrus sauce or poached in an aromatic broth, spring lamb in its season – and some creatures appear in more than one guise: pigeon breast in a beef broth with pulses as a starter; with mushrooms in a red wine sauce as a main course; venison liver with an onion confit to start, noisettes of venison saddle with red wine and port as a main. Caramelised apple pastry with caramel sauce is a favourite sweet; others include a trio of nut desserts, pineapple and grenadine with a fresh fruit platter, and a little pot of chocolate and rosemary. France and Germany are listed separately on the exceptional wine list – other countries appear by grape variety. Super selection, plenty of half bottles, very keen prices. ***Seats** 48. Private Room 24. L at 1 D 7-9.30. Closed Sun & Mon. Set L £18.50 Set D from £28.* AMERICAN EXPRESS *Access, Diners, Visa.*

Rooms £130

The Residence, built in 1987, offers eight luxurious suites, each with high-quality fabrics and period French furniture chosen by design graduate Patricia. Italian marble bathrooms.

Peebles Cringletie House 65% £86

Tel 0721 730233 Fax 0721 730244 **HR**

Peebles Borders EH45 8PL **Map 3 C6**

Set well back from the A703, three miles north of Peebles, this Scottish baronial-style mansion offers peace and quiet and enjoys views of the distant Meldon and Moorfoot Hills. Open fires, fresh flowers from the gardens and antiques enhance the traditional decor. Most impressive of the day rooms is the panelled drawing room with fine painted ceiling. Well-kept bedrooms offer considerable comfort and excellent bathrooms boast big soft towels. ***Rooms** 13. Garden, tennis, putting. Closed 2nd week Jan-1st week Mar. Access, Visa.*

Restaurant £60

A two-acre walled kitchen garden provides much of the fresh produce served in the lofty twin dining rooms. Cooking is soundly based, with

See over

dishes such as prawn and dill roulade, poached sole with ginger and chives, spinach-sauced vegetarian pancakes and medallions of beef with bacon and mushrooms. Prices are extremely favourable on a sound wine list. ***Seats** 56. Parties 12. Private Room 28. L 1-1.45 D 7.30-8.30. Set L £14 Set D £23.50.*

Peebles — Park Hotel — 62% — £89

Tel 0721 720451 Fax 0721 723510 — **H**

Innerleithen Road Peebles Borders EH45 8BA — **Map 3 C6**

A handsome, whitewashed building on the A72. Views of gardens and hills are enjoyed by many of the bedrooms, which include one with a four-poster. Guests may use the extensive leisure facilities of the *Peebles Hotel Hydro*, a sister hotel under the same ownership. ***Rooms** 24. Garden, putting.* AMERICAN EXPRESS *Access, Diners, Visa.*

Peebles — Peebles Hotel Hydro — 70% — £103

Tel 0721 720602 Fax 0721 722999 — **H**

Innerleithen Road Peebles Borders EH45 8LX — **Map 3 C6**

A fine holiday hotel overlooking the Tweed valley, run by energetic Pieter van Dijk, manager for over 20 years. Formally a hydropathic hotel, its extensive sports facilities in the 30 acres of grounds are a major attraction, keeping even the most active guests fully occupied. Public rooms of grand proportions are both attractive and comfortable; in the bar there's a good selection of malt whiskies. A sun room overlooks the valley, as do some of the good-size bedrooms, which are charmingly furnished and well kept. Families are well catered for with the likes of baby-sitting and baby-changing facilities in Bubbles leisure centre; a small charge for children covers breakfast and high tea. The hotel also offers adaptable conference and function facilities for up to 400 delegates. Weekend dinner dances. ***Rooms** 137. Garden, indoor swimming pool, sauna, solarium, spa bath, gymnasium, beautician, hairdressing, tennis, squash, badminton, pitch & putt, putting, riding, games room, snooker, coffee shop (10am-11pm), kiosk, children's playground & playroom.* AMERICAN EXPRESS *Access, Diners, Visa.*

Peebles — Tontine Hotel — 57% — £80

Tel 0721 720892 Fax 0721 729732 — **H**

High Street Peebles Borders EH45 8AJ — **Map 3 C6**

Modest, practical accommodation at an agreeable hotel established in 1808. Upgrading of bedrooms continues. Forte Heritage. ***Rooms** 37.* AMERICAN EXPRESS *Access, Diners, Visa.*

Peebles — Places of Interest

Tourist Information Tel 0721 720138.
Traquair Castle Innerleithen Tel 0896 830323.
Robert Smails Printing Works Innerleithen
Ardchattan Gardens Ardchattan Priory Tel 063175 274.
Argyll Boat Cruises Tel 0631 65687.

Perth — Number Thirty Three — £45

Tel 0738 33771 — **R**

33 George Street Perth Tayside PH1 5LA — **Map 3 C5**

Choose between the light meal menu of the oyster bar (ideal for theatre-goers) and the more substantial dishes offered in the dining area beyond at this art deco nearly-all-seafood restaurant near the centre of town. The former might include seafood soup, gravad lax, creamed mushroom pancake and Scottish oysters, the latter grilled hake rolled in sesame seeds, monkfish and spring vegetables en papillote, and roast duck in honey and lemon sauce. Both menus show the list of puds, sticky toffee pudding with butterscotch soufflé being typical. ***Seats** 35. Parties 24. L 12.30-2.30 D 6.30-9.30. Closed Sun & Mon, 10 days Christmas/New Year.* AMERICAN EXPRESS® *Access, Visa.*

Perth **Royal George Hotel** **62%** **£95**

Tel 0738 24455 Fax 0738 30345 **H**

Tay Street Perth Tayside PH1 5LD **Map 3 C5**

A Georgian jumble of a hotel close to the city centre with some rooms facing the river Tay. Refurbished day rooms are quite extensive and offer many quiet, comfortable seating areas. Some bedrooms are old-fashioned, while the more recently updated are most appealing, with floral fabrics, easy chairs, darkwood furniture and up-to-date bathrooms. A limited room service is offered. ***Rooms** 42. Garden.* AMERICAN EXPRESS® *Access, Diners, Visa.*

Perth **Stakis City Mills Hotel** **59%** **£90**

Tel 0738 28281 Fax 0738 43423 **H**

West Mill Street Perth Tayside PH1 5QP **Map 3 C5**

Right in the heart of Perth, the Stakis is based on a watermill dating back to the 15th century. Single, double and twin rooms, plus a couple of family rooms. Conferences up to 235 theatre-style. ***Rooms** 76.* AMERICAN EXPRESS® *Access, Diners, Visa.*

Perth **Places of Interest**

Tourist Information Tel 0738 38353.
Perth Theatre Tel 0738 21031.
St Ninian's Cathedral Tel 0738 21373.
Perth Museum and Art Gallery Tel 0738 32488.
Dewars Ice Rinks Tel 0738 37810.
Perth Showgrounds Tel 0738 23780.
Perth Hunt Racecourse Tel 0738 51597.
Caithness Glass Visitor Centre Inveralmond Tel 0783 37373.
Historic Houses, Castles and Gardens
Branklyn Garden (NT) Tel 0738 25535.
Megginch Castle Gardens Errol. Tel 08212 222.

Peterhead **Waterside Inn** **67%** **£89**

Tel 0779 71121 Fax 0779 70670 **H**

Fraserburgh Road Peterhead Grampian AB42 7BN **Map 2 D3**

A modern hotel which is comfortable and efficiently run. There's a series of bars to suit every taste, and several conference rooms (maximum capacity 250). 40 studio bedrooms in a separate block are compact and functional, while those in the main building are more spacious and luxurious; children stay free in parents' room. Turn left at a grassy roundabout as you approach Peterhead from Aberdeen (A92) and follow signs to St Fergus. ***Rooms** 110. Garden, indoor swimming pool, keep-fit equipment, sauna, spa bath, solarium, snooker, grill room (7am-10pm Tue-Sat).* AMERICAN EXPRESS® *Access, Diners, Visa.*

Peterhead **Places of Interest**

Tourist Information Tel 0779 71904.
Arbuthnot Museum Tel 0779 77778.

Pitlochry **Green Park Hotel** **58%** **£76**

Tel 0796 473248 Fax 0796 473520 **H**

Cluny Bridge Road Pitlochry Tayside PH16 5JY **Map 3 C4**

From manicured lawns to neat carpeted bathrooms, this Victorian lochside hotel is very well kept. Fresh flowers and an original tapestry frieze adorn the panelled entrance hall but it is the splendid view across the loch from

See over

the lounge which is the major attraction. Bedrooms feature good Japanese elm furniture and pretty matching bedcovers and curtains. ***Rooms** 37. Garden, putting, game fishing, games room. Closed Nov-Mar. Access, Visa.*

Pitlochry — Pitlochry Hydro — 64% — £98

Tel 0796 472666 Fax 0796 472238 — **H**

Knockard Road Pitlochry Tayside PH16 5JH — **Map 3 C4**

Set high above Pitlochry, the Hydro is a sturdily-built, well-maintained and well-run late-Victorian hotel. Its attractions are supplemented by good leisure facilities, mostly housed in the Hydro Club. Bedrooms, including a couple of suites, have modern tiled bathrooms. Children up to 14 stay free in parents' room. No dogs. ***Rooms** 62. Garden, indoor swimming pool, gymnasium, spa bath, sauna, solarium, snooker, putting. Closed Jan & Feb.* AMERICAN EXPRESS® *Access, Diners, Visa.*

Pitlochry — Places of Interest

Tourist Information Tel 0796 472215.
Pitlochry Theatre Festival Tel 0796 472680. *May-Oct.*
Blair Castle Blair Atholl. Tel 0796 4781207.

Port Appin — Airds Hotel — 76% — £220*

Tel 063 173 236 Fax 063 173 535 — **HR**

Port Appin Appin Strathclyde PA38 4DF — **Map 3 B5**

Once a ferry inn for "those in passage" to the island of Lismore, the Allen family's hotel enjoys a fine setting in two acres of gardens with splendid views of Loch Linnhe. Day rooms are ideal for relaxation, with inviting chairs and sofas, coal fires and plenty of reading material. Bedrooms are not large but make good use of high-quality fabrics and have well-kept modern bathrooms. Dogs by prior arrangement only. *Half-board terms only. ***Rooms** 13. Garden. Closed early Jan-early Mar. Access, Visa.*

Restaurant — £78

The best local produce goes into Betty and Graeme Allen's kitchen and sympathetic, essentially simple treatment results in very enjoyable daily-changing four-course dinners. Lightly cooked oysters with smoked salmon and champagne jelly, open ravioli of mushrooms with a Muscadet and parsley sauce or a salad of roast quail with truffle oil dressing could start the meal, followed by soup (perhaps cream of tomato and basil) and a trio of main courses such as fillet of halibut on a bed of honeyed aubergines with champagne and chive sauce or roast saddle of roe deer on a potato cake with thyme and juniper sauce. Desserts are a strong point and it could be difficult to choose between, for example, mango mousse with walnut shortbread, chocolate ice cream gateau with crème anglaise or prune and armagnac ice cream. The fabulous wine list (Eric Allen's domain) will delight all wine-lovers. Front tables get the best loch views. No smoking. ***Seats** 36. L 12.30-1.30 D 8-8.30. Set D £33.*

Port William — Corsemalzie House — 61% — £75

Tel 098 886 254 — **H**

Port William by Newton Stewart Dumfries & Galloway DG8 9RL — **Map 4 A3**

A popular and unpretentious hotel in a 19th-century stone mansion surrounded by the secluded setting of forty wooded acres. Among its many sporting attractions, fishing is a major activity (rights on stretches of the Rivers Bladnoch and Tarff, plus nearby lochs) and there's good rough shooting and arrangements with local golf courses. The lounge and bar provide easy relaxation, and bedrooms are generally of a decent size; all have private bath or shower. Children under 13 in parents' room are charged at £3 a night; high tea served in the bar. ***Rooms** 14. Garden, putting, game fishing, shooting. Closed 25 & 26 Dec, 14 Jan-mid Mar. Access, Visa.*

Portpatrick **Knockinaam Lodge** 73% £100

Tel 077 681 471 Fax 077 681 435 **HR**

Portpatrick nr Stranraer Dumfries & Galloway DG9 9AD Map 4 A2

An air of contentment surrounds this most welcoming and comfortable country house, nestling in a secluded cove (follow signs from the A77) with private foreshore and beach, that is as much the home of the Frichots as their numerous returning guests. An eclectic clock collection graces most public rooms, which include a warmly panelled bar complete with stags head, and open-fire-warmed sitting rooms with a wealth of plump-cushioned sofas, magazines and board games. Bedrooms are equally gracious, prettily decorated but not over-fussy, and bathrooms include a splendid tub used by Winston Churchill. Excellent breakfasts and delightful service from Scots lassies. ***Rooms 10.*** *Garden. Closed Jan-mid Mar.* AMERICAN EXPRESS *Access, Diners, Visa.*

Restaurant £80

Former sous chef Stuart Muir has taken hold of the reins, producing consistently enjoyable food of the likes of *raviolis aux champignons sauvages et tagliatelle légumes, aiguillette de canard fermier roti et son étuve de choux à la crème*, with *crème brulée à la cassonnade de cannelle sa tuile à l'orange* to finish. Produce, some supplied from their own garden, is of the highest quality and Stuart's touch is assured. Soup, salads and sandwiches can be had in the bar at lunchtime, or a three-course lunch can be served in the dining room by prior arrangement. ***Seats*** *26. L 12.30-2 D 7.30-9. Set L £19 Set D £30.*

Portree **Rosedale Hotel** 54% £70

Tel 0478 3131 Fax 0478 2531 **H**

Beaumont Crescent Portree Isle of Skye Highland IV51 9DB Map 2 A3

Situated right on the quayside of a quaint, picturesque fishing harbour, the Rosedale continues to offer simple but comfortable accommodation in often small but well-kept bedrooms, reached through a maze of narrow staircases and corridors. A new serviced suite with sauna and jacuzzi adds a luxurious dimension to the annexed Beaumont House, a cottage at the other end of the terrace. The bar in original 1970s purple and green is now almost a museum piece. ***Rooms*** *24. Garden. Closed Oct-mid April. Access, Visa.*

Portree **Places of Interest**

Tourist Information Tel 0478 612137.
An Tuireann Arts Centre Tel 0478 613306.
Old Skye Crofter's House Folk Museum Luib Tel 0471 822427.
Skye Woollen Mill Tel 0478 612889.
The Museum of the Isles Isle of Skye. Tel 04714 305.
Talisker Distillery Carbost Tel 0478 640203 *20 miles.*

Quothquan **Shieldhill** 75% £98

Tel 0899 20035 Fax 0899 21092 **HR**

Quothquan Biggar Strathclyde ML12 6NA Map 3 C6

Shieldhill exudes the warmth of continuous habitation since 1199: crested carpeting laid throughout the public areas owes its origins to the Chancellor family, residents for seven centuries. With open fires and deep sofas, the atmosphere is one of a Scottish baronial mansion, while the laid-back welcome is more firmly rooted in contemporary California (Jack Greenwald and Christine Dunstan also own Santa Barbara's *Cheshire Cat*). Bedrooms are individually styled in restful tones of Laura Ashley prints, to which fresh flowers, fruit bowl and sherry decanter add an apposite welcome. Several baths are jacuzzis; and all the beds are supremely comfortable. Substantial Scottish breakfasts and attentive service overall; no smoking in the bedrooms or restaurant. Stronger on humanities than

See over

unabashed luxury. No dogs. ***Rooms*** *11. Garden, fishing.* AMERICAN EXPRESS *Access, Diners, Visa.*

Restaurant **£65**

A civilised restaurant where Jack Greenwald presides with an informal urbanity. New chefs this year are continuing the modern style with fixed-price-only 3- or 4-course menus offering a short choice, perhaps sautéed scallops with shredded vegetables and raspberry vinegar dressing followed by smoked Finnan haddock and green lentil chowder, Angus beef Wellington with pickled walnut essence and lemon and rhubarb tart with rhubarb and ginger ice cream. No smoking. ***Seats*** *32. Parties 6. Private Room 12. L 12-2 D 7-9 (Sat to 9.30). Set D from £24.50.*

Quothquan — Place of Interest

New Lanark Conservation Village Tel 0555 661345 *8 miles.*

Rockcliffe — Baron's Craig 65% £90

Tel 055 663 225 Fax 055 663 328 **H**

Rockcliffe by Dalbeattie Dumfries & Galloway DG5 4QF **Map 4 B3**

An 1880 granite house set in 12 acres of woods, lawns and gardens from which there are fine views of the Solway Firth. Walkers and golfers love it (the latter have six courses within close reach), and enjoy returning to lounges stocked with books and newspapers. Many sea-borne activities can also be arranged. Bedrooms are warm and comfortable. Children up to 14 stay free in parents' room. ***Rooms*** *27. Garden, golf practice net, putting, sailing, windsurfing, water-skiing. Closed Nov-Easter. Access, Visa.*

Rockcliffe — Places of Interest

Kircudbright Tourist Information Tel 0557 30494.
Threave Garden nr Castle Douglas Tel 0556 2575 *12 miles.*

Rothes — Rothes Glen Hotel 65% £110

Tel 03403 254 Fax 03403 566 **H**

Rothes nr Elgin Grampian AB38 7AH **Map 2 C3**

Forty acres of grounds at the head of the Glen of Rothes provide rural peace at a baronial house designed by the architect of Balmoral Castle. Inside, there's an elegant lounge with ribbed ceiling and white marble fireplace, plus a bar and TV room. Antique furniture graces most of the variously-sized bedrooms. 14 rooms have bath/shower/WC, two have shower/WC only. ***Rooms*** *16. Garden, putting. Closed Christmas-Jan.* AMERICAN EXPRESS *Access, Diners, Visa.*

St Andrews — Rufflets Country House 65% £104

Tel 0334 72594 Fax 0334 78703 **H**

Strathkinness Low Road St Andrews Fife KY16 9TX **Map 3 D5**

They are justly proud of their ten acres of award-winning gardens at this 1920s-built hotel on the B939 a mile and a half west of St Andrews. Inside, the hotel is as well kept as the gardens, with pretty floral fabrics and wallpapers and mostly traditional darkwood furniture. Three particularly attractive rooms are in a rose-covered cottage in the grounds. Children up to 10 stay free in parents' room. Additional bedrooms came on stream in mid-1993. Public areas include an appealing entrance hall, lounge and formal drawing room. ***Rooms*** *26. Garden, putting.* AMERICAN EXPRESS *Access, Diners, Visa.*

St Andrews — Rusacks Hotel — 74% — £150

Tel 0334 74321 Fax 0334 77896 — **H**

Pilmour Links St Andrews Fife KY16 9JQ — **Map 3 D5**

Public rooms at this grand Victorian hotel are sumptuous, with trompe l'oeil marble columns and crystal chandeliers in the foyer-lounge plus high-quality furnishings throughout. The spacious sun lounge affords panoramic views of the Old Course and the golf-themed Champions Bar is a good place to re-live the triumphs and disasters of the day's golf. Traditionally furnished bedrooms, the best of which have some antique pieces, feature a variety of stylish fabrics and easy chairs. Smart bathrooms have generous towelling bathrobes. Well-turned-out staff provide a high level of service that includes valet parking, automatic luggage porterage and proper bedroom service in the evenings. Forte Grand. ***Rooms** 50. Sauna, solarium.*

AMERICAN EXPRESS® *Access, Diners, Visa.*

St Andrews — St Andrews Old Course Hotel — 82% — £200

Tel 0334 74371 Fax 0334 77668 — **H**

St Andrews Fife KY16 9SP — **Map 3 D5**

Alongside the 17th hole of the famous Old Course, the hotel also commands views of the city, St Andrews Bay and the Highlands beyond from the glorious day rooms. Exemplary service from smart, friendly staff combines with the baronial feel of the building to produce real luxury. The slate-floored foyer with stone-effect walls leads through to a spacious reception area with darkwood panelling, stencilled ceiling and silk Oriental rugs on the parquet floor. The book-lined library, sunny conservatory (open from 6.30am-10pm) and convivial Road Hole bar with its two fireplaces all offer top-class comfort. Attention to detail in the bedrooms is equally meticulous, with traditional wooden furniture, TVs hidden away in cabinets and footstools with the comfortable armchairs. High-class toiletries and generously-sized bathrobes add to the exuberance in the marble bathrooms. The Spa is an extensively equipped health and leisure centre with facilities that range from beauty treatments to a 50' pool under a glass roof. Golfing guests wishing to play the Old Course should apply to the hotel's golf steward. The hotel also provides fine facilities for banqueting and conferences (up to 300 people). Children up to 12 stay free in parents' room. Special children's menu available. ***Rooms** 125. Garden, indoor swimming pool, gymnasium, spa bath, steam room, solarium, golf shop.*

AMERICAN EXPRESS® *Access, Diners, Visa.*

St Andrews — Places of Interest

Tourist Information Tel 0334 72021.
Buchanan Theatre Tel 0334 76161.
Earlshall Castle and Gardens Leuchars Tel 0334 839205.
British Golf Museum Tel 0334 78880.
East Sands Leisure Centre Tel 0334 76506.

St Fillans — Four Seasons Hotel — 60% — £70

Tel & Fax 0764 685 333 — **H**

St Fillans nr Crieff Tayside PH26 2NF — **Map 3 C5**

The setting for the Scott family's agreeable little hotel, in four acres of grounds, is one of outstanding natural beauty, with Loch Earn in the foreground and the mountains beyond. Simple but comfortable public rooms take advantage of the location: there are several small lounges, the Tarken Bar (where good snacks are served in hearty-sized or children's portions), restaurant and coffee shop. Much redecoration has taken place over the last few years. Bedrooms are also unfussy in their appointments and include six chalets on a wooded hillside behind the main building; families with dogs should choose the chalets. Children up to 7 stay free in parents' room. ***Rooms** 18. Garden, water-skiing. Closed Christmas-end Feb.*

AMERICAN EXPRESS® *Access, Visa.*

Scarista — Scarista House 67% — £90

Tel 0859 550238 Fax 0859 550277 — **HR**

Scarista Isle of Harris Highland PA85 3HX — **Map 2 A3**

The Callaghans' former manse on the Atlantic coast of Harris (15 miles south-west of Tarbert on the A859) must be one of the most remote hotels in Britain. Ruggedly beautiful countryside and endless deserted beaches are a magnet for walkers, bird-watchers and fishermen, who also appreciate the warm welcome and homely comforts of Scarista House. One of the two lounges is lined with books and there is a record collection available for guests' use. Bedrooms in the annexe are larger and more modern than those in the main house, which have a touch more character; three are reserved for non-smokers; one new bedroom was added last year. No children under 8. Well-trained dogs are welcome so long as they do not disturb the hill sheep. ***Rooms*** *8. Garden. Closed mid Oct-Mar. No credit cards.*

Restaurant — £54

Jane Callaghan's simple, hearty dinners are served in a candle-lit dining room and are based on good local produce using only free-range eggs and meat, and avoiding farmed seafood. The choice is fixed, so advise in advance of any dislikes ("or, indeed, any likes"). Bread, cakes and preserves are all home-made. ***Seats*** *20. Private Room 8. D only at 8. Set D £25.*

Scone — Murrayshall House 72% — £125

Tel 0738 51171 Fax 0738 52595 — **HR**

Scone Tayside PH2 7PH — **Map 3 C5**

Golf is a major attraction at this turn-of-the-century stone mansion, with a professional on hand to give tuition, a golf shop and a clubhouse with bar. Fabric-covered walls feature in the stylish day rooms, dark blue damask to match the soft furnishings in the quiet lounge and a bold floral pattern in the lounge bar. Best bedrooms are those in the original part of the house, those in the newer wing being somewhat smaller, but all offer many extras like fresh flowers, fruit, magazines and mineral water. Rooms are properly serviced in the evenings as are the bathrooms which boast robes and large bath sheets. Children up to 10 stay free in parents' room. ***Rooms*** *19. Garden, tennis, bowling, golf (18).* AMERICAN EXPRESS *Access, Diners, Visa.*

Old Masters Restaurant — £56

With a change of personnel in the kitchen has come a reduction of prices on the menu at this luxuriously appointed hotel restaurant. The new light lunch menu might include cullen skink (a traditional Scottish fish soup), samosas and goujons of plaice with French fries and a herb dip while the evening à la carte offerings are typified by gravad lax with marinated cucumber and an Arran mustard dressing, breast of guinea fowl with black pudding and a port and lentil sauce, and a hot pot of smoked and fresh fish in a saffron sauce. ***Seats*** *60. Parties 12. Private Room 30. L 12-2 D 6.30-9.30. Set D £17.50.*

Scone — Place of Interest

Scone Palace Tel 0738 52300.

Scourie — Eddrachilles Hotel 60% — £68

Tel 0971 502080 Fax 0971 502477 — **H**

Badcall Bay Scourie Highland IV27 4TH — **Map 2 B2**

This 200-year-old hotel enjoys a setting of outstanding peace and rugged beauty at the head of Badcall Bay. Handa Island bird sanctuary is a few miles to the north, and boat trips can be made from nearby Tarbet. It's also a great base for walking, exploring, climbing and fishing. Seven of the neatly-kept bedrooms have shower/WC only. No children under 3. No dogs. ***Rooms** 11. Garden, boat hire. Closed Nov-Feb. Access, Visa.*

Scourie **Scourie Hotel** 60% £68

Tel 0971 2396 Fax 0971 2423 **H**

Scourie by Lairg Highland IV27 4SX **Map 2 B2**

Built by the second Duke of Sutherland as a coaching inn, this is now a fishing hotel *par excellence.* Brown trout, sea trout and salmon are all to be found in the 25,000 acres of grounds, and boats can be supplied for many of the beats. Tales swapped in the lounges and cocktail bar are naturally fairly fishy. Bedrooms, including two garden suites, are modern and well kept, with fitted furniture and good-sized bathrooms (two rooms are without en-suite facilities). There are no TVs, but the views from the windows are very watchable. Children up to 12 stay free in parents' room. ***Rooms** 21. Garden, game fishing. Closed mid Oct-Mar..* AMERICAN EXPRESS *Access, Diners, Visa.*

Selkirk **Philipburn House** 60% £99

Tel 0750 20747 Fax 0750 21690 **H**

Lingle Road Selkirk Borders TD7 5LS **Map 4 C1**

Set back from the A707/A708 junction, a mile from the town centre on the Peebles road, this extended 18th-century house has been turned into a delightful family hotel with a Tyrolean-style interior. Jim and Anne Hill, owners since 1971, cater for all kinds of visitors – business, fishing, tourist, family – and friendly hospitality is their watchword. Bedrooms – in the house, by the pool or in the 'log cabin' – feature pine, pretty fabrics and a host of extras. Parents will appreciate the privacy provided by many separate but connecting children's rooms. An interesting 'light bite' menu is served in the characterful pine-panelled bar. ***Rooms** 16. Garden, outdoor swimming pool, games room, children's playground, crèche. Access, Visa.*

Selkirk **Places of Interest**

Tourist Information Tel 0750 20054.
Bowhill Tel 0750 20732.
Halliwell's House Museum Tel 0750 20096.

Skeabost Bridge **Skeabost House** 60% £86

Tel 047 032 202 Fax 047 032 454 **H**

Skeabost Bridge by Portree Isle of Skye Highland IV51 9NP **Map 2 A3**

Twelve acres of woodland and gardens surround a former hunting lodge on Loch Snizort. It's a comfortable place, with the same family owners since 1970, and relaxation is easy in the lounges, the flagstoned sun lounge, the cosy bar and the billiard room. Pretty bedrooms include one with a four-poster and a few in the nearby Garden House. One is a large family room. The hotel owns eight miles of the river Snizort, which runs through the grounds, and has a boat on a nearby loch. ***Rooms** 26. Garden, golf (9-hole), fishing, snooker. Closed mid Oct-mid Apr. Access, Visa.*

Skeabost Bridge **Place of Interest**

Edinbane Pottery Tel 047082 234.

Skelmorlie **Manor Park** 61% £75

Tel 0475 520832 Fax 0475 520832 **H**

Skelmorlie nr Largs Strathclyde PA17 5HE **Map 3 B6**

Built in 1840 and modernised with some care, the hotel stands on a hill above the coast road (A78) midway between Skelmorlie and Largs. The gardens are a source of great pride with 15 acres of lawns, shrubberies, *See over* water gardens, rhododendron walks and woodland. The main talking point inside is the bar, notable for its vast stock of whiskies and a unique map of the Clyde carved in walnut and sycamore. In one of the conference suites Churchill and Eisenhower met to plan the D-day landings. Seven bedrooms are in the main building, the rest in the nearby Stables Court. No dogs. ***Rooms** 23. Garden.* AMERICAN EXPRESS *Access, Diners, Visa.*

Sleat — Kinloch Lodge — 67% — £100

Tel 047 13 214 Fax 047 13 277 — **HR**

Sleat Isle of Skye Highland IV43 8QY — **Map 3 A4**

Kinloch Lodge is a white stone building at the head of Loch Na Dal in the south of the island. Built in 1680, it is now the home of Lord and Lady Macdonald, and guests are made to feel like family friends. Its isolated position makes it a haven of peace and the views are truly outstanding. Two stylish drawing rooms enjoy the spectacular views and are adorned with ancestral portraits, fine antiques, porcelain pieces and each with a roaring fire provide the perfect spot for afternoon tea or a pre-dinner drink. Bedrooms, mostly rather small, are comfortable and quiet, with no phones or TVs to disturb the peace; prices vary to reflect their size and outlook (prices are also greatly reduced during low season – March and April, mid-October and November). Furniture is a mixture of antique and modern pieces and the two rooms not en suite have bathrooms across the corridor. Children by arrangement only. ***Rooms** 10. Garden, shooting, fishing. Closed Dec-Mar. Access, Visa.*

Dining Room — £75

Good home cooking by Lady Macdonald and three others. Local ingredients, hearty portions, friendly staff. Some typical dishes from the five-course, limited-choice menu: watercress roulade stuffed with smoked salmon and fromage frais, mushroom and garlic soup, baked fillet of cod or roast leg of lamb with spiced apricot sauce and rosemary and red wine gravy; cinnamon pavlova with blackcurrant cream or dark chocolate and vanilla cheesecake to finish. No smoking in the dining rooms. Coffee with fudge is served in the drawing rooms. Concise, carefully selected wine list. ***Seats** 28. Parties 10. D at 8. Set D £30.*

Sleat — Places of Interest

Clan Donald Centre Armadale Castle Tel 04714 305.
Kylerhea Otter Haven.

South Queensferry — Forth Bridges Moat House 61% — £114

Tel 031-331 1199 Fax 031-319 1733 — **H**

South Queensferry Lothian EH30 9SF — **Map 3 C5**

60s' hotel with spectacular views of both Forth bridges and good leisure facilities. 5 miles from Edinburgh airport. Conference/banqueting facilities for 200. Children up to 14 stay free in parents' room. ***Rooms** 108. Garden, indoor swimming pool, gymnasium, squash, sauna, spa bath, solarium, beauty & hair salon, snooker.* AMERICAN EXPRESS *Access, Diners, Visa.*

South Queensferry — Places of Interest

Dalmeny House Tel 031-331 1888.
Hopetoun House Tel 031-331 2451.

Spean Bridge — Letterfinlay Lodge — 55% — £68

Tel 0397 712622 — **H**

Spean Bridge Highland PH34 4DZ — **Map 3 B4**

Here since 1963, the Forsyth family have created a comfortable and very Scottish atmosphere in a ruggedly beautiful setting on the banks of Loch Lochy (seven miles north of Spean Bridge). The public rooms include

a cosy little bar, a homely TV lounge and a sun lounge with glorious views. Bedrooms furnished in various styles are named by colour and decorated accordingly; all have private bathrooms, three not en suite. Five rooms are considered suitable for family use. ***Rooms** 13.*
Closed Nov-mid Mar. AMERICAN EXPRESS *Access, Diners, Visa.*

Stewarton **Chapeltoun House** **71%** **£90**

Tel 0560 482696 Fax 0560 485100 **H**

Stewarton-Irvine Road Stewarton Strathclyde KA3 3ED **Map 3 B6**

A turn-of-the-century mansion set in private gardens off the B769 Irvine road two miles out of Stewarton. Its bedrooms, ranging in size from medium to spacious, all boast antique furniture and a range of extras such as fruit, sweets, mineral water, sherry, flowers and sewing kits; the bathrooms are similarly well equipped with toiletries, bathrobes and good towels. Of the public rooms, the hall/lounge is the best, with panelled walls and a pargeted frieze below the coffered ceiling; the drawing room has reproduction coffee tables and green draylon seating. No children under 12.
***Rooms** 8. Garden, fishing. Closed 2 weeks Jan.* AMERICAN EXPRESS *Access, Visa.*

Stirling **Granada Lodge** **£45**

Tel 0786 815033 Fax 0786 815900 **L**

M90/M80 Junction 9 Stirling Central FK7 8EU **Map 3 C5**

***Rooms** 37.* AMERICAN EXPRESS *Access, Diners, Visa.*

Stirling **Places of Interest**

Tourist Information Tel 0786 475019.
MacRobert Arts Centre Tel 0786 461081.
Stirling Castle Tel 0786 450000.
Smith Art Gallery and Museum Tel 0786 471917.
Regimental Museum of Argyll and Sutherland Highlanders Tel 0786 475165.

Stornoway **Cabarfeidh Hotel** **64%** **£85**

Tel 0851 702604 Fax 0851 705572 **H**

Manor Park Stornoway Isle of Lewis Highland PA87 2EU **Map 2 A2**

An early-70s hotel with a rather faceless exterior (belying the inviting interior) on the edge of town, a brisk walk from the Ullapool ferry terminal. The Viking Bar (with a longship for a counter), a cocktail bar and a restaurant divided into three differently styled areas comprise the public rooms. Cheerful bedrooms, all en suite. Open all year round.
***Rooms** 46. Garden.* AMERICAN EXPRESS *Access, Diners, Visa.*

Stornoway **Places of Interest**

Tourist Information Tel 0851 703088,

Strachur **Creggans Inn** **61%** **£98**

Tel 036 986 279 Fax 036 986 637 **H**

Strachur Strathclyde PA27 8BX **Map 3 B5**

Sir Fitzroy and Lady Maclean's white-painted inn stands by Loch Fyne on the Road to the Isles. It's a great part of the world for fishing, walking and touring, after which a glass of the hotel's own Old MacPhunn ten-year-old vatted malt goes down well in the bar. There's a peaceful sitting room and a large garden lounge, both with delightful views. Decor varies in the small but charming bedrooms, almost all of which have bathrooms en suite. ***Rooms** 21. Garden, fishing.* AMERICAN EXPRESS *Access, Diners, Visa.*

Strachur Places of Interest

Crarae Glen Garden Minard. Tel 0546 86614.
Inveraray Castle Tel 0499 2203 *20 miles.*
Argyll Wildlife Park Inveraray Tel 0499 2264.
European Sheep and Wool Centre Lochgoiliead Tel 03013 247 *10 miles.*

Stranraer North West Castle 68% £70

Tel 0776 4413 Fax 0776 2646 **H**

Portrodie Stranraer Dumfries & Galloway DG9 8EH **Map 4 A2**

Tastefully extended since being built in 1820, the hotel stands opposite the ferry port. It was once the home of explorer Sir John Ross, whose name is commemorated in the panelled bar. Bedrooms include six suites, and 20 rooms are considered suitable for family occupation. Conference and banqueting facilities for 150 delegates; enquire about special arrangements for residents at two local golf courses and nearby squash courts. Sister establishment to the *Cally Palace Hotel* in Gatehouse of Fleet and *Kirroughtree Hotel*, Newton Stewart. ***Rooms** 72. Indoor swimming pool, curling rink, sauna, solarium, spa bath, gymnasium, snooker, coffee shop (10am-9.30pm). No credit cards.*

Stranraer Places of Interest

Tourist Information Tel 0776 2595.
Historic Houses, Castles and Gardens
Castle Kennedy and Lochinch Gardens Tel 0776 2024.
Logan House and Botanic Garden Tel 077686 231.
Glenwhan Gardens Dunragit Tel 05814 222.

Strathblane Kirkhouse Inn £72

Tel 0360 770621 Fax 0360 770896 **I**

Glasgow Road Strathblane Central G63 9AA **Map 3 B5**

On the A81 Stirling to Aberfoyle road, ten miles north of Glasgow, this roadside inn is at the foot of the Campsie Fells and thus popular with walkers. An ideal touring centre as Loch Lomond, the Trossachs, Glasgow and Stirling are all within 30 minutes by car. Sprucely kept public areas include a busy public bar and quieter lounge and restaurant. Pastel colours are used in the bedrooms, which include a honeymoon suite with a sunken bath. Children up to 12 stay free in parents' room. Adventure weekends are a big attraction. ***Rooms** 15. Garden, pool table.* AMERICAN EXPRESS *Access, Diners, Visa.*

Strathtummel Port-an-Eilean Hotel 65% £58

Tel 0882 634233 **H**

Strathtummel by Pitlochry Tayside PH16 5RU **Map 3 C4**

The Hallewells are in their 20th year at this Victorian hunting lodge beautifully situated on the shore of Loch Tummel. Large, traditionally furnished bedrooms are well supplied with books and have no TVs or telephones to disturb the peace. Lounges and the cosy cocktail bar enjoy splendid views of mountain and loch and throughout the hotel there's a fine collection of paintings, mainly by Scottish artists. On the B8019 about nine miles west of Pitlochry. ***Rooms** 8. Garden, coarse & game fishing. Closed Oct-Apr. No credit cards.*

We welcome bona fide complaints and recommendations on the tear-out pages at the back of the book for readers' comments. They are followed up by our professional team.

Talladale — Loch Maree Hotel — £70

Tel 044 584 288 Fax 044 584 241 — **I**

Achnasheen Talladale Highland IV2 2HC — **Map 2 B3**

A purpose-built fishing hotel beautifully situated on the banks of the loch between Gairloch and Kinlochewe. The glorious outdoors is certainly a major attraction, and inside things have changed dramatically from the former time-warp Victorian cosiness. The hotel owns eight boats (complete with mandatory ghillies) for sea trout and salmon fishing on the loch. ***Rooms** 18. Garden, fishing, boating, games room. Access, Visa.*

Tarbert — Stonefield Castle — 58% — £122

Tel 0880 820836 Fax 0880 820929 — **H**

Loch Fyne Tarbert Strathclyde PA29 6YJ — **Map 3 B6**

Sixty acres of grounds surround the 19th-century former baronial home and many of the rooms command spectacular views over Loch Fyne. Day rooms are in comfortable, traditional style, so too the bedrooms in the main house. Wing rooms are more ordinary but certainly adequate. Two miles north of Tarbert – look out for hotel signs. ***Rooms** 33. Garden, outdoor swimming pool (summer only), sauna, solarium, snooker, mooring.* AMERICAN EXPRESS *Access, Diners, Visa.*

Tarbert — Places of Interest

Tourist Information Tel 0880 820429.

Tiroran — Tiroran House — 70% — £186*

Tel & Fax 068 15 232 — **HR**

Tiroran Isle of Mull Strathclyde PA69 6ES — **Map 3 A5**

Owing much of its uniqueness to the hospitality of Wing Commander and Mrs Blockey (who converted their sporting lodge for guests' use in 1977), Tiroran House is a pleasing mix of home and hotel. Many guests return annually to enjoy, among other things, the spectacular views of Loch Scridain across some 15 acres of gardens and woodland. The house, furnished with antiques and family silver, contains six bedrooms of individual decor and charm; the rest are in adjacent pine cottages looking down the garden and across a burn running its length. Biscuits, cheese and a half bottle of wine are typical of the thoughtful touches that await arriving guests; breakfast, too, is exemplary. No phones, no TVs, no children under ten. *Half-board terms only. ***Rooms** 9. Garden, games room. Closed early Oct-mid May. No credit cards.*

Restaurant — £70

Non-residents, welcomed if space allows, will encounter a dinner party atmosphere ably enhanced by Sue Blockey's well-judged cooking. Her table d'hote main course (no choice) may be noisettes of venison with red wine and pink peppercorn sauce with fan-roasted potatoes, braised leeks and fingered carrots or roast duckling with Seville oranges, new potatoes, cabbage and red wine casserole and broccoli. Starters and puddings (choice of three of each) look to the garden for salad crops, herbs, soft fruits and chicken and duck eggs. Excellent bread is baked daily and fine Scottish cheeses and Stilton are fitting additions. Lunch, for residents only, is served on the verandah; packed lunches are also provided on request. Some good wines (and growers) at affordable prices on the helpful wine list. ***Seats** 20. D only at 7.45. Closed L except residents. Set D £28.50.*

Tiroran — Places of Interest

Iona Community Tel 06817 407
Fingal's Cave Staffa Tel 041-552 8391.

Tobermory — Tobermory Hotel 57% — £60

Tel 0688 2091 Fax 0688 2140 — **H**

53 Main Street Tobermory Isle of Mull Strathclyde PA75 6NT — **Map 3 A4**

Ring the bell to gain access to this small, carefully maintained hotel on the waterfront of Tobermory Bay. The owners Martin and Kay Sutton put hospitality top of their list, and two cosy lounges furnished with floral sofas and easy chairs, well-chosen ornaments and pictures offer welcoming touches like magazines and fresh flowers. Compact bedrooms have been recently refurbished; 'superior' rooms have king-size beds. The bathrooms are well kept; nine are currently en suite; eight have shared facilities, although plans are afoot to make them all en suite. ***Rooms** 17. Access, Visa.*

Tobermory — Places of Interest

Tourist Information Tel 0688 2182

Troon — Marine Highland Hotel 67% — £138

Tel 0292 314444 Fax 0292 316922 — **H**

Crosbie Road Troon Strathclyde KA10 6HE — **Map 4 A1**

This handsome Victorian sandstone structure overlooks the 18th fairway of Royal Troon championship golf course. Accommodation options are standard, de luxe or top-of-the-range Ambassador suites. Families welcome, with entertainment during festive periods, baby-sitting and baby-listening offered. Good conference facilities. Leave the A77 and follow the B789 to Troon. ***Rooms** 72. Indoor swimming pool, gymnasium, squash, sauna, spa bath, steam room, solarium, beauty salon, putting, snooker.* AMERICAN EXPRESS *Access, Diners, Visa.*

Troon — Piersland House 64% — £85

Tel 0292 314747 Fax 0292 315613 — **H**

15 Craigend Road Troon Strathclyde KA10 6HD — **Map 4 A1**

A sandstone and timbered building dating from 1890 and originally owned by the grandson of whisky man Johnnie Walker. From the reception, stairs lead up to a galleried landing with exposed roof timbers. Further pleasing architectural features are to be found in the bar/lounge, which boasts stone-mullioned windows, an embroidered frieze and a ribbed ceiling. Bedrooms are individually and prettily appointed. Banqueting/conference facilities for up to 150/110. The hotel stands opposite Royal Troon golf club. ***Rooms** 19. Garden, putting.* AMERICAN EXPRESS *Access, Diners, Visa.*

Troon — Places of Interest

Tourist Information Tel 0292 317696.

Turnberry — Turnberry Hotel 84% — £190

Tel 0655 31000 Fax 0655 31706 — **HR**

Turnberry Strathclyde KA26 9LT — **Map 4 A2**

When Turnberry opened in 1906 it became the world's first hotel and golf resort, and the country club and spa keep it today in the forefront of sporting hotels. It is also established as a top-flight conference and banqueting venue (up to 150 delegates in the self-contained Turnberry Suite). The hotel overlooks the famous links of Ailsa and Arran, to the islands of that name and towards the Mull of Kintyre beyond. Day rooms combine comfort and splendour at a high level, and bedrooms, too, are notably stylish, with luxuriously equipped bathrooms. Informal eating in a new golf Clubhouse (8am-7pm) which opened last year. Children up to 12 stay free in parents' room; 24hr room service includes a children's menu. ***Rooms** 132. Garden, indoor swimming pool, gymnasium, spa bath,* *sauna, solarium, beauty & hair salon, 2 18-hole golf courses, 12-hole pitch & putt, health spa, tennis, riding, snooker, helipad.* AMERICAN EXPRESS *Access, Diners, Visa.*

Restaurant

£90

The main restaurant offers a luxurious menu of classics and modernised variants (crab bisque, tournedos Rossini, roast duck with sage and onion stuffing and apple sauce, blackberry and Bramley crumble), while the restaurant at the Spa, called The Bay at Turnberry, is open for lunch and dinner seven days a week providing a healthy menu that eschews red meat and rich sauces. Unusually, some excellent Swiss wines are to be found on a fine all-round list that features some of the best French producers.
***Seats** 200. Private Room 8. L (Sun only) 1-2.30 D 7.30-10. Set L £18.75 Set D £35.*

Tweedsmuir — Crook Inn — 59%

£52

H

Tel 089 97 272 Fax 089 97 294

Tweedsmuir nr Biggar Borders ML12 6QN

Map 4 C1

Standing on the A701 Moffat-Edinburgh road and set in the ruggedly beautiful Tweed valley, the Crook is a good base for walking, climbing and touring holidays. Guests can also enjoy free fishing on 30 miles of the River Tweed. Burns wrote *Willie Wastle's Wife* in what is now the bar, and locally-born John Buchan set many of his novels in the area. Neat bedrooms are simple in their appointments, with no TVs or telephones. There are a few Art Deco features in the lounge and some of the bathrooms. A craft centre (glass-making a speciality) has recently been created from the old stable block. ***Rooms** 7. Garden, fishing, putting.* AMERICAN EXPRESS *Access, Diners, Visa.*

Uig — Uig Hotel — 59%

£75

H

Tel 047 042 205 Fax 047 042 308

Uig Isle of Skye Highland IV51 9YE

Map 2 A3

On a hillside at the north end of the island, the former coaching inn is handy for the ferry to Uist and Harris. It was established as a hotel in 1946 by Grace Graham, who still plays an active role. You come here to enjoy the peace and solitude, the wonderful scenery, the walks and the wildlife. Day rooms are neat and homely, and there are sea views from the glass-fronted sun lounge, which features fine water colours and etchings of distinction. Comfortable bedrooms with smart co-ordinated colour schemes include six in Sobhraig House, a converted steading next to the hotel. Popular for bridge congresses, plus garden and wildlife tours. ***Rooms** 16. Garden, pony trekking. Closed mid Oct-1 Apr.* AMERICAN EXPRESS *Access, Diners, Visa.*

Ullapool — Altnaharrie Inn — 73%

£230*

HR

Tel 085 483 230

Ullapool Wester Ross Highland IV26 2SS

Map 2 B2

A small launch transfers you from the quayside at Ullapool across Loch Broom. The trip takes approximately 10 minutes and transports you to the crock of gold at the end of a rainbow. Wisteria-clad and painted white with a cottage garden at the front, the impression from the sea as you approach is of a delightful house surrounded by trees nestling below heather-clad hills. The welcome extended by Fred Brown as you walk up the path to the front door is as warm and charming as the wonderful interior. The smell of log fires mingles with the heady perfume of gigantic lily blooms in the entrance hall, which doubles as a small but comfortable lounge. There's a further, more spacious lounge upstairs. Decor throughout is a very tasteful mix of styles – the rough white-painted walls hung with all manner of artwork, beautiful paintings and craftwork. Books abound as do vases of simply arranged but stunning flowers. Bedrooms, whether upstairs in the main house or in the little cottages close by in the grounds,

See over

are brightly decorated, spotless and possess all the charm and style you'd expect from a very well-run small country hotel. While there are no radios or TVs, little extras which are provided include fresh fruit and water. Candles and torches are there for night-time use when the generator is switched off. Bathrooms are equally bright and immaculately maintained. Fine toiletries more than compensate for the sometimes peaty appearance of the water, which is inevitable in such a remote location. Rooms are serviced to a very professional and high standard with beds turned down at night and bathrooms tidied up with fresh towels provided. Breakfasts in the morning are a simpler extension of the previous night's dinner with a wonderful selection of carefully prepared items, from porridge to venison sausages and buttery croissants, home-made jams and marmalades – a meal that will help sustain you almost till dinner-time. The ferry leaves shortly after breakfast returning to Ullapool where cars are parked in a private quayside car park. This is a strictly no-smoking hotel. No children under 7. *Half-board terms only. ***Rooms** 8. Garden. Closed mid Nov-week before Easter.* AMERICAN EXPRESS

Restaurant ★★★ £120

A phenomenal restaurant in an idyllic location. The dining room is a picture of style and informal elegance. A polished lightwood-strip floor partly overlaid with Oriental rugs, beautiful artwork on the stark white walls and highly polished mahogany tables together with gleaming glassware, candles, fresh flowers and the views from the windows of the loch, which laps the edge of the garden, all create one of the most beautifully romantic settings imaginable. Gunn Eriksen almost never emerges from her kitchen, remaining behind the scenes and almost singlehandedly creating dishes of great visual appeal and artistry. Her sources are mainly the rich wealth of local produce and in the thirteen years she has been cooking here suppliers have come to know that she will countenance only the very best. This laudable fastidiousness manifests itself in such sights as the living larder of crabs, scallops and lobsters, their sea-bed locations marked by numerous red buoys. With the great dependence on the delivery of supplies to this remote location it's a marvel that the menus change on a daily basis. When reservations are taken guests are asked whether they have any food dislikes or allergies as there is no choice on the five-course menu except at the dessert stage when a choice of three is available, often all three being offered, and not in half portions! The use of rare or little known foods is common, with Gunn drawing from the land and sea almost anything that takes her fancy, fashioning it into a dish that totally captivates the palate. Natural flavours and textures abound, subtly enhanced by the delicate use of fresh herbs and well-considered seasonings. Sauces too are perfect accompaniments to the dishes, most being simply the reduced pan juices of the main ingredient to which a few discreet additions are made. Menus are well-balanced, dishes complementing one another to create a meal that will remain imprinted on the memory for a long, long time. A typical repast will begin with featherlight crisp puff pastry shells filled with capelin roe blended with sour cream and topped with Oscietre caviar. Excellent breads, naturally all home-baked, accompany a starter of thinly sliced scallops, interleaved with rounds of summer truffles laid on a circle of puff pastry with coral butter, and two sauces – one of the reduced scallop juices with butter and Barsac, the other of veal stock with a hint of wild deer stock – a sharp and enlivening contrast that works magically. To follow, a lobster soup – the clear stock delicately imbued with ginger, coriander, chervil, dill and lots of champagne, the lobster meltingly tender and presented, sliced, with a single claw. Main course of lamb fillet, cooked to a delicious pink tenderness is accompanied by a small parcel of more of the fillet wrapped in leek with foie gras and herbs. In the centre of the plate is a round of paper-thin slices of new potatoes baked with garlic and rosemary in lamb fat. Chopped oyster and chanterelle mushrooms scattered in the reduced meat juices and a tiny cherry tomato stuffed with fresh thyme salad completes a stunning dish. Next, a choice of some 25 very special British cheeses – the chosen selection served with fruit bread and fresh fruit. For lessert the choice is the likes of pistachio and lemon tart; a pear dessert of ayers of bitter chocolate, vanilla ice cream and pear balls surrounded by a yrup of pear juice with Poire William eau de vie; or perhaps an apple aked in very fine puff-pastry leaves with a Calvados ice cream and a aramel sauce on the side – the ice cream just beginning to melt, creating a ensational finale. Though the cheapest champagne is 50p short of £40, the est of the excellent wine list is fairly priced with some real gems. Notable ouse and half bottle selections. Delicious petits fours and coffee are served n one of the two lounges. Service led by Fred Brown is informal and aultless. ***Seats** 18. Parties 14. D only 7.30 for 8.*

Jllapool Ceilidh Place £90

Tel 0854 612103 Fax 0854 612886 **I**

14 West Argyle Street Ullapool Highland IV26 2TY **Map 2 B2**

.iterally meaning 'Meeting Place', Ceilidh Place is much more: bookshop, rts centre, coffee shop, evening restaurant and venue for theatre, music and oetry all housed in a cosy collection of welcoming rooms. Such is the xtent of the live entertainment that the single little TV is more than dequate. The pretty bedrooms are comfortable and spotless; ten rooms ow have en-suite facilities. Eleven additional rooms in a separate building cross the street offer more spartan, budget accommodation with shared acilities. Families are well catered for. ***Rooms** 13. Coffee shop (9.30am-9pm) Closed 2 weeks Jan.* AMERICAN EXPRESS *Access, Diners, Visa.*

Jllapool Places of Interest

Tourist Information Tel 0854 612135.

Jphall Houstoun House 68% £110

Tel 0506 853831 Fax 0506 854220 **H**

Jphall Lothian EH52 6JS **Map 3 C5**

Three buildings, the main one distinctively gabled, and set in 20 acres of fine gardens that include yew hedges and copper beeches of great ntiquity. Apart from its convenience, it also offers comfortable and roomy ccommodation in bedrooms that are either contemporary in style or more raditional, some with four-posters. Tower bedrooms retain some of the riginal 17th-century panelling. Day rooms also vary in age and character; here's a pleasantly modern lounge overlooking the tree-lined drive and hree panelled dining rooms. ***Rooms** 30. Garden.* AMERICAN EXPRESS *Access, Diners, Visa.*

Our inspectors are full-time employees; they are professionally trained by us.

Vhitebridge Knockie Lodge 71% £150*

Tel 0456 486276 Fax 0456 486389 **HR**

Vhitebridge Highland IV1 2UP **Map 3 B4**

ust 20 minutes from Fort Augustus but a world away from the tourist-eaten track, Knockie Lodge enjoys a glorious setting above Loch Nan ann surrounded by sheep, the occasional deer and with mountain views ll around. Built as a hunting lodge in 1789 the building is not grand but s immensely civilised with a timelessly tranquil atmosphere nurtured y the warm hospitality of Ian and Brenda Milward. Peat and log fires

See over

warm the antique-filled hall and appealing morning room (where the honesty bar is to be found) with family photos and ornaments adding to the charm. Traditionally furnished bedrooms (some with antiques) are prettily decorated and boast fresh flowers, mineral water and lots of books. All have direct dial phones but no radio or TV. No children under ten. *Half-board terms only. ***Rooms** 10. Garden, fishing, sailing, snooker. Closed Nov-Apr.* AMERICAN EXPRESS *Access, Diners, Visa.*

Restaurant £70

Booking is essential as non-resident diners cannot always be accommodated in this delightful dado-panelled dining room where polished antique tables gleam in the candle-light. Good use is made of local ingredients on the no-choice (except at the pud stage) five-course set menu that might consist of monkfish lasagne followed by soup before the likes of local lamb fillet with a mushroom and aubergine timbale and honey-roasted garlic-flavoured sauce or Scottish salmon baked with herbs on a bed of creamed spinach with saffron mayonnaise. Apple tatin or blackcurrant bavarois perhaps before cheese with home-baked walnut bread to complete an entirely satisfactory meal. No children under ten. No smoking. ***Seats** 20. D only 7.30 for 8. Set D £28.*

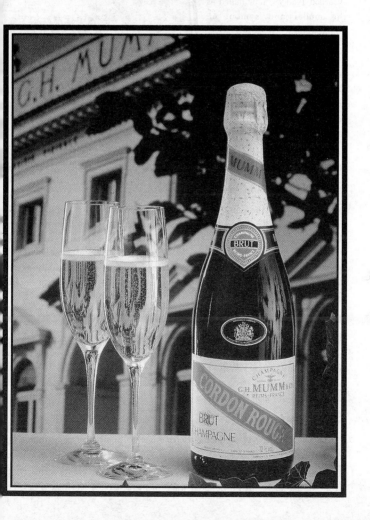

A great Champagne is born

Reims, March 1, 1827 saw the birth of a new house of champagne, "P.A. Mumm et Co.". The founding fathers, Gottlieb Mumm and his two brothers, Jules and Edouard, recognised masters of the art, came from a long line of wealthy German wine-makers and owned vineyards in the Rhine Valley.

From the very first year, Mumm met with resounding success that was even further inspired, in 1875, with the creation of the incomparable "Cordon Rouge", now hailed as the model and symbol of champagne. In 1838, with Gottlieb's son, Georges Hermann de Mumm, the position and prestige of the house of Mumm were established and it took on the name "G.H.Mumm & Cie".

Ever since, the perfection and style of Mumm have been acclaimed the world over.

Fine soils and noble wines

Since the turn of the century Mumm has been recognised as one of the most famous "vineyard houses" in the Champagne region. The estate contains some of the finest crus - Côte des Blancs, Montagne de Reims, Vallée de la Marne and now covers more than three hundred hectares of superlative soil. With such quality grapes, Mumm produces champagnes from a palette of the finest crus, each with an individual flavour, every cuvée endowed with finesse, elegance and freshness.

Harmony

Each Mumm champagne is unique. Tradition, precision and true affection go into each and every bottle of Mumm champagne. To achieve perfection for such harmony, from twenty-five to as many as forty crus are blended to produce one single cuvée. A great champagne can only enjoy grace, elegance and longevity through the blending of the finest grape varieties.

A subtle art

Every year, the art of producing a cuvée is a truly creative endeavour. By increasing the number of sources and maintaining strict control of the quality of the wines, Mumm has expanded the subtle range of its incomparable style. After tasting more than a hundred wines in the cellars, a selection is made of those to be blended. Subtle marriages of taste depend on the skill and art of the cellar-master and on the entire team.

For perfect balance, the best wines, best crus and best grapes are selected: Chardonnays from the Côte des Blancs offer elegance and finesse, Pinots Noirs from the Montagne de Reims adds a rich wine flavour, while Pinots Meunier from the Vallée de la Marne are lively and fruity. Subtlety, nobility and grace,. together with strength and longevity combine in precious alchemy, yielding the perfection of Mumm champagnes. And so the unparalleled quality of Mumm wines continues from year to year.

The prestige of Mumm

First produced in 1875, the celebrated cuvée Cordon Rouge, bearing the emblem of the French Légion d'Honneur is now a symbol of refinement and respect for tradition. Ever since the Roaring Twenties, no celebration nor gala has been complete without the magic bottles bearing the name of Mumm. Seven other cuvées now make up the full range: vintage and non-vintage Cordon Rouge brut, vintage Cordon Rosé, Cordon Vert, Mumm de Cramant, René Lalou and, the height of perfection, Grand Cordon de Mumm.

Inspiration, transcending style

As ambassadors of excellence and a unique lifestyle, Mumm champagnes have long been partners in artistic ventures and noble endeavours. The famous Cordon Rouge has inspired such creative geniuses as Utrillo, Brayer, Chapelain-Midy, Carzou and Foujita who decorated the chapel of "Notre Dame de la Paix" in Reims. Mumm has also been a source of inspiration for great sailors. Since 1977 it has organised the famous "Champagne Mumm Admiral's Cup" and, more recently, the prestigious "Champagne Mumm World Cup".

Tasting Notes
by the Cellar-master at Mumm!

Cordon Rouge

Colour
Eager, exciting bubbles. Brilliant, full and laced with dreams. Golden on wheat straw background.

Nose
Ample, colourful and fruity. Redolent of smoking greengage jam.

Palate
A strong personality and decisive character... with velvet roundness. Chivalrous courtship of tastebuds. Transient touch of almond and peach. Lingering powerfully, charming and virile.

Tasting
A loyal, steady cuvée, the blend showing powerful body yet delicate form. Acts magnetically, for apéritif, and is a sprightly companion throughout a meal. A gem of a champagne, harmoniously combining many crus.

Vintage Cordon Rouge

Colour
Delicate and harmonious bright tints. Light straw with a touch of mellow gold. Attractively eager yet gentle bubbles.

Nose
Earthy caress on a fresh spring morning. Aromas of healthy, fleshy yellow apples. Decisive, frank and full of go.

Palate
Reassuringly soft-angled robustness. Gallant and vivacious. A gentle touch on the tastebuds.

Tasting
A robust, lively wine eager to live long. It will enhance meat and poultry in the midst of a meal. A happy marriage of power and elegance and a smiling cuvée.

Cordon Vert

Colour
Mellow gold with amber tints. Bold confident bubbles.

Nose
Pulpy and fleshy. Penetratingly soothing. Velvet aromas of melting pear.

Palate
Heralding untold pleasures. Tastebuds under sugary spell. Top-bred glucose languorous and long.

Tasting
A symphony of many crus brought together in sweet alliance. A wine made from fully ripe selected grapes. An indispensable companion of refined desserts.

Vintage Cordon Rosé

Colour

Twirling, pink salmon. Subtle hints of gold and crimson. Springtime sprightliness and freshness.

Nose

Convincing and teasing. Aromas of cunningly-scented red fruit.

Palate

Generously firm, yet full of courteousness. Soothingly round, velvety and fresh. A fleetingly... lingering dream.

Tasting

Its youthful finesse is its hope and pride. The table's pleasures it sees as white meats and cheeses. It is at any time to be desired a symbol of love and happiness.

Grand Cordon

Colour

Laced with jade and gold. Roguishly gracious bubbles.

Nose

Floral and convincingly persuasive. Aromas of delicate earthy flavours. Ample, balanced and fruity.

Palate

Grace and charm, finesse and elegance, showing a smilingly personable presence. A discreet personality and a fine character.

Tasting

A fine, enchanting cuvée, caressingly and poetically evocative of pleasure. A champagne full of freshness and jollity, sweet at any time of the day, a byword for pleasure and love. An excellent apéritif, it is better still before meat, with starters and fish if the meal is to be champagne only.

René Lalou

Colour

Noble, eager bubbles. Stylish and proud in its bearing. Gold and jade form its colour.

Nose

Unctuous and enthralling. Aromas of blossoming hawthorn. Proud and fiery all along.

Palate

Strikes as frank and heady. Fruity, pressing, sweet and long. Generous, powerful, smiling and strong.

Tasting

A harmonious, pulpy, yet gracious wine. A desirable cuvée for the inquiring and informed palate. A champagne for all seasons, a noble wine to preside over a grand dinner.

Mumm de Cramant

Colour

A blend of jade and light. A light froth is to this champagne what delicate features are to a woman's face.

Nose

Full of freshness and youth. Noble wood seasoned with great spirits. Perky aromas of new-born vine-shoots.

Palate

Gentle, remarkably delicate impression. Lingering and caressingly voluptuous. Graceful, poetical finish.

Tasting

Fond of smiling lips, it will give joy and cheerfulness as an apéritif. Early in the meal, it will get on fine with fish, pastry and shellfish.

CHAMPAGNE MUMM ADMIRAL'S CUP

Every two years the small town of Cowes on the Isle of Wight plays host to an international yachting regatta of world renown – the Champagne Mumm Admiral's Cup. It was here in 1815 that one of the world's oldest and most exclusive Yacht Clubs was founded, known today as the Royal Yacht Squadron. British and foreign royalty attend and participate in the Cowes Week racing adding a social dimension to make the event a classic in the international sporting calendar.

To win the Champagne Mumm Admiral's Cup is to win one of the most competitive trophies in yacht racing. The crews represent each country's best sailors – America's Cup helmsmen and Olympic medalists combined with the best yachts from the top designers. The racing takes place between July 26th and August 12th, including inshore and offshore courses, culminating in the famous 600 mile Fastnet Race.

For 16 years Champagne Mumm has been closely involved in the world of international sailing, a sport which symbolises adventure and challenge combined with a respect for the natural environment.

Through the Champagne Mumm Admiral's Cup and the Champagne Mumm World Cup circuit, the message of excellence, craftsmanship and tradition is reflected in the partnership between Grand Prix racing and champagne.

These events promote the image of Mumm to an important loyal and upscale audience and also provide many local sales and promotional opportunities to affiliates and distributors internationally.

CHAMPAGNE MUMM WORLD CUP

Wales

Abercynon — Llechwen Hall — £60

Tel 0443 742050 Fax 0443 742189 — **I**

Abercynon nr Llanfabon Mid Glamorgan CF37 4HP — **Map 9 C6**

Literally at the head of the valley (signposted from the A4054), Llechwen Hall is a 17th-century farmhouse, converted to a gentleman's residence in Victorian times, whence to country hotel five years ago. Victorian character is retained in bedroom extensions whose accoutrements are nevertheless up-to-date, with neat bathrooms en suite. A lively local trade adds welcoming warmth to the bars and restaurant and there are banqueting and conference facilities (for up to 80) in the Nelson suite. ***Rooms** 11. Garden.* AMERICAN EXPRESS *Access, Diners, Visa.*

Aberdovey — Plas Penhelig — 62% — £83

Tel 0654 767676 Fax 0654 767783 — **H**

Aberdovey Gwynedd LL35 0NA — **Map 8 C3**

A wooded driveway leads from the A493 to the house, whose seven acres of award-winning grounds include a walled kitchen garden. The views are splendid, whether over the gardens or out across the Dovey estuary. Inside, the feel is Edwardian in the oak-panelled hall and in the south-facing lounge, while bedrooms are more modern in aspect; larger rooms have a table and two chairs. The terrace is an agreeable spot for an alfresco drink. ***Rooms** 11. Garden, putting, tennis. Closed Jan-Mar. Access, Visa.*

Aberdovey — Trefeddian Hotel — 58% — £88*

Tel 0654 767213 Fax 0654 767777 — **H**

Aberdovey Gwynedd LL35 0SB — **Map 8 C3**

Trefeddian stands back from the A493, half a mile north of Aberdovey, with fine views across Cardigan Bay. Day rooms, which include lounge, reading room and bar, offer a choice of peace and quiet or conviviality. Neat, practical bedrooms include several with balconies. *Half-board terms only in the hotel. Self-catering accommodation is also available in a house, flat and bungalow. Family facilities. ***Rooms** 46. Garden, indoor swimming pool, tennis, putting, snooker. Closed end Dec-mid Mar. Access, Visa.*

Abergavenny — Llanwenarth Arms Hotel — NEW — £59

Tel 0873 810550 Fax 0873 811880 — **I**

Brecon Road Abergavenny Gwent NP8 1EP — **Map 9 D5**

A refurbished roadside inn (on the A40) some 3 miles to the west of Abergavenny standing on an escarpment above the Usk valley. Residents enjoy use of their own lounge, and a Victorian-style conservatory furnished with comfortable cane furniture. Bedrooms, approached by way of a sheltered courtyard, are attractively furnished and immaculately kept, each one enjoying its fair share of the view across to Sugar Loaf mountain. ***Rooms** 18.* AMERICAN EXPRESS *Access, Diners, Visa.*

Abergavenny — Walnut Tree Inn — ★★ — £77

Tel 0873 852797 Fax 0873 859764 — **R**

Llandewi Skirrid Abergavenny Gwent NP7 8AW — **Map 9 D5**

The look is of a country pub, the whitewashed building bedecked with baskets of flowers. Inside, an informal bar leads through to the main dining area, a long, narrow room with tables set along the walls. But this is no ordinary pub, as Franco and Ann Taruschio have been demonstrating since 1963. Franco's cooking has found fame literally worldwide; based on a Mediterranean theme, but taking in many other influences, dishes on his daily-changing menu have an instant, honest appeal. Some are homely and familiar – lasagne bolognese is an all-time favourite – while others are attuned to modern fashion: carpaccio of warm salmon and lime, panaché of fish with balsamic vinaigrette. Home-made cotechino is served with lentils, lamb with polenta, herby-crusted baked cod with a tomato coulis. Local ingredients feature in many dishes, including asparagus (au gratin or hollandaise), Llanover salt duck with pickled gooseberries and salmon with rhubarb and ginger. A now established feature is an 18th-century recipe of pasta with porcini, truffles and Parma ham. The sweet menu (Welsh winner of Dessert of the Year) has always been a strength (Sicilian cheesecake, ice creams and sorbets, a chocolate trio) and there are first-rate Italian and British cheeses. Always a fine wine list here, and naturally a stupendous Italian section (ask advice) though there's good balance elsewhere. ***Seats** 44. L 12-3 D 7.15-10. Closed Sun & Mon, Christmas, 2 weeks Feb. No credit cards.*

Abergavenny — Places of Interest

Tourist Information Tel 0873 857588.
Abergavenny Showground Tel 0873 3152.

Aberkenfig — New Garden — £35

Tel 0656 724361 — **R**

40 Pandy Road Aberkenfig nr Bridgend Mid Glamorgan — **Map 9 D5**

Stylishly modern behind an unassuming frontage, New Garden offers a mainly Cantonese menu that keeps the crowds rolling in. Stuffed crab claws, black bean mussels or honey-roast spare ribs could precede soup, then perhaps grilled fish with crabmeat sauce, a filling hot pot dish or one of a dozen ways with duck. Various set meals for 2 or more. ***Seats** 160. Parties 100. L 12-2 D 5.30-12. Closed L Sun, 3 days Christmas. Set meals from £13.* AMERICAN EXPRESS *Access, Diners, Visa.*

Abersoch — Porth Tocyn Hotel — 69% — £94

Tel 0758 713303 Fax 0758 713538 — **HR**

Bwlchtocyn Abersoch Gwynedd LL53 7BU — **Map 8 B3**

Once a row of lead-miners' cottages, the hotel stands high above Cardigan Bay. It's about $2\frac{1}{2}$ miles south of Abersoch, through the hamlets of Sarn Bach and Bwlchtocyn. The Fletcher-Brewer family have guarded their reputation for attentive hospitality for three generations, and the chintzy lounges contribute just the right degree of homeliness. Bedrooms, though generally small, are individually furnished in a similar style, many with restful sea views, all with private bathrooms and showers. Families with children are well catered for (children stay free in parents' room).
***Rooms** 17. Garden, outdoor swimming pool, tennis. Closed mid Nov-week before Easter. Access.*

Restaurant — £60

The focal point of Louise Fletcher-Brewer's culinary output is her short-choice two-or five-course dinner menu, completely changed each day. Salmon and cucumber mousse, venison brochettes with port and rosemary sauce, onion and thyme leaf soup, prawn-stuffed baked bream and veal escalopes with cassis sauce show the style. Steamed Snowdon pudding with gin sauce is a tempting desert. Lunch is casual, maybe alfresco by the pool, with a hot and cold buffet on Sundays. An evolving and sensibly priced wine list includes good-value wines from around the world. House selection offers terrific value. ***Seats** 50. L 12.30-2 D 7.30-9.30. Set L (Sun) £14 Set D £17.50/£23.*

Abersoch — Riverside Hotel — 59% — £80

Tel 0758 712419 Fax 0758 712671 — **H**

Abersoch Gwynedd LL53 7HW — **Map 8 B3**

Messing about on the river is a favourite pastime at the Bakewell family's cheerful hotel, the river in question being the Soch (canoe and rowing boat available). At the front is a harbour, overlooked by the little lounge.

See over

Bedrooms are neat, modern and functional. Reduced rates for children with many facilities supplied including cots, high-chairs and a laundry room. No dogs. ***Rooms** 12. Garden, indoor swimming pool (open Apr-end of Sept). Closed mid Nov-end Feb.* AMERICAN EXPRESS *Access, Diners, Visa.*

Aberystwyth — Conrah Country Hotel — 63% — £79

Tel 0970 617941 Fax 0970 624546 — **H**

Chancery Aberystwyth Dyfed SY23 4DF — **Map 9 B4**

Tucked away at the end of a long drive, three miles south of Aberystwyth, set in 22 acres of grounds and woods, the Conrah puts peace, friendliness and fine views high on the agenda, and the three drawing rooms provide them in abundance. 11 of the bedrooms are in the main house, the rest around a courtyard. All are comfortable and cheerful; all bathrooms are now en suite. ***Rooms** 20. Garden, indoor swimming pool, sauna, table tennis. Closed 1 week Christmas.* AMERICAN EXPRESS *Access, Diners, Visa.*

Aberystwyth — Places of Interest

Tourist Information Tel 0970 612125.
Aberystwyth Arts Centre Tel 0970 623232.
Llywernog Silver-Lead Mine Museum Ponterwyd Tel 0970 85620.
Strata Florida Abbey Tel 09745 261 *10 miles.*
Vale of Rheidol Railway Brecon Mountain Railway Tel 0970 675993/625819.

Barry — Bunbury's — £50

Tel 0446 732075 — **R**

14 High Street Barry South Glamorgan CF6 8EA — **Map 9 C6**

30s' sounds and setting behind the Barry Hotel. The main menu covers a good range of dishes, in individual and often fairly adventurous style: aubergine and walnut caviar, chicory-stuffed chicken. There's also a lunchtime blackboard menu with dishes like cottage pie or spicy peanut chicken priced at around £4. ***Seats** 32. L 10.30-2.30 D 7.30-10 (Sat to 10.30). Closed Sun & Mon, Bank Holidays. Access, Visa.*

Barry — Mount Sorrel Hotel — 59% — £85

Tel 0446 740069 Fax 0446 746600 — **H**

Porthkerry Road Barry South Glamorgan CF6 8AY — **Map 9 C6**

Converted from two Victorian houses 30 years ago, with more recent additions for extra accommodation, meeting rooms and leisure facilities. Comfortable day rooms, very acceptable bedrooms (children up to 12 stay free when sharing with parents); two suites have interconnecting rooms and six other rooms are suitable for families. ***Rooms** 43. Indoor swimming pool, keep-fit equipment, sauna, coffee shop (7am-8pm).* AMERICAN EXPRESS *Access, Diners, Visa.*

Barry — Places of Interest

Knap Swimming Pool Tel 0446 735 175.
Barry Island Pleasure Park Tel 0446 741250.

Beaumaris — Bulkeley Arms — 59% — £77

Tel 0248 810415 Fax 0248 810146 — **H**

Castle Street Beaumaris Anglesey Gwynedd LL58 8AW — **Map 8 B1**

A sturdy Georgian building opposite the pier with splendid views across the Menai Straits to Snowdonia. Families and individual guests are equally well catered for, and children up to 12 stay free in parents' rooms; informal eating in the Castle Bar bistro. Bedrooms are delightfully old-fashioned, with light oak furniture, writing desks and armchairs. There are two bars,

a sunny residents' lounge and a ballroom where functions and regular dances are held. ***Rooms** 43. Garden, beauty salon, massage, chiropodist.*
AMERICAN EXPRESS *Access, Visa.*

Beaumaris Places of Interest

Bangor Information Centre Tel 0248 352786.
Theatr Gwynedd Bangor Tel 0248 351708 *7 miles.*
Cathedral Church of St. Deiniol Bangor Tel 0248 351693.
Historic Houses, Castles and Gardens
Beaumaris Castle Tel 0248 810361.
Beaumaris Gaol Museum Tel 0248 810921.
Penrhyn Castle (NT) Nr Bangor Tel 0248 353084.
Pencarreg Glyn Garth Nr Beaumaris Tel 0248 713545.

Beddgelert Royal Goat Hotel 60% £68

Tel 076 686 224 Fax 076 686 422 **H**

Beddgelert Gwynedd LL55 4YE **Map 8 B2**

The Roberts family play host to the regulars who come for Snowdonia's fishing, walking and climbing. Beyond the white-painted facade an entrance hall/reception has heavily carved furniture and brass ornaments, more of which feature in the comfortable residents-only bar; there's plenty of lounge space and two dining rooms. Some of the bedrooms have four-posters. Children up to 11 stay free in parents' room. Function facilities for up to 150. ***Rooms** 34. Garden, games room, fishing.*
AMERICAN EXPRESS *Access, Diners, Visa.*

Beddgelert Places of Interest

National Trust Information Point Tel 076 686 293.
Sygun Copper Mine Tel 076 686 595.

Betws-y-Coed Royal Oak 59% £74

Tel 0690 710219 Fax 0690 710603 **H**

Holyhead Road Betws-y-Coed Gwynedd LL24 0AY **Map 8 C2**

A solid stone edifice on the river Llugwy where there's a traditional and welcoming air in both the reception and bar with studded brown leather and antique oak furniture. Bedrooms have restful autumnal decor, simple modern furniture and two armchairs; six annexe rooms have glossy laminated furniture with eye-catching mirrored bedheads. No dogs. ***Rooms** 27. Garden, coffee shop (7.30am-9pm).* AMERICAN EXPRESS *Access, Diners, Visa.*

Betws-y-Coed Places of Interest

Plas-y-Brenin National Centre for Mountain Activities Capel Curig Tel 06904 214.
Swallow Falls Tel 0690 710796.

Bontddu Bontddu Hall 62% £90

Tel 0341 49661 Fax 0341 49284 **H**

Bontddu nr Dolgellau Gwynedd LL40 2SU **Map 8 C3**

Michael and Margaretta Ball's Victorian Gothic country mansion stands in Snowdonia National Park off the A496, halfway between Dolgellau and Barmouth. The views are outstanding, particularly from the day rooms and the sun terrace, a popular spot for summer teas. There's a strong period feel, with features like marble columns, a colourful skylight above the main staircase and Victorian church benches in the bar. Bedrooms, the majority also offering fine views over the estuary, include a four-poster room and

See over

one with a spa bath. Six lodge suites are in the hotel grounds. No children under 3, but up-to-16s stay free in parents' room. ***Rooms** 20. Garden. Closed Nov-Mar.* AMERICAN EXPRESS *Access, Diners, Visa.*

Brechfa — Ty Mawr — 60% — £68

Tel 0267 202332 Fax 0267 202437 — **H**

Brechfa nr Carmarthen Dyfed SA32 7RA — **Map 9 B5**

Three stone-built cottages dating from the 15th century make up Beryl and Dick Tudhope's tiny hotel, which stands by the bridge over the river Marlais (the middle name of Dylan Thomas). Relaxation is the name of the game, whether it's over a book in the lounge or a drink in the cosy stone-walled bar, and peace is guaranteed by the absence of phones and TVs in the cottagey, pine-furnished bedrooms. The hotel stands on the B4310. ***Rooms** 5. Garden. Closed last week Nov & 2 weeks Jan.* AMERICAN EXPRESS *Access, Visa.*

Bridgend — Forte Travelodge — £42

Tel 0656 659218 — **L**

Sarn Park Service Area nr Bridgend Mid Glamorgan CF32 9RW — **Map 9 C6**

Located on the M4 at junction 36 at the Welcome Break Service Area. Situated midway between Cardiff and Swansea, 2 miles from Bridgend. ***Rooms** 40.* AMERICAN EXPRESS *Access, Visa.*

Cardiff — Angel Hotel — 66% — £114

Tel 0222 232633 Fax 0222 396212 — **H**

Castle Street Cardiff South Glamorgan CF1 2QZ — **Map 9 D6**

Between the Castle and Arms Park rugby stadium, the distinctive Angel has kept its individual character for over 100 years. Liveried doormen show guests into the foyer, where chandeliers, pillars and a mural of clouds and cherubs try to make a good impression. Bedrooms are generally roomy, and there are several function rooms catering for 300+. Queens Moat Houses. ***Rooms** 91. Gymnasium, sauna, solarium, snooker.* AMERICAN EXPRESS *Access, Diners, Visa.*

Cardiff — Armless Dragon — £50

Tel 0222 382357 — **R**

97 Wyeverne Road Cathays Cardiff South Glamorgan CF2 4BG — **Map 9 D6**

Ostensibly courting the 'adventurous end of a staid market', this bustling bistro is handily placed for the Sherman Theatre and University College. Seafood is always popular, with dishes like fried cod's roe with chive vinaigrette, scallops in sorrel sauce and cod, hake or monkfish grilled, *bonne femme* or in a spicy tomato sauce. Meaty options are no less interesting (red pepper stuffed with lamb, Barbary duck with lemon and almond sauce) and laverballs with mushrooms remains a favourite starter. ***Seats** 45. L 12.30-2.15 D7.30-10.30 (Sat to 11). Closed L Sat, all Sun & Mon, Bank Holidays except Good Friday.* AMERICAN EXPRESS *Access, Diners, Visa.*

Cardiff — Campanile Hotel — £44

Tel 0222 549044 Fax 0222 549000 — **L**

Caxton Place Pentwyn Cardiff South Glamorgan CF2 7HA — **Map 9 D6**

Closest M4 junction is J29; off the Pentwyn interchange of the A48. ***Rooms** 50.* AMERICAN EXPRESS *Access, Diners, Visa.*

Changes in data sometimes occur in establishments after the Guide goes to press. Prices should be taken as indications rather than firm quotes.

Cardiff **Cardiff International** **67%** **£82**

Tel 0222 341441 Fax 0222 223742 **H**

Mary Ann Street Cardiff South Glamorgan CF1 2EQ **Map 9 D6**

A striking modern hotel opposite Cardiff International Arena and next to the National ice rink. Victorian brick and cast iron are cleverly matched, and an arcade-style interior echoes the architecture of Cardiff's markets. Bedrooms, all twin or double-bedded, include two floors upgraded to Executive Standard. Valet parking in a neighbouring NCP car park is a bonus. Smart and keen staff. Children up to 12 accommodated free in their parents' room. Banqueting/conference facilities for 120/40. Free parking for up to 50 cars. ***Rooms** 143.* AMERICAN EXPRESS® *Access, Diners, Visa.*

Cardiff **Cardiff Marriott Hotel** **69%** **£131**

Tel 0222 399944 Fax 0222 395578 **H**

Mill Lane Cardiff South Glamorgan CF1 1EZ **Map 9 D6**

Modern hotel, handy for the station and Arms Park. Bright public areas, decent leisure centre, conference and banqueting facilities for up to 300. ***Rooms** 182. Gymnasium, indoor swimming pool, squash, sauna, spa bath, solarium.* AMERICAN EXPRESS® *Access, Diners, Visa.*

Cardiff **Copthorne Hotel** **70%** **NEW** **£119**

Tel 0222 599100 Fax 0222 599080 **H**

Culverhouse Cross Cardiff South Glamorgan CF5 6XJ **Map 9 D6**

A large new five-storey hotel to the west of town off the A48 near the HTV studios. Lots of wood panelling and rich autumnal colour schemes predominate in appealing public areas, some of which overlook the hotel's own small lake. All the good-sized bedrooms are well laid out with large desks (to which the phone is easily movable) with comfortable armchairs in addition to breakfast table and proper armchair. Good bathrooms feature polished red-granite vanitory units. Rooms on the Connoisseur Floor get extras like bathrobes and slippers plus use of an executive lounge with free soft drinks and Continental breakfast. ***Rooms** 135. Garden, indoor swimming pool, gymnasium, sauna, spa bath, steam room, solarium, beauty salon, snooker, coffee shop (10-10).* AMERICAN EXPRESS® *Access, Diners, Visa.*

Cardiff **Forte Crest** **69%** **£93**

Tel 0222 388681 Fax 0222 371495 **H**

Castle Street Cardiff South Glamorgan CF1 2XB **Map 9 D6**

City-centre hotel located between the river Taff and Arms Park. A business centre supports conferences of up to 180 delegates. ***Rooms** 155. Snooker.* AMERICAN EXPRESS® *Access, Diners, Visa.*

We welcome bona fide complaints and recommendations on the tear-out pages at the back of the book for readers' comments. They are followed up by our professional team.

Cardiff **Forte Posthouse** **63%** **£68**

Tel 0222 731212 Fax 0222 549147 **H**

Pentwyn Road Cardiff South Glamorgan CF2 7XA **Map 9 D6**

Modern hotel near J29 of the M4, four miles from the city. Day rooms were refurbished last year. Conference facilities (up to 140) and a leisure centre. ***Rooms** 139. Indoor swimming pool, gymnasium, sauna, spa bath, solarium.* AMERICAN EXPRESS® *Access, Diners, Visa.*

Cardiff **Forte Travelodge** **£42**

Tel 0222 549564 **L**

Circle Way East Llanederyn Cardiff South Glamorgan CF3 7ND **Map 9 D6**

4 miles north-east of Cardiff city centre. Off the A48(M) on the road to Coed-y-Gores. 3 miles from junction 29 of the M4. ***Rooms*** *32.* AMERICAN EXPRESS *Access, Visa.*

Cardiff **Moat House** **70%** **£103**

Tel 0222 732520 Fax 0222 549092 **H**

Circle Way East Llanederyn Cardiff South Glamorgan CF3 7XF **Map 9 D6**

Set in its own grounds east of Cardiff, this Moat House is smart, comfortable and practical behind its unexciting modern exterior. Day rooms are in open plan, providing plenty of space in which to unwind. The conference complex (for up to 300 delegates) is on the first floor. Good-sized bedrooms, with extra touches of luxury plus evening maid service in Executive rooms. Travelling west on the M4, leave at junction 29 and take the A48(M). Heading east from West Wales, take the A470 at junction 32. ***Rooms*** *135. Indoor swimming pool, keep-fit equipment, spa bath, sauna, solarium. Closed Christmas/New Year.* AMERICAN EXPRESS *Access, Diners, Visa.*

Cardiff **Le Monde** **£40**

Tel 0222 387376 **R**

60 St Mary Street Cardiff South Glamorgan **Map 9 D6**

One of a trio of atmospheric restaurants-cum-wine bars, this one appeals primarily to fish-eaters with a wide array of shell, sea and freshwater fish. Its siblings are *La Brasserie* (0222 372164) specialising in grilled meats and seasonal game and *Champers* (0222 373363) with a Spanish slant to both menu and wine list – over 100 Riojas! *Champers* is open Sunday evening. ***Seats*** *150. L 12-2.30 D 7-12. Closed Sun, 25 Dec.* AMERICAN EXPRESS *Access, Diners, Visa.*

Cardiff **Park Hotel** **70%** **£108**

Tel 0222 383471 Fax 0222 399309 **H**

Park Place Cardiff South Glamorgan CF1 3UD **Map 9 D6**

The Park's impressive stone-clad facade is a striking landmark on Cardiff's pedestrianised Queen Street and today's lack of traffic is a bonus for those occupying the best, front-facing bedrooms. Entry, however, is from Park Place and vehicular access (to the rear) is tricky. Mount Charlotte Thistle's restorations have retained the traditional air of elegance in the reception hall and writing lounge. Caernarvon Room and Harlech Lounge apart, much of the ground and first floors is given over to extensive function and conference facilities with a capacity of up to 300. ***Rooms*** *119.* AMERICAN EXPRESS *Access, Diners, Visa.*

Cardiff **Quayles** **£60**

Tel 0222 341264 **R**

6/8 Romilly Crescent Cardiff South Glamorgan CF1 9NR **Map 9 D6**

Agreeable neighbourhood brasserie with smart black and white tiled floor, black bentwood chairs and art deco mirrors, close to Sophia Gardens. Modern, sensibly-priced no-frills cooking by the Canning family with extremely good value fixed-price lunches and early dinners plus à la carte dinners in a 'Mediterranean' style. Assorted tapas, grilled tomato polenta with blue cheese sauce and Parmesan, tagliatelle verdi with wild mushrooms and ham, salmon baked with thyme and orange, devilled kidneys with mushrooms, warm lemon tart and almond meringues with cream and apricot sauce typify the style, and there's great effort behind

it (which includes making their own breads, growing their own herbs for curing gravad lax and making their own sausages, plus seeking out the best local suppliers). More elaborate Sunday lunch and leisurely brunch (kippers, fish cakes, devilled kidneys, haddock Monte Carlo, prairie oysters, frozen pepper vodka *inter alia*). Occasional themed evenings with music. ***Seats** 46. L 12-2.30 (Sun 11.30-3.30) D 7.30-10.30. Closed D Sun, all Tues, Bank Holidays. Set L £5.25/£11.95 Set D £7.75 (before 8pm).*
Access, Visa.

Cardiff — Travel Inn — £43

Tel 0633 680070 Fax 0633 681143 — **L**

Newport Road Castleton nr Cardiff South Glamorgan CF3 8UQ — **Map 9 D6**

***Rooms** 49. Access, Diners, Visa.*

Cardiff — Places of Interest

Cardiff Tourist Information Tel 0222 227281.
Caerphilly Tourist Information Tel 0222 851378.
Cardiff Arms Park Tel 0222 390111.
Cathedral Church of St. Peter and St. Paul Tel 0222 561545.
The National Museum of Wales Tel 0222 397951.
Welsh Folk Museum St. Fagans Tel 0222 569441.
Wales Empire Pool Tel 0222 382296.
Sophia Gardens Cricket Ground Tel 0222 343478.
Wales National Ice Rink Tel 0222 383451.
Theatres and Concert Halls
Chapter Arts Centre Tel 0222 396061.
New Theatre Tel 0222 394844.
Sherman Theatre Tel 0222 230451.
St. David's Hall Tel 0222 371236.
Historic Houses, Castles and Gardens
Caerphilly Castle Tel 0222 883143 *5 miles.*
Cardiff Castle Tel 0222 822083.
Castle Coch Tongwynlais Tel 0222 810101.
Dyffryn Botanic Garden Tel 0222 593328.

Carmarthen — Ivy Bush Royal — 59% — £60

Tel 0267 235111 Fax 0267 234914 — **H**

Spilman Street Carmarthen Dyfed SA31 1LG — **Map 9 B5**

Once a favoured retreat of Lord Nelson and Lady Hamilton, today a Forte Heritage hotel on the West Wales heritage trail. Slightly fewer bedrooms – some singles have been made into twins/doubles. Coach tours and conferences (max 200). ***Rooms** 75. Garden. Access, Diners, Visa.*

Carmarthen — Places of Interest

Tourist Information Tel 0267 231557.
Carmarthen Museum Tel 0267 231691.
Pembrey Beach *20 miles.*

Chepstow — Beckfords — £60

Tel 0291 626547 — **R**

15-16 Upper Church Street Chepstow Gwent NP6 5EX — **Map 9 D6**

In his elegant Georgian-style restaurant 100 yards from St Mary's Church Jeremy Hector prepares a short menu that changes weekly. Soup, garlic king prawns or mushrooms with paprika and cream could be your starting choice, followed by the day's fish dish, roast grouse with bread sauce or rack of lamb with pink peppercorn or leek, honey and orange sauce. Good cooking, with a touch of imagination. ***Seats** 38. Private Room 12. L 12.30-1.45 (Sun to 2.30) D 7.30-10. Closed L Mon, D Sun, Bank Holidays. Access, Visa.*

Chepstow — Castle View Hotel — £60

Tel 0291 620349 Fax 0291 627397 — **I**

16 Bridge Street Chepstow Gwent NP6 5EZ — **Map 9 D6**

This friendly little hotel was built in the 17th century as a private residence, perhaps with stones from neighbouring Chepstow Castle, which commands the Wye riverbank opposite. Ivy-covered now, and genuinely welcoming, it's immaculately kept by Martin and Vicky Cardale. Original walls and timbers may still be seen, both in the public area and in some bedrooms, most of which have recently been refurbished with smart mahogany pieces. One room, with its own lounge and sleeping up to four, is in a small cottage next door and there are two spacious family rooms overlooking the garden. Good variety of snacks in the bar. ***Rooms** 11.*
AMERICAN EXPRESS *Access, Diners, Visa.*

Chepstow — Leadon's Brasserie — £42

Tel 0291 627402 — **R**

Beaufort Square Chepstow Gwent NP6 5XJ — **Map 9 D6**

A bustling basement with a lively atmosphere and skilled cooking by the chef/patron. Regular items on an ever-changing blackboard menu include terrine of crab and smoked salmon, chicken liver paté with onion marmalade, halibut with avocado mayonnaise and lamb cutlets with courgette fritters. ***Seats** 46. L 12-2 D 6-10. Closed Sat & Sun. Set D £12.50.*

Chepstow — St Pierre Hotel — 66% — £100

Tel 0291 625261 Fax 0291 629975 — **H**

St Pierre Park Chepstow Gwent NP6 6YA — **Map 9 D6**

The heart of the hotel is a 14th-century mansion standing in 400 acres complete with a large lake. An extensive leisure club, two golf courses and a conference area (up to 220 delegates theatre-style) make it a fine base for work or leisure. Among the day rooms are spacious lounges, three restaurants and a poolside bar. Bedrooms, many with splendid views, include 30 of Executive standard and 43 in the Lakeside village. Children up to 16 stay free in parents' room. Direct reservations line 0291 624444. Country Club Hotels. ***Rooms** 147. Garden, indoor swimming pool, squash, badminton, sauna, spa bath, solarium, beauty salon, tennis, bowling, coffee shop (10am-10pm).* AMERICAN EXPRESS *Access, Diners, Visa.*

Chepstow — Places of Interest

Tourist Information Tel 0291 623772.
Chepstow Castle Tel 0291 624065.
Chepstow Museum Tel 0291 625981.
Chepstow Racecourse Tel 0291 622260.
Caldicot Castle Tel 0291 420241 *5 miles.*

Chirk — Starlings Castle — £50

Tel 0691 718464 — **RR**

Bron Y Garth Oswestry Shropshire SY10 7NU — **Map 8 D2**

It's handy to note that despite a Shropshire address Bron Y Garth lies across the border into Clwyd, high atop an escarpment overlooking Offa's Dyke; and it's certainly advisable to obtain directions when booking (they will be happy to send you a map). This is less historic Welsh castle than hidden 18th-century sandstone farmhouse whose whitewashed dining room exudes a cool, Mediterranean feel. Antony Pitt's food is also firmly down-to-earth, its roots in fine fresh produce and abundant flavours. Half a dozen starters may include an interesting soup (tomato and coriander consommé), escabeche of tuna, *jambon persillé*, followed by the likes of Provençal pigeon casserole, fillet of halibut with oysters and dill, raspberry and water melon soup, hot chocolate soufflé, lemon tart and a mix of Welsh and Continental cheeses. Ten tables in the garden in really good weather. A new pottery studio provides an interesting distraction. Family facilities. Service is relaxed and informal, Jools Pitt a refined and engaging hostess. ***Seats** 24. Private Room 28. L (Sun only) 12-2.30 D 7-10. Closed 2 weeks end Feb. Access, Visa.*

Rooms **£44**

The eight bedrooms share a couple of bathrooms along a single landing. Set under low eaves, they're cosy enough, with truly comfortable beds, thick duvets and water bottles in winter. Great country breakfasts with home-made bread and preserves.

Clydach The Drum and Monkey NEW

£50

Tel 0873 831980 **R**

Clydach Blackrock Abergavenny Gwent **Map 9 D5**

Skilful conversion of a derelict pub alongside the A465 has created a refined restaurant and lounge bar whose views of Clydach Gorge are superb. Jon West's cooking skills shine throughout a dinner of plaice mousse with garlic prawns hollandaise, Cajun seasoned halibut steak, chicken breast with avocado and Stilton and traditional desserts such as jam sponge and custard or milk chocolate cheesecake. Lighter bar snacks daily: early evening menu £11.95 for three courses. Check directions when booking. ***Seats** 45. Parties 15. Private Room 25. L 12-2 D 6-10. Set D £11.95. No credit cards.*

Colwyn Bay Café Niçoise NEW

£45

Tel 0492 531555 **R**

124 Abergele Road Colwyn Bay Clwyd **Map 8 C1**

Traditional and modern French cooking in a romantic setting with French background music. Typical dishes on owner Carl Swift's menu could include smoked salmon paupiettes with a lime and cucumber dressing, Welsh lamb with boulangère potatoes and Paris-Brest with apricot sauce. Fish specials; vegetarian list. ***Seats** 32. Parties 20. L 12-2 D 7-10. Closed L Mon, all Sun, 26 Dec & 1 Jan. Set D £12.95. Access, Visa.*

Colwyn Bay Hotel Seventy Degrees 61%

£53

Tel 0492 516555 Fax 0492 515565 **H**

Penmaenhead Colwyn Bay Clwyd LL29 9LD **Map 8 C1**

High on a cliff that affords panoramic sea and mountain views, this distinctive hotel takes its name not from its 70s origin but from the unusual angle at which it was built. Day rooms are light and airy, and bedrooms are given a touch of character by Impressionist posters. The hotel is easily and quickly reached from the A55. Children up to 12 stay free in parents' room. ***Rooms** 43.* AMERICAN EXPRESS *Access, Diners, Visa.*

Colwyn Bay Places of Interest

Tourist Information Tel 0492 530478.
Bodnant Garden Tal-y-Cafn Tel 0492 650460.
Bodelwyddan Castle Bodelwyddan Tel 0745 583539 *10 miles.*
Welsh Mountain Zoo Tel 0492 532938.

Conwy Sychnant Pass Hotel 60%

£60

Tel 0492 596868 Fax 0492 870009 **HR**

Sychnant Pass Road Conwy Gwynedd LL32 8BJ **Map 8 C1**

A substantial white-pebbledash house set in three acres of grounds that include a stream, a pond and woods. It's lovely walking country but when the weather's not so kind the lounge and bar are good places to relax. Fine

See over

views can be enjoyed from the bedrooms, the best and largest of which are those in the original part of the house where furnishings are traditional; other rooms have modern units. The Conwy Tunnel considerably eases access to this pleasant location. Children up to 12 stay free in parents' room. ***Rooms** 14. Garden.* AMERICAN EXPRESS *Access, Diners, Visa.*

Conwy Places of Interest

Tourist Information Tel 0492 592248.
Conwy Castle Tel 0492 592358.
Aberconwy House Tel 0492 592246
Smallest House Quayside

Coychurch Coed-y-Mwstwr Hotel 70% £95

Tel 0656 860621 Fax 0656 863122 **HR**

Coychurch Bridgend Mid Glamorgan CF35 6AF **Map 9 C6**

High above the Vale of Glamorgan, the "whispering trees" of this Victorian hotel's name are easily heard among the 17 acres of ancient woodland in which Coed-y-Mwstwr stands, one of the most attractively positioned country mansions in South Wales. True to its Victorian origins, decor and furnishings are a blend of homely charm and elegant period style: private suites and function rooms have high ceilings, chandeliers, oak panelling and huge fireplaces. Bedrooms throughout are spacious and comfortable with crown-canopied beds and carpeted bathrooms containing bathrobes and a good supply of toiletries. Children up to 14 stay free in parents' room. Leave the M4 at Junction 35. ***Rooms** 24. Outdoor swimming pool, tennis, garden, snooker.* AMERICAN EXPRESS *Access, Diners, Visa.*

Elliot Room £75

The setting is one of high-beamed ceiling, chandeliers and wood-panelled walls, and fixed-priced lunch and dinner menus are equally serious affairs, designed to reflect the best ingredients of the locality. Welsh specialities feature on the à la carte: healthy options weigh in with the likes of marinated tofu and Oriental stir-fry vegetables. Careful attention is paid to both the all-Welsh cheeseboard and the well-stocked cellar. ***Seats** 50. L 12-2.30 D 7.30-10.15 (Sat to 10.30, Sun to 9.30). Set L £12.50/£16 Set D £24.*

Crickhowell Bear Hotel £48

Tel 0873 810408 Fax 0873 811696 **I**

High Street Crickhowell Powys NP8 1BW **Map 9 D5**

Dating back to the 15th century and once a stopping-off point on the London-West Wales coaching route, the Bear continues its tradition of hospitality as the focal point of the market town. The evocative bars, with low black beams, sturdy old furniture and open fires, are good places for a snack, a drink or a chat with owners and locals, and upstairs there's a quiet residents' lounge. Bedrooms, some grouped round a courtyard, have good-quality furniture and warm, well-chosen fabrics. Top of the range is a four-poster room with jacuzzi. Three rooms, including one suite, have recently been completed in an annexe. ***Rooms** 28. Garden.* AMERICAN EXPRESS *Access, Visa.*

Crickhowell Gliffaes Country House Hotel 63% £63

Tel 0874 730371 Fax 0874 730463 **H**

Crickhowell Powys NP8 1RH **Map 9 D5**

Fishing is the favourite pastime at this distinctive late-Victorian house (spot the campanile), which overlooks a mile of water on the left bank of the Usk. Many other outdoor activities have a following here, while the sitting room and drawing room are splendid places for doing nothing. Bedrooms are spacious and attractively furnished with old or antique pieces. The hotel stands in its own attractive grounds west of Crickhowell. Dogs permitted in the lodge. ***Rooms** 22. Garden, fishing, tennis, putting, golf practice net, snooker. Closed 31 Dec – 25 Feb.* AMERICAN EXPRESS® *Access, Diners, Visa.*

Crickhowell — Places of Interest

Tretower Court & Castle Tel 0874 730279.

Cross Hands — Forte Travelodge

£42

Tel 0269 845700

L

A48 Cross Hands nr Llanelli Dyfed SA14 6NW

Map 9 B5

On the A48 eastbound, 11 miles east of Carmarthen. ***Rooms** 32.* AMERICAN EXPRESS® *Access, Visa.*

Eglwysfach — Ynyshir Hall — 70%

£110

Tel 0654 781209 Fax 0654 781366

HR

Eglwysfach Machynlleth Powys SY20 8TA

Map 8 C3

Queen Victoria once owned this modestly sized Georgian house, now the home of Joan and Rob Reen. Rob is an accomplished artist whose work is to be found in bedrooms, each named after a famous painter, and throughout the immaculate day rooms which also feature a collection of Oriental rugs. An artist's eye is also evident in the stylish decor of the bedrooms, which are furnished with antiques and come with magazines, books and mineral water (best rooms also get sherry) amongst other comforts. Good bathrooms are equally well appointed. Breakfast includes freshly squeezed orange juice and home-made conserves. Check-out time on day of departure is a rather early 10.30am. No children under 9 years. ***Rooms** 9. Garden, pitch & putt.* AMERICAN EXPRESS® *Access, Diners, Visa.*

Restaurant

£60

Rob's most recent works tend to feature on the walls of the dining room with its well-spaced, crisply-clothed tables. Just five choices at each step of the fixed-price, monthly-changing menu but an extra starter and main course of the day helps to provide variety for guests staying for more than a day or two. Starter might include a turbot and salmon millefeuille with blackcurrant, crab and truffle ravioli with asparagus and a leek and chicken roulade with ginger and coriander with an orange and lime sauce. Main courses, which come with vegetables chosen to suit each individual dish, range from saddle of Welsh lamb with onion marmalade with orange and rosemary stuffing to rabbit and Calvados pie. Good wine list includes about a dozen house wines available by the glass. ***Seats** 20. Private Room 12. L (Sun only) 12.30-1.30 D 7-8.30. Set L £15 Set D £23.*

Ewloe — St David's Park Hotel — 69%

£107

Tel 0244 520800 Fax 0244 520930

H

St David's Park Ewloe Clwyd CH5 3YB

Map 8 D2

Purpose-built on Georgian inspiration, this fine example of modern hotel construction stands by the junction of the A55 and A494. Its interior continues the Georgian theme, with the period's decorative style used throughout. The business and conference markets are well catered for (250+ delegates can be seated theatre-style) and there's a well-equipped leisure club. Bedrooms, furnished in light oak, include suites and studio rooms, ladies' executive rooms, family rooms and some designed for disabled guests. Children up to 16 stay free in parents' room. In mid-1994 the hotel is due to open Northop Country Park, a few minutes away, which comprises golf, tennis and country club. ***Rooms** 121. Indoor swimming pool, gymnasium, spa bath, steam room, sauna, solarium, beautician, games room, children's playroom, snooker.* AMERICAN EXPRESS® *Access, Diners, Visa.*

Fishguard — Fishguard Bay Hotel — 59% — £60

Tel 0348 873571 Fax 0348 873030 — **H**

Quay Road Goodwick Fishguard Dyfed SA64 0BT — **Map 9 A5**

Ten acres of woodland stand at the back while Cardigan Bay is straight ahead and the ferry service to Rosslare is only minutes away. A popular venue for functions, with conferences accommodating up to 200, banqueting up to 300. Best bedrooms have bay-facing balconies: only seven rooms don't have en-suite bathrooms. Children up to 14 stay free in their parents' room. ***Rooms** 62. Garden.* AMERICAN EXPRESS *Access, Diners, Visa.*

Gowerton — Cefn Goleu Park — 69% — £80

Tel 0792 873099 — **HR**

Cefn Stylle Road Gowerton West Glamorgan SA4 3QS — **Map 9 B6**

Bought by Emma and Claude Rossi in 1987, the manor house, which stands in 48 acres of gardens, has been restored with love, patience and the skills of local craftsmen. A stunning vaulted central hall contains unique showcases of china dolls, and is ringed by a minstrel's gallery leading to four master bedrooms with Victorian elegance recreated. Further similarly appointed accommodation is available in the adjoining coach house. No dogs. ***Rooms** 6. Garden. Closed Jan. Access, Visa.*

Restaurant — £60

From Claude and Bernard's kitchen come hearty, full-flavoured dishes such as chicken in a mustard sauce, trout stuffed with garlic, parsley, breadcrumbs and cheese, and veal escalope with vermouth and orange. Sunday lunchtime brings soup, melon or paté, four main courses including a couple of roasts, and the sweet trolley. ***Seats** 40. Private Room 20. L (Sun only) 12.30-2 D 7.30-9.30. Closed D Sun, all Mon. Set L £11.50.*

Gwbert-on-Sea — Cliff Hotel — 60% — £79

Tel 0239 613241 Fax 0239 615391 — **H**

Gwbert-on-Sea Cardigan Dyfed SA43 1PP — **Map 9 B4**

Dramatically located on 30 acres of headland overlooking Cardigan Island, a privately owned hotel whose convivial atmosphere is augmented by friendly staff and high-profile management. There's a wealth of recreational facilities, both on and off site, for all the family (under-12s free in parents' room); conference and banqueting (max 200). Self-catering apartments offering full use of the hotel facilities are also available. ***Rooms** 73. Garden, outdoor swimming pool, gymnasium, squash, sauna, solarium, golf (9), snooker.* AMERICAN EXPRESS *Access, Diners, Visa.*

Halkyn — Forte Travelodge — £42

Tel 0352 780952 — **L**

A55 Halkyn Clwyd CH8 8RF — **Map 8 D1**

On the A55 westbound 13 miles west of Chester, 5 miles south of Holywell and 15 miles north-west of Wrexham. ***Rooms** 31.* AMERICAN EXPRESS *Access, Visa.*

Harlech — The Cemlyn — £55

Tel 0766 780425 — **RR**

High Street Harlech Gwynedd LL46 2YA — **Map 8 B2**

A large picture window provides wonderful views from Ken Goody's unpretentious little restaurant, but his nightly menus provide the greatest draw, with two or three courses offered at fixed prices. Local produce (with interesting combinations of natural flavours) and the best local seafood are the highlights: gratin of mussels, sautéed monkfish with fresh mango and mild curry sauce, cream of pea soup with tarragon, wild rabbit with mustard sauce, roast smoked ham with Madeira sauce and baked peach; lemon sorbet brulée, Kentucky rum and chocolate pie or good unpasteurised Welsh cheeses to finish. The wine list has been very carefully honed since last year. No smoking in the sea view extension. ***Seats** 52. Parties 12. Private Room 10. L by arrangement only D 7-9 (Sat to 9.30). Closed Nov-mid Mar. Set D £14.50/£16.50. Access, Visa.*

Room **£40**

There is one twin-bedded room with comfortable armchairs, hundreds of books and the same great view as the restaurant. Don't miss the marvellous breakfast. No children under 8. No dogs.

Harlech — Places of Interest

Tourist Information Tel 0766 780658.
Theatr Ardudwy Tel 0766 780667.
Harlech Castle Tel 0766 780552.

Lake Vyrnwy — Lake Vyrnwy Hotel — 64% — £70

Tel 069 173 692 Fax 069 173 289 **H**

Lake Vyrnwy (via Oswestry) Llanwyddyn Powys SY10 0LY **Map 8 C3**

25,000 acres of shooting rights and fly fishing on the man-made lake (begun in 1881 and officially opened in 1910 in order to expand the water supply to Liverpool, 68 miles away) make this tranquil retreat a popular sporting hotel. There are miles of splendid walks, while inside the house (built at the same time as the dam) there's tea by the fireside, a convivial drink in the bar or an hour or two with a board game. Bedrooms are brightly decorated in unfussy style with a mixture of antique and period furniture; the very best rooms have magnificent views over the lake and its splendid Gothic tower, a balcony, four-poster bed or jacuzzi bath; larger rooms and interconnecting rooms are suitable for families, who can also eat informally in The Tavern. Other outdoor pursuits include cycling (bikes can be hired from the hotel), nature trails, bird watching, archery and canoeing. Banqueting and conference facilities for up to 120/150. ***Rooms** 38. Garden, tennis, shooting, fishing, sailing.* AMERICAN EXPRESS *Access, Diners, Visa.*

Lake Vyrnwy — Places of Interest

Powysland Museum & Montgomery Canal Centre The Canal Wharf, Welshpool Tel 0938 554656.
Montgomeryshire Showground Welshpool Tel 0938 554818.
Powis Castle (NT) Welshpool Tel 0938 554336.
Glebe House Garden Welshpool Tel 0938 553602.

Lampeter — Peppers Bistro — NEW — £20

Tel 0570 423796 **R**

14 High Street Lampeter Dyfed SA4 8BG **Map 9 B4**

Choice and quality are both commendable at Stephanie Warne's wholefood and vegetarian bistro, which is open for lunch, evening meals and an all-day selection of speciality teas, light snacks and home baking. From the main menu come the likes of cashewnut paté, parsnip goulash with pasta shells, carrot and cheese pie and pineapple upside-down cake. ***Seats** 42. Parties 10. Private Room 30. L 12-2.30. Closed Sun, Bank Holidays, 7 days Christmas. No credit cards.*

> Our inspectors *never* book in the name of Egon Ronay's Guides. They disclose their identity only if they are considering an establishment for inclusion in the next edition of the Guide.

Lamphey Court Hotel 59% £99

Tel 0646 672273 Fax 0646 672480 **H**

Lamphey Pembroke Dyfed SA71 5NT **Map 9 A5**

A hotel since 1978, the Court is peacefully situated in extensive grounds just a mile from the south Pembrokeshire coast (take the M4 to Carmarthen, then A477 Pembroke Road; at Milton village turn left for Lamphey). The reception hall, with its handsome staircase, and the day rooms have a charm and elegance that echoes their Georgian origins; main-house bedrooms enjoy fine views, good facilities and large, newly retiled bathrooms. The Westminster annexe houses purpose-designed studios with sitting rooms and sofa beds: ideal for families. Children under 16 are accommodated free in their parents' room. Conference suite (for up to 90), and leisure centre with sun terrace. A refurbishment programme was due for completion at the end of 1993, plus larger leisure facilities and tennis courts. ***Rooms** 31. Garden, indoor swimming pool, keep-fit equipment, sauna, solarium.* AMERICAN EXPRESS *Access, Diners, Visa.*

Lamphey Places of Interest

Pembroke Tourist Information Tel 0646 682148.
Tenby Tourist Information Tel 0834 842402.
Colby Woodland Garden (NT) Amroth, Tenby Tel 0558 822800/0834 811725 *13 miles.*
National Museum of Gypsy Caravans, Romany Crafts and Lore Pembroke Tel 0646 681308.
Manor House Wildlife and Leisure Park Tenby Tel 0646 651201.
Tenby Museum and Picture Gallery Tel 0834 842809.
Tenby Beach
Torch Theatre Milford Haven Tel 06462 5267 *15 miles.*

Llanarmon Dyffryn Ceiriog Hand Hotel £58

Tel 069 176 666 Fax 069 176 262 **I**

Llanarmon Dyffryn Ceiriog nr Llangollen Clwyd LL20 7LD **Map 8 D2**

Originally a 16th-century farmhouse, the hotel stands in beautiful countryside in a picturesque village at the head of the Ceiriog Valley. An old black range in reception, antiques in lounge and bar plus a log fire all add up to a cosy, traditional atmosphere. Bedrooms are neat and simple, with plain walls and white fitted furniture. ***Rooms** 13. Garden, tennis.* AMERICAN EXPRESS *Access, Diners, Visa.*

Llanarmon Dyffryn Ceiriog West Arms Hotel £78

Tel 069 176 665 Fax 069 176 622 **I**

Llanarmon Dyffryn Ceiriog nr Llangollen Clwyd LL20 7LD **Map 8 D2**

Nestling in the lovely Ceiriog Valley, this 400-year-old country inn has lost none of its charm through recent restoration. Slate-flagged floors, vast inglenooks and beams offset by period furnishings preserve the atmosphere of a bygone age. Though six of the bedrooms are now fairly modern, the rest retain exposed beams, brass bedsteads and antique furniture, to which neatly added bathrooms provide the requisite modern comforts. A private garden suite accommodates meetings and dinner parties for up to 70 guests. ***Rooms** 14. Garden, fishing.* AMERICAN EXPRESS *Access, Diners, Visa.*

Llanberis Y Bistro £50

Tel 0286 871278 **R**

43-45 High Street Llanberis Gwynedd LL55 4EU **Map 8 B2**

Danny and Nerys Roberts have been here since 1979, and their friendly and informal restaurant remains a popular spot for dinner. Fixed-priced meals, from two to four courses, include canapés, side salad and home-baked bread plus coffee with chocolate florentines. Local produce is put to good use in dishes like lamb riblets, salmon with leeks and dill, and beef with a garlic, port and mushroom sauce. Vegetarian options, excellent cheesecake, farmhouse cheeses. ***Seats** 50. Private Room 44. D only 7.30-9.30 (Sat to 9.45). Closed Sun & Mon in winter. Set D £18/£24. Access, Visa.*

Llanberis — Places of Interest

Museum of the North, Power of Wales Tel 0286 870636.
Snowdon Mountain Railway Tel 0286 870223.
Welsh Slate Museum Tel 0286 870630.

Llandderfel — Palé Hall — 68% — £110

Tel 06783 285 Fax 06783 220 — **H**

Llandderfel nr Bala Gwynedd LL23 7PS — **Map 8 C2**

An imposing Victorian mansion in the beautiful Dee valley, Palé Hall boasts some particularly grand public rooms including a panelled central hall with fine parquet flooring, elegantly proportioned drawing room and blue Boudoir lounge with exquisite hand-painted domed ceiling. Breakfast is served in the original kitchen of the house, still with its old black range. Part of the electricity for the house comes from their own mini-hydro-electric plant and the ancient dials can still be seen recording the current being produced. More, or sometimes less, stylishly decorated bedrooms vary enormously in size and shape with a variety of furniture that is rarely antique although one room has an old oak half-tester once slept in by Queen Victoria along with the original bath tub she used during her stay. Other mainly spacious, carpeted bathrooms vary even more than the bedrooms with sinks in every colour imaginable or decoratively painted – one even has a gold swan's-neck tap. Good towelling and huge bottles of bath foam and shampoo. ***Rooms** 17. Garden, coarse fishing. Access, Visa.*

Llandeilo — Cawdor Arms — 65% — £57

Tel 0558 823500 — **H**

Llandeilo Dyfed SA19 6EN — **Map 9 C5**

Clearly signposted at the end of the M4, the former Bear has long been associated with the Cawdor family, whose coat of arms is its emblem. Handsome proportions and a slightly faded elegance are hallmarks of the Georgian day rooms, and bedrooms include the four-poster Rose and Victorian suites and Howard's Room, where Howard Hughes stayed in 1927 after making a forced landing on his transatlantic flight. ***Rooms** 17. Access, Diners, Visa.*

Llandrillo — Tyddyn Llan — 65% — £84

Tel & Fax 049 084 264 — **HR**

Llandrillo nr Corwen Clwyd LL21 0ST — **Map 8 C2**

Peter and Bridget Kindred run a delightful country hotel surrounded by lawns midway between Bala and Corwen on the B4401. Outdoor pursuits include four miles of fishing (for grayling, trout and some salmon) on the River Dee, with a ghillie provided if required; further local lake and reservoir fishing. Fine paintings, prints and ornaments take the eye in the lounge, and there are antiques in the bedrooms. ***Rooms** 10. Garden, fishing. Access, Visa.*

Restaurant — £60

The dining room is in Georgian style and provides a splendid setting for getting away from it all for a quiet meal at your own pace. The 3- or 4-course, fixed-price menu offers a good range – from roast breast of wood pigeon with lentils and smitaine sauce or warm salad of brill with raspberry vinaigrette to start, followed by carrot and cumin soup, then sirloin of prime Welsh beef with shallot confit and red wine jus, monkfish, local lamb and a vegetarian option. Rich pickings among the choice of four desserts – try the Snowdon pudding with Madeira sauce (a steamed,

See over

moulded fruit suet pudding). Farmhouse cheeses are served with biscuits, celery and nuts. Decently-priced wine list. ***Seats** 45. Parties 25. Private Room 30. L 12.30-2 D 7.30-9.30. Closed 1st week Feb. Set L £9/£11 (£13.50 Sun) Set D £19.50.*

Llandudno — Bodysgallen Hall — 77% — £155

Tel 0492 584466 Fax 0492 582519 — **HR**

Llandudno Gwynedd LL30 1RS — **Map 8 C1**

A 13th-century tower is the oldest part of a building that has seen additions in most centuries since with the latest dating from 1905. Set in over 200 acres of grounds that include some fine formal gardens, the house has been carefully restored by Historic House Hotels and furnished in true country house style with antiques and oil paintings to complement the mellow oak panelling, ornate pargeting and other original features of day rooms which boast numerous sofas plump with feather-filled cushions. Bedrooms, which include nine one- or two-bedroom suites around a charming garden, vary considerably in size and shape but all are decorated and furnished to the same high standard with antique and fabric-draped pieces plus flowering plants, porcelain ornaments and comforts like mineral water and home-made biscuits. Cork-floored bathrooms feature huge bath sheets and luxurious toiletries. Attentive, friendly staff take their cue from general manager Richard Carr. Signposted from the A470 just out of town. No children under eight. ***Rooms** 28. Garden, tennis.* AMERICAN EXPRESS *Access, Diners, Visa.*

Restaurant — £82

There are fine views of the estate from the stone-mullioned windows of twin dining rooms where a fixed-price menu, slightly shorter at lunchtime, offers plenty of choice. Dishes such as veal, bacon and herb terrine with hot toasted brioche; quenelles of smoked trout mousse on a cucumber and yoghurt sauce; honey roast duck with port and orange sauce; pastry-wrapped loin of Welsh lamb with chicken mousse, and lemon sole with a sauce of smoked salmon, dill and saffron are confidently handled by young chef Mair Lewis – who has worked her way up to the top job since arriving here direct from catering college – and her team. Note the Cellarman's Choice (15 wines at £14) on the good all-round wine list, which somewhat confusingly lists New World wines by grape variety. No smoking. ***Seats** 60. Private Room 40. L 12.30-2 D 7.30-9.45. Set L £13.90/£15.90 Set D £27.50/£29.50.*

Llandudno — Empire Hotel — 69% — £70

Tel 0492 860555 Fax 0492 860791 — **H**

Church Walks Llandudno Gwynedd LL30 2HE — **Map 8 C1**

Courtesy and care are the watchwords of owners Len and Elizabeth Maddocks, here since 1960, and their reward is a very high level of repeat business. Russell Flint prints add distinction to the homely lounge, and there's a choice of bars and restaurants. Bedrooms vary considerably in size and price, from budget singles to de luxe rooms in the Victorian house next to the main building; antiques, cast-iron beds, silk drapes and marble-floored bathrooms with whirlpool baths are features. Multi-channel TV and video recorders (large library of films available) in all rooms. Dogs in budget rooms only. ***Rooms** 58. Indoor & outdoor swimming pools, spa bath, sauna, steam room, roof garden and sun terrace. Closed 10 days Christmas.* AMERICAN EXPRESS *Access, Diners, Visa.*

Llandudno — St George's Hotel — 61% — £72

Tel 0492 877544 Fax 0492 878477 — **H**

St George's Place Llandudno Gwynedd LL30 2LG — **Map 8 C1**

Llandudno's oldest hotel, restored to its former glory, houses conferences and banqueting for up to 250. The Shape Club offers top-to-toe health hair and cosmetic care. Many bedrooms afford views of the sea and Great Orme, and the best have balconies. Under-12s stay free in their parents' room. ***Rooms** 86. Keep-fit equipment, sauna, spa bath, solarium, beauty & hair salon. Closed 10 days Jan.* AMERICAN EXPRESS *Access, Diners, Visa.*

Llandudno — St Tudno Hotel — 69% — £104

Tel 0492 874411 Fax 0492 860407 — **HR**

The Promenade Llandudno Gwynedd LL30 2LP — **Map 8 C1**

The enthusiastic Blands have been welcoming guests to their charming seafront hotel for over 21 years now with a winning combination of friendliness and professionalism. Either side of the entrance hall the bar/lounge and sitting room (reserved for non-smokers) are Victorian in style – parlour plants, original fire places – in contrast to a bright coffee lounge to be found behond the reception desk where fresh flowers compete with the receptionists' smiles. A small bottle of sparkling wine greets guests in bedrooms that, though generally not large, are individually decorated in pretty co-ordinating fabrics and wall coverings with a good eye for detail. Rooms are properly serviced in the evenings as are the bathrooms with their generous towelling and good toiletries. In 1861 Alice Liddell, later to be immortalised in Lewis Carroll's *Alice's Adventures in Wonderland*, spent a holiday here. Limited parking (for up to eight cars). ***Rooms** 21. Patio, indoor swimming pool.* AMERICAN EXPRESS *Access, Visa.*

Garden Room Restaurant — £65

Painted greenery and trellis work on the walls together with potted plants and conservatory-style furniture provide the garden atmosphere while David Harding in the kitchen provides competently cooked dishes for the fixed-price menus that offer some half-a-dozen choices at each stage. Smoked haddock and leek tart with butter sauce, chilled fresh orange or grapefruit juice, tomato and basil soup, Welsh lamb cutlets with plum and port wine sauce, and poached halibut with prawns and parsley sauce demonstrate the range. There's a good house selection on the comprehensive wine list, which has an expanded New World section this year. Plenty of good drinking under £25. No smoking. ***Seats** 60. L 12.30-2 D 7-9.30. Set L £11.50/£13.50 (Sun £14.50) Set D £19/£22/£25.*

Llandudno — Places of Interest

Tourist Information Tel 0492 876413.
Mostyn Art Gallery Tel 0492 874151.
Llandudno Dry Ski Slope Tel 0492 874707.
Alice in Wonderland Visitor Centre Tel 0492 860082.

Llangammarch Wells — Lake Country House Hotel — 68% — £98

Tel 059 12 202 Fax 059 12 457 — **HR**

Llangammarch Wells Powys LD4 4BS — **Map 9 C4**

Standing in 50 acres of parkland and enjoying genuine tranquillity, a mainly Edwardian building run along personable lines by Jean-Pierre and Jan Mifsud. Grandly proportioned day rooms include a handsome parlour lounge that retains much of the period character by using traditional furnishings and fabrics. Bedrooms have fine views and are individually styled with a combination of antiques and restful colour schemes. Smart, efficient staff mirror the owners' enthusiasm. Popular with fishermen as the river Irfon runs through the grounds. ***Rooms** 19. Garden, pitch & putt, tennis, fishing, snooker.* AMERICAN EXPRESS *Access, Visa.*

Restaurant — £65

Fixed-price, five-course dinners with a choice of three or four dishes at each stage are typified by cream of celery and apple soup, wild mushroom-filled saffron ravioli with avocado, roulade of chicken with pistachio nuts, sweet peppers, tomatoes and chestnuts, panaché of fish (including hake, monkfish, salmon and red mullet), and *langue du chat* basket filled with orange and cardamom ice cream and cinnamon sauce. Table d'hote lunches are served in the restaurant, lighter lunches in the lounge; good choice at Sunday lunchtime. No children under 12 in the dining room. Plenty of choice on the varied wine list. ***Seats** 50. L 1-2 (non-residents by arrangement only) D 7-8.45. Set L £15.50 (Sun) Set D £24.50.*

Llangefni Tre-Ysgawen Hall 79% £107

Tel 0248 750750 Fax 0248 750035 **HR**

Capel Coch nr Llangefni Anglesey Gwynedd LL77 7UR **Map 8 B1**

A tree-lined drive leads from the B5111 to this fine Victorian mansion with friendly owners and staff. Handsome public rooms leading off a grand entrance include a bar and a traditionally styled lounge that looks southward over the gardens. Bedrooms are of a very good size and appointed to a high degree of comfort and elegance, with beautiful fabrics complementing hand-picked, mainly antique furniture. Bathrooms, too, are excellent, particularly two with corner whirlpool baths. 3,000 acres of private shooting. Function facilities for up to 120. ***Rooms** 19. Garden, helipad, shooting, kennels.* AMERICAN EXPRESS *Access, Diners, Visa.*

Restaurant £70

Housed in a large conservatory-style extension, the restaurant is both elegant and formal, much in keeping with the house's atmosphere. ***Seats** 60. L 12-2.30 (Sat from 12.30) D 7-9.30. Set L £11/£14 Set D £20.*

Llangefni Places of Interest

Holyhead Tourist Information Tel 0407 762622.
Wylfa Nuclear Power Station Tel 0407 710471 *10 miles.*

Llangollen Hand Hotel 55% £66

Tel 0978 860303 Fax 0978 861277 **H**

Bridge Street Llangollen Clywd LL20 8PL **Map 8 D2**

Country hotel with gardens reaching down to the river Dee. Simple, attractive rooms. Banqueting and conference facilities for up to 80. ***Rooms** 57. Garden, fishing.* AMERICAN EXPRESS *Access, Diners, Visa.*

Llangollen Royal Hotel 59% £82

Tel 0978 860202 Fax 0978 861824 **H**

Bridge Street Llangollen Clywd LL20 8PG **Map 8 D2**

Looking just a little like a fairy-tale castle, the Royal overlooks a 14th-century stone bridge on the banks of the Dee. Simple bedrooms, two bars and a comfortable lounge. Forte Heritage. ***Rooms** 33.* AMERICAN EXPRESS *Access, Diners, Visa.*

Llangollen Places of Interest

Tourist Information Tel 0978 860828.
European Centre for Traditional and Regional Cultures Tel 0978 861292.
Llangollen Railway Tel 0978 860951.
Valle Crucis Abbey Tel 0978 860326 *2 miles.*
Chirk Castle Tel 0691 777701 *6 miles.*

Llangybi Cwrt Bleddyn Hotel 71% £100

Tel 0633 49521 Fax 0633 49220 **H**

Tredunnock nr Usk Gwent NP5 1PG **Map 9 D6**

A large house standing in 17 acres of countryside three miles from Caerleon, between Llangybi and Tredunnock. Some original features date back to the 17th century but the interior is modernised to a great extent, including spacious bedrooms with separate seating areas. The lounge and private meeting rooms feature carved panelling and fireplaces. There's a new residents' library. Good family facilities; informal eating in the club house restaurant. Conference facilities for up to 200. No dogs. ***Rooms** 36. Garden, indoor swimming pool, sauna, solarium, spa bath, hair salon, games room, tennis, squash.* AMERICAN EXPRESS *Access, Diners, Visa.*

Llanrug — Seiont Manor — 71% — £97

Tel 0286 673366 Fax 0286 672840 — **H**

Llanrug Caernarfon Gwynedd LL55 2AQ — **Map 8 B2**

150 acres of parkland provide pleasant walks, and Snowdonia National Park and the Isle of Anglesey are both a short drive away. Fishing is available on the river Seiont, and guests have complimentary access to a nearby golf course. Improvements to the on-site leisure club include an enlarged gym and new sauna. Public rooms, including a traditional oak-panelled bar, a lounge and a very comfortable library (the last two serving morning coffee, lunch and afternoon tea), are also furnished in a manner that befits the ancient character of the building. Bedrooms are in two purpose-built blocks which extend from the original stone building and are in a style sympathetic to it. Rooms have either little balconies or patio doors, are of a good size and all boast antique or good-quality period furniture. Children up to 14 stay free in parents' room. Conference facilities for up to 100 delegates. The hotel stands on the A4086 on the left before entering the village if coming from Caernarfon. ***Rooms** 28. Garden, indoor swimming pool, sauna, solarium, fishing.* AMERICAN EXPRESS *Access, Diners, Visa.*

Llanrug — Places of Interest

Caernarfon Tourist Information Tel 0286 672232.
Caernarfon Castle Tel 0286 677617 *World Heritage Listed Site.*
Segontium Roman Fort Museum Caernarfon Tel 0286 675625.

Llansanffraid Glan Conwy — Old Rectory — 73% — £89

Tel 0492 580611 Fax 0492 584555 — **HR**

Llanrwst Road Llansanffraid Glan Conwy Gwynedd LL28 5LF — **Map 8 C1**

Michael and Wendy Vaughan's attractive Georgian house stands on a hillside just off the A470 (within half a mile of the A55), affording excellent views over the Conwy estuary and Snowdonia. On the ground floor there is a fine sitting room with pine panelling, groups of comfortable armchairs and sofas, and a cosy morning room offering a quiet and peaceful atmosphere: ornaments, paintings and prints make the rooms traditional and homely throughout. The bedrooms contain armchairs, antique furniture and quality fabrics; bathrooms are excellent. Two coach-house rooms allow smoking and entertain small dogs – both of which are otherwise actively discouraged. No children under 5. ***Rooms** 6. Garden. Closed 20 Dec-1 Feb.* AMERICAN EXPRESS *Access, Diners, Visa.*

Restaurant — £70

Guests may dine separately or at a communal table, with dinner served at 8 o'clock. Local produce is used by Wendy in her four-course menus, notably Welsh black beef and mountain lamb; the cream is from the nearby Vale of Clwyd. Vegetable terrine on a tomato vinaigrette, roast fillet of lamb with red wine sauce and gremolata, poached fillet of brill with salmon caviar sauce and roulade of chicken with lentils and bacon are typical of the excellent fare she provides. Home-made ices are always available, plus cheese – a board, and either grilled goat's cheese or a soufflé. Fairly priced wine list with notes on every bin. Lots of half bottles. ***Seats** 16. Parties 12. D only at 8. Set D £26.*

Set menu prices may not always include service or wine.

Llanvihangel Gobion — Llansantffraed Court 66% — £70

Tel 0873 840678 Fax 0873 840674 — **H**

Llanvihangel Gobion Abergavenny Gwent NP7 9BA — **Map 9 D5**

The owners describe the house as neo-classical Lutyens with strong Georgian influences. It stands on the B4598 Abergavenny road, in extensive parkland on the fringe of the Usk valley with the Black Mountains as a backdrop. Most characterful of the bedrooms are on the top floor, with oak beams and dormer windows. Children up to 12 stay free in parents' room. The lounge and bar provide ample space for a relaxing chat or drink. ***Rooms*** *21. Garden.* AMERICAN EXPRESS *Access, Diners, Visa.*

Llanwnda — Stables Hotel 57% — £49

Tel 0286 830711 Fax 0286 830413 — **H**

Llanwnda nr Caernarfon Gwynedd LL54 5SD — **Map 8 B2**

Three miles south-west of Caernarfon on the A499, this is a modest single-storey hotel set around original Victorian stables which now house a bar and restaurant. Children up to 12 stay free in parents' room. New owners. ***Rooms*** *14. Garden, outdoor swimming pool.* AMERICAN EXPRESS *Access, Diners, Visa.*

Llyswen — Llangoed Hall 80% — £145

Tel 0874 754525 Fax 0874 754545 — **HR**

Llyswen Brecon Powys LD3 0YP — **Map 9 D5**

Distinguished buildings have occupied this site for many centuries, but the present magnificent hall (the work of Sir Clough Williams-Ellis of Portmeirion fame) dates only from 1912; the south wing alone survives from the 1632 Jacobean mansion. The hall has been restored in marvellous style, and the day room feature fine paintings, antiques, chintzes and large sofas. Elegance is a keynote in the bedrooms, whose individual decor is complemented by all sorts of thoughtful extras. Wood-floored bathrooms epitomise the quality. High standard of service. Children under eight at the management's discretion. Dogs are not allowed in the hotel, but heated kennels are available. ***Rooms*** *23. Garden, tennis, fishing, snooker, helipad.* AMERICAN EXPRESS *Access, Diners, Visa.*

Restaurant — £100

NEW CHEF

The dining room, graciously done out in yellow and cornflower blue, is a splendid setting for enjoying the talents of Mark Salter. His cooking is modern classical, with many innovative touches and an emphasis on lightness. Many of the ingredients are grown in the kitchen garden, while others are supplied locally where possible. Five-course dinner menus and the à la carte make mouthwatering reading, and results on the plate do not disappoint: beetroot consommé garnished with poached squab and fresh thyme, chargrilled fillet of red mullet on home-made noodles with a rosemary sauce, honey-glazed shank of Welsh lamb with seasonal vegetables and a sun-dried tomato sauce, noisettes of wild mushrooms with red pepper pasta and sorrel sauce, apple and sultana sponge with caramelised apple and a cinnamon anglaise. There are helpful notes on a fine wine list with many mature clarets and burgundies, as well as interesting house recommendations. Splendid choice of half bottles. See Cellar of the Year Wales winner. ***Seats*** *46. Private Room 36. L 12.15-2.30 D 7.15-9.30. Set L £16 Set D £35.*

Llyswen — Places of Interest

Brecon Tourist Information Tel 0874 622485.
Builth Wells Tourist Information Tel 0982 553307.
Wyeside Arts Centre Builth Wells Tel 0982 552555.
Royal Welsh Showground Llanelwedd Tel 0982 553683.

Machynlleth Wynnstay Arms £53

Tel 0654 702941 Fax 0654 703884 **H**

Maengwyn Street Machynlleth Powys SY20 8AE **Map 8 C3**

Main-street hotel with a neo-Georgian facade. Convivial bar, choice of lounges (including non-smoking). Children up to 16 stay free in parents' room. ***Rooms** 20.* AMERICAN EXPRESS® *Access, Diners, Visa.*

Machynlleth Places of Interest

Centre for Alternative Technology Llwyngwern Quarry Tel 0654 702400 *2½ miles.*

Merthyr Tydfil Baverstock Hotel 57% £55

Tel 0685 386221 Fax 0685 723670 **H**

Heads of the Valley Road Merthyr Tydfil Mid Glamorgan CF44 0LX **Map 9 C5**

Privately-owned modern hotel in an elevated position on the A465. A good deal of business comes from conferences and meetings in a variety of rooms (50 residential, 400 daytime). Reduced rates at weekends when businessmen are thin on the ground. ***Rooms** 53. Garden.* AMERICAN EXPRESS® *Access, Diners, Visa.*

Merthyr Tydfil Places of Interest

Ynysfach Engine House Tel 0685 721858/83704.
Cyfarthfa Castle Museum and Art Gallery Tel 0685 723112.

Miskin Miskin Manor 70% £100

Tel 0443 224204 Fax 0443 237606 **H**

Penddylan Road Pontyclun Miskin Mid Glamorgan CF7 8ND **Map 9 C6**

A handsome stone mansion in 20 acres of garden and woodland, Miskin Manor was built in 1858. Day rooms are very comfortable and deep sofas in floral fabrics invite guests to relax and gaze out over the gardens. The bedrooms are vast – even singles have sofas – and are luxurious without being ostentatious. Some have four-posters and there are two suites. Children stay free in parents' room. There's a sports and leisure complex and conference facilities for up to 150 delegates. The hotel is undergoing an extensive programme of refurbishment. M4 Junction 34. ***Rooms** 32. Garden, indoor swimming pool, gymnasium, spa bath, steam room, sauna, solarium, beauty salon, badminton, coffee shop (10am-10pm), crèche (9am-3pm Mon-Fri).* AMERICAN EXPRESS® *Access, Diners, Visa.*

Monmouth King's Head 64% £65

Tel 0600 712177 Fax 0600 713545 **H**

Agincourt Square Monmouth Gwent NP5 3DY **Map 9 D5**

This timber-fronted former coaching inn retains its links with a notable past; Kings Henry V and Charles I, Lord Nelson and the Hon CS Rolls all having played their part in the King's Head's history. Bedrooms are full of character with their blackened beams and antique furniture; four are suitable for family use, with under-5s staying free. Falstaff's wine bar and brasserie is open all day for light meals and teas; a supervised crèche is provided at Sunday lunchtime for parents who want an hour of peace! Separate conference and banqueting rooms accommodate up to 200. ***Rooms** 29.* AMERICAN EXPRESS® *Access, Diners, Visa.*

Monmouth Places of Interest

Tourist Information Tel 0600 713899.
Nelson Collection and Local History Centre Tel 0600 713519.

Mumbles Norton House 65% £70

Tel 0792 404891 Fax 0792 403210 **HR**

17 Norton Road Mumbles Swansea West Glamorgan SA3 5TQ **Map 9 C6**

A pretty white-painted Georgian house with wisteria round the door, personally run in friendly fashion by Jan and John Powers. The main day room is the bar with an unusual umbrella-vaulted ceiling, and there is a small lounge on the first floor, but it's only just big enough for a single three-piece suite. Bedrooms vary from three rooms with four-posters and one with rough stone walls and timbered ceiling, to the majority of smaller rooms in a newer wing. All have homely touches like fresh flowers, mineral water and a welcoming decanter of sherry. Many of the bathrooms have very small washbasins and three have shower and WC only, but all have good towelling. Excellent breakfasts begin with a huge glass of freshly squeezed orange juice. No children under 10. No dogs. ***Rooms*** *15. Garden. Closed 25 & 26 Dec.* AMERICAN EXPRESS *Access, Diners, Visa.*

Restaurant £60

Although dishes on the fixed-price dinner menu have Welsh names, with clear English explanations, the cooking is not native to the Principality. Flat mushrooms filled with laverbread, cockles and bacon, duck with black cherries, pork tenderloin with brandy, cream and peppercorn sauce, vegetable lasagne plus 'catch of the day' are among the five or so dishes at each stage. Orange and Grand Marnier syllabub, trio of chocolates (cake, mousse and white sorbet), sorbets and local cheeses complete the picture. ***Seats*** *36. Parties 10. Private Room 16. L by arrangement D 7.15-9.30 (Sun 7-9). Set D £19.50/£23.50.*

Mumbles PA's Winebar £45

Tel 0792 367723 **R**

95 Newton Road Mumbles West Glamorgan SA3 4BN **Map 9 C6**

A wine bar/brasserie overlooking Oystermouth Castle. Typical dishes on the weekly-changing menu run from grilled garlic mussels and salad of avocado and bacon to seared salmon with a balsamic reduction, partridge with mostarda and sirloin steak béarnaise. Tables outside in summer. ***Seats*** *32. L 12-2.30 D 6-9.30. Closed Sun, 3 weeks Oct, 2 days Christmas. Access, Visa.*

Mumbles Place of Interest

Caswell Bay Beach

Newport Celtic Manor 75% £117

Tel 0633 413000 Fax 0633 412910 **H**

Coldra Woods Newport Gwent NP6 2YA **Map 9 D6**

A 300-acre estate provides the setting for this 19th-century manor house, which is only one minute from Junction 24 of the M4. Well set up for both business and pleasure, the hotel maintains high standards of decor, maintenance and service. Six conference suites cater for up to 350 delegates, and the leisure facilities are impressive. The extended frontage of the manor houses two bars, one in pub style, an elegant drawing room and a large patio conservatory (used for breakfast). Bedrooms are of a good size and feature triple glazing, freestanding darkwood furniture with ample writing space, attractive window seating and smartly tiled, well-lit bathrooms. ***Rooms*** *73. Garden, indoor swimming pool, gymnasium, sauna, solarium, helipad.* AMERICAN EXPRESS *Access, Diners, Visa.*

> Many hotels offer reduced rates for weekend or out-of-season bookings. Always ask about special deals.

Newport **Hilton National** **61%** **£93**

Tel 0633 412777 Fax 0633 413087 **H**

The Coldra Newport Gwent NP6 2YG **Map 9 D6**

Practical modern hotel at Junction 24 of the M4, with leisure and business centres. Conference/banqueting facilities for 500/400. ***Rooms*** *119. Indoor swimming pool, keep-fit equipment, sauna, steam room, sun bed.* AMERICAN EXPRESS *Access, Diners, Visa.*

Newport **Kings Hotel** **62%** **£51**

Tel 0633 842020 Fax 0633 244667 **H**

7 High Street Newport Gwent NP9 1QU **Map 9 D6**

Victorian town-centre hotel opposite the railway station (and just off the M4 at Junction 26). Boardroom suites for 20-80 people and ballroom catering for up to 220. Roomy bedrooms (under-12s accommodated free in parents' room), large traditional lounge and a cheerful bar. ***Rooms*** *47.* AMERICAN EXPRESS *Access, Diners, Visa.*

Newport **Stakis Country Court Hotel** **69%** **£112**

Tel 0633 413733 Fax 0633 413713 **H**

Chepstow Road Newport Gwent NP6 2LX **Map 9 D6**

Stakis hotel built round a courtyard garden. Roomy overnight accommodation, leisure centre, self-contained facilities for business meetings. ***Rooms*** *141. Indoor swimming pool, gymnasium, sauna, spa bath, solarium.* AMERICAN EXPRESS *Access, Diners, Visa.*

Newport **Places of Interest**

Tourist Information Tel 0633 842962.
Dolman Theatre Tel 0633 263670.
Newport Centre Tel 0633 259676.
Tredegar House Tel 0633 815880.
Cathedral Church of St. Woolos Tel 0633 63338.
Museum and Art Gallery Tel 0633 840064.
Roman Legionary Museum Caerleon Tel 0633 423.

Northop **Soughton Hall** **79%** **£99**

Tel 0352 840811 Fax 0352 840382 **HR**

Northop nr Mold Clwyd CH7 6AB **Map 8 D2**

Set in 10 acres of gardens on its own 150-acre estate, grand Soughton Hall retains much of the charm and character derived from its origins as a bishop's palace, built in 1714. On the ground floor there's a cosy library and bar; on an upper floor the baronial-style drawing room has a carved stone fireplace, tapestries, drapes and Oriental carpets. Period furniture, co-ordinated decor and plenty of extras, from the pair of armchairs, fruit and mineral water to the generous toiletries and towels in well-equipped bathrooms, make these arguably the best hotel bedrooms in North Wales. Breakfast is taken in the original Servants' Hall where a black-leaded range still features. Welcoming and attentive staff, directed by the resident Rodenhurst family, contribute greatly to the feeling of relaxation and well-being. Private meeting rooms for 40. No children under 12. No dogs. ***Rooms*** *12. Garden, snooker, archery, chauffeur service. Closed first 2 weeks Jan.* AMERICAN EXPRESS *Access, Visa.*

Restaurant **£70**

The splendid State Dining Room, with its polished tables, crystal glass and fine china, is on the first floor overlooking the garden. Fixed-price dinner menus incorporate old classics and traditional dishes, with care taken to reflect the current interest in lighter eating. Nightly specialities; notable sweets and cheeses. The fairly-priced wine list, which has good

See over

balance, offers mostly young wines, though there are some mature clarets. Smoking is not encouraged. ***Seats** 40. Private Room 22. L Sun 12-2 D 7-9.30 (Sat to 10, Sun to 7.30). Set L £18.50 Set D £24.*

Northop — Places of Interest

Mold Tourist Information Tel 0352 759331.
Clwyd Theatre Mold Tel 0352 755114 *4 miles.*

Northop Hall — Forte Travelodge — £42

Tel 0244 816473 — **L**

Northop Hall Mold Clwyd CH7 6HB — **Map 8 D2**

Located on the A55 eastbound, 3 miles north east of Mold. Approximately 10 miles west of Chester. ***Rooms** 40. American Express Access, Visa.*

Pant Mawr — Glansevern Arms — £55

Tel 055 15 240 — **I**

Pant Mawr nr Llangurig Powys SY18 6SY — **Map 9 C4**

Personally owned and managed for 27 years by Mr Edwards and family, the Glansevern Arms commands a magnificent position overlooking the upper reaches of the Wye, on the A44, four miles west of Llangurig. An intimate bar and lounge soak in the glorious hill scenery by day and glow with warmth from log fires at night. Residents equally enjoy the peace and quiet afforded by bedrooms with private sitting areas, uninterrupted by any phones, where the views should provide a greater attraction than television. ***Rooms** 7. Closed 1 week Christmas. No credit cards.*

Pant Mawr — Places of Interest

Newtown Tourist Information Tel 0686 625580.
Gregynog House and Gardens Newtown Tel 0686 650224 *28 miles.*
Robert Owen Memorial Museum Newtown Tel 0686 626345.
W H Smith Museum Newtown Tel 0686 626280.

Penally — Penally Abbey — 65% — £86

Tel 0834 843033 Fax 0834 844714 — **HR**

Penally nr Tenby Dyfed — **Map 9 B5**

In a tranquil hillside setting overlooking sand dunes and Carmarthen Bay, Penally Abbey is a gothic-style stone-built mansion with an adjoining coach house, 1½ miles from Tenby. There's a tiny bar, a vine-shaded conservatory and a homely lounge where guests can play various musical instruments. Four bedrooms have four-posters (two are in the Coach House), others pine wardrobes and period wash-stands. Cheerful staff and welcoming hosts. Good breakfasts. No dogs. ***Rooms** 11. Garden, indoor swimming pool, games room. Access, Visa.*

Restaurant — £50

Elleen Warren puts prime ingredients to good use on her fixed-price dinner menus. Typical dishes could include smoked salmon and trout terrine, herring fillets marinated in dill, dressed Pembrokeshire crab, rack of Welsh lamb with apple mint and white wine, and baked ham caramelised with apples, brown sugar and Calvados. No children under seven. No smoking. ***Seats** 30. Parties 20. L by arrangement D 7.30-9.30. Set D £22.*

Pencoed — Forte Travelodge — £42

Tel 0656 864404 — **L**

Old Mill Felindre Road Pencoed nr Bridgend Mid Glamorgan CF3 5HU — **Map 9 C6**

Head north on the A473 from junction 35 of the M4, taking first right into Felindre Road. 10 minutes from Bridgend. ***Rooms** 40. American Express Access, Visa.*

Penmaenpool — George III Hotel — £88

Tel 0341 422525 Fax 0341 423565 — **I**

Penmaenpool nr Dolgellau Gwynedd LL40 1YD — **Map 8 C3**

Now under the new ownership of the Cartwright family, the George III is a 17th-century inn boasting a superb situation at the head of the Mawddach estuary. A new reception has been created in the former porch and all the decent-sized bedrooms are now en suite, with brighter decor and quality furniture. Friendly staff give an air of hospitality to the bar, with its antique oak tables, brasses and paintings; there's also a very cosy residents' lounge. Children under eight stay free in their parents' room. Free fishing permits to guests staying two or more nights on half board. ***Rooms** 11. Garden, fishing.* AMERICAN EXPRESS® *Access, Visa.*

Port Talbot — Travel Inn — £43

Tel 0639 813017 Fax 0639 823096 — **L**

Baglan Road Port Talbot West Glamorgan SA12 8ES — **Map 9 C6**

***Rooms** 40.* AMERICAN EXPRESS® *Access, Diners, Visa*

Porthkerry — Egerton Grey — 73% — £85

Tel 0446 711666 Fax 0446 711690 — **H**

Porthkerry nr Cardiff South Glamorgan CF6 9BZ — **Map 9 C6**

This former rectory is tucked away in a lovely little valley ten miles from Cardiff and three from Barry (leave the M4 at Junction 33, follow signs to Rhoose and look for hotel sign one mile east of Rhoose village). Anthony and Magda Pitkin generate an air of peaceful informality which is evident as soon as you enter the parquet-floored foyer, and personal attention is the order of the day. Rugs, plump-cushioned seating, period decor and a piano grace the lounge, and the library is charming. Bedrooms, including two suites, vary in size, shape and design but all boast pretty, well-chosen fabrics, light, restful colour schemes and antique or period furniture. The carpeted bathrooms are first rate, many of them offering wonderful old baths with huge shower heads. ***Rooms** 10. Garden, tennis.* AMERICAN EXPRESS® *Access, Diners, Visa.*

Portmeirion — Hotel Portmeirion — 74% — £129

Tel 0766 770228 Fax 0766 771331 — **HR**

Portmeirion Gwynedd LL48 6ER — **Map 8 B2**

Portmeirion was created (and opened in 1926) by Sir Clough Williams-Ellis on a secluded peninsula on the Traeth Bach estuary. It's a fairytale village comprising 50 buildings arranged round a central piazza. The hotel is based on an early-Victorian villa near the shore and contains some stunning public rooms: among others the black and white marble-floored hall and the Indian-themed Jaipur Bar particularly take the eye. Guests stay either in the main hotel building with the pick of the sea views or in the surrounding suites and cottages that make up the village. The latter are newly refurbished to the high standard of the others and are within very comfortable walking distance of the hotel. Five de luxe suites in the Anchor and Fountain building overlook the swimming pool and estuary. Children under four stay free in parents' room. No dogs. Conference/banqueting facilities for up to 100. ***Rooms** 34. Garden, outdoor swimming pool, golf (18), tennis, sea fishing, coffee shop (10am-5pm), village shops (closed Jan-Mar). Closed 3 weeks Jan.* AMERICAN EXPRESS® *Access, Diners, Visa.*

Restaurant — £65

A light, spacious, curvilinear dining room with faux-marble pillars and fine vistas across the estuary is home to Craig Hindley's careful cooking, which utilises first-rate raw materials in modern style. Loin of Welsh lamb comes with a charlotte of courgette and glazed radish, maize-fed chicken with

See over

oyster mushrooms and grain mustard sauce and grilled turbot with aubergine, sun-dried tomatoes and olive oil. The fixed-price dinner menus offer about six choices at each stage, the good-value lunch menu about half that number. The fairly-priced wine list is both well balanced and comprehensive, and offers exceptionally good drinking under £13 (house wines). No smoking. ***Seats** 100. Private Room 40. L 12.30-2 D 7-9.30. Set L £13.50 Set D £20/£25.*

Portmeirion Places of Interest

Portmeirion Village Tel 0766 770228.
Gloddfa Slate Mine and Llechwedd Slate Caverns Blaenau Festiniog Tel 0766 830664.
Ffestiniog Railway Porthmadog Tel 0766 831654.
Llechwedd Slate Caverns Tel 0766 830306.

Presteigne Radnorshire Arms 61% £124*

Tel 0544 267406 Fax 0544 260418 **H**

High Street Presteigne Powys LD8 2BE **Map 9 D4**

A small country inn that's a fine example of Elizabethan magpie architecture. Good-sized, well-furnished bedrooms, plus a characterful bar with oak beams and high-back settles. Forte Heritage. *Half-board terms only. ***Rooms** 16. Garden. AMERICAN EXPRESS Access, Diners, Visa.*

Pwllheli Plas Bodegroes £75

Tel 0758 612363 Fax 0758 701247 **RR**

Nefyn Road Pwllheli Gwynedd LL53 5TH **Map 8 B2**

At their secluded Georgian manor house (on the A497 a mile west of Pwllheli) Chris and Gunna Chown pride themselves on finding the finest ingredients virtually on their doorstep, in an area renowned for succulent seafood, Welsh lamb and beef, free-range chickens and ducks and their eggs. Many herbs and vegetables come straight from the restaurant's gardens. Chris's five-course, fixed-price dinners offer plenty of choice and great value: typical examples from recent menus include tartlet of wild mushrooms with Parmesan and rocket salad, lobster fishcake with tartare sauce, roast duck with Calvados, chargrilled lamb kebab with garlic cream, hot chocolate tart with spiced pears and strudel of Welsh cheeses with celery and walnut salad. Splendid and keenly-priced wine list with a fine house selection, good notes, as well as denoting the relative sweetness of white wines. The striking modern decor includes some 50 works by contemporary Welsh artists. No smoking. ***Seats** 35. Private Room 16. D only 7-9.30 (Sun to 9). Closed Mon, Jan-Feb. Set D £30.* AMERICAN EXPRESS *Access, Visa.*

Rooms from £130*

The eight en-suite bedrooms echo the delightful house's inherent charm, their co-ordinated colours and fabrics combining with either antique or modern pine furniture. No smoking. * Half-board terms.

Reynoldston Fairyhill 64% £75

Tel 0792 390139 Fax 0792 391358 **HR**

Reynoldston Gower Swansea West Glamorgan SA3 1BS **Map 9 B6**

Rescued from dereliction by its current owners, Fairyhill today offers a tranquil retreat in 24 acres of park and woodland containing a meandering trout stream. Signs of its 18th-century origins are evident in irregular oak doorways and uneven landings; antique Welsh dressers are in keeping. Superior main-house bedrooms have full-sized baths en suite, the remainder shower/WC only, and a two-bedroomed converted stable with a walled garden is offered as a 'super de luxe' suite; two rooms in the coach house are suitable as a family suite. ***Rooms** 15. Garden, fishing. Closed November-January. Access, Visa.*

Restaurant

£64

French with Welsh overtones describes the weekly-changing menu prepared by Julie Bishop. Matchsticks of smoked chicken and chicory with walnuts and walnut oil dressing, warm salad of grilled goat's cheese with bacon and pine nuts, escalope of cod with cucumber sauce, and sautéed calf's liver with Dubonnet and sage are typical dishes. A central buffet groans with a range of home-made desserts. Short wine list assembled by grape variety. ***Seats** 70. Parties 40. Private Room 16. L (Sun only) 12.30-1.15 D 7.30-9. Set L (Sun) £12.95.*

Rossett — Llyndir Hall — 71%

£110

Tel 0244 571648 Fax 0244 571258

H

Llyndir Lane Rossett nr Wrexham Clywd LL12 0AY — **Map 8 D2**

Ten minutes drive from the centre of Chester, this 'Strawberry Gothic' hall is surrounded by beautiful parkland. Bedrooms are well sized and furnished with antique pieces, the effect being both tasteful and elegant without being ostentatious. Most of the rooms are in a sympathetic new building. A gracious and sunny drawing room looks out over the lush lawns. Children up to 14 stay free in parents' room. Banquet and conference facilities for up to 90/150. Guests have free entry to some local sights. ***Rooms** 38. Garden, indoor swimming pool, spa bath, steam room, solarium, coffee shop (7am-10pm, till 11 weekends).* AMERICAN EXPRESS *Access, Diners, Visa.*

Rossett — Places of Interest

Wrexham Tourist Information Tel 0978 357845.
Bersham Industrial Heritage Museum Centre Bersham Tel 0978 261529 *8 miles.*
Chirk Castle (NT) Tel 0691 777701.
Erddig (NT) Tel 0978 355314.
Bangor-on-Dee Racecourse Tel 0978 780323 *10 miles.*

Ruthin — Ruthin Castle — 62%

£79

Tel 0824 702664 Fax 0824 705978

H

Corwen Road Ruthin Clwyd LL15 2NU — **Map 8 C2**

30 acres of grounds surround ancient Ruthin Castle, where relics of the past include a drowning pool, whipping pit and dungeons. The castle has known attack, siege and virtual destruction, but more peaceful diversions today centre around the cocktail bar, splendid lounge, or comfortable bedrooms appointed in traditional style. The Great Hall is the scene of regular medieval banquets. No dogs. ***Rooms** 58. Garden, snooker, fishing.* AMERICAN EXPRESS *Access, Diners, Visa.*

Ruthin — Places of Interest

Ruthin Tourist Information and Craft Centre Tel 08242 4774/5675/3992.
Cathedral Church of St. Asaph Tel 0745 583597 *16 miles.*

St David's — St Non's Hotel — 56%

£73

Tel 0437 720239 Fax 0437 721839

H

St David's Dyfed SA62 6RJ — **Map 9 A5**

A friendly family hotel half a mile from the town centre offering some of the best children's terms around: under-6s stay free in parents' room and enjoy free breakfast and high tea. Other bonuses include five ground-floor bedrooms for the less mobile, and free golf at the picturesque St David's 9-hole course. ***Rooms** 24. Garden.* AMERICAN EXPRESS *Access, Diners, Visa.*

St David's — Warpool Court 62% £111

Tel 0437 720300 Fax 0437 720676 **H**

St David's Dyfed SA62 6BN **Map 9 A5**

Bordering National Trust parkland, Warpool Court enjoys spectacular scenery and panoramic views over St Brides Bay to the offshore islands beyond. Equally eye-catching within is the Ada Williams collection of unique armorial and ornamental hand-painted tiles which bedeck the public areas and a number of the bedrooms (many of which have been recently refurbished). Private rooms for functions and conferences accommodate up to 70 people. Children under 14 stay free in parents' room; outdoor playground for children. Free golf at the St David's course. The hotel was built in the 1860s as St David's Cathedral School. ***Rooms** 25. Garden, tennis, covered outdoor swimming pool (Easter-Oct), keep-fit equipment, sauna, games room, children's play area. Closed January.* AMERICAN EXPRESS *Access, Diners, Visa.*

St David's — Places of Interest

Haverfordwest Tourist Information Tel 0437 763110.
County Showground Haverfordwest Tel 0437 764331.
St David's Bishop's Palace Tel 0437 720517.
Cathedral Church of St David and St Andrew Tel 0437 720202.
Museums and Art Galleries
Scolton Manor Museum Spittal Tel 0437 731328.
Graham Sutherland Gallery Haverfordwest Tel 0437 751297.

Swansea — Forte Crest 69% £95

Tel 0792 651074 Fax 0792 456044 **H**

39 The Kingsway Swansea West Glamorgan SA1 5LS **Map 9 C6**

High-riser in the city centre, updated from its 60s' look. Leisure and business centres (conference facilities for 200+). ***Rooms** 99. Indoor swimming pool, gymnasium, sauna, solarium.* AMERICAN EXPRESS *Access, Diners, Visa.*

Swansea — Hilton National 65% £88

Tel 0792 310330 Fax 0792 797535 **H**

Phoenix Way Enterprise Park Llansamlet Swansea West Glamorgan SA7 9EG **Map 9 C6**

Two-storey, purpose-built redbrick hotel three miles from the city centre and two from the M4 (Junctions 44 or 45). Conference facilities for up to 200. 24hr room service. ***Rooms** 120. Keep-fit equipment, sauna.* AMERICAN EXPRESS *Access, Diners, Visa.*

> is our symbol for an outstanding wine list.

Swansea — Langland Court Hotel £78

Tel 0792 361545 Fax 0792 362302 **I**

31 Langland Court Road Langland Swansea West Glamorgan SA3 4TD **Map 9 C6**

Take the coastal road from Swansea to Mumbles (five miles) and follow signs to Langland Bay to find this comfortable clifftop inn. Public areas take the form of a Tudor-style residence, to which *Polly's*, the Dylan Thomas-themed wine bar, adds much character. Period-style main-house bedrooms mostly have fine views of the Bristol Channel, while further rooms occupy the adjacent former coach house (dogs allowed here only). Children up to 16 stay free in parents' room. Popular for conferences and functions. ***Rooms** 21. Garden, hair salon.* AMERICAN EXPRESS *Access, Diners, Visa.*

Swansea — Number One

£52

Tel 0792 456996

R

1 Wind Street Swansea West Glamorgan SA1 1DE

Map 9 C6

The atmosphere at Kate Taylor's bistro is convivial and the seating strictly limited, so booking is advised. There's nothing pretentious about either the surroundings or her no-nonsense cooking. Fish and shellfish are popular choices – hot oysters with laverbread and Stilton, quenelles of pike with prawn sauce – while meat dishes might include wood pigeon with bacon and port, saddle of hare or magret of duck with Madeira sauce. Separate menus for desserts and cheese, with Welsh varieties heading the latter. Good-value 2- and 3-course lunches with a small choice (perhaps gratin of seafood with garlic followed by ragout of duck with shallots and peas). ***Seats** 28. L 12-2.30 D 7-9.30. Closed D Mon & Tue, all Sun, 25-30 Dec. Set L £8.95/£10.95.* AMERICAN EXPRESS *Access, Visa.*

Swansea — Swansea Marriott 67%

£123

Tel 0792 642020 Fax 0792 650345

H

Maritime Quarter Swansea West Glamorgan SA1 3SS

Map 9 C6

Modern, four-storey redbrick hotel in a bayside location. Good-size bedrooms look out over either the bay or the marina. Children up to 18 stay free in parents' room; junior diners' menu in Abernethys restaurant. Sparse public areas. ***Rooms** 118. Indoor swimming pool, keep-fit equipment, spa bath, sauna.* AMERICAN EXPRESS *Access, Diners, Visa.*

Swansea — Places of Interest

Tourist Information Tel 0792 468321.
Clyne Gardens Tel 0792 401737.
Caswell Bay Beach.
Pembrey Motor Racing Circuit Tel 0554 891042.
Pembrey Sands Beach.
Afan Lido Swimming Pools Port Talbot Tel 0639 884141 *12 miles.*
St Helen's Cricket Ground Tel 0792 466321.
Singleton Park Showground Tel 0792 302429.

Theatres and Concert Halls

Brangwyn Hall Tel 0792 470002.
Dylan Thomas Theatre Tel 0792 473238.
Grand Theatre Tel 0792 462028.
Taliesin Arts Centre Tel 0792 295438.

Museums and Art Galleries

Cery Richards Gallery Tel 0792 295438.
Glynn Vivian Art Gallery Tel 0792 655006/651738.
Maritime and Industrial Museum Tel 0792 470371/650351.
Parc Howard Museum and Art Gallery Llanelli Tel 0554 773538 *16 miles.*

Talsarnau — Maes-y-Neaudd 72%

£109

Tel 0766 780200 Fax 0766 780211

HR

Talsarnau nr Harlech Gwynedd LL47 6YA

Map 8 C2

Signposted off the B4573 between Talsarnau and Harlech, Maes-y-Neaudd enjoys a tranquil setting on one side of an almost secret valley with fine views across the Snowdonia National Park. The oldest part of the building, now the bar with stone inglenook and leather upholstery, dates from the 15th century with later additions from the 16th and 19th. Other day rooms include a central lobby/lounge with large skylight and decorated bedrooms vary considerably in style from a small single with shower and WC only, a few with pine furniture, others with antique pieces and a four-poster with oak furniture to a splendidly large room (one of four in the adjacent stable block) with black beams, high pitched ceiling and log-burning stove. All have armchairs and/or sofas and bathrooms (three with

See over

spa baths) offer good towelling and robes. Personally run in friendly fashion by the Horsfalls and the Slatters who have been continually improving the hotel over the last 11 years. ***Rooms** 16. Garden.* AMERICAN EXPRESS *Access, Diners, Visa.*

Restaurant

£68

Dinner is officially a five-course affair but add the complimentary starter and the fact that one is encouraged to have cheese plus both puds before rounding off with one of their unusual ices (grain-mustard ice cream, apricot and thyme sorbet) and it can be more like eight or nine. The well-balanced, daily-changing menu offers a small choice at some stages; between stuffed quail with mustard dressing and a salad of asparagus and oyster mushrooms with basil to start perhaps to be followed by a soup and a fish dish before deciding between venison on a bed of Calvados onion jam, breast and "ballantine" of Trelough duck with citrus essence, a Welsh lamb dish and vegetarian option. A variety of home-baked breads testifies to the care taken by chef Peter Jackson who also makes good use of an extensive herb garden. Outstanding cheeses as befits this year's regional British Cheeseboard Winner. Well-balanced wine list with more New World than before. Fair prices, good house selection. No smoking. No children under 7 at night. ***Seats** 40. Parties 10. Private Room 50. L 12-2 (Mon-Sat by arrangement) D 7-9. Set L £8.75/£10.75 Set D £19.15/£23/£26.*

Talyllyn Tynycornel Hotel 59%

£80

Tel 0654 782282 Fax 0654 782679 **H**

Talyllyn Tywyn Gwynedd LL36 9AJ **Map 8 C3**

Fishing is the main attraction here, but the marvellous setting on Talyllyn Lake in Snowdonia National Park makes it a popular base for hikers and lovers of the great outdoors. The atmosphere is cosy and relaxed in the lounge and bar. Accommodation includes recently refurbished rooms in an annexe. Children stay free in parents' room. ***Rooms** 15. Garden, outdoor swimming pool, sauna, solarium, fishing.* AMERICAN EXPRESS *Access, Diners, Visa.*

Talyllyn Place of Interest

Talyllyn Railway and Narrow-gauge Railway Museum Tel 0654 710472.

Tintern Abbey Beaufort Hotel 60%

£92

Tel 0291 689777 Fax 0291 689727 **H**

Tintern Abbey nr Chepstow Gwent NP6 6SF **Map 9 D5**

Stone-built hotel whose front rooms look out on to the ruins of 800-year-old Tintern Abbey. Jarvis Hotels. ***Rooms** 24. Garden, games room.* AMERICAN EXPRESS *Access, Diners, Visa.*

Tintern Abbey Royal George 59%

£67

Tel 0291 689205 Fax 0291 689448 **H**

Tintern Abbey nr Chepstow Gwent NP6 6SF **Map 9 D5**

Tony and Maureen Pearce offer a warm welcome at their friendly hotel set at the foot of a lovely wooded hillside. A trout stream runs alongside, and the ruins of Tintern Abbey are just a short walk away. There's ample bar and lounge space (one lounge is stocked with board games) and a large function room. Some of the bedrooms have balconies overlooking the gardens. One child under 14 free in parents' room; ten rooms are suitable for family occupation. ***Rooms** 19. Garden, fishing.* AMERICAN EXPRESS *Access, Diners, Visa.*

Tintern Abbey Places of Interest

Tourist Information Tel 0291 689431.
Tintern Abbey Tel 0291 624647.

Trellech Village Green

£45

Tel 0600 860119

RR

Trellech nr Monmouth Gwent NP5 4PA

Map 9 D5

Jane and Bob Evans work hard to create warmth and atmosphere while housing two types of diner in a single setting. The bistroesque blackboard menu lists a long choice in the brasserie: seafood lasagne, casserole pheasant, chili beef and beans, Welsh lamb pie. The à la carte menu in the restaurant offers starters such as pigeon and basil terrine or king prawns with orange and ginger, then maybe paupiettes of salmon and turbot with a chervil butter sauce, or pan-fried fillet of beef with a port sauce topped with foie gras. Sweets include a little-of-everything *assiette gourmande.* ***Seats*** *70. Parties 24. Private Room 18. L 12-1.45 D 7-9.45 (Sat to 10). Closed D Sun, all Mon (open D Bank Holidays), 10 days Jan. Access, Visa.*

Rooms

£45

An adjacent stable conversion houses two basic, en-suite cottagey bedrooms (in phone-free privacy): one double, one twin. Bed and breakfast or self-catering terms.

Welsh Hook Stone Hall

£52

Tel 0348 840212 Fax 0348 840815

RR

Welsh Hook Wolfscastle nr Haverfordwest Dyfed SA62 5NS

Map 9 A5

Check directions carefully to seek out this charming 14th-century manor house hidden down lanes near Wolfscastle, 1½ miles west of the A40. Owner Martine Watson oversees while new chef Manuel Antunes works away in the kitchen. Moules marinière, snails with mushrooms in a cream sauce, fillet of brill with a cucumber sauce, confit de canard, and tarte tatin and profiteroles typify the à la carte style; a 4-course table d'hote dinner is also offered. Recommendations from a French-dominated wine list are impeccably handled by host Dr Alan Watson. ***Seats*** *34. Private Room 30. D only 7.30-9.30. Closed Mon, 2 weeks Dec. Set D £15.* AMERICAN EXPRESS *Access, Visa.*

Rooms

£58

Three double and two single bedrooms, all with neat bathrooms, are simply furnished and softly decorated. Residents have a private lounge for post-prandial relaxation.

Whitebrook Crown at Whitebrook

£65

Tel 0600 860254 Fax 0600 860607

RR

Whitebrook nr Monmouth Gwent NP5 4TX

Map 14 B2

Deep in the steeply wooded Whitebrook Valley an old inn has been virtually lost within a modern, white-painted rectangular building now run by Roger and Sandra Bates as a restaurant with rooms. A comfortable lounge (which houses the reception desk and small dispense bar) leads on to a cottagey, beamed dining room with wheelback chairs and pink and blue tablecloths. A fixed-price dinner menu offers a choice of seven or eight dishes at each stage with the likes of goat's cheese and leek tart with pine nut and herb crust; duck liver parfait on toasted brioche with home-pickled vegetables; chicken and morel mousse-stuffed breast of chicken with lobster ravioli, and calf's liver and grilled polenta on a bed of onion with a piquant sherry sauce. Sandra makes everything herself from the bread and gravad lax to the stocks that are at the heart of some excellent sauces, while Roger is the chatty host front of house. Lunchtime brings a shorter, simpler prix-fixe plus a varied light lunch menu also served

See over

in the lounge. A well-rounded and fairly-priced wine list has plenty of half bottles and helpful notes. Check out the bin ends. ***Seats** 30.*
Private Room 14. L 12-2 D 7-9.30 (Sat till 9.30). Closed L Mon, D Sun (except for residents), 25 & 26 Dec, 2 weeks Jan. Set L £14 Set D £14.
AMERICAN EXPRESS *Access, Diners, Visa.*

Rooms £80

Twelve well-kept, modestly furnished bedrooms with compact en-suite bathrooms offer good overnight accommodation. All have direct-dial phones, remote-control TV, radio-alarm, hairdryer and tea/coffee making facilities. The terrace makes a good spot for breakfast if the weather is kind.

Wrexham Forte Travelodge £42

Tel 0978 365705 **L**

Wrexham Bypass Rhostyllen Wrexham Clwyd LL14 4EJ **Map 8 D2**

At the A483/A5152 roundabout, 4 miles south of Wrexham and 6 miles east of Llangollen. ***Rooms** 32.* AMERICAN EXPRESS *Access, Visa.*

Channel Islands & Isle of Man

Alderney

Braye — First & Last

£30

Tel 0481 823162

R

Braye Alderney

Map 13 E4

The only restaurant on the island to benefit from the sea view with a panoramic dining room on the first-floor. The blue decor is strongly marine. Fish is of course a speciality with a beautiful crab bisque made from local crab and simply prepared catch of the day. Vegetarians and meat-lovers are also well catered for. In the evening, red lanterns are lit for a more romantic atmosphere. ***Seats** 65. Parties 40. L 12.15-1.30 D 7-10. Closed Mon, Oct-Apr.* AMERICAN EXPRESS® *Access, Diners, Visa.*

St Anne — Chez André — 63%

£62

Tel 0481 822777 Fax 0481 822962

H

Victoria Street St Anne Alderney

Map 13 E4

Located in the town centre, the hotel is under new ownership. The homely lounge and breakfast conservatory adjacent to the restaurant are attractive features. En-suite bedrooms have recently been redecorated and upgraded with trouser press, satellite TV, hairdryer and tea/coffee facilities. They are small but comfortable. 50% reduction for children under 12. ***Rooms** 11.* AMERICAN EXPRESS® *Access, Visa.*

St Anne — Georgian House

£45

Tel 0481 822471

R

Victoria Street St Anne Alderney

Map 13 E4

Charming, cosy pub with an elegant, traditional feel, located in the centre of St Anne. If the lunch menu is kept simple and offers the likes of Alderney whole fresh crab or moules à la crème, dinners are more special and the à la carte menu will extend to platter of fruits de mer or 12oz sirloin steak in cream and brandy. Tempting Sunday lunch menus (£7.75) and barbecues in the garden. A star entry in our Pub Guide. ***Seats** 48. Parties 40. Private Room 24. L 12-2.30 D 7-10. Closed D Tue.* AMERICAN EXPRESS® *Access, Diners, Visa.*

St Anne — Inchalla Hotel — 64%

£73

Tel 0481 823220 Fax 0481 823551

HR

The Val St Anne Alderney

Map 13 E4

Small hotel located on the heights of St Anne which benefits from a pleasant view of the town roofs with the sea in the background. Bedrooms are bright and well maintained with colour TV and well-stocked mini-bar. The surrounding gardens are peaceful and restful and the owner Valerie Willis will take care of the smallest details like ordering a cab for airport transfer. The use of jacuzzi, sauna and solarium is by appointment only with a £5 charge. ***Rooms** 10. Garden, sauna, spa bath, solarium. Closed 10 days Christmas.* AMERICAN EXPRESS® *Access, Visa.*

Restaurant

£52

The simply decorated dining room matches the well-executed, unpretentious cooking. The evening table d'hote menu offers simple fare of cauliflower and Stilton soup, almond trout and boeuf bourguignon where excellent ingredients are brought to their best. From the more extensive à la carte menu, choose the catch of the day cooked to your liking or fresh Alderney crab and lobster. Good-value bottles on the short wine list. ***Seats** 35. L (Sun only) 1-1.45 D 7-8.30. Closed D Sun. Set D £12.*

ALDERNEY — Place of Interest

Tourist Information Tel 0481 822994.

Guernsey

Castel — Hougue du Pommier

£71

Tel 0481 56531 Fax 0481 56260

I

Castel Guernsey

Map 13 E4

Lovely inn set in 10 acres of a former farm orchard. Quiet bedrooms which overlook the gardens are comfortable with remote-control colour TV and tea/coffee facilities. Gardens are particularly well kept. The solar heated swimming pool is remote and sheltered by trees. Nearby is a 10-hole pitch and putt golf course and a putting green. The restaurant, a succession of small dining rooms, retains the charm of the old farmhouse. ***Rooms*** *38. Garden, outdoor swimming pool, sauna, solarium, golf (18), games room.* AMERICAN EXPRESS® *Access, Diners, Visa.*

Castel — La Grande Mare — 73%

£134*

Tel 0481 56576 Fax 0481 56532

HR

Vazon Bay Castel Guernsey

Map 13 E4

Set in 100 acres of land with a 9-hole golf course, La Grande Mare is an unusual hotel which has the feel of a country inn and caters mainly for families. Although a few double bedrooms are available, most are studios or suites, which can accommodate up to 8 guests. Bedrooms, although with four poster beds, are minimally furnished. Suites have breakfast bar and comfortable sitting areas. All bedrooms have satellite TV, trouser press and hairdryer. Bathrooms are particularly large and agreeable. *Half-board terms only. ***Rooms*** *27. Outdoor swimming pool, spa bath, golf (9), fishing.* AMERICAN EXPRESS® *Access, Diners, Visa.*

Restaurant

£70

With a comfortable open-air layout and picture windows looking out on to the golf course, the restaurant has a strong country club atmosphere. The service has a bygone *je ne sais quoi* with waiters in white gloves and flambé trolleys. Chef Adrian Davison, who trained at the Dorchester in London, plays comfortably with meat and fruit combinations. The à la carte menu offers a refreshing and delicate first course of fresh Guernsey scallops with a pink peppercorn vinaigrette and is equally interesting with robust dishes like saddle of venison with cranberries, chestnuts and port-flavoured game jus. Particular attention is given to the wine selection both on the wine list and through a set dinner menu which offers a different glass of wine with each course. Simple but well-executed desserts. ***Seats*** *75. L 12-2 D 7-9.30.*

NEW CHEF

> We welcome bona fide complaints and recommendations on the tear-out pages at the back of the book for readers' comments. They are followed up by our professional team.

L'Erée — The Taste of India

£35

Tel 0481 64516

R

Sunset Cottage L'Eree Guernsey

Map 13 E4

One of the few Indian restaurants on the island, it is well located at the end of Rocquaine Bay near Lihou island. No sea view but an attractive intimate decor. The menu is strong on tandoori. Dishes are prepared with quality ingredients and a delicate mix of spices. There is a branch in St Peter's Port (Tel 0481 723730). ***Seats*** *52. L 12-2 D 6-12. Set L £6.95 (Sun £9.95) Set D £12.* AMERICAN EXPRESS® *Access, Diners, Visa.*

Forest — Mallard Hotel — 67% — £63

Tel 0481 64164 Fax 0481 65732 — **H**

Forest Guernsey — **Map 13 E4**

Conveniently located near the airport, the hotel offers good accommodation at kind prices. Public rooms are particularly large and the big attraction is of course the outdoor solar-heated swimming pool with plenty of sun beds and outdoor tables. Bedrooms are comfortable with trouser press, hairdryer, colour TV, tea/coffee facilities. Rooms overlooking the swimming pool have balconies facing south. Rooms facing the back of the building are quieter. Perfect for families. ***Rooms*** *47. Garden, outdoor swimming pool, keep-fit equipment, sauna, spa bath, solarium, tennis, games room, 2 cinemas.* AMERICAN EXPRESS *Access, Visa.*

Pleinmont — Imperial Hotel — £57

Tel 0481 64044 Fax 0481 66139 — **I**

Pleinmont Torteval Guernsey — **Map 13 E4**

Attractive little hotel ideally located at the south end of Rocquaine Bay. Bar, restaurant and most of the bedrooms benefit from a beautiful view of the bay. Four rooms have attractive balconies with patio furniture. Ongoing refurbishment ensures clean and bright accommodation with tea/coffee facilities, colour TV and direct-dial telephone. Children are welcome if well behaved with a 50% discount for children under 11. Special rates include a car hire. ***Rooms*** *17. Closed Nov-Apr. Access, Visa.*

St Martin — Bon Port Hotel — 66% — £90

Tel 0481 39249 — **H**

Moulin Huet Bay St Martin Guernsey — **Map 13 E4**

Ideally located with a breathtaking view and direct access to a private beach, the hotel caters for those who are looking for peace. Bedrooms are sparkling clean, with colour TV, trouser press, hairdryer, and tea/coffee facilities. Rooms with the sea view and private balconies are the best. Mr and Mrs Henke, the German owners, will make sure all your needs are fulfilled. Comfortable self-catering house at the back of the hotel with side sea view. ***Rooms*** *14. Garden, outdoor swimming pool. Access, Visa.*

St Martin — St Margaret's Lodge — 63% — £76

Tel 0481 35757 Fax 0481 37594 — **H**

Forest Road St Martin Guernsey — **Map 13 E4**

Midway between the airport and St Peter Port, the lodge is close to the south coast with its beaches and cliff paths. The modern interior includes a comfortable lounge and lounge bar. Bedrooms, all with en-suite facilities, include three suites. Guests can take a twice-daily courtesy coach for shopping in town. Conference/banqueting for 120. ***Rooms*** *47. Garden, outdoor swimming pool, sauna, solarium.* AMERICAN EXPRESS *Access, Diners, Visa.*

St Martin — La Trelade Hotel — 61% — £70

Tel 0481 35454 Fax 0481 37855 — **H**

Forest Road St Martin Guernsey — **Map 13 E4**

A holiday hotel in three acres of grounds off the main airport road. Two split-level lounge areas (one non-smoking) have modern brown leather-look seating, and the bar has smart and comfortable salmon-pink upholstery. Bedrooms are decent-sized and are equipped with simple white built-in units and clean bathrooms, some with shower and bath, others with shower only. Friendly staff. Families are well catered for with a children's playground and baby-listening available. Children up to 16 pay for meals but not accommodation in parents' room. ***Rooms*** *45. Garden, outdoor swimming pool, putting, games room.* AMERICAN EXPRESS *Access, Diners, Visa.*

St Peter Port — Absolute End

£50

Tel 0481 723822 Fax 0481 729129

R

St George's Esplanade St Peter Port Guernsey

Map 13 E4

On the seafront about a mile from the town centre, this is a pretty, cottagey restaurant specialising in fish and shellfish. The choice runs from home-smoked brill, salmon, scallops, mackerel and trout to prawn and asparagus pancakes, grilled sardines, salmon coulibiac and Dover sole grilled or meunière. Some meat dishes, too, and a decent choice for vegetarians. Good-value table d'hote lunch. Garden terrace for summer eating (cold food and drinks). ***Seats*** *60. Parties 50. Private Room 20. L 12-2 D 7-10. Closed Sun, Jan. Set L £10.* AMERICAN EXPRESS *Access, Diners, Visa.*

St Peter Port — Braye Lodge

£63

Tel 0481 723787 Fax 0481 712876

H

Ruette Braye St Peter Port Guernsey

Map 13 E4

New owners took over in 1993, with major improvement plans that included management and staff structure as well as bricks and mortar. These and other changes (more rooms, a leisure centre) were too late for us to grade the hotel. ***Rooms*** *25. Garden, outdoor swimming pool.* AMERICAN EXPRESS *Access, Diners, Visa.*

St Peter Port — Duke of Richmond — 63%

£75

Tel 0481 726221 Fax 0481 728945

H

Cambridge Park St Peter Port Guernsey

Map 13 E4

The hotel's position high above St Peter Port, between Cambridge Park and Candie Gardens, provides spectacular views from many of the bedrooms, some of which have balconies. Inland rooms are the cheapest, while top of the range is the penthouse suite. Public rooms include the Saumarez Cabin (ship's cabin motif), the Victorian Bar and a comfortable, roomy lounge that opens on to a terrace. Conference/banqueting facilities for 100/200. Children under 11 free if sharing parents' room. ***Rooms*** *74. Outdoor swimming pool.* AMERICAN EXPRESS *Access, Diners, Visa.*

St Peter Port — La Frégate — 64%

£111

Tel 0481 724624 Fax 0481 720443

H

Les Cotils St Peter Port Guernsey

Map 13 E4

An 18th-century manor house providing high standards of comfort and service along with views of the harbour from most of the bedrooms. Some rooms have double-glazed patio doors opening on to private balconies. Best sited of the public areas is the terrace next to the bar and restaurant. No children under 8. No dogs. ***Rooms*** *13.* AMERICAN EXPRESS *Access, Diners, Visa.*

St Peter Port — Louisiana

£60

Tel 0481 713157 Fax 0481 712191

R

South Esplanade St Peter Port Guernsey

Map 13 E4

Located on Havelet Bay with a beautiful view of Herm and Sark, this is an up-market restaurant for special occasions. Surprisingly there are only a few Cajun Creole specialities on the menu, which contains mainly pleasantly executed French and Italian dishes. ***Seats*** *90. Parties 30. Private Room 25. L 12-2.30 D 6-10.30. Closed Mon, Bank Holidays. Set L £8 Set D £14.95.* AMERICAN EXPRESS *Access, Visa.*

St Peter Port **Le Nautique** £50

Tel 0481 721714 **R**

The Quay Steps St Peter Port Guernsey **Map 13 E4**

Long-established French restaurant standing on the seafront, overlooking the harbour and marina. Fish is the pick of the menu, as you might expect. Sole comes grilled, meunière or with a champagne and lobster sauce; lobster itself is offered grilled and flambéed with whisky, Thermidor or cold with mayonnaise and salad; monkfish is presented with dugléré or orange and pepper sauce. Duck, lamb and steaks are also popular and there's a selection of three vegetarian dishes. Service is polished and efficient, booking essential. Smart dress is preferred. Short wine list with many bottles also offered in halves. ***Seats** 68. Parties 14. Private Room 30. L 12-2 D 7-10. Closed Sun, 1st 2 weeks Jan.* AMERICAN EXPRESS® *Access, Diners, Visa.*

St Peter Port **Old Government House** 68% £110

Tel 0481 724921 Fax 0481 724429 **H**

Ann's Place St Peter Port Guernsey **Map 13 E4**

Traditional standards of decor and service are to be found at this hillside hotel, where the classically elegant entrance hall is a reminder of the days when it actually was the Governor's residence. The Governor's Bar is cosy and intimate with its military memorabilia and the Centenary Bar, opened in 1958 to mark 100 years of the hotel's existence, features dancing to the hotel band Monday to Saturday in summer and weekends in winter. Best bedrooms are in a modern wing. Recent developments include a winter garden and brasserie. Conference/banqueting facilities for 150. ***Rooms** 72. Garden, outdoor swimming pool, solarium.* AMERICAN EXPRESS® *Access, Diners, Visa.*

St Peter Port **St Pierre Park** 71% £130

Tel 0481 728282 Fax 0481 712041 **H**

Rohais St Peter Port Guernsey **Map 13 E4**

Located in a quiet setting of 45 acres of parkland, away from the town's activity, it provides the island's most impressive leisure complex, with Tony Jacklin-designed 9-hole golf course, three outdoor tennis courts, a 25m indoor swimming pool and a fully-equipped health suite. Recently renovated public rooms are airy and elegant. The lounge/bar and some bedrooms overlook the garden and ornamental lake. Bedrooms, some yet to be redecorated, offer comfortable accommodation with up-to-date accessories. Children under 11 stay free in their parents' room. ***Rooms** 134. Garden, indoor swimming pool, gymnasium, sauna, spa bath, solarium, beauty & hair salons, tennis, 9-hole golf course, snooker, coffee shop (10am-10pm).* AMERICAN EXPRESS® *Access, Diners, Visa.*

GUERNSEY **Places of Interest**

Tourist Information Tel 0481 723552.
Aquarium Tel 723301
Auberge du Val Herb Garden Tel 63862.
Castle Cornet Tel 726518.
26 Cornet Street (Nat Trust of Guernsey) Tel 728451.
Fort Grey Shipwreck Museum Tel 726518.
German Occupation Museum Tel 38205.
German Underground Hospital Tel 39100.
German Botanical Gardens Tel 36690.
Guernsey Clockmakers Tel 36360.
Guernsey Coppercraft Tel 65112.
Guernsey Folk Museum Tel 55384.
Guernsey Museum & Art Gallery Tel 726518.
Guernsey Shires Tel 43923.
Guernsey Toys Tel 723871.
Guernsey Woodcarvers Tel 65373.

Hauteville House (Maison de Victor Hugo) Tel 721911.
La Valette Underground Tel 722300.
Military Museum.
Le Friquet Butterfly Centre Tel 54378.
Le Planel Dolls Tel 64326.
Le Tricoteur Tel 64040.
Les Rouvets Tropical Vinery Tel 63566.
Manor Railways Tel 38655.
Moulin Huet Pottery Tel 37201.
Oatlands Craft Centre Tel 44282.
Philatelic Bureau (GPO) Tel 726241.
Sausmarez Manor Tel 35571.
The Dolls House Collection Tel 35904.
The Rose Centre Tel 36580.
The Strawberry Farm Tel 64428.
The Telphone Museum Gel 711221.
Wild Sub-Tropical Gardens Tel 35571.

Herm

Herm White House 64% £116*

Tel 0481 722159 Fax 0481 710066 **H**

Herm **Map 13 E4**

The only hotel on the island, the White House offers comfortable accommodation for those who want to escape the hurly-burly of mainland life. The hotel produces its own electricity and there are no televisions or telephones in the bedrooms; a small butane cooker is used to heat up the kettles. The best bedrooms have sea view and balcony; some newly refurbished ones are brighter with brand new bathrooms. The hotel is self-contained with a succession of homely lounges, an elegant sea view restaurant and the Ship Inn, a pub with a Carvery dining room. Children are very welcome. *Half-board terms only. Self-catering cottages and flats also available. ***Rooms** 38. Garden, outdoor swimming pool, tennis. Closed mid Oct-end Mar. Access, Visa.*

Restaurant £40

Meals are served in an elegant dining room where smoking is not allowed. No à la carte, but a tempting four-course menu proposing the likes of duck liver risotto, cream of mushroom soup or grilled whole plaice with herb butter and fresh lime as well as vegetarian alternatives. The gourmet menu, well priced with a choice of five courses is only available on Saturday nights. ***Seats** 100. Parties 50. L 12.30-1.30 D 7-9. Set D £14.45.*

Jersey

Bouley Bay Water's Edge Hotel 64% £104

Tel 0534 862777 Fax 0534 863645 **H**

The Slipway Bouley Bay Trinity Jersey JE3 5AS **Map 13 F4**

A unique location on the island, as it stands alone in Bouley Bay with a beautiful view, direct access to the pebble beach and outdoor swimming pool. Bar and dining rooms, both overlooking the sea, have recently been refurbished. Bedrooms are comfortable but slightly dated. The best ones have small balconies and sea views. On a recent visit, service was not

See over

up to the general hotel standard. ***Rooms** 51. Garden, outdoor swimming pool, sauna, solarium, coffee shop (10am-5.30pm), Black Dog Bar (10am-11pm). Closed mid Oct-mid April.* AMERICAN EXPRESS *Access, Diners, Visa.*

Gorey **Jersey Pottery** ↑ **£60**

Tel 0534 851119 Fax 0534 856403 **R**

Gorey Village Gorey Jersey **Map 13 F4**

The pottery has become Jersey's most popular tourist attraction. The modern premises have an attractive restaurant, set in a flowery conservatory with garden furniture, umbrellas, and climbing vines. The menu is strong on summer dishes with fat-reduced sauces or light concoctions of warm carrot mousse with mussels and Muscadet cream, boned wing of skate, rolled and served on a bed of diced tomato with balsamic vinegar. Beautiful fresh seafood salads and plateaux de fruits de mer using locally caught seafood are a speciality. Orders are taken until 4.30pm. The next-door self-service café offers cold dishes (mainly seafood salads), pastries and afternoon teas. Children are very welcome in both restaurants. ***Seats** 300. Meals 9-5.30. Closed Sat & Sun, Bank Holidays, 10 days Christmas.* AMERICAN EXPRESS *Access, Diners, Visa.*

Gorey **Moorings Hotel** **62%** **£96**

Tel 0534 853633 Fax 0534 857618 **H**

Gorey Pier Gorey Jersey JE3 6EW **Map 13 F4**

A small, friendly waterfront hotel huddled between Mont Orgueil Castle and Gorey Harbour. It's also just a short distance from Grouville Bay beach. Two bars provide a choice for relaxing over a drink, and there's a lounge and roof garden. Bedrooms are furnished in simple style, and three are suitable for family occupation. Baby-listening available. Free use of swimming pool and night club (no unaccompanied under-18s) in sister hotel one mile away. No dogs. ***Rooms** 16.* AMERICAN EXPRESS *Access, Visa.*

> We endeavour to be as up-to-the-minute as possible, but inevitably some changes to key personnel may occur at restaurants and hotels after the Guide goes to press.

Gorey **Old Court House** **64%** **£89**

Tel 0534 854444 Fax 0534 853587 **H**

Gorey Jersey JE3 9EX **Map 13 F4**

On the edge of Gorey, and handy for Royal Bay beach, the Old Court House is a popular place for family holidays. Public areas include a beamed restaurant dating in part from the 15th century. New-wing bedrooms have balconies, while the pleasant older rooms are more spacious. No dogs. ***Rooms** 58. Garden, outdoor swimming pool, sauna, solarium. Closed Nov-Feb.* AMERICAN EXPRESS *Access, Diners, Visa.*

Grouville **Grouville Bay Hotel** **62%** **£80**

Tel 0534 51004 Fax 0534 57416 **H**

Grouville Jersey **Map 13 F4**

Located right next to the Royal Jersey Golf course, the hotel has no golf concession but enjoys attractive views over the greens. Outdoor heated swimming pool and footpath to the nearby beaches are pluses. Comfortable public rooms and basic bedrooms (40% for family use) with colour TV and tea/coffee facilities. ***Rooms** 56. Garden, outdoor swimming pool, children's swimming pool, games room. Closed 2nd week Oct-2nd week Apr.* AMERICAN EXPRESS *Access, Diners, Visa.*

Havre des Pas — Ommaroo Hotel — 59% — £75

Tel 0534 23493 Fax 0534 59912 — **H**

Havre des Pas St Helier Jersey JE2 4UQ — **Map 13 F4**

Traditional seaside hotel whose best rooms (available with a supplement) have sea-facing balconies. All rooms now have en-suite facilities. Child-friendly. Note that the hotel is now open all year. ***Rooms** 85. Garden.* AMERICAN EXPRESS *Access, Diners, Visa.*

Havre des Pas — Hotel de la Plage — 66% — £84

Tel 0534 23474 Fax 0534 68642 — **H**

Havre des Pas St Helier Jersey JE2 4UQ — **Map 13 F4**

A well-run modern hotel on the seafront, with picture windows to enhance the views. Day rooms are in various styles: subdued and modern in the split-level lounge-bar, tropical in the Caribbean Bar, bamboo in the sun lounge. Sea-facing bedrooms have balconies; inland-view rooms are cheaper. Snacks are served all day in the lounges, in the bedrooms or on the terrace. No dogs. ***Rooms** 78. Keep-fit facilities, solarium, games room. Closed end Oct-early Apr.* AMERICAN EXPRESS *Access, Diners, Visa.*

Portelet Bay — Portelet Hotel — 66% — £100

Tel 0534 41204 Fax 0534 46625 — **H**

Portelet Bay St Brelade Jersey — **Map 13 F4**

A well-kept modern hotel open only in summer. Most popular of the public rooms is the sun lounge overlooking the pool to St Brelade's Bay beyond. Elsewhere there's a quiet residents' lounge and a 70s'-style cocktail bar. Many of the bedrooms have private balconies. Free early-morning tea or coffee and paper, mini-bus to town. No dogs. ***Rooms** 86. Garden, outdoor swimming pool, tennis, putting, games room. Closed Oct-Apr.* AMERICAN EXPRESS *Access, Diners, Visa.*

> Never leave money, credit cards or valuables lying around in your hotel room. Use the hotel safe or the mini-safe in your room.

Rozel Bay — Chateau la Chaire — 74% — £105

Tel 0534 863354 Fax 0534 865137 — **HR**

Rozel Bay Jersey JE3 6AJ — **Map 13 F4**

Built in 1843 just above the charming harbour of Rozel Bay, the hotel's public rooms have the proportions and elegance of the last century, from the welcoming reception hall, with its large staircase, to the high-ceilinged rococo lounge or the intimate, oak-panelled dining room. Bedrooms have been redecorated, privileging the first-floor Executive rooms with the highest standard including stylish decor, comfortable sitting areas and jacuzzi bathtubs. Regular double bedrooms are much smaller, with the charming cosiness of lower ceilings under slanted roofs and small windows. Complimentary water, fruit basket and biscuits in all bedrooms. ***Rooms** 14. Garden.* AMERICAN EXPRESS *Access, Diners, Visa.*

Restaurant — £65

From the oak-panelled dining room with a traditional atmosphere extends a contemporary conservatory with a view of the hotel terrace and surrounding trees. Here a simple menu is well executed with a strong emphasis on freshness and well-mastered, creamy sauces: steamed supreme of turbot with poached leeks and a champagne and mussel beurre blanc, corn-fed chicken supreme with a fricassee of woodland mushrooms veiled in Madeira and cream sauce. Inspired desserts like an iced pistachio nougatine parfait with a caramel sauce perfumed with honey. Well-stocked wine list. ***Seats** 65. Parties 30. L 12-2 D 7-10 Set D £22.50.*

St Aubin — Old Court House Inn — £80

Tel 0534 46433 Fax 0534 45103 — I

St Aubin Harbour St Aubin Jersey — Map 13 F4

A pleasant inn with surviving historical features and a lot of character. Meals are served in the restaurant with an attractive courtyard or in the downstairs pubby bar with its sunny terrace. One of the house's best features is the Mizzen Mast bar, shaped as a barge and used as the Royal Barge pub in *Bergerac*. Bedrooms, recently renovated, have fashionable fabrics, old pine and brand new bathrooms. One large suite, with a beautiful view and private patio, is ideal for families. ***Rooms** 9.* AMERICAN EXPRESS *Access, Diners, Visa.*

St Brelade — Atlantic Hotel — 70% — £130

Tel 0534 44101 Fax 0534 44102 — H

La Moye St Brelade Jersey JE3 8HE — Map 13 F4

A functional 70s' block high above St Ouen's Bay, the Atlantic Hotel is surrounded by three acres of grounds. All rooms have balconies to take advantage of the views (of either La Moye golf course or the bay and sea) and are furnished to a very high standard, with top-quality mahogany furniture, fine floral fabrics and Chinese-style china; some of the larger rooms have sofa beds and the Garden studios and two luxury suites have their own terraces. In the spacious entrance hall, glazed terracotta flooring, brown leather armchairs and a pool with waterfall please the eye; another major feature is the Palm Club, a well-equipped health and leisure centre. Besides the restaurant menus there are light lunches and children's high teas. No dogs. ***Rooms** 50. Garden, indoor & outdoor swimming pools, keep-fit equipment, sauna, spa bath, solarium, tennis. Closed Jan & Feb.* AMERICAN EXPRESS *Access, Diners, Visa.*

St Brelade — Hotel Chateau Valeuse — 65% — £74

Tel 0534 46281 Fax 0534 47110 — HR

St Brelade Jersey JE3 8EE — Map 13 F4

Quiet hotel on the heights of St Brelade, away from the main road with a beautiful view of the bay. South-facing bedrooms with balconies are of course the best, but all are simply and comfortably furnished. No amenities except for colour TV, but room service is particularly prompt and efficient. The heated outdoor swimming pool in the middle of well-kept gardens is just the place to relax. No children under five. ***Rooms** 33. Garden, outdoor swimming pool, putting. Closed mid Oct-Apr. Access, Visa.*

Restaurant — £50

Popular with non-residents and on Sunday lunch, with some tables overlooking the bay, the menu is simple and well prepared: *moules marinière*, sole with lobster sauce, *veau à la crème*. ***Seats** 70. Parties 50. L 12.45-1.45 D 8-9. Set L £8.50 Set D £14.50.*

St Brelade — La Place Hotel — 67% — £110

Tel 0534 44261 Fax 0534 45164 — H

Route du Coin La Haule St Brelade Jersey JE3 8BF — Map 13 F4

Once a farmhouse but now much enlarged by modern extensions, La Place is for those who like rural surroundings. The main public rooms are part of the original, 400-year-old building. There's a delightful open-air seating area in a south-facing courtyard, a bright bar with green bamboo furniture and two lounges, one of which has a black-beamed ceiling, a pink granite fireplace, antique furniture and polished brass ornaments. Bedrooms include seven around the pool. Children up to seven stay free in parents' room; children's high tea is offered. ***Rooms** 40. Outdoor swimming pool, sauna.* AMERICAN EXPRESS *Access, Diners, Visa.*

St Brelade **Sea Crest** **64%** **£84**

Tel 0534 46353 Fax 0534 47316 **HR**

Petit Port St Brelade Jersey JE3 8HH **Map 13 F4**

Julian and Martha Bernstein are personally in charge of their relaxing white-painted hotel, which overlooks a rocky bay at the south-west end of the island. The restaurant, which features modern artwork, includes a cocktail bar opening on to a sun lounge and terrace. Bedrooms, recently refurbished, include five with balconies. Children under twelve stay free in parents' room. No dogs. ***Rooms*** *7. Garden, outdoor swimming pool. Closed Feb.* AMERICAN EXPRESS® *Access, Visa.*

Restaurant **£68**

Local seafood appears regularly on a menu which daily specials and dishes prepared at the table (scampi dijonnaise, veal Marsala, steak Diane). Book a table by the window for the best views. ***Seats*** *60. Parties 10. L 12.30-2 (Sun to 3) D 7.30-10. Closed all Mon, also D Sun in winter. Set L £10 Set D £18.50.*

St Brelade **Taj Mahal** **£50**

Tel 0534 44400 **R**

La Pulente St Brelade Jersey **Map 13 F4**

An interesting discovery at the southern edge of St Ouen's Bay. Both the small bar and dining room overlook the bay and are elegantly decorated. In the summer, the terrace provides additional seating but booking is advisable. The menu is strong on charcoal-grilled dishes and fresh seafood according to availabilities. The chef's specialities include half-lobster Botera cooked in garlic, ginger, coconut butter and fresh coriander, Taj Mahal tandoori chicken topped with a sweet peanut tomato sauce or delicious Kashmiri vegetables mixed with mango and topped with coconut milk. There is a second Taj Mahal in la Motte Street, St Helier (Tel 0534 20147). ***Seats*** *28. L 12-2 D 6-11. Closed L Mon.* AMERICAN EXPRESS® *Access, Diners, Visa.*

St Brelade's Bay **Hotel L'Horizon** **72%** **£160**

Tel 0534 43101 Fax 0534 46269 **H**

St Brelade's Bay Jersey **Map 13 F4**

Leisure facilities shine at this Clipper hotel, which overlooks a sandy beach in the heart of St Brelade's Bay. Club L'Horizon is a well-equipped centre for relaxing or keeping fit, and a 40ft motor yacht, *Clipper L'Horizon*, is available for day charter. Public areas include a bar with picture windows and beach views, a drawing room, a library and three restaurants. Good-sized bedrooms have decent-quality furniture and well-equipped bathrooms. Banqueting/conference facilities for 200/150. No dogs. ***Rooms*** *107. Garden, indoor swimming pool, keep-fit equipment, sauna, spa bath, solarium, hairdressing, coffee shop (10am-11pm). Access, Visa.*

St Brelade's Bay **St Brelade's Bay Hotel** **70%** **£140**

Tel 0534 46141 Fax 0534 47278 **H**

St Brelade's Bay Jersey JE3 8EF **Map 13 F4**

This smartly whitewashed, low-level hotel bears evidence of the long-term care and pride heaped upon it by the Colley family. Behind it is a lovely garden set with sun-loungers where parents can relax while a lifeguard teaches their children to swim; inside, an airy, spacious foyer leads you to the elegant and comfortable lounge, with antiques, chesterfields, parquet floors and beautiful rugs. There's live music in the cocktail bar, and a club room and games room for younger guests. First-and second-floor rooms are traditional, while those on the third floor are more modern; all are attractively and tastefully decorated and furnished. Families are well catered for. ***Rooms*** *82. Garden, outdoor swimming pool, keep-fit equipment, sauna, solarium, games room, tennis, putting. Closed mid Oct-end Apr. Access, Visa.*

St Clement's Bay — Hotel Ambassadeur — 63% — £70

Tel 0534 24455 Fax 0534 23185 — **H**

St Clement's Bay Jersey JE2 6SB — **Map 13 F4**

Modern hotel with fine views over St Clement's Bay from the sunny lounge and the best of the bedrooms. These rooms overloook the bay and have large patio windows and wrought-iron balustrades. ***Rooms** 69. Outdoor swimming pool, games room. Closed 3 Jan-15 Feb.* AMERICAN EXPRESS *Access, Visa.*

St Helier — Apollo Hotel — 63% — £88

Tel 0534 25441 Fax 0534 22120 — **H**

9 St Saviour's Road St Helier Jersey JE2 4LA — **Map 13 F4**

A modern two-storey hotel built round a courtyard. Public areas provide plenty of space to relax: there are two bars (one in pub style), a coffee shop serving snacks throughout the day, an indoor leisure centre and a sun-trap terrace. Bedrooms, some with balconies, include many suitable for family occupation. ***Rooms** 85. Indoor swimming pool, gymnasium, sauna, spa bath, solarium, coffee shop (11am-9pm).* AMERICAN EXPRESS *Access, Diners, Visa.*

St Helier — Beaufort Hotel — 60% — £92

Tel 0534 32471 Fax 0534 20371 — **H**

Green Street St Helier Jersey — **Map 13 F4**

A few minutes' walk from the beach and the town centre, this friendly modern hotel offers comfortable accommodation, free car parking and leisure facilities. A pianist plays nightly in the bar, and the large terrace is fun when the sun shines. Bedrooms each have two armchairs. Suites and four-poster rooms available. No dogs. ***Rooms** 54. Indoor swimming pool, spa bath, games room (summer).* AMERICAN EXPRESS *Access, Diners, Visa.*

St Helier — La Capannina — £60

Tel 0534 34602 Fax 0534 77626 — **R**

65 Halkett Place St Helier Jersey — **Map 13 F4**

Popular and cheerful Italian restaurant whose straight-down-the-line menu is supplemented by daily specials – usually seafood, such as lobster bisque, stuffed clams, red mullet or brill meunière. Extensive wine list. ***Seats** 130. Parties 40. Private Room 20. L 12-2 D 7-10. Closed Sun, Bank Holidays, 1 week Christmas. Access, Diners, Visa.*

St Helier — Hotel de France — 71% — £120

Tel 0534 38990 Fax 0534 35354 — **H**

St Saviour's Road St Helier Jersey — **Map 13 F4**

Located in the northern part of St Helier, on St Saviour's Road, the hotel has the elegance of a mid-nineteenth century palace spoiled by the construction of modern conference and leisure buildings. The extraordinary conference facilities include a 600-delegate auditorium, the 1,200 sq. ft. Skyline Hall and a profusion of banqueting suites and boardrooms.
To accommodate the 320 bedrooms, a large conservatory restaurant and two bars are adequate – unlike the tiny indoor and outdoor swimming pools. Bedrooms in the old wing are large although not as well equipped as the smaller rooms in the new wing. The hotel caters for families particularly well. Children under 12 stay free in their parents' room between April and October. ***Rooms** 320. Terrace, outdoor and indoor swimming pool, keep-fit equipment, squash, sauna, spa bath, solarium, beauty & hair salon, games room, snooker, news kiosk (8-12, 4-7).* AMERICAN EXPRESS *Access, Diners, Visa.*

St Helier **Grand Hotel** **68%** **£120**

Tel 0534 22301 Fax 0534 37815 **HR**

The Esplanade St Helier Jersey JE4 8WD **Map 13 F4**

The long, gabled frontage of the Grand is a distinctive feature on the seafront and the entrance is appropriately impressive, with ornate, coloured pillars and a marble floor. The smart period-style bar and lounge have fine views and so do balconied front bedrooms, which attract a hefty surcharge. It's a busy hotel catering for both holiday and business visitors (conference/banqueting facilities for 180/250). Families are well provided for with free accommodation for under-14s in their parents' room, plus baby-sitting and special children's meals also available. De Vere Hotels. ***Rooms** 115. Indoor swimming pool, keep-fit equipment, sauna, spa bath, solarium, beauty salon, hairdressing, snooker.* AMERICAN EXPRESS *Access, Diners, Visa.*

Victoria's **£70**

Formal elegance and a traditional French/British à la carte menu. There's a second restaurant, the Regency. ***Seats** 250. L 12.15-2.15 D 7-10 (Sun to 9.30). Set L £14 Set D £19.50.*

St Helier **Pomme d'Or Hotel** **65%** **£90**

Tel 0534 78644 Fax 0534 37781 **H**

The Esplanade St Helier Jersey JE2 3NF **Map 13 F4**

A convenient harbourside location in the town centre helps make this large, white-painted and green-tiled hotel popular with tourists. Air-conditioned public rooms include Le Pommier coffee shop and The Wharf pub. Pleasant, well-designed bedrooms and spotless bathrooms are equipped with everything needed for a comfortable stay. Some rooms have recently been refurbished and two suites are now available. Conference/banqueting facilities for 300. No dogs. ***Rooms** 150. Coffee shop (7am-11pm).* AMERICAN EXPRESS *Access, Diners, Visa.*

St Ouen **The Lobster Pot** **£65**

Tel 0534 482888 Fax 0534 481574 **RR**

L'Etacq St Ouen Jersey **Map 13 F4**

A popular spot with tours and coaches where booking is recommended for weekends. The location is attractive, overlooking St Ouen's Bay. The speciality is of course locally caught lobster served grilled, à la nage, Newburg or Thermidor, but an extensive menu will please all tastes. Well-prepared flambé desserts. ***Seats** 90. Private Room 40. L 12.30-2.15 D 7.30-10. Set D £14.50.* AMERICAN EXPRESS *Access, Diners, Visa.*

Rooms **£88**

Thirteen large bedrooms with the usual modern amenities of TV, trouser press, hairdryer and even a small bar area with tea and coffee facilities and a small refrigerator. The best rooms naturally have a sea view. Good for families.

St Peter **Mermaid Hotel** **64%** **£92**

Tel 0534 41255 Fax 0534 45826 **H**

Airport Road St Peter Jersey JE3 7BN **Map 13 F4**

A modern hotel located near the airport and built next to a natural lake. Bedrooms all have the expected facilities and though not large they benefit from south-facing balconies with a lake view. The hotel is self-contained with restaurants, bar, pub and impressive leisure facilities. No dogs. ***Rooms** 68. Garden, outdoor & indoor swimming pools, keep-fit equipment, sauna, spa bath, tennis, putting.* AMERICAN EXPRESS *Access, Diners, Visa.*

St Saviour **Longueville Manor** 80% £144

Tel 0534 25501 Fax 0534 31613 **HR**

St Saviour Jersey JE2 7SA **Map 13 F4**

Now managed by the third generation of Lewis and Dufty families who ensure quality with the same warmth and elegance, the manor still reigns supreme among the Island's hotels. The carved-panelled dining room and lounge, part of the architectural interest of the house, are beautifully complemented by stylish yet not overdone decor. Bedrooms are of course up to the standard of the rest, each with its own style, some with original stone fireplaces. Bathrooms feel more like anterooms, with strong attention to detail. Master bedrooms, located at the front of the building, closer to the road, tend to be smaller and not as quiet. Fifteen acres of grounds provide peaceful walks and of course tables are set outside near the swimming pool for light lunches, afternoon teas or cocktails. Charming staff lavish care and attention on the guests. ***Rooms** 32. Garden, outdoor swimming pool, tennis.* AMERICAN EXPRESS *Access, Diners, Visa.*

Restaurant £90

The two dining rooms cater for different moods, from the solemn atmosphere of the 13th-century carved-panelled oak room to the more relaxed armchairs of the second done in warm tones of beige. Table d'hôte, à la carte, menu dégustation or vegetarian, the chef caters for many tastes using some home-grown herbs and vegetables. *Courgettes en fleur* with a salmon soufflé, fricassee of maize chicken, lobster and baby vegetables, roast best end of lamb with glazed shallots and artichoke, are examples of lightly-prepared dishes, some too elaborate for their own good when simplicity is best. Impressive cheese trolley of British and French selections and beautiful desserts like a cherry Bakewell tart with Jersey cream. ***Seats** 65. Parties 20. Private Room 30. L 12.30-2 D 7.30-9.30. Set L £17.50 Set D £28.50.*

St Saviour **Merton Hotel** 60% £86*

Tel 0534 24231 Fax 0534 68603 **H**

Belvedere St Saviour Jersey **Map 13 F4**

Located right outside St Helier, on a sloped street off the A3, a spacious hotel with basic accommodation and the amazing Aquadome complex of indoor and outdoor swimming pools. Good for children, with entertainment for them in the evening. *Half-board terms. ***Rooms** 330. Garden, indoor and outdoor swimming pool, children's swimming pool, squash, spa bath, tennis, bistro (10.30-2, 3-6, 9.30-12).* AMERICAN EXPRESS *Access, Diners, Visa.*

JERSEY Places of Interest

Tourist Information Tel 0534 500777.
Battle of Flowers Museum St Ouen Tel 482408.
Berni Gallery St Helier Tel 68080.
Channel Island Military Museum St Ouen Tel 23136.
Elizabeth Castle St Helier Tel 23971.
Fantastic Tropical Gardens St Peter Tel 481585.
Fort Regent Leisure Centre St Helier Tel 500000.
German Command Bunker St Brelade Tel 482089.
German Underground Hospital St Lawrence Tel 863442.
Jersey Butterfly Centre St Mary Tel 481707.
Jersey Flower Centre St Lawrence Tel 865665.
Jersey Museum St Helier Tel 30511.
Jersey Zoo, Trinity Tel 864666.
Les Mielles Visitor Centre St Ouen Tel 483651.
La Hougue Bie Grouville Tel 853823.
Le Moulin de Quètivel St Peter Tel 45408.

Living Legend St Peter Tel 485496.
Micro World St Ouen Tel 483390.
Mont Orgueil Castle Gorey Tel 853292.
Samarès Manor St Clement Tel 70551.
St Matthews (Glass) Church St Lawrence Tel 20934.
St Peter's Bunker Museum St Peter Tel 481048.

Sark

Sark Aval Du Creux Hotel 57% £63

Tel 0481 832036 Fax 0481 832368 **HR**

Sark **Map 13 E4**

Eight miles east of Guernsey is the island of Sark, a peaceful retreat with forty miles of coastline, bracing walks and no traffic. Peter and Cheryl Tonks' friendly little hotel, originally a farmhouse, is a good place for family holidays, with four of the bedrooms of a suitable size for families. There are two lounges and a small bar hung with local pictures. ***Rooms** 12. Garden, outdoor swimming pool, boules. Closed Oct-Apr. Access, Visa.*

Restaurant £52

Seafood plays the leading role here, with local crab served hot in a shell with cheese glaze, plus oysters, lobster (surf'n'turf) and monkfish. Fresh asparagus from Guernsey (in season) and pan-fried pigeon breast with gingerbread sauce, and guinea fowl in filo pastry with sweet red peppers show that care is taken not only in preparation but also in obtaining quality ingredients. ***Seats** 40. Private Room 15. L 12-2 D 7-8. Set D £15.95.*

Sark Dixcart Hotel 64% £90

Tel 0481 832015 Fax 0481 832164 **HR**

Sark **Map 13 E4**

Sark's oldest established hotel, whose guests included Victor Hugo. Managed by the owners, the hotel has been through a major refurbishment. Converted bedrooms have been tastefully done, exposing the original stone walls and using the warmth of pinewood panelling. Bathrooms have good-quality modern showers. The owners are planning more improvements over the years. Homely lounge and bar for the occasional rainy day and fifty acres of land with private access to the Dixcart Bay beach. Children welcome if well behaved. Open all year. ***Rooms** 18. Garden, playroom.* AMERICAN EXPRESS *Access, Diners, Visa.*

Restaurant £38

The restaurant's beautiful view over the sloping gardens is peaceful and relaxing. The table d'hote menu, the cheapest on the island, is of high quality, using freshly caught fish or local lamb and beef. Typical dishes are clear beef consommé with batons of carrots, scallops in bacon, lamb chops and kidneys with rosemary sauce, or fresh lobster. The dessert menu includes delicious Sark ice creams. Well-priced wine list. ***Seats** 100. L 12-2.30 D 7-9.30. Set D £13.50.*

Sark Hotel Petit Champ 61% £68

Tel 0481 832046 Fax 0481 832469 **H**

Sark **Map 13 E4**

Splendid sea views are a feature at this small hotel, in a quiet setting on carless Sark's west coast. There's a tiny bar, leafy sun lounges and a quiet, homely lounge. Bedrooms are best described as cosy, and are undisturbed by TVs or telephones; some rooms have sliding patio doors. No children

See over

under seven. No dogs. ***Rooms** 16. Garden, outdoor swimming pool, putting, horse & carriage hire, bicycle hire, sea fishing, yacht charters. Closed Oct-Easter.* AMERICAN EXPRESS *Access, Diners, Visa.*

Sark La Sablonnerie 66% £65

Tel 0481 832061 Fax 0481 832408 **HR**

Sark **Map 13 E4**

As there are no cars on the island, the hotel provides a horse-drawn carriage to bring guests from the harbour to Little Sark, the southern part of the island connected by a narrow bridge with breathtaking views. The hotel is a lesson in *savoir vivre,* where the charming owner Elizabeth Perrée treats her guests lovingly. The heart of the hotel is the cosy bar with low ceiling, granite walls and blue velvet decor. The hotel is surrounded by beautifully kept flowery gardens. The bright comfortable bedrooms are individually decorated with simple pine furniture; half of them are not ensuite.
In addition to the elaborate meals served in the intimate restaurant, a lovely tea garden located a few yards from the main building is open all day for light meals and afternoon teas. ***Rooms** 22. Closed Oct-Easter. Garden.*

Restaurant £52

A small dining room done in red with simple pine furniture and candle-lit in the evening. The only self-sufficient establishment on the island. Food for the table comes from the hotel's own nearby farm which produces all the organic dairy products, meat and vegetables needed with, of course, local fish and seafood. Dinner begins with large plates of canapés in the bar, followed by a delicious five-course fixed-price menu which might include langoustines and king prawns with brandy mayonnaise, cream of asparagus soup with lemon croutons and fillet of pork en croute. ***Seats** 36.*
L 12.30-2.30 D 7.30-9.30. Set L £16.50 Set D £18.50.

See the Conference and Banqueting section for lists of hotels arranged by county.

Sark Stocks Hotel 61% £102*

Tel 0481 832001 Fax 0481 832130 **HR**

Sark **Map 13 E4**

Peace and relaxation come without too much trouble at the Armorgie family's granite-built hotel, which lies in a wooded valley 20 minutes walk from the harbour. There's a homely atmosphere in the lounge, and comfortable, unfussy bedrooms are decorated with darkwood furniture and floral fabrics. No TVs in the rooms. *Half-board terms only. ***Rooms** 25. Garden, outdoor swimming pool, coffee shop (10am-10pm).*
Closed mid Oct-Easter. Access, Diners, Visa.

Cider Press Restaurant £50

Both table d'hote and à la carte menus are offered, with local fish, shellfish and meat always featuring. Mussels Catalan-style, crab and smoked bacon soup, roast shoulder of veal, grilled turbot and lobster prepared several ways all use Island produce. Coffee, lunch, cream teas and light evening meals are served in the *Courtyard Bistro,* with alfresco tables in summer adjacent to the swimming pool; children's supper menu served here from 5-7pm. ***Seats** 60. Private Room 12. L 12-2.30 D 7.30-9 (Sun to 9).*
Set D £12.50/£15.50.

SARK Place of Interest

Tourist Information Tel 0481 832345.

Isle of Man

Ballasalla La Rosette

£50

Tel 0624 822940

R

Main Road Ballasalla Isle of Man

Map 4 B4

Local seafood, including crab and queenies (little scallops), and straightforward meat dishes get simple classic treatment in a French-style restaurant with several alcoves and private rooms. The restaurant is 5 minutes drive from the airport. ***Seats** 45. Parties 6. Private Room 16. L 12-3 D 7-10. Closed Sun, 1st 2 weeks Jan. Set L £12.50. Access, Visa.*

Douglas Palace Hotel 65%

£95

Tel 0624 662662 Fax 0624 625535

H

Central Promenade Douglas Isle of Man

Map 4 B4

The excellent leisure complex, with its own bar/café, the cinemas, the night club and the public casino provide plenty of entertainment for guests at the modern Palace, one of the focal points of the island's night life. Other day rooms are smart and spacious, and bedrooms, though not large, are quite well equipped. There are four suites. Banqueting and conference facilities for 300+. Pleasant, helpful staff. No dogs. ***Rooms** 135. Indoor swimming pool, sauna, spa bath, solarium, beauty & hair salon, casino, night club, coffee shop (7am-10pm).* AMERICAN EXPRESS *Access, Diners, Visa.*

Douglas Sefton Hotel 63%

£70

Tel 0624 626011 Fax 0624 676004

H

Harris Promenade Douglas Isle of Man

Map 4 B4

A turn-of-the-century seafront hotel with smart rooms behind its grand white frontage. The spacious interior is modern with just a hint of days gone by. There are good sea views from the lounge and the best bedrooms. Popular for weekend and special breaks (golf, rambling, bird-watching etc). Access through a secret door to the adjacent Gaiety Theatre. Conference and banqueting facilities for 100. ***Rooms** 80. Indoor swimming pool, keep-fit equipment, sauna, spa bath, steam room, solarium, beauty salon, coffee shop (9.45am-11pm).* AMERICAN EXPRESS *Access, Diners, Visa.*

Ramsey Grand Island Hotel 67%

£90

Tel 0624 812455 Fax 0624 815291

H

Bride Road Ramsey Isle of Man

Map 4 B4

One mile north of Ramsey on the Bride Road, the handsome white-painted hotel looks down past terraced lawns to Ramsey Bay. Originally a Georgian manor house, it has a traditional look and feel, and there are a few antiques among the furnishings. Bedrooms are done out prettily, with pinks and blues predominating. There are extensive conference facilities (for up to 300/200). ***Rooms** 54. Garden, indoor swimming pool, sauna, spa bath, steam room, beauty and hair salon, putting, snooker, coarse fishing.* AMERICAN EXPRESS *Access, Diners, Visa.*

Ramsey Harbour Bistro

£45

Tel 0624 814182

R

5 East Street Ramsey Isle of Man

Map 4 B4

Informal eating in a friendly bistro near the quay. Seafood is quite a feature on the menu: local queenie scallops cooked with Mornay sauce, with a garlic sauce on a bed of spinach, or with bacon, onion and black pepper; deep-fried or baked plaice, fisherman's pie, lobster and Dover sole. There's also plenty of choice for meat-eaters, plus indulgent desserts. ***Seats** 46. L 12.15-2.30 D 6.30-10.30. Closed Christmas, 5 July, 2 weeks Oct. Set L (Sun) £9.95. Access, Visa.*

Northern Ireland

Annalong — Glassdrumman House — 69% — £85 — HR

Tel 039 67 68451 Fax 039 67 67041

85 Mill Road Annalong Co Down BT34 4RH — Map 22 D2

Situated just off the A2 coast road, with lovely views over the sea or back into the Mournes, this former farmhouse now has luxurious bedrooms with fresh flowers, fruit, mineral water and exceptionally well-appointed bathrooms. Service is a high priority, including 24hr room service, overnight laundry and a secretarial service, and breakfast a speciality – you can even go and choose your own newly-laid egg if you like. Beaches, walking, climbing, and fishing available locally. ***Rooms** 10. Garden, tennis, riding. Access, Visa.*

Restaurant — £60

At the French-style Memories restaurant good use is made of organically grown vegetables and naturally reared beef and pork from the hotel farm and seafood from local ports. ***Seats** 40. Private Room 20. L by reservation only to residents. D 8-9.30. Set D from £19.50.*

Belfast — Bengal Brasserie — £30 — R

Tel 0232 640099

339 Ormeau Road Belfast Co Antrim BT7 3GL — Map 22 D2

About a mile south of the city centre, this recently refurbished Indian restaurant is situated in a modern shopping arcade. Sound Bengali cooking includes a list of daily blackboard specials such as scampi masala, tandoori duck and Indian river fish as well as a wide choice on the main menu with lamb and chicken dishes jostling for space beside prawns, lobster and crayfish. Friendly, helpful staff. ***Seats** 46. Private Room 50. L 12-2 D 5.30-11.15 (Sun to 10.15). Closed L Sun, 25 Dec, 1 Jan. Access, Diners, Visa.*

Belfast — Dukes Hotel — 67% — £92 — H

Tel 0232 236666 Fax 0232 237177

65 University Street Belfast Co Antrim BT7 1HL — Map 22 D2

In a residential area close to Queen's University and the Botanic Gardens, the black leather and chrome seating in the foyer typical of its modern interior may surprise first time visitors to this Victorian building. The work of a different impressionist painter sets the tone in each spacious, uncluttered bedroom and extra-large fluffy bath sheets soften the hard modernity of the bathrooms. There are two bars, conference facilities for 130 and a health club. Children up to 16 stay free in parents' room. Five non-smoking rooms. Very attractive weekend rates. No dogs. ***Rooms** 21. Keep-fit equipment, sauna.* AMERICAN EXPRESS *Access, Diners, Visa.*

Belfast — Manor House Cantonese Cuisine — £40 — R

Tel 0232 238755

43-47 Donegall Pass Belfast Co Antrim BT7 1DQ — Map 22 D2

The long, personally constructed menu at this family-run Cantonese restaurant includes instructions on the use of chopsticks and a historical outline of the cuisine of the Guangzhou area of Canton. Pastel decor and air conditioning provide a comfortable background in which to enjoy the sound cooking, including unusual dishes for the adventurous such as braised duck's web with fish lip or fish heads with bean curd, as well as many more familiar ones. ***Seats** 120. Private Room 50. Meals 12-12. Closed 25 & 26 Dec. Set L from £5.50 Set D from £13.50. Access, Diners, Visa.*

Consult page 16 for a full list of starred restaurants

3elfast Nick's Warehouse £45

Tel 0232 439690 **R**

35-39 Hill Street Belfast Co Antrim BT1 2LB **Map 22 D2**

Lively, colourful, uncomplicated dishes characterise the main menu at this :onverted warehouse, served in the first-floor restaurant (popular with ɔusiness people) at lunchtime and also in the ground floor wine bar ıt night. Try a platter of smoked fish (marinated kippers, eel and salmon), ɔerhaps, breast of chicken with a chocolate and chili sauce or pasta with ı rich red wine and aubergine sauce. Informal lunchtime wine bar menus ıre equally interesting and both carry imaginative vegetarian choices. *Seats 45. Private Room 45. Wine bar open for drinks 11.30-11 L 12-3 D 6-9. Closed L Sat, all Sun, D Mon, Bank Holidays. Access, Diners, Visa.*

3elfast Plaza Hotel 64% £76

Tel 0232 333555 Fax 0232 232999 **H**

15 Brunswick Street Belfast Co Antrim BT2 7GE **Map 22 D2**

Jltra-modern city-centre business hotel with well-equipped bedrooms, all with satellite TV, hairdryer and trouser press as standard, and five :onference suites (capacity 70 theatre-style, 30 restaurant-style). There ıre 14 rooms reserved for non-smokers. Children up to 10 stay free n parents' room. No dogs. ***Rooms** 83.* AMERICAN EXPRESS *Access, Diners, Visa.*

3elfast Roscoff ★ £74

Tel 0232 331532 **R**

Lesley House Shaftesbury Square Belfast Co Antrim BT2 7DB **Map 22 D2**

Stainless steel and black leather chairs in the foyer/bar set the tone for ı minimalistic decor more London than Belfast, Paul Rankin's confident *uisine créative* is more Gallic than Gaelic – and there's a shaft of Californian unshine thrown into both the cooking and Jeanne Rankin's dazzling front of house smile: a great combination, especially given genuine Northern reland prices which, although they have crept up during the last year, till make Roscoff exceptional value in comparison with other restaurants of this calibre. Sophisticated menus based on the best of local ingredients offer the likes of grilled scallops with fresh pasta and a chili and garlic oil, monkfish tempura with a sesame and ginger vinaigrette or crispy duck :onfit with soft polenta and mushrooms on a porcini jus, followed by one of pastry chef Jeanne's special desserts (Northern Ireland winner of Dessert of the Year) – bourbon pecan tart with caramelised bananas, ɔerhaps, or apricot cheesecake with an apricot and orange compote – or selection of Irish, English and French farmhouse cheeses. ***Seats** 70. L 12.15-2.15 D 6.30-10.30. Closed L Sat, all Sun, 11 & 12 Jul, 26 Dec, Jan. Set L £13.50 Set D £18.50.* AMERICAN EXPRESS *Access, Diners, Visa.*

3elfast Strand Restaurant £35

Tel 0232 682266 **R**

12 Stranmillis Road Belfast Co Antrim BT9 5AA **Map 22 D2**

This welcoming restaurant and wine bar in the university area has a great following and Anne Turkington makes an excellent hostess. Dining areas re broken up and given privacy by café curtains on brass rails and upstairs here's an attractive conservatory bar. Food is served throughout the day nd, although the flexible menus change regularly, they always offer good portions of carefully cooked food. A couple of starters, such as curried hicken pancakes and leek tart, might make a light lunch, or move on to nain courses like liver and bacon or chili con carne (a house speciality). ***Seats** 80. Parties 12. Private Room 25. L Sun 12-3 D Sun 5-10 Meals Mon-Sat 12-12. Closed 25 & 26 Dec, 12 & 13 July.* AMERICAN EXPRESS *Access, Diners, Visa.*

Belfast — Welcome Restaurant

£40

Tel 0232 381359

R

22 Stranmillis Road Belfast Co Antrim BT9 5AA

Map 22 D2

Beside the Ulster Museum, the Welcome is easily found and, beyond the pagoda roof at the entrance, decorative lanterns, dragons, screens and Chinese ornaments set an oriental tone, although table settings are western. The long menu includes most of the popular Chinese dishes and there are one or two less familiar hotpots and vegetarian options, like Lo Hon Chai (Ginko nut, carrot, bamboo shoot, straw mushroom, button mushroom, white fungus and beansprout). ***Seats** 80. Parties 25. Private Room 30. L 12-2 D 5-11.30 (Sun to 10.30). Closed L Sat & Sun, 24-26 Dec. Set L from £5. Access, Diners, Visa.*

Belfast — Wellington Park 59%

£90

Tel 0232 381111 Fax 0232 665410

H

21 Malone Road Belfast Co Antrim BT9 6RU

Map 22 D2

Public areas in this bustling university area hotel have been redesigned to extend the foyer, amalgamate bar and restaurant areas and upgrade rooms. The locality and a thriving conference business (capacity 150 theatre-style) ensure a lively atmosphere, but one of the three bars is kept exclusively for residents. Children up to 12 stay free in parents' room. No dogs. ***Rooms** 50.* AMERICAN EXPRESS *Access, Diners, Visa.*

Belfast — Places of Interest

Tourist Information Tel 0232 246609.
Mount Stewart House and Gardens (NT) Greyabbey Tel 024774 387 *17 miles.*
Northern Ireland Aquarium Portaferry Tel 02477 28062 *25 miles.*
Ulster Museum and Botanic Gardens Tel 0232 381251.
Belfast Zoo Tel 0232 776277 *5 miles North.*
Malone House Art Gallery and Gardens Upper Malone Rd Tel 0232 681246.
Dixon Park Upper Malone Rd Tel 0232 320202.
Transport Museum Tel 0232 451519.
Theatres and Concert Halls
Grand Opera House Great Victoria St Tel 0232 241919.
Lyric Theatre Ridgeway St Tel 0232 381081.
Ulster Hall Bedford St Tel 0232 323900.
Group Theatre Bradford St Tel 0232 229685.

> If we recommend meals in a hotel or inn a separate entry is made for its restaurant.

Bushmills — Bushmills Inn

£68

Tel 026 57 32339 Fax 026 57 32048

I

25 Main Street Bushmills Co Antrim BT57 8QA

Map 22 C

This town gave its name to the world's oldest distillery and is only a couple of miles from the Giant's Causeway, so there is no shortage of things to do around Bushmills. The hotel, originally a 19th-century inn, features stripped pine in some of the rooms and the bar is a special attraction. Conferences are held in an oak-beamed loft. ***Rooms** 11. Garden. Access, Visa.*

Bushmills — Places of Interest

Giant's Causeway Tourist Information Tel 02657 31855/31582.

Comber — La Mon House — 59% — £85

Tel 0232 448631 Fax 0232 448026 — H

The Mills 41 Gransha Road Comber Co Down BT23 5RF — Map 22 D2

Situated in the countryside just 5 miles from Belfast city centre, public areas in this low-rise modern hotel include a bar featuring copper-topped tables, a small residents' lounge (which may be in private use), carvery restaurant and a fun bar with karaoke. Practical bedrooms have simple fitted furniture; nine large rooms have balconies and there are eight small singles with shower only. Banqueting facilities for 450, conference up to 1,100 theatre-style. No dogs. ***Rooms** 38. Garden, indoor swimming pool, gymnasium, sauna, solarium, whirlpool bath, riding.* AMERICAN EXPRESS *Access, Visa.*

Comber — Places of Interest

Down Country Museum Downpatrick Tel 0396 615218.
Mount Stewart Newtownards Tel 024774 387.
Wildfowl and Wetlands Centre Castle Espie Tel 0242 874146 *3 miles.*

Crawfordsburn — Old Inn — £80

Tel 0247 853255 Fax 0247 852775 — I

15 Main Street Crawfordsburn Co Down BT19 1JH — Map 22 D2

The pretty village setting of this 16th century inn – the oldest in continuous use in all Ireland – belies its convenient location, close to Belfast and its City Airport. Oak beams, antiques and gas lighting emphasise the natural character of the building, an attractive venue for business people (conference facilities for 100) and private guests alike. Individually decorated bedrooms vary in size and style, most have antiques, some four-posters and a few have private sitting rooms. Free private car parking for overnight guests. Children up to 10 stay free in parents' room. No dogs. ***Rooms** 33. Garden.* AMERICAN EXPRESS *Access, Visa.*

Dunadry — Dunadry Inn — 64% — £98

Tel 084 94 32474 Fax 084 94 33389 — H

2 Islandreagh Drive Dunadry Co Antrim BT41 2HA — Map 22 D2

Once a linen mill, this famous riverside hotel is set in ten acres, adjacent to the Dunadry Country Club and conveniently close to Belfast International Airport. The Copper Bar is a popular venue for the lunchtime buffet and families can eat informally in the conservatory. Conference facilities for up to 350 theatre-style (banquets 300) ensure a constant bustle. Some bedrooms are rather masculine, with darkwood furniture and neat bathrooms; best rooms are on the ground floor and have access to the garden. Children up to 5 stay free in parents' room. No dogs. ***Rooms** 67. Garden, indoor swimming pool, keep-fit equipment, spa bath, sauna, solarium. Closed 24-27 Dec.* AMERICAN EXPRESS *Access, Diners, Visa.*

Dunmurry — Forte Crest Belfast — 67% — £95

Tel 0232 612101 Fax 0232 626546 — H

300 Kingsway Dunmurry Co Antrim BT17 9ES — Map 22 D2

Ten minutes' drive from the city centre, this business-oriented modern hotel is set in 14 acres of gardens and has conference facilities for 450 theatre-style and 350 banquet-style, six meeting rooms and full office amenities. Thirty-five rooms are designated non-smoking. Children under 12 stay free in parents' room. Ample car parking. ***Rooms** 82. Keep-fit equipment, squash.* AMERICAN EXPRESS *Access, Diners, Visa.*

Garvagh Blackheath House & MacDuff's Restaurant £60

Tel & Fax 0265 868433 **RR**

112 Killeague Road Blackhill Garvagh Co Londonderry BT51 4HH **Map 22 C1**

Set in two acres of gardens, this listed former rectory provides the atmosphere and Joseph and Margaret Erwin add charm and friendliness. Margaret makes skilful use of local ingredients in Irish country house cooking, with seasonal game a speciality and inspired starters such as spiced salmon and prawn puffs with Indian dip balanced by Cranachan, an Irish version of flummery, to finish. ***Seats** 36. Private Room 12. D only 7-9.30. Closed Sun & Mon, 25 & 26 Dec, 12 Jul. Access, Visa.*

Rooms £60

The five spacious bedrooms are individually furnished with good bathrooms and fresh flowers, books and fruit. There is also a delightfully grand drawing room for guests.

Holywood Culloden Hotel 72% £140

Tel 0232 425223 Fax 0232 426777 **HR**

142 Bangor Road Craigavad Holywood Co Down BT18 0EX **Map 22 D2**

Overlooking Belfast Lough and surrounded by 12 acres of mature gardens, the Victorian Gothic Culloden makes a splendid local landmark. Features such as painted arches, ribbed ceilings and stained glass remain in most public areas, although the red-plush bar is a modern interpretation of the theme. Bedrooms are all good-sized and well-furnished, although most are in an extension and furniture varies in style. Four function suites can accommodate up to 500 people and the Elysium health and fitness club is popular with locals and residents alike. No dogs. ***Rooms** 91. Garden, indoor swimming pool, keep-fit equipment, squash, sauna, spa bath, solarium, tennis, snooker. Closed 24-25 Dec.* AMERICAN EXPRESS *Access, Diners, Visa.*

Restaurant £65

Comfortable and restful, with views over the garden, the restaurant has soft pink decor, well-upholstered chairs and plenty of well-trained staff on hand to provide efficient, friendly service. The menu in the main restaurant is strong on grills and there is also an all-day grill bar in the complex, 'The Cultural Inn', open 11-10. ***Seats** 150. Parties 20. Private Room 50. L 12.30-2.30 D 7-9.45 (Sun to 8.30). Closed L Sat. Set L & D £17.*

Holywood Place of Interest

Ulster Folk and Transport Museum Cultra Tel 0232 428428.

Larne Magheramorne House 63% £66

Tel 0574 279444 Fax 0574 260138 **H**

59 Shore Road Magheramorne Larne Co Antrim BT40 3HW **Map 22 D1**

Set in 40 acres of woodland with water views, this Victorian house (dating from about 1880) has a conservatory style entrance hall and the traditional drawing room has a peaceful atmosphere. Conference/banqueting facilities for up to 200. Children up to 2 free in parents' room; cots and high-chairs available, baby-sitting by arrangement. No dogs. ***Rooms** 22. Garden.* AMERICAN EXPRESS *Access, Diners, Visa.*

Londonderry Everglades Hotel 59% £76

Tel 0504 46722 Fax 0504 49200 **H**

Prehen Road Londonderry Co Londonderry BT47 2PA **Map 22 C1**

This modern, low-rise hotel is south of the town, on the banks of the River Foyle and close to Eglinton Airport. Conference facilities for up to 350 are supported by business services and there is banqueting for 250. Children

up to 12 stay free in parents' rooms; cots, high-chairs, baby-listening available, baby-sitting by arrangement. ***Rooms** 52. Garden.*
Closed 24 & 25 Dec. AMERICAN EXPRESS *Access, Diners, Visa.*

Londonderry Places of Interest

Tourist Information Tel 0504 267284.
Derry's Walls.
St. Columb's Cathedral off London St Tel 0504 262746.
O'Doherty's Tower Magazine St Tel 0504 265238.
Display Centre Butcher St Tel 0504 362016.
Ulster-American Folk Park Omagh Tel 0662 243292.
Brachmore Stone Circus Nr Cookstown.

Newtownards Strangford Arms 58%

£88 **H**

Tel 0247 814141 Fax 0247 818846

92 Church Street Newtownards Co Down BT23 4AL

Map 22 D2

A well-run, friendly local meeting place and businessman's hotel, the Strangford Arms has an interesting history of might-have-beens. It now has comfortable bedrooms with modern facilities including trouser press and same day laundry service – and all rooms have working desk facilities. The Horseshoe bar is the place to unwind. No dogs. ***Rooms** 40. Garden.*
Closed 25 Dec, 12 Jul. AMERICAN EXPRESS *Access, Diners, Visa.*

Portballintrae Bayview Hotel 58%

£65 **H**

Tel 026 57 31453 Fax 026 57 32360

2 Bayhead Road Portballintrae nr Bushmills Co Antrim BT57 8RZ

Map 22 C1

Overlooking the tiny harbour and the bay, the long pebbledash hotel building stands on the scenic north Antrim coast road and provides conference facilities for 150. Functions, including wedding receptions, often create a stir but residents can escape to their own sitting room, or have a drink in the convivial Porthole bar. Bedrooms include one semi-suite with a small sitting room area and generally have modern bathrooms. No dogs. ***Rooms** 16. Indoor swimming pool, sauna, solarium, snooker.*
AMERICAN EXPRESS *Access, Visa.*

Portrush Ramore ★

£72 **R**

Tel 0265 824313

The Harbour Portrush Co Antrim BT56 8VM

Map 22 C1

Changes have been taking place at the Ramore – they've taken a wall away and brought the kitchen out so guests can watch George McAlpin and his staff cooking. It also has the advantage of making the restaurant seem bigger and brighter, totally in tune with a parallel shift of emphasis on the menu, which now has a much wider choice of food and a distinct leaning towards Californian and Mediterranean style cuisines. The emphasis on seafood is still there, of course, but the approach is more flexible, with seats at the counter where you can have just a one-course meal if you like. Home-made breads are a speciality and the wide-ranging menu really has something to please everyone, ranging from crustacea, served in the shell – prawns, lobster, crab and mussels, served on ice with dipping sauces – to Tuscan chicken with parma ham and Emmenthal cheese, served on a raw tomato butter sauce or peppered rump steak with onion rings, frites – and panache. Desserts are a speciality and always include soufflés on the list. Exceptionally friendly prices on a sensible wine list. New World well represented. ***Seats** 60. D only 7-10.30 (lunchtime wine bar downstairs).*
Closed Sun & Mon, 2 weeks Feb, Christmas/New Year. Access, Visa.

Portrush Place of Interest

Dunluce Castle *3 miles.*

Templepatrick Templeton Hotel 66% £100

Tel 084 94 32984 Fax 084 94 33406 **H**

882 Antrim Road Templepatrick Ballyclare Co Antrim BT39 0AH **Map 22 D2**

Situated a mile from the Templepatrick exit on the M2 and convenient to Belfast International Airport, this striking modern hotel has public areas varying in style from the sleek black and gold cocktail bar to Sam's bar, with its flagstone floor, open fire and traditional wooden chairs appealing to more conventional tastes. Spacious bedrooms are furnished to a high standard in warm colours, with a lot of light woodwork in furniture and, in some cases, ceilings. Children up to 4 stay free in parents' room; cots, baby-listening and high chairs available. Extensive conference facilities for up to 400/350; ample convenient parking, 24hr room service and helpful, friendly staff all make a good impression. Golf course and sports centre nearby. ***Rooms** 20. Garden.* AMERICAN EXPRESS *Access, Diners, Visa.*

Republic of Ireland

When calling from outside the Republic omit the initial zero and prefix the number with 010-353. For example, Park Hotel Kenmare 010-353 64 41200.

Prices quoted are expressed in Irish Punts.

Adare — Adare Manor — 79% — £201

Tel 061 396566 Fax 061 396124 — **HR**

Adare Co Limerick — **Map 23 B5**

The former home of the Earls of Dunraven, this magnificent neo-Gothic mansion is set in 900 acres on the banks of the river Maigue. Its splendid chandeliered drawing room and the glazed cloister of the dining room look over formal box-hedged gardens towards the Robert Trent Jones golf course. Other grand public areas include the gallery, named after the Palace of Versailles, with its unique 15th-century choir stalls and fine stained glass windows; banqueting for up to 220. Gracious bedrooms have individual hand carved fireplaces, fine locally-made mahogany furniture, cut-glass table lamps and impressive marble bathrooms with strong showers over huge bathtubs. Children under 12 are accommodated free in their parents' room. ***Rooms** 64. Garden, indoor swimming pool, gymnasium, sauna, golf, riding, fishing, clay-pigeon shooting.* AMERICAN EXPRESS *Access, Diners, Visa.*

Restaurant — £95

The arrival of Gerard Costelloe as Chef de Cuisine in 1993 has brought a change of direction. Local produce, including vegetables from the estate's own gardens, still takes pride of place on the menu but although the skills of the kitchen brigade are based on classical cuisine, the style is now more consciously Irish. ***Seats** 65. Private Room 25. L 12.30-2.30 (Sun to 3) D 7.30-10. Set L £15 Set D £35.*

Adare — Dunraven Arms — 65% — £120

Tel 061 396209 Fax 061 396541 — **H**

Adare Co Limerick — **Map 23 B5**

Set in one of Ireland's most picturesque villages, the Dunraven Arms is an excellent base for the many sporting activities in the area. Golf and fishing are available nearby, equestrian holidays are a speciality and guests may ride to hounds with manager Bryan Murphy. Frequent functions (facilities for 400) create a lot of activity, but newer rooms in an adjoining block are quieter than those in the house; most rooms overlook gardens or have views of the village and all are furnished in traditional style with antiques. Under-12s stay free in parents' room. ***Rooms** 45. Garden, news kiosk, shop.* AMERICAN EXPRESS *Access, Diners, Visa.*

Adare — Mustard Seed — £65

Tel 061 396451 — **R**

Main Street Adare Co Limerick — **Map 23 B5**

Just beside the gates of Adare Manor, this charming restaurant is housed in a series of cosy rooms with open fires and Victorian clutter in a particularly picturesque cottage. Skilful and imaginative use of the best local produce is the key to its success and chef Michael Weir creates a new menu daily for his modern dishes with an Irish flavour such as baked mousse of black pudding with tomato, olives and leeks or braised oxtail with cabbage and bacon in its own gravy. Desserts range from the updated but homely, such as hot rhubarb crumble with ginger and vanilla sauce, to the exotic, as in mousse of passion fruit with a mango coulis. Good Irish farmhouse cheeses. ***Seats** 46. Parties 18. Private Room 30. D only 7-10. Closed Sun & Mon, 25 & 26 Dec, Feb.* AMERICAN EXPRESS *Access, Diners, Visa.*

Ahakista — Shiro — ★ — £80

Tel 027 67030 — **RR**

Ahakista nr Bantry Co Cork — **Map 23 A6**

The Shiro Japanese Dinner House, situated in a fine, meticulously maintained Georgian house overlooking Dunmanus Bay, may only accommodate small numbers, but both the welcome and the food are big-hearted. Often referred to as an experience which defies description, Kei Pilz's authentic Japanese food is so exquisite in both preparation and presentation that it remains in the mind as a finely detailed patchwork, an impressionistic mirage of culinary delights. With great charm Werner Pilz guides newcomers through the menu, which changes daily, and consists of three short courses – *zensai* (flower-decked appetisers), *moriawase* (delicate egg dishes and sushi) and *suimono* (a seasonal soup), followed by a choice of eight main courses including a selection of lightly-battered deep-fried *tempura* dishes, *sashimi* (seasonal raw fish, served with soy sauce and *wasabi* – hot green mustard) and *yakitori* (chicken breast, liver and vegetables on bamboo skewers, with a traditional spicy sauce). A selection of home-made ices, including green tea, dramatically arranged with some colourful fruit against a black plate and followed by a choice of teas and coffees, rounds off a unique experience. There's a pleasant but somewhat confusing wine list – Crozes Hermitage appearing under Chablis! 5% supplement for paying by credit card. Bookings only. ***Seats** 12.* *Private Room 8. D only 7-9. Set D £32.* AMERICAN EXPRESS *Access, Diners, Visa.*

Rooms **£30**

A small traditional cottage in the grounds of Shiro, renovated to a high standard, is available for self-catering. Breakfast can be provided, £4 supplement per person.

Athy Tonlegee House £55

Tel 0507 31473 Fax 0507 31473 **RR**

Athy Co Kildare **Map 23 C4**

Mark and Marjorie Molloy combine comfort with style at their Georgian restaurant with rooms just outside Athy. While Marjorie looks after guests with friendly charm, Mark demonstrates his skills in the kitchen with dishes like ravioli of crab and cockles with fennel sauce, brill with garlic potatoes and lobster sauce, and rack of lamb with tarragon. Finish with good, uncomplicated desserts like lemon tart or fresh raspberries with cream or, for a small extra charge, make the most of a good Irish farmhouse cheeseboard. ***Seats** 40. L by arrangement D 7-10.30.* *Closed D Sun, 25 & 26 Dec, Good Friday. Set D from £15. Access, Visa.*

Rooms **£55**

There are five individually furnished en-suite bedrooms. Children under 10 may stay free in their parents' room. Dogs allowed if house-trained. *Garden.*

Aughrim Aughrim Schoolhouse Restaurant NEW £45

Tel 0905 73936 **R**

Aughrim nr Ballinasloe Co Galway **Map 23 B4**

Converting Michael and Geraldine Harrison's schoolhouse to make it into the delightful and very practical restaurant it is today was a labour of love recorded in a scrap book kept beside the fire in the comfortable reception area. It, like the menu, makes interesting reading – and, since they opened in spring 1992, the Harrisons have achieved a fine balance for a small country restaurant, providing lively, modern food which pleases a local clientele with a liking for hearty portions and those in the know who come from afar. From a wide choice of first courses start, perhaps, with warm crab tart on a saffron and chive sauce – very fresh, natural-tasting, in an enclosed light pastry shell with good saffron flavour in the sauce, or a roasted red onion and sweet pepper salad. Well-balanced main courses might include chicken supreme filled with cheese and basil on a seed mustard sauce, a pleasingly piquant combination, or at Sunday lunch (especially good value) pot-roasted shoulder of lamb with braised onions. Good vegetables are served on a large platter (left on the table for seconds); lovely gimmick-free desserts. ***Seats** 50. L 12-3 (Sun only) D 6.30-11.* *Closed D Sun, Mon in winter, 24-26 Dec. Set L £8.50 Set D £16.* *Access, Visa.*

Aughrim — Place of Interest

Battle of Aughrim Centre Tel 0905 73939.

Ballina — Downhill Hotel — 65% — £110

Tel 096 21033 Fax 096 21338 — **H**

Downhill Road Ballina Co Mayo — **Map 22 B3**

Extensive leisure and conference facilities are a major attraction at this popular hotel set in landscaped gardens overlooking the river Brosna. The purpose-built conference centre and hospitality rooms accommodate groups from 10 to 400 and the leisure centre has not only a 50 foot oval swimming pool but nightly entertainment at the adjacent Frog's Pavilion piano bar. Facilities for children include cots, high chairs, baby-listening, baby-sitting (by arrangement), playroom and supervised creche. ***Rooms** 52. Garden, indoor swimming pool, keep-fit equipment, squash, sauna, spa bath, solarium, tennis, games room, snooker. Closed 4 days Christmas.* AMERICAN EXPRESS *Access, Diners, Visa.*

Ballina — Mount Falcon Castle — 60% — £88

Tel & Fax 096 21172 — **HR**

Ballina Co Mayo — **Map 22 B3**

Once described as a lady who 'dispenses wine and wit in equal measure', Constance Aldridge has run her Victorian castle with relish for over half a century. Although renowned for hearty country pursuits, huge log fires and convivial company, quiet relaxation is also an alternative, whether walking in the surrounding woodlands or nearby beaches, fishing on the River Moy or Lough Conn, or simply curling into a deep armchair with a book in the relaxingly lived-in drawing room. Simple bedrooms are furnished with antiques. ***Rooms** 10. Garden, tennis, game fishing. Closed Christmas week, Feb & Mar.* AMERICAN EXPRESS *Access, Diners, Visa.*

Restaurant — £50

Milk, cream, butter, freshly laid free-range eggs, fresh fruit and vegetables are all produced on the farm or in the garden, so the style is real Irish country house cooking, with the emphasis firmly on fresh ingredients. Mrs Aldridge presides at a long candlelit table and although you may choose to dine separately, most people enjoy the friendly atmosphere of the communal table. Specialities of the house include gravad lax and jugged hare, wonderful soups served from a big silver tureen and traditional main courses such as a roast or, perhaps, some local salmon, served with home-grown vegetables. Good Irish farmhouse cheeses. ***Seats** 22. D only at 8. Set D £18.*

Ballyconnell — Slieve Russell Hotel — 78% — £110

Tel 049 264444 Fax 049 26474 — **H**

Ballyconnell Co Cavan — **Map 22 C3**

Situated in a lovely fishing area just south of the attractive town of Ballyconnell (famous for the canal linking the Shannon and Lough Erne, currently under reconstruction), this surprising hotel is aptly named after a nearby mountain. Recently completed and, under the careful management of Raymond Maguire, operating to high international standards, it is not at all what might be expected in the quiet Cavan countryside: a spacious foyer complete with marble colonnades and grand central staircase sets the tone for all the public areas. Spacious bedrooms have extra large beds, with good amenities including trouser press as standard and large marble bathrooms, all with jacuzzi air baths. The championship golf course is now operational and excellent leisure facilities in the Golf and Country Club adjoining the hotel include a 20 metre pool. ***Rooms** 150. Indoor swimming pool, children's pool, gymnasium, squash, sauna, spa bath, steam room, tennis, golf (18).* AMERICAN EXPRESS *Access, Diners, Visa.*

Ballyhack **Neptune Restaurant** **£50**

Tel & Fax 051 89284 **R**

Ballyhack Harbour Ballyhack Co Wexford **Map 23 C5**

On arrival at the Wexford side of the Passage East car ferry, ignore the main Wexford road which draws traffic away from Ballyhack to the right – and head for the castle. Nestling underneath it you will find this delightfully informal bistro/restaurant, with three rooms decorated in sunny Mediterranean blues, soft yellows and white and a little patio overlooking the harbour. Specialities including Neptune creamy fish soup, warm bacon salad, hot crab Brehat and scallops in orange and gin with rice feature on a variety of menus ranging from a light à la carte lunch to set lunch and dinners. Good desserts and home-made bread. **Seats** 45. *Parties 20. Private Room 30. L 12.30-3 D 6.30-10 (Sat to 10.30). Closed Mon (except Jul & Aug), Christmas-17 Mar. Set Sun L £9.90 Set D from £11.90.* AMERICAN EXPRESS *Access, Diners, Visa.*

Ballylickey **Ballylickey Manor House** **67%** **£150**

Tel 027 50071 Fax 027 50124 **H**

Ballylickey Bantry Co Cork **Map 23 B6**

Home of the Franco-Irish Graves family for four generations, Ballylickey is set in 10 acres of award-winning gardens with wonderful views over Bantry Bay. There are five spacious suites in the main house and, near the swimming pool and garden restaurant, wooden garden cottages offer seven simpler rooms, all en suite. ***Rooms** 12. Garden. Closed Nov-Mar.* AMERICAN EXPRESS *Access, Visa.*

Ballylickey **Seaview Hotel** **69%** **£100**

Tel 027 50462 Fax 027 51555 **HR**

Ballylickey Bantry Co Cork **Map 23 B6**

Secluded in private grounds close to Ballylickey Bridge, with views of Bantry Bay and the mountains beyond, this immaculately maintained hotel has earned a reputation for consistently high standards over many years under the personal management of Miss Kathleen O'Sullivan. A large sitting room, library and television room provide ample space for guests to relax and spacious bedrooms, all en-suite and some with sea views, are prettily decorated. Ground floor accommodation is suitable for disabled guests. No dogs. ***Rooms** 17. Garden. Closed Nov-Mar.* AMERICAN EXPRESS *Access, Visa.*

Restaurant **£55**

Several rooms linked by arches and decorated in warm tones of pink make up the dining area, which is elegantly furnished with antiques and fresh flowers. The five-course dinner menu specialises in local produce, especially seafood in classic dishes such as Dover sole on the bone with lemon butter, brill mornay or coquilles St Jacques, and changes daily. A carefully compiled and fairly-priced wine list relies on reputable shippers. ***Seats** 50. L (Sun only) 12.45-2 D 7-9.30. Set D £19.50.*

Ballymote **Temple House** **NEW** **£60**

Tel 071 83329 Fax 071 83808 **PH**

Ballymote Co Sligo **Map 22 B2**

If you've ever wondered what a Georgian mansion was like, visit Temple House: huge and austere in its parkland setting, the front door opens onto a massive outer hall complete with all the trophies and paraphernalia of outdoor pursuits and then into an even larger, elegant inner one with all manner of rooms opening mysteriously off. Bedrooms are also on the grand scale with furnishings going back to the last redecoration in 1864 (hence the polite request not to touch the curtains) and fascinating bric-a-

See over

brac going back to who knows when – the Percevals have lived here since 1665. 20th century comforts have crept in, however, in the shape of central heating and relatively modern bathrooms which work well despite a slight air of eccentricity. The beds are comfortable, the view which greets you when you open the big wooden shutters in the morning is wonderful and there is a real country breakfast to look forward to – Deb Perceval oversees the kitchen herself and what you get is good, wholesome home cooking, much of it from their own big walled garden, which is run on broadly organic principles. Babies in cots free, baby-listening/sitting available. For crack, including traditional Irish music sessions, consult Sandy Perceval about local pubs. ***Rooms** 5. Garden, coarse fishing, snooker, lake boats (3). Closed Dec-Mar (except shooting parties Dec & Jan).* AMERICAN EXPRESS *Access, Visa.*

Ballynahinch — Ballynahinch Castle — 71% — £94

Tel 095 31006 Fax 095 31085 — **H**

Recess Ballynahinch Co Galway — **Map 22 A3**

Standing in 350 acres of private grounds and overlooking the famous Owenmore River, this crenellated mansion dates back to 1784. The renowned Ballynahinch Fishery is the main attraction, although anyone drawn to the country will enjoy the log fires and atmosphere in the Fishermans pub, where the catches are measured, weighed and entered in the fishing log. Open fires and antiques in public rooms set the tone and bedrooms, furnished with traditional mahogany, have views of the river and the Twelve Bens mountains. Facilities for small (25) conferences. ***Rooms** 28. Garden, tennis, fishing, shooting, bicycles.* AMERICAN EXPRESS *Access, Diners, Visa.*

We welcome bona fide complaints and recommendations on the tear-out pages at the back of the book for readers' comments. They are followed up by our professional team.

Ballyvaughan — Gregans Castle — 71% — £88

Tel 065 77005 Fax 065 77111 — **HR**

Ballyvaughan Co Clare — **Map 23 B4**

With magnificent mountain views over the unique limestone scenery of The Burren towards Galway Bay, the exterior of this family-run hotel is appropriately austere and in no way prepares the first-time visitor for the comfort and style within. Public rooms include an elegant traditional drawing room, library and, across the impressive marbled hall, the Corkscrew Bar (which unexpectedly turns out to be named after a nearby hill) where excellent light meals are served all day and, in fine weather, may be taken out in the garden. Rooms, which vary in size and shape but are all decorated to a high standard, some with four-posters, have a refreshing emphasis on peace and quiet, without radios or televisions. The hotel is situated on the direct inland road between Ballyvaughan and Lisdoonvarna. No dogs. ***Rooms** 22. Garden. Closed Nov-Mar. Access, Visa.*

Restaurant — £75

Before settling into the elegant dining room, relax in the bar and order from Margaret Cronin's carefully constructed five-course menus which change daily but are always based on the best of local ingredients, notably lamb and seafood, in dishes like king scallop and mussel broth, pheasant and lentil terrine, coulibiac of wild salmon and noisettes of Burren spring lamb with ratatouille and a cream of garlic sauce. Good locally-made Irish farmhouse cheeses. ***Seats** 60. L 12-3 (in bar) D 7-8.30. Set D £26.*

Ballyvaughan — Places of Interest

Tourist Information Tel 065 81171.
Aillwee Cave Tel 065 77036.
Cliffs of Moher.
The Burren.

Baltimore — Chez Youen

£75

Tel 028 21036

R

The Pier Baltimore Co Cork

Map 23 B6

Youen Jacob has been delighting visitors to Baltimore with his distinctly Breton style of seafood cooking since 1978 and it's a case of *plus ça change:* concessions will be made to non fish eaters in the shape of an occasional vegetable soup or melon with port and perhaps a steak with green peppercorn sauce, but it is the dramatic presentation of seafood in the shell which draws admiring sighs. Lobster is very much a speciality and available all year round and the shellfish platter on the £28 dinner menu includes Dublin Bay prawns, oysters or Baltimore shrimps, crab and velvet crab as well as lobster – all served in shell, this dish is indeed a sight to behold. ***Seats** 45. Parties 12. Private Room 50. Meals 12.30-midnight in summer L 12.30-3 (summer only) D 6.30-11. Closed L (low season), mid Nov-mid Feb, booking essential in winter. Set L from £12.50 Set D from £19.50.* AMERICAN EXPRESS *Access, Diners, Visa.*

Beaufort — Dunloe Castle 71%

£92

Tel 064 44111 Fax 064 44583

H

Beaufort nr Killarney Co Kerry

Map 23 A5

All that remains of the original 13th-century castle is the empty shell of the keep but, although the hotel is modern, the lovely parkland setting gives a good first impression and all public areas, including the cocktail bar and restaurant, have recently been completely refurbished. The main public room is a spacious, comfortably furnished first-floor drawing room with some well-chosen antiques and lovely views of the Gap of Dunloe. All bedrooms have newly-refurbished bathrooms. Sister hotel to *Hotel Europe* (Killarney) and *Ard-na-Sidhe* (Caragh Lake). Banqueting/conference facilities for 400/800. ***Rooms** 120. Garden, indoor swimming pool, sauna, tennis, riding, putting, game fishing, cycling. Closed Oct-Apr.* AMERICAN EXPRESS *Access, Diners, Visa.*

Birr — Dooly's Hotel 60%

£50

Tel 0509 20032 Fax 0509 21332

H

Birr Co Offaly

Map 23 C4

One of Ireland's oldest coaching inns, dating back to 1747, this attractively old-fashioned hotel is right on Emmet Square, the centre of Georgian Birr. A good holiday centre with plenty to do locally – Birr Castle gardens are very near, also golfing, fishing, riding and river excursions. Public rooms including two characterful bars, are traditional in furnishing style and well-maintained. Pleasant, modest bedrooms are all en-suite; some may be noisy when there's a function in the night-club. ***Rooms** 18. Garden, coffee shop (10am-10pm), night club. Closed 25 Dec.* AMERICAN EXPRESS *Access, Diners, Visa.*

Birr — Tullanisk NEW

£60

Tel 0509 20572 Fax 0509 20572

PH

Birr Co Offaly

Map 23 C4

18th-century Dower House in the demesne of the Earls of Rosse (still resident at Birr Castle), Tullanisk has been carefully restored by George and Susie Gossip who have run it as private country house since 1989. The house is beautiful, interesting and comfortable, the surrounding gardens and

See over

parkland lovely and full of wildlife, of which a fair cross-section may make an appearance while you watch from the big mahogany dining table at dinner. George is an excellent chef and enjoys producing memorable no-choice dinners – asparagus from the demesne gardens perhaps, with a wispy puff-pastry lid and butter sauce, followed by a main course which may be unusual, such as brochettes of sweetbreads, served with lots of home-grown vegetables, home-made biscuits with the farmhouse cheeses and a dessert like hot chocolate soufflé for the grand finale. Breakfasts live up to the promise of the night before and more. ***Rooms** 7. Garden. D only 8.30. Closed Christmas week. Access, Visa.*

Blacklion MacNean Bistro NEW

£40

Tel 072 53022

R

Blacklion Co Cavan

Map 22 C2

Vera Maguire and her son Nevan transform top class local ingredients into imaginative, stylish meals at this unassuming little front room restaurant, on the main street of Blacklion. An ideal partnership of Vera's traditional skills and Nevan's creativity and interest in new trends results in a sophisticated but generous style. Starters on well-balanced menus with plenty of choice might include avocado mousse with seafood and Marie Rose sauce: a gleaming green moulded mousse, good mixture of seafood, subtle pink sauce and colourful mixed leaf garnish presented dramatically on a large black plate. Typical main courses range from big portions of local free-range duckling to unusual fish dishes such as roast fillet of smoked cod with red wine sauce and wispy crisp-fried leeks, a surprising but successful combination. Organic vegetables accompany and desserts, especially those on the Chef's Specials menu, are outstanding. ***Seats** 35. L 12.30-3 light meals 3-6 D 6-9.30. Closed Mon, Good Friday, 25 & 26 Dec. Set L (Sun) £9.50 Set D from £12.* AMERICAN EXPRESS *Access, .*

Blackrock Ayumi-Ya

£40

Tel 01 283 1767

R

Newpark Centre Newtownpark Avenue Blackrock Co Dublin

Map 23 D4

Situated in a small shopping centre, Ayumi-Ya was Dublin's first Japanese restaurant and still offers the widest range of authentic dishes. Diners are offered the choice of western or Japanese-style seating when booking – also the time to opt for a teppanyaki table if you want food cooked in front of you. In addition to teppanyaki and an à la carte menu for old hands, set menus ranging from vegetarian, through the Ayumi-Ya dinner course to a special seasonal dinner make the choices easier. Staff are helpful and may wisely advise a series of starters to maximise on the Japanese eating experience – tempura (deep-fried food in light batter), yakitori (skewered poultry), osashimi (assorted raw fish) and miso soup might all be tried together for example, with sake or green tea. ***Seats** 60. Private Room 25. D only 7-11 (Sun 6-10). Closed 24-26 Dec, Good Friday. Set D from £10.25.* AMERICAN EXPRESS *Access, Diners, Visa.*

Blackrock Clarets

£70

Tel 01 288 2008 Fax 01 283 3273

R

63 Main Street Blackrock Co Dublin

Map 23 D4

Owner-chef Alan O'Reilly works consistently in his style of progressive Irish cooking to create interesting, innovative menus at this unpretentious but comfortable and welcoming restaurant. There may be a special tasting menu one week, or a theme menu based on a specific cuisine another, but there will always be imaginative, carefully cooked food at fair prices – typically, a salad of mixed leaves, fresh herbs and edible flowers presented in a dramatic pastry basket or pigeon breast wrapped in cabbage and cooked in a filo parcel; well-balanced vegetables may give a nod to traditional Irish specialities such as colcannon. Game is a speciality

in season; breads are good, also their tangy lemon tart. ***Seats** 50.
L 12.30-2.30 D 7-10. Closed L Sat, all Sun & Mon, Bank Holidays.
Set L £12.95 Set D £22.95.* AMERICAN EXPRESS *Access, Visa.*

Blessington Downshire House 57% £63

Tel 045 65199 Fax 045 65335 **H**

Blessington Co Wicklow **Map 23 D4**

Situated on the N81 just 18 miles from Dublin, in the tree-lined main street of Blessington, this comfortable village hotel is not only in an area of archaeological interest and great natural beauty, but is very close to Ireland's great Palladian mansion, Russborough House, home of the world-famous Beit art collection. The present owner, Rhoda Byrne, has run the hotel since 1959 and instigated many improvements, including conference facilities for up to 100 and recent refurbishment of public areas. Simply furnished bedrooms all have en-suite bathrooms. ***Rooms** 25. Garden, tennis. Closed mid Dec-6 Jan. Access, Visa.*

Boyle Cromleach Lodge 78% £118

Tel 071 65155 Fax 071 65455 **HR**

Ballindoon Castlebaldwin nr Boyle Co Sligo **Map 22 B3**

In a uniquely beautiful location overlooking Lough Arrow, Christy and Moira Tighe have furnished this purpose-built modern country house to the highest international standards and it is impeccably maintained. Comfort is a high priority throughout: public rooms include a cosy sitting room and bar with an open fire and a cane-furnished conservatory along the front of the building. All rooms, including the spacious, individually decorated bedrooms, enjoy breathtakingly beautiful views over the Lough and the countryside beyond. Exceptionally well-appointed bedrooms have queen-size and single bed, safe, mini-bar, hairdryer, comfortable armchairs, writing and dressing areas, tea/coffee-making facilities with teapot and fresh milk daily in the fridge. Ice machine and trouser press with ironing board are available on the landing outside (in addition to a full laundry/ironing service). Fully-tiled bathrooms are also large and well-planned, with full-size bath, strong overbath shower, efficient extraction, generous towels and good toiletries. *Garden. **Rooms** 10. Closed 3 days Christmas, 3 weeks Jan.* AMERICAN EXPRESS *Access, Visa.*

Restaurant ★ £75

The restaurant is made up of a number of dining areas, all carefully designed to take full advantage of the beautiful views over Lough Arrow and table settings, including wonderful Villeroy & Boch china, are exquisite. Menus are sophisticated and Moira, a self-taught cook, combines flair, imagination and lightness of touch. Start, perhaps, with a tartlet of organic bacon and baby leeks (a dainty little tart of very light, crisp pastry filled with finely sliced juicy leeks and bacon) or a chicken and crabmeat 'sausage' on a carrot and Sauternes sauce (light, delicately flavoured sausage with a crispy crust, set in a pool of rich, aromatic orange, the Sauternes perfectly complementing the natural sweetness of the carrot). Soups are intensely flavoured, salads colourful and vibrant. For main course, try marinated beef with watercress (two thick slices marinated overnight, filled with a vegetable stuffing and served with a caramelised sauce – superb), or a dashing millefeuille of monkfish and asparagus (the pastry lid set at a jaunty angle with asparagus spears jutting up through the corners), garnished with a dainty bouquet of organic vegetables. Well conceived and beautifully presented dessert plates might include a selection such as a trio of ices in a tuile tulip, a floating island sprinkled with praline and set under an exquisite spun sugar basket, a little strawberry sablé tower and a dark/white chocolate mousse, all set in a pool of vanilla crème anglaise, and garnished with little twists of candied orange zest: magnificent (Irish winner of Dessert of the Year). Good recommendations under £15 on decent wine list. ***Seats** 50. Private Room 20. L by arrangement D 7-9 (Sun 6.30-8). Set L £16.95 Set D £26.50.*

Bray **Tree of Idleness** £65

Tel 01 286 3498 **R**

Seafront Bray Co Wicklow **Map 23 D4**

In one of Ireland's best-loved and longest-established restaurants, the Greek-Cypriot tradition established by the late Akis Courtellas has been successfully continued by his widow Susan and head chef Ismail Basaran, who joined them in 1980. In addition to a wide range of classical Greek-Cypriot specialities, the menu includes much else to choose from – warm pigeon breast salad, for instance, or roast venison in a red wine sauce with green peppercorns. Exotic fruits come in many guises for dessert and ice creams are excellent. The renowned wine list has great depth in its clarets (especially), burgundies and Rhone. Note the Massandra collection from Russia. ***Seats** 50. Parties 18. D only 7.30-11 (Sun to 10). Closed Mon, Bank Holidays, 1 week Christmas, 2 weeks Sep. Set D from £15.50. Access, Diners, Visa.*

Bunratty **Fitzpatricks Shannon Shamrock 60%** £125

Tel 061 361177 Fax 061 471252 **H**

Bunratty Co Clare **Map 23 B4**

This low-rise modern hotel seems to be nestling in beside Bunratty Castle and has a leisure centre with indoor swimming pool and banqueting facilities for up to 200. Only four miles from Shannon airport, this would make a good base for touring Clare and the Burren; children under 12 stay free in parents' room. ***Rooms** 115. Indoor swimming pool, sauna, steam room. Closed 25 Dec.* AMERICAN EXPRESS *Access, Diners, Visa.*

Bunratty **MacCloskey's** £70

Tel 061 364082 **R**

Bunratty House Mews Bunratty Co Clare **Map 23 B4**

Situated in the cellars of Bunratty House, which overlooks the Castle and Folk Park, this characterful restaurant has rough white-washed walls and is dimly-lit with candles and natural light from one small window. Run by Gerry and Marie MacCloskey since 1982, the format is now well-established: the five-course fixed-price menu offers a wide choice of dishes starting, perhaps, with grilled lamb's kidneys with caramelised onions or chicken liver paté with a redcurrant glaze, followed by roast pork fillet with tarragon or escalope of pork with lemon and chive sauce. Round off, perhaps, with lemon mousse or home-made ice cream. Tables near the entrance may be affected by noise from the kitchen. ***Seats** 60. Private Room 22. D only 7-10. Closed Sun & Mon, Jan, Good Friday. Set D £25.* AMERICAN EXPRESS *Access, Diners, Visa.*

Caherdaniel **Loaves & Fishes** NEW £55

Tel 066 75273 **R**

Caherdaniel nr Derrynane Co Kerry **Map 23 A5**

Helen Mullane and Armel Whyte came from the *Mustard Seed* (see entry in Adare) to set up this charming little restaurant in 1990. The style is comfortably cottagey, with an old range, low ceilings and random plate collection and, new this year, an interesting little bar/reception area at the back with light filtering through a stained-glass skylight. Armel's imaginative, shortish à la carte menu offers plenty of interest starting, perhaps, with confit of duck with a marmalade of onion (tender, juicy cold duck with a pretty salad garnish and delicious home-made relish) or country terrine of pork with garlic and a tomato and mustard-seed relish – for serious garlic-lovers, also with an excellent relish. Well-balanced main courses include favourites like crab claws, sirloin steak and local Kerry lamb, with a rosemary scented potato stuffing and port jus, perhaps, and fish, typically pan-fried brill with a fennel and citrus butter. Good desserts include a tangy lemon tart. ***Seats** 30. Parties 8. Private Room 12. D only 6-9.30. Closed Mon Jun-Aug, Mon & Tues Sep, Oct-Easter. Access, Visa.*

Caragh Lake — Hotel Ard-na-Sidhe — 70% — £110

Tel 066 69105 Fax 066 69282 — **H**

Caragh Lake nr Killorglin Co Kerry — **Map 23 A5**

This handsome Victorian mansion has recently been completely refurbished, but otherwise its charms remain the same – the main attraction is the beautiful lakeside setting, the peace and quiet of wooded gardens and grassy terraces. In the house there are 12 good-sized bedrooms furnished with antiques and a further eight rooms with private patios are available in the garden house at slightly lower rates. Sister hotel to Hotel Europe (Killarney) and Dunloe Castle (Beaufort). ***Rooms** 20. Garden, game fishing. Closed Oct-Apr.* AMERICAN EXPRESS *Access, Diners, Visa.*

Caragh Lake — Caragh Lodge — 65% — £72

Tel 066 69115 Fax 066 69316 — **H**

Caragh Lake nr Killorglin Co Kerry — **Map 23 A5**

Set on the shores of Caragh Lake in award-winning gardens, with views of the McGillicuddy Reeks, this Victorian fishing lodge offers both tranquillity and relaxing activities like boating, fishing and swimming. With five championship courses nearby, it makes an ideal centre for a golfing holiday and horse riding can also be arranged locally. Comfortable day rooms are furnished with antiques and the owner Mary Gaunt personally supervises the kitchen. Children under 6 stay free in parents' rooms (some in cottages); no television. No dogs. ***Rooms** 10. Garden, sauna, tennis, game fishing, rowing boat, bicycles. Closed mid Oct-Easter.* AMERICAN EXPRESS *Access, Visa.*

Carlingford — Jordan's Bar & Restaurant — NEW — £55

Tel 042 73223 — **R**

Carlingford Co Louth — **Map 22 D3**

Harry and Marian Jordan take turns in the kitchen of their soft-toned warmly decorated restaurant, but the day always starts with a baking session to produce their delicious brown soda bread and white yeast rolls. Menus are nicely balanced between the traditional and modern, in dishes such as a black pudding and muesli mousse served on an onion confit with a rich game sauce or local Carlingford oysters, served natural or cooked. Local lamb and seafood feature strongly as in grilled hake with capers on a saffron sauce or, a lunchtime speciality, braised shank of lamb wrapped in herbs and puff pastry, with a rosemary and port sauce, all served with varied, thoughtfully presented vegetables. Desserts include a good selection of home-made ices with a duo of white and dark chocolate mousse and 'cranachan', an Irish version of tiramisu made with Irish whiskey. ***Seats** 34. Parties 12. Private Room 16. L 12.30-2.30 (Sun) D 7-10. Closed L (except Sun Apr-end Sep), 25 & 26 Dec, 2 weeks Jan.* AMERICAN EXPRESS *Access, Diners, Visa.*

Carne — Lobster Pot — NEW — £50

Tel 053 31110 — **R**

Carne Co Wexford — **Map 23 D5**

Pub, seafood bar and restaurant – the award-winning Lobster Pot has it all and attracts a loyal clientele from all over Ireland. In a prime roadside location, the long, low building is typical of traditional houses in the area; inside several small, cosy interconnecting bar areas are furnished in simple, practical style with sturdy furniture designed for comfortable eating – augmented, in fine weather, by an ample supply of picnic tables out at the front. One room is given over to the more formal restaurant, but the

See over

atmosphere throughout is very relaxed and the emphasis is on providing good value and efficient service. Many of the most popular dishes on the menu may seem somewhat predictable – mussels in garlic, shrimp cocktail, prawn mayonnaise – but everything is freshly home-made – the more unusual choices, such as poached sea bass or lobster pot-pourri, as well as all the old favourites. ***Seats** 28. L 12.30-2.30 (Sun only Sep-end May), D 6-9. Closed L Mon-Sat and Sun Jun-Sep (except bar meals), D Tue-Sat in winter, Good Friday, 25 Dec, all Jan.* AMERICAN EXPRESS® *Access, Visa.*

Carrickmacross Nuremore Hotel 72% £120

Tel 042 61438 Fax 042 61853 **H**

Carrickmacross Co Monaghan **Map 22 C3**

Situated on the N2, this modern low-rise hotel is set in 100 acres of woods and parkland just south of the town. Major refurbishment over the last few years has seen bedrooms, public rooms, leisure and conference facilities upgraded to a high standard, Many of the bright, airy bedrooms overlook the lake. Banqueting facilities for 200 (conferences 400). No dogs. ***Rooms** 69. Garden, indoor swimming pool, gymnasium, squash, sauna, spa bath, solarium, tennis, golf (18), games room.* AMERICAN EXPRESS® *Access, Diners, Visa.*

Cashel Cashel House 76% £120

Tel 095 31001 Fax 095 31077 **HR**

Cashel Co Galway **Map 22 A3**

Set in acres of award-winning gardens that run down to their own private beach and formerly one of Connemara's most gracious homes, Cashel House was opened as a hotel by Dermot and Kay McEvilly in 1968 and, when General and Madame de Gaulle chose to spend two weeks there in 1969, it became a legend almost overnight. Since then, friendly professionalism, comfort, good food and ever-improving standards have continued to earn the hotel an international reputation for excellence. Log fires burn throughout the year, day rooms are furnished with antiques and filled with fresh flowers and bedrooms are individually decorated; the ground floor Garden Suite rooms are especially stylish, with separate seating areas and access on to the patio. Service is excellent and breakfast includes a wide range of home-made produce, from soda bread and marmalade to black pudding. ***Rooms** 32. Garden, tennis, sea & game fishing, boating, horse riding (inc dressage).* AMERICAN EXPRESS® *Access, Visa.*

Restaurant £70

A large conservatory extension enhances this sunny split-level restaurant and fixed-price five-course dinners make imaginative use of the best of local produce in dishes ranging from the strong simplicity of their own Cashel House smoked salmon, roast Connemara lamb with garlic, rosemary and its juices or lobster from their own tank, poached or grilled, to the sophistication of, say, smoked chicken mousse with hazelnut sauce or baked fillet of fresh Corrib trout in filo pastry, with chervil sauce. Desserts offer a similar range, from rhubarb tart with crème anglaise to a milk and white chocolate terrine with coffee sauce, and there is an excellent selection of Irish farmhouse cheeses. ***Seats** 70. Parties 12. Private Room 10. L 1-2 D 7.30-8.30 (Sun 7.30-9). Closed 10-31 Jan. Set D from £26.*

Our inspectors *never* book in the name of Egon Ronay's Guides. They disclose their identity only if they are considering an establishment for inclusion in the next edition of the Guide.

Cashel — Zetland House — 65% — £99

Tel 095 31111 Fax 095 31117 — **H**

Cashel Co Galway — **Map 22 A3**

Built as a sporting lodge in the early 19th century, the Zetland is situated in an area of outstanding natural beauty overlooking Cashel Bay and is still a popular base for sporting holidays. All kinds of fishing are available, also snipe and woodcock shooting in winter. Cosy sitting rooms are comfortable and most rooms have wonderful sea views. ***Rooms** 20. Garden, tennis, fishing, snooker. Closed Nov-Easter.* AMERICAN EXPRESS *Access, Diners, Visa.*

> Changes in data sometimes occur in establishments after the Guide goes to press. Prices should be taken as indications rather than firm quotes.

Cashel — Chez Hans — £70

Tel 062 61177 — **R**

Rockside Cashel Co Tipperary — **Map 23 C5**

At the foot of the Rock of Cashel, this former Wesleyan chapel with panelled bar and welcoming fire has provided a characterful setting since 1968 for Hans-Peter Mattia's generous interpretation of classics based on the best of local meat and seafood, Typical dishes might include quenelles of brill and turbot with butter sauce, Kinsale lobster bisque, rack of local lamb with a herb crust and tarragon sauce or half a free-range duckling with honey and thyme. ***Seats** 60. Parties 80. D only 6.30-10. Closed Sun & Mon, Bank Holidays, 3 weeks Jan. Access, Visa.*

Cashel — Place of Interest

Cahir Castle Cahir Tel 052 41011.

Castledermot — Doyle's School House Country Inn — £50

Tel 0503 4482 — **RR**

Main Street Castledermot Co Kildare — **Map 23 C4**

The surroundings don't match up to John Doyle's strong, inexpensive country cooking. Patés, game in season, beef and oyster pie. Farmhouse cheeses are served with home-made oat biscuits. ***Seats** 35. Private Room 25. L 12.30-2 D Nov-Mar 7.30-10.30, Apr-Oct 6.30-10.30. Closed L Tues-Sat unless by arrangement, D Sun, all Mon, mid Jan-mid Feb. Set L £10, Set D £18.50.* AMERICAN EXPRESS *Access, Diners, Visa.*

Rooms — £70

Four double rooms, all en-suite.

Castledermot — Kilkea Castle — 70% — £118

Tel 0503 45156 Fax 0503 45187 — **HR**

Kilkea Castledermot Co Kildare — **Map 23 C4**

The oldest inhabited castle in Ireland, Kilkea dates back to the twelfth century and has been renovated and converted to its use as an hotel with skill and sensitivity that allow it to retain its inherent elegance and

See over

grandeur. Rooms, many with wonderful views over the formal gardens and surrounding countryside, are splendidly furnished to incorporate modern comforts in a manner appropriate to their age and style. The adjoining leisure centre, although architecturally discreet, offers state-of-the-art facilities and includes indoor swimming pool, saunas, jacuzzi, steam room, well-equipped exercise room and sun bed. Outdoor sports include clay pigeon shooting, archery, tennis and fishing on the nearby River Griese. An 18-hole championship golf course is due to open early in 1994. *Rooms 45.* AMERICAN EXPRESS *Access, Diners, Visa.*

De Lacy's

£75

Named after Hugh de Lacy, who built Kilkea Castle in 1180, this first-floor restaurant is appropriately grand with magnificent views over the countryside and a bright, airy atmosphere. Scottish chef George Smith has a distinctive style and the lengthy descriptions on the menu give an indication of the complexity of what is to follow. But, despite a uniquely decorative approach to presentation in some dishes, the quality of ingredients shines through and, in specialities such as the roast of the day, there are excellent simpler alternatives available. Local produce features strongly, much of it taken from the gardens below, where guests can take coffee in summer and wander around to see the old fruit trees, vegetables and herbs. Salads and vegetables are a speciality and desserts beautiful and sophisticated, to match their surroundings. ***Seats** 45. Parties 14. L 12.30-2.30. D 7-9.30. Closed 25 Dec. Set L £13.95 Set D £23.50.*

Castletownshend — Mary Ann's Bar & Restaurant NEW

£50

Tel 028 36146 — R

Castletownshend nr Skibbereen Co Cork — Map 23 B6

This famous low-ceilinged haven from the 'soft' West Cork weather has been in the capable hands of Fergus and Patricia O'Mahony since 1983 and celebrates its 150th birthday this year (1994). Although most famous for its excellent bar food, Patricia O'Mahony's good home cooking is now making a name for the restaurant upstairs, with excellent super-fresh local seafood the main speciality but also local lamb and good steaks. Their seafood platter is outstanding, with jumbo prawns, crab claws, oysters, fresh crabmeat and poached and smoked salmon jostling for space on a bed of salad, or your could try rack of lamb – no less than 5 lean, tender, meaty chops cooked just as you like them. Desserts lean towards homely favourites like lemon meringue pie or strawberry shortcake and the farmhouse cheese plate is as generous as it is good. ***Seats** 30. L 12-30-2.30 (in bar: also Sun low-season in restaurant) D from 6 (bar) 6.30 (res). Closed D Sun, all Mon Nov-Mar (except Christmas period). Set L £13 (winter Sun only) Set D £18.50. Access, Visa.*

Prices quoted for the Republic of Ireland are in Irish punts.

Clifden — Abbeyglen Castle — 60%

£102

Tel 095 21201 Fax 095 21797 — H

Sky Road Clifden Co Galway — Map 22 A3

Since 1970 owner/manager Paul Hughes has personally welcomed guests, many of whom return year after year, to this crenellated hotel. Landscaped gardens provide the setting for an outdoor pool and, since 1992, full-size tennis court. Public areas include a spacious drawing room for residents and a relaxing pubby bar with open peat fire. Good-sized bedrooms have recently been refurbished. Conference facilities for up to 200. ***Rooms** 40. Outdoor swimming pool, sauna, solarium, tennis, pitch and putt, snooker. Closed 10 Jan-1 Feb.* AMERICAN EXPRESS *Access, Diners, Visa.*

Clifden — Ardagh Hotel — 60% — £75

Tel 095 21384 Fax 095 21314 — **HR**

Ballyconneely Road Clifden Co Galway — **Map 22 A3**

About two miles south of Clifden, this modern hotel has an excellent location overlooking Ardbear Bay. Bedrooms are spacious and extensive; public areas include a very comfortable bar furnished with sofas and armchairs and an attractive plant-filled sun room on the top floor. Golf, fishing and horse riding are available near-by. No dogs. ***Rooms** 21. Garden, solarium. Closed Nov-Mar.* AMERICAN EXPRESS *Access, Diners, Visa.*

Restaurant — £60

The first-floor restaurant has lovely views to add to the enjoyment of Monique Bauvet's imaginative way with local produce. Baked Irish goat's cheese on a nutty salad, seafood chowder and fillet of wild salmon on a bed of spinach, sorrel and a raw tomato butter are typical of the restaurant; lighter lunches in the bar. ***Seats** 55. Parties 30. D only 7.15-9.30. Closed Nov-Mar. Set D from £21.*

Clifden — Destry Rides Again — NEW — £35

Tel 095 21722 — **R**

Clifden Co Galway — **Map 22 A3**

Paddy Foyle of *Rosleague Manor* (see entry under Letterfrack) has opened this amusing little restaurant with his wife Julia and two ex-Rosleague chefs Dermot Gannon and Grainne Wall. Decor is predictably whacky – an old Georgian fanlight decorates one wall and has a real skull balanced on top, a collection of silver food domes and a variety of 'boys in the backroom' memorabilia all create atmosphere. Settings on closely-packed modern black tables are modishly cost-conscious (paper napkins, nice but cheapish cutlery and glasses) but snazzy little black Italian carvers are comfortable. Fashionable fare includes an excellent olive bread, served with aromatic olive oil, Destry's terrine, a richly flavoursome duck terrine served with a slightly piquant Cumberland-type sauce, main courses like fillet of hake with sesame seed crust served on a smashing gingered cabbage stir-fry or escalope of chicken with spinach and cream cheese, served with a tarragon jus – light and lively. Desserts include good home-made ices and a rich 'Lethal Chocolate Pud', made to a secret recipe. Confident, classy cooking and great fun. Short, user-friendly, keenly-priced wine list. Wheelchair facilities. ***Seats** 30. Open 11am-10pm L 12-3 D 6.30-10. Access, Visa.*

Clifden — O'Grady's Seafood Restaurant — NEW — £50

Tel 095 21450 — **RR**

Market Street Clifden Co Galway — **Map 22 A3**

Since the mid-60s an appreciative clientele has been drawn to this traditional seafood restaurant with well-spaced tables, some in alcoves but all with a degree of privacy – you get a level of comfort and service which is not always a feature of newer restaurants. Try starting with a speciality like Jack's smoked fish bisque – smooth, creamy but with just the right amount of texture and smokiness to be interesting, served with a choice of good home-made white yeast bread or wholemeal soda. Sophisticated main courses from a wide choice, predominantly but not exclusively seafood, on the à la carte dinner menu might include grilled fillet of turbot with a compote of rhubarb and champagne butter cream or best end of lamb on a jus of wild mushrooms with a hint of pesto, while lunch offerings are simpler – marinière style mussels, perhaps, or braised kidneys with a creamy mushroom and pink peppercorn sauce. Follow with 'sinful desserts' or farmhouse cheese. Informal piano bistro serving one-plate specialities opened summer 1993. ***Seats** 50. Parties 20. Private Room 12. L 12.30-3.30 D 6.30-10. Closed mid-Nov-end Feb. Set L £8.95.* AMERICAN EXPRESS *Access, Diners, Visa.*

See over

Rooms **£36**

Accommodation is of a high standard with eleven en-suite bedrooms available nearby with gardens, outdoor swimming pool, sauna and tennis. Tel 095 21437 for details.

Clifden — Rock Glen Manor — 61% — £84

Tel 095 21035 Fax 095 21737 — H

Ballyconneely Road Clifden Co Galway — **Map 22 A3**

A mile and a half from Clifden on the Ballyconneely road, turn right at the pottery and you will find this magnificently located 18th-century shooting lodge which has been run as a hotel by John and Evangeline Roche since 1973. Public areas include a sun room and drawing room, both ideally situated for full enjoyment of the views, and a cosy print-lined bar. Fourteen of the recently refurbished, well-equipped bedrooms are on the ground floor. Golf, horse-riding, fishing, mountain climbing and beaches are all available nearby. ***Rooms** 29. Garden, tennis, putting green, fishing, snooker. Closed Oct-mid Mar.* AMERICAN EXPRESS *Access, Diners, Visa.*

Clifden — Place of Interest

Connemara National Park Tel 095 41054.

Clonmel — Clonmel Arms — 61% — £82

Tel 052 21233 Fax 052 21526 — H

Sarsfield Street Conmel Co Tipperary — **Map 23 C5**

Right in the town centre, with parking along the quayside, this popular hotel has banqueting facilities for up to 350 (conferences 450). Bedrooms in pastel colours are all en-suite, some with shower/WC only. Several rooms are suitable for families and there are two family suites; children under 12 stay free in parents' rooms. Golf available at special rates at Clonmel golf course. ***Rooms** 31. Terrace, coffee shop (10am-10pm).* AMERICAN EXPRESS *Access, Diners, Visa.*

Clonmel — Place of Interest

Ormond Castle Carrick-on-Suir Tel 051 40787.

Collooney — Markree Castle — 60% — NEW — £96

Tel 071 67800 Fax 071 67840 — H

Collooney Co Sligo — **Map 22 B2**

Set in hundreds of acres of gardens, meadows and woods stretching down to the Unsin river, Sligo's oldest inhabited castle has been the home of the Cooper family since 1640. The present owner, Charles Cooper, took on the mammoth task of restoration after the castle had been empty for many years and has succeeded remarkably well in recreating a family atmosphere and retaining the character of the castle whilst modernising it to meet contemporary standards of comfort. Spacious rooms and characterful bathrooms house a wide variety of antiques. Children up to 4 stay free in parents' room; small charge (£12) for under 12s. Peace and quiet, outdoor pursuits (including falconry) and good food – with an excellent full Irish breakfast and an afternoon tea which any home baker could take pride in – are the hallmarks of Markree. ***Rooms** 15. Garden, fishing. Closed Feb.* AMERICAN EXPRESS *Access, Diners, Visa.*

Our inspectors are full-time employees; they are professionally trained by us.

Cong Ashford Castle 86% £199

Tel 092 46003 Fax 092 46260 **HR**

Cong Co Mayo **Map 22 B3**

Ireland's grandest castle hotel, Ashford is set in 350 acres of parkland and has a history going back to the early 13th century. Exclusivity, formality and tranquillity are the essential characteristics, first seen in the grandeur of the entrance and formal gardens and, inside, in a succession of impressive public rooms complete with all the trappings of a long and proud history – panelled walls, oil paintings. balustrades, suits of armour and magnificent fireplaces. Immaculately maintained bedrooms and luxurious suites are elegantly furnished with period furniture, with appropriately vast hedonistic bathrooms reflecting the special qualities of this unique hotel. Spacious, discreet conference facilities for 110 (banquets 90). Children under 6 stay free in their parents' room. No dogs. ***Rooms** 83. Garden, golf (9), equestrian centre, fishing, lake cruising, bicycles, boutique, coffee shop (10am-4.30 pm).* AMERICAN EXPRESS *Access, Diners, Visa.*

Restaurant £95

The room itself is large, with handsome panelling, chandeliers and vast windows looking out to the grounds, its spaciousness scarcely conducive to intimacy. Service, however, is as discreet and professional as ever, and daily menus present a wide choice: from "A Taste of Ireland" come potato and garlic grass soup and traditional Irish stew. On the table d'hote Clew Bay scallops, Connemara hill lamb and local farmhouse cheeses reassert reliance on the finest of Irish produce. Predictable wine list with high prices. ***Seats** 130. L 12.45-2 D 7-9.30. Set L £19 Set D £32.*

Connaught Room £95

Part of the original Georgian house built in 1715, the Connaught Room is opulent and exclusive, with chandeliers, sparkling crystal and immaculate table settings. Denis Lenihan is in charge of the cooking in both restaurants and the menus are fairly similar. ***Seats** 40. Private Room 40. L 1-2.30 D 7-9.30.*

Cork Arbutus Lodge 65% £72

Tel 021 501237 Fax 021 502893 **HR**

Montenotte Cork Co Cork **Map 23 B6**

The former home of a Lord Mayor of Cork looks proudly over award-winning gardens to the city below. The house is furnished with fine antiques and famous for the Ryans' private art collection, especially modern paintings by Irish artists. Public areas are a comfortable mixture of old and new, with views from both the bar and the rather grand dining room. Bedrooms vary considerably: the most recently refurbished are spacious and less impressive. Staff are friendly and helpful and there is always a member of the Ryan family present to welcome guests. ***Rooms** 19. Garden, tennis.* AMERICAN EXPRESS *Access, Diners, Visa.*

Restaurant £74

With able assistance from Helen Ward, Declan Ryan offers a wide range of dishes with a mixture of classical French and modern Irish influences, but always based on the best of seasonal local ingredients. Typically, Irish Atlantic smoked salmon might feature alongside warm duck leg salad with Puy lentils, followed perhaps by grilled turbot with oyster and champagne sauce or bacon and cabbage, Arbutus style. An excellent cheeseboard normally gives a choice of seven or eight Irish farmhouse cheeses and there is a tempting sweet trolley. Superb wine list with some bargains and wonderful old clarets and burgundies. See also Irish Regional Wine Cellar of the Year. ***Seats** 50. Parties 30. Private Room 25. L 1-2 D 7-9.30. Closed Sun, 1 week Christmas. Set L £12.50 Set D £21.*

Cork Bully's — £25

Tel 021 273555 — **R**

40 Paul Street Cork Co Cork — **Map 23 B6**

In this tiny, informal restaurant close to the Paul Street shopping centre, owner-chef Eugene Buckley cooks superb pizzas with exceptionally light, crisp bases in a special wood-burning oven run on off-cuts from a local furniture factory. Also simple, wholesome fresh fish, omelettes and grills. There is another branch, serving very similar food, across the city at Douglas. ***Seats** 40. Parties 20. Meals 12-11.30. Closed 25 & 26 Dec, Good Friday. No credit cards.*

Cork Clifford's ★ — £70

Tel 021 275333 — **R**

18 Dyke Parade Cork Co Cork — **Map 23 B6**

A heady atmosphere of sheer professionalism hits you as you enter Cliffords – an old building (once a library) has been decorated with dash in modern style and pastel colours, enhanced by Michael and Deirdre Clifford's personal collection of Irish art. There is a small upstairs cocktail bar, or you can go straight to your table: a picture of simplicity, with comfortable modern high-back chairs, beautiful coarse linen and a single flower floating in a glass bowl. Uniformed staff are discreet and extremely efficient under Deirdre's expert supervision. Michael's style of cooking – inspired but precise and controlled, each dish an exercise in balance of flavours, textures and presentation – is well-established and utterly confident, his imaginative, sometimes witty, use of the best of local ingredients legendary. Presentation. although original and always pleasing, is not allowed to overshadow the food. Start, perhaps, with a super little appetiser of Clonakilty black pudding with puréed mushrooms and a tiny wedge of blini; a selection of warm-from-the-oven breads is handed separately, with delicious unsalted butter. A typical first course is hamburger of free-range duck and rabbit with a purée of white spring vegetables – tiny little flavoured-packed mini-burgers, complemented by the juicy, slightly spicy vegetable purée – or new season lamb kidneys with mangetout in a sherry vinegar jus, the pink, piquant, tender kidneys nicely contrasting in flavour and colour with the crisp, green mangetout. Mid-day main courses might include breast of chicken scented with vermouth in grain mustard sauce – a perfect lunch dish, the pan-fried chicken juicy, tender, its flavour highlighted by the very lightly spiked grainy sauce – or fillets of John Dory with a compote of tomato and cucumber in a light dill sauce; side vegetables tend to be very individual, colourful and interesting, often including Clifford's variations on traditional Irish themes. Finish with an elegant dessert – a warm gateau of almonds flavoured with apricots, perhaps, or 'Cliffords' medley of chocolate – or with a selection from their outstanding presentation of French and Irish farmhouse cheeses. Round the meal off with headily aromatic coffee or tisane with petits fours. ***Seats** 40. Parties 10. Private Room 50. L 12.30-2.30 D 7.30-10.30. Closed L Sat & Mon, all Sun, Bank Holidays, 2 weeks Aug. Set L £12.75 Set D £27.* AMERICAN EXPRESS *Access, Diners, Visa.*

Cork Crawford Gallery Café — £45

Tel 021 274415 — **R**

Emmet Place Cork Co Cork — **Map 23 B6**

Right in the city centre, next to the Opera House, stands the Crawford Art Gallery, a fine 1724 building which houses an excellent collection of 18th and 19th century landscapes, notably the work of Nathaniel Grogan (1740-1804) – and one of the best informal eating places in Cork. Managed since 1986 by Fern Allen, the link with Ballymaloe House at Shanagarry is immediately obvious with Ballymaloe dessert plate, ices and even petits fours rubbing metaphorical shoulders with the catch from Ballycotton, free-range meat and vegetables grown on Ballymaloe farm – and jostling for space with trendier items like bruschetta, *salade tiède* with Cashel blue and bacon, pork and chicken satay and fresh pasta with olive oil and spring herbs ***Seats** 70. Private Room 200. L 12-2.30 D 6.30-9.30. Closed D Mon, Tue & Sat, all Sun, Bank Holidays, 2 weeks Christmas. Access, Visa.*

Cork **Fitzpatrick Silver Springs** 64% £107

Tel 021 507533 Fax 021 507641 **H**

Tivoli Cork Co Cork **Map 23 B6**

Situated on a bank above the main Dublin road about five minutes drive from the city centre (courtesy coach service all day), this modern tower block hotel has an eye-catching external glass lift and overlooks the commercial traffic of the River Lee. Two self-contained conference/banqueting suites can each accommodate up to 800 guests and a well-equipped leisure centre has indoor tennis as well as a 25-metre pool. Rooms have recently been refurbished and children under five stay free in their parents' room. ***Rooms** 110. Garden, indoor swimming pool, gymnasium, sauna, spa bath, steam room, solarium, beauty salon, tennis, golf (9).* AMERICAN EXPRESS *Access, Diners, Visa.*

Cork **Flemings** NEW £55

Tel 021 821621 **RR**

Silver Grange House Tivoli Cork Co Cork **Map 23 B6**

Just off the main Cork-Dublin road, overlooking the (now commercial) harbour at Tivoli, this large Georgian family house is set in well-maintained grounds, including a kitchen garden large enough to allow virtual self-sufficiency in fruit, vegetables and herbs during the summer. The light, airy double dining room is graciously proportioned, with two marble fireplaces and impressive gilt overmantel mirrors, allowing space to be increased or reduced without loss of style; elegant drapes, well-furnished tables, comfortably upholstered chairs and uniformed waiters give a sense of occasion appropriate to Michael Fleming's skilful cooking. Soups are good, or try tarte italienne, a light pastry crust filled with slivers of smoked bacon, beef tomatoes and best mozzarella, set in a pool of herby fresh tomato sauce or, for main course, pork with mushroom and brandy cream, a well-conceived dish of tender pan-fried pork appealingly garnished with a tiny apple and red cabbage tartlet, its crispness, colour and slight sharpness contrasting well with the rich sauce. Vegetables are imaginative in selection and presentation, desserts classical. ***Seats** 50. Parties 22. Private Room 36. L 12.30-2.30 D 6.30-11. Set L £10.50/12.50 Set D £18.50. Closed Good Friday, 24-26 Dec.*

Rooms £61

Accommodation is available in four spacious rooms, comfortably furnished in a style appropriate to the age and graciousness of the house. All have en-suite bathrooms. *Garden.*

Cork **Forte Travelodge** £42

Tel 021 310722 **L**

Jct South Ring Road/Kinsale Road Cork Airport Blackash nr Cork Co Cork **Map 23 B6**

1½ miles south of Cork city centre on the main airport road, 1 mile from it. AMERICAN EXPRESS *Access, Visa.*

Cork **Huguenot** £25

Tel 021 273357 **R**

French Church Street Cork Co Cork **Map 23 B6**

Bistro-style restaurant in the pedestrianised 'French' area of old Cork, run by Michael Callaghan and his family. In a characterful room, complete with minstrel's gallery, try inexpensive dishes such as West Cork black

See over

pudding with peppered pears or chicken stir-fry with lime and ginger, from menus that change with the seasons. ***Seats*** *70. L 10.30-2.30 D 6-10.30 (Sun Jun-Aug 6-10), Sat Jun-Aug 12.30-11. Closed L Sun (all Sun in winter), 25 & 26 Dec. Set D £6.95. Access, Visa.*

Cork Imperial Hotel 69% **£110**

Tel 021 274040 Fax ext 2507 **H**

South Mall Cork Co Cork **Map 23 B6**

Dermot Kelly has headed a consistent management team at this thriving, conveniently sited city centre hotel for twenty years now. Recently refurbished rooms are all en-suite, with a mixture of furnishings, and conference facilities for up to 600 (banqueting 350) ensure a lively atmosphere. Attractive weekend rates. Private car park with valet parking. ***Rooms*** *101. Closed 1 week Christmas.* AMERICAN EXPRESS *Access, Diners, Visa.*

Cork Isaacs **£40**

Tel 021 503805 **R**

48 MacCurtain Street Cork Co Cork **Map 23 B6**

When the Ryan family (of *Arbutus Lodge*) and chef Canice Sharkey got together to open this relaxed middle-market restaurant in an 18th-century warehouse in an unfashionable area of the city in 1992, it took Cork by storm – and, it seems, this is no flash-in-the-pan success. Softly aged bricks, terracotta paint work and vibrant modern paintings provide a perfect background for an eclectic mixture of culinary styles and influences all brought together in cheerful harmony under Sharkey's watchful eye. Quality and value are successfully combined in dishes like grilled goats cheese salad with sun-dried tomatoes, a gutsy blackeye bean stew with mushrooms or grilled breast of chicken with cherry tomatoes and fresh basil. Irresistible desserts can also be memorable, as in a shimmering palette of barely-warmed soft fruit with home-made aromatic ice cream. **Seats** 90. *Parties 30. Private Room 60. L 12-2.30 D 6.30-10.30 (Sun to 9). Closed L Sun, 3 days Christmas. Access, Visa.*

Cork Jacques **£55**

Tel 021 277387 **R**

9 Phoenix Street Cork Co Cork **Map 23 B6**

Since 1982, Jacqueline and Eithne Barry have run this cosy, informal restaurant close to the GPO. It has a dual personality, first providing interesting, inexpensive day-time food, then changing into a more serious restaurant in the evening when the menu includes fashionable fare like smoked fish salad – eel, mackerel and salmon with a horseradish cream, garnished with deep-fried leeks and ginger – and fresh duck with apricot and potato stuffing, served with a tamarind and apricot sauce. Classic dishes are enlivened with up-to-the-minute garnishes and lively flavourings like ginger, fresh herbs, garlic and olive oil. ***Seats*** *55. Parties 16. L 12-4 D 6-10.30. Closed D Mon, all Sun, Bank Holidays, 10 days Christmas. Set D from £7.90 (6-7pm)* AMERICAN EXPRESS *Access, Diners, Visa.*

Cork Jurys Hotel 66% **£133**

Tel 021 276622 Fax 021 274477 **H**

Western Road Cork Co Cork **Map 23 B6**

Comfortable low-rise hotel in an attractive riverside setting half a mile from the city centre. All bedrooms have recently been refurbished and upgraded to include double and single beds; children up to 14 may stay free in their parents' room. Banqueting/conference facilities for up to 520/700. No dogs. ***Rooms*** *200. Garden, indoor and outdoor swimming pool, gymnasium, squash, sauna, spa bath, tennis. Closed 24-26 Dec.* AMERICAN EXPRESS *Access, Diners, Visa.*

Cork Lovetts

£72

Tel 021 294909 Fax 021 508568

R

Churchyard Lane off Well Road Douglas Cork Co Cork

Map 23 B6

Situated in a fashionable residential area to the south of the city and convenient for the airport, the Lovett family's comfortable, confident restaurant has attracted many ardent supporters over the years. Portraits by an unknown 19th-century Cork artist provide a perennial talking point and a lively background for Margaret Lovett's imaginative cooking: seafood is its main strength, but the best of all local seasonal produce features throughout the menus. Start perhaps with deep-fried crab cakes with salsa rosa, a hot tomato and chili dressing, or with Berhaven squid, simmered in olive oil and garlic, served with garlic soda bread – or try a local cheese in Chetwynd blue cheese salad. Main courses tend to be more classic, but the origin of ingredients is stated with price and they are treated with respect. ***Seats** 45. Private Room 24. L 12.30-2 D 7-10. Closed L Sat, all Sun, Bank Holidays. Set L £13.50 Set D £22.* AMERICAN EXPRESS *Access, Diners, Visa.*

Cork Morrisons Island Hotel 69%

£109

Tel 021 275858 Fax 021 275833

H

Morrisons Quay Cork Co Cork

Map 23 B6

Very central and right on the river bank so you can watch the mullet in the water below from your window, this compact all-suites hotel is run by a related consortium and on the same lines as *Stephen's Hall* in Dublin. Each well-equipped suite has its own lobby and kitchenette in addition to a bedroom with seating area or separate sitting room. The decor is in pleasingly modern Irish idiom, with good fabrics including tweeds in understated shades, specially commissioned pictures by Irish artists and a refreshing emphasis on simply stylish Irish-made furniture, notably in the restaurant. Thoughtful design is evident throughout and the foyer, although small, has visual impact with its oriental rugs and rich colours. ***Rooms** 40. Closed (possibly) 1 week Christmas.* AMERICAN EXPRESS *Access, Diners, Visa.*

Cork O'Keeffe's

£65

Tel 021 275645

R

23 Washington Street West Cork Co Cork

Map 23 B6

Marie and Tony O'Keeffe have been running this hospitable restaurant since 1990 and the menu changes every month. Portions are generous and influences wide-ranging, but fresh local ingredients at the height of their season provide the basis for menus which might include starters like venison and port terrine with a cranberry coulis or fresh prawns or scallops in garlic butter followed, perhaps, by kassler with a colcannon cake and a Brecon Lodge mustard sauce or salmon three ways – grilled, smoked and gravad lax. ***Seats** 33. Parties 33. L by arrangement D 6.30-10.30. Closed Sun, Bank Holidays, 10 days Christmas.* AMERICAN EXPRESS *Access, Diners, Visa.*

Cork Rochestown Park Hotel 67%

£85

Tel 021 892233 Fax 021 892178

H

Rochestown Road Cork Co Cork

Map 23 B6

Close to both Cork airport and the ferry port, this attractive hotel stands in lovely grounds and has conference facilities for 250 (banquets 180). The original part of the building was the home of former Lord Mayors of Cork and features gracious, well-proportioned public rooms. Modern bedrooms are functional and comfortable, with all amenities and a new wing including five suites was completed in 1993, when a new health and leisure club with indoor swimming pool was also opened. Children up to six stay

See over

free in parents' room. ***Rooms** 63. Garden, indoor swimming pool, gymnasium, sauna, steam room, solarium, whirlpool bath. Closed 25 Dec.* AMERICAN EXPRESS *Access, Diners, Visa.*

Cork Seven North Mall NEW £50

Tel 021 397191 Fax 021 300811 **PH**

7 North Mall Cork Co Cork **Map 23 B6**

This elegant 240-year-old guest house belongs to the family of Cork city architect Niall Hegarty and is run by his wife, Angela. It's centrally situated on a tree-lined south-facing mall overlooking the River Lee. Rooms are all spacious, individually furnished in a pleasing restrained style in keeping with the house itself and with new bathrooms cleverly added to look as if they have always been there. Some rooms have river views and there is a ground-floor room especially designed for disabled guests. Excellent breakfasts. A nice touch is the personalised map of the city centre given to guests, which shows clearly all the best restaurants, pubs, museums, galleries and theatres, mostly reassuringly near. ***Rooms** 5.* *Closed 18 Dec-6 Jan. Access, Visa.*

Cork Places of Interest

Tourist Information Tel 021 273251.
The Queenstown Story Cobh Tel 021 813591.
Jameson Heritage Centre Midleton Tel 021 613594.
Triskell Arts Centre off South Main Street Tel 021 272022.
Crawford School of Art and Gallery Emmett Place Tel 021 966777.
G.A.A. Athletic Grounds Pairc Chaoimh Tel 021 963311.
Cork City Gaol Tel 021 542478.
Church of St. Francis Liberty Street.
St. Finbarre's Cathedral Sharman Crawford Street.
St. Colman's Cathedral Cobh.
Everyman Palace MacCurtain Street Tel 021 501673.
Opera House Emmett Place Tel 021 270022.
Historic Houses, Castles and Gardens
Blarney Castle House and Gardens Tel 021 385252.
Fota Wildlife Park Carrigtwohill, Nr Cobh Tel 021 812678.

Crossmolina Enniscoe House 63% £88

Tel 096 31112 Fax 096 31773 **H**

Castlehill nr Crossmolina Ballina Co Mayo **Map 22 B3**

Generations of the same family have lived here on the shores of Lough Conn since the 17th century and the mature woodland, antique furniture and family portraits all contribute to today's enjoyment of Irish hospitality and country house life. The main bedrooms have four-posters or canopy beds and lovely views of the parkland and trout-filled lake. Other fishing, golf and riding can be arranged in the neighbourhood. Susan Kellett, current owner of Enniscoe, is a keen genealogist and has established a Heritage and Family History Research Centre in converted yard buildings behind the house, where there is also some self-catering accommodation. ***Rooms** 6. Garden, game fishing. Closed mid Oct-end Mar.* AMERICAN EXPRESS *Access, Visa.*

Dalkey Il Ristorante £60

Tel 01 284 0800 **R**

108 Coliemore Road Dalkey Co Dublin **Map 23 D4**

Situated above 'The Club' bar, this intimate little restaurant has just six tables in a pretty, rag-painted room. Italian Roberto Pons is the power in the kitchen, while his Irish wife Celine provides the warm welcome. The classical North Italian cooking is enlivened by attractive modern presentation in dishes like carpaccio with shavings of fresh parmesan, spaghettini with garlic, oil and chili, scampi risotto, sea trout cooked in sea salt and rosemary and veal escalope with parma ham and sage. ***Seats** 26. Parties 22. D only 7.30-10.30. Closed Mon, Bank Holidays except Good Friday, 1 week Christmas, end Jan-mid Feb.* AMERICAN EXPRESS *Access, Visa.*

Delgany Glenview Hotel 63% £70

Tel 01 287 3399 Fax 01 287 7511 **H**

Glen of the Downs Delgany Co Wicklow **Map 23 D4**

Renowned for its wonderful views, this hotel changed hands in 1992 and the new owners have already made major improvements. The building has been extended, providing a new conference area with state-of-the-art facilities at one end and extra bedrooms at the other, and the building has been redecorated throughout. Well-equipped bedrooms have tea and coffee-making facilities, hairdryer and trouser press as standard and children under 5 stay free in parents' room. Conferences for up to 300 (banquets 200). ***Rooms** 42. Garden. Access, Visa.*

Dingle Beginish Restaurant NEW £55

Tel 066 51588 Fax 066 51591 **R**

Green Street Dingle Co Kerry **Map 23 A5**

Named after one of the nearby Blasket Islands and situated in a terrace of large houses, Pat and John Moore's stylish restaurant is in two well-proportioned, high-ceilinged rooms and opens into a conservatory overlooking a lovely garden, flood-lit at night. Understated decor provides a comfortable atmosphere and an uncompetitive background for some very good pictures, impressively framed. John is an excellent host and Pat a skilful cook with an interest in food trends. Seafood is the speciality, with a token nod to carnivores and vegetarians. To start, try a lively salad of tossed greens with lardons and a tangy blue cheese dressing or a good home-made soup such as subtle celery and lovage, followed perhaps by roasted turbot fillet with olive oil scented potato purée and chive sauce or poached lobster with lemon butter – or perhaps some Kerry lamb or beef fillet with rösti and a cognac and green peppercorn sauce. Delicious desserts could include an unusual hot rhubarb soufflé tart. Good farmhouse cheese selection. ***Seats** 48. Private Room 12. L 12.30-2.15 D 6-9.30. Closed Mon, mid Nov-Mar.* AMERICAN EXPRESS *Access, Diners, Visa.*

Dingle Dingle Skellig Hotel 61% NEW £86

Tel 066 51144 Fax 066 51501 **H**

Dingle Co Kerry **Map 23 A5**

Family-friendly, well-run 60s' hotel with a shoreside location on the edge of the town. Public areas are comfortably furnished in practical materials and quite stylishly decorated, fair-sized bedrooms have small but neat bathrooms. Good use is made of sea views throughout, especially in a recently added conservatory restaurant with special anti-glare glass. Children are well catered for, with entertainment in high season, but the top floor is reserved for guests travelling without families. ***Rooms** 115. Garden, indoor swimming pool, sauna, solarium, beauty & hair salon, tennis, games room, snooker, deep-sea fishing. Closed mid Nov-mid Mar.* AMERICAN EXPRESS *Access, Diners, Visa.*

Dingle Doyle's Seafood Bar & Townhouse £50

Tel 066 51174 Fax 066 51816 **RR**

4 John Street Dingle Co Kerry **Map 23 A5**

Flagstone floors and old pine furniture give this family-run restaurant lots of character. Local seafood is the main attraction, with menus made up daily according to the catch landed by the Dingle boats and lobster, selected from a tank in the bar, is a speciality. Cooking is straightforward, allowing the natural flavour and freshness of prime ingredients to come through. Start, perhaps, with seafood chowder, oysters, home-smoked

See over

salmon or salmon tartare with horseradish cream and choose a main course from another wide selection of fish and seafood. Finish with a homely dessert such as strawberry shortcake or choose from a selection of Irish farmhouse cheeses. ***Seats*** *50. Parties 12. D only 6-9. Closed Sun, also mid Nov-mid Mar. Access, Diners, Visa.*

Rooms — £59

High quality accommodation includes a residents' sitting room as well as eight stylish bedrooms furnished with antiques and luxurious bathrooms.

Dingle — The Half Door — NEW — £55

Tel 066 51600 Fax 066 51206 — **R**

John Street Dingle Co Kerry — **Map 23 A5**

Denis and Teresa O'Connor's cosy, cottagey restaurant is very welcoming – low-ceilinged, with the old range still in situ, exposed stone walls, copper pots and lovely fresh flowers leading the eye out to a bright conservatory area at the back. There's a nice air of professionalism too, with a proper bar and good linen on the tables and Denis's mainly seafood menus are full of interest. Dingle Bay seafood chowder is great for lunch or a cold evening and there's an outstanding seafood platter, available hot or cold, with lobster, oysters, Dublin Bay prawns, scallops, crab claws and mussels conveniently presented with garlic or lemon butter. Mouthwatering desserts typically include pear and apple crumble with warm *crème anglaise* or a good selection of home-made ices, prettily presented. Air-conditioning. ***Seats*** *50. Parties 12. Private Room 20. L 12.30-2.30 D 6-10. Closed Tue (except Jul & Aug), early Jan-Easter.* AMERICAN EXPRESS *Access, Diners, Visa.*

Dingle — Lord Baker's Bar & Restaurant — NEW — £50

Tel 066 51277 — **R**

Main Street Dingle Co Kerry — **Map 23 A5**

The winning Kerry format – bar with informal eating area gradually developing into fully-fledged restaurant at the back – is at work here, with good bar food backed up by more formal value-conscious meals, especially Sunday lunch. High ceilings, allowing dramatic display of locally-made wall hangings, give way to glass, and back tables are in a conservatory extension leading into the garden. Evening menus are more elaborate than lunch, but offer a good choice on the set dinner, leaning towards seafood but with about four other main course alternatives. Starters on any of the menus might include smoked Dingle Bay mackerel with horseradish sauce, well-presented with lots of salad alongside a well-smoked (not dyed) fish or a simple tomato and onion salad with a sound olive oil dressing. Cromane mussels *bonne femme*, wild salmon steak with lemon butter and stir-fry beef with seasonal vegetables are typical main courses. Good, simple sweets. Cocktails a speciality in the bar. ***Seats*** *85. L 12.30-2.30 D 6-10. Closed 25 Dec. Access, Visa.*

Dingle — Place of Interest

Great Blasket Island Tel 01 6613111

Dublin — Ayumi-Ya Japanese Steakhouse — £40

Tel 01 622233 — **R**

132 Lower Baggot Street Dublin — **Map 23 D4**

This informal basement restaurant, an offshoot of the Ayumi-Ya Restaurant in Blackrock, serves simple tasty dishes inexpensively and is clearly signed from the street. Crisp, colourful specialities include kushi-yaki (food cooked on skewers), teriyaki (food marinated then grilled over charcoal) and teppanyaki steaks (cooked on a hot iron plate). Try ebifari (big prawns, deep-fried in breadcrumbs) or mushroom panko age (mushrooms stuffed with salted plums, breadcrumbed and deep-fried), both served with a green salad with wakame (seaweed) and bean curd and soy sauce. Main courses include beef teriyaki and salmon teriyaki, both presented sizzling on board-mounted iron dishes. ***Seats** 40. Parties 20. L 12.30-2.30 D 6.30-12.30. Closed L Sat, all Sun. Set L from £6.95. Access, Visa.*

Dublin **Berkeley Court** 76% £182

Tel 01 601711 Fax 01 617238 **H**

Lansdowne Road Dublin 4 **Map 23 D4**

The flagship of the Doyle group, the luxurious Berkeley Court has an impressively large split-level lobby-lounge with mirrored columns, brass-potted parlour palms and reproduction furniture in a mixture of styles. The elegant Berkeley Room, Gothic panelled bar and bright conservatory Grill Room are quieter in tone. Ballroom, boardroom and several suites provide function facilities for up to 275 people. Accommodation includes a proportion of spacious Executive suites with classic furnishings and guests have use of the well-equipped Riverview racquet and fitness centre, about 5 minutes drive from the hotel. ***Rooms** 207. Indoor swimming pool, sauna, solarium, hair salon, news kiosk, boutique.* AMERICAN EXPRESS *Access, Diners, Visa.*

Dublin **Blooms Hotel** 60% £120

Tel 01 715622 Fax 01 715997 **H**

Anglesea Street Dublin 2 **Map 23 D4**

Modern city-centre hotel named after one of Joyce's most famous characters. The public bar and night-club are popular with locals; other public areas are rather limited. Standardised bedrooms all have telephone extensions in bathrooms. ***Rooms** 86. Whirlpool bath. Closed 25 & 26 Dec.* AMERICAN EXPRESS *Access, Diners, Visa.*

Dublin **Burlington Hotel** 70% £152

Tel 01 6605222 Fax 01 6608496 **H**

Upper Leeson Street Dublin 4 **Map 23 D4**

A '70s building just outside the city centre, the Burlington is Ireland's largest hotel and always bustling with commercial business. Public rooms are on a grand scale, with large chandeliers in the main lobby/lounge area and a very big bar recently refurbished in a strange confusion of styles. Bedrooms are thoughtfully designed and well-equipped, with good working space for the business guest and neat tiled bathrooms with ample shelf space and bathrobes. The Burlington has a good reputation for banquets and has conference facilities for up to 1,000. No dogs. ***Rooms** 500. Hair salon, kiosk, boutique.* AMERICAN EXPRESS *Access, Diners, Visa.*

Dublin **Central Hotel** 58% £120

Tel 01 6797302 Fax 01 6797303 **H**

1-5 Exchequer Street Dublin 2 **Map 23 D4**

This aptly-named hotel has a unique parking arrangement with local offices, who allow use of their secure parking overnight and at weekends, suiting both business and private guests. A late 19th-century building, the hotel was completely refurbished in 1990; public areas have generally been well maintained, but bedrooms vary considerably in size, facilities (some have bath, others only a shower), decor and maintenance; the quietest ones overlook Dame Court, whereas the traffic on the South Great George's Street side is heavy during business hours. Attractive weekend offers. 20 family rooms and two interconnecting; baby-listening/sitting by arrangement. ***Rooms** 72. Closed 25 & 26 Dec.* AMERICAN EXPRESS*, Access.*

Dublin Chapter One £70

Tel 01 8732266 **R**

18/19 Pannell Square Dublin 1 **Map 23 D4**

The franchise for this characterful vaulted cellar restaurant underneath the Dublin Writers Museum has changed hands and it is now run as a sister restaurant to the *Old Dublin*. However, although menus now lean slightly towards Russian/Scandinavian themes, there has been no dramatic change of style in the kitchen and chef Ross Lewis offers starters like warm salads, baked goat's cheese and duck livers with garlic croutons alongside blinis and gravad lax. For main course, roast duck might come with apricot sauce and endives, or griddled calf's liver with black olives, rosemary, red onion and a balsamic vinegar gravy. Desserts include good pastry dishes such as open fruit tarts and delicious mille feuilles with mascarpone and fruit. Concise wine list with some good growers on it. The Museum Coffee Shop, upstairs, serves more informal food all day. ***Seats** 100. Parties 30. Private Room 24. L 12-2.30 (Sun from 12.30) D 5.45-11 (pre-theatre menu from 5.45). Closed L Sat & Sun, Bank Holidays (except coffee shop), 25 & 26 Dec. Set L £10.50 Set D from £18.50.* AMERICAN EXPRESS *Access, Diners, Visa.*

Dublin The Chili Club NEW £45

Tel 01 6773721 **R**

1 Anns Lane Dublin 2 **Map 23 D4**

Just off bustling South Ann Street, in Dublin's most fashionable shopping area, this intimate, low-ceilinged restaurant provides an oasis of serenity. Anna, the Thai chef, cooks the hot and spicy food of her homeland to be 'as traditional as the market will allow'. Satays, sweet and sours and even most of the curries are easy on the palate, but watch out for her fiery Tom Yum Gung, an innocent looking clear prawn soup with fresh green chilis lurking amongst the kaffir, lime and coriander, or Phat Prik Neur, where bright green spring onions provide camouflage. ***Seats** 42. Parties 12. L 12.30-2.30 D 6.30-10.30. Closed L Sat & Sun, Bank Holidays, 25 Dec, Good Friday.* AMERICAN EXPRESS *Access, Diners, Visa.*

Dublin Commons Restaurant NEW £80

Tel 01 4752597 Fax 01 4780551 **R**

Newman House 85-86 St Stephen's Green Dublin 2 **Map 23 D4**

In the basement of one of Dublin's most historic buildings, this soothing, airy restaurant looks out onto mature trees in a large courtyard and has access to 5 acres of private gardens beyond. Classic dark blues and creams, warmed by oriental rugs, fresh flowers and an interesting selection of specially commissioned pictures by Irish artists, provide an elegant setting for Gerard Kirwan's eclectic cuisine, a well-established style based firmly on the best of local produce but open to a wide range of influences. Colourful, lively dishes are typical, in a John Dory salad with poppy seed vinaigrette, for instance – the warm, pale fish contrasting with the colourful, cool, crisp mixed leaves and enlivened by a striking nut-oil vinaigrette. Or, in sautéed lamb with cucumber, mint and yoghurt, the Middle-Eastern flavours of the salad perfectly complement tender, pink slices of loin of lamb. Main courses lean slightly towards seafood – steamed turbot might be set in a pretty green-flecked, slightly spicy coriander beurre blanc – balanced for carnivores by fillet of beef, or breast of duck seared, sliced and served with a raspberry vinegar to cut the richness of the meat. Simple, well-cooked vegetables are served on the plate. Pretty desserts might include blackcurrant and vanilla bavarois, a swirl of contrasting colours and flavours, set on a pool of crème anglaise and garnished with a little spray of jewel-like redcurrants, a single raspberry and a tiny brandy snap. Farmhouse cheeses available in the evening. Delicious Java coffee and petits fours. ***Seats** 60. Parties 12. Private Room 30. L 12.30-2.15 D 7-10.15. Closed L Sat, all Sun, Bank Holidays, 25 & 26 Dec.* AMERICAN EXPRESS *Access, Diners, Visa.*

Dublin — Hotel Conrad — 73% — £210

Tel 01 6765555 Fax 01 6765424 — **H**

Earlsfort Terrace Dublin 2 — **Map 23 D4**

Just off St Stephen's Green, opposite the National Concert Hall, this modern international hotel is only a few minutes walk from the south city-centre shopping and business areas. Public areas include an open-plan marbled foyer and lobby/lounge, cocktail bar, all-day brasserie restaurant and, Alfie Byrne's, a pubby bar in the basement. Spacious bedrooms have air-conditioning, individual temperature controls, mini-bar and executive desk and there are hairdryers and bathrobes in the marbled bathrooms. Conference facilities for 300, banquets 250. 60 bedrooms designated non-smoking; children up to 10 stay free in parents' room. ***Rooms** 190 (including 9 suites). News kiosk, brasserie (7am-11.30pm).* AMERICAN EXPRESS *Access, Diners, Visa.*

Dublin — Cooke's Café — NEW — £40

Tel 01 6790536 Fax 01 6790546 — **R**

14 South William Street Dublin 2 — **Map 23 D4**

Owner-chef John Cooke moved from Polo One in 1992 to set up his own cafe on the other side of Grafton Street. Now Dublin's most fashionable place to eat, trompe l'oeil decor and a great sense of style make this people-watching if rather cramped restaurant an interesting place to be, but the Californian/Mediterranean influenced food is good too. Try lobster salad, for instance, a riot of mixed salad leaves with huge chunks of pink lobster threaded through it, or melt-in-the-mouth duck confit with Puy lentils and pancetta. Their range of breads is second to none and, like the pastries and desserts, can be bought at their Francis Street bakery. ***Seats** 40 (plus 30 outdoors in summer). Open 12-12. L 12-2.30 D 6-8. Closed Bank Holidays, 3 days Christmas.* AMERICAN EXPRESS *Access, Diners, Visa.*

> Any person using our name to obtain free hospitality is a fraud.
> Proprietors, please inform the police and us.

Dublin — Le Coq Hardi — £95

Tel 01 689070 — **R**

35 Pembroke Road Ballsbridge Dublin 4 — **Map 23 D4**

Food fashions have come and gone in the sixteen years since they opened this restaurant in an end-of-terrace Georgian house, but John Howard continues to produce the classical French cuisine that is so close to his heart and his wife Catherine to supervise this calm, club-like restaurant with style. High ceilings, ornate plasterwork and immaculate napery and glassware make a fine setting for seasonal cuisine based firmly on the best of local ingredients. Typical offerings might include terrine of rabbit, chicken liver and leek with apple and celeriac vinaigrette or, a house speciality, Coq Hardi smokies – smoked haddock marbled with tomato, Irish farmhouse cheese and double cream, baked 'en cocotte' – followed perhaps by steamed skate wing, served with nut-brown butter and hazelnuts or soy sauce and ginger; Wicklow lamb may be served in a navarin, or as a rack, cooked very pink and there is always a good choice of game in season. Delicious desserts usually include an old favourite like bread and butter pudding or diplomat pudding and good ice creams, or you can finish with a selection of Irish farmhouse cheeses. Famous for its collection of Chateau Mouton Rothschild (the 1870 is a snip at £5000) – not all for sale, the wine list has special appeal for the connoisseur. Mostly French. ***Seats** 50. Private Room 34. L 12-2.30 D 7-11. Closed L Sat, all Sun, Bank Holidays, 1 week Christmas, 2 weeks Aug. Set L £14.50 Set D £24.50.* AMERICAN EXPRESS *Access, Diners, Visa.*

Dublin The Davenport Hotel 76% NEW £177

Tel 01 6616799 Fax 01 6615663 **H**

Merrion Square Dublin 2 **Map 23 D4**

Hidden behind the neo-classical facade of a Victorian church and only a stone's throw from Trinity College and the National Gallery, the impressive exterior of The Davenport is carried through into the marble-pillared lobby, an atrium encircled by Georgian windows which soars up through six storeys to the domed roof and cupola above. Rooms beyond are on a more human scale, with relatively low ceilings creating an unexpectedly intimate atmosphere throughout the hotel. Colour schemes tend to be bold, giving each area a specific character – the bar is masculine, club-like, for example, the restaurant lighter and more feminine – with stylish drapes and quality materials, notably marble and a variety of woods, used throughout. Although not individually decorated there is considerable variety amongst the rooms, which tend to have a homely, almost country atmosphere which is emphasised by the irregular shapes in some rooms and (well-furnished) bathrooms. Nice touches include a safe as well as trouser press in all rooms, air-conditioning, good American over-bath showers and an attractive Irish-made range of toiletries. Private 24 hour valet parking. Some lady executive designated rooms. ***Rooms** 120.* AMERICAN EXPRESS® *Access, Diners, Visa.*

Dublin Doyle Montrose see under Dublin Montrose.

Dublin Ernie's £80

Tel 01 2693260/2693300 **R**

Mulberry Gardens Donnybrook Dublin 4 **Map 23 D4**

The Evans family have owned this elegant south-city restaurant since 1984 and its most remarkable feature is the late Ernie Evans' personal collection of paintings, mostly of Irish interest and many of his beloved Kerry, which take up every available inch of wall space – closely followed by the pretty little central courtyard garden which makes an especially attractive feature when floodlit at night. Chef Sandra Earl is very much in control in the kitchen, producing refreshingly up-dated versions of the classics. Tian of celeriac with crab claws, warm parcel of tomato and mozzarella with tomato coulis, feuilleté of queen scallops with ginger and soy sauce and galantine of poussin stuffed with hazelnuts and apricots are all typical of her style and desserts include comfort food like apple and date tart with crème anglaise as well as elegant concoctions appropriate to a grand finale. ***Seats** 60. L 12.30-2.30 D 7.15-10.15. Closed L Sat, all Sun & Mon, Bank Holidays, 1 week Christmas. Set L £13.95 Set D £19.95.* AMERICAN EXPRESS® *Access, Diners, Visa.*

Dublin Les Frères Jacques £80

Tel 01 6794555 **R**

74 Dame Street Dublin **Map 23 D4**

Evocative prints, French-speaking staff and a theatreland location (next door to the Olympia) and the frequent presence of French diners imbue this restaurant with a distinctively Parisian atmosphere, to which le patron adds his infectious Gallic charm. French cuisine from the best of Irish raw materials is the basis for daily-changing fixed-price menus: native lobsters from the tank, cassolette of mussels with saffron and roasted fennel, baked oysters on a bed of cabbage with lime butter, fillet of turbot with garlic and shiitake sauce all reflect a bias towards seafood and a lively, colourful approach. Pigeon is a favourite too, also lamb, lamb's kidneys and game in season, all handled with the same flair. ***Seats** 65. Private Room 40. L 12.30-2.30 D 7.30-10.30 (Fri & Sat to 11). Closed L Sat, all Sun, Open some Bank Holidays, 1st week January. Set L £13 Set D £20.* AMERICAN EXPRESS® *Access, Visa.*

Dublin George's Bistro & Piano Bar £70

Tel 01 6797000 Fax 01 6797560 **R**

29 South Frederick Street Dublin 2 **Map 23 D4**

The menu is distinctly old-fashioned, but food is correctly cooked and based on top-quality ingredients – a combination which suits the conservative tastes of the well-heeled post-theatre crowd who frequent this popular bistro in a side street between the Dail and Trinity College. Steaks, racks of lamb and Dover sole are favourite main courses, with something like avocado with crab or garlic mushrooms to start. The other attraction is live music (piano with female vocal), which tends to inhibit conversation but fuels the late-night buzz. Lunch is served on the ground floor, dinner in the basement. ***Seats** 90. Private Room 50. L 12-3.30 D 7-12.30. Closed Sun & Mon, Bank Holidays, 1 week Christmas. Set L £8 Set D £23.50.* AMERICAN EXPRESS *Access, Diners, Visa.*

Dublin The Grafton Plaza Hotel 64% NEW £85

Tel 01 4750888 Fax 01 4750908 **H**

Johnsons Place Dublin 2 **Map 23 D4**

Don't expect a spacious lobby or a heavy emphasis on service in this well-located new hotel and you won't be disappointed: dispensing with wasteful extras has helped keep costs down and, within these self-imposed limitations, the public areas (including corridors) are surprisingly stylish and the rooms impressive and thoughtfully designed. Although not individually decorated, rooms are well-furnished, with specially Irish-made co-ordinating carpets throughout and all furniture except antiques made to order in Ireland. Rooms vary in size, but have good amenities – trouser press, hair dryer, multi-channel TV, tea-and coffee-making facilities and, in some cases, a mini-bar; smallish bathrooms are well-designed, with bath and over-bath shower, plenty of shelf space, telephones and quality Irish-made toiletries. No private parking; guests use a nearby multi-storey car park. ***Rooms** 75. Closed 25 & 26 Dec.* AMERICAN EXPRESS *Access, Diners, Visa.*

Dublin Gresham Hotel 64% £140

Tel 01 746881 Fax 01 787175 **H**

O'Connell Street Dublin **Map 23 D4**

Free, secure valet parking is a major asset at this famous north-city hotel. The comfortably furnished chandelier-lit lobby/lounge is a popular meeting place, especially for morning coffee or afternoon tea, and Toddy's Bar (named after an illustrious former manager) is an all-day eating spot. Front bedrooms are best, with smart modern bathrooms, and there are nine full suites. Banqueting/conference facilities for 200/325. ***Rooms** 200. Closed 25 & 26 Dec.* AMERICAN EXPRESS *Access, Diners, Visa.*

Prices quoted for the Republic of Ireland are in Irish punts.

Dublin Grey Door £99

Tel 01 763286 Fax 01 763287 **PH**

22 Upper Pembroke Street Dublin 2 **Map 23 D4**

Situated conveniently close to the main south city-centre shopping and business areas, this discreet hotel is in a fine Georgian terrace near Fitzwilliam Square. Bedrooms are spacious and appointed to a high standard with mahogany furniture and fine fabrics in pale blues and reds and thoughtfully designed bathrooms have powerful over-bath showers and generous towels. There is an elegant, traditionally furnished period drawing room for residents' use, with a marble fireplace and antiques. Staff are friendly and helpful. ***Rooms** 7.* AMERICAN EXPRESS *Access, Diners, Visa.*

Dublin — Hibernian Hotel 70% NEW — £120

Tel 01 6687666 Fax 01 6602655 — **HR**

Eastmoreland Place Ballsbridge Dublin 4 — **Map 23 D4**

Named after a much-missed Dublin institution (now the site of a shopping mall), this conveniently located small hotel is itself a conversion, the Victorian building having been a nurses' residence until recently. Public areas are quietly impressive, with the occasional well-placed pillar adding a touch of grandeur, and the overall impression is of understated elegance: immaculate furnishings and stylish decor, predominantly in soothing tones of deep green and terracotta, convey a delightful country house feeling. A quiet library, comfortably furnished with chesterfields and decorated in rather masculine, deep tones, doubles as residents' sitting room or small conference room and a second cosy sitting room, opening on to the bright, airy restaurant, also serves as a reception room for diners. Bedrooms, which vary somewhat in size and shape, are individually decorated and thoughtfully furnished with keen attention to detail, including good pictures and striking fresh flower arrangements. Bathrooms are neat but tend to be on the small side. The small scale throughout the hotel creates a homely atmosphere, underlined by an overall emphasis on a high standard of service. ***Rooms** 30. Patio, private car park.* AMERICAN EXPRESS *Access, Diners, Visa.*

Restaurant — £55

An oasis of tranquillity in the city, this restaurant offers relaxing dining in an elegantly appointed dining room decorated in deep terracotta, dark green and cream or under stylish cream parasols on the terrace. French chef Frederic Souty produces limited but lively daily-changing menus with a choice of about four first and main courses typically in a warm bacon salad with diced tomatoes and garlic croutons or duo of black and white pudding with black peppercorns and parsley followed by soup and sorbet at dinner. Well-balanced main courses might include a duo of salmon and hake with fresh scallions and roast almonds and panfried fillet of beef with chanterelles and garlic. French cheeseboard. ***Seats** 40. Parties 15. Private Room 20. L 12.30-2.30 D 6.30-10.30. Set D £19.95. Closed L Sat, Good Friday, Christmas.* AMERICAN EXPRESS *Access, Diners, Visa.*

Dublin — Jurys Christchurch Inn 55% NEW — £43

Tel 01 4750111 Fax 01 4704888 — **H**

Christchurch Place Dublin 8 — **Map 23 D4**

New budget hotel run on the same lines as sister hotel *Jurys Galway Inn* (see entry, Galway). Spacious rooms, some with views over Christchurch cathedral and its environs, accommodate up to four people for a flat-rate room tariff. Basic requirements are well provided for, with good-sized beds, neat bathrooms with over-bath showers, decent towels and toiletries, direct-dial phone and colour TV. No tea/coffee-making facilities, but there is an ice-machine on each floor, a reasonably priced self-service restaurant, and bar. City centre within walking distance; multi-storey car park nearby. ***Rooms** 183. Closed 25 & 26 Dec.* AMERICAN EXPRESS *Access, Diners, Visa.*

Dublin — Jurys Hotel and Towers 76% — £158

Tel 01 605000 Fax 01 605540 — **H**

Pembroke Road Ballsbridge Dublin 4 — **Map 23 D4**

Close to Lansdowne Road rugby ground and the Royal Dublin Society showgrounds, this lively modern hotel has extensive banqueting/conference facilities (for 600/850 guests respectively), two restaurants, a coffee shop, two bars and a popular nightly dinner cabaret (May-October), all planned to take place in or around a central pavilion and water-garden. For the quieter life, The Towers is a hotel within a hotel with its own security access, hospitality room, library and boardroom in addition to 100 Executive bedrooms. Throughout the hotel, rooms are spacious, very comfortable and well-equipped with good, well-planned bathrooms and a well-selected range of toiletries. The hotel has earned a special EC commendation for its disabled guest facilities. Children under 14 stay free in their parents' room. No dogs. ***Rooms** 400. Garden, indoor & outdoor swimming pools, spa bath, beauty & hair salon, coffee shop (6.30am-4.30am), gift shop, car rental & airline desks.* AMERICAN EXPRESS *Access, Diners, Visa.*

Dublin Kapriol £64

Tel 01 4751235 **R**

45 Lower Camden Street Dublin 2 **Map 23 D4**

This popular Italian restaurant is near the famous *Bleeding Horse* pub and within walking distance of many of the main hotels. Family-run by the Peruzzis since 1978, the Kapriol has delighted more than one generation of diners with its caring atmosphere and traditional Italian menu based entirely on fresh produce in a wide range of home-made pasta dishes, seafood ranging from risotto alla veneziana (with squid) to real scampi made with jumbo Dublin Bay Prawns, a good choice of veal dishes and game in season. ***Seats** 30. D only 7.30-12. Closed Sun, Bank Holidays, last 2 weeks Aug.* AMERICAN EXPRESS *Access, Diners, Visa.*

Dublin Locks £82

Tel 01 543391 **R**

1 Windsor Terrace Portobello Dublin 8 **Map 23 D4**

Claire Douglas has run this canal-side restaurant since 1980, to frequent acclaim. Portions are generous and food imaginative as in a vegetarian Chinese salad, panfried monkfish and prawns in a Thai curry sauce and suckling pig with an apple and horseradish sauce. Good farmhouse cheeses. ***Seats** 47. Private Room 30. L 12.30-2 D 7.15-11. Closed L Sat, all Sun, Bank Holidays, 1 week Christmas. Set L from £12.95 Set D from £18.95.* AMERICAN EXPRESS *Access, Diners, Visa.*

Dublin Mont Clare Hotel 64% £155

Tel 01 6616799 Fax 01 6615663 **H**

Merrion Square Dublin 2 **Map 23 D4**

Almost next to the National Gallery, the Mont Clare underwent major structural changes and refurbishment in 1990, leaving only the large stained glass and mahogany bar, which is popular with local business people. Most bedrooms are not large, but polished wood fitted furniture provides business guests with plenty of work space, with phones on the desks. Bathrooms are on the small side, but well finished in marble. No dogs. ***Rooms** 74. Valet parking.* AMERICAN EXPRESS *Access, Diners, Visa.*

Dublin Montrose Hotel 65% £134

Tel 01 2693311 Fax 01 2691164 **H**

Stillorgan Road Dublin **Map 23 D4**

This south-city hotel near the University College campus has undergone extensive refurbishment. Removing balconies and rebuilding the whole front has updated the exterior, while interior improvements include the addition of more suites and rooms for the disabled. ***Rooms** 180.* AMERICAN EXPRESS *Access, Diners, Visa.*

Dublin Oisins £72

Tel & Fax 01 4753433 **R**

31 Upper Camden Street Dublin **Map 23 D4**

Original Irish Specialities In Nostalgic Surroundings. Oisins doesn't actually mean that, but it could, with a menu that includes crubeens (pig's trotters), pigeon breast with Guinness and mustard sauce and Irish stew with dumplings. Nettle soup is a popular starter, carrageen moss with Bailey's *See over* (a blancmange set with gelatinous seaweed from the west coast) a favourite dessert. Friendly service, regular live music. ***Seats** 40. D only 6.30-10.30. Closed Sun & Mon in winter, Bank Holidays, Christmas week. Set D £35 (main course only £18).* AMERICAN EXPRESS *Access, Diners, Visa.*

Dublin Old Dublin NEW £60

Tel 01 542028 Fax 01 541406 **R**

90/91 Francis Street Dublin 8 **Map 23 D4**

Since 1980 owner/chef Eamonn Walsh has exercised his skills in Russian/Scandinavian cuisine here – especially appropriate in this area of the city, which goes right back to Viking times, but the service is bang up to date with a doorman to greet you and keep an eye on the street parking. Inside, a series of warmly-decorated rooms makes up the ground floor restaurant, each with its own marble fireplace, soft wall lights illuminating a collection of good pictures, well-upholstered chairs and a refreshing emphasis on old-fashioned comfort. Menus range from a popular set lunch to a flexibly constructed dinner menu which can include variations from a short carte of specialities, at small extra charges. Authentic versions of popularised classics like borsch, gravad lax, chicken kiev and beef stroganoff are there, of course, alongside many more exotic-sounding dishes like bresaola (home-cured beef), planked sirloin Hussar (the steak baked between oak planks and served on an oak platter with sweet pickle) and Georgian lamb shaslyk (marinated leg of lamb, served with rice and minted yoghurt). A good cheeseboard includes unusual French and Irish farmhouse specialities. ***Seats** 65. Parties 30. Private Room 16. L 12.30-2.30 D 7.15-11. Closed L Sat, all Sun, Bank Holidays, 3 days Christmas. Set L from £10 Set D from £19.* AMERICAN EXPRESS *Access, Diners, Visa.*

Dublin 101 Talbot £32

Tel 01 745011 **R**

101 Talbot Street Dublin 1 **Map 23 D4**

Upstairs in a busy shopping street, close to O'Connell Street and the Abbey and Peacock Theatres, this bright, airy restaurant has a rather arty cheap and cheerful atmosphere which harmonises well with the wholesome Mediterranean-influenced and spicy eastern food. Leanings towards wholefoods and vegetarian dishes – Italian mixed bean soup, for instance, or spicy Indonesian vegetable casserole with basmati rice – are balanced by interesting things for carnivores, good home baking and some very tempting desserts – and, for once, the cheap and cheerful description carries through to the bill. Only one wine over £15 on list! ***Seats** 80. L 12-3 D 6.30-11 (light meals 10am-11pm). Closed Sun, Bank Holidays. Access, Visa.*

Dublin Pasta Fresca £30

Tel 01 6792402 **R**

3-4 Chatham Street Dublin 2 **Map 23 D4**

Chic Italian wine bar-delicatessen just off the Grafton Street shopping area. The popular all-day menu is based on good home-made pastas, interesting vegetarian options and a wide range of salads with well-made dressings. ***Seats** 75. Meals 8am-11.30pm (Mon to 7). Closed Sun, Bank Holidays. Set D £8.50. Access, Visa.*

Dublin Patrick Guilbaud ★ £100

Tel 01 6764192 Fax 01 6601546 **R**

46 James Place off Lower Baggot Street Dublin 2 **Map 23 D4**

It is eleven years since M. Guilbaud opened here in Dublin's first purpose-built restaurant and, once again, the last year has been an improvement on the one before. The success is well-deserved: the restaurant exudes sophisticated elegance with its plant-filled atrium entrance and strong abstract paintings and front-of-house staff make it all look easy with a relaxed professionalism which allows maximum enjoyment of Guillaume Le Brun's cooking. The no-choice table d'hote menu is handled with commendable flexibility and the wine list is refreshingly free of snobbery, with a good, user-friendly selection of house wines and reasonably-priced choice (plenty under £20). A la carte, taste sensations include sliced foie gras served with fig purée, panfried fillet of turbot with spices and roast duck with a Seville orange and ginger sauce. In addition there's a six-course *menu surprise*, dependent on what is freshest from the market that day, and an excellent French cheeseboard. ***Seats** 50. L 12.30-2 D 7.30-10.15. Closed Sun & Mon, Bank Holidays. Set L £15.50 Set D £25 & £45.* AMERICAN EXPRESS *Access, Diners, Visa.*

Dublin **Pizzeria Italia** **NEW** **£25**

Tel 01 6778528 Fax 01 6601546 **R**

23 Temple Bar Dublin 2 **Map 23 D4**

Since 1986 the Alambi family have run this tiny one-room pizza-bar and restaurant in what has since become the trendy Left Bank area of Dublin. Efficient, humorous staff and delicious, herby aromas set the tone: traditional minestrone is convincingly home-made and although pizzas and classic pasta dishes predominate, of course, there's also a good choice of steaks at very reasonable prices, plus the likes of pollo cacciatore (chicken cooked in red wine with mushrooms, onion, tomato and oregano) and a very good crème caramel to go with the cappuccino. ***Seats** 65. Meals 12-11. Closed Sun, Bank Holidays, 2 weeks June, 2 weeks from 24 Dec. No credit cards.*

Dublin **Il Primo** **£40**

Tel 01 783373 **R**

16 Montague Street Dublin 2 **Map 23 D4**

The determinedly simple, almost austere surroundings at this little Italian place belie the imagination, sound cooking and value of the food in lively, colourful dishes like rustic canapés of coarse chicken liver paté, pizza with roast aubergine, peppers, sun-dried tomatoes and mozzarella, or flat pasta with wild mushrooms and cream or extra virgin olive oil. The short carte changes with the seasons and is always boosted by a few daily specials. Home-made pasta is excellent, Italian and Irish cheeses in good condition served with fruit. Any wine under £30 available by the glass. ***Seats** 44. Parties 30. L 12-3 D 6-11.Closed Sun, Bank Holidays. Access, Diners, Visa.*

Dublin **Rajdoot** **£40**

Tel 01 6794274 **R**

26 Clarendon Street Westbury Centre Dublin 2 **Map 23 D4**

Authentic North Indian cuisine from a member of the small UK chain. Tandoori dishes are the main speciality, based on a wide range of ingredients including lamb's kidneys, quail and mackerel as well as the more usual chicken, prawns and lamb. Set price daily menus include a keenly priced 3-course lunch. ***Seats** 92. Parties 20. L 12-2.30 D 6.30-11.30. Closed 25 & 26 Dec, 1 Jan, Good Friday (L only other Bank Holidays), Sun. Set L £6.95 Set D £14.95.* AMERICAN EXPRESS *Access, Diners, Visa.*

Dublin **Roly's Bistro** **NEW** **£50**

Tel 01 6682611/6682379 **R**

7 Ballsbridge Terrace Ballsbridge Dublin 4 **Map 23 D4**

Well-known Dun Laoghaire restaurateur Roly Saul and chef Colin O'Daly (ex-*The Park*, Blackrock) have created a winning formula for this large, air-conditioned, two-storey French-style bistro: the crowd, the buzz, the *See over* quality of the food and, above all, the reasonable prices are more Paris than Dublin. Set lunch menus are surprisingly long on choice at the price, while the evening à la carte menu offers a very wide selection, typically ranging from a wild mushroom soup with sorrel or tian of crab with pink grapefruit, through main courses like roast guinea hen with grapes and lime sauce, rabbit and pigeon pie with red cabbage or shellfish bake, an aromatic combination of, say, scallops, prawns and mussels with tomato and basil. Vegetables include traditional dishes such as colcannon (potato with kale, onion and herbs) and desserts vary from comfort food like apple rice meringue to elegant concoctions of assorted chocolate mousses served on a coffee sauce. A limited selection of cheese, including Long Clawson Stilton and an Irish farmhouse cheese such as Milleens or Gubbeen, changes regularly. Short, user-friendly wine list includes a wide selection of house wines. Saturday brunch. ***Seats** 120. L 12-3 D 6-10 (Sun to 9). Closed Good Friday, 25 & 26 Dec.* AMERICAN EXPRESS *Access, Visa.*

Dublin **Royal Dublin Hotel** **63%** **£98**

Tel 01 8733666 Fax 01 8733120 **H**

40 Upper O'Connell Street Dublin 1 **Map 23 D4**

Well-situated on Dublin's most famous street, this recently refurbished modern hotel has identical bedrooms and an all-day bar and brasserie. A striking conference venue in O' Connell Hall has conference facilities for 250 (banquets 230). Children under 12 stay free in parents' room. Limited amount of secure parking in a basement garage. ***Rooms** 117. News kiosk, brasserie (7am-midnight).* AMERICAN EXPRESS *Access, Visa, Diners.*

Dublin **Sachs Hotel** **62%** **£98**

Tel 01 6680995 Fax 01 6686147 **H**

19 Morehampton Road Donnybrook Dublin 4 **Map 23 D4**

Although this attractive small hotel in a Georgian terrace is a lively night-spot, it also manages to provide townhouse comfort and a discreet ambience; front windows are double-glazed and bedrooms are individually decorated in period style. Live music includes Friday night sessions in the Tiffany-style bar and a popular jazz brunch on Sundays and there is also a nightly disco. Seminar rooms cater for small groups, conference facilities for 170 (banquets 120). Free private parking. ***Rooms** 20. Closed 25 Dec.* AMERICAN EXPRESS *Access, Diners, Visa.*

Dublin **Shalimar** **£50**

Tel 01 6710738 **R**

17 South Great George's Street Dublin 2 **Map 23 D4**

Welcoming, well-appointed basement restaurant serving generous portions of hearty Indian food. ***Seats** 56. Parties 20. L 12.30-2.30 D 6-12 (Fri & Sat to 12.30). Closed L Sat, Bank Holidays, 1 week Christmas, Muslim Holidays. Set L from £6.95 Set D from £14.* AMERICAN EXPRESS *Access, Diners, Visa.*

Dublin **Shelbourne Hotel** **74%** **£174**

Tel 01 6766471 Fax 01 6616006 **H**

St Stephen's Green Dublin 2 **Map 23 D4**

One of Ireland's most historic buildings – the constitution was drafted here – this opulent 18th-century hotel is still central to Dublin life and many a scandal has originated from the famous Horseshoe Bar or, recently, the new Shelbourne Bar on Kildare Street which opened in 1992. Friday nights are best for people-watching, here and in several other near-by hostelries which share an exalted clientele of politicians and other famous faces. The hotel has retained all its grandeur, with a magnificent faux-marbre entrance hall and refurbished Lord Mayor's lounge (a popular spot for morning coffee or afternoon tea). Spacious, elegantly furnished superior and de-luxe rooms and suites have traditional polished wood furniture and impressive drapes, while standard rooms in a newer wing are smaller. Rooms on lower floors can suffer from external noise, but all rooms are well-appointed, with bathrobes, mini-bars and three telephones as standard. Valet parking. No leisure facilities in the hotel, but golfing is available at the *Royal Dublin Club*. Forte. ***Rooms** 164. Beauty salon, news kiosk, food served all day in Shelbourne Bar.* AMERICAN EXPRESS *Access, Diners, Visa.*

Dublin La Stampa NEW £55

Tel 01 6778611 Fax 01 6773336 **R**

35 Dawson Street Dublin 2 **Map 23 D4**

In a strikingly beautiful, large room warmly decorated in extravagant Renaissance style, the noise level hits you at first, but is easily forgotten. New chef Michael Martin (ex-*Le Gavroche*) produces a stylish French-influenced meal at a surprisingly reasonable price. The formula clearly works, with locals fighting for the opportunity to sample dishes like saddle of lamb stuffed with wild mushrooms and spinach or grilled red mullet with a confit of fennel. Good classic desserts include a sharp lemon tart and a chocolate marquise served with an orange anglaise. Farmhouse cheese comes with an interesting mixed leaf salad. In addition to the set menus, there is a short carte at lunch and a more extensive one for dinner. ***Seats** 160. L 12-2.30 D 6-11.30 (w/e to 12). Closed Sun, Good Friday, 3 days Christmas.* AMERICAN EXPRESS *Access, Diners, Visa.*

Dublin Stephen's Hall Hotel 65% NEW £103

Tel 01 6610585 Fax 01 6610606 **HR**

14/17 Lower Leeson Street Dublin 2 **Map 23 D4**

Situated in a thriving business and tourist area just off St Stephen's Green and run on the same lines as *Morrison's Island* in Cork (see entry), this is Dublin's first all-suites hotel. Each suite has its own lobby and kitchenette in addition to a dining area and sitting room. Degrees of spaciousness vary considerably, with two-bedroom and penthouse suites (for up to 4 guests) having ample space for private dining at very reasonable prices, while smaller ones may seem a little cramped. But all are well-furnished in a pleasingly understated modern Irish style, with thoughtfully planned bathrooms and well-designed furniture. In addition to full room service and 24-hour porter service, a special shopping service is available for guests who wish to cook in their suite; all meals, including breakfast, can also be taken in the restaurant. ***Rooms** 37. Free secure parking. Closed (possibly) 1 week Christmas.* AMERICAN EXPRESS *Access, Diners, Visa.*

The Terrace Bistro £45

This semi-basement restaurant overlooks a large courtyard (complete with chef Giles O'Reilly's herb planting and used for outdoor tables in summer) and is bright and warmly decorated, with formal white-clothed tables. Well-balanced menus favour classical French cuisine but succeed in being a little out of the ordinary without pretentiousness; typically wholesome, well-presented dishes might include an eel terrine, flavoured with beer and herbs, a gutsy feta, garlic and olive salad or casserole of venison with cranberry and ginger. French farmhouse cheeses are a speciality and value overall is good. ***Seats** 48. Parties 12. L 12.15-2.30 D 6.15-9.30. Closed L Sat, all Sun, 24 Dec-early Jan. Set L from £7.50 Set D from £12.50.*

Dublin Ta Se Mohogani Gaspipes £45

Tel 01 6798138 **R**

17 Manor Street Stoneybatter Dublin 7 **Map 23 D4**

Stylish little American restaurant in a neglected part of town features an eclectic menu strong on spicy fare like Thailand spring rolls with hot dipping sauce or bruschetta with spicy marinara and Ragato cheese. There's a fresh fish special daily and a late night jazz menu. ***Seats** 40. Parties 16. L 12-3 D 7-11 (Fri & Sat to 2.30 am). Closed Sun & Mon, 2 weeks end July, Bank Holidays. Access, Diners, Visa.*

Dublin **The Westbury** 79% £180

Tel 01 6791122 Fax 01 6797078 **HR**

Off Grafton Street Dublin 2 **Map 23 D4**

Nestled in the heart of Grafton Street, with its own integral shopping mall, the Westbury exudes the warmth of a home-from-home, albeit a very grand one. Mannequins meandering among the tables constitute a typical tea-time diversion; there's slick table service in the Terrace Bar and Dublin's Joycean traditions are echoed in the lively Sandbank seafood bar with its stained glass and rosewood panelling. Pinks and blues are key colours in the bedrooms, which offer a high standard of comfort and accessories; they range from newly modernised singles to luxury penthouse suites. Business gatherings and banquets (to a maximum of 200) are accommodated in elegantly furnished boardrooms and function suites. Here, as elsewhere, the Westbury has the atmosphere of a top-class hotel with legions of staff providing a good level of service. ***Rooms** 205. Gymnasium, beauty & hair salon, news kiosk, coffee shop (10am-10pm, Sun to 8pm).* AMERICAN EXPRESS *Access, Diners, Visa.*

Russell Room £85

The traditional French menu holds few surprises, though the cooking is sound and both service and surroundings suitably stylish. Praiseworthy Irish salmon and seafoods make a strong showing, and flambéed crepes Suzette a completely apposite dessert for the setting. A three-course table d'hote lunch (four courses at dinner) offers a choice of five or so dishes at each course. Easy-to-use, but unspectacular wine list. 15% service charge is added to all menu prices. ***Seats** 100. Parties 40. L 12.30-2.30 D 6.30-10.30 (Sun to 9.30). Set L £14.50 Set D £18.50.*

Dublin Airport **Forte Crest** 57% £134

Tel 01 8444211 Fax 01 8425874 **H**

Collinstown Dublin Airport Co Dublin **Map 22 D3**

Modern, sound-proofed accommodation, including some non-smoking rooms, close to the airport, with 24 hour courtesy coach service to the terminal. 24 hour room service. Conference and exhibition facilities for 150; leisure facilities nearby. Choice of restaurants includes *Sampans* Chinese. ***Rooms** 192.* AMERICAN EXPRESS *Access, Diners, Visa.*

Dublin Places of Interest

Tourist Information Tel 01 2844768.
Dublin Airport Tel 01 8445387.
Bank of Ireland College Green Tel 01 6615933.
Trinity College (Book of Kells) and Dublin Experience University of Dublin Tel 01 6772941.
Dublin Zoo Phoenix Park Tel 01 6771425.
Fairyhouse Racecourse Ratoath Tel 01 8256777.
The Curragh Co Kildare Tel 01 289288.
Gaelic Athletic Association (GAA) Tel 046 23638.
Croke Park Football Ground Hurling and Gaelic Football Tel 01 363222.
Irish Rugby Union and Lansdowne Road Rugby Ground Baub Bridge Tel 01 6684601.
Theatres and Concert Halls
Abbey and Peacock Theatres Lower Abbey Street Tel 01 8787222.
Andrew's Lane Theatre Exchequer Street Tel 01 6795720.
Gaiety Theatre South King Street Tel 01 6771717.
Gate Theatre Cavendish Row Tel 01 8744045.
Olympia Theatre Dame Street Tel 01 6777744.
Tivoli Theatre Francis Street Tel 01 544472.
National Concert Hall Earlsfoot Terrace Tel 01 6711888.

Point Depot (Exhibitions and Concerts) North Wall Quay Tel 01 366000.
Irish Film Centre Eustace Street Tel 01 6793477.

Museums and Art Galleries

Dublinia, Christchurch Tel 01 4758137.
Chester Beatty Library and Gallery of Oriental Art Shrewsbury Road Tel 01 2692386.
Civic Museum South William Street Tel 01 6794260.
Dublin Writer's Museum Parnell Square North Tel 01 8722077.
Fry Model Railway Museum Malahide Castle Tel 01 452758.
Irish Museum of Modern Art/Royal Hospital Kilmainham Tel 01 6718666.
Guinness Brewery James's Gate Tel 01 536700 *ext. 5155.*
Hugh Lane Municipal Gallery Parnell Square Tel 01 8741903.
National Gallery of Ireland Merrion Square West Tel 01 66615133.
National Museum of Ireland Kildare Street Tel 01 6618811.
National Wax Museum Granby Row, Parnell Square Tel 01 8726340.
Natural History Museum Merrion Street Tel 01 618811.

Historic Houses, Castles and Gardens

Ashtown Castle Phoenix Park Tel 01 613111.
Dublin Castle Dame Street Tel 01 6777129.
Joyce Tower Sandycove Tel 01 2809265.
Kilmainham Gaol Kilmainham Tel 01 535984.
Malahide Castle Malahide Tel 01 8452655.
Marsh's Library St. Patrick Close Tel 01 543511.
National Botanic Gardens Glasnevin Tel 01 377596.
Newbridge House Donabate Tel 045 31301.
Newman House St. Stephen's Green Tel 01 4757255.
Number Twenty Nine Lower Fitzwilliam Street Tel 01 7026165.

Cathedrals

Christ Church Cathedral Christ Church Place Tel 01 6778099.
St. Patrick's Cathedral Patrick's Close Tel 01 4754817.
Whitefriar Street Carmelite Church Aungier Street Tel 01 4758821.
Pro Cathedral Marlborough Street Tel 01 874292.

Dun Laoghaire Restaurant Na Mara £75

Tel 01 280 0509 Fax 01 284 4649 **R**

1 Harbour Road Dun Laoghaire Co Dublin **Map 23 D4**

Railway buffs will be fascinated by this elegant harbourside restaurant, as it is the old Kingstown terminal building and is owned by Irish Rail Catering Services. The interior is classical with bar and reception areas recently stylishly refurbished and decor throughout in soft soothing tones. French-influenced menus are a mixture of traditional and modern styles, with a strong emphasis on seafood in dishes like lobster bisque, salad of smoked eel with hazelnut dressing, roasted monkfish with ragout of mushrooms and shallots or simply poached fillet of sole with lemon. tomato and sorrel sauce. Flambéed specialities feature and there is a short choice of meat and vegetarian dishes. ***Seats** 80. Private Room 75. L 12.30-2.30 D 7-10.30. Closed Sun, 1 week Christmas. Set L £12.75 Set D £23.* AMERICAN EXPRESS *Access, Diners, Visa.*

Dun Laoghaire Royal Marine Hotel 67% £85

Tel 01 280 1911 Fax 01 280 1089 **H**

Marine Road Dun Laoghaire Co Dublin **Map 23 D4**

Overlooking Dun Laoghaire harbour and the car ferry terminal, this imposing Ryan Group hotel stands in 4 acres of gardens and has extensive conference and banqueting facilities for up to 600. Children under 16 may stay free in parents' room. 38 deluxe bedrooms, lively bars and helpful staff. ***Rooms** 104. Garden.* AMERICAN EXPRESS *Access, Diners, Visa.*

Dun Laoghaire — Places of Interest

Tourist Information Tel 01 2806984/5/6.
National Maritime Museum Haigh Terrace Tel 01 2800969.

Dundalk — Ballymascanlon House 59% — £73

Tel 042 71124 Fax 042 71598 — **H**

Ballymascanlon Dundalk Co Louth — **Map 22 D3**

Two miles out of Dundalk on the Belfast road, this Victorian mansion is set in 130 acres of parkland. Bedrooms vary considerably in size, the largest being arranged around a glass-domed circular landing. There is a well planned leisure complex, good golf course and conference facilities for 250. ***Rooms** 36. Garden, indoor swimming pool, gymnasium, squash, sauna, solarium, floodlit tennis, 9-hole golf course. Closed 24-27 Dec.* AMERICAN EXPRESS *Access, Diners, Visa.*

Dundalk — Places of Interest

Tourist Information Tel 042 35484.
Basement Gallery Town Hall Tel 042 32276.

Dunderry — Dunderry Lodge Restaurant — £75

Tel 046 31671 — **R**

Dunderry Navan Co Meath — **Map 22 C3**

Although it is in a comfortably furnished, characterful old stone building, formally set tables with white linen and fine glasses create a sense of occasion at this well-known country restaurant. Owner-chef Paul Groves uses home-grown and local produce to good effect in menus which are imaginative without being pretentious. Game paté might be served with an elderberry and nut oil dressing, for example, or creamy scrambled eggs served as a starter with wild mushrooms and herbs. Game often features when in season, also local free-range poultry and pork. The dessert trolley is famous for its wide range of temptations, including floating islands, white and dark chocolate or coffee mousse and ices set in a bowl of hazelnut meringue gateau. Sunday lunch offers exceptional value. ***Seats** 40. Parties 12. L Sun 1-2 (also open L Sat May-Aug, other days by arrangement) D 7-9.30. Closed D Sun, all Mon, Bank Holidays. Set L £13 Set D £16.75.* AMERICAN EXPRESS *Access, Diners, Visa.*

Dundrum — Dundrum House 66% — £96

Tel 062 71116 Fax 062 71366 — **H**

Dundrum Cashel Co Tipperary — **Map 23 B5**

The Crowe family take great pride in their hotel, a large Georgian house set in beautiful parkland with a trout-filled river. Public rooms include a lofty reception hall, a comfortable drawing room furnished with wing chairs and, in the old chapel, a bar with live music every night in summer. Spacious, simply decorated bedrooms are furnished with antiques. An 18-hole golf course was opened in 1993. ***Rooms** 55. Garden, golf (18), fishing, snooker.* AMERICAN EXPRESS *Access, Diners, Visa.*

Dunlavin — Rathsallagh House 67% — £110

Tel 045 53112 Fax 045 53343 — **HR**

Dunlavin Co Wicklow — **Map 23 C4**

Built in the former stables of a Queen Anne house which burned down in 1798, Joe and Kay O'Flynn's delightful, rambling country house has an award-winning walled kitchen garden, 280-acre farm and seemingly endless rolling parkland. Fishing and deer-stalking are easily arranged (also hunting in season) and an 18-hole golf course is due for completion in spring 1994 – or you can simply catch up with your reading by the fireside in the delightfully lived-in drawing room. Rooms are generally spacious and quite luxurious in an understated way, with lovely country views; some smaller, simpler rooms in the stable yard have a special cottagey charm. There is a completely separate private conference facility for up to 50 in a courtyard conversion at the back. Outstanding breakfasts are served in the traditional way from a huge sideboard. No children under 12. ***Rooms** 14. Garden, indoor swimming pool, tennis, practice golf, snooker, helipad. Access, Diners, Visa.*

Restaurant

£65

Take in the easy-going atmosphere in the old kitchen bar while reading the menu, then settle down in the traditional dining room and enjoy the evening shadows falling on parkland and the hills beyond. Good home cooking is the order of the day, allowing the freshness and quality of prime local produce to come through. Typical offerings on the limited choice four-course menu might include oxtail soup, grilled scallops or woodland salad with quails' eggs, followed by baked brill with hollandaise or smoked bacon and spiced potatoes. Roast local beef is a speciality, also Wicklow lamb. Leave some room for a tempting dessert from the trolley, or some Irish farmhouse cheese. ***Seats** 50. Private Room 15. L (Sun only) 1-2 D 7.30-9. Closed Mon in winter, 3 days Christmas, 1 week from 2 Jan. Set L £14.95 Set D £25.*

Dunworley — Dunworley Cottage

£60

Tel 023 40314 — **R**

Butlerstown Clonakilty Dunworley Co Cork — **Map 23 B6**

Signposted from Timoleague now, this well-known restaurant is easier to find than it used to be, but remote nevertheless. But it is worth the trouble: they take their food seriously here, using produce supplied by the Organic Growers of Ireland whenever possible and anything wild that is good to eat. Katherine Noren, who runs the kitchen, is from Sweden and the food reflects a happy blend of cultures. Marinated herring is a regular starter and soups are a special feature – mussels, vegetables and the oft-quoted Dunworley Nettle soup – and they serve a local speciality, Clonakilty black and white pudding, with a sherry sauce and loganberries. Good steaks are always popular and menus are constructed around the local catch of the day. Any special dietary needs are willingly looked after and there's a special children's menu, with Swedish meatballs the number one favourite. ***Seats** 50. Private Room 20. L 1-5 D 6.30-10. Closed Mon & Tue, also Nov and Jan-Feb. Set D £18.* AMERICAN EXPRESS *Access, Diners, Visa.*

Many establishments are currently on the market, so ownership could change after we go to press.

Durrus — Blairs Cove House Restaurant

£60

Tel 027 61127 — **R**

Blairs Cove Durrus nr Bantry Co Cork — **Map 23 A6**

Philippe and Sabine de Mey's characterful restaurant is in the sympathetically restored outbuildings of an 18th-century manor house, with views over Dunmanus Bay. Begin with a plate of starters from the renowned buffet, then move on to locally caught fish – wild salmon with horseradish crust and beurre blanc, perhaps, or John Dory with orange sauce, or steaks and spring lamb cooked before your eyes over a wood-fired grill. Finish with desserts displayed on the grand piano, or wonderful local farmhouse cheeses. Half bottles make a feeble show on a decent wine list – ask to see the supplementary claret and burgundy list. Accommodation in comfortable self-catering apartments nearby can be arranged by ringing 027 61041. ***Seats** 70. D only 7.30-9.30. Closed Sun (also Mon Sep-Jun), Nov-Feb. Set D £23.* AMERICAN EXPRESS *Access, Diners, Visa.*

Ennis — Auburn Lodge — 61% — £65

Tel 065 21247 Fax 065 21202 — **H**

Galway Road Ennis Co Clare — **Map 23 B4**

A good base for exploring The Burren, this sprawling modern hotel on the N18 has well-equipped bedrooms, good conference and banqueting facilities for up to 500 and friendly, helpful staff. ***Rooms** 100. Garden, tennis.* AMERICAN EXPRESS *Access, Diners, Visa.*

Ennis — Old Ground Hotel — 66% — £98

Tel 065 28127 Fax 065 28112 — **H**

Ennis Co Clare — **Map 23 B4**

Famous old ivy-clad hotel next to Ennis cathedral, with ground-floor bedrooms suitable for disabled guests and conference facilities for up to 250 (banquets 180). A convenient base for touring Clare; children under 16 may stay free in their parents' room. Forte Heritage. ***Rooms** 58.* AMERICAN EXPRESS *Access, Diners, Visa.*

Ennis — West County Inn — 59% — £77

Tel 065 28421 Fax 065 28801 — **H**

Clare Road Ennis Co Clare — **Map 23 B4**

Bright, modern hotel on the outskirts of town with a garden conservatory and lively night life at Ebonys night club, scene of a 'Taste of Ireland' summer season cabaret. Children under 12 may stay free in their parents' room and there are rooms for disabled guests. Extensive conference facilities for up to 800 (banquets 550). Leisure centre available at nearby sister hotel, the *Clare Inn* (see entry Newmarket-on-Fergus). ***Rooms** 110. Snooker.* AMERICAN EXPRESS *Access, Diners, Visa.*

Ennis — Places of Interest

Tourist Information Tel 065 28366.
Graggaunowen Bronze Age Project Quin Tel 061 367178.

Enniskerry — Curtlestown House — £50

Tel 01 2825083 — **R**

Curtlestown Enniskerry Co Wicklow — **Map 23 D4**

Just half an hour's drive from Dublin, 2½ miles from Enniskerry on the Glencree road, Teresa and Colin Pielow's cosy little farmhouse makes a charming country restaurant. Colin's traditional menus specialise in game in season, local lamb and seafood in summer. Typical offerings for Sunday lunch might include home-made soup or smoked fillets of trout raifort (well-smoked fillets with an attractive and tasty salad of mixed leaves and horseradish sauce) all served with freshly baked bread and butter followed, perhaps, by a home-cooked roast served with a communal dish of small potatoes steamed in their jackets, chunky carrot batons and lightly cooked broccoli spears – simple and delicious. Home-made apple crumble is served with real egg custard. ***Seats** 40. Parties 20. Private Room 25. L (Sun only) 12.30-2.30 D 8-10. Closed Mon. Set L £11.50 Set D from £17. Access, Visa*

Enniskerry — Enniscree Lodge — 59% — £75

Tel 01 286 3542 Fax 01 286 6037 — **HR**

Cloon Enniskerry Co Wicklow — **Map 23 D4**

Boasting a view to match that of any restaurant in Ireland, this friendly old inn also has a cosy bar for winter, a terrace for sunny weather and good all-day bar good. Recently refurbished rooms are comfortably furnished in country style and most have stunning views; bathrooms are slightly dated but neat and functional. A residents' lounge doubles as a small function room. Children up to 12 may stay free in parents' room. ***Rooms** 10. Closed Mon-Thur in Jan & Feb.* AMERICAN EXPRESS® *Access, Diners, Visa.*

Restaurant

£60

Since his arrival in the spring of 1993, chef Paul Moroney has established a new and more sophisticated style in this attractive restaurant overlooking Glencree. Traditional Irish fare may be missed but dishes like a well-balanced, colourful summer salad with fresh prawns, toasted pine kernels and walnut dressing or rack of local Wicklow lamb in a mustard crust with home-made mint chutney on the present lively, French-influenced menu are an overall improvement. ***Seats** 40. Parties 12. L 12.30-2.30 D 7.30-9.30 (Sat to 10, Sun to 9). Set L £12.50.*

Ferrycarrig Bridge — Ferrycarrig Hotel 61%

£90

Tel 053 22999 Fax 053 41982

H

Ferrycarrig Bridge nr Wexford Co Wexford

Map 23 D5

All bedrooms in this well-run modern waterside hotel overlook the Slaney estuary and there is a path leading to Ferrycarrig Castle. Comfortably furnished public rooms look onto landscaped gardens and stylish bedrooms have well-equipped bathrooms with plenty of shelf space. There are conference facilities for up to 400 and a new leisure centre was opened in 1992. ***Rooms** 40. Garden, gymnasium, sauna, steam room, solarium, whirlpool bath, beauty salon.* AMERICAN EXPRESS® *Access, Diners, Visa.*

Galway — Ardilaun House 66%

£90

Tel 091 21433 Fax 091 21546

H

Taylors Hill Galway Co Galway

Map 23 B4

Friendly, helpful staff and a bustling atmosphere are the most striking features of this much-extended hotel. Public rooms in the original Georgian building are graciously proportioned with fine plasterwork, but good use has been made of the attractive garden setting throughout; all bedrooms have a pleasant leafy outlook and the large dining room opens onto a patio and lawn. Unpretentious, traditionally furnished bedrooms vary somewhat in size and the best have been recently refurbished; children up to 10 may stay free in parents' room. Eight non-smoking rooms. Conference facilities for 400 (banquets 250). Good housekeeping and maintenance throughout. No dogs. ***Rooms** 90. Garden, gymnasium, sauna, solarium, snooker. Closed 6 days Christmas.* AMERICAN EXPRESS® *Access, Diners, Visa.*

> We do not accept free meals or hospitality – our inspectors pay their own bills.

Galway — Brennans Yard 64% NEW

£70

Tel 091 68166 Fax 091 68262

H

Lower Merchants Road Galway Co Galway

Map 23 B4

Interesting old warehousing near the river has been stylishly converted to make this new hotel. First impressions are of an attractive building with unexpectedly cramped entrance, but the second phase of development, which will include the foyer as originally planned, has yet to be completed. Public rooms currently in operation include a pleasantly bright if smallish dining room (also to be extended) and, at the back, the striking Oyster Bar for informal meals, especially local seafood. Individually decorated bedrooms make up in style what is lacking in space – well-planned, clean-lined rooms have old stripped pine pieces, locally-made pottery and neat, functional bathrooms. Direct-dial phones, radio and TV, tea/coffee-making facilities, hairdryer and toiletries included as standard. ***Rooms** 24. Closed 2 weeks Christmas.* AMERICAN EXPRESS® *Access, Diners, Visa.*

Galway **Casey's Westwood Restaurant** NEW £55

Tel 091 21442/21645 R

Dangan Upper Newcastle Galway Co Galway Map 23 B4

The Casey family have been running this popular eating place since 1982 and the long, low building houses a number of bars and restaurant areas to suit various types of occasion. An evening in the main restaurant starts in the cocktail lounge, where orders are taken before you settle into a comfortable carver or banquette at a well-appointed table to enjoy John Casey's sound cooking. Menus offer a wide choice and demand a few minutes' concentration to take in a complicated pricing structure, which allows flexibility between menus, and the day's specials. From a 5-course dinner menu, typical starters include salad of duck livers with mixed leaves and smoked quails' eggs and tartlet of mussels with smoked bacon and leeks with a saffron sauce; a selection of home-made bread is handed. Medallions of monkfish studded with pancetta are served with home-made tagliatelle and a pretty, piquant tomato and red pepper coulis. Vegetables are imaginative, desserts unusual and prettily presented and petits fours home-made. Low-cholesterol and vegetarian dishes available. ***Seats 120.*** *L 12.30-2.15 D 6.30-10. Closed Good Friday, 24-26 Dec. Set L £10.80 Set D £18.50.* AMERICAN EXPRESS *Access, Visa.*

Galway **Corrib Great Southern Hotel** 68% £109

Tel 091 55281 Fax 091 51390 H

Dublin Road Galway Co Galway Map 23 B4

On the edge of the city, overlooking Galway Bay, this large modern hotel offers a wide range of facilities for business guests and family holidays. Bedrooms vary considerably; recently refurbished rooms are much improved and new spacious 'superior' rooms are well-planned with good attention to detail and stylish bathrooms. Children under 2 stay free in parents' room, favourable half-board rate for under 12s. The (smallish) swimming pool has a lifeguard at all times and in high season and busy weekends children's entertainment and a crèche are provided. New state-of-the-art business/convention centre has facilities for groups of 8 to 850, with banqueting for up to 650. Public areas include *O'Malleys Pub*, a big, lively bar with sea views, and a cosy residents' lounge. ***Rooms 180.*** *Indoor swimming pool, steam room, whirlpool bath, snooker.* AMERICAN EXPRESS *Access, Diners, Visa.*

Our inspectors *never* book in the name of Egon Ronay's Guides. They disclose their identity only if they are considering an establishment for inclusion in the next edition of the Guide.

Galway **Glenlo Abbey** 66% NEW £110

Tel 091 26666 Fax 091 27800 H

Bushy Park Galway Co Galway Map 23 B4

First impressions may be off-putting at this 18th-century abbey conversion as the reception area, although attractively furnished with antiques, can be unwelcoming and inefficient. Things improve thereafter, however; public areas, furnished to a high standard and varied in size and style, include an especially attractive large dining/function room with river and countryside views and a nice pubby basement bar furnished with country antiques. Spacious bedrooms with king size beds, safe and trouser press have well-designed marbled bathrooms, complete with shaving mirror, ample shelf space, good over-bath shower, efficient extraction, generous towels and a nice big bar of soap in a travel box. Conference facilities for 48, banqueting up to 75. ***Rooms*** *20. Garden. Closed 25-27 Dec.* AMERICAN EXPRESS *Access, Diners, Visa.*

Galway — Great Southern — 69% — £113

Tel 091 64041 Fax 091 66704 — H

Eyre Square Galway Co Galway — **Map 23 B4**

Built in 1845 overlooking Eyre Square right in the heart of Galway, this historic railway hotel has retained many of its original features and old-world charm mixes easily with modern facilities. Public rooms are quite grand (foyer and restaurant have recently been refurbished) and include O'Flahertys Pub bar as well as a cocktail lounge. Bedrooms, which vary somewhat but are generally spacious, are traditionally furnished with dark mahogany and brass light fittings. Conference facilities for up to 450 (banquets 350). ***Rooms** 116. Indoor swimming pool, sauna, steam room, hair salon.* AMERICAN EXPRESS *Access, Diners, Visa.*

Galway — Jurys Galway Inn — 55% — NEW — £49

Tel 091 66444 Fax 091 68415 — H

Quay Street Galway Co Galway — **Map 23 B4**

Run on the same lines as the new *Jurys Christchurch Inn*, Dublin, this room-only 'inn' offers a good standard of basic accommodation without frills. Rooms, almost all with lovely views, are large (sleeping up to four people) with everything required for comfort and convenience – neat en-suite bathroom, TV, phone – but no extras. Beds are generous, with good-quality bedding, but wardrobes are open. No tea/coffee-making facilities, no room service. Public areas include an impressive, well-designed foyer with seating areas, a pubby bar with good atmosphere and self-service cafeteria. ***Rooms** 128.* AMERICAN EXPRESS *Access, Diners, Visa.*

Galway — Places of Interest

Tourist Information Tel 091 63081.
Thoor Ballylee Gort Tel 091 31436 *W B Yeats' home.*
Coole Gort Tel 091 31804 *Nature Reserve.*
Ballybrit Racecourse Tel 091 53870.

Glasson — Glasson Village Restaurant — NEW — £45

Tel 0902 85001 — R

Glasson Athlone Westmeath — **Map 22 B3**

A converted barracks overlooking fields, this attractive stone building has a pleasant country atmosphere with soft colours, old pine furniture and a conservatory. Owner-chef Michael Brooks prepares imaginative meals with a good variety of local meats included but, remarkably for a Midlands restaurant, specialises in seafood. Dinner might begin with a hot terrine of salmon and hake with sweet red pepper sauce or cassolette of seafood with home-made pasta, followed by salmon en croute with saffron sauce, fillet of pork with mushrooms and green peppercorns, or rack of lamb. Styles of presentation can be mixed, but portions are generous and, at Sunday lunch especially, the atmosphere is welcoming to families, while also relaxing for adults without children – a difficult balance to achieve. ***Seats** 50. Parties 12. Private Room 14. L 12.30 & 2.15 (Sun only, 2 sittings) D 7.15-10.15. Closed D Sun, 3 weeks Oct, Christmas week. Set L £8.50 Set D £15.75.* AMERICAN EXPRESS *Access, Visa.*

Glen of Aherlow — Aherlow House — 63% — £56

Tel 062 56153 Fax 061 355405 — H

Glen of Aherlow nr Tipperary Co Tipperary — **Map 23 B5**

Set in the middle of a coniferous forest in the Galtee Mountains, this Tudor-inspired building was once a hunting lodge. Open beams, lots of dark wood and big log fires create a good atmosphere in the public

See over

rooms and a large terrace outside the bar commands views of the Glen of Aherlow. Well-appointed bedrooms are individually furnished; three are suitable for families (under 10s may stay free in parents' room) and there are facilities for disabled guests. Separate conference facilities for up to 280 people (banquets 220). No dogs. ***Rooms** 10. Closed Mon-Thu Nov-mid Dec & mid Jan to early March.* AMERICAN EXPRESS *Access, Diners, Visa.*

Gorey Marlfield House 81% £146

Tel 055 21124 Fax 055 21572 **HR**

Gorey Co Wexford **Map 23 D5**

At this fine period house in beautiful gardens and woodland, Ray and Mary Bowe provide discerning guests with a fine base for touring the beauty spots of Wicklow and the south-east of Ireland. A large oval foyer with fluted Doric columns, marble floor, busts and palms sets the tone for a seriously sumptuous interior which includes a grand drawing room and a very stylish bar, both decorated in period style with great attention to detail. Bedrooms are individually decorated and vary from charming smaller rooms at the top of the house – some with four-posters but all with good facilities and beautiful bedding including fine, broderie anglaise trimmed, cotton sheets – to a very grand series of six luxurious suites on the ground floor, each different but all with elaborate use of exclusive fabrics, carefully chosen antiques and pictures and appropriately large, well-appointed bathrooms. Colours throughout the house are rich and subtle and beautiful fresh flowers abound. No dogs. ***Rooms** 19. Garden, sauna, lawn tennis, helipad. Closed Dec & Jan.* AMERICAN EXPRESS *Access, Visa.*

Restaurant £90

Almost an extension of the garden, the combination of trompe-l'oeil and real plants plus the proximity of the conservatory extension, confuses the senses in this exotic dining room. Chef Rose Brannock has established a confident style and uses the best of local ingredients, including produce grown in the kitchen garden, in interesting fixed-price menus which offer a good choice. Lunch might begin with a terrine of salmon and sweetbreads with Noilly Prat sauce, followed by pan-fried lamb kidneys with potato cake and orange liqueur sauce, then white chocolate mousse with a fresh raspberry coulis. Dinner menus are more sophisticated: Bannow Bay oysters may be wrapped in filo and served with hollandaise and vegetable butter sauce or terrine of pheasant and pigeon served with pear purée and blackcurrant sauce. Pan-fried fillet of beef with a bone marrow and herb crust and peppercorn sauce and fillets of sole grilled with fresh asparagus and a tomato and chive sauce are typical of the main-course style. No children under seven in the evening. ***Seats** 60. L 12.30-2 D 7-9.30. Set L £15.50 Set D £26.50.*

Prices quoted for the Republic of Ireland are in Irish punts.

Greystones The Hungry Monk £55

Tel 01 2875759 **R**

Greystones Co Wicklow **Map 23 D4**

Monk-related decor, much of it humorous, sets the tone at this informal first-floor restaurant, where jovial host and wine buff Pat Keown practises his skill at providing interesting quality food at affordable prices. Table d'hote menus and Sunday lunch offer starters like lamb kidneys dijonnaise, moules normande and vegetarian samosas and main courses of rack of Wicklow lamb or salmon with watercress sauce. Daily blackboard specials offer a wide choice of locally caught seafood and game in season, also frequently changed and keenly priced wine suggestions. His connoisseur's list has great depth and there are several house wines under £10, plus a good choice of half bottles. ***Seats** 40. L 12.30-3.30 D 7-11. Closed L Tue-Sat, all Mon. Set L £10.95 Set D £14.95.* AMERICAN EXPRESS *Access, Diners, Visa.*

Hodson Bay — Hodson Bay Hotel — 65% — NEW — £90*

Tel 0902 92444 Fax 0902 92688 — H

Hodson Bay Athlone Co Roscommon — Map 22 C3

Conferences and sport and leisure activities, often combined, are the main attractions of this lively hotel on the shores of Lough Ree. Golfing is available at the Athlone Golf Club, located next to the hotel, boating and watersports on the lough and River Shannon and a wide number of pursuits in the hotel's excellent leisure and activity centre. Conference facilities for 500 (banquets 400). Practical en-suite rooms are backed by extensive facilities including formal and informal dining and a waterside bar. *Half-board terms only. ***Rooms** 46. Garden, indoor swimming pool, gymnasium, keep-fit equipment, sauna, solarium, fishing, tennis.* AMERICAN EXPRESS *Access, Diners, Visa.*

Hodson Bay — Place of Interest

Athlone Castle Athlone Tel 0902 92912.

Howth — Adrian's — £50

Tel 01 391696 — R

3 Abbey Street Howth Co Dublin — Map 23 D4

At dinner time, crudités and a herby dip welcome you to this little family-run restaurant, quickly followed by yeast rolls, garlic bread with sesame seeds and olive bread, still warm from the oven. Service may then slow down but Catriona Holden's imaginative, carefully cooked food is worth waiting for. Although carnivores and vegetarians are well catered for, the bias is towards fresh fish from the harbour. Try the Howth bisque followed, perhaps, by poached selection of seafood – salmon, brill, fresh prawns and a couple of huge mussels in the half shell, served on a very delicate mustard sauce. Pretty, sophisticated desserts are available separately, or as a trio of, for example, hazelnut biscuit glacé, Amaretto cheesecake and chocolate mousse, with nutty wafers and raspberry coulis. Informal day-time menu averages under £10 for 3 courses ***Seats** 32. Private Room 36. Meals 12-9.30 (Sun 12-7). Set D £16.* AMERICAN EXPRESS *Access, Diners, Visa.*

Howth — King Sitric — £70

Tel 01 326729 Fax 01 392442 — R

East Pier Harbour Road Howth Co Dublin — Map 23 D4

Local seafood, much of it both caught and landed within sight, is very much the speciality at this well-established fish restaurant on the harbour front in Howth. Owner-chef Aidan MacManus gives a token nod to carnivores with dishes such as chicken Kiev or rack of lamb with redcurrant sauce, but it is with the great, simple fish dishes like sole on the bone or lobster with butter sauce that he excels. In addition to dinner, an upstairs seafood bar opens for lunch in summer: less expensive dishes ranging from crab bisque with the famous King Sitric brown bread, through fisherman's platters and Balscadden Bay lobster mayonnaise to meringue Sitric or farmhouse cheeses are served at tables overlooking Balscadden Bay and Howth Harbour. You need look no further than the house recommendations on the excellent wine list (predominantly white wines), which has more than 25 Chablis. ***Seats** 60. Private Room 22. L 12.30-3 (summer and pre-Christmas only) D 6.30-11. Closed Sun, Bank Holidays, 10 days Christmas & Easter. Set D £22.* AMERICAN EXPRESS *Access, Diners, Visa.*

Howth — Places of Interest

Howth Castle Gardens Tel 01 322624.

Innishannon — Innishannon House Hotel 63% NEW

£85

Tel 021 775121 Fax 021 775609

H

Innishannon Co Cork

Map 23 B6

In a very romantic riverside location, this early-18th-century house has much natural charm. Rooms, all en-suite, vary in shape and character and are individually decorated with antiques; the best rooms have river views, but others overlook the gardens and all have original wooden shutters and are thoughtfully furnished, with good attention to detail. Bathrooms vary in style and age, but are appropriately appointed. Public rooms, including a cosy residents' bar, sitting room and conservatory, are unpretentious but comfortable and feature a large personal collection of traditional and modern paintings. In addition to formal lunch and dinner in the restaurant, there is an imaginative bar menu and special afternoon teas are served in the drawing room from 3-7 pm daily. ***Rooms*** *13. Garden, fishing, boating.* AMERICAN EXPRESS *Access, Diners, Visa.*

Kanturk — Assolas Country House 66%

£108

Tel 029 50015 Fax 029 50795

HR

Kanturk Co Cork

Map 23 B5

Set in award-winning gardens reaching down to a picturesque river-bank and home of the Bourke family for several generations, this charming creeper-clad 17th-century house has been run by the current owner, Joe Bourke, and his wife Hazel since 1984. Well-situated, only an hour's drive from Cork, this welcoming family home with its antiques, log fires and excellent housekeeping makes a comfortable base for touring the south-west – Kinsale, Bantry, the Ring of Kerry, Dingle are all easily accessible. No dogs. ***Rooms*** *9 (6 in main house, 3 in courtyard). Garden, tennis, fishing, boating. Closed Nov-mid-Mar. Access, Diners, Visa.*

Restaurant

£65

Deep red walls, well-polished antique tables and uniformed staff provide an elegant background for Hazel Bourke's imaginative use of their own garden and regional produce in menus which change daily and often have seafood as a main course – scallops with a chive beurre blanc, perhaps, or baked fillet of John Dory with a bacon and herb cream sauce. Or local lamb might be roasted and served with Hazel's mint jelly, or venison with wild rowanberry jelly. Desserts like lemon tart or rhubarb fool with vanilla shortbread follow on the trolley, or finish with local farmhouse cheeses. Coffee and petits fours are served in the drawing room. ***Seats*** *30. Private Room 34. D only 7-8.30 (Sun to 8). Set D £25.*

Kenmare — The Old Bank House NEW

£50

Tel 064 41589 Fax 064 41589

RR

Main Street Kenmare Co Kerry

Map 23 A6

Matthew d'Arcy moved across the road from the *Park Hotel* in 1992 to set up in this converted bank and his wife Aileen provides a warm welcome. There's a real fire glowing where the main banking hall used to be and the vault at the back is opened up on busy nights. Staff are informal and friendly and the menu longish and ambitious – Matthew's style is modern classical and *Park* enthusiasts will recognise the signature. Start, perhaps, with an attractive, generous tartlet of mussels, set in a pool of rich prawn sauce, or an unusual soup of seafood and melon – rich, deeply-flavoured, interesting. From a main course selection which spreads its favours very fairly, typical offerings would include roast lamb with a walnut and basil stuffing, honey and thyme sauce – tiny little eyes of loin, cooked pinkish with a rich, complex sauce – or guinea fowl with a herby, crunchy stuffing. Desserts include an excellent orange and Cointreau soufflé. Service can be slow. ***Seats*** *40. D 7-9 (from 5 high season). Closed Sun, Mon & Tues in winter, 25 Dec, 2 weeks Feb. Access, Visa.*

Rooms

£26

Five neat, comfortably furnished rooms are individually decorated in homely style. Smallish bathrooms (some shower only) have plenty of thick towels and toiletries supplied. Sitting room with TV.

Kenmare Packie's NEW

£45

Tel 064 41508 **R**

Henry Street Kenmare Co Kerry **Map 23 A6**

Maura Foley used to cook up the road at The Lime Tree but since 1992 she has been drawing the crowds to her new venture. Packie's is bang up to date: punchy, fashionable food at reasonable prices served in stylish but no-nonsense surroundings: small tables, a big squeeze – but this place has class. The menu encompasses the Californian/Mediterranean influences in dishes like intensely-flavoured bruschetta of sun-dried tomatoes, basil and hand-rolled mozzarella, or home-made pasta in a generous tagliatelle with mussels in cream and garlic or crispy crab and coriander bundles with a light curry sabayon. A high proportion of dishes are interchangeable as starter or main course portions, desserts are good and homely, service informal and swift. Round off with one of a wide choice of teas and coffees. ***Seats** 35. Private Room 15. D only 5.30-10. Closed Sun, Nov-Easter. Access, Visa.*

Kenmare Park Hotel 85%

£210

Tel 064 41200 Fax 064 41402 **HR**

Kenmare Co Kerry **Map 23 A6**

Francis Brennan has not only achieved a reputation for outstanding professionalism for his quietly luxurious Victorian hotel, but his personal attention to detail has ensured a warmth of welcome and hospitality often missing from very grand establishments. It has an enviable situation, with the town to stroll around on one side and the estuary and mountains to admire on the other. There's always a fire in the hall, the whole building, including corridors as well as main public rooms and bedrooms, is filled with a personal and often entertaining collection of antiques and pictures and fresh flowers are everywhere, creating an atmosphere of splendour without pomposity. Public rooms are gracious, with lovely views. Bedrooms vary from nine luxurious suites with large well-equipped bathrooms and all the accessories, through the majority – good, spacious rooms with separate seating areas and well-finished marbled bathrooms – to a few which have shower/WC only. Most rooms have individual heat control. Excellent breakfasts. No dogs. ***Rooms** 50. Garden, tennis, golf (9), games room. Closed mid Nov-22 Dec, 4 Jan-Easter. Access, Visa.*

Restaurant

£85

An elegant high-ceilinged room with beautiful views over the estuary, classic white linen and impeccable table settings lend the perfect background for Jim McCarthy and his efficient staff to provide the exemplary service for which they are famous. Complete redevelopment of the kitchen in 1993 has greatly improved facilities for head chef Brian Cleere and his team, and their aim to make stylish use of local produce remains the driving force. Set menus are changed daily and, although leaning towards local seafood, have plenty of choice. Typically, starters might include fresh asparagus with a light orange sauce or a salad of goat's cheese with tomatoes and a balsamic vinaigrette followed at dinner by a fresh prawn bisque, perhaps. Well-balanced main courses might include simple panfried fillets of sea trout and brill with a lemon butter sauce or baked fillet of salmon on a bed of spinach with a shallot cream sauce, along with choices based on the best meat and poultry. Desserts are beautifully presented and there's a good choice of local farmhouse cheeses. There's a serious wine list with great depth – note the Californian section – though there's little of note under *£20.* ***Seats** 80. Private Room 30. L 1-1.45 D 7-8.45. Set L £17.50 Set D £35.*

Kenmare **Sheen Falls Lodge** 86% £220

Tel 064 41600 Fax 064 41386 **HR**

Kenmare Co Kerry **Map 23 A6**

The setting, high on a promontory, surrounded by woodland and gardens with expansive views of Kenmare Bay on one side and the turbulent waters and rapids of Sheen Falls on the other, is the making of this distinctive yellow-ochre hotel, especially when floodlit at night. Although it is mostly new, part of the original 17th-century house has been retained and worked into an imaginative plan – immediately creating an impression of age in the spacious marbled-columned foyer, for example, which is in the old house and has an impressive fireplace with a log fire burning all year. The same warm atmosphere is created in the other public rooms, notably a well-stocked mahogany-panelled library with green leather chesterfields, a traditional bar and sunny yellow lounge which still has the original stone fireplace and wooden floor. Full advantage is taken of the natural beauty of the site, with every window having its own special view, a feature followed through to the bedrooms, which all overlook the bay or the waterfall. Rooms include 8 suites (one designed for disabled guests) and, while not individually decorated, are all spacious, with extra large beds and fine linen sheets, and are exceptionally well-appointed, with iron and trouser press, fresh fruit, mineral water and personal safe included as standard. Marble bathrooms with gold-plated fittings and twin wash-basins all have enormous towels, bathrobes, slippers, shaving kit and hair dryer. Beside the main building there is also a discreet 3-bedroom apartment, with separate entrance from the grounds, popular for small business conferences, and in the basement an impressive state-of-the-art conference suite, the William Petty Conference Centre, named after the original owner of the land, which has facilities for up to 150, theatre-style. An otherwise well-appointed and luxurious leisure centre is remarkable for having only a post-sauna plunge-pool. ***Rooms** 40. Garden, gymnasium, sauna, spa bath, steam room, solarium, tennis, riding, coarse & game fishing, games room, boutique, helipad. Closed Jan-mid Mar.* AMERICAN EXPRESS *Access, Diners, Visa.*

La Cascade Restaurant £90

Views of the falls, floodlit at night, are an attraction here, but the sophisticated menu is always of interest too. Both a daily table d'hote and an extravagant à la carte are offered and should please even the most discerning diner. Typical starters might include hot foie gras with balsamic vinegar and freshly toasted brioche or saffron-scented seawater consommé with shellfish; main courses continue the theme using expensive ingredients in dishes like fresh scallops panfried on an essence of lobster and Chartreuse or panfried noisettes of lamb with crisp-fried lamb sweetbreads. Local wild Atlantic salmon is cured and smoked on the premises. Finish perhaps with cardamon ice cream with a soup of seasonal fruits scented with allspice and mirabelle. Excellent service to match the setting. Weekday lunch is served in the lounge (oysters, open sandwiches, fish casserole, stir-fried chicken, tasting plate of desserts), followed by afternoon tea (£7.50 3-5pm). The long, long wine list is quite steeply priced – entry price for champagne is £40! ***Seats** 120. Parties 8. Private Room 24. L Sun only 1-2 D 7.30-9.30. Set D from £30.*

Kilcoran **Kilcoran Lodge** 58% £66

Tel 052 41288 Fax 052 41994 **H**

Kilcoran Cahir Co Tipperary **Map 23 C5**

Set in 20 acres of grounds, this former hunting lodge overlooking the Suir Valley was taken over by Waverney Inns, Ireland, just before we went to press. Conference/banqueting facilities for 300/220. ***Rooms** 23. Indoor swimming pool, keep-fit equipment, sauna, spa bath, solarium, riding, coarse & game fishing.* AMERICAN EXPRESS *Access, Diners, Visa.*

Kilkenny **Kilkenny Kitchen** **NEW** **£20**

Tel 056 22118 **R**

Kilkenny Design Centre Castle Street Kilkenny **Map 23 C5**

Situated in beautiful outbuildings opposite the Castle, the Kilkenny Kitchen offers good home cooking on the premises and, in the shape of crusty home-made breads and delicious cakes, also to take away. Both hot and cold meals are much admired for their variety and general wholesomeness – all the more enjoyable when taken in such pleasing surroundings. Afternoon tea, with a slice of cherry flapjack or a finger of buttery shortbread, is delicious. ***Seats** 85. Light meals 9-5 L 12-4 (Sun 10-5). Closed Good Friday, Christmas, Sun Jan-Easter.* AMERICAN EXPRESS *Access, Diners, Visa.*

Kilkenny **Lacken House** **NEW** **£60**

Tel 056 61085 Fax 056 62435 **RR**

Dublin Road Kilkenny Co Kilkenny **Map 23 C5**

Over the last decade Eugene and Breda McSweeney have built up Lacken House to become the leading restaurant in the Kilkenny area. Situated on the edge of the town in a Victorian house with a pleasant, well-proportioned drawing room/bar, the basement restaurant has rather small tables, but the quality of the food is adequate compensation. Eugene uses fresh local produce – much of it organic – in his progressive Irish cooking. The dinner menu offers a well-balanced choice based on the classics but with concessions to current trends, in dishes such as fresh salmon pizza, yellow and grey oyster mushrooms in garlic butter, steamed fillet of salmon Chinese style or breasts of pigeon served with lentils and smoked bacon. A varied Irish farmhouse cheese plate includes local specialities, notably the new Abbey Blue. ***Seats** 35. D only 7-10.30. Closed all Sun & Mon except for residents, 1 week Christmas.* AMERICAN EXPRESS *Access, Diners, Visa.*

Rooms **£55**

Eight rooms, all with shower or bath, provide simple accommodation; children up to 4 stay free in parents' room. Breakfast is excellent.

Kilkenny **Newpark Hotel** **58%** **£90**

Tel 056 22122 Fax 056 61111 **H**

Castlecomer Road Kilkenny Co Kilkenny **Map 23 C5**

Basic bedrooms but a good leisure centre at this 1960s hotel on the N77. Conference/banqueting facilities for 500/400. Children up to 4 free in parents' room. ***Rooms** 60. Indoor swimming pool, children's pool, keep-fit equipment, sauna, spa bath, steam room, solarium, tennis.* AMERICAN EXPRESS *Access, Diners, Visa.*

Kilkenny **Places of Interest**

Tourist Information Tel 056 21755.
Irish National Design Centre Tel 056 22118.
Dunmore Cave Tel 056 67726.
Kilkenny Castle Tel 056 21450.
Jerrpoint Abbey Tel 056 24623.

Killarney **Aghadoe Heights Hotel** **70%** **£136**

Tel 064 31766 Fax 064 31345 **H**

Aghadoe Killarney Co Kerry **Map 23 A5**

Low-rise concrete and glass hotel of 1960s origin has been refurbished in varying styles but to a generally high standard in public areas and the views over Lake Killarney and the mountains beyond are wonderful, especially from the elegantly appointed dining room. Recently expanded

See over

leisure facilities, although conspicuous from the road, do not intrude. Bedrooms and bathrooms are neat, although not large. Conference/banqueting facilities for 130/100. Sister hotel to *Fredrick's* in Maidenhead, England. ***Rooms*** *60. Garden, indoor swimming pool, gymnasium, sauna, spa bath, steam room, solarium, beauty salon, tennis, fishing, boutique, helipad.* AMERICAN EXPRESS *Access, Diners, Visa.*

Killarney — Cahernane Hotel — 66% — £110

Tel 064 31895 Fax 064 34340 — **HR**

Muckross Road Killarney Co Kerry — **Map 23 A5**

Formerly the residence of the Earls of Pembroke, this beautifully situated hotel is set in parkland with wonderful views of Killarney's lakes and mountains. Rooms vary from traditional master bedrooms in the manor house furnished with antiques to the simpler but spacious and well-appointed rooms with good bathrooms in a cleverly integrated new wing. Good porterage and housekeeping and a warm, friendly atmosphere add to a high level of comfort. Children under 12 may stay free in parents' room. ***Rooms*** *52. Garden, hair salon, tennis, pitch & putt, game fishing, boutique. Closed 4 Jan-Easter.* AMERICAN EXPRESS *Access, Diners, Visa.*

Restaurant — £65

There is plenty of variety on chef Eddie Hayes' menus – the table d'hote offers a choice of six starters, main courses and desserts on his five-course menu and there's also a substantial à la carte menu. The style on the set menu tends to be fairly traditional (marinated wild salmon with dill sauce, terrine of woodcock; entrecote steak with roasted shallots, roast saddle of lamb with cream and garlic sauce; vacherin glacé or strawberries Berkoff) while the carte is best described as eclectic, a veritable hotchpotch of influences from a wide variety of cuisines especially, perhaps, modern Italian: fettucine with smoked salmon, exotic fruit plate, escargots porto fieno – snails in port with wild mushrooms, gorgonzola and black pasta – are typical. Finish, perhaps, with a good cheeseboard and hand-made chocolates. A comprehensive wine list with depth – New World well-represented. ***Seats*** *90. Parties 30. Private Room 14. D only 7-9.30. Set D £25.*

Killarney — Hotel Europe — 72% — £84

Tel 064 31900 Fax 064 32118 — **H**

Killorglin Road Fossa Killarney Co Kerry — **Map 23 A5**

Views of lake and mountains are enjoyed from this large, modern hotel and most of the bedrooms have balconies to make the most of the setting. Pine-furnished bedrooms offer a generous amount of space and there is a luxurious penthouse floor. In the same group as *Dunloe Castle* and *Ard-na-Sidhe*, the hotel caters equally well for private guests and conference (up to 500 delegates theatre-style) and there is an excellent health and fitness centre. No dogs. ***Rooms*** *210. Garden, indoor swimming pool, gymnasium, sauna, spa bath, hair salon, tennis, riding. Closed Nov-Mar.* AMERICAN EXPRESS *Access, Diners, Visa.*

Killarney — Gaby's Seafood Restaurant — £50

Tel 064 32519 Fax 064 32747 — **R**

27 High Street Killarney Co Kerry — **Map 23 A5**

Geert Maes, owner-chef at Gaby's since 1976, moved a few doors up the street to a new, larger purpose-built restaurant in 1992 but, except for a change of decor and the benefits of a full bar menu, it's more or less a case of *plus ça change*: Geert is still in the business of taking fresh local fish, cooking it simply and accurately and serving it with a smile. Menus change a little with the times, but specialities remain, in the chef's hot salmon starter, for instance, or a range of cold main courses like Kerry shellfish platter and lobster salad. Finish, perhaps with imaginative home-made ice

creams or a local farmhouse cheese selection. Splendid wine list, with particular emphasis on white burgundies, though good choice elsewhere. Informal menu at lunchtime. ***Seats** 72. L 12.30-2.30 D 6-10.*
Closed all Sun & L Mon, Feb. AMERICAN EXPRESS *Access, Diners, Visa.*

Killarney **Great Southern** **69%** **£129**

Tel 064 31262 Fax 064 31642 **H**

Killarney Co Kerry **Map 23 A5**

Situated close to the town centre, this former railway hotel is a substantial building set in extensive gardens. The entrance hall is impressive, with Ionic columns, chandeliers and a large seating area. Bedrooms vary considerably in size and style; some were refurbished in 1993. Main public areas have also been extensively refurbished recently. Leisure facilities are good and the hotel can take conferences up to 1,000, theatre style. ***Rooms** 183. Garden, indoor swimming pool, sauna, solarium, spa bath, gymnasium, snooker, tennis, hairdressing, baby-sitting. Closed 6 weeks Jan/Feb.* AMERICAN EXPRESS *Access, Diners, Visa.*

Killarney **The Killarney Park Hotel** **73%** **NEW** **£110**

Tel 064 35555 Fax 064 352266 **H**

Kenmare Place Killarney Co Kerry **Map 23 A5**

Although new and very centrally situated, this hotel is pleasantly set in gardens with mature trees and its classical lines and fresh yellow and white colour scheme are easy on the eye. First impressions are carried through to the smart foyer, which is spacious, with fires, plenty of comfortable seating and, in common with most of the other public areas, notably the bar, has a pleasingly bold colour scheme and mixes fabrics with good effect. The restaurant is more restrained and has a cosy area especially appropriate for winter dining. Although not individually furnished, bedrooms are planned in groups to have variety in shape and size as well as colour schemes; all are spacious, several very large and especially suitable for families, and marbled bathrooms are well appointed. Banqueting/conference facilities for 160/150. The leisure centre opens out onto its own furnished patio. No dogs. ***Rooms** 55. (10 non-smoking). Garden, indoor swimming pool, children's pool, gymnasium, keep-fit equipment.* AMERICAN EXPRESS *Access, Diners, Visa.*

Killarney **Killarney Towers Hotel** **57%** **NEW** **£85**

Tel 064 31038 Fax 064 31755 **H**

College Square Killarney Co Kerry **Map 23 A5**

Very centrally located, this new hotel has quite spacious, identical, but comfortably furnished bedrooms with tea-making facilities, multi-channel TV and neat en-suite bathrooms. Two bars include a residents' lounge and the pubby Scruffy's. Lock-up car park. ***Rooms** 102. Access, Visa.*

Killarney **Torc Great Southern** **65%** **£85**

Tel 064 31611 Fax 064 31824 **H**

Park Road Killarney Co Kerry **Map 23 A5**

Modern, low-rise hotel half a mile from the town centre on the main Cork road. Well-run, with views of the Kerry mountains, it makes a good base for a holiday in the area. Improvements in 1993 include the addition of a new bar and refurbishment of 20 bedrooms. ***Rooms** 96. Garden, indoor swimming pool, sauna, tennis. Closed Oct-Mar.* AMERICAN EXPRESS *Access, Diners, Visa.*

Killarney — Places of Interest

Tourist Information Tel 064 31633.
Killarney National Park Tel 064 31947.
Ross Castle Tel 064 32402.
Crag Cave Castle Island Tel 066 41244.

Killiney — Court Hotel — 68% — £97

Tel 01 2851622 Fax 01 2852085 — H

Killiney Bay Killiney Co Dublin — **Map 23 D4**

Half an hour from the city centre by car or DART, this extended Victorian mansion looks over landscaped gardens to Killiney Bay. The most recent additions include a new cocktail bar and conservatory and the reception area has also been enlarged and modernised. Bedrooms, most with sea views, are spacious and pleasantly decorated with darkwood furniture and co-ordinated fabrics; under-12s stay free in parents' room. An international conference centre has facilities for up to 300. No dogs. ***Rooms** 86. Garden.* AMERICAN EXPRESS *Access, Diners, Visa.*

Killiney — Fitzpatrick's Castle — 68% — £147

Tel 01 2851533 Fax 01 2850207 — H

Killiney Co Dublin — **Map 23 D4**

Dating back to 1741 and converted by the present owners in 1974, this imposing castle hotel is half an hour's drive from Dublin city centre and, despite its size and style, has a surprisingly lived-in atmosphere. Extensive facilities include two large lounges, two restaurants, a basement disco and a conference suite for up to 550 delegates. Roomy bedrooms, including some mini-suites, have darkwood furniture and draped curtains. Children under 12 may stay free in parents' room. ***Rooms** 85. Garden, indoor swimming pool, gymnasium, squash, sauna, steam room, hair & beauty salon, tennis.* AMERICAN EXPRESS *Access, Diners, Visa.*

Killiney — Place of Interest

Ayesha Castle Tel 01 2852323.

Killorglin — Nick's Restaurant — £65

Tel 066 61219 Fax 066 61233 — R

Lower Bridge Street Killorglin Co Kerry — **Map 23 A5**

Nick and Anne Foley's popular seafood restaurant always has a good buzz and Nick's cooking, which relies entirely on daily catches for its seafood and local suppliers for lamb, beef and organically grown vegetables, is mainly traditional French. Moules marinière or provençale, grilled salmon steak beurre blanc, shellfish mornay and peppered steak in brandy cream sauce are typical. There are also a couple of vegetarian options – asparagus tips with hollandaise, perhaps, and a stir-fry – a choice of six desserts, changed daily, and a good cheeseboard. Thoughtfully compiled wine list with some tasting notes and good drinking under £20. ***Seats** 80. Parties 50. Private Room 35. D only 6-10. Closed Nov-Easter, Mon & Tues, 25 & 26 Dec.* AMERICAN EXPRESS *Access, Diners, Visa.*

Kinnegad — The Cottage — NEW — £20

Tel 044 75284 — R

Kinnegad Co Westmeath — **Map 22 C3**

A magic spot for a break on the main Dublin-Galway road, this delightfully homely cottage restaurant is in a league of its own, serving real home-made food ranging from the option of proper meals at given times to snacks at any time and a really great afternoon tea – baking is a speciality, with scones and home-made preserves, a wide variety of cakes and irresistible cookies always available. Home-made soups, hot dishes like poached salmon, quiches and omelettes served with salad are all typical, also desserts like apple pie, pavlova or fresh fruit tarts according to season. ***Seats** 30. Parties 14. Private Room 26. L 12-3 D 6-8. Closed D Sat, all Sun, 10 days Christmas. No credit cards.*

Kinsale — Actons Hotel — 60% — £100

Tel 021 772135 Fax 021 772231 — **H**

Pier Road Kinsale Co Cork — **Map 23 B6**

Overlooking the harbour, this attractive quayside hotel was created from several substantial period houses. Conference facilities for up to 400. Forte Heritage. ***Rooms** 57. Indoor swimming pool, gymnasium, sauna, solarium.* AMERICAN EXPRESS® *Access, Diners, Visa.*

Kinsale — Blue Haven Hotel — £84

Tel 021 772209 Fax 021 774268 — **IR**

3 Pearse Street Kinsale Co Cork — **Map 23 B6**

Bedrooms at this small blue-and-white hotel near the quay vary from quite small to reasonably large, but all are neat with smart white furniture and pictures by local artists. Only one has a bath, the rest have showers or share a bathroom. The bar, which serves a wide choice of good food, is very attractive, with wood panelling, natural stone and a log fire, and has lots of cosy corners opening on to a cane-furnished conservatory which, in turn, leads on to a patio. The entrance has been upgraded and a new wine shop/delicatessen opened just off the lobby. No dogs. ***Rooms** 10. Sea fishing, coffee shop (10.30am-11.30pm). Closed 25 Dec.* AMERICAN EXPRESS® *Access, Diners, Visa.*

Restaurant — £60

Overlooking an attractive courtyard garden, the characterful restaurant has a strong maritime theme which leaves the diner with no doubt as to the specialities of the house – and chef Stanley Matthews does not disappoint. Typical starters might include 'Molly Malone', a mixture of mussels and prawns with garlic crumbs, classic coquilles St Jacques or baked oysters glazed with hollandaise, followed by brill and scallop bake or a simply grilled sole on the bone. Seafood is balanced by dishes like rack of lamb, chicken Madeira, steaks and an oriental vegetarian special. Good local farmhouse cheeses. ***Seats** 45. Parties 18. D only 7-10.30. Closed 2 days mid-week Nov-Feb and 25 Dec.*

Kinsale — Chez Jean-Marc — NEW — £55

Tel 021 774625 Fax 021 774680 — **R**

Lower O'Connell Street Kinsale Co Cork — **Map 23 B6**

Formerly the excellent but short-lived *Skippers*. Jean-Marc and Fiona Tsai moved here form Tralee in 1992 and transformed the previous minimalistic decor: the exterior is now a cheerful yellow with deep-blue paint work, the interior restored to its natural cottagey style. Open beams and stonework, decorative china and gentle country colours, notably dark green and, on the tables, deep peony red, create a warm ambience, echoed by the friendly welcome and efficient service. Jean-Marc's skilful cooking is an unusual blend of classical French and oriental styles – and, aware of visitors' interest in the food of the country, he also offers a 'Taste of Ireland' set dinner at £18 (except Saturday night). A typical dinner from the carte might start with millefeuille of crispy vegetables with 'Chinese' drumsticks – a large, varied and very crisp vegetable stir-fry, topped with a wisp of crisp puff pastry and surrounded by a guard of tender, caramelised drumsticks, dramatically presented on a very large plate. Follow, perhaps with home-made fettucine with clams, mussels and salmon marinated in fresh thyme – a huge bowl of seafood with a layer of fresh pasta at the base to soak up its juices and a fresh parmesan and basil sauce forked

See over

through it. Desserts are simple in concept – ices, soufflés – but witty and dramatic in presentation. Good house selection of 10 wines at £12.50. ***Seats** 55. L (Sun only, low season) 12.30-3 D 6.45-10.30 (winter 7-10). Closed Sun (summer) D Sun, all Mon (winter), 3 days Christmas, 15 Feb-15 Mar.* AMERICAN EXPRESS *Access, Diners, Visa.*

Kinsale Man Friday NEW £55

Tel 021 772260 **R**

Scilly Kinsale Co Cork **Map 23 B6**

High up over the harbour, this popular, characterful restaurant is housed in a series of rooms and is much larger than it seems. Seafood is the speciality, but there's a very wide choice. Typical starters include Crusoe's warm salad, a huge mixed leaf salad with very crispy croutons and bacon and scampi served with sweet and sour sauce, a generous serving of large fresh Dublin Bay prawns with a piquant dipping sauce. Main courses may include escalopes of monkfish with a light chive and mustard sauce, turbot à la bretonne, served stuffed with prawns, crab and leeks with a white wine sauce – or an excellent black sole on the bone, simply grilled. Duck, steak and lamb are all regular alternatives to seafood. Simple, well-presented desserts include good ice creams. Efficient service. ***Seats** 80. Private Room 35. L by arrangement only (groups) D 7-10. Closed Sun (Nov-Mar), 24-26 Dec.* AMERICAN EXPRESS *Access, Visa.*

Kinsale Max's Wine Bar £40

Tel 021 772443 **R**

Main Street Kinsale Co Cork **Map 23 B6**

Wendy Tisdall has run this delightful little restaurant for 18 years and, despite improvements including the addition of a conservatory, it remains reassuringly unchanged and never ceases to charm. Highly varnished table tops reflect fresh flowers and plants and creative menus are always light and tempting. Starters and salads are especially interesting and many people make a meal from a selection which might typically include grilled mussels with garlic butter and breadcrumbs, spinach pasta with fresh salmon, lamb's brains with capers in black butter and Caesar salad. Seafood is strong, as in monkfish chunks simmered in white wine, with cream and tarragons, but carnivores and vegetarians are well looked after too. The early bird menu is especially good value. ***Seats** 40. Parties 12. L 1-3 D 7-10.30. Closed Nov-Feb. Set D £12. Access, Visa.*

Kinsale The Old Bank House NEW £53

Tel 021 774075 **PH**

Pearse Street Kinsale Co Cork **Map 23 B6**

Right in the centre of Kinsale, Marie and Michael Riese offer classy individually furnished rooms, all en-suite. Amenities include direct-dial phone and multi-channel TV in all rooms and there's a nice range of toiletries in the well-finished bathrooms. Good antiques and quality fabrics are used throughout and there's a very pleasant residents' sitting room. Good breakfast. ***Rooms** 9. Garden. Closed 3 days at Christmas.* AMERICAN EXPRESS *Access, Visa.*

Kinsale Old Presbytery £36

Tel 021 772027 **RR**

Cork Street Kinsale Co Cork **Map 23 B6**

Ken and Cathleen Buggy offer peace and comfort in abundance in this unusual house. Its most striking feature is their personal collection of antiques, many of particular rural interest, and all of which have to find a home somewhere, whether hanging from the ceiling in the dining room, perched on a landing at the turn of the stairs or in one of the bedrooms. There is a comfortable sitting room with an open fire and very individual bedrooms have big beds and fresh linen, most with en suite facilities. An enjoyable breakfast may be taken in the conservatory. No children under 14. No dogs. ***Rooms** 6. Closed 1 week Christmas. No credit cards.*

Dining Room £38

The old kitchen has been turned into a small restaurant, giving residents a change from the rich offerings of Kinsale's many eating houses. Ken Buggy is a confident cook and his menu changes daily, depending mostly on the catch of the day as local seafood is a speciality. Particularly good bread. ***Seats** 14. D only 7.30-8.30. Closed Sun, 1 week Christmas. Set D £13.*

Kinsale Scilly House 65% NEW £80

Tel 021 772413 **H**

Scilly Kinsale Co Cork **Map 23 B6**

Bill Skelly and Californian Karin Young's stylish old house overlooking the harbour has a very country American feel, with lots of old pine furniture, antiques, traditional quilting and good local paintings. Bright, airy and immaculately maintained, Scilly House has fine public rooms including a bar/library with grand piano, a second cosy sitting room and dining room with views over the extensive garden down to the sea. Splendid bedrooms, nearly all with views, have great individuality and good bathrooms. Breakfast, which can be served in the garden, has an original Californian bias. ***Rooms** 7 (2 non-smoking). Closed Dec-Feb.* AMERICAN EXPRESS *Access, Visa.*

Kinsale Place of Interest

Charles Fort Tel 021 772263.

Leighlinbridge The Lord Bagenal Inn £45

Tel 0503 21668 **R**

Leighlinbridge Co Carlow **Map 23 C4**

Over the last decade this famous old inn has built up a formidable reputation for good food, interesting wines and hospitality. Whether you need to break a journey for a snack or a quick meal, take Sunday lunch with the family or have a special evening out, the Lord Bagenal can provide something appropriate, ranging from excellent home-made patés, through prime local steaks to seafood from the nearby Wexford coast and wild Slaney salmon. Good farmhouse cheeses. An interesting list of wines under £12.50 completes a well-balanced list with helpful tasting notes and fair prices. ***Seats** 90. Parties 25. Private Room 40. L 12.30-2.30 D 6-10.30 (bar food 12.30-10.30). Closed 25 Dec, Good Friday. Set L £9 Set D £17.50. Access, Diners, Visa.*

Letterfrack Rosleague Manor 72% £90

Tel 095 41101 Fax 095 41168 **HR**

Letterfrack Connemara Co Galway **Map 22 A3**

Character and charm are major attractions at this delightfully situated Georgian house in 30 acres of landscaped gardens overlooking Ballinakill Bay. Family-owned and managed by siblings Paddy and Anne Foyle, it has all the amenities expected of a small first-class hotel – central heating, peat fires, good bathrooms, suites, fine antique furniture and paintings – and a great deal more. Most bedrooms are large, with separate seating areas or full suites and public rooms – two drawing rooms and a leafy black and white-tiled conservatory bar – are comfortably furnished with style and elegance. But it is the special warmth and friendliness of the owners and their staff which keeps so many guests returning. ***Rooms** 20. Garden, sauna, tennis, billiards, sea & coarse fishing. Closed Nov-Easter. Access, Visa.*

See over

Restaurant **£60**

Round antique tables, glittering chandeliers and a lovely outlook on bright summer evenings create the right ambience for Nigel Rush's short but well-balanced fixed-priced four-course menus. The best of local ingredients, including fresh fruit, vegetables and herbs from their own garden, provide the starting point for dishes like baked devilled crab, or smoked trout mousse with smoked salmon followed by a choice of soups and main courses such as medallions of monkfish with garlic and pine kernels, poached wild salmon or rack of Connemara lamb. Irish farmhouse cheeses, good home-made ice creams and desserts like hot marinated berries gratinated with Grand Marnier or a superb rhubarb tart round off the meal. No children under 10 for dinner. ***Seats** 60. Parties 8. Private Room 10. L 1-2.30 D 8-9.30 (Sun to 9). Set D from £23.*

Letterfrack Place of Interest

Kylemore Abbey Connemara Tel 095 41146.

Limerick Castletroy Park Hotel 73% NEW **£124**

Tel 061 335566 Fax 061 331117 **H**

Dublin Road Limerick **Map 23 B5**

Despite its somewhat forbidding appearance from the road, this new red brick hotel has a warm and welcoming atmosphere in all the public areas and, although not individually decorated, the attractive rooms are thoughtfully furnished with special attention to the needs of the business traveller, with second phone, fax and computer points. Twenty rooms are designated non-smoking and there are two especially equipped for disabled guests. The purpose-built, up-to-the-minute conference centre is designed to cope equally well with a small board meeting or conference for 450 and you can have a complete cardio-vascular check-up at the well-equipped leisure centre. On a social note, the *Merry Pedlar Pub* aims to get away from the usual hotel bar atmosphere and features regular live traditional Irish music sessions. Children under 12 may stay free in parents' room. No dogs. ***Rooms** 107. Garden, indoor swimming pool, children's pool, keep-fit equipment, sauna, spa bath, solarium, massage, aromatherapy, reflexology. Closed 25 & 26 Dec.* AMERICAN EXPRESS *Access, Diners, Visa.*

Limerick Greenhills Hotel 57% **£69**

Tel 061 53033 Fax 061 53307 **H**

Ennis Road Limerick Co Limerick **Map 23 B5**

The Greene family own and manage this friendly hotel just 5 minutes from the city and 20 minutes from Shannon airport. The health and leisure complex is a major attraction, but the hotel also caters well for the business community (conferences up to 350, banquets 300) and is well situated for touring a wide area from the lakes of Killarney to Galway. Under 12s may stay free in parents' room. ***Rooms** 60. Garden, indoor swimming pool, children's pool, gymnasium, sauna, spa bath, steam room, solarium, beauty salon, tennis. Closed 25 Dec.* AMERICAN EXPRESS *Access, Diners, Visa.*

Limerick Jurys Hotel 66% **£113**

Tel 061 327777 Fax 061 326400 **H**

Ennis Road Limerick **Map 23 B5**

Recently refurbished throughout, this low-rise 1960s hotel is set in 5 acres of gardens on the banks of the Shannon. Attractive conference facilities can cater for up to 150 (banquets 120) and there is a good health and leisure centre, including a separate children's pool. Rooms are decorated to a high standard with neat bathrooms; children under 14 may stay free in their parents' room. ***Rooms** 96. Garden, indoor swimming pool, gymnasium, sauna, steam room, sun bed, tennis, coffee shop. Closed 24 & 25 Dec.* AMERICAN EXPRESS *Access, Diners, Visa.*

Limerick Limerick Inn 66%

£115

Tel 061 326666 Fax 061 326281

H

Ennis Road Limerick

Map 23 B5

The Ryan family owns this sprawling modern hotel a few miles out of town on the Shannon airport road. Recent refurbishment has seen improvements in the lobby area, which now includes a lounge, and 20 bedrooms have been upgraded to Executive standard. In addition, some of the conference rooms have been totally refurbished. There is also a popular health and leisure centre; children up to 12 may stay free in their parents' room. ***Rooms*** *153. Garden, indoor swimming pool, gymnasium, sauna, solarium, whirlpool bath, tennis, putting, snooker, coffee shop (7.30am -11pm). Closed 25 Dec.* AMERICAN EXPRESS *Access, Diners, Visa.*

Limerick Two Mile Inn 60%

£78

Tel 061 326255 Fax 061 453783

H

Ennis Road Limerick

Map 23 B5

A long single-storey building just outside the city on the N19; the most striking feature of this modern hotel is its pyramid-shaped roof. Bedroom wings surround a neat garden and many rooms have recently been refurbished. Entertainment is a major attraction: a big complex features cabaret artists and bands and there is also a popular discotheque. No dogs. ***Rooms*** *125. Garden. Closed 24-26 Dec.* AMERICAN EXPRESS *Access, Diners, Visa.*

Limerick Places of Interest

Tourist Information Tel 061 317522.
City Gallery of Art Tel 061 310663.
King John's Castle Tel 061 411201.

Malahide Bon Appétit

£80

Tel 01 845 0314

R

9 St James Terrace Malahide Dublin

Map 22 D3

Only 15 minutes from Dublin airport, Bon Appétit attracts a regular clientele to its elegant Georgian terrace setting overlooking the estuary. Aperitifs are served in the ground-floor drawing room/bar – notable for some pleasing local watercolours, and the cosy restaurant, decorated in warm tones of red and dark green, is in the basement. Here, chef/patron Patsy McGuirk serves classical French food based on top-quality local ingredients, especially luxury seafood in dishes such as Wexford crab claws in butter sauce or Dover sole (Creation McGuirk – a whole boned sole stuffed with turbot, prawns and mushrooms in a white wine sauce, baked in the oven). ***Seats*** *55. Private Room 24. L 12.30-2 D 7-11. Closed L Sat, all Sun, Bank Holidays, 1 week Christmas. Set L £10 Set D £20.* AMERICAN EXPRESS *Access, Diners, Visa.*

Malahide Roches Bistro

£55

Tel 01 845 2777

R

12 New Street Malahide Co Dublin

Map 22 D3

Family-run by sisters Orla Roche and Niamh Boylan, this is probably nearest to a French local restaurant to be found in Co Dublin. Set in Malahide's attractive main street, it's a small, intimate place with cheerful blue and white check linen and an open fire in winter. The wide-ranging set menus change daily and show a strong bias towards French country cooking and lots of seafood dishes – all cooked in an open kitchen, watched by guests taking an aperitif or coffee at the dividing bar. Go for specialities like crab soufflé à la crème or seafood pancakes or try an unusual combination like monkfish with fresh mint. Meat-lovers will find strip loin steak with pink and green peppercorns thick, tender and piquant.

See over

Apple and frangipane tart is a speciality and there's a good selection of farmhouse cheeses, then as much freshly brewed coffee as you like. The short French wine list is mostly under £20. ***Seats** 35. Parties 30. Private Room 36. L 12-2.30 D 7-10.30. Closed L Mon Jan-Jun, D Mon-Wed, all Sun, Bank Holidays, 2 weeks Jan. Set L £9.95 Set D £18.95.* AMERICAN EXPRESS *Access, Diners, Visa.*

Mallow — Longueville House — 72% — £110

Tel 022 47156 Fax 022 47459 — **HR**

Mallow Co Cork — **Map 23 B5**

A handsome Georgian house built in 1720, Longueville has been run as a hotel since 1969 by Michael O'Callaghan and his family, descendants of the original occupants. While grandly proportioned, this gracious house has an easy informality which makes it seem natural to be surrounded by gilt-framed mirrors, family portraits and impressive fireplaces with log fires burning. Bedrooms are stylishly furnished with antiques, good fabrics and thoughtfully equipped modern bathrooms. Very attractive half-board rates; friendly, helpful staff. No dogs. ***Rooms** 16. Garden, game & coarse fishing, games room, snooker. Closed 20 Dec-28 Feb.* AMERICAN EXPRESS *Access, Diners, Visa.*

Presidents' Restaurant — £65

Portraits of all the previous presidents of Ireland take pride of place in this elegant, high-ceilinged room – a fitting backdrop for William O'Callaghan's creative, imaginative cooking. Well-balanced set menus offer a sensibly limited choice, augmented by a short à la carte. Produce from their private fishing on the Blackwater and his father's farm and gardens supplies most of William's needs in the kitchen, an appropriate beginning for starters such as charlotte of vegetables and Longueville lamb fillet, a substantial dish with slivers of lean tender lamb and courgette batons bound with tomato concassé and wrapped in tender spinach, laid on a lovely pool of vinaigrette with snipped chives and saffron strands threaded through it, gradually releasing its rich colour in swirling patterns. Follow this, perhaps, with a poached fillet of John Dory, set on a little bed of bright green spinach and surrounded by a slightly acid sorrel sauce simply served on a plain white plate. Garden vegetables, served in little bouquets, are what they claim to be and have great depth of flavour. Desserts often come from the garden too, as in a delicious hot rhubarb and raspberry soup, with a scoop of home-made vanilla ice cream gently melting into it. Irish farmhouse cheeses are excellent and home-made chocolates and petits fours come with the coffee. ***Seats** 80. Parties 15. Private Room 20. L 12.30-2 D 7-9. Set L £14 Set D £24.*

Maynooth — Moyglare Manor — 77% — £110

Tel 01 628 6351 Fax 01 628 5405 — **HR**

Moyglare Maynooth Co Kildare — **Map 23 C4**

At the end of a tree-lined avenue, this impressive Georgian house just west of Dublin overlooks hundreds of acres of parkland and mountains. Renowned for its period decor, the family-owned hotel has been run by Norah Devlin since 1983 and its impressive public rooms are filled with antiques, paintings, mirrors and flowers. The marble fireplace in the bar has a peat fire burning and there's an attractive sun lounge with ruched blinds and rattan furniture. Rooms are also furnished in period style, many with four-poster or half-tester beds, but all the modern comforts are provided, including good bathrooms. No children under 12. No dogs. ***Rooms** 17. Garden, tennis. Closed 3 days Christmas.* AMERICAN EXPRESS *Access, Diners, Visa.*

Restaurant — £70

Candlelight and traditional furnishings set the tone for dishes like smoked salmon stuffed with shrimps and mayonnaise or panfried John Dory with lemon and butter, followed perhaps by roast free-range duckling with orange sauce or roast brace of quail with chestnut stuffing and burgundy sauce. Lunch menus are simpler, but also favour seafood and game in season. There's an amazing collection of Bordeaux, good burgundies and Rhone on a list that's short in the New World. ***Seats** 80. Private Room 50. L 12.30-2.30 D 7-9 (Sun to 8.30). Closed L Sat. Set L £9.95 Set D £21.*

Monkstown Mr Hung's

£64

Tel 01 2843982

R

5a The Crescent Monkstown Co Dublin

Map 23 D4

Standard Western-style Cantonese cooking is popular with locals at this comfortable, well-appointed and friendly restaurant. Typical offerings include starters like spare ribs, pancake roll or stuffed crab claws; chicken, beef and seafood dishes, sizzling or otherwise, can be good main courses. ***Seats** 80. L 12.30-2.30 D 6-12.30. Closed L Mon-Thu, all Sun, Good Friday, 25 & 26 Dec.* AMERICAN EXPRESS *Access, Diners, Visa.*

Mountrath Roundwood House 58%

£64

Tel 0502 32120

HR

Mountrath Co Laois

Map 23 C4

Secluded in mature woods of lime, beech and chestnut, this Palladian villa from the early Georgian period offers something special to the visitor with a sense of history and, perhaps, a sense of humour: do not expect 'every modern convenience' and you will not be disappointed. Instead, enjoy staying in an unspoilt, characterful old house with shutters on the windows of the old-fashioned bedrooms instead of curtains and hot water bottles laid out ready in your bathroom. Children, who will love the unusual animals and their young in the back yard, are free in parents' room under 3; tea at 6.30. ***Rooms** 6. Garden.* AMERICAN EXPRESS *Access, Diners, Visa.*

Restaurant

£60

Rosemarie Kennan's food suits the house perfectly – good interesting cooking without unnecessary frills – and Frank is a good host. Sunday lunch is especially good value. ***Seats** 26. Parties 16. L Sun only at 1.30 D at 8.30. Set L £11 Set D £19.*

Moycullen Cloonabinnia House Hotel 61% NEW

£50

Tel 091 85555 Fax 091 85640

H

Ross Lake Moycullen Co Galway

Map 23 B4

Situated in landscaped gardens overlooking Ross Lake, this unpretentious 1960s hotel owes its charm to the warmth and genuine hospitality of the Kavanagh family. Nora-Anne, a former BIM (Irish Fisheries Board) demonstrator, supervises the kitchen personally, Tommy runs the atmospheric bar, popular with locals and guests alike and often the scene for much talk of fishing and son Cathal looks after the restaurant. Public areas generally are a homely mixture of old and new, with comfort and a relaxed atmosphere the key-notes. Modest bedrooms are all en-suite, with lovely views; function rooms (conferences 300/banquets 240) are downstairs, well away from residents and with a separate entrance. Four rooms are designated non-smoking. ***Rooms** 14. Garden, fishing, hunting, shooting. Closed Nov-Mar. Access, Visa.*

Moycullen Drimcong House Restaurant ★

£60

Tel 091 85115

R

Moycullen Co Galway

Map 23 B4

The world has been beating a path to the door of much-feted restaurateurs Gerry and Marie Galvin at Drimcong since 1984 and interest in this very fine restaurant shows no sign of abating. Enjoy a drink in the relaxing, book-filled bar before settling down at a polished oak table for dinner. Gerry's inventive, imaginative cooking puts a modern accent on classical skills and both 5-course table d'hote and à la carte menus change regularly

See over

according to the best produce available. Local seafood, Connemara lamb, free-range poultry and game in season all feature regularly in dashing starters like game sausage with couscous and chutney sauce, grilled oysters with garlic and gruyère or seafood stir-fir. Chinese broth might be offered as an alternative to mussel soup and typical main courses could include grilled fillet of beef with polenta and mushroom sauce, panfried venison with onion marmalade and red vermouth sauce or an unusual vegetarian option such as avocado and blue cheese with filo pastry and sweet pepper compote. Desserts are wide-ranging – a fruit sorbet and its purée, hot steamed lemon and raspberry pudding – and there's an excellent farmhouse cheeseboard. Children are made especially welcome.There are separate menus for vegetarians (5-course £15.50) and children (3-course £8.50). ***Seats** 50. Private Room 32. D only 7-10.30. Closed Sun, Mon, Bank Hols, Jan & Feb. Set D £14.95.* AMERICAN EXPRESS *Access, Diners, Visa.*

Mullingar Crookedwood House £55

Tel 044 72165 Fax 044 72166 **R**

Crookedwood Mullingar Co Meath **Map 22 C3**

Noel and Julie Kenny give the lie to any suggestion that the Irish Midlands are a culinary desert in this very attractive, welcoming and professional restaurant. Noel bases his seasonal menu firmly on the best of local produce in delicious starters like sauté of duck livers with raspberry and red wine sauce or potato pancake with garlic butter and chives. Soup – cream of leek, perhaps, or Atlantic fish – and sorbet to follow on the 6-course dinner menu, then main courses like loin of venison and wild duck in a red wine sauce with grapes and bacon or a vegetarian option like rösti with creamed mushrooms. Finish perhaps with a luscious chocolate gateau or a cheeseboard of Irish farmhouse cheeses and Stilton. ***Seats** 35. Parties 14. Private Room 35. L (Sun only) 12.30-2 D 7-10. Closed D Sun & Mon, Bank Holidays, 2 weeks Oct. Set L £13 Set D £17.* AMERICAN EXPRESS *Access, Diners, Visa.*

Changes in data sometimes occur in establishments after the Guide goes to press. Prices should be taken as indications rather than firm quotes.

Navan Ardboyne Hotel 60% £75

Tel 046 23119 Fax 046 22355 **HR**

Dublin Road Navan Co Meath **Map 22 C3**

Standing in its own grounds on the outskirts of town, the Ardboyne is a well-run modern hotel with a thriving conference and function trade (conference/banqueting facilities for 700/400). The bar is cosy and convivial, with dark timbers, deep red seating, an open fire and low lighting, while the lounge is bright and welcoming, with fresh flowers and plenty of comfortable seats. Simple, well-equipped bedrooms have fitted furniture, good desk/dressing table space and compact, tiled bathrooms. High standard of housekeeping. No dogs. ***Rooms** 27. Garden, coffee shop (7am-10pm), disco (Fri & Sat). Closed 24-27 Dec.* AMERICAN EXPRESS *Access, Diners, Visa.*

Terrace Restaurant £55

This attractive, busy restaurant serves simple, unpretentious food and does it well. The carvery is their speciality and serves quality local meats to any degree of 'doneness', but don't overlook dishes like steak and Guinness casserole. Particularly good desserts from the buffet. ***Seats** 150. Private Room 50. L 12.30-2.30 D 5.30-10 (Sun till 9). Set L £6.50/£9.50 Set D £11.95/£16.95.*

Navan Place of Interest

Hill of Tara Tel 046 25903.

Newbawn — Cedar Lodge — 62% — £75

Tel 051 28386 Fax 051 28222 — H

Carrigbyrne Newbawn Co Wexford — Map 23 C5

14 miles from Wexford on the main Rosslare-Waterford road, this family-run hotel stands in lush countryside beneath the slopes of Carrigbyrne Forest. Red brick walls, wooden ceilings and open fires create a warm and welcoming atmosphere in the public rooms and paintings and frescos by local artists provide interesting focal points. Bedrooms are practical and neatly-appointed. Conference/function suite for up to 100 (banquets 70) in adjoining low-rise wings. ***Rooms** 18. Garden. Closed 25 & 26 Dec, Jan. Access, Visa.*

Newbawn — Place of Interest

John F Kennedy Arboretum Tel 051 88195.

Newbay — Newbay Country House — NEW — £60

Tel 053 42779 Fax 053 46318 — PH

Newbay nr Wexford Co Wexford — Map 23 D5

Conveniently situated close to the ferry port of Rosslare, the Drum family's large early-19th-century house is both impressive and relaxed with a lofty hall, an elegant, shallow staircase, imposingly proportioned drawing and dining rooms and a fascinating collection of antiques, including many curiosities. Bedrooms vary, but all are large, individually furnished, with four-posters, Mientje's original dried flower arrangements, en-suite facilities and views over gardens and countryside. Although the proportions of the house demand a somewhat grand style, this is a family home so don't expect hotel-type facilities such as phones and televisions in rooms. Dinner, for residents only and taken at one large table, is cooked by Paul and of a very high standard although there is no choice; pre-dinner drinks, coffee and petits fours are served in the drawing room. ***Rooms** 6. Garden. Closed mid Nov-mid Mar except for groups. Access, Diners, Visa.*

Newbridge — Hotel Keadeen — 68% — £85

Tel 045 31666 Fax 045 34402 — H

Ballymany Newbridge Co Kildare — Map 23 C4

Set in 8 acres of fine landscaped gardens, this hotel is well back from the main road, just south of the town and quite near the Curragh racecourse. Extensive conference and banqueting facilities cater for anything from 5 to 500 people. Well-furnished and maintained throughout; the best public area is probably the main bar, decorated in rustic style with plenty of quiet corners. Good-sized bedrooms are furnished in a variety of styles. ***Rooms** 37. Garden. Closed 25-27 Dec.* AMERICAN EXPRESS *Access, Diners, Visa.*

Newmarket-on-Fergus — Clare Inn Hotel — 64% — £70

Tel 061 368161 Fax 061 368622 — H

Dromoland Newmarket-on-Fergus Co Clare — Map 23 B4

This low-rise modern hotel is built on a hilltop, in the grounds of Dromoland Castle and shares the castle's 18-hole golf course. Public areas are spacious and well-kept, including a well-equipped leisure centre and conference facilities for up to 400. Bedrooms are functional but large, bathrooms rather cramped; there are some decorative variations between rooms and family rooms sleep up to four – children up to 12 stay free in parents' room. Sea angling can be arranged from the hotel's boat, *Lady Christeen*. ***Rooms** 121. Garden, indoor swimming pool, gymnasium, sauna, spa bath, solarium, pitch & putt, games room, coffee shop (2.30pm-10pm).* AMERICAN EXPRESS *Access, Diners, Visa.*

Newmarket-on-Fergus Dromoland Castle 78% £208

Tel 061 368144 Fax 061 363355 **HR**

Newmarket-on-Fergus Co Clare **Map 23 B4**

Set in a 375-acre estate, complete with 18-hole golf course, this 19th-century castle has a full complement of towers and crenallations yet, despite its undeniably impressive character, has a relaxed and surprisingly intimate atmosphere. Family portraits line the walls, creating a sense of continuity with Dromoland's long history as a family home (going back to Brian Boru, High King of Ireland, who died at the Battle of Clontarf in 1014) and, since 1963, as a hotel. Although elegant and high-ceilinged, with gilded Gothic cornices and glittering chandeliers, even the major public rooms are on a human scale, comfortably furnished and comfortable to be in – a feeling enhanced by the aroma of woodsmoke which wafts around the castle from its innumerable log fires. Bedrooms vary considerably in size, aspect and outlook, but all are decorated with a pleasing combination of style and restraint; some are due for refurbishment, with a few bathrooms perhaps overdue, so it may be wise to inquire – but generally both rooms and bathrooms are finished to a high standard, with many thoughtful extras. A new wing, built to match the castle, was opened in 1993 and includes the Brian Boru Hall, with banqueting/conference seating for 450. Children up to 12 stay free in parents' rooms. No dogs. ***Rooms** 73. Garden, golf, riding, fishing, tennis, snooker.* AMERICAN EXPRESS *Access, Diners, Visa.*

The Earl of Thomond £100

Jean-Baptiste Molinari provides a sophisticated French menu appropriate to the elegance of the setting: through the length of the interconnecting rooms which form the restaurant, huge chandeliers hang from a soft blue, gold-corniced ceiling, the colours echoed in magnificent drapes and accented by Coalport china with deep blue and gold rims. Tables are well-spaced and music provided by a duo of harpist and fiddler adds to the sense of occasion. Service is efficient, without pomposity. The main menu is an extensive 5-course affair, starting with an appetiser of, perhaps, a little fish quenelle set in a pool of wine sauce, followed by a choice of four first courses, typically including a salade gourmande of mixed leaves and, perhaps, confit of goose and calf's sweetbreads, or a steamed selection of the day's catch, served with lightly cooked vegetables tossed in a parsley vinaigrette. Soups may offer a choice of a deeply-flavoured beef consommé or a rich Provençal fish soup with rouille. Four main courses will include at least one fish dish, something simple – rack of lamb, perhaps – to appeal to conservative tastes and a confidently-executed French flourish such as a confit of leg and breast of duck accompanied by 'pommes grenaille', garnished with chopped truffles. Accompanying locally grown organic vegetables may include lesser known varieties such as salsify or scorzonera. A wide choice of desserts ranges from classics such as crème brulée to original locally-inspired inventions like Baileys-flavoured sailing boats on a sea of orange (the mousse boats topped by chocolate sails and set in an intensely orange sauce). Alternatively, there is a good cheeseboard, well-balanced between French and local Irish farmhouse cheeses. Good petits fours and a choice of freshly brewed coffee, tea or tisanes to finish. Mostly French wines on a pricy and extensive list that's light on half bottles. ***Seats** 90. Parties 10. L 12.30-2 D 7.30-10. Set L £18 Set D £32.*

Newport Newport House 67% £116

Tel 098 41222 Fax 098 41613 **HR**

Newport Co Mayo **Map 22 A3**

Kieran and Thelma Thompson's creeper-clad Georgian house stands in large gardens adjoining the town and overlooking the Newport river and quay – an unusual location for one of the most attractive and hospitable country houses in Ireland. Fishing is the major attraction, with salmon and sea trout fishing on the river and nearby loughs. Golf, horseriding and pony trekking are also available locally, but the appeal of the house itself with its beautiful central hall, sweeping staircase and gracious drawing room is enough to draw guests without sporting interests. Bedrooms, like the rest of the house, are furnished in style with antiques and fine paintings and bathrooms which can be eccentric but work well. The day's catch is weighed and displayed in the hall and a cosy fisherman's bar provides the perfect venue for a reconstruction of the day's sport. ***Rooms** 20. Garden, sea & game fishing, snooker. Closed 7 Oct-18 Mar.* AMERICAN EXPRESS *Access, Visa.*

Restaurant

£60

A high-ceilinged dining room overlooking the gardens and decorated in restrained period style provides an elegant setting for John Gavin's confident cooking, based on the best of local produce, much of it coming from the organically-worked walled kitchen garden. Salmon, home-smoked by Owen Mullins who has been at Newport since 1946, makes a perfect starter on a 6-course dinner menu, followed by soup and, perhaps, escalope of monkfish with julienne of vegetables and vermouth sauce or charcoal-grilled sirloin steak with red wine butter. Vegetables and salad are as fresh as it is possible to be and there's a choice of farmhouse cheese or a fine dessert menu to finish. An amazing wine list has good house recommendations and a huge selection of French wines (especially clarets and Rhones). ***Seats** 39. Parties 16. D only 7.30-9.30. Set D £27.*

Oughterard — Connemara Gateway Hotel 65%

£100

Tel 091 82328 Fax 091 82332

H

Oughterard Co Galway

Map 22 B3

Originally a 1960s motel, this building has been systematically improved over the years and now conceals some characterful public areas, especially the foyer with its old pine boarding and the bar, where a surprisingly rural atmosphere has been created through choice of furnishings and agricultural memorabilia. Open turf fires are welcoming and an abundance of fresh and dried flower arrangements bring colour and add interest throughout, as does the work of local artists and sculptors. Bedrooms are variable, the best having co-ordinated floral schemes, tweedy bedcovers and well-finished bathrooms. Good children's facilities. Golf available nearby. Conference/banqueting for 100/150. ***Rooms** 62. Garden, indoor swimming pool, sauna, solarium, snooker, tennis. Closed Jan (usually).* AMERICAN EXPRESS *Access, Visa.*

Oughterard — Currarevagh House 65%

£78

Tel 091 82313 Fax 091 82731

HR

Oughterard Co Galway

Map 22 B3

An early-Victorian manor house set in parkland, woods and gardens beside Lough Corrib, Currarevagh has been in the family for five generations and the current owners, Harry and June Hodgson, run it as a country house, with the emphasis on old-fashioned hospitality and service. Traditionally furnished day rooms have a warm, homely appeal and afternoon tea, served in the garden or drawing room, is a time-honoured ritual. Bedrooms are peaceful, with no phones or TVs. The hotel has sporting rights over 5000 acres and fishing facilities that include boats and ghillies. ***Rooms** 15. Garden, tennis, fishing, mooring, swimming, hotel boats. Closed Nov-Mar. No credit cards.*

Restaurant

£50

June Hodgson bases her cooking firmly of the best of fresh local ingredients, with simplicity the keynote of her no-choice five-course dinner menu: game broth to start, perhaps, followed by prawns in garlic butter and rack of lamb with honey and Guinness with potato loaves and stir-fry vegetables. Black cherry brulée, then Irish farmhouse cheeses to finish. Helpful notes on a carefully compiled wine list; note the bin ends. No smoking. Snack lunches. ***Seats** 28. D only at 8. Set D £17.50.*

Oughterard — Sweeny's Oughterard House — 59% — £98

Tel 091 82207 Fax 091 82161 — **H**

Oughterard Co Galway — **Map 22 B3**

An attractive 200 year-old roadside house on the Clifden side of the town, prettily situated opposite the river and surrounded by mature trees, Sweeny's has been owner-run by the Higgins family for several generations. The comfortable, cottagey public rooms are furnished with antiques and bedrooms vary considerably; some have four-posters. Fishing is the main attraction, but there are plenty of other outdoor pursuits including the gentler pleasures of scenic driving and taking tea on the lawn. Children under 12 may stay free in their parents' room. ***Rooms** 20. Garden, patio. Closed 4 weeks Dec/Jan.* AMERICAN EXPRESS *Access, Diners, Visa.*

Oughterard — Place of Interest

Aughnanure Castle Tel 091 82214.

Oysterhaven — The Oystercatcher — £65

Tel 021 770822 — **R**

Oysterhaven Co Cork — **Map 23 B6**

Bill and Sylvia Patterson run this olde worlde restaurant in a flower-clad cottage filled with pictures and antiques down beside a creek near Kinsale. But the extensive set menu is modern and Bill Patterson presents fashionable dishes based on the best of local ingredients including game in season. Starters could include a warm salad of goat's cheese and snails with ham and garlic perfumed with Pernod followed, perhaps, by oven-roasted scallops on a bitter orange sauce or roast partridge with a sauce of wild mushrooms. Prettily presented desserts include a good crème brulée. Mark-ups on the wine list are somewhat inconsistent – particularly champagnes, which are steeply priced. ***Seats** 30. Parties 20. L by arrangement for parties of 7 or more D 7.30-9.30 (bookings only in winter). Closed Jan. Set D £21.95. Access, Visa.*

Parknasilla — Great Southern — 72% — £151

Tel 064 45122 Fax 064 45323 — **H**

Parknasilla Sneem Co Kerry — **Map 23 A6**

Overlooking Kenmare Bay and set in 300 acres of sub-tropical parkland, this late-Victorian building blends well with its exotic surroundings. An air of tranquillity is immediately conveyed by a sense of space, antiques and fresh flowers in the foyer and the tone of restful luxury is continued through all the public areas to elegantly decorated bedrooms. Good indoor leisure facilities are matched by a wide range of outdoor attractions, including a recently-completed series of scenic walks through the estate. ***Rooms** 83. Garden, indoor & outdoor swimming pool, outdoor Canadian hot-tub, sauna, spa bath, steam room, tennis, golf (9), riding, games room, snooker, sea-fishing, water sports. Closed Jan-Mar.* AMERICAN EXPRESS *Access, Diners, Visa.*

Parknasilla — Place of Interest

Derrynane National Historic Park Caherdaniel Tel 066 75113.

Rathmullan — Rathmullan House — 62% — £72

Tel 074 58188 Fax 074 58200 — **H**

Rathmullan nr Letterkenny Co Donegal — **Map 22 C1**

Since 1962 Bob and Robin Wheeler have been running this attractively extended informal Georgian house set in lovely gardens which stretch down to the beaches of Lough Swilly. Public areas furnished with antiques and paintings include a period drawing room, library and characterful cellar bar and turf or log fires ensure a cosy atmosphere even in winter. Accommodation ranges from well-appointed master suites to family rooms and budget rooms without bathrooms. An unusual pool complex includes imaginatively conceived Egyptian Baths with ionised saltwater indoor pool and steam room. Deserted sandy beaches and all the splendours of the little-known north-west are within convenient reach of this comfortable, friendly base. Outstanding breakfasts. ***Rooms** 23. Garden, indoor swimming pool, sauna, steam room, tennis. Closed Nov-mid Mar.* AMERICAN EXPRESS *Access, Diners, Visa.*

Rathmullan Places of Interest

Glebe House and Gallery Church Hill Letterkenny Tel 074 37071.
Glenveagh National Park Tel 074 37088.

Rathnew Hunter's Hotel 60% £75

Tel 0404 40106 Fax 0404 40338 **HR**

Newrath Bridge Rathnew Co Wicklow **Map 23 D4**

The Gelletlie family and their forbears have been running this delightfully old-fashioned coaching inn since 1820, so it is not surprising that it should encompass a mixture of styles, including some interesting antiques. The current owner, Maureen Gelletlie, adds just the right element of eccentricity to the very real charm of the place. Rooms vary considerably; co-ordinated schemes are not to be expected and some have no en-suite facilities. More important is the meticulously maintained garden leading down to a river at the back, with its wonderful herbaceous borders – the perfect place for their famous afternoon tea, an aperitif or coffee after a meal. Inclement weather is also anticipated, with a welcoming open fire in the cosy bar. Friendly, informal service is excellent. ***Rooms** 17. Garden. Closed 25-28 Dec.* AMERICAN EXPRESS *Access, Diners, Visa.*

Restaurant £50

Several steps back in time, the restaurant overlooks the garden and everything about it, including the service, is refreshingly old-fashioned. Go for Wexford mussels with garlic butter, roast Wicklow lamb with fresh herbs, vegetables from the garden and nursery puddings such as rhubarb tart or lemon meringue pie from the daily-changing 3- and 4-course set menus. Prices are fair on a cosmopolitan wine list. ***Seats** 54. Parties 14. L 1-2.30 (Sat & Sun to 3) D 7.30-9. Set L £12.50 Set D £18.50*

Rathnew Tinakilly House 70% £100

Tel 0404 69274 Fax 0404 67806 **HR**

Rathnew Wicklow Co Wicklow **Map 23 D4**

Set in extensive gardens overlooking a bird sanctuary, this substantial mansion was built in the 1870s by Captain Halpin, Commander of the *Great Eastern*, which laid the first telegraph cable linking Europe and America. Since 1983 it has been run as a hotel by William and Bee Power, who have been responsible for extensive renovations and the addition of a period-style wing. The interior has been restored and furnished to a high standard with antiques, good pictures and an interesting collection of Halpin memorabilia. Comfortably furnished period bedrooms vary; the best have four-posters and most have lovely sea views. The new wing has added an extra fifteen bedrooms, relocated the restaurant and now accommodates conferences and banqueting for up to 150. Friendly, professional service. Very good breakfasts. No dogs. ***Rooms** 29. Garden, tennis, putting green.* AMERICAN EXPRESS *Access, Diners, Visa.*

Restaurant £75

The best of old and new combine in John Moloney's cooking. Bee's renowned brown bread is always on the table and John's creative seasonal menus are based on the best of local produce, especially seafood and fresh fruit and vegetables grown on the premises. Start, perhaps, with confit

over

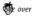

of duck with endive and Puy lentils, followed by soup, often based on home-grown vegetables and herbs, and a main course such as poached fillet of turbot with prawn butter sauce or lamb with a herb mousse and rosemary sauce. Finish with a sophisticated dessert or a selection from the French and Irish cheeseboard. Set dinner menu changes daily. ***Seats*** *70. Private Room 40. L 12.30-2 D 7.30-9 (Sun till 8). Set L £16.50 Set D £25.*

Renvyle — Renvyle House — 64% — £109

Tel 095 43511 Fax 095 43515 — **H**

Renvyle Co Galway — **Map 22 A3**

Heading towards Clifden on the N59, Renvyle is sign-posted from Recess. On the edge of the Atlantic, backed by farmland and with its own private lake, the hotel offers a wealth of leisure pursuits and, since suffering storm damage several years ago, the golf course has been upgraded. Conference facilities for up to 120, banqueting for 150. Bedrooms vary from family-size rooms with balconies to attic rooms with dormer windows. ***Rooms*** *74. Garden, tennis, golf (9), putting, bowling green, riding, fishing, snooker. Closed 1 Jan-17 Mar.* AMERICAN EXPRESS *Access, Diners, Visa.*

Riverstown — Coopershill House — 68% — £80

Tel 071 65108 Fax 071 65466 — **HR**

Coopershill Riverstown Co Sligo — **Map 22 B2**

Standing at the centre of a 500-acre estate, this Georgian mansion has been home to seven generations of the O'Hara family since it was built in 1774 and now successfully combines the spaciousness and elegance of the past with modern amenities. The rooms retain their original regal dimensions and are furnished in period style with family portraits and antiques. Spacious bedrooms all have en-suite bathrooms and most have four-poster or canopy beds. Peace and tranquillity sum up the atmosphere: no TVs or radios, but books and personal touches like fresh flowers and mineral water. ***Rooms*** *7. Garden, coarse and game fishing, boating. Closed end Oct-mid Mar.* AMERICAN EXPRESS *Access, Diners, Visa.*

Restaurant — £50

Antique polished tables, silver candelabra and a log fire in the white marble fireplace provide a fitting setting for Lindy O'Hara's good home cooking. A no-choice 5-course menu might include cheese parcels, a traditional soup, stuffed pork with fresh apricot sauce, farmhouse cheeses and, perhaps, lemon mousse. No smoking. ***Seats*** *14. D only 8-8.45. Set D £20.*

Rosslare — Great Southern — 62% — £76

Tel 053 33233 Fax 053 33543 — **H**

Rosslare Co Wexford — **Map 23 D5**

Its position overlooking Rosslare harbour makes this modern hotel a useful stopover for ferry users and there's plenty to keep children happy with a crèche and playground. Public rooms are light and spacious, with ample seating; many of the simply-furnished bedrooms are suitable for family occupation. Up to 150 conference delegates can be accommodated theatre-style. ***Rooms*** *99. Garden, indoor swimming pool, keep-fit equipment, tennis, sauna, steam room, snooker, hairdressing, children's play area. Closed Jan-Mar.* AMERICAN EXPRESS *Access, Diners, Visa.*

Rosslare — Kelly's Strand Hotel — 71% — £84

Tel 053 32114 Fax 053 32222 — **H**

Rosslare Co Wexford — **Map 23 D5**

Since their original tea room was established here in 1895 and later developed into a guesthouse and, in 1905, a hotel, the Kelly family has built up a formidable reputation for personal service at the hotel where other Irish hoteliers take their families on holiday. Excellent facilities include a leisure complex with a 15-metre exercise pool, counter-swimming jet, Canadian hot tub, Turkish bath and beauty treatments like aromatherapy and hydrotherapy. Children are well catered for, with a playroom, outdoor playground and supervised crèche. There's live entertainment every night. Bedrooms are light, modern and practical. No dogs. ***Rooms** 99. Garden, indoor swimming pools, gymnasium, squash, sauna, spa bath, solarium, beauty & hair salon, tennis, badminton, bicycles, games rooms, crazy golf, snooker, crèche, children's play area, giant chess and draughts. Closed early Dec-late Feb. Access, Visa.*

Rosslare Places of Interest

Ferry Terminal Tourist Information Tel 053 33622.
Windsurfing Centre Tel 053 32101.

Rossnowlagh Sand House 68%

£88

Tel 072 51777 Fax 072 52100

H

Rossnowlagh Co Donegal

Map 22 B2

Sitting right by a large sandy beach overlooking Donegal Bay, the crenellated Sand House hotel has a new Atlantic conservatory lounge to take advantage of views that are also enjoyed by many of the bedrooms. The Britton family and their staff extend a warm welcome which is reinforced by a fire in the Victorian-style lobby. Bedrooms, immaculate like the rest of the hotel, are individually decorated with expensive, stylish fabrics; furniture varies from antiques to fairly modest fitted units, and superior rooms have chaises longues. A delightful, peaceful hotel, as the many regular guests will testify. ***Rooms** 40. Garden, tennis, surfing, canoeing, sea, game & coarse fishing, games room. Closed mid Oct-Easter.* AMERICAN EXPRESS *Access, Diners, Visa.*

Roundwood Roundwood Inn

£60

Tel 01 2818107

R

Roundwood Co Wicklow

Map 23 D4

Set amidst spectacular scenery in the highest village in the Wicklow Hills, this 17th-century inn is furnished in traditional style with wooden floors, dark wood furniture and huge log fires throughout. Excellent bar food is available every day and includes substantial soups, specialities like Galway oysters, smoked Wicklow trout, smoked salmon and Irish stew, and blackboard specials such as home-made gravad lax, lobster salad and a speciality dessert, triple liquor parfait, all eaten at sturdy tables in front of the fire. The restaurant is in the same style and only slightly more formal but the restaurant menu leans towards bigger dishes like rack of Wicklow lamb, roast wild Wicklow venison and other game in season. German influences are evident in long-established specialities wiener schnitzel and a feather-light fresh cream gateau which is not to be missed. A mainly European wine list favours France and Germany, with some bottles under £10. ***Seats** 45. Parties 35. Private Room 32. L 1-2.30 D 7.30-9.30 (Sat to 10). Closed D Sun, all Mon, 25 Dec, Good Friday. Set L £13.95. Access, Visa.*

Scotshouse Hilton Park

£111

Tel 047 56007 Fax 047 56033

PH

Scotshouse nr Clones Co Monaghan

Map 22 C3

To avoid confusion it is best to enter the estate by the main entrance on the Clones-Scotshouse road; just a third of a mile from the Clones Golf Club, look out for a black gate with silver falcons. Once inside, Hilton Park will work its charm on you – magnificent woodlands give way to gardens and the 18th-century mansion, overlooking its own lake. Johnny and Lucy are the eighth generation of Maddens to live here and they run it very much as a family home which takes in guests. Large rooms, some with dressing rooms and characterful bathrooms, have wonderful views and the house

See over

is full of interest with heirlooms, portraits and four-poster beds. Lucy cooks an excellent no-choice 5-course dinner based on the best of local produce, especially vegetables, herbs and fruit from their own organic gardens. An outstanding breakfast is served in the Green Room, a bright semi-basement which is full of charm. Not suitable for very young children. No dogs. ***Rooms** 5. Garden, golf (9), shooting, coarse & game fishing, boating. Closed Oct-Easter except for parties by arrangement.* AMERICAN EXPRESS *Access, Visa.*

Shanagarry — Ballymaloe House — 63% — £108

Tel 021 652531 Fax 021 652021 — **HR**

Shanagarry Co Cork — **Map 23 C6**

Ivan and Myrtle Allen's large old family farmhouse is surrounded by their 400-acre farm and only two miles from the coast, near the fishing village of Ballycotton. The house is big and impressive in a comfortable sort of way, with large rooms furnished with a homely mixture of old and new and an outstanding collection of modern paintings. Rooms in the main house are traditional, those in converted outhouses spacious and cottagey, but all have individuality and are thoughtfully furnished. Ground-floor courtyard rooms are suitable for wheelchairs. Delightful breakfasts. ***Rooms** 30. Garden, outdoor swimming pool, tennis, outdoor children's play area. Closed 24-26 Dec.* AMERICAN EXPRESS *Access, Diners, Visa.*

Restaurant ↑ — £80

Have an aperitif and peruse the menu in the conservatory, then move into one of the four rooms, all furnished with antiques and Irish art, which make up the restaurant. Local produce, much of it from their own farm and garden as well as seafood from Ballycotton and Kenmare, provides the material for an exercise in simplicity, designed to ensure that the freshness and flavour of ingredients will take centre stage, rather than the obvious skills of the cook. Typical dishes on constantly changing menus include excellent patés and terrines, turbot with sea kale and hollandaise, warm smoked salmon with cucumber and fennel, roast spring lamb and escalopes of beef with peppers and chilis. The fame of the place has spread far and wide, and for many years Ballymaloe has been at the forefront of Irish hospitality. ***Seats** 90. Private Room 30. L at 1 D 7-9.30 (Sun buffet only at 7.30). Set L £15 Set D £29.*

Shannon — Great Southern — 64% — £110

Tel 061 471122 Fax 061 471982 — **H**

Shannon Airport Shannon Co Clare — **Map 23 B4**

Modern airport hotel directly opposite the main terminal building, recently totally refurbished. Soundproofed bedrooms include 11 Executive rooms and 3 suites. Fourteen rooms designated non-smoking. Conference facilities for up to 130. ***Rooms** 115. Garden, coffee shop. Closed 25 & 26 Dec.* AMERICAN EXPRESS *Access, Diners, Visa.*

Shannon — Oakwood Arms Hotel — 63% — NEW — £75

Tel 061 361500 Fax 061 361414 — **H**

Shannon Co Clare — **Map 23 B4**

This new (1991) family-owned red brick hotel creates a good impression with neatly laid-out flower beds. If the mock-Tudor style of the hotel is somewhat surprising in this setting, its aviation theme is less so: the lounge bar and function room both honour the memory of the pioneer female pilot Sophie Pearse, who came from the area, and the restaurant is maned after Howard Hughes' famous flying boat, *The Spruce Goose.* Public areas are quite spacious and comfortably furnished and, although not individually decorated, rooms have all the necessary comforts and are double-glazed. ***Rooms** 42. Patio. Closed 25 Dec, Good Friday.* AMERICAN EXPRESS *Access, Diners, Visa.*

Shannon Places of Interest

Airport Tourist Information Tel 061 471664/471565.

Skerries Red Bank Restaurant £60

Tel 01 8491005 Fax 01 8491598 **R**

7 Church Street Skerries Co Dublin **Map 22 D3**

Owner-chef Terry McCoy creates imaginative, generous dishes based on local seafood in this well-known north Dublin restaurant located in a converted bank. Have a drink and read the menu in the comfortable reception area, then settle down to specialities such as baked crab 'Loughshinney' (blended with dry sherry and served in its own shell), whole Dublin Bay prawns, cooked in fish stock and served with garlic butter or black sole 'Red Bank' (stuffed with mussels and prawns). Tempting desserts, including a very good baked chocolate cheesecake, are served from the trolley and there's a farmhouse cheeseboard, Menus change with the seasons and favour organic produce. ***Seats** 45. Parties 14. Private Room 10. D only 7-10. Closed D Sun, all Mon, 4 days Christmas, 2 weeks Nov. Set L (Sun only) £13 Set D £17.95.* AMERICAN EXPRESS *Access, Diners, Visa.*

Sligo Sligo Park 58% £95

Tel 071 60291 Fax 071 69556 **H**

Pearse Road Sligo Co Sligo **Map 22 B2**

Just south of town, Sligo Park is a modern hotel with a leisure centre, set in seven acres of parkland. A continuing programme of improvement and refurbishment has seen the addition of a new lobby and an upgraded bar. Conference and banqueting facilities can cater for up to 450. Children under six stay free in their parents' room. ***Rooms** 89. Indoor swimming pool, gymnasium, sauna, spa bath, steam room, solarium, snooker, tennis, coffee shop (10am-7pm).* AMERICAN EXPRESS *Access, Diners, Visa.*

> If we recommend meals in a hotel or inn a separate entry is made for its restaurant.

Sligo Truffles Restaurant NEW £22

Tel 071 44226 **R**

The Mall Sligo Co Sligo **Map 22 B2**

A visit to Bernadette O'Shea's unusual 'new age Pizza' restaurant has become a high point of many a trip to Sligo in recent years. First her adventurous mind sought original treatments for the humble pizza, producing variations based on a wide range of influences – the Californian Classic will include sun-dried tomatoes and roasted garlic, the Mexicano, spicy sausage and fresh hot chili peppers and so on, but the best of all is the Irish Cheese Board, a surprisingly light taste experience adding melting goat's cheese, Cashel blue, smoked Brie, cream cheese, cottage cheese and Irish mozzarella, and fresh herbs to a crisp base and fresh tomato sauce. Then she got into wonderful main course salads – Italian, Roquefort, Greek, you name it – based on local organic produce. Now it's fresh pastas, all enjoyed in a delightfully whacky room, with trompe l'oeil decorations and a peat fire. ***Seats** 38. Parties 10. D only 5-10.30. Closed Mon, 3 days Christmas, 4 days Easter.*

Sligo Places of Interest

Tourist Information Tel 071 61201.
Parkes Castle Tel 071 64149.

Spiddal Boluisce Seafood Bar

£45

R

Tel 091 83286 Fax 091 83285

Spiddal Connemara Co Galway

Map 23 B4

Since 1974 the Glanville family have been providing everything from the simplest snacks to seafood chowder, fish and vegetarian salads in their downstairs bar and, upstairs in the convivial first-floor restaurant, an impressive array of seafood. Try anything from a wide range of specialities from mussels in cream sauce, crab claws with garlic butter, monkfish, prawns and scallops through to an excellent lobster Thermidor. But carnivores are well looked after too, with good steaks, duckling and dishes like lasagne or stir-fried chicken. Good home baking (brown bread, apple pie) and an Irish farmhouse cheeseboard. ***Seats** 60. Parties 10. Meals 12-10 (Sun 4-10). Closed L Sun, 24-26 Dec.* AMERICAN EXPRESS *Access, Visa.*

Spiddal Bridge House Hotel

£65

I

Tel 091 83118

Spiddal Connemara Co Galway

Map 23 B4

Esther Feeney has managed this immaculately kept family-owned hotel on Galway Bay for many years. The neat pine-clad bar has French windows opening onto the garden and the Stirrup Room is open for food all day. Modest bedrooms are attractively decorated with co-ordinating fabrics; some have shower/WC only. No children under 2. No dogs. ***Rooms** 14. Garden. Closed Christmas-mid Feb.* AMERICAN EXPRESS *Access, Diners, Visa.*

Stillorgan China-Sichuan Restaurant

£50

R

Tel 01 2884817

4 Lower Kilmacud Road Stillorgan Co Dublin

Map 23 D4

Five miles south of Dublin city centre is the only Chinese restaurant sponsored by China Sichuan Food Authority in the British Isles, with its chef and special spices supplied direct from Sichuan province. Although limited, the menu provides interest, with spicy and chili-hot dishes marked as such. Try smoked duckling – juicy, succulent meat with a delicate and subtle smoky flavour; try also Ma-Po tofu, braised bean curd cooked with minced pork in a wonderful hot and spicy sauce. Steamed black sole with ginger sauce is another must, not to mention spiced beef, fried lamb and chicken with cashew nuts. Excellent value for money, even if prices are higher than London, but service is average. Extensive wine list covers the world. Smart decor and intimate atmosphere. ***Seats** 50. Parties 20. L 12.30-2.30 (Sun & Bank Holidays 1-2.30) D 6-11. Closed 25-27 Dec. Set L from £7 Set D £16.50.* AMERICAN EXPRESS *Access, Visa.*

Straffan Kildare Hotel 86%

£245

HR

Tel 01 6273333 Fax 01 6273312

Straffan Co Kildare

Map 23 C4

Set in lush countryside and overlooking its own 18-hole Arnold Palmer-designed golf course, this hotel (formerly *Straffan House*) holds a unique position of unrivalled opulence and a sense of other-worldliness which is heightened by a distinctly French atmosphere, a legacy from the Barton wine family who lived here in the 19th century. The interior is magnificent in concept, with superb furnishings and a wonderful collection of original paintings by well-known artists, including William Orpen and Jack B Yeats, who has a room devoted to his work. All rooms and bathrooms are individually designed in the grand style, with great attention to detail. Country Club golf and fishing facilities are available at half the rate charged to non-residents. Conference facilities for up to 70 in the main house (banquets 50), but up to 600 in the sports centre. 17 miles from Dublin, 24 miles from the airport. ***Rooms** 45. Garden, indoor* *swimming pool, gymnasium, squash, sauna, solarium, hair & beauty salon, golf (18), tennis, snooker, coarse and game fishing.* AMERICAN EXPRESS *Access, Diners, Visa.*

The Byerley Turk

£100

Although the restaurant is in a new wing, the impressively draped tall windows, marble columns and rich decor in tones of deep terracotta, cream and green harmonise perfectly with the style of the original house and it takes a sharp eye to detect the differences. The room is cleverly shaped to create semi-private areas and make the most of window tables, laid with crested china, monogrammed white linen, gleaming modern crystal and silver. Chef Michel Flamme's leanings towards classical French cuisine are tempered by traditional Irish influences – in, for example, layers of crubeens and ox tongue with a cream of spinach with a confit of onions and mustard sauce – and, with his kitchen garden now in full production, by local and home-grown seasonal produce, as in warm asparagus salad with garden leaves in a walnut dressing or supreme of chicken with a stew of broad beans scented with garlic and basil. Set menus for lunch and dinner are changed daily and there is an additional Seasonal Fayre Menu: sophisticated dishes on the 3- course table d'hote dinner menu might include roast monkfish accompanied by a cream of lobster sprinkled with mussels, followed by roast spring lamb with its vegetable parcel and finishing, perhaps, with a plate of caramel desserts or a selection of Irish and French cheeses. ***Seats** 80. Parties 30. L 12.30-2 D 7-10. Set L £22 Set D £29.*

Straffan Places of Interest

Steam Museum Tel 01 6273155.
Castletown House Celbridge Tel 01 628 8252.
Irish National Stud Tully Tel 045 21617.
Japanese Gardens Tully Tel 045 21251.

Swords Le Chateau

£55

Tel 01 406353

R

River Mall Main Street Swords Dublin Co Dublin

Map 22 D3

In a shopping mall near Dublin airport, John Dowd's cooking easily outclasses the surroundings. The menu is mainly French with a few more original offerings – such as pasta Tara, a well-balanced dish of home-made pasta with garlic, cream, bacon and baby mushrooms – added for good measure. Lunch is especially good value. No children after 8.30pm. ***Seats** 60. Parties 20. L 12.15-2.30 D 7-11. Closed Mon, Bank Holidays, 1 week Christmas/New Year. Set L £10.50 Set D £19.75.* AMERICAN EXPRESS *Access, Diners, Visa.*

Swords Forte Travelodge

£42

Tel 1 800 709 709 (in Ireland) 0800 850 950 (from England)

L

N1 Dublin/Belfast Road Swords Bypass nr Dublin Co Dublin

Map 22 D3

On the southbound carriageway of the Swords bypass at Swords roundabout, $1\frac{1}{2}$ miles north of Dublin airport, 16 miles north of Dublin city centre. AMERICAN EXPRESS *Access, Visa.*

Swords The Old Schoolhouse NEW

£50

Tel 01 840 4160 Fax 01 840 5060

R

Coolbanagher Swords Co Dublin

Map 22 D3

Set in a quiet backwater away from the main road, this old stone building has been sympathetically restored and converted to make a delightful restaurant. Although well-established, the place has taken an upturn under new chef Paul Lewis and the food now comes closer to matching the surroundings. There are always daily specials on the blackboard, patés,

See over

soups and offal are good choices and fish from nearby harbours Skerries and Howth often features in dishes such as a meal-in-a-soup-bowl chowder or simple grilled black sole on the bone. Country desserts like apple and blackberry crumble are hard to resist. ***Seats** 70. Parties 20. Private Room 20. L 12.30-2.30 D 6.30-10.30. Closed L Sat, all Sun, Bank Holidays, 3 days Christmas. Set L from £10.95 Set D £18.50.* AMERICAN EXPRESS *Access, Diners, Visa.*

Thomastown — Mount Juliet Hotel — 81% — £240

Tel 056 24455 Fax 056 24522 — **HR**

Mount Juliet Thomastown Co Kilkenny — **Map 23 C5**

The imposing 18th-century Mount Juliet House stands in 1500 acres of parkland and formal gardens through which flow the rivers Kings and Nore; a traditional stone bridge crosses the latter for access to the hotel. Its exquisite interior is no less striking: public rooms feature wonderful moulded plasterwork and the Parlour boasts a colourful marble fireplace. The bedrooms and generously proportioned suites are individually styled, with soft floral fabrics, solid oak furniture and deep-cushioned sofas; most have fine Adam fireplaces. Bathrooms are equally luxurious with many extras. Three suites are in Ballylinch House on the estate. Recreational facilities include a Jack Nicklaus-designed golf course, and a brand new leisure centre abutting the clubhouse. Children under 16 stay free in their parents' room. Kennelling for dogs. Meeting rooms for up to 50, banqueting for 140. ***Rooms** 32. Garden, tennis, game fishing, golf, archery, riding, snooker, helipad.* AMERICAN EXPRESS *Access, Diners, Visa.*

Lady Helen McCalmont Restaurant — £75

Although grand, this gracefully elegant high-ceilinged room, softly decorated in pastel shades and with sweeping views over the grounds, is not forbidding and has a pleasant atmosphere. To match these beautiful surroundings, Chris Farrell uses the finest ingredients to create colourful, flavoursome dishes, many of them garnished with fresh seasonal fruit and flowers. Local meat is a speciality, as in noisettes of new season's lamb, rolled in chopped herbs, panfried and served with a cream tansy sauce, a complicated but successful dish. Wild salmon from the River Nore often features too – poached in a citrus bouillon, perhaps, and served with saffron sauce. Pretty desserts might include a light strawberry mousse surrounded by bittersweet fruit coulis or a plate of regional Irish cheese garnished with grapes. Service is efficient and friendly. ***Seats** 55. Parties 20. Private Room 60. Closed 2 weeks after New Year. L 12.30-2.30 D 7-9. Set L £16 Set D £29.*

Tralee — Ballyseede Castle Hotel — 60% — NEW — £85

Tel 066 25799 Fax 066 25287 — **H**

Tralee Co Kerry — **Map 23 A5**

Just off the Killarney road, this 15th-century castle was once the chief garrison of the legendary Fitzgeralds, Earls of Desmond, and has had a colourful history. Impressive public rooms include a lobby with Doric columns, two drawing rooms with fine plasterwork and a dining room overlooking ancient oaks. Bedrooms are spacious and comfortable; bathrooms vary considerably. Conference/banqueting for 180/80. Golf, fishing, riding and shooting available nearby. No dogs. ***Rooms** 15. Garden. Access, Diners, Visa.*

Tralee — Place of Interest

Kerry The Kingdom Tel 066 27777.

Waterford — Dwyer's Restaurant — £55

Tel 051 77478 — **R**

8 Mary Street Waterford Co Waterford — **Map 23 C5**

In a backstreet near the bridge Martin O'Dwyer's comfortable, low-key converted barracks provides an undemonstrative background for his quietly confident cooking. A limited choice 3-course early evening menu is extremely good value, or there's a more flexible table d'hote with a wider choice, plus a good à la carte menu. Lively starters might include profiteroles of crab with tomato coulis, perhaps, or a refreshing, colourful mixed lettuce salad with bacon and fresh parmesan. Then soup, which could be a creamy fish chowder, or a sorbet such as cider and lemon. Main courses include a good choice of local fish, as in poached brill maltaise (with orange-flavoured mayonnaise) or panfried wild salmon with onion and sorrel sauce balanced by interesting meat and poultry dishes, typically medallions of pork fillet with lemon and thyme. Unusual food combinations make for original but gimmick-free presentation; attention to detail, and to contrasts of flavour and texture, is consistently good. Desserts such as a wicked marquise of three chocolates or wholesome pear and almond tart are equally irresistible. Good Irish farmhouse cheeseboard. ***Seats** 30. Parties 10. D only 6-10 (early evening menu 6-7.30). Closed Sun, Christmas, Easter, 2 weeks Jul. Set D £12.* AMERICAN EXPRESS *Access, Diners, Visa.*

Waterford Granville Hotel 69% £79

Tel 051 55111 Fax 051 70307 **H**

Waterford Co Waterford **Map 23 C5**

Once the home of Thomas Meagher, mayor of Waterford in the early 1800s and later of Carlo Bianconi who started Ireland's first transport system, the Cusack family's historic quayside hotel is kept shipshape inside and out. The chandeliered hall sets the tone for the interior, with its white marble fireplace, paintings and antiques, including a grandfather clock. Stylishly decorated bedrooms vary in size but all have good bathrooms and children under 12 may stay free in their parents' room. Traditional darkwood furniture is used throughout, including the panelled bar and library with homely fires. Conference facilities for up to 300 (banquets 200). No dogs. ***Rooms** 74.* AMERICAN EXPRESS *Access, Diners, Visa.*

Waterford Jurys Hotel 60% £103

Tel 051 32111 Fax 051 32863 **H**

Ferrybank Waterford Co Waterford **Map 23 C5**

Situated high up over the river Suir, all the bedrooms have good views of Waterford City and are comfortably furnished with darkwood furniture. Children up to 14 may stay free in their parents' rooms and there are special activities for children in July and August. The well-equipped leisure centre is a popular attraction and has a good-sized pool. Conference facilities for up to 700 (banquets 600). ***Rooms** 99. Indoor swimming pool, plunge pool, gymnasium, sauna, spa bath, steam room, tennis. Closed 24-26 Dec.* AMERICAN EXPRESS *Access, Diners, Visa.*

Waterford Prendiville's Restaurant and Guesthouse £60

Tel 051 78851 **RR**

Cork Road Waterford Co Waterford **Map 23 C5**

Peter and Paula Prendiville serve imaginative food at reasonable prices and with professionalism at their converted gate lodge – something to plan around if you are travelling to Ireland via Rosslare as traffic off the ferry hits Waterford in the early evening, just in time for dinner. Paula plans her menus around the best of local ingredients, notably organic produce, and transforms it into creative dishes with an original twist such as panfried pigeon breasts with sweet and sour vegetables, or squid and crab claws deep-fried in tempura batter with garlic mayonnaise. Elegant desserts – typically strawberry tartlet served with hot grape brulée – are irresistible. ***Seats** 50. Parties 16. Private Room 20. L 12.30-2.15 D 6.30-10.30. Closed Sun, 24-26 Dec. Set L £9.95. Access, Visa.*

See over

Rooms

£44

Nine recently redecorated simply-furnished rooms are available, five with en-suite facilities and all with phones. Some have crochet bedspreads and three rooms have TVs.

Waterford — Tower Hotel — 57%

£124

Tel 051 75801 Fax 051 70129

H

The Mall Waterford Co Waterford

Map 23 C5

Beside the River Suir, near Reginald's Tower, this city-centre hotel offers practical accommodation and has a good leisure centre. Fifteen extra bedrooms have been added recently. Conference/banqueting facilities for 600/500. ***Rooms** 125. Indoor swimming pool, gymnasium, sauna, spa bath. Closed 25 & 26 Dec.* AMERICAN EXPRESS *Access, Diners, Visa.*

Waterford — Waterford Castle — 80%

£193

Tel 051 78203 Fax 051 79316

HR

The Island Ballinakill Waterford Co Waterford

Map 23 C5

Situated on its own private island and reached only by ferry, it's hard to imagine a more peaceful setting for this 18th-century castle. Stone arches and walls above old panelling, a fine ribbon plaster ceiling, a log fire burning in a huge stone fireplace and antique leather chairs all combine to make the entrance hall and the drawing room, although more refined in style, is equally grand. Bedrooms vary somewhat in size and situation – the best are very spacious with wonderful views of parkland and water – but all are individually decorated in keeping with the building and have fine bathrooms with Victorian tubs. Dogs in kennels only. ***Rooms** 19. Garden, indoor swimming pool, tennis, golf (18), riding, bicycles.* AMERICAN EXPRESS *Access, Diners, Visa.*

Restaurant

£80

Old oak panelling under an intricate Elizabethan-style plaster ceiling, oil paintings, comfortable Regency-striped chairs, fine table settings and a pianist add up to a splendid setting in which to enjoy Paul McCluskey's accomplished cooking. Based on local produce, especially the vegetables, salads and herbs grown in the castle gardens, a 3-course lunch menu might include island salad with smoked duck and a hazelnut dressing or a spicy turnip soup, followed perhaps by monkfish medallions on a chive sauce with tomato or a traditional dish like boiled ham with parsley sauce. Dinner menus have an extra course but are on similar lines, not over-complicated and emphasising natural flavours: panfried lemon sole on a saffron and thyme sauce, broccoli soup, duckling sauté with honey and ginger. Vegetarian dishes make the most of the island produce. Short à la carte and set menus for both lunch and dinner. ***Seats** 60. Private Room 26. L 12.30-2 D 7-10 (Sun to 9). Set L £15.50 Set D £29.50.*

Waterford — Places of Interest

Tourist Information Tel 051 75788.
Waterford Cathedral Tel 051 74757.
Waterford Crystal Glass Factory Kilbarry Tel 051 73311.

Wexford — White's Hotel — 60%

£69

Tel 053 22311 Fax 053 45000

H

George Street Wexford Co Wexford

Map 23 D5

Although the present building is largely modern, the history of this famous hotel goes back to 1779, when it was founded by John White as a lodging for militiamen, and Oscar Wilde's mother, Speranza, lived here once. Now public areas include a large old-style bar and a spacious foyer with easy chairs and, as in other public rooms, a real fire. Bedrooms are practical, with fitted units and neat, fully tiled bathrooms. Conference/function facilities for up to 600. No dogs. ***Rooms** 82. Coffee shop (8am-9.30pm).* AMERICAN EXPRESS *Access, Diners, Visa.*

Wexford Places of Interest

Tourist Information Tel 053 23111.
Westgate Heritage Centre Tel 053 42611.
Johnstown Castle Demesne and Agricultural Museum Tel 053 42888.
Irish National Heritage Park Ferry Carrig Tel 053 41733.

Wicklow Old Rectory 59%

£84

Tel 0404 67048 Fax 0404 69181

HR

Wicklow Co Wicklow

Map 23 D4

Since 1977 Paul and Linda Saunders have been welcoming hosts at their delightful pink-washed Victorian rectory on the edge of town, near the famous Mount Usher gardens. It's decorated with great individuality throughout; the cosy sitting room has a white marble fireplace and traditional furnishings are brought to life by some unusual collections, notably ex-fireman Paul's display of helmets and related paraphernalia. Colourfully decorated bedrooms are all en-suite and have many homely extras. There's an outstanding choice at breakfast. ***Rooms** 6. Garden. Closed Nov-Easter.* AMERICAN EXPRESS *Access, Diners, Visa.*

Restaurant

£60

Since the new Orangery dining room area was opened in 1993 the background for Linda's imaginative food has been more spacious and comfortable, but her meals are still a gastronomic treat prepared with an artist's eye. Not only do flowers play a regular part in garnishing (and for eating), but there is a vegetarian floral selection menu – an idea which has now been developed into regular weekly floral menus in early summer, to coincide with the Wicklow Gardens Festival. Beautiful desserts. Spanish wines are the best bet on an otherwise predictable list. No smoking. ***Seats** 12 à la carte (20 for set menu). Parties 8. D only at 8. Set D £24.*

Wicklow Places of Interest

Tourist Information Tel 0404 69117.
Mount Usher Gardens Tel 0404 40205.

Youghal Aherne's Seafood Restaurant

£60

Tel 024 92424

RR

163 North Main Street Youghal Co Cork

Map 23 C6

The Fitzgibbon family's renowned bar and seafood restaurant is a hard place to pass – best to give in to the warm welcome and swift service which awaits in the cocktail bar (where the bar menu is served). Menus, changed daily and presented against a soft watercolour background, offer a wide choice of local seafood in dishes such as their famous chowder, served with a superb dark moist malty yeastbread, an unusual hot potato and smoked salmon gratin or Youghal Bay lobster, served simply hot buttered or Thermidor at surprisingly reasonable prices. Lovely desserts are best of all served as a tasting plate. ***Seats** 50. Private Room 20. L 12.30-2 (Sun to 1.45 in bar) D 6.30-9.30. Closed 4 days Christmas. Set L £12.50 Set D £19.50. Access, Visa.*

Rooms

£75

Aherne's ten stylish en-suite bedrooms, individually decorated to a very high standard and furnished with antiques.

Making hygienic prac

New recipe for hygiene

Eating out is one of life's pleasures, but not if it damages your health. To counteract the seemingly unprecedented increase in food-borne illnesses, the Government introduced the Food Safety Act 1990 with the aim of providing greater controls through the food chain from source to consumption. It carries with it powerful penalties and responsibility is placed entirely on the individual establishment to ensure its food safety.

Britannia Food Safety & Hygiene Award Scheme

This award scheme was set up by Britannia to guide those establishments towards superior standards of food safety and hygiene matters as a whole. Aimed at restaurants, hotels, pubs, bars, cafés, etc. who join the scheme, it charts their progress and if, following rigorous monitoring, they meet Britannia's exacting standards, they are finally presented with the award which they can display to their staff and customers. Valid for only one year, the award also ensures that food handling premises keep their standards up – and their competitors!

Customised Hygiene Manual

When they join the scheme, an environmental health specialist visits the premises and carries out a comprehensive inspection. The objective is to highlight areas where hygiene practices or the

Receiving their awards last May'9
Barbara Dadoush and J
and Mr and Mrs Reed,

condition of the premises or equipment falls belc Britannia's high standards. They are then provid with a customised manual which sets out, step-b step, the routines that need to be followed to ensu compliance with the Food Safety Act. Areas that w be covered include food storage, temperatu monitoring, cleaning routines, pest prevention a staff training. Altogether it adds up to a comple food safety and hygiene management system. Aft three months, the inspector returns to review t situation and if procedures are up to scratch awards the certificate. Follow-up checks are made six monthly or quarterly intervals to confirm th they are maintaining standards.

Scheme participants also benefit from emerger 24-hour advice for technical and legal informati and advance warning of legislative changes that w

ce a menu for success.

rnemouth from left to right are:
ves, Oatlands Park Hotel
s Country House Hotel.

fect their premises. In the unlikely event of a osecution being served, Britannia even give a legal penses guarantee up to £25,000 per claim providing eir manual instructions have been carried out.

onfidence

People are now eating out more than ever and e acutely aware of food-related illnesses. The public eeds assurance that the food they eat is safe and epared in premises which conform to high andards of hygiene. The Britannia Food Safety and ygiene Award gives people that confidence.

Wherever you see the award, be it a five star otel or the pub down the road, you can be sure that ey operate to the same high standards.

For more information about the award scheme, ease call in confidence FREE on 0800 212364 and k for Paula Rousen.

Current Britannia Food Safety and Hygiene Award holders include:-

LONDON
The Dorchester Hotel, Park Lane W1A 2HJ.
071 629 8888
Lloyds of London, One Lime Street EC3M.
071 623 7100
La Capannina, 24 Romilly Street W1. **071 437 2473**

DEVON
Fairwater Head Hotel, Hawkeschurch
Nr Axminster, Devon EX13 5TX. **0297 678349**

BEDFORDSHIRE
Knife & Cleaver, The Grove, Houghton Crescent, Bedford MK4 3LA. **0234 740387**

DORSET
Alexandra Hotel, Pound Street, Lyme Regis DT7 3HZ.
0297 442010

CORNWALL
Castle Rock Hotel, 4 New Road, Port Isaac,
North Cornwall PL29 3SB. **0208 880300**

NORFOLK
The Historical Thomas Paine, White Hart Street,
Thetford IP24 1AA. **0842 755631**

SURREY
Oatlands Park Hotel, Oatlands Drive, Weybridge
KT13 9HB. **0932 847242**

BERKSHIRE
Stirrups Country House Hotel, Maidens Green,
Nr Bracknell RG12 6LD. **0344 882284**

OXON
The Marlborough Hotel, 28 Market Square, Witney,
Oxon OX8 7BB. **0993 776353**

CLEVELAND
Parkmore Hotel, 636 Yarm Road, Eaglescliffe.
0642 786815

CUMBRIA
Derwentwater Hotel, Portinscale, Keswick, Cumbria
CA12 5RE. **0768 772538**

(Also, the catering facilities at the British Shoe Corporation Ltd, Sunningdale Road, Leicester LE3 1UR)

BRITANNIA FOOD SAFETY SERVICE LTD

Britannia Food Safety Service Ltd is part of one National Britannia group of companies.

Quick Reference Lists: Outside London

Hotels under £65 for 2

England

Acle Forte Travelodge
Aldeburgh Uplands
All Stretton Stretton Hall Hotel
Alton Forte Travelodge
Alton Grange Hotel
Altrincham George & Dragon
Amesbury Forte Travelodge
Ashford Travel Inn
Axbridge Oak House
Bainbridge Rose & Crown Inn
Baldock Forte Travelodge
Bamburgh Lord Crewe Arms
Barnard Castle Jersey Farm Hotel
Barnsley Ardsley Moat House
Barnsley Forte Travelodge
Barton Mills Forte Travelodge
Barton Stacey Forte Travelodge
Barton-under-Needwood Forte Travelodge (N)
Barton-under-Needwood Forte Travelodge (S)
Basildon Campanile Hotel
Basildon Travel Inn
Basingstoke Forte Travelodge
Basingstoke The Ringway
Basingstoke Travel Inn
Bebington Forte Travelodge
Beccles Waveney House
Billingshurst Forte Travelodge
Birmingham Campanile Hotel
Birmingham Granada Lodge
Blyth Forte Travelodge
Blyth Granada Lodge
Bolton Pack Horse Hotel
Boroughbridge The Crown
Braithwaite Ivy House
Branscombe Masons Arms
Brentwood Forte Travelodge
Bridlington Expanse Hotel
Bucklow Hill The Swan
Burnham Grovefield Hotel
Burnley Forte Travelodge
Burtonwood Forte Travelodge
Bury St Edmunds Butterfly Hotel
Cambridge Arundel House
Cannock Travel Inn
Canterbury Canterbury Hotel
Canterbury Ebury Hotel
Carcroft Forte Travelodge
Carlisle Granada Lodge
Castle Cary Bond's
Cheltenham On The Park
Cheltenham Travel Inn
Chessington Travel Inn
Chester Chester Resort Hotel
Chesterfield Forte Travelodge
Chiddingfold Crown Inn
Chippenham Granada Lodge
Christchurch Travel Inn
Clayton-le-Woods Pines Hotel
Colchester Butterfly Hotel
Colsterworth Forte Travelodge
Corsham Methuen Arms
Coventry (North) Campanile Hotel
Coventry (South) Campanile Hotel
Crewe Forte Travelodge
Croydon Travel Inn
Derby International Hotel
Desborough Forte Travelodge
Dinnington Dinnington Hall
Doncaster Campanile Hotel
Dorking Forte Travelodge
Dover Travel Inn
Droitwich Forte Travelodge
Dudley Forte Travelodge
Dunchurch Forte Travelodge
Dunstable Forte Travelodge
East Dereham King's Head
East Grinstead Woodbury House
East Stoke Kemps Country House Hotel
Eastleigh Forte Travelodge
Eccleshall St George Hotel
Ely Forte Travelodge
Ely Lamb Hotel
Fairford Bull Hotel
Fareham Red Lion
Farnham Trevena House
Faugh String of Horses Inn
Fenstanton Forte Travelodge
Ferrybridge Granada Lodge
Findon Findon Manor
Fleet Forte Travelodge
Fontwell Forte Travelodge
Fossebridge Fossebridge Inn
Frilford Heath Dog House Hotel
Gateshead Forte Travelodge
Gayton Travel Inn
Gloucester Travel Inn
Gloucester Travel Inn
Goathland Mallyan Spout
Gordano Forte Travelodge
Goudhurst Star & Eagle Inn
Grantham Forte Travelodge
Grantham Granada Lodge
Grindleford Maynard Arms
Hagley Travel Inn
Hailey The Bird In Hand
Hailsham Forte Travelodge

Hartlebury Forte Travelodge
Hartlepool Grand Hotel
Hartshead Moor Forte Travelodge
Hatherleigh George Hotel
Haydock Forte Travelodge
Hayes Travel Inn
Heathrow Airport Granada Lodge
Hereford Travel Inn
Hollingbourne Great Danes
Horndon-on-the-Hill Bell Inn
Horsham Travel Inn
Hull Campanile Hotel
Hurstbourne Tarrant Esseborne Manor
Ilminster Forte Travelodge
Kenton Travel Inn
Kidderminster Stone Manor
King's Lynn Forte Travelodge
Kintbury Dundas Arms
Knutsford Forte Travelodge
Langho Northcote Manor
Leicester Granada Lodge
Letchworth Broadway Toby Hotel
Liverpool Campanile Hotel
Lolworth Forte Travelodge
Long Melford Black Lion
Longham Bridge House
Lower Swell Old Farmhouse
Ludlow Forte Travelodge
Luton Forte Crest
Luton Hotel Ibis
Luton Leaside Hotel
Lutterworth Denbigh Arms
Lympsham Batch Farm Country Hotel
Malvern Cottage in the Wood
Manchester Granada Lodge
Market Drayton Corbet Arms
Marlborough Ivy House
Marston Forte Travelodge
Melksham King's Arms Hotel
Melton Mowbray George Hotel
Mere Old Ship Hotel
Middleton-in-Teesdale Teesdale Hotel
Midhurst Angel Hotel
Montacute King's Arms Inn
Morden Forte Travelodge
Moretonhampstead White Hart Inn
Much Birch Pilgrim Hotel
Neasham Newbus Arms
Needham Market Pipps Ford
Newark Forte Travelodge
Newark Grange Hotel
Newby Wiske Solberge Hall
Newmarket White Hart
Northampton Forte Travelodge
Northampton Travel Inn
Norwich Hotel Norwich
Norwich Norwich Sport Village Hotel
Nuneaton Forte Travelodge
Nuneaton Travel Inn
Okehampton Forte Travelodge
Old Harlow Travel Inn
Oldbury Forte Travelodge
Ormesby St Margaret Ormesby Lodge
Oswestry Forte Travelodge
Oxford Forte Travelodge
Parkgate Ship Hotel
Penrith Forte Travelodge
Peterborough Forte Travelodge
Petersfield Langrish House
Plymouth Boringdon Hall
Plymouth Campanile Hotel
Pocklington Feathers Hotel
Podimore Forte Travelodge
Powburn Breamish House
Preston Travel Inn
Ravenstonedale Black Swan Inn
Reading Forte Travelodge
Redditch Campanile Hotel
Reeth Burgoyne Hotel
Renishaw Sitwell Arms
Retford Forte Travelodge
Rotherham Campanile Hotel
Rotherham Travel Inn
Ruckhall Ancient Camp Inn
Rugeley Forte Travelodge
Runcorn Campanile Hotel
Rushden Forte Travelodge
Saffron Walden Saffron Hotel
St Austell White Hart
St Ives Slepe Hall
St Margaret's Wallett's Court
Saltash Granada Lodge
Scole Scole Inn
Scotch Corner Forte Travelodge
Seahouses Olde Ship Hotel
Sedgemoor Forte Travelodge
Sedlescombe Brickwall Hotel
Shipdham Shipdham Place
Silloth-on-Solway Skinburness Hotel
Skipton Forte Travelodge
Slaidburn Hark to Bounty Inn
Sleaford Forte Travelodge
Solihull Travel Inn
Somerton Lynch Country House Hotel
South Cave Forte Travelodge
South Mimms Forte Travelodge
South Witham Forte Travelodge
Southport New Bold Hotel
Southwold The Crown
Stilton Bell Inn
Stockport Forte Travelodge
Stockport Travel Inn
Stoke-on-Trent Haydon House Hotel
Stokesley Chapters
Stourbridge Talbot Hotel
Stourport-on-Severn Moat House
Stowmarket Forte Travelodge
Stratford-upon-Avon Dukes Hotel
Street Bear Hotel
Stretton Ram Jam Inn
Sutton Coldfield Forte Travelodge
Sutton Scotney North Forte Travelodge
Sutton Scotney South Forte Travelodge
Swavesey Forte Travelodge
Tamworth Granada Lodge
Taunton Travel Inn
Telford Forte Travelodge
Tetbury Calcot Manor
Thrapston Forte Travelodge
Thrussington Forte Travelodge
Thurrock Granada Lodge
Tickton Tickton Grange
Tintagel Trebrea Lodge
Tiverton Forte Travelodge
Toddington Granada Lodge
Towcester Forte Travelodge

Tring Travel Inn
Uppingham Forte Travelodge
Uttoxeter Forte Travelodge
Uttoxeter White Hart
Wakefield Campanile Hotel
Wakefield Granada Lodge
Walsall Wood Baron's Court Hotel
Wantage Bear Hotel
Warminster Granada Lodge
Warrington Travel Inn
Washington Campanile Hotel
Washington Granada Lodge
Wateringbury Wateringbury Hotel
Weedon Crossroads Hotel
Wentbridge Forte Travelodge
Weobley Olde Salutation Inn
Whitewell Inn at Whitewell
Wilmington Home Farm
Winchester Royal Hotel
Winkton Fisherman's Haunt Hotel
Woburn Bell Inn
Wolverhampton Goldthorn Hotel
Woodhall Spa Dower House
Worcester Giffard Hotel
Worksop Forte Travelodge
Wrotham Heath Travel Inn
York Forte Travelodge
Yoxford Satis House

Scotland

Aberdeen Travel Inn
Abington Forte Travelodge
Alyth Lands of Loyal Hotel
Cumbernauld Travel Inn
Dulnain Bridge Auchendean Lodge
Dumbarton Forte Travelodge
Dundee Travel Inn
Edinburgh Forte Travelodge
Edinburgh Granada Lodge
Forfar Royal Hotel
Garve Inchbae Lodge
Glencarse Newton House Hotel
Gretna Green Forte Travelodge
Harray Loch Merkister Hotel
Helmsdale Navidale House
Isle of Raasay Isle of Raasay Hotel
Kilmelford Cuilfail Hotel
Kinross Granada Lodge
Kirkmichael Log Cabin Hotel
Newhouse Travel Inn
Oban Columba Hotel
Stirling Granada Lodge
Strathtummel Port-an-Eilean Hotel
Tobermory Tobermory Hotel
Tweedsmuir Crook Inn

Wales

Abercynon Llechwen Hall
Abergavenny Llanwenarth Arms Hotel
Bridgend Forte Travelodge
Cardiff Campanile Hotel
Cardiff Forte Travelodge
Cardiff Travel Inn
Carmarthen Ivy Bush Royal
Chepstow Castle View Hotel
Colwyn Bay Hotel Seventy Degrees
Conwy Sychnant Pass Hotel
Crickhowell Bear Hotel
Crickhowell Gliffaes Country House Hotel
Cross Hands Forte Travelodge
Fishguard Fishguard Bay Hotel
Halkyn Forte Travelodge
Llanarmon Dyffryn Ceiriog Hand Hotel
Llandeilo Cawdor Arms
Llanwnda Stables Hotel
Machynlleth Wynnstay Arms
Merthyr Tydfil Baverstock Hotel
Monmouth King's Head
Newport Kings Hotel
Northop Hall Forte Travelodge
Pantmawr Glansevern Arms
Pencoed Forte Travelodge
Port Talbot Travel Inn
Wrexham Forte Travelodge

Channel Islands

Alderney Chez André
Guernsey, Forest Mallard Hotel
Guernsey, St Peter Port Braye Lodge
Guernsey, Pleinmont Imperial Hotel
Sark Aval Du Creux
Sark La Sablonnerie

Northern Ireland

Portballintrae Bayview Hotel

Republic of Ireland

Ballymote Temple House
Birr Dooly's Hotel
Birr Tullanisk
Blessington Downshire House
Cork Forte Travelodge
Cork Seven North Mall
Dublin Jurys Christchurch Inn
Ennis Auburn Lodge
Galway Jurys Galway Inn
Glen of Aherlow Aherlow House
Kinsale Old Bank House
Mountrath Roundwood House
Moycullen Cloonabinnia House Hotel
Newbay Newbay Country House
Spiddal Bridge House Inn
Swords Forte Travelodge

15 Minutes Off Motorway

Eating in the motorway service areas may cut out extra travelling time, but it also cuts out any possibility of pleasing the discerning palate.
Yet throughout the land outstanding eating is available just a short drive from the motorway network, and the list that follows pinpoints STARRED RESTAURANTS that need no more than a 15-minute detour. And if you're looking for somewhere to spend the night in style, we also feature DE LUXE AND GRADE 1 HOTELS within a similar range.
So even when time is important, you don't have to leave out the good things – just leave the motorway! For further details of these establishments, see individual entries in the main section of the Guide.

England

M1

J12 **Flitwick** Flitwick Manor
J13 **Aspley Guise** Moore Place Hotel
J16 **Daventry** Daventry Resort Hotel
Northampton Swallow Hotel
J22 **Leicester** Holiday Inn
J23 **Quorn** The Quorn
J24 **Castle Donington** Donington Thistle Hotel
J25 **Nottingham** Forte Crest
Nottingham Royal Moat House International Hotel
Nottingham Rutland Square Hotel
J47 **Leeds** Haley's Hotel

M3

J2 **Egham** Runnymede Hotel
J3 **Ascot** Royal Berkshire Hotel
Bagshot Pennyhill Park Hotel
J5 **Rotherwick** Tylney Hall
J6 **Basingstoke** Audleys Wood Thistle Hotel
J8 **Winchester** Lainston House

M4

J4 **Heathrow Airport** Edwardian Hotel
Heathrow Airport (West Drayton) Excelsior Hotel
Heathrow Airport Heathrow Hilton
Heathrow Airport (West Drayton) Holiday Inn Crowne Plaza
Heathrow Airport Sheraton-Heathrow
Heathrow Airport (Hayes) Sheraton Skyline
J6 **Slough** Marriott Hotel
Slough Copthorne Hotel
Windsor Oakley Court Hotel
J8/9 **Bray-on-Thames** Waterside Inn
Maidenhead Fredrick's Hotel
Taplow Cliveden
J10 **Sindlesham** Reading Moat House
J11 **Reading** Holiday Inn Hotel
Shinfield L'Ortolan
J13 **Newbury** Foley Lodge Hotel
Newbury Regency Park Hotel
Woolton Hill Hollington House
J16 **Purton** Pear Tree
J17 **Beanacre** Beechfield House
Castle Combe Manor House
Easton Grey Whatley Manor Hotel
J18 **Bath** Bath Spa Hotel
Bath Priory Hotel
Bath Royal Crescent Hotel & Restaurant
Colerne Lucknam Park Hotel

M5

J4 **Bromsgrove** Grafton Manor
Chaddesley Corbett Brockencote Hall
J5 **Abberley** Elms Hotel
Droitwich Spa Chateau Impney Hotel
J7 **Worcester** Fownes Resort Hotel
J9 **Corse Lawn** Corse Lawn House
J11 **Cheltenham** The Epicurean
Cheltenham The Greenway
Gloucester Hatton Court
J13 **Painswick** Painswick Hotel
Stroud Oakes
J14 **Thornbury** Thornbury Castle
J25 **Hatch Beauchamp** Farthings Country House Hotel
Taunton Castle Hotel & Restaurant
J29 **Whimple** Woodhayes
J31 **Exeter** Royal Clarence

M6

J2/3 **Ansty** Ansty Hall
J6 **Birmingham** Copthorne Hotel
Birmingham Holiday Inn
Birmingham Hyatt Regency Birmingham
Birmingham Swallow Hotel
Sutton Coldfield New Hall

J15 **Hanchurch** Hanchurch Manor
J17 **Nantwich** Rookery Hall
J19 **Alderley Edge** Alderley Edge Hotel
J32 **Longridge** Heathcote's
J40 **Penrith** North Lakes Gateway Hotel
Ullswater Leeming House Hotel
Ullswater Sharrow Bay Hotel & Restaurant
J42 **Wetheral** Crown Hotel
J43 **Brampton** Farlam Hall Hotel

M11

J8 **Broxted** Whitehall Hotel
J8 **Hatfield Heath** Down Hall Hotel
J12 **Cambridge** Midsummer House Restaurant

M20

J8 **Lenham** Chilston Park
J9 **Ashford** Eastwell Manor
Ashford Ashford International
J11 **Hythe** Hythe Imperial Hotel

M23

J9 **Horley** Langshott Manor
J10 **East Grinstead** Gravetye Manor & Restaurant
Gatwick Airport Gatwick Hilton International
Gatwick Airport (Horley) Ramada Hotel Gatwick
Gatwick Airport Forte Crest Gatwick
Turners Hill Alexander House
J11 **Cuckfield** Ockenden Manor Hotel
Lower Beeding South Lodge

M25

J9 **Sutton** Holiday Inn
J14 **Heathrow Airport** Heathrow Hilton

M27

J9 **Fareham** Solent Hotel
J12 **Portsmouth** Portsmouth Marriott Hotel

M40

J4 **Marlow** Compleat Angler Hotel
Medmenham Danesfield House
J7 **Great Milton** Le Manoir aux Quat'Saisons & Restaurant
J9 **Oxford** Old Parsonage
J15 **Leamington Spa** Mallory Court & Restaurant
Stratford upon Avon Billesley Manor
Stratford upon Avon Ettington Park
Stratford upon Avon Moat House International
Stratford upon Avon Welcombe Hotel

M42

J4 **Hockley Heath** Nuthurst Grange
J6 **Birmingham** Birmingham Metropole
Meriden Forest of Arden Hotel
J9 **Wishaw** Belfry Hotel

M50

J1 **Puckrup** Puckrup Hall
J2 **Ledbury** Hope End Country House

M53

J5 **Puddington** Craxton Wood Hotel
J12 **Chester** Chester Grosvenor
Chester Crabwall Manor

M54

J4 **Shifnal** Park House Hotel

M56

J5 **Manchester Airport** Hilton International
J6 **Handforth** Belfry Hotel
Wilmslow Stanneylands Hotel

M62

J26 **Bradford** Restaurant Nineteen

M63

J9 **Manchester** Charterhouse Hotel
Manchester Copthorne Hotel
Manchester Holiday Inn Crowne Plaza
Manchester Hotel Piccadilly
Manchester Ramada Hotel
Manchester Yang Sing

A1M

JN **Newcastle-upon-Tyne** Swallow Gosforth Park Hotel
Newcastle-upon-Tyne Holiday Inn
Newcastle-upon-Tyne 21 Queen Street

Scotland

M8

J2	**Edinburgh** The Balmoral
	Edinburgh Caledonian Hotel
	Edinburgh George Inter-Continental Hotel
	Edinburgh Howard Hotel
	Edinburgh King James Thistle Hotel
	Edinburgh Royal Terrace Hotel
	Edinburgh Sheraton Grand
J17	**Glasgow** One Devonshire Gardens
J17/18	**Glasgow** Forte Crest
	Glasgow Glasgow Hilton
	Glasgow Town House
J18	**Glasgow** Glasgow Marriott Hotel

M9

J9	**Linlithgow** Champany Inn Restaurant
	Dunblane Cromlix House

M80

J4	**Cumbernauld** Westerwood Hotel

Wales

M4

J24	**Newport** Celtic Manor Hotel
	Llangybi Cwrt Bleddyn Hotel
J32	**Cardiff** Moat House
	Cardiff Park Hotel
J34	**Miskin** Miskin Manor

Restaurants with Rooms

England

Barnstaple Lynwood House
Baslow Fischer's Baslow Hall
Birdlip Kingshead House
Blandford Forum La Belle Alliance
Bradford Restaurant 19
Bray-on-Thames The Waterside Inn
Brimfield Poppies Restaurant
Campsea Ashe Old Rectory
Cartmel Uplands
Cawston Grey Gables
Cheltenham Redmond's
Cowan Bridge Cobwebs
Dedham Fountain House & Dedham Hall
Dorchester Yalbury Cottage
Dorrington Country Friends
East Buckland Lower Pitt
Erpingham Ark
Glastonbury No. 3 Restaurant & Hotel
Great Dunmow The Starr
Gulworthy Horn of Plenty
Harwich Pier at Harwich
Haworth Weavers
Hayfield Bridge End Restaurant
Helford Riverside
Horndon on the Hill Hill House
Kington Penrhos Court
Knutsford La Belle Epoque
Lavenham Great House
Lympstone River House
Manchester Airport Moss Nook
New Alresford Hunters
Oxford Bath Place Hotel & Restaurant
Padstow Seafood Restaurant
Paulerspury Vine House
Pool-in-Wharfedale Pool Court
Powerstock Three Horseshoes Inn
Ross-on-Wye Pheasants
Stonor Stonor Arms
Storrington Manley's
Sturminster Newton Plumber Manor
Thornton-le-Fylde River House
Ulverston Bay Horse Inn & Bistro
Uppingham The Lake Isle
Waterhouses Old Beams
Wath-in-Nidderdale Sportsman's Arms
Watlington Well House
Williton White House
Winteringham Winteringham Fields
Wylam Laburnum House
Yeovil Little Barwick House

Scotland

Alyth Drumnacree House
Canonbie Riverside Inn
Fort William The Factor's House
Kingussie The Cross
Muir-of-Ord Dower House
Peat Inn Peat Inn

Wales

Chirk Starlings Castle
Harlech The Cemlyn
Pwllheli Plas Bodegroes
Trellech Village Green
Welsh Hook Stone Hall
Whitebrook Crown at Whitebrook

Channel Islands

St Ouen The Lobster Pot

Northern Ireland

Garvagh Blackheath House & MacDuff's

Republic of Ireland

Ahakista Shiro
Athy Tonlegee House
Cork Flemings
Dingle Doyle's Seafood Bar & Townhouse
Enniskerry Enniscree Lodge
Kenmare The Old Bank House
Kilkenny Lacken House
Kinsale Old Presbytery
Waterford Prendiville's Restaurant/Guesthouse
Youghal Aherne's Seafood Restaurant

Inns offering accommodation (ungraded as hotels)

England

Alcester Arrow Mill
Andover White Hart Inn
Ashington Mill House Hotel
Axbridge Oak House
Bainbridge Rose & Crown Inn
Buckler's Hard Master Builder's House
Burford Lamb Inn
Burton-on-Trent Riverside Inn
Canterbury Falstaff Hotel
Castle Ashby Falcon Inn
Charlbury Bell Hotel
Chiddingfold Crown Inn
Chipping Norton Crown & Cushion
Clanfield The Plough at Clanfield
Corsham Methuen Arms
Dartmouth Royal Castle Hotel
Dorchester-on-Thames George Hotel
Driffield Bell Hotel
East Dereham King's Head
Eccleshall St George Hotel
Eton Christopher Hotel
Faugh String of Horses Inn
Frilford Heath Dog House Hotel
Goudhurst Star & Eagle Inn
Greta Bridge Morritt Arms
Grindleford Maynard Arms
Hailey The Bird In Hand
Hatherleigh George Hotel
Hathersage Hathersage Inn
Horndon-on-the-Hill Bell Inn
Kintbury Dundas Arms
Lacock At The Sign of The Angel
Ledbury The Feathers
Lower Swell Old Farmhouse
Lynmouth Rising Sun Inn
Macclesfield Sutton Hall
Market Drayton Corbet Arms
Melksham King's Arms Hotel
Mellor Millstone Hotel
Mere Old Ship Hotel
Middleton Stoney Jersey Arms
Midhurst Angel Hotel
Montacute King's Arms Inn
Moretonhampstead White Hart Inn
Odiham George Hotel
Pocklington Feathers Hotel
Ravenstonedale Black Swan Inn
Romaldkirk Rose and Crown
Ruckhall Ancient Camp Inn
St Austell White Hart
Scole Scole Inn
Seahouses Olde Ship Hotel
Shepperton Warren Lodge
Slaidburn Hark to Bounty Inn
Southwold The Crown
Stilton Bell Inn
Stratfield Turgis Wellington Arms
Troutbeck Mortal Man Inn
Tutbury Ye Olde Dog & Partridge Inn
Uttoxeter White Hart
Weobley Olde Salutation Inn
Whitewell Inn at Whitewell
Winchester Wykeham Arms
Winkton Fisherman's Haunt Hotel
Winsford Royal Oak Inn
Yattendon Royal Oak

Scotland

Gatehouse of Fleet Murray Arms Inn
Glenelg Glenelg Inn

Kilfinan Kilfinan Hotel
Melrose Burts Hotel
Strathblane Kirkhouse Inn
Talladale Loch Maree Hotel
Ullapool Ceilidh Place

Wales

Abercynon Llechwen Hall
Abergavenny Llanwenarth Arms Hotel
Chepstow Castle View Hotel
Crickhowell Bear Hotel
Llanarmon Dyffryn Ceiriog Hand Hotel
Llanarmon Dyffryn Ceiriog West Arms Hotel
Pantmawr Glansevern Arms
Penmaenpool George III Hotel
Swansea Langland Court Hotel

Channel Islands

Castel Hougue du Pommier
Pleinmont Imperial Hotel
St Aubin Old Court House Inn

Northern Ireland

Bushmills Bushmills Inn
Crawfordsburn Old Inn Crawfordsburn

Republic of Ireland

Spiddal Bridge House Inn
Kinsale Blue Haven Hotel

Town House Hotels

This exclusive category highlights a small number of hotels of distinctive personality. Most are conversions of town residences which retain not only their period facades but also interior character and, to some extent, the feel of a private house. Noe of them has more than 50 bedrooms, and very few are owned by groups. Excellent personal service is another attribute.

England

Bedford Woodlands Manor
Brighton Topps Hotel
Bury St Edmunds Angel Hotel
Cheltenham On The Park
Chipping Campden Cotswold House
Poole Mansion House
Sherborne Eastbury Hotel
Tetbury The Close
Wareham Priory Hotel
York Grange Hotel
York Mount Royale

Scotland

Edinburgh Howard Hotel
Elgin Mansion House
Glasgow One Devonshire Gardens
Nairn Clifton Hotel

Wales

Llandudno St Tudno Hotel

Republic of Ireland

Cork Arbutus Lodge
Dublin Hibernian Hotel

Private House Hotels

Private House hotels are de luxe 'bed and breakfast' establishments. This handful of hotels offers guests comfortable, often luxurious accommodation and personal service, but they do not have public restaurants or day rooms, though some may have a drawing room. With the usual percentage rating, they would have suffered by not having normal hotel facilities and are therefore not graded.

England

Bath Fountain House
Chartham Thruxted Oast
Chedington Hazel Barton
Golden Green Goldhill Mill
Leeds 42 The Calls
Lincoln D'Isney Place
Prestbury White House Manor
Teignmouth Thomas Luny House

Scotland

Edinburgh Channings
Glasgow Devonshire Hotel

Republic of Ireland

Ballymote Temple House
Birr Tullanisk
Cork Seven North Mall
Dublin Grey Door
Kinsale The Old Bank House
Newbay Newbay Country House
Scotshouse Hilton Park

Country House Hotels

This is a select category of small hotels offering civilised comfort, good service and fine food in an attractive and peaceful rural setting. Most of them are imposing country mansions, converted and run with loving care by dedicated owners, often a husband-and-wife team. They have no more than 35 bedrooms; all have recommended in-house restaurants, many of star standard.

England

Amberley Amberley Castle
Battle Netherfield Place
Bilbrough Bilbrough Manor
Bowness-on-Windermere Linthwaite House
Bradford-on-Avon Woolley Grange
Buckland Buckland Manor
Chagford Gidleigh Park
Charingworth Charingworth Manor
Chedington Chedington Court
Cheltenham Greenway
East Grinstead Gravetye Manor
Freshford Homewood Park
Grasmere Michael's Nook
Great Milton Le Manoir aux Quat'Saisons
Grimston Congham Hall
Horley Langshott Manor
Leamington Spa Mallory Court
Lewdown Lewtrenchard Manor
Maiden Newton Maiden Newton House
Mawnan Smith Nansidwell
Monkton Combe Combe Grove Manor
Nidd Nidd Hall
Oakham Hambleton Hall
Puckrup Puckrup Hall
South Molton Whitechapel Manor
Ston Easton Ston Easton Park
Storrington Abingworth Hall
Storrington Little Thakeham
Taplow Cliveden
Ullswater Sharrow Bay
Walkington Manor House
Woolton Hill Hollington House Hotel

Scotland

Alexandria Cameron House
Arisaig Arisaig House
Ballater Tullich Lodge
Banchory Invery House
Dunblane Cromlix House
Eriska Isle of Eriska
Fort William Inverlochy Castle
Portpatrick Knockinaam Lodge

Wales

Llandudno Bodysgallen Hall
Llangefni Tre-Ysgawen Hall
Llyswen Llangoed Hall
Northop Soughton Hall
Porthkerry Egerton Grey

Republic of Ireland

Gorey Marlfield House
Innishannon Innishannon House Hotel
Letterfrack Rosleague Manor
Rathnew Hunter's Hotel
Riverstown Coopershill House

Beautifully Situated Hotels

England

Abberley Elms Hotel
Alcester Arrow Mill
Alston Lovelady Shield
Amberley Amberley Castle
Amberley Amberley Inn
Ambleside Rothay Manor Hotel
Applethwaite Underscar Manor
Ashbourne Callow Hall
Ashford Eastwell Manor
Aylesbury Hartwell House
Bagshot Pennyhill Park
Bakewell Hassop Hall
Baslow Cavendish Hotel
Bassenthwaite Armathwaite Hall
Battle Netherfield Place
Beanacre Beechfield House
Bilbrough Bilbrough Manor
Bishop's Tawton Halmpstone Manor
Borrowdale Borrowdale Hotel
Borrowdale Stakis Lodore Swiss Hotel
Boughton Monchelsea Tanyard Hotel
Bradford-on-Avon Woolley Grange
Brampton Farlam Hall
Bromsgrove Grafton Manor
Broxted Whitehall
Buckland Buckland Manor
Burley Burley Manor
Calstock Danescombe Valley Hotel
Canterbury Howfield Manor
Carlyon Bay Carlyon Bay Hotel
Carlyon Bay Porth Avallen Hotel
Cartmel Aynsome Manor
Castle Combe Manor House
Chaddesley Corbett Brockencote Hall
Chadlington The Manor
Chagford Gidleigh Park
Chagford Great Tree Hotel
Chagford Mill End
Charingworth Charingworth Manor
Chedington Chedington Court
Cheltenham Greenway
Chittlehamholt Highbullen
Churt Frensham Pond Hotel
Climping Bailiffscourt
Colerne Lucknam Park
Cornhill-on-Tweed Tillmouth Park
Corse Lawn Corse Lawn House
Cranbrook Kennel Holt Hotel
Crathorne Crathorne Hall
Crosby-on-Eden Crosby Lodge
Dovedale Izaak Walton Hotel
Dulverton Ashwick House
Easington Grinkle Park
East Grinstead Gravetye Manor
Easton Grey Whatley Manor
Elcot Elcot Park Resort Hotel
Evershot Summer Lodge
Fairy Cross Portledge Hotel
Flitwick Flitwick Manor
Freshford Homewood Park
Freshwater Farringford Hotel
Gillingham Stock Hill House
Gittisham Combe House
Golant Cormorant Hotel
Grasmere Michael's Nook
Grasmere Wordsworth Hotel
Great Snoring Old Rectory
Grizedale Grizedale Lodge
Hackness Hackness Grange
Haslemere Lythe Hill Hotel
Hatfield Heath Down Hall
Hawkchurch Fairwater Head Hotel
Haytor Bel Alp House
Hintlesham Hintlesham Hall
Hockley Heath Nuthurst Grange
Holbeton Alston Hall
Hope Cove Cottage Hotel
Hope Cove Lantern Lodge
Horton-cum-Studley Studley Priory
Hunstrete Hunstrete House
Huntsham Huntsham Court
Hurstbourne Tarrant Esseborne Manor
Jervaulx Jervaulx Hall
Kilve Meadow House
Lamorna Cove Lamorna Cove Hotel
Land's End State House
Langar Langar Hall
Langley-on-Tyne Langley Castle
Leamington Spa Mallory Court
Ledbury Hope End
Lenham Chilston Park
Lewdown Lewtrenchard Manor
Linton Wood Hall
Liskeard Well House
Longhorsley Linden Hall
Looe Talland Bay Hotel
Lower Beeding South Lodge
Lower Slaughter Lower Slaughter Manor
Malvern Cottage in the Wood
Markington Hob Green
Marlow Compleat Angler Hotel
Matlock Riber Hall
Mawnan Smith Budock Vean Hotel
Mawnan Smith Meudon Hotel
Mawnan Smith Nansidwell
Medmenham Danesfield House
Middlecombe Periton Park
Monkton Combe Combe Grove Manor
Morston Morston Hall
Mullion Polurrian Hotel
Nantwich Rookery Hall
New Milton Chewton Glen
North Stoke Springs Hotel
Oakham Hambleton Hall
Otley Chevin Lodge
Poole Haven Hotel
Porlock Oaks Hotel
Portloe Lugger Hotel
Puddington Craxton Wood
Purton Pear Tree
Richmond Petersham Hotel
Rotherwick Tylney Hall
Rothley Rothley Court
Ruckhall Ancient Camp Inn

Salcombe Marine Hotel
Salcombe Soar Mill Cove
Sandiway Nunsmere Hall
Saunton Saunton Sands
Scalby Wrea Head
South Molton Whitechapel Manor
St Martin's St Martin's Hotel
St Mawes Hotel Tresanton
Stapleford Stapleford Park
Ston Easton Ston Easton Park
Storrington Abingworth Hall
Storrington Little Thakeham
Stow-on-the-Wold Wyck Hill House
Stratford-upon-Avon Billesley Manor
Stratford-upon-Avon Ettington Park
Stratford-upon-Avon Welcombe Hotel
Studland Bay Knoll House
Sutton Coldfield New Hall
Swinfen Swinfen Hall
Taplow Cliveden
Teffont Evias Howard's House
Tetbury Calcot Manor
Thornbury Thornbury Castle
Thurlestone Thurlestone Hotel
Torquay Osborne Hotel
Tresco Island Hotel
Turners Hill Alexander House
Ullswater Leeming House
Ullswater Old Church Hotel
Ullswater Rampsbeck Country House Hotel
Ullswater Sharrow Bay
Upper Slaughter Lords of the Manor
Veryan Nare Hotel
Walkington Manor House
Warminster Bishopstrow House
West Bexington Manor Hotel
Whimple Woodhayes Hotel
Whitewell Inn at Whitewell
Winchester Lainston House
Windermere Merewood Hotel
Windsor Oakley Court
Winsford Royal Oak Inn
Woody Bay Woody Bay Hotel
Woolton Hill Hollington House Hotel
York Middlethorpe Hall

Scotland

Aberfeldy Farleyer House
Achiltibuie Summer Isles
Advie Tulchan Lodge
Airth Airth Castle
Altnaharra Altnaharra Hotel
Ardentinny Ardentinny Hotel
Arduaine Loch Melfort Hotel
Arisaig Arisaig House
Auchterarder Auchterarder House
Auchterarder Gleneagles Hotel
Ballater Tullich Lodge
Banchory Invery House
Banchory Raemoir House
Beattock Auchen Castle
Chapel of Garioch Pittodrie House
Crinan Crinan Hotel
Dalguise Kinnaird
Drumnadrochit Polmaily House
Dryburgh Dryburgh Abbey
Dulnain Bridge Auchendean Lodge
Dunblane Cromlix House
Duror Stewart Hotel
Eriska Isle of Eriska
Ettrickbridge Ettrickshaws Hotel
Fort William Inverlochy Castle
Fort William Mercury Hotel
Garve Inchbae Lodge
Gatehouse of Fleet Cally Palace
Glenborrodale Glenborrodale Castle
Glenelg Glenelg Inn
Gullane Greywalls Hotel
Harray Loch Merkister Hotel
Helmsdale Navidale House
Inverness Bunchrew House
Inverness Culloden House
Inverness Dunain Park
Isle of Raasay Isle of Raasay Hotel
Kelso Ednam House
Kelso Sunlaws House
Kentallen of Appin Ardsheal House
Kentallen of Appin Holly Tree
Kilchrenan Ardanaiseig
Kilchrenan Taychreggan Hotel
Kildrummy Kildrummy Castle
Killiecrankie Killiecrankie Hotel
Kilmore Glenfeochan House
Kilwinning Montgreenan Mansion
Kinclaven by Stanley Ballathie House
Langbank Gleddoch House
Maryculter Maryculter House
Newton Stewart Kirroughtree Hotel
North Berwick Marine Hotel
North Middleton Borthwick Castle
Oban Knipoch Hotel
Onich Allt-nan-Ros Hotel
Onich Lodge on the Loch
Onich Onich Hotel
Peebles Cringletie House
Peebles Peebles Hotel Hydro
Pitlochry Green Park Hotel
Port Appin Airds Hotel
Port William Corsemalzie House
Portpatrick Knockinaam Lodge
Rockcliffe Baron's Craig
Scarista Scarista House
Scourie Eddrachilles Hotel
Skelmorlie Manor Park
Sleat Kinloch Lodge
Spean Bridge Letterfinlay Lodge
St Fillans Four Seasons Hotel
Strachur Creggans Inn
Strathtummel Port-an-Eilean Hotel
Talladale Loch Maree Hotel
Tarbert Stonefield Castle
Tiroran Tiroran House
Turnberry Turnberry Hotel
Ullapool Altnaharrie Inn
Whitebridge Knockie Lodge

Wales

Aberdovey Plas Penhelig
Abersoch Porth Tocyn Hotel
Aberystwyth Conrah Country Hotel

Beaumaris Bulkeley Arms
Beddgelert Royal Goat Hotel
Bontddu Bontddu Hall
Conwy Sychnant Pass Hotel
Crickhowell Gliffaes Country House Hotel
Eglwysfach Ynyshir Hall
Gwbert-on-Sea Cliff Hotel
Lake Vyrnwy Lake Vyrnwy Hotel
Llanarmon Dyffryn Ceiriog Hand Hotel
Llanarmon Dyffryn Ceiriog West Arms Hotel
Llandderfel Pale Hall
Llandudno Bodysgallen Hall
Llangammarch Wells Lake Country House Hotel
Llansanffraid Glan Conwy Old Rectory
Llyswen Llangoed Hall
Northop Soughton Hall
Pantmawr Glansevern Arms
Penmaenpool George III Hotel
Porthkerry Egerton Grey
Portmeirion Hotel Portmeirion
Reynoldston Fairyhill
Rossett Llyndir Hall
St David's Warpool Court
Talsarnau Maes-y-Neaudd

Channel Islands

Rozel Bay Chateau la Chaire
St Brelade's Bay Hotel L'Horizon
St Saviour Longueville Manor
Sark Hotel Petit Champ
Sark Stocks Hotel

Republic of Ireland

Adare Adare Manor
Ballylickey Ballylickey Manor House
Ballylickey Sea View Hotel
Ballynahinch Ballynahinch Castle
Ballyvaughan Gregans Castle
Beaufort Dunloe Castle
Caragh Lake Hotel Ard-na-Sidhe
Caragh Lake Caragh Lodge
Cashel Cashel House
Clifden Abbeyglen Castle
Clifden Ardagh Hotel
Clifden Rock Glen Manor
Delgany Glenview Hotel
Dingle Dingle Skellig Hotel
Dundrum Dundrum House
Dunlavin Rathsallagh House
Ferrycarrig Bridge Ferrycarrig Hotel
Glen of Aherlow Aherlow House
Gorey Marlfield House
Innishannon Innishannon House Hotel
Kanturk Assolas Country House
Kenmare Sheen Falls Lodge
Killarney Aghadoe Heights Hotel
Killarney Cahernane Hotel
Killarney Hotel Europe
Letterfrack Rosleague Manor
Mallow Longueville House
Maynooth Moyglare Manor
Newmarket-on-Fergus Dromoland Castle
Oughterard Currarevagh House
Parknasilla Great Southern
Rathmullan Rathmullan House
Rathnew Hunter's Hotel
Renvyle Renvyle House
Riverstown Coopershill House
Scotshouse Hilton Park
Shanagarry Ballymaloe House
Straffan Kildare Hotel
Thomastown Mount Juliet Hotel
Waterford Waterford Castle
Wicklow Old Rectory

Hotels with Sporting Facilities

Fishing

England

Alcester Arrow Mill
Allendale Bishop Field
Ambleside Nanny Brow
Appleby-in-Westmorland Tufton Arms
Aylesbury Hartwell House
Bagshot Pennyhill Park
Baslow Cavendish Hotel
Bassenthwaite Armathwaite Hall
Beccles Waveney House
Belton Belton Woods Hotel
Bibury The Swan
Bigbury-on-Sea Burgh Island Hotel
Bodymoor Heath Marston Farm
Bolton Abbey Devonshire Arms
Bowness-on-Windermere Linthwaite House
Burton-on-Trent Riverside Inn
Calbourne Swainston Manor
Castle Combe Manor House
Chagford Gidleigh Park
Chagford Mill End
Chittlehamholt Highbullen
Clearwell Clearwell Castle
Donnington Donnington Valley Hotel
Dovedale Izaak Walton Hotel
Dulverton Carnarvon Arms

Easington Grinkle Park
East Grinstead Gravetye Manor
Egham Runnymede Hotel
Fairford Bull Hotel
Falmouth Greenbank Hotel
Fossebridge Fossebridge Inn
Gittisham Combe House
Grasmere White Moss House
Hanchurch Hanchurch Manor
Harvington The Mill
Hintlesham Hintlesham Hall
Hinton Hinton Grange
Hollingbourne Great Danes
Huntsham Huntsham Court
Kingham Mill House
Lenham Chilston Park
Lewdown Lewtrenchard Manor
Lifton Arundell Arms
Linton Wood Hall
Longham Bridge House
Lower Slaughter Lower Slaughter Manor
Lympsham Batch Farm Country Hotel
Maiden Newton Maiden Newton House
Marlow Compleat Angler Hotel
Mawnan Smith Meudon Hotel
Meriden Forest of Arden Hotel
Minster Lovell Old Swan
Mullion Polurrian Hotel
Needham Market Pipps Ford
Newbury Millwaters
Newby Bridge The Swan
Otley Chevin Lodge
Puckrup Puckrup Hall
Quorn The Quorn
Ravenstonedale Black Swan Inn
Ross-on-Wye Pengethley Manor
Rowsley Peacock Hotel
Ruckhall Ancient Camp Inn
Salcombe Marine Hotel
Samlesbury Tickled Trout
Seaview Seaview Hotel
Stanstead Abbots Briggens House
Stapleford Stapleford Park
Stonehouse Stonehouse Court
Stratfield Turgis Wellington Arms
Stratford-upon-Avon Ettington Park
Sudbury Mill Hotel
Taplow Cliveden
Tresco Island Hotel
Ullswater Old Church Hotel
Ullswater Rampsbeck Country House Hotel
Upper Slaughter Lords of the Manor
Wallingford Shillingford Bridge Hotel
Wansford-in-England Haycock Hotel
Wareham Priory Hotel
Warminster Bishopstrow House
Weston-under-Penyard Wharton Lodge
Whitewell Inn at Whitewell
Winchester Lainston House
Windsor Oakley Court
Winsford Royal Oak Inn
Woodbridge Seckford Hall
Worthington Kilhey Court

Scotland

Advie Tulchan Lodge
Alexandria Cameron House
Altnaharra Altnaharra Hotel
Annan Warmanbie Hotel
Ardentinny Ardentinny Hotel
Auchterarder Gleneagles Hotel
Ballachulish Ballachulish Hotel
Banchory Invery House
Banchory Raemoir House
Beattock Auchen Castle
Bonnyrigg Dalhousie Castle
Callander Roman Camp
Dalguise Kinnaird
Dryburgh Dryburgh Abbey
Dulnain Bridge Muckrach Lodge
Dunblane Cromlix House
Eriska Isle of Eriska
Ettrickbridge Ettrickshaws Hotel
Fort William Inverlochy Castle
Garve Inchbae Lodge
Gatehouse of Fleet Cally Palace
Glenborrodale Glenborrodale Castle
Glenelg Glenelg Inn
Harray Loch Merkister Hotel
Helmsdale Navidale House
Inverness Bunchrew House
Kelso Ednam House
Kelso Sunlaws House
Kenmore Kenmore Hotel
Kentallen of Appin Holly Tree
Kilchrenan Ardanaiseig
Kilchrenan Taychreggan Hotel
Kilfinan Kilfinan Hotel
Kilmore Glenfeochan House
Kinclaven by Stanley Ballathie House
Kinlochbervie Kinlochbervie Hotel
Kirkmichael Log Cabin Hotel
Lochinver Inver Lodge Hotel
Melrose George & Abbotsford Hotel
Pitlochry Green Park Hotel
Port William Corsemalzie House
Portpatrick Knockinaam Lodge
Scourie Scourie Hotel
Skeabost Bridge Skeabost House
Sleat Kinloch Lodge
Stewarton Chapeltoun House
Strachur Creggans Inn
Strathtummel Port-an-Eilean Hotel
Talladale Loch Maree Hotel
Tobermory Tobermory Hotel
Tweedsmuir Crook Inn
Whitebridge Knockie Lodge

Wales

Beddgelert Royal Goat Hotel
Crickhowell Gliffaes Country House Hotel
Lake Vyrnwy Lake Vyrnwy Hotel
Llanarmon Dyffryn Ceiriog Hand Hotel
Llanarmon Dyffryn Ceiriog West Arms Hotel
Llandderfel Pale Hall
Llandrillo Tyddyn Llan
Llangammarch Wells Lake Country House Hotel
Llangollen Hand Hotel
Llangollen Royal Hotel

Llanrug Seiont Manor
Llyswen Llangoed Hall
Penmaenpool George III Hotel
Reynoldston Fairyhill
Ruthin Ruthin Castle
Talyllyn Tynycornel Hotel

Channel Islands

Castel La Grande Mare Hotel

Isle of Man

Ramsey Grand Island Hotel

Republic of Ireland

Adare Adare Manor
Ballina Mount Falcon Castle
Ballyconnell Slieve Russell Hotel
Ballylickey Ballylickey Manor House
Ballymote Temple House
Ballynahinch Ballynahinch Castle
Beaufort Dunloe Castle
Caragh Lake Hotel Ard-na-Sidhe
Caragh Lake Caragh Lodge
Cashel Cashel House
Cashel Zetland House
Castledermot Kilkea Castle
Clifden Rock Glen Manor
Cong Ashford Castle
Crossmolina Enniscoe House
Dundrum Dundrum House
Ennis Auburn Lodge
Hodson Bay Hodson Bay Hotel
Kanturk Assolas Country House
Kenmare Sheen Falls Lodge
Kilcoran Kilcoran Lodge
Killarney Aghadoe Heights Hotel
Killarney Cahernane Hotel
Killiney Court Hotel
Kinsale Blue Haven Hotel
Letterfrack Rosleague Manor
Mallow Longueville House
Moycullen Cloonabinnia House Hotel
Newmarket-on-Fergus Dromoland Castle
Newport Newport House
Oughterard Currarevagh House
Parknasilla Great Southern
Renvyle Renvyle House
Riverstown Coopershill House
Rossnowlagh Sand House
Scotshouse Hilton Park
Straffan Kildare Hotel
Thomastown Mount Juliet Hotel

Golf

England

Barnham Broom Barnham Broom Hotel
Bearsted Tudor Park
Belton Belton Woods Hotel
Cambridge Cambridgeshire Moat House
Carlyon Bay Carlyon Bay Hotel
Chedington Chedington Court
Croydon Selsdon Park
Goodwood Goodwood Park
Heathrow Airport Holiday Inn Crowne Plaza Heathrow
Hintlesham Hintlesham Hall
Hinton Hinton Grange
Hythe Hythe Imperial
Meriden Forest of Arden Hotel
Morley Breadsall Priory
Mottram St Andrew Mottram Hall
Sawbridgeworth Manor of Groves
Stratford-upon-Avon Welcombe Hotel
Telford Telford Hotel
Tewkesbury Tewkesbury Park
Thundridge Hanbury Manor
Uckfield Horsted Place
Washington Moat House
Weston-under-Redcastle Hawkstone Park
Windsor Oakley Court
Wishaw The Belfry

Scotland

Auchterarder Gleneagles Hotel
Cumbernauld Westerwood Hotel
Gatehouse of Fleet Cally Palace
Irvine Hospitality Inn
Kenmore Kenmore Hotel
Kirknewton Dalmahoy Hotel, Golf & Country Club
Langbank Gleddoch House
Melrose Burts Hotel
Scone Murrayshall House
Turnberry Turnberry Hotel

Wales

Chepstow St Pierre Hotel
Portmeirion Hotel Portmeirion

Channel Islands

Castel La Grande Mare Hotel
Castel Hougue du Pommier

Republic of Ireland

Ballyconnell Slieve Russell Hotel
Carrickmacross Nuremore Hotel
Dundrum Dundrum House
Kenmare Park Hotel
Newmarket-on-Fergus Clare Inn Hotel
Newmarket-on-Fergus Dromoland Castle
Scotshouse Hilton Park
Straffan Kildare Hotel
Thomastown Mount Juliet Hotel
Waterford Waterford Castle

Indoor Swimming

England

Alsager Manor House
Appleby-in-Westmorland Appleby Manor Hotel
Ascot Royal Berkshire
Ashford Ashford International
Aylesbury Forte Posthouse
Aylesbury Hartwell House
Barford Glebe Hotel
Barnham Broom Barnham Broom Hotel
Basingstoke Hilton National
Basingstoke The Ringway
Bassenthwaite Armathwaite Hall
Bath Bath Spa Hotel
Bath Hilton National
Beaconsfield Bellhouse Hotel
Bearsted Tudor Park
Belton Belton Woods Hotel
Bexleyheath Swallow Hotel
Birmingham Copthorne Hotel
Birmingham Forte Posthouse
Birmingham Forte Crest
Birmingham Holiday Inn
Birmingham Hyatt Regency
Birmingham Swallow Hotel
Blackpool Imperial Hotel
Blackpool Pembroke Hotel
Blakeney Blakeney Hotel
Bolton Last Drop Village Hotel
Borrowdale Stakis Lodore Swiss Hotel
Bournemouth Chine Hotel
Bournemouth Norfolk Royale
Bournemouth Palace Court
Bournemouth Royal Bath Hotel
Bowness-on-Windermere Belsfield Hotel
Bracknell Coppid Beech Hotel
Bramhope Forte Crest
Bramhope Parkway Hotel
Brentwood Forte Posthouse
Brierley Hill Copthorne Hotel
Brighouse Forte Crest
Brighton Brighton Metropole
Brighton Grand Hotel
Brighton Hospitality Inn
Bristol Aztec Hotel
Bristol Bristol Marriott Hotel
Bristol Forte Crest
Bristol Hilton Hotel
Bristol Redwood Lodge
Bristol Stakis Bristol Hotel
Bristol Swallow Royal Hotel
Broadway Lygon Arms
Brockenhurst Balmer Lawn Hotel
Brockenhurst Careys Manor
Bromsgrove Stakis Country Court
Broughton Broughton Park
Broxbourne Cheshunt Marriott Hotel
Burnham Burnham Beeches Moat House
Burnley Oaks Hotel
Calbourne Swainston Manor
Cambridge Cambridgeshire Moat House
Cambridge Forte Posthouse
Cambridge Holiday Inn
Canterbury Ebury Hotel
Carlisle Swallow Hilltop
Carlyon Bay Carlyon Bay Hotel
Castle Donington Donington Thistle
Charingworth Charingworth Manor
Cheltenham Golden Valley Thistle
Chester Abbots Well
Chester Forte Posthouse
Chester Mollington Banastre
Chester Rowton Hall
Chesterfield Chesterfield Hotel
Chipping Norton Crown & Cushion
Chiseldon Chiseldon House
Chittlehamholt Highbullen
Chollerford George Hotel
Churt Frensham Pond Hotel
Coatham Mundeville Hall garth
Cobham Hilton National
Colerne Lucknam Park
Constantine Bay Treglos Hotel
Cooden Cooden Resort Hotel
Copdock Ipswich Moat House
Coventry Forte Crest
Crick Forte Posthouse Northampton Rugby
Croydon Croydon Park
Croydon Selsdon Park
Dartmouth Stoke Lodge
Doncaster Moat House
Dover Moat House
Driffield Bell Hotel
Durham Royal County Hotel
Eastbourne Grand Hotel
Egham Runnymede Hotel
Elcot Elcot Park Resort Hotel

Evesham Evesham Hotel
Exeter Forte Crest
Falmouth Falmouth Hotel
Falmouth Royal Duchy Hotel
Falmouth St Michael's Hotel
Fareham Forte Posthouse
Fareham Solent Hotel
Farnborough Forte Crest
Fawkham Brandshatch Place
Ferndown Dormy Hotel
Garforth Hilton National
Gateshead Newcastle Marriott Hotel
Gateshead Swallow Hotel
Gatwick Airport Chequers Thistle
Gatwick Airport Copthorne Effingham Park
Gatwick Airport Europa Gatwick
Gatwick Airport Forte Crest Gatwick
Gatwick Airport Gatwick Hilton International
Gatwick Airport Holiday Inn Gatwick
Gatwick Airport Ramada Hotel Gatwick
Gloucester Forte Crest
Golant Cormorant Hotel
Goodwood Goodwood Park
Grasmere Wordsworth Hotel
Great Baddow Pontlands Park
Guildford Forte Crest
Hackness Hackness Grange
Harome Pheasant Hotel
Harrogate Majestic Hotel
Harrogate Hotel St George
Hatfield Heath Down Hall
Havant Forte Posthouse
Haydock Forte Posthouse
Haydock Haydock Thistle
Heathrow Airport Edwardian International
Heathrow Airport Excelsior Hotel
Heathrow Airport Heathrow Hilton Hotel
Heathrow Airport Holiday Inn Crowne Plaza Heathrow
Heathrow Airport Ramada Hotel Heathrow
Heathrow Airport Sheraton Skyline
Hethersett Park Farm
Hinckley Hinckley Island Hotel
Hintlesham Hintlesham Hall
Hinton Hinton Grange
Holbeton Alston Hall
Hollingbourne Great Danes
Hope Cove Lantern Lodge
Huddersfield Pennine Hilton National
Hull Forte Crest
Hythe Hythe Imperial
Hythe Stade Court
Knaresborough Dower House
Knutsford Cottons Hotel
Lancaster Forte Posthouse
Langdale Langdale Hotel
Leeds Holiday Inn Crowne Plaza
Leicester Holiday Inn
Leicester Stakis Country Court
Linton Wood Hall
Liverpool Britannia Adelphi Hotel
Liverpool Moat House
Lockington Hilton National E Midlands Airport
Lower Beeding Cisswood House
Lower Slaughter Lower Slaughter Manor
Lymington Passford House
Lytham St Annes Dalmeny Hotel
Maidenhead Holiday Inn
Maidstone Stakis Country Court Hotel
Manchester Britannia Hotel
Manchester Copthorne Hotel
Manchester Holiday Inn Crowne Plaza
Manchester Hotel Piccadilly
Manchester Portland Thistle
Manchester Sachas Hotel
Manchester Airport Forte Crest
Manchester Airport Hilton International
Matlock Bath New Bath Hotel
Mawnan Smith Budock Vean Hotel
Meriden Forest of Arden Hotel
Milton Keynes Forte Crest
Milton Keynes Friendly Hotel
Monkton Combe Combe Grove Manor
Moreton-in-Marsh Manor House
Morley Breadsall Priory
Mottram St Andrew Mottram Hall
Mullion Polurrian Hotel
New Milton Chewton Glen
Newbury Foley Lodge
Newbury Hilton National
Newbury Stakis Newbury Hotel
Newcastle-under-Lyme Forte Posthouse
Newcastle-upon-Tyne Copthorne Hotel
Newcastle-upon-Tyne Holiday Inn
Newcastle-upon-Tyne Novotel
Newcastle-upon-Tyne Swallow Gosforth Park
Newquay Hotel Bristol
Newton Abbot Passage House
Nidd Nidd Hall
Northampton Stakis Country Court
Northampton Swallow Hotel
Norwich Airport Ambassador Hotel
Norwich Forte Posthouse
Norwich Friendly Hotel
Norwich Norwich Sport Village Hotel
Norwich Hotel Norwich
Norwich Sprowston Manor
Nutfield Nutfield Priory
Oxford Moat House
Penrith North Lakes Hotel
Peterborough Forte Posthouse
Peterborough Moat House
Peterborough Swallow Hotel
Pingewood Kirtons Farm Country Club
Plymouth Boringdon Hall
Plymouth Copthorne Hotel
Plymouth Moat House
Poole Haven Hotel
Poole Sandbanks Hotel
Portsmouth Forte Posthouse
Portsmouth Portsmouth Marriott Hotel
Reading Forte Posthouse
Reading Holiday Inn
Reading Ramada Hotel
Rochester Bridgewood Manor Hotel
Rochester Forte Posthouse
Rotherwick Tylney Hall
Runcorn Forte Posthouse
St Albans Sopwell House
St Ives Garrack Hotel
St Martin's St Martin's Hotel

Salcombe Marine Hotel
Salcombe Soar Mill Cove
Salcombe South Sands Hotel
Salcombe Tides Reach
Samlesbury Swallow Trafalgar
Samlesbury Tickled Trout
Saunton Saunton Sands
Seale Hog's Back Hotel
Shaftesbury Royal Chase Hotel
Shanklin Cliff Tops Hotel
Sheffield Forte Crest
Sheffield Moat House
Sheffield St George Swallow Hotel
Shifnal Park House
Sidmouth Fortfield Hotel
Sidmouth Victoria Hotel
Skipton Randell's Hotel
Slough Copthorne Hotel Slough/Windsor
Slough Heathrow/Slough Marriott Hotel
Solihull Moat House
Solihull St John's Swallow Hotel
South Milford Forte Posthouse Leeds/Selby
South Mimms Forte Posthouse
South Normanton Swallow Hotel
South Wootton Knights Hill Hotel
Southampton Forte Posthouse
Southampton Southampton Park Hotel
Stafford Tillington Hall
Standish Almond Brook Moat House
Stockton-on-Tees Swallow Hotel
Stoke-on-Trent Stakis Grand Hotel
Stoke-on-Trent Stoke-on-Trent Moat House
Stratford-upon-Avon Billesley Manor
Stratford-upon-Avon Ettington Park
Stratford-upon-Avon Moat House International
Stratford-upon-Avon Windmill Park
Sunderland Swallow Hotel
Sutton Holiday Inn
Sutton Coldfield Moor Hall
Sutton Coldfield Penns Hall
Swindon Blunsdon House
Swindon De Vere Hotel
Swindon Forte Posthouse
Swindon Swindon Marriott Hotel
Taplow Cliveden
Telford Holiday Inn Telford/Ironbridge
Telford Moat House
Telford Telford Hotel
Tewkesbury Tewkesbury Park
Thundridge Hanbury Manor
Thurlestone Thurlestone Hotel
Torquay Grand Hotel
Torquay Imperial Hotel
Torquay Osborne Hotel
Torquay Palace Hotel
Tunbridge Wells Spa Hotel
Uckfield Horsted Place
Walberton Avisford Park
Walsall Wood Baron's Court Hotel
Wareham Springfield Country Hotel
Warminster Bishopstrow House
Warrington Lord Daresbury Hotel
Warwick Hilton National
Washington Moat House
Watford Hilton National
West Runton The Links Country Park Hotel & G C
Wetheral The Crown
Willerby Grange Park
Wilmslow Moat House
Winterbourne Grange Resort Hotel
Wishaw The Belfry
Witney Witney Lodge
Wokingham Stakis St Anne's Manor
Woodbridge Seckford Hall
Woolacombe Woolacombe Bay Hotel
Worthington Kilhey Court
Wrotham Heath Forte Posthouse Maidstone Sevenoaks
York Novotel
York Swallow Hotel

Scotland

Aberdeen Holiday Inn Crowne Plaza
Aberdeen Stakis Tree Tops
Aberdeen Airport Aberdeen Marriott Hotel
Airth Airth Castle
Alexandria Cameron House
Auchterarder Gleneagles Hotel
Aviemore Stakis Aviemore Four Seasons
Aviemore Stakis Coylumbridge Resort Hotel
Ayr Caledonian Hotel
Ballater Craigendarroch Hotel
Contin Craigdarroch Lodge
Crieff Crieff Hydro
Cumbernauld Westerwood Hotel
Drymen Buchanan Highland Hotel
Dunblane Stakis Dunblane Hydro
East Kilbride Westpoint Hotel
Edinburgh The Balmoral
Edinburgh Carlton Highland
Edinburgh Royal Terrace Hotel
Edinburgh Scandic Crown Hotel
Edinburgh Sheraton Grand Hotel
Edinburgh Swallow Royal Scot
Elgin Mansion House
Erskine Forte Posthouse
Forfar Royal Hotel
Gatehouse of Fleet Cally Palace
Glasgow Glasgow Hilton
Glasgow Glasgow Marriott Hotel
Glasgow Jurys Pond Hotel
Glasgow Moat House International
Glasgow Swallow Hotel
Gourock Stakis Gantock Hotel
Inverness Caledonian Hotel
Inverness Dunain Park
Inverness Kingsmills Hotel
Irvine Hospitality Inn
Kinross Windlestrae Hotel
Kirknewton Dalmahoy Hotel, Golf & Country Club
Lerwick Shetland Hotel
Peebles Peebles Hotel Hydro
Peterhead Waterside Inn
Pitlochry Pitlochry Hydro
St Andrews St Andrews Old Course Hotel

South Queensferry Forth Bridges Moat House
Stranraer North West Castle
Troon Marine Highland Hotel
Turnberry Turnberry Hotel

Wales

Aberdovey Trefeddian Hotel
Abersoch Riverside Hotel
Aberystwyth Conrah Country Hotel
Barry Mount Sorrel Hotel
Cardiff Cardiff Marriott Hotel
Cardiff Copthorne Hotel
Cardiff Forte Posthouse
Cardiff Moat House
Chepstow St Pierre Hotel
Ewloe St David's Park Hotel
Lamphey Court Hotel
Llandudno Empire Hotel
Llandudno St Tudno Hotel
Llangybi Cwrt Bleddyn Hotel
Llanrug Seiont Manor
Miskin Miskin Manor
Newport Celtic Manor
Newport Hilton National
Newport Stakis Country Court Hotel
Penally Penally Abbey
Rossett Llyndir Hall
St David's Warpool Court
Swansea Forte Crest
Swansea Swansea Marriott Hotel

Channel Islands

St Brelade Atlantic Hotel
St Brelade's Bay Hotel L'Horizon
St Helier Apollo Hotel
St Helier Beaufort Hotel
St Helier Grand Hotel
St Helier Hotel de France
St Peter Mermaid Hotel
St Peter Port St Pierre Park
St Saviour Merton Hotel & Leisure Centre

Isle of Man

Douglas Palace Hotel
Douglas Sefton Hotel
Ramsey Grand Island Hotel

Northern Ireland

Comber La Mon House
Dunadry Dunadry Inn
Holywood Culloden Hotel
Portballintrae Bayview Hotel

Republic of Ireland

Adare Adare Manor
Ballina Downhill Hotel
Ballyconnell Slieve Russell Hotel
Beaufort Dunloe Castle
Bunratty Fitzpatricks Shannon Shamrock
Carrickmacross Nuremore Hotel
Castledermot Kilkea Castle
Cork Fitzpatrick Silver Springs
Cork Jurys Hotel
Cork Rochestown Park Hotel
Dingle Dingle Skellig Hotel
Dublin Berkeley Court
Dublin Jurys Hotel and Towers
Dublin Airport Forte Crest
Dundalk Ballymascanlon House
Dunlavin Rathsallagh House
Galway Corrib Great Southern Hotel
Galway Great Southern
Hodson Bay Hodson Bay Hotel
Kilcoran Kilcoran Lodge
Kilkenny Newpark Hotel
Killarney Aghadoe Heights Hotel
Killarney Hotel Europe
Killarney Great Southern
Killarney Killarney Park Hotel
Killarney Torc Great Southern
Killiney Fitzpatrick's Castle
Kinsale Actons Hotel
Kinsale Blue Haven Hotel
Limerick Castletroy Park Hotel
Limerick Greenhills Hotel
Limerick Jurys Hotel
Limerick Limerick Inn
Newmarket-on-Fergus Clare Inn Hotel
Oughterard Connemara Gateway Hotel
Parknasilla Great Southern
Rathmullan Rathmullan House
Rosslare Great Southern
Rosslare Kelly's Strand Hotel
Sligo Sligo Park
Straffan Kildare Hotel
Thomastown Mount Juliet Hotel
Waterford Jurys Hotel
Waterford Tower Hotel
Waterford Waterford Castle

Outdoor Swimming

England

Aldridge Fairlawns
Alveston Forte Posthouse
Ascot Berystede Hotel
Bagshot Pennyhill Park

Bath Priory Hotel
Beanacre Beechfield House
Birmingham Forte Posthouse
Bognor Regis Royal Norfolk
Bonchurch Winterbourne Hotel
Borrowdale Stakis Lodore Swiss Hotel
Bournemouth Carlton Hotel
Bournemouth Chine Hotel
Bournemouth Swallow Highcliff Hotel
Bowness-on-Windermere Old England Hotel
Bradford Novotel
Bradford-on-Avon Woolley Grange
Bristol Redwood Lodge
Broadway Collin House
Brockenhurst Balmer Lawn Hotel
Broxted Whitehall
Buckland Buckland Manor
Burley Burley Manor
Carlyon Bay Carlyon Bay Hotel
Castle Combe Manor House
Charlecote Charlecote Pheasant
Cheltenham Hotel de la Bere
Chittlehamholt Highbullen
Climping Bailiffscourt
Cooden Cooden Resort Hotel
Corse Lawn Corse Lawn House
Coventry Novotel
Croydon Selsdon Park
Dartmouth Stoke Lodge
Dorking White Horse
Dulverton Carnarvon Arms
Eastbourne Grand Hotel
Easton Grey Whatley Manor
Egham Great Fosters
Evershot Summer Lodge
Exmouth Imperial Hotel
Fairy Cross Portledge Hotel
Falmouth Falmouth Hotel
Farnham Trevena House
Faugh String of Horses Inn
Freshwater Farringford Hotel
Gatwick Airport Chequers Thistle
Gatwick Airport Forte Posthouse
Gloucester Hatton Court
Great Baddow Pontlands Park
Great Milton Le Manoir aux Quat'Saisons
Grimston Congham Hall
Harvington The Mill
Hatherleigh George Hotel
Helland Bridge Tredethy Country Hotel
Helmsley Feversham Arms
Holbeton Alston Hall
Hunstrete Hunstrete House
Ipswich Forte Posthouse
Kidderminster Stone Manor
Lamorna Cove Lamorna Cove Hotel
Leamington Spa Mallory Court
Liskeard Well House
Looe Talland Bay Hotel
Lymington Passford House
Lyndhurst Lyndhurst Park
Lyndhurst Parkhill Hotel
Manchester Novotel
Matlock Bath New Bath Hotel
Medmenham Danesfield House
Monkton Combe Combe Grove Manor
Mudeford Avonmouth Hotel
Mullion Polurrian Hotel
Needham Market Pipps Ford
New Milton Chewton Glen
Newlyn Higher Faugan Country House Hotel
Newquay Hotel Riviera
North Stoke Springs Hotel
Nottingham Novotel
Oakham Hambleton Hall
Paignton Palace Hotel
Paignton Redcliffe Hotel
Plymouth Forte Posthouse
Plymouth Novotel
Poole Haven Hotel
Preston Novotel
Ross-on-Wye Pengethley Manor
Rotherwick Tylney Hall
St Austell Boscundle Manor
Salcombe Soar Mill Cove
Saunton Saunton Sands
Sawbridgeworth Manor of Groves
Sedlescombe Brickwall Hotel
Sidmouth Victoria Hotel
Silchester Romans Hotel
Stanstead Abbots Briggens House
Stevenage Novotel
Storrington Abingworth Hall
Storrington Little Thakeham
Stourport-on-Severn Moat House
Studland Bay Knoll House
Taplow Cliveden
Tetbury Calcot Manor
Thurlestone Thurlestone Hotel
Torquay Grand Hotel
Torquay Imperial Hotel
Torquay Livermead Cliff Hotel
Torquay Livermead House
Torquay Osborne Hotel
Torquay Palace Hotel
Tresco Island Hotel
Ventnor Royal Hotel
Veryan Nare Hotel
Walberton Avisford Park
Wallingford Shillingford Bridge Hotel
Wareham Springfield Country Hotel
Warminster Bishopstrow House
Weedon Crossroads Hotel
Weston-on-the-Green Weston Manor
Weston-super-Mare Grand Atlantic
Weston-under-Redcastle Hawkstone Park
Woolacombe Woolacombe Bay Hotel
Woolton Hill Hollington House Hotel
York Mount Royale

Scotland

Aberdeen Airport Airport Skean Dhu Hotel
Auchterhouse Old Mansion House
Drumnadrochit Polmaily House
Nairn Golf View Hotel
North Berwick Marine Hotel
Selkirk Philipburn House
Tarbert Stonefield Castle

Wales

Abersoch Porth Tocyn Hotel
Coychurch Coed-y-Mwstwr Hotel
Gwbert-on-Sea Cliff Hotel
Llandudno Empire Hotel
Llanwnda Stables Hotel
Portmeirion Hotel Portmeirion
Talyllyn Tynycornel Hotel

Channel Islands

Bouley Bay Water's Edge Hotel
Castel La Grande Mare Hotel
Castel Hougue du Pommier
Forest Mallard Hotel
Grouville Grouville Bay Hotel
Herm White House
Portelet Bay Portelet Hotel
St Aubin Old Court House Inn
St Brelade Atlantic Hotel
St Brelade Hotel Chateau Valeuse
St Brelade La Place Hotel
St Brelade Sea Crest
St Brelade's Bay St Brelade's Bay Hotel
St Clement's Bay Hotel Ambassadeur
St Helier Hotel de France
St Martin Hotel Bon Port
St Martin St Margaret's Lodge
St Martin La Trelade Hotel
St Peter Mermaid Hotel
St Peter Port Braye Lodge
St Peter Port Duke of Richmond
St Peter Port Old Government House
St Saviour Longueville Manor
St Saviour Merton Hotel & Leisure Centre
Sark Aval Du Creux
Sark Hotel Petit Champ
Sark Stocks Hotel

Republic of Ireland

Ballylickey Ballylickey Manor House
Clifden Abbeyglen Castle
Cork Jurys Hotel
Dublin Jurys Hotel and Towers
Renvyle Renvyle House
Rosslare Kelly's Strand Hotel
Shanagarry Ballymaloe House

Leisure Centres

England

Ashford Ashford International
Barford Glebe Hotel
Bassenthwaite Armathwaite Hall
Bath Bath Spa Hotel
Bath Hilton National
Beaconsfield Bellhouse Hotel
Bearsted Tudor Park
Belton Belton Woods Hotel
Birmingham Copthorne Hotel
Birmingham Forte Posthouse
Birmingham Holiday Inn
Birmingham Hyatt Regency
Blackpool Imperial Hotel
Bolton Last Drop Village Hotel
Borrowdale Stakis Lodore Swiss Hotel
Bournemouth Royal Bath Hotel
Bowness-on-Windermere Belsfield Hotel
Bramhope Forte Crest
Brierley Hill Copthorne Hotel
Brighouse Forte Crest
Brighton Brighton Metropole
Brighton Grand Hotel
Bristol Aztec Hotel
Bristol Bristol Marriott Hotel
Bristol Forte Crest
Bristol Hilton Hotel
Bristol Redwood Lodge
Bristol Stakis Bristol Hotel
Bristol Swallow Royal Hotel
Brockenhurst Careys Manor
Bromsgrove Stakis Country Court
Broxbourne Cheshunt Marriott Hotel
Cambridge Forte Posthouse
Carlisle Swallow Hilltop
Charingworth Charingworth Manor
Cheltenham Hotel de la Bere
Chester Abbots Well
Chester Forte Posthouse
Chester Mollington Banastre
Chester Rowton Hall
Chesterfield Chesterfield Hotel
Chipping Norton Crown & Cushion
Churt Frensham Pond Hotel
Colerne Lucknam Park
Cooden Cooden Resort Hotel
Copdock Ipswich Moat House
Coventry Forte Crest
Crick Forte Posthouse Northampton Rugby
Croydon Croydon Park
Croydon Selsdon Park
Dartmouth Stoke Lodge
Doncaster Moat House
Dover Moat House
Durham Royal County Hotel
Eastbourne Grand Hotel
Elcot Elcot Park Resort Hotel
Falmouth Falmouth Hotel
Fareham Forte Posthouse
Fareham Solent Hotel
Farnborough Forte Crest
Fawkham Brandshatch Place
Ferndown Dormy Hotel
Garforth Hilton National

Gateshead Swallow Hotel
Gatwick Airport Copthorne Effingham Park
Gatwick Airport Forte Crest Gatwick
Gatwick Airport Gatwick Hilton International
Gatwick Airport Holiday Inn Gatwick
Gatwick Airport Ramada Hotel Gatwick
Gloucester Forte Crest
Grasmere Wordsworth Hotel
Great Baddow Pontlands Park
Harrogate Majestic Hotel
Harrogate Hotel St George
Havant Forte Posthouse
Haydock Forte Posthouse
Haydock Haydock Thistle
Heathrow Airport Edwardian International
Heathrow Airport Excelsior Hotel
Heathrow Airport Heathrow Hilton Hotel
Heathrow Airport Holiday Inn Crowne Plaza Heathrow
Hinckley Hinckley Island Hotel
Holbeton Alston Hall
Hollingbourne Great Danes
Huddersfield Pennine Hilton National
Hythe Hythe Imperial
Knutsford Cottons Hotel
Lancaster Forte Posthouse
Langdale Langdale Hotel
Leeds Holiday Inn Crowne Plaza
Leicester Holiday Inn
Leicester Stakis Country Court
Liverpool Britannia Adelphi Hotel
Liverpool Moat House
Lockington Hilton National E Midlands Airport
Lymington Passford House
Maidstone Stakis Country Court Hotel
Manchester Copthorne Hotel
Manchester Holiday Inn Crowne Plaza
Manchester Portland Thistle
Manchester Sachas Hotel
Manchester Airport Forte Crest
Manchester Airport Hilton International
Meriden Forest of Arden Hotel
Milton Keynes Forte Crest
Monkton Combe Combe Grove Manor
Morley Breadsall Priory
Mullion Polurrian Hotel
New Milton Chewton Glen
Newbury Hilton National
Newbury Stakis Newbury Hotel
Newcastle-under-Lyme Forte Posthouse
Newcastle-upon-Tyne Holiday Inn
Newcastle-upon-Tyne Moat House
Newton Abbot Passage House
Northampton Swallow Hotel
Norwich Forte Posthouse
Norwich Hotel Norwich
Norwich Norwich Sport Village Hotel
Norwich Sprowston Manor
Nutfield Nutfield Priory
Oxford Moat House
Penrith North Lakes Hotel
Peterborough Moat House
Peterborough Swallow Hotel
Portsmouth Portsmouth Marriott Hotel
Reading Forte Posthouse
Reading Ramada Hotel
Rochester Bridgewood Manor Hotel
St Albans Sopwell House
Salcombe Marine Hotel
Salcombe Tides Reach
Samlesbury Swallow Trafalgar
Seale Hog's Back Hotel
Shanklin Cliff Tops Hotel
Sheffield Forte Crest
Sheffield Moat House
Sidmouth Victoria Hotel
Slough Copthorne Hotel Slough/Windsor
Slough Heathrow/Slough Marriott Hotel
Solihull Moat House
Solihull St John's Swallow Hotel
South Mimms Forte Posthouse
South Normanton Swallow Hotel
South Wootton Knights Hill Hotel
Southampton Forte Posthouse
Southampton Southampton Park Hotel
Stafford Tillington Hall
Stoke-on-Trent Stakis Grand Hotel
Stoke-on-Trent Stoke-on-Trent Moat House
Stratford-upon-Avon Moat House International
Stratford-upon-Avon Windmill Park
Sunderland Swallow Hotel
Sutton Holiday Inn
Sutton Coldfield Penns Hall
Swindon Blunsdon House
Swindon De Vere Hotel
Swindon Forte Posthouse
Swindon Swindon Marriott Hotel
Taplow Cliveden
Telford Moat House
Telford Telford Hotel
Tewkesbury Tewkesbury Park
Thundridge Hanbury Manor
Thurlestone Thurlestone Hotel
Torquay Grand Hotel
Torquay Imperial Hotel
Tunbridge Wells Spa Hotel
Walberton Avisford Park
Walsall Wood Baron's Court Hotel
Wareham Springfield Country Hotel
Warrington Lord Daresbury Hotel
Watford Hilton National
Wetheral The Crown
Willerby Grange Park
Wilmslow Moat House
Wishaw The Belfry
Woolacombe Woolacombe Bay Hotel
Wrotham Heath Forte Posthouse Maidstone Sevenoaks
York Swallow Hotel

Scotland

Aberdeen Holiday Inn Crowne Plaza
Aberdeen Stakis Tree Tops
Aberdeen Airport Aberdeen Marriott Hotel
Alexandria Cameron House
Auchterarder Gleneagles Hotel
Aviemore Stakis Aviemore Four Seasons
Aviemore Stakis Coylumbridge Resort Hotel

Ayr Caledonian Hotel
Crieff Crieff Hydro
Dunblane Stakis Dunblane Hydro
East Kilbride Westpoint Hotel
Edinburgh The Balmoral
Edinburgh Carlton Highland
Edinburgh Royal Terrace Hotel
Edinburgh Sheraton Grand Hotel
Edinburgh Swallow Royal Scot
Elgin Mansion House
Erskine Forte Posthouse
Forfar Royal Hotel
Glasgow Glasgow Marriott Hotel
Glasgow Glasgow Hilton
Glasgow Jurys Pond Hotel
Glasgow Moat House International
Glasgow Swallow Hotel
Gourock Stakis Gantock Hotel
Inverness Caledonian Hotel
Inverness Kingsmills Hotel
Kilchrenan Ardanaiseig
Kinross Windlestrae Hotel
Kirknewton Dalmahoy Hotel, Golf & Country Club
Peebles Peebles Hotel Hydro
Peterhead Waterside Inn
St Andrews St Andrews Old Course Hotel
Stranraer North West Castle
Troon Marine Highland Hotel
Turnberry Turnberry Hotel

Wales

Cardiff Cardiff Marriott Hotel
Cardiff Copthorne Hotel
Cardiff Forte Posthouse
Cardiff Moat House
Chepstow St Pierre Hotel
Ewloe St David's Park Hotel
Llangybi Cwrt Bleddyn Hotel
Miskin Miskin Manor
Newport Hilton National
Newport Stakis Country Court Hotel
Rossett Llyndir Hall
Swansea Forte Crest
Swansea Swansea Marriott Hotel

Channel Islands

St Brelade Atlantic Hotel
St Helier Grand Hotel
St Helier Hotel de France
St Peter Port St Pierre Park

Isle of Man

Douglas Palace Hotel
Douglas Sefton Hotel
Ramsey Grand Island Hotel

Northern Ireland

Comber La Mon House
Dunadry Dunadry Inn

Republic of Ireland

Ballina Downhill Hotel
Ballyconnell Slieve Russell Hotel
Bunratty Fitzpatricks Shannon Shamrock
Carrickmacross Nuremore Hotel
Cork Fitzpatrick Silver Springs
Cork Jurys Hotel
Dundalk Ballymascanlon House
Ferrycarrig Bridge Ferrycarrig Hotel
Kilcoran Kilcoran Lodge
Kilkenny Newpark Hotel
Killarney Aghadoe Heights Hotel
Killarney Great Southern
Killiney Fitzpatrick's Castle
Kinsale Actons Hotel
Limerick Castletroy Park Hotel
Limerick Greenhills Hotel
Limerick Jurys Hotel
Limerick Limerick Inn
Parknasilla Great Southern
Rosslare Great Southern
Sligo Sligo Park
Straffan Kildare Hotel
Thomastown Mount Juliet Hotel
Waterford Tower Hotel

Riding

England

Aspley Guise Moore Place
Bagshot Pennyhill Park
Bassenthwaite Armathwaite Hall
Broughton Broughton Park
Burley Burley Manor
Hintlesham Hintlesham Hall
Hinton Hinton Grange
Hunstrete Hunstrete House
Middlecombe Periton Park
Porlock Oaks Hotel
Stratford-upon-Avon Ettington Park
Taplow Cliveden
Thundridge Hanbury Manor
Thurlestone Thurlestone Hotel
Weston-under-Penyard Wharton Lodge
Woolacombe Woolacombe Bay Hotel

Scotland

Auchterarder Gleneagles Hotel
Crieff Crieff Hydro
Duror Stewart Hotel

Eriska Isle of Eriska
Peebles Peebles Hotel Hydro
Turnberry Turnberry Hotel

Northern Ireland

Comber La Mon House

Republic of Ireland

Adare Adare Manor
Beaufort Dunloe Castle
Cong Ashford Castle
Glen of Aherlow Aherlow House
Kenmare Sheen Falls Lodge
Killarney Hotel Europe
Newmarket-on-Fergus Clare Inn Hotel
Newmarket-on-Fergus Dromoland Castle
Parknasilla Great Southern
Renvyle Renvyle House
Thomastown Mount Juliet Hotel

Squash

England

Ascot Royal Berkshire
Barnham Broom Barnham Broom Hotel
Beaconsfield Bellhouse Hotel
Bearsted Tudor Park
Belton Belton Woods Hotel
Birmingham Forte Crest
Bolton Last Drop Village Hotel
Borrowdale Stakis Lodore Swiss Hotel
Brandon Brandon Hall
Bristol Aztec Hotel
Bristol Redwood Lodge
Brockenhurst Balmer Lawn Hotel
Broughton Broughton Park
Burnley Oaks Hotel
Cambridge Cambridgeshire Moat House
Cheltenham Golden Valley Thistle
Cheltenham Hotel de la Bere
Chester Mollington Banastre
Chester Rowton Hall
Chipping Norton Crown & Cushion
Chittlehamholt Highbullen
Churt Frensham Pond Hotel
Cobham Hilton National
Cooden Cooden Resort Hotel
Croydon Croydon Park
Croydon Selsdon Park
Driffield Bell Hotel
Fareham Solent Hotel
Fawkham Brandshatch Place
Ferndown Dormy Hotel
Gatwick Airport Copthorne London Gatwick
Gatwick Airport Europa Gatwick
Gatwick Airport Ramada Hotel Gatwick
Goodwood Goodwood Park
Harrogate Majestic Hotel
Hythe Hythe Imperial
Land's End State House
Langdale Langdale Hotel
Leamington Spa Mallory Court
Ledbury The Feathers
Liverpool Britannia Adelphi Hotel
Lytham St Annes Dalmeny Hotel
Maidenhead Holiday Inn
Manchester Holiday Inn Crowne Plaza
Medmenham Danesfield House
Meriden Forest of Arden Hotel
Morley Breadsall Priory
Mottram St Andrew Mottram Hall
Mullion Polurrian Hotel
Neasham Newbus Arms
Newcastle-upon-Tyne Swallow Gosforth Park
Newquay Hotel Riviera
Nidd Nidd Hall
Norwich Norwich Sport Village Hotel
Nottingham Royal Moat House
Nutfield Nutfield Priory
Oxford Moat House
Penrith North Lakes Hotel
Pingewood Kirtons Farm Country Club
Poole Haven Hotel
Portsmouth Portsmouth Marriott Hotel
Richmond Richmond Gate Hotel
Salcombe Tides Reach
Samlesbury Swallow Trafalgar
Saunton Saunton Sands
Sidmouth Victoria Hotel
Skipton Randell's Hotel
Stourport-on-Severn Moat House
Sutton Coldfield Penns Hall
Swindon Blunsdon House
Swindon Swindon Marriott Hotel
Taplow Cliveden
Tewkesbury Tewkesbury Park
Thundridge Hanbury Manor
Thurlestone Thurlestone Hotel
Torquay Imperial Hotel
Torquay Livermead House
Torquay Palace Hotel
Walberton Avisford Park
Wallingford Shillingford Bridge Hotel
Warrington Lord Daresbury Hotel
Washington Moat House
Weston-on-the-Green Weston Manor
Westonbirt Hare & Hounds
Wilmslow Moat House
Wishaw The Belfry
Woolacombe Woolacombe Bay Hotel

Scotland

Alexandria Cameron House
Auchterarder Gleneagles Hotel
Auchterhouse Old Mansion House
Aviemore Stakis Coylumbridge Resort Hotel
Ballater Craigendarroch Hotel
Banchory Tor-na-Coille Hotel
Chapel of Garioch Pittodrie House
Crieff Crieff Hydro
Drymen Buchanan Highland Hotel
East Kilbride Westpoint Hotel
Edinburgh Carlton Highland
Glasgow Glasgow Marriott Hotel
Kirknewton Dalmahoy Hotel, Golf & Country Club
Langbank Gleddoch House
Peebles Peebles Hotel Hydro
South Queensferry Forth Bridges Moat House
Troon Marine Highland Hotel
Turnberry Turnberry Hotel

Wales

Cardiff Cardiff Marriott Hotel
Chepstow St Pierre Hotel
Gwbert-on-Sea Cliff Hotel
Llangybi Cwrt Bleddyn Hotel
Llanrug Seiont Manor
Miskin Miskin Manor
Talyllyn Tynycornel Hotel

Channel Islands

St Helier Hotel de France
St Saviour Merton Hotel & Leisure Centre

Northern Ireland

Dunmurry Forte Crest Belfast
Holywood Culloden Hotel

Republic of Ireland

Ballina Downhill Hotel
Ballyconnell Slieve Russell Hotel
Carrickmacross Nuremore Hotel
Cork Jurys Hotel
Dundalk Ballymascanlon House
Killiney Fitzpatrick's Castle
Rosslare Kelly's Strand Hotel
Straffan Kildare Hotel

Tennis

England

Abberley Elms Hotel
Abbot's Salford Salford Hall
Alston Lovelady Shield
Ambleside Nanny Brow
Ascot Royal Berkshire
Ashford Eastwell Manor
Aylesbury Hartwell House
Bagshot Pennyhill Park
Bakewell Hassop Hall
Barnham Broom Barnham Broom Hotel
Bassenthwaite Armathwaite Hall
Bath Bath Spa Hotel
Battle Netherfield Place
Beanacre Beechfield House
Bearsted Tudor Park
Belton Belton Woods Hotel
Bigbury-on-Sea Burgh Island Hotel
Bodymoor Heath Marston Farm
Bognor Regis Royal Norfolk
Borrowdale Stakis Lodore Swiss Hotel
Bournemouth Swallow Highcliff Hotel
Bowness-on-Windermere Belsfield Hotel
Bradford-on-Avon Woolley Grange
Bramhope Parkway Hotel
Bramley Bramley Grange
Bristol Redwood Lodge
Broadway Lygon Arms
Brockenhurst Balmer Lawn Hotel
Broxted Whitehall
Buckland Buckland Manor
Burnham Burnham Beeches Moat House
Cambridge Cambridgeshire Moat House
Carlyon Bay Carlyon Bay Hotel
Castle Combe Manor House
Chagford Gidleigh Park
Cheltenham Golden Valley Thistle
Cheltenham Hotel de la Bere
Chipping Gibbon Bridge Country House
Chittlehamholt Highbullen
Climping Bailiffscourt
Coatham Mundeville Hall Garth
Cobham Hilton National
Cobham Woodlands Park
Colerne Lucknam Park
Corse Lawn Corse Lawn House
Croydon Selsdon Park
Dane End Green End Park
Dartmouth Stoke Lodge
Dovedale Peveril of the Peak
Droitwich Spa Chateau Impney
Dulverton Carnarvon Arms
Easington Grinkle Park
East Dereham King's Head
Easton Grey Whatley Manor

Egham Great Fosters
Egham Runnymede Hotel
Elcot Elcot Park Resort Hotel
Evershot Summer Lodge
Exmouth Imperial Hotel
Fairy Cross Portledge Hotel
Farnham Trevena House
Fawkham Brandshatch Place
Ferndown Dormy Hotel
Flitwick Flitwick Manor
Freshford Homewood Park
Freshwater Farringford Hotel
Gillingham Stock Hill House
Goodwood Goodwood Park
Great Ayton Ayton Hall
Great Milton Le Manoir aux Quat'Saisons
Grimston Congham Hall
Hackness Hackness Grange
Harrogate Majestic Hotel
Harvington The Mill
Haslemere Lythe Hill Hotel
Hatfield Heath Down Hall
Hawkhurst Tudor Court
Helmsley Feversham Arms
Hethersett Park Farm
Hintlesham Hintlesham Hall
Hinton Hinton Grange
Holbeton Alston Hall
Hollingbourne Great Danes
Horton-cum-Studley Studley Priory
Hunstrete Hunstrete House
Huntsham Huntsham Court
Hurstbourne Tarrant Esseborne Manor
Hythe Hythe Imperial
Kidderminster Stone Manor
Knutsford Cottons Hotel
Langdale Langdale Hotel
Leamington Spa Mallory Court
Lenham Chilston Park
Liskeard Well House
Longhorsley Linden Hall
Lower Beeding South Lodge
Lower Slaughter Lower Slaughter Manor
Lymington Passford House
Lyndhurst Lyndhurst Park
Lyndhurst Parkhill Hotel
Marlow Compleat Angler Hotel
Matlock Riber Hall
Matlock Bath New Bath Hotel
Mawnan Smith Budock Vean Hotel
Mawnan Smith Nansidwell
Medmenham Danesfield House
Meriden Forest of Arden Hotel
Minster Lovell Old Swan
Monkton Combe Combe Grove Manor
Morley Breadsall Priory
Mottram St Andrew Mottram Hall
Mullion Polurrian Hotel
Nantwich Rookery Hall
Needham Market Pipps Ford
New Milton Chewton Glen
Newcastle-upon-Tyne Swallow Gosforth Park
Newlyn Higher Faugan Country House Hotel
Nidd Nidd Hall
North Stifford Moat House
North Stoke Springs Hotel
Norwich Norwich Sport Village Hotel
Oakham Hambleton Hall
Otley Chevin Lodge
Paignton Palace Hotel
Pingewood Kirtons Farm Country Club
Plymouth Boringdon Hall
Poole Haven Hotel
Ravenstonedale Black Swan Inn
Rochester Bridgewood Manor Hotel
Rotherwick Tylney Hall
Rusper Ghyll Manor
Salcombe Soar Mill Cove
Saunton Saunton Sands
Sawbridgeworth Manor of Groves
Sevenoaks Royal Oak
Sidmouth Victoria Hotel
Silchester Romans Hotel
Six Mile Bottom Swynford Paddocks
Slough Heathrow/Slough Marriott Hotel
South Milford Forte Posthouse Leeds/Selby
South Wootton Knights Hill Hotel
St Margaret's Wallett's Court
Stafford Tillington Hall
Stanstead Abbots Briggens House
Stapleford Stapleford Park
Ston Easton Ston Easton Park
Storrington Abingworth Hall
Storrington Little Thakeham
Stourport-on-Severn Moat House
Stratford-upon-Avon Billesley Manor
Stratford-upon-Avon Ettington Park
Stratford-upon-Avon Welcombe Hotel
Stratford-upon-Avon Windmill Park
Studland Bay Knoll House
Swindon Blunsdon House
Swindon Swindon Marriott Hotel
Taplow Cliveden
Tewkesbury Tewkesbury Park
Thundridge Hanbury Manor
Thurlestone Thurlestone Hotel
Torquay Grand Hotel
Torquay Imperial Hotel
Torquay Livermead House
Torquay Osborne Hotel
Torquay Palace Hotel
Tresco Island Hotel
Tunbridge Wells Spa Hotel
Turners Hill Alexander House
Uckfield Horsted Place
Veryan Nare Hotel
Walberton Avisford Park
Wareham Springfield Country Hotel
Warminster Bishopstrow House
Weedon Crossroads Hotel
West Runton The Links Country Park Hotel & G C
Weston-super-Mare Grand Atlantic
Weston-under-Redcastle Hawkstone Park
Westonbirt Hare & Hounds
Weybridge Oatlands Park
Whimple Woodhayes Hotel
Winchester Lainston House
Wishaw The Belfry
Witherslack Old Vicarage
Wokingham Stakis St Anne's Manor
Woolacombe Woolacombe Bay Hotel
Woolton Hill Hollington House Hotel
Yelverton Moorland Links

Scotland

Aberdeen Stakis Tree Tops
Advie Tulchan Lodge
Alexandria Cameron House
Auchterarder Gleneagles Hotel
Auchterhouse Old Mansion House
Aviemore Stakis Coylumbridge Resort Hotel
Ballater Craigendarroch Hotel
Banchory Invery House
Banchory Raemoir House
Chapel of Garioch Pittodrie House
Contin Craigdarroch Lodge
Crieff Crieff Hydro
Cumbernauld Westerwood Hotel
Dalguise Kinnaird
Drumnadrochit Polmaily House
Drymen Buchanan Highland Hotel
Dunblane Cromlix House
Dunblane Stakis Dunblane Hydro
Eriska Isle of Eriska
Fort William Inverlochy Castle
Gatehouse of Fleet Cally Palace
Glenborrodale Glenborrodale Castle
Gourock Stakis Gantock Hotel
Gullane Greywalls Hotel
Inverness Culloden House
Kelso Sunlaws House
Kenmore Kenmore Hotel
Kentallen of Appin Ardsheal House
Kilchrenan Ardanaseig
Kilwinning Montgreenan Mansion
Kinclaven by Stanley Ballathie House
Kirknewton Dalmahoy Hotel, Golf & Country Club
Nairn Golf View Hotel
Nairn Newton Hotel
Newton Stewart Kirroughtree Hotel
North Berwick Marine Hotel
Peebles Cringletie House
Peebles Peebles Hotel Hydro
Scone Murrayshall House
Turnberry Turnberry Hotel

Wales

Aberdovey Plas Penhelig
Aberdovey Trefeddian Hotel
Abersoch Porth Tocyn Hotel
Chepstow St Pierre Hotel
Coychurch Coed-y-Mwstwr Hotel
Crickhowell Gliffaes Country House Hotel
Lake Vyrnwy Lake Vyrnwy Hotel
Llanarmon Dyffryn Ceiriog Hand Hotel
Llanarmon Dyffryn Ceiriog West Arms Hotel
Llandudno Bodysgallen Hall
Llangammarch Wells Lake Country House Hotel
Llangybi Cwrt Bleddyn Hotel
Llyswen Llangoed Hall
Northop Soughton Hall
Porthkerry Egerton Grey
Portmeirion Hotel Portmeirion
St David's Warpool Court

Channel Islands

Forest Mallard Hotel
Herm White House
Portelet Bay Portelet Hotel
St Brelade Atlantic Hotel
St Brelade's Bay St Brelade's Bay Hotel
St Peter Mermaid Hotel
St Peter Port St Pierre Park
St Saviour Longueville Manor
St Saviour Merton Hotel & Leisure Centre

Northern Ireland

Annalong Glassdrumman Lodge
Holywood Culloden Hotel

Republic of Ireland

Ballina Downhill Hotel
Ballina Mount Falcon Castle
Ballyconnell Slieve Russell Hotel
Ballynahinch Ballynahinch Castle
Beaufort Dunloe Castle
Blessington Downshire House
Caragh Lake Caragh Lodge
Cashel Cashel House
Cashel Zetland House
Castledermot Kilkea Castle
Clifden Abbeyglen Castle
Clifden Rock Glen Manor
Cong Ashford Castle
Cork Arbutus Lodge
Cork Fitzpatrick Silver Springs
Cork Jurys Hotel
Dingle Dingle Skellig Hotel
Dundalk Ballymascanlon House
Dunlavin Rathsallagh House
Ennis Auburn Lodge
Gorey Marlfield House
Hodson Bay Hodson Bay Hotel
Kanturk Assolas Country House
Kenmare Park Hotel
Kenmare Sheen Falls Lodge
Kilkenny Newpark Hotel
Killarney Aghadoe Heights Hotel
Killarney Cahernane Hotel
Killarney Hotel Europe
Killarney Great Southern
Killarney Torc Great Southern
Killiney Fitzpatrick's Castle
Letterfrack Rosleague Manor
Limerick Jurys Hotel
Limerick Limerick Inn
Maynooth Moyglare Manor
Newmarket-on-Fergus Clare Inn Hotel
Newmarket-on-Fergus Dromoland Castle
Oughterard Connemara Gateway Hotel
Oughterard Currarevagh House
Parknasilla Great Southern
Rathmullan Rathmullan House
Rathnew Tinakilly House

Renvyle Renvyle House
Rosslare Great Southern
Rosslare Kelly's Strand Hotel
Rossnowlagh Sand House
Shanagarry Ballymaloe House
Sligo Sligo Park
Straffan Kildare Hotel
Thomastown Mount Juliet Hotel
Waterford Jurys Hotel
Waterford Waterford Castle

Hotels with Wheelchair facilities

Compiled in association with the Holiday Care Service (Tel 0293 774535)

England

Abingdon Abingdon Lodge
Aldeburgh Brudenell Hotel
Aldeburgh Uplands
Ambleside Rothay Manor
Appleby-in-Westmorland Appleby Manor
Ashford Ashford International Hotel
Ashford Forte Posthouse
Bassenthwaite Armathwaite Hall
Bearsted Tudor Park
Beeston Wild Boar
Bolton Abbey Devonshire Arms
Boreham Street Whitefriars Hotel
Bramley Bramley Grange
Brands Hatch Brands Hatch Thistle
Brighton Bedford Hotel
Brighton Brighton Metropole
Bristol Bristol Marriott
Broxbourne Cheshunt Marriott
Bury St Edmunds Butterfly
Cambridge Arundel House
Cambridge Gonville
Cambridge Holiday Inn
Cambridge University Arms
Canterbury County Hotel
Chester Crabwall Manor
Chester-le-Street Lumley Castle
Coventry Novotel
Darlington Blackwell Grange Moat House
Dover Dover Moat House
Durham Royal County Hotel
Elcot Elcot Park
Gatwick Airport Chequers Thistle
Gatwick Airport Copthorne London Gatwick
Gatwick Airport Gatwick Concorde
Gatwick Airport Gatwick Hilton International
Gatwick Airport Gatwick Moat House
Gatwick Airport Holiday Inn
Goodwood Goodwood Park
Grasmere Wordsworth
Hackness Hackness Grange
Hastings Cinque Ports Hotel
Hastings Royal Victoria Hotel
Haydock Haydock Thistle
Hereford Hereford Moat House
Jervaulx Jervaulx Hall
Kings Lynn Butterfly
Langley Langley Castle
Leeds Holiday Inn
Longhorsley Linden Hall
Loughborough Quorn Grange
Maidstone Stakis Country Court
Manchester Copthorne Hotel
Needham Market Pipps Ford
Newbury Millwaters
Newbury Regency Park Hotel
Newcastle Holiday Inn
Newmarket Newmarket Moat House
North Stifford Stifford Moat House
Norwich Hotel Nelson
Norwich Hotel Norwich
Norwich Friendly Hotel
Norwich Sprowston Manor
Otley Chevin Lodge
Peterborough Butterfly
Peterborough Moat House
Peterborough Swallow Hotel
Plymouth Copthorne Hotel
Romaldkirk Rose and Crown
Ross-on-Wye Pengethley Manor
Seale Hogs Back
Slough Copthorne Hotel
Southampton Novotel
Southampton Polygon
Standish Almond Brook Moat House
Wallingford Springs Hotel
Warwick Hilton International
Washington Washington Moat House
Wateringbury Wateringbury Hotel
Witney Witney Lodge
Worfield Old Vicarage
York Grange

Scotland

Aberdeen Aiport Skean Dhu Hotel
Crieff Crieff Hydro
Dulnain Bridge Muckrach Lodge
Dumbarton Forte Travelodge
Edinburgh Caledonian Hotel
Edinburgh Forte Travelodge
Edinburgh Sheraton Hotel
Edinburgh Stakis Grosvenor Hotel
Glasgow Hospitality Inn
Irvine Hospitality Inn
Kinclaven by Stanley Ballathie House
Lerwick Shetland Hotel
Markinch Balbirnie House
Oban Alexandra Hotel
Onich Lodge on the Loch
Pitlochry Pitlochry Hydro

Wales

Beaumaris Bulkeley Arms
Cardiff Cardiff Marriott
Cardiff Copthorne Hotel
Fishguard Fishguard Bay Hotel
Llangammarch Wells Lake Country House Hotel
Llangefni Tre-Ysgawen Hall
Llangybi Cwrt Bleddyn Hotel
Llanwnda Stables Hotel
Penmaenpool George III Hotel
Swansea Marriott
Talsarnau Maes-y-Neuadd

Channel Islands

St Peter Port St Pierre Park

Northern Ireland

Larne Magheramorne House

Republic of Ireland

Ballyvaughan Gregans Castle
Cork Jurys Hotel
Dublin Jurys Hotel
Dublin Montrose Hotel
Dublin Airport Forte Crest
Dundrum Dundrum House
Ennis West Country Inn
Galway Corrib Great Southern Hotel
Kenmare Sheen Falls Lodge
Limerick Castleray Park Hotel
Limerick Limerick Inn
Limerick Two Mile Inn

Restaurants with Private Dining Rooms

England

Alderley Edge Alderley Edge Hotel (22)
Amberley Amberley Castle (48)
Ambleside Rothay Manor Hotel (30)
Applethwaite Underscar Manor (20)
Ascot Royal Berkshire (75)
Ashford Eastwell Manor (90)
Aston Clinton Bell Inn (20)
Aylesbury Hartwell House (30)
Barnsley Armstrongs (20)
Barnsley Restaurant Peano (10)
Barnstaple Lynwood House (20)
Basingstoke Audleys Wood (40)
Baslow Fischer's Baslow Hall (24)
Bath Bath Spa Hotel (150)
Bath Circus Restaurant (40)
Bath Garlands (35)
Bath Priory Hotel (60)
Bath Queensberry Hotel (25)
Bath Royal Crescent Hotel (80)
Battle Netherfield Place ( )
Beckingham Black Swan (28)
Berwick-upon-Tweed Funnywayt'mekalivin (24)
Bibury The Swan (12)
Bilbrough Bilbrough Manor (20)
Birmingham Adil Restaurant (25)
Birmingham Chung Ying Garden (240)
Birmingham Days of the Raj (15)
Birmingham Henry's (40)
Birmingham Henry Wong (20)
Birmingham Hyatt Regency (200)
Birmingham New Happy Gathering (60)
Birmingham Purple Rooms (30)
Birmingham Royal Alfaisal (50)
Birmingham Swallow Hotel (20)
Bishop's Tawton Halmpstone Manor (30)
Blandford Forum La Belle Alliance (40)
Botley Cobbett's (14)
Bournemouth Ocean Palace (40)
Bowness-on-Windermere Gilpin Lodge (16)
Bowness-on-Windermere Linthwaite House (20)
Bracknell Coppid Beech Hotel (25)
Bradford K2 (36)
Bradford Nawaab (30)
Bradford-on-Avon Woolley Grange (40)
Brampton Farlam Hall (30)
Bray-on-Thames The Waterside Inn (8)
Brightling Jack Fuller's (25)
Brighton Browns (50)
Brighton China Garden (40)
Brighton La Marinade (35)
Brimfield Poppies Restaurant (16)
Bristol Blue Goose (80)
Bristol Browns Restaurant & Bar (230)
Bristol Harveys Restaurant (60)
Bristol Howard's (40)
Bristol Jameson's Restaurant (40)
Bristol Markwick's (20)
Bristol Michael's Restaurant (38)
Bristol Swallow Royal Hotel (250)
Broadway Dormy House (40)
Broadway Hunters Lodge (34)
Broadway Lygon Arms (60)
Bromsgrove Grafton Manor (12)
Broughton Broughton Park (50)
Broxted Whitehall (120)
Camberley Tithas (16)
Cambridge Browns (50)
Cambridge Charlie Chan (100)
Cambridge Midsummer House (50)
Campsea Ashe Old Rectory (30)

Canterbury County Hotel (120)
Canterbury River Kwai (30)
Castle Combe Manor House (20)
Cawston Grey Gables (22)
Chaddesley Corbett Brockencote Hall (50)
Chadlington The Manor (10)
Chagford Gidleigh Park (24)
Charingworth Charingworth Manor (40)
Chedington Chedington Court (20)
Cheltenham Bonnets Bistro at Staithes (12)
Cheltenham Epicurean (18)
Cheltenham Greenway (18)
Cheltenham Redmond's (28)
Chester Francs (60)
Chichester The Droveway (12)
Chilgrove White Horse Inn (14)
Chinnor Sir Charles Napier Inn (45)
Chiseldon Chiseldon House (20)
Christchurch Splinters Restaurant (22)
Clanfield The Plough at Clanfield (12)
Colerne Lucknam Park (30)
Corse Lawn Corse Lawn House (70)
Crosby-on-Eden Crosby Lodge (20)
Cuckfield Murray's (18)
Dartmouth Carved Angel (18)
Dedham Fountain House & Dedham Hall (15)
Dedham Le Talbooth (24)
Diss Weavers (45)
Dorchester Mock Turtle (14)
Dorking Partners West Street (30)
Dulverton Ashwick House (12)
Dunbridge Mill Arms Inn (40)
Duxford Duxford Lodge (36)
East Buckland Lower Pitt (18)
East Grinstead Gravetye Manor (18)
Eastbourne Grand Hotel (20)
Elcot Elcot Park Resort Hotel (150)
Ely Old Fire Engine House (35)
Emsworth 36 On The Quay (10)
Eton Antico (25)
Evershot Summer Lodge (20)
Eversley New Mill Restaurant (35)
Falmouth Pandora Inn (10)
Farnham Krug's (60)
Faversham Read's (12)
Fawkham Brandshatch Place (120)
Felsted Rumbles Cottage (10)
Flitwick Flitwick Manor (30)
Freshford Homewood Park (30)
Gillingham Stock Hill House (12)
Glastonbury No. 3 Restaurant & Hotel (10)
Gloucester Hatton Court (40)
Goring-on-Thames The Leatherne Bottel (20)
Grasmere Michael's Nook (36)
Grasmere Wordsworth Hotel (100)
Great Dunmow The Starr (36)
Great Gonerby Harry's Place (4)
Great Milton Le Manoir aux Quat'Saisons (46)
Great Yarmouth Seafood Restaurant (40)
Grimston Congham Hall (12)
Grizedale Grizedale Lodge (35)
Gulworthy Horn of Plenty (12)
Handforth Belfry Hotel (180)
Harrogate Tannin Level (12)
Haslemere Morel's (15)
Hastings Roser's (35)
Hayfield Bridge End Restaurant (20)
Hersham The Dining Room (30)
Herstmonceux Sundial Restaurant (22)
Highclere The Yew Tree (20)
Hindhead Xian (20)
Hintlesham Hintlesham Hall (80)
Hinton Hinton Grange (18)
Hockley Heath Nuthurst Grange (95)
Horley Langshott Manor (12)
Hull Ceruttis (24)
Hunstrete Hunstrete House (18)
Huntingdon Old Bridge Hotel (50)
Huntsham Huntsham Court (28)
Hurstbourne Tarrant Esseborne Manor (12)
Ide Old Mill (8)
Ilkley Rombalds Hotel (50)
Jevington Hungry Monk Restaurant (16)
Kendal The Moon (40)
Kington Penrhos Court (90)
Kintbury Dundas Arms (20)
Kinver Berkley's Bistro (40)
Knutsford La Belle Epoque (100)
Lacock At The Sign of The Angel (20)
Langar Langar Hall (16)
Langho Northcote Manor (40)
Lavenham Great House (50)
Lavenham The Swan (40)
Leamington Spa Mallory Court (50)
Leamington Spa Regent Hotel (20)
Leeds Bhavani Junction (100)
Leeds Brasserie Forty Four (60)
Leeds Haley's Hotel (24)
Leeds Maxi's Chinese Restaurant (40)
Leeds Olive Tree (40)
Leeds Sang Sang (30)
Leeds Sous le Nez en Ville (28)
Leicester Curry Pot (30)
Leicester Man Ho (60)
Leicester Rise of the Raj (40)
Lewdown Lewtrenchard Manor (30)
Linton Wood Hall (110)
Liverpool La Grande Bouffe (20)
Long Melford Chimneys (50)
Lower Beeding Cisswood House (150)
Lower Beeding South Lodge (15)
Lower Slaughter Lower Slaughter Manor (26)
Lymington Gordleton Mill (30)
Lympstone River House (14)
Maidenhead Fredrick's (14)
Malvern Cottage in the Wood (14)
Malvern Croque-en-Bouche (8)
Manchester Quan Ju De (48)
Manchester That Café (36)
Manchester Victoria & Albert Hotel (16)
Manchester Yang Sing (200)
Manchester Airport Etrop Grange (50)
Marlow Compleat Angler Hotel (100)
Marston Moreteyne Moreteyne Manor (85)
Matlock Riber Hall (34)
Medmenham Danesfield House (20)
Melbourn Pink Geranium (16)

Melksham Toxique (24)
Midhurst Angel Hotel (40)
Moreton-in-Marsh Annie's (12)
Moulsford-on-Thames Beetle & Wedge (65)
Moulton Black Bull (30)
Nantwich Rookery Hall (65)
New Alresford Hunters (80)
New Milton Chewton Glen (12)
Newcastle-upon-Tyne Fisherman's Lodge (40)
Newcastle-upon-Tyne King Neptune (50)
Northleach Wickens (20)
Norwich Marco's (10)
Oakham Hambleton Hall (60)
Old Burghclere Dew Pond (25)
Oxford Browns (50)
Oxford Restaurant Elizabeth (40)
Paulerspury Vine House (12)
Penzance Harris's (26)
Penzance Berkeley Restaurant (34)
Pitton Silver Plough (34)
Plumtree Perkins Bar Bistro (30)
Pool-in-Wharfedale Pool Court (36)
Poole Mansion House (40)
Powerstock Three Horseshoes Inn (20)
Puckrup Puckrup Hall (200)
Puddington Craxton Wood (35)
Pulborough Stane Street Hollow (24)
Quorn Quorn Grange (120)
Ramsbottom Village Restaurant (14)
Reigate La Barbe (35)
Richmond Petersham Hotel (20)
Ridgeway Old Vicarage (45)
Ripley Michels' (12)
Romsey Old Manor House (24)
Rotherwick Tylney Hall (15)
Rowde George & Dragon (35)
St Martin's St Martin's Hotel (14)
Salcombe Spinnakers (30)
Sandiway Nunsmere Hall (42)
Sevenoaks Royal Oak (24)
Shanklin Old Village The Cottage (11)
Sheffield Nirmal's (50)
Shinfield L'Ortolan (30)
Sourton Collaven Manor (25)
South Godstone La Bonne Auberge (100)
South Molton Whitechapel Manor (10)
Southwold The Crown (25)
Southwold The Swan (44)
Staddle Bridge McCoy's (25)
Stamford The George of Stamford (26)
Stanton St Quintin Stanton Manor (50)
Stapleford Stapleford Park (200)
Stilton Bell Inn (12)
Ston Easton Ston Easton Park (24)
Stonham Mr Underhill's (14)
Stonor Stonor Arms (24)
Storrington Abingworth Hall (54)
Storrington Little Thakeham (40)
Storrington Manley's (20)
Storrington Old Forge (12)
Stow Bardolph Hare Arms (45)
Stow-on-the-Wold Wyck Hill House (40)
Stratford-upon-Avon Billesley Manor (100)
Streatley-on-Thames Swan Diplomat (100)
Stretton Ram Jam Inn (25)
Sturminster Newton Plumber Manor (40)
Sudbury Mabey's Brasserie (25)
Surbiton Chez Max (50)
Sutton Coldfield New Hall (8)
Taplow Cliveden (42)
Taplow Cliveden, Waldo's Restaurant (12)
Taunton Castle Hotel (125)
Tetbury Calcot Manor (50)
Thornton-le-Fylde River House (40)
Thundridge Hanbury Manor (100)
Tresco Island Hotel (10)
Tuckenhay Floyd's Inn (Sometimes) (8)
Tunbridge Wells Spa Hotel (180)
Tunbridge Wells Thackeray's House (50)
Turners Hill Alexander House (50)
Twickenham Hamiltons (8)
Uckfield Horsted Place (22)
Ullswater Leeming House (20)
Ullswater Rampsbeck Country House Hotel (20)
Ulverston Bay Horse Inn & Bistro (30)
Upper Slaughter Lords of the Manor (10)
Uppingham The Lake Isle (12)
Wadhurst Spindlewood (24)
Walkington Manor House (20)
Wansford-in-England Haycock Hotel (28)
Wareham Priory Hotel (24)
Warminster Bishopstrow House (22)
Waterhouses Old Beams (12)
Wath-in-Nidderdale Sportsman's Arms (8)
Wells Ritcher's (18)
Weymouth Perry's (40)
Whitstable Whitstable Oyster Fishery Co (30)
Wickham Old House Hotel (14)
Wilmslow Harry's (40)
Wilmslow Stanneylands (100)
Windermere Holbeck Ghyll (12)
Windermere Roger's Restaurant (26)
Windsor Oakley Court (20)
Winteringham Winteringham Fields (10)
Witherslack Old Vicarage (18)
Wiveliscombe Langley House (20)
Woburn Paris House (16)
Woodstock Bear Hotel (65)
Woodstock Feathers Hotel (25)
Woolton Hill Hollington House Hotel (45)
Worfield Old Vicarage (14)
Wymondham Number Twenty Four (22)
Yattendon Royal Oak (8)
Yeovil Little Barwick House (20)
York Grange Hotel (60)
York Melton's (12)
York Middlethorpe Hall (50)
York 19 Grape Lane (22)

Scotland

Aberdeen Gerard's (50)
Aberfeldy Farleyer House (32)
Auchterarder Auchterarder House (60)

Auchterhouse Old Mansion House (20)
Ayr Fouters Bistro (36)
Banchory Raemoir House ( )
Blairgowrie Kinloch House (30)
Colbost Three Chimneys Restaurant (21)
Craigellachie Craigellachie Hotel (20)
Cupar Ostlers Close (20)
Dunblane Cromlix House (20)
Edinburgh Alp-Horn (24)
Edinburgh L'Auberge (30)
Edinburgh The Balmoral (10)
Edinburgh Indian Cavalry Club (50)
Edinburgh Kelly's (36)
Edinburgh Martin's (8)
Edinburgh Ristorante Raffaelli (30)
Edinburgh Shamiana (14)
Edinburgh Szechuan House (25)
Edinburgh Vintners Room (36)
Fort William Inverlochy Castle (15)
Glasgow Brasserie on West Regent Street (55)
Glasgow Buttery (8)
Glasgow Glasgow Hilton (12)
Glasgow Mata Hari (15)
Glasgow One Devonshire Gardens (20)
Glasgow Ristorante Caprese (25)
Glasgow Rogano (16)
Glasgow Ubiquitous Chip (25)
Gullane Greywalls Hotel (20)
Inverness Culloden House (34)
Kilchrenan Taychreggan Hotel (10)
Kilfinan Kilfinan Hotel (26)
Kinclaven by Stanley Ballathie House (32)
Kirknewton Dalmahoy Hotel, Golf & Country Club (24)
Nairn Clifton Hotel (14)
Newton Stewart Kirroughtree Hotel (30)
Newtown St Boswells Le Provencale (46)
Oban Knipoch Hotel (24)
Peat Inn Peat Inn (24)
Peebles Cringletie House (28)
Quothquan Shieldhill (20)
Scarista Scarista House (10)
Scone Murrayshall House (30)
Turnberry Turnberry Hotel (8)

Wales

Chepstow Beckfords (12)
Clydach Drum & Monkey (25)
Coychurch Coed-y-Mwstwr Hotel (150)
Eglwysfach Ynyshir Hall (12)
Gowerton Cefn Goleu Park (20)
Harlech The Cemlyn (10)
Lampeter Peppers Bistro (30)
Llanberis Y Bistro (44)
Llandrillo Tyddyn Llan (45)
Llandudno Bodysgallen Hall (40)
Llangefni Tre-Ysgawen Hall (30)
Llyswen Llangoed Hall (36)
Mumbles Norton House (16)
Northop Soughton Hall (22)
Penally Penally Abbey (20)
Portmeirion Hotel Portmeirion (40)
Pwllheli Plas Bodegroes (16)
Talsarnau Maes-y-Neaudd (14)
Trellech Village Green (18)
Welsh Hook Stone Hall (30)
Whitebrook Crown at Whitebrook (14)

Channel Islands

St Anne Georgian House (24)
St Helier La Capannina (18)
St Ouen The Lobster Pot (40)
St Peter Port Absolute End (20)
St Peter Port Louisiana (18)
St Peter Port Le Nautique (30)
St Saviour Longueville Manor (20)
Sark Aval Du Creux (15)
Sark Stocks Hotel (12)

Isle of Man

Ballasalla La Rosette (16)

Northern Ireland

Annalong Glassdrumman Lodge (20)
Belfast Bengal Brasserie (50)
Belfast Manor House (50)
Belfast Nick's Warehouse (45)
Belfast Strand Restaurant (25)
Belfast Welcome Restaurant (30)
Garvagh Blackheath House & MacDuff's (12)
Holywood Culloden Hotel (50)

Republic of Ireland

Adare Adare Manor (25)
Adare Mustard Seed (20)
Ahakista Shiro (8)
Ballyhack Neptune Restaurant (20)
Ballyvaughan Gregans Castle (40)
Baltimore Chez Youen (12)
Boyle Cromleach Lodge (20)
Bunratty MacCloskey's (22)
Caherdaniel Loaves & Fishes (12)
Carlingford Jordan's Bar & Restaurant (16)
Carne Lobster Pot (28)
Cashel Cashel House (10)
Castledermot Doyle's School House Country Inn (25)
Castletownshend Mary Ann's Bar & Restaurant (14)
Clifden O'Grady's Seafood Restaurant (12)
Cong Ashford Castle, Connaught Room (40)
Cork Arbutus Lodge (25)
Cork Clifford's (50)
Cork Crawford Gallery Café (200)
Cork Flemings (36)
Cork Isaacs (60)
Cork Lovetts (24)

Dingle Beginish Restaurant (12)
Dingle Half Door (20)
Dublin Ayumi-Ya (20)
Dublin Chapter One (24)
Dublin The Chili Club (16)
Dublin Commons Restaurant (30)
Dublin Le Coq Hardi (34)
Dublin Les Frères Jacques (40)
Dublin George's Bistro & Piano Bar (50)
Dublin Hibernian Hotel (20)
Dublin Locks (30)
Dublin Old Dublin Restaurant (16)
Dublin Patrick Guilbaud (28)
Dublin Roly's Bistro (60)
Dublin Stephen's Hall Hotel (12)
Dun Laoghaire Restaurant Na Mara (75)
Dunlavin Rathsallagh House (15)
Dunworley Dunworley Cottage (20)
Enniskerry Curtlestown House (25)
Enniskerry Enniscree Lodge (10)
Glasson Glasson Village Restaurant (12)
Gorey Marlfield House (24)
Howth Adrian's (36)
Howth King Sitric (22)
Kanturk Assolas Country House (18)
Kenmare The Old Bank House (12)
Kenmare Packies (15)
Kenmare Park Hotel (12)
Kenmare Sheen Falls Lodge (24)
Kilkenny Kilkenny Kitchen (65)
Kilkenny Lacken House (20)
Killarney Cahernane Hotel (14)
Killorglin Nick's Restaurant (35)
Kinnegad The Cottage (26)
Kinsale Chez Jean-Marc (25)
Kinsale Man Friday (35)
Kinsale Old Presbytery (10)
Leighlinbridge The Lord Bagenal Inn (40)
Letterfrack Rosleague Manor (10)
Malahide Bon Appetit (20)
Malahide Roches Bistro (36)
Mallow Longueville House (20)
Maynooth Moyglare Manor (50)
Moycullen Drimcong House Restaurant (32)
Mullingar Crookedwood House (35)
Navan Ardboyne Hotel (50)
Newmarket-on-Fergus Dromoland Castle (120)
Newport Newport House (35)
Oysterhaven The Oystercatcher (20)
Rathnew Hunter's Hotel (20)
Rathnew Tinakilly House (40)
Roundwood Roundwood Inn (32)
Shanagarry Ballymaloe House (30)
Skerries Red Bank Restaurant (10)
Straffan Kildare Hotel (50)
Swords Le Chateau (20)
Swords Old Schoolhouse (20)
Thomastown Mount Juliet Hotel (60)
Waterford Dwyer's Restaurant (10)
Waterford Prendiville's Restaurant/Guesthouse (50)
Waterford Waterford Castle (26)
Youghal Aherne's Seafood Restaurant (20)

Restaurants with a non-smoking area

The following is a list of establishments where smoking is not allowed in the restaurant (or in some cases, anywhere). In addition, many hotels have bedrooms designated non-smoking, or a non-smoking lounge, and some restaurants have a non-smoking section or room. Ask what they've got to offer when you book – and remember that puffing companions can usually retire to bar, lounge, garden etc.

England

Amberley Amberley Castle
Ambleside Rothay Manor Hotel
Ambleside Wateredge Hotel
Appleby-in-Westmorland Appleby Manor Hotel
Applethwaite Underscar Manor
Ashford Eastwell Manor
Aston Clinton Bell Inn
Barnstaple Lynwood House
Baslow Fischer's Baslow Hall
Bath Bath Spa Hotel
Bath Priory Hotel
Beckingham Black Swan
Berwick-upon-Tweed Funnywayt'mekalivin
Bibury The Swan
Bilbrough Bilbrough Manor
Birmingham Hyatt Regency
Birmingham Rajdoot
Birmingham Swallow Hotel
Blackpool September Brasserie
Blandford Forum La Belle Alliance
Bournemouth Royal Bath Hotel
Bowness-on-Windermere Gilpin Lodge
Bowness-on-Windermere Linthwaite House
Bradford Bombay Brasserie
Bradford Nawaab
Braunton Otters Restaurant
Brightling Jack Fuller's
Brighton Browns
Brighton La Marinade
Brimfield Poppies Restaurant
Bristol Harveys Restaurant

Bristol Howard's
Bristol Michael's Restaurant
Broadway Dormy House
Brockenhurst Le Poussin
Broughton Broughton Park
Buckland Buckland Manor
Burford Lamb Inn
Calstock Danescombe Valley Hotel
Cambridge Browns
Campsea Ashe Old Rectory
Cartmel Uplands
Cawston Grey Gables
Chaddesley Corbett Brockencote Hall
Chadlington The Manor
Chagford Gidleigh Park
Chapeltown Greenhead House
Cheltenham Bonnets Bistro at Staithes
Cheltenham Redmond's
Chester Francs
Chinnor Sir Charles Napier Inn
Chiseldon Chiseldon House
Clanfield The Plough at Clanfield
Cockermouth Quince & Medlar
Corse Lawn Corse Lawn House
Cowan Bridge Cobwebs
Crosby-on-Eden Crosby Lodge
Cuckfield Murray's
Dedham Fountain House & Dedham Hall
Diss Weavers
Dorchester Mock Turtle
Dorking Partners West Street
Dorrington Country Friends
Dulverton Ashwick House
Dunbridge Mill Arms Inn
East Grinstead Gravetye Manor
Ely Old Fire Engine House
Erpingham Ark
Eyton Marsh Country Hotel
Fawkham Brandshatch Place
Felsted Rumbles Cottage
Flitwick Flitwick Manor
Folkestone La Tavernetta
Freshford Homewood Park
Gillingham Stock Hill House
Glastonbury No. 3 Restaurant & Hotel
Grasmere Michael's Nook
Grasmere White Moss House
Grasmere Wordsworth Hotel
Great Dunmow The Starr
Great Gonerby Harry's Place
Great Milton Le Manoir aux Quat'Saisons
Grimston Congham Hall
Grizedale Grizedale Lodge
Guist Tollbridge
Harrogate Café Fleur
Harrogate Old Swan Hotel
Harrogate Tannin Level
Haslemere Morel's
Haworth Weavers
Hayfield Bridge End Restaurant
Herstmonceux Sundial Restaurant
Highclere The Yew Tree
Hintlesham Hintlesham Hall
Hockley Heath Nuthurst Grange
Horley Langshott Manor
Hull Ceruttis
Hunstrete Hunstrete House
Ilkley Rombalds Hotel
Ixworth Theobalds
Jevington Hungry Monk Restaurant
Kendal The Moon
Kendal Posh Nosh
Kintbury Dundas Arms
Lavenham The Swan
Leamington Spa Regent Hotel
Ledbury Hope End
Leeds Bhavani Junction
Lewdown Lewtrenchard Manor
Linton Wood Hall
Long Melford Chimneys
Longridge Paul Heathcote's Restaurant
Lower Beeding South Lodge
Lower Slaughter Lower Slaughter Manor
Lymington Gordleton Mill
Lympstone River House
Lytham St Annes Dalmeny Hotel
Maiden Newton Le Petit Canard
Malvern Cottage in the Wood
Malvern Croque-en-Bouche
Manchester Gaylord
Manchester Quan Ju De
Manchester Victoria & Albert Hotel
Marlow Compleat Angler Hotel
Melbourn Pink Geranium
Melksham Toxique
Melmerby Village Bakery
Nantwich Rookery Hall
Newark Gannets Café-Bistrot
Newcastle-upon-Tyne Fisherman's Lodge
Northleach Wickens
Norwich Marco's
Old Burghclere Dew Pond
Oxford Bath Place Hotel & Restaurant
Oxford Browns
Paulerspury Vine House
Plumtree Perkins Bar Bistro
Poole Haven Hotel: La Roche Restaurant
Porlock Oaks Hotel
Powerstock Three Horseshoes Inn
Puckrup Puckrup Hall
Pulborough Stane Street Hollow
Ramsbottom Village Restaurant
Richmond River Terrace
Ridgeway Old Vicarage
Rotherwick Tylney Hall
St Martin's St Martin's Hotel
St Mawes Idle Rocks Hotel
Sandiway Nunsmere Hall
Shanklin Old Village The Cottage
Sissinghurst Rankins
South Godstone La Bonne Auberge
South Molton Whitechapel Manor
Southall Asian Tandoori Centre
Southampton Browns Brasserie
Southwold The Crown
Southwold The Swan
Spark Bridge Bridgefield House
Stapleford Stapleford Park
Stonham Mr Underhill's
Storrington Abingworth Hall
Stow-on-the-Wold Wyck Hill House
Stretton Ram Jam Inn
Sutton Coldfield New Hall
Taplow Cliveden: Waldo's Restaurant
Taunton Porters Wine Bar

Tetbury Calcot Manor
Thornton-le-Fylde River House
Tintagel Trebrea Lodge
Torquay Table Restaurant
Tunbridge Wells Spa Hotel
Turners Hill Alexander House
Uckfield Horsted Place
Ullswater Leeming House
Ullswater Old Church Hotel
Ullswater Rampsbeck Country House Hotel
Ullswater Sharrow Bay
Ulverston Bay Horse Inn & Bistro
Wansford-in-England Haycock Hotel
Waterhouses Old Beams
Williton White House
Wimborne Les Bouviers
Winchester Wykeham Arms
Windermere Holbeck Ghyll
Windsor Oakley Court
Winteringham Winteringham Fields
Witherslack Old Vicarage
Wiveliscombe Langley House
Woodstock Bear Hotel
Worfield Old Vicarage
Yeovil Little Barwick House
York 19 Grape Lane

Scotland

Aberfeldy Farleyer House
Achiltibuie Summer Isles
Alexandria Cameron House
Anstruther Cellar
Arisaig Arisaig House
Auchterarder Auchterarder House
Auchterhouse Old Mansion House
Ayr Fouters Bistro
Ayr The Stables
Ballater Tullich Lodge
Blairgowrie Kinloch House
Cairndow Loch Fyne Oyster Bar
Canonbie Riverside Inn
Colbost Three Chimneys Restaurant
Craigellachie Craigellachie Hotel
Dalguise Kinnaird
Drumnadrochit Polmaily House
Drybridge Old Monastery Restaurant
Dulnain Bridge Auchendean Lodge
Dunblane Cromlix House
Edinburgh Alp-Horn
Edinburgh The Balmoral
Edinburgh Caledonian Hotel
Edinburgh Indian Cavalry Club
Edinburgh Kalpna
Edinburgh Kelly's
Edinburgh Martin's
Edinburgh Vintners Room
Fort William Crannog Seafood Restaurant
Fort William Inverlochy Castle
Glamis Castleton House
Glasgow D'Arcy's
Glasgow Mata Hari
Glenborrodale Glenborrodale Castle
Gullane La Potiniere
Kentallen of Appin Ardsheal House
Kilchrenan Ardanaiseig
Kilfinan Kilfinan Hotel
Kilmore Glenfeochan House
Kinclaven by Stanley Ballathie House
Kingussie The Cross
Maybole Ladyburn
Muir-of-Ord Dower House
Nairn Clifton Hotel
Newton Stewart Kirroughtree Hotel
Newtonmore Ard-na-Coille Hotel
Newtown St Boswells Le Provencale
Onich Allt-nan-Ros Hotel
Peat Inn Peat Inn
Port Appin Airds Hotel
Portpatrick Knockinaam Lodge
Quothquan Shieldhill
Scarista Scarista House
Sleat Kinloch Lodge
Tiroran Tiroran House
Ullapool Altnaharrie Inn

Wales

Cardiff Quayles
Coychurch Coed-y-Mwstwr Hotel
Eglwysfach Ynyshir Hall
Harlech The Cemlyn
Llanberis Y Bistro
Llandudno Bodysgallen Hall
Llandudno St Tudno Hotel
Llangammarch Wells Lake Country House Hotel
Llansanffraid Glan Conwy Old Rectory
Llyswen Llangoed Hall
Penally Penally Abbey
Portmeirion Hotel Portmeirion
Pwllheli Plas Bodegroes
Talsarnau Maes-y-Neaudd

Channel Islands

Gorey Jersey Pottery
Rozel Bay Chateau la Chaire
St Anne Inchalla Hotel
St Helier Grand Hotel
St Peter Port Louisiana
St Saviour Longueville Manor
Sark Stocks Hotel

Northern Ireland

Belfast Roscoff
Garvagh Blackheath House & MacDuff's
Holywood Culloden Hotel

Republic of Ireland

Athy Tonlegee House
Ballina Mount Falcon Castle
Blackrock Clarets

Boyle Cromleach Lodge
Bray Tree of Idleness
Cashel Cashel House
Castletownshend Mary Ann's Bar & Restaurant
Clifden Ardagh Hotel
Clifden O'Grady's Seafood Restaurant
Cong Ashford Castle
Cork Arbutus Lodge
Cork Bully's
Cork Clifford's
Cork Crawford Gallery Café
Cork Jacques
Cork Lovetts
Cork O'Keeffe's
Dingle Doyle's Seafood Bar & Townhouse
Dingle Half Door
Dublin Le Coq Hardi
Dublin Ernie's
Dublin Les Freres Jacques
Dublin Kapriol
Dublin Locks
Dublin Oisins
Dublin Old Dublin Restaurant
Dublin Pasta Fresca
Dublin Patrick Guilbaud
Dublin Polo One
Dublin Il Primo
Dublin Rajdoot
Dublin Stephen's Hall Hotel
Dublin Ta Se Mohogani Gaspipes
Dublin The Westbury
Dun Laoghaire Restaurant Na Mara
Dunderry Dunderry Lodge Restaurant
Dunlavin Rathsallagh House
Dunworley Dunworley Cottage
Durrus Blairs Cove House Restaurant
Enniskerry Enniscree Lodge
Glasson Glasson Village Restaurant
Greystones The Hungry Monk
Howth King Sitric
Kenmare Park Hotel
Killarney Cahernane Hotel
Killarney Gaby's Seafood Restaurant
Killorglin Nick's Restaurant
Kinsale Blue Haven Hotel
Kinsale Max's Wine Bar
Letterfrack Rosleague Manor
Malahide Bon Appetit
Malahide Roches Bistro
Mallow Longueville House
Moycullen Drimcong House Restaurant
Navan Ardboyne Hotel
Newport Newport House
Oughterard Currarevagh House
Rathnew Hunter's Hotel
Rathnew Tinakilly House
Riverstown Coopershill House
Roundwood Roundwood Inn
Shanagarry Ballymaloe House
Spiddal Boluisce Seafood Bar
Stillorgan Mr Hung's Sawadee Thai Restaurant
Swords Le Chateau
Thomastown Mount Juliet Hotel
Waterford Waterford Castle
Wicklow Old Rectory
Youghal Aherne's Seafood Restaurant

Sunday Eating

England

Alderley Edge Alderley Edge Hotel
Altrincham Francs **(L)**
Amberley Amberley Castle
Ambleside Rothay Manor Hotel
Ambleside Wateredge Hotel
Appleby-in-Westmorland Appleby Manor Hotel
Applethwaite Underscar Manor
Ascot Hyn's
Ascot Royal Berkshire
Ashford Eastwell Manor
Ashington The Willows **(L)**
Aston Clinton Bell Inn
Aylesbury Hartwell House
Basingstoke Audleys Wood
Basingstoke Hee's **(D)**
Baslow Fischer's Baslow Hall **(L)**
Bath Bath Spa Hotel
Bath Circus Restaurant **from 10am to L**
Bath Clos du Roy **(L)**
Bath Garlands
Bath The New Moon **from 9am**
Bath Priory Hotel
Bath Royal Crescent Hotel
Battle Netherfield Place
Bibury The Swan
Bilbrough Bilbrough Manor
Birdlip Kingshead House **(L)**
Birmingham Adil Restaurant
Birmingham Chung Ying
Birmingham Chung Ying Garden
Birmingham Days of the Raj **(D)**
Birmingham New Happy Gathering
Birmingham Purple Rooms
Birmingham Rajdoot 23:30
Birmingham Royal Alfaisal **from 11.30 am**
Birmingham Swallow Hotel
Botley Cobbett's **(L)**
Bournemouth Ocean Palace
Bowness-on-Windermere Gilpin Lodge
Bowness-on-Windermere Linthwaite House
Bracknell Coppid Beech Hotel
Bradford Bombay Brasserie
Bradford K2 **from 11 am**
Bradford Nawaab
Bradford-on-Avon Woolley Grange
Brampton Farlam Hall **(D)**

Bray-on-Thames The Waterside Inn
Bridport Riverside Restaurant **(L from 11.30)**
Brightling Jack Fuller's **(L)**
Brighton Black Chapati **(L from 1)**
Brighton Browns
Brighton China Garden
Brighton La Marinade **(L)**
Brighton Topps Hotel **(D)**
Bristol Browns Restaurant & Bar
Bristol Jameson's Restaurant **(L)**
Bristol Rajdoot **(D)**
Bristol Swallow Royal Hotel
Broadhembury Drewe Arms **(L)**
Broadway Collin House
Broadway Dormy House
Broadway Hunters Lodge **(L)**
Broadway Lygon Arms
Brockenhurst Le Poussin **(L)**
Bromsgrove Grafton Manor
Broughton Broughton Park
Broxted Whitehall
Buckland Buckland Manor
Burford Lamb Inn
Calstock Danescombe Valley Hotel **(D)**
Camberley Tithas
Cambridge Browns
Cambridge Charlie Chan
Canterbury County Hotel
Cartmel Uplands
Castle Cary Bond's **(D)**
Castle Combe Manor House
Cavendish Alfonso's **(L)**
Cawston Grey Gables **(D)**
Chaddesley Corbett Brockencote Hall
Chadlington The Manor **(D)**
Chagford Gidleigh Park
Charingworth Charingworth Manor
Charlbury The Bull at Charlbury **(L)**
Chedington Chedington Court **(D)**
Cheltenham Epicurean **(L)**
Cheltenham Greenway
Cheltenham Redmond's **(L)**
Chelwood Chelwood House
Chester Francs
Chichester Comme Ca **(L)**
Chichester The Droveway **(L)**
Chilgrove White Horse Inn **(L)**
Chinnor Sir Charles Napier Inn **(L)**
Chiseldon Chiseldon House
Chobham Quails Restaurant **(L)**
Cirencester Tatyan's **(D)**
Clanfield The Plough at Clanfield
Cockermouth Quince & Medlar **(D)**
Coggeshall White Hart **(L)**
Colerne Lucknam Park
Corse Lawn Corse Lawn House
Cranleigh La Barbe Encore **(L)**
Crosby-on-Eden Crosby Lodge
Dartmouth Carved Angel **(L)**
Dedham Fountain House & Dedham Hall **(L)**
Dedham Le Talbooth
Dorchester Yalbury Cottage **(L)**
Dorking Partners West Street **(L)**
Dulverton Ashwick House
Dunbridge Mill Arms Inn
Duxford Duxford Lodge
East Grinstead Gravetye Manor
Edenbridge Honours Mill Restaurant **(L)**
Elcot Elcot Park Resort Hotel
Elton Loch Fyne Oyster Bar **from 9am**
Ely Old Fire Engine House **(L)**
Emsworth 36 On The Quay **(L)**
Erpingham Ark **(L)**
Esher Good Earth
Evershot Summer Lodge
Eversley New Mill Restaurant
Evesham Riverside Hotel **(L)**
Eyton Marsh Country Hotel **(D)**
Falmouth Pandora Inn **(D)**
Falmouth Seafood Bar **(D)**
Fawkham Brandshatch Place
Felsted Rumbles Cottage **(L)**
Flitwick Flitwick Manor
Folkestone Paul's
Freshford Homewood Park
Fressingfield Fox and Goose
Gillingham Stock Hill House **(L)**
Gloucester Hatton Court
Goring-on-Thames The Leatherne Bottel
Grasmere Michael's Nook
Grasmere Wordsworth Hotel
Great Dunmow The Starr **(L)**
Great Milton Le Manoir aux Quat'Saisons
Grimston Congham Hall
Grizedale Grizedale Lodge
Guildford Mandarin **(D)**
Guiseley Prachee
Guist Tollbridge **(L)**
Gulworthy Horn of Plenty
Hampton Wick Le Petit Max
Handforth Belfry Hotel
Handforth Handforth Chinese Restaurant **(D)**
Harrogate Café Fleur **(D)**
Harrogate Miller's The Bistro **(L)**
Harrogate Old Swan Hotel
Harvington The Mill
Harwich Pier at Harwich
Haworth Weavers **(L)**
Hayfield Bridge End Restaurant **(L)**
Helford Riverside
Herne Bay L'Escargot
Hersham The Dining Room **(L)**
Herstmonceux Sundial Restaurant **(L)**
Highclere The Yew Tree
Hintlesham Hintlesham Hall
Hinton Hinton Grange
Hockley Heath Nuthurst Grange
Horley Langshott Manor **(D)**
Hunstrete Hunstrete House
Huntingdon Old Bridge Hotel
Huntsham Huntsham Court **(D)**
Hurstbourne Tarrant Esseborne Manor
Ilkley Rombalds Hotel
Ixworth Theobalds **(L)**
Jevington Hungry Monk Restaurant
Kendal The Moon **(D)**
Keyston Pheasant Inn
Kington Penrhos Court
Lacock At The Sign of The Angel **(L from 1)**
Langho Northcote Manor
Lavenham Great House **(L)**
Lavenham The Swan

Leamington Spa Mallory Court
Ledbury Hope End **(D)**
Leeds Adriano Flying Pizza
Leeds Bhavani Junction **(D)**
Leeds Darbar **L from 11.30**
Leeds Haley's Hotel **(L)**
Leeds Maxi's Chinese Restaurant
Leeds New Asia
Leeds Olive Tree
Leeds Sang Sang
Leeds Thai Siam **(D)**
Leicester Man Ho
Leicester Rise of the Raj
Lewdown Lewtrenchard Manor
Linton Wood Hall
Liskeard Well House
Liverpool La Grande Bouffe **(D)**
Long Melford Chimneys **(L)**
Longridge Paul Heathcote's Restaurant
Lower Beeding South Lodge
Lower Slaughter Lower Slaughter Manor
Lymington Gordleton Mill **(L)**
Lympstone River House
Madingley Three Horseshoes
Maiden Newton Maiden Newton House **(D at 8)**
Maidenhead Fredrick's
Maidstone Mandarin Chef
Malvern Anupam
Malvern Cottage in the Wood
Manchester Gaylord
Manchester Penang Village
Manchester Quan Ju De
Manchester Rajdoot **(D)**
Manchester Siam Orchid **(D)**
Manchester Sonarga **(D)**
Manchester That Café **(L)**
Manchester Yang Sing
Manchester Airport Etrop Grange
Marlow Compleat Angler Hotel
Marston Moreteyne Moreteyne Manor **(L)**
Matlock Riber Hall
Mawnan Smith Nansidwell
Medmenham Danesfield House
Melbourn Pink Geranium **(L)**
Melksham Toxique **(L)**
Melmerby Village Bakery **from 9:30 & L**
Midhurst Angel Hotel
Milford-on-Sea Rocher's **(L)**
Moreton-in-Marsh Annie's **(L)**
Moreton-in-Marsh Marsh Goose **(L)**
Moulsford-on-Thames Beetle & Wedge **(L)**
Nantwich Rookery Hall
New Alresford Hunters **(L)**
New Barnet Mims Restaurant
New Milton Chewton Glen
Newcastle-upon-Tyne King Neptune
Nottingham Higoi **(D)**
Nottingham Noble House
Nottingham Ocean City
Nottingham Sonny's
Oakham Hambleton Hall
Oxford Al-Shami
Oxford Bath Place Hotel & Restaurant **(L)**
Oxford Browns
Oxford Cherwell Boathouse **(L)**
Oxford Restaurant Elizabeth
Oxford 15 North Parade **(L)**
Paulerspury Vine House **(L)**
Penkridge William Harding's House **(L)**
Penzance Abbey Hotel **(D)**
Pitton Silver Plough **(L)**
Polperro Kitchen at Polperro **(D)**
Poole Mansion House
Porlock Oaks Hotel **(D)**
Powerstock Three Horseshoes Inn
Puckrup Puckrup Hall
Pulborough Stane Street Hollow **(L)**
Purton Pear Tree
Quorn Quorn Grange
Richmond Petersham Hotel
Richmond River Terrace
Ridgeway Old Vicarage **(L)**
Ripley Michels' **(L)**
Roade Roadhouse
Romaldkirk Rose and Crown
Romsey Old Manor House **(L)**
Rotherwick Tylney Hall
Rowde George & Dragon **(L)**
St Martin's St Martin's Hotel **(D)**
St Mawes Idle Rocks Hotel **(D)**
Salcombe Spinnakers **(L)**
Sandiway Nunsmere Hall
Seaview Seaview Hotel **(L)**
Sevenoaks Royal Oak
Shanklin Old Village The Cottage **(L)**
Sheffield Nirmal's **(D)**
Shinfield L'Ortolan **(L)**
Silverton Silverton Inn & Restaurant **(L)**
Sissinghurst Rankins **(L)**
Sourton Collaven Manor
South Godstone La Bonne Auberge **(L)**
South Molton Whitechapel Manor
Southall Asian Tandoori Centre **from 9am**
Southampton Kuti's
Southwold The Crown
Southwold The Swan
Spark Bridge Bridgefield House **(D)**
Stamford The George of Stamford
Stapleford Stapleford Park
Stilton Bell Inn **(D)**
Ston Easton Ston Easton Park
Storrington Abingworth Hall
Storrington Little Thakeham **(L)**
Storrington Manley's **(L)**
Storrington Old Forge **(L)**
Stow-on-the-Wold Wyck Hill House
Stratford-upon-Avon Billesley Manor
Stratford-upon-Avon The Opposition
Streatley-on-Thames Swan Diplomat
Stretton Ram Jam Inn
Stroud Oakes **(L)**
Sturminster Newton Plumber Manor **(D)**
Sutton Partners Brasserie **(L)**
Sutton Coldfield New Hall
Tadworth Gemini Restaurant **(L)**
Taplow Cliveden
Taunton Castle Hotel
Teffont Evias Howard's House
Tetbury Calcot Manor **(L)**
Thornton-le-Fylde River House **(L)**
Thundridge Hanbury Manor **(L)**
Tintagel Trebrea Lodge **(D)**
Torquay Table Restaurant **(D)**
Tresco Island Hotel

Tuckenhay Floyd's Inn (Sometimes)
Tunbridge Wells Spa Hotel
Tunbridge Wells Thackeray's House **(L)**
Turners Hill Alexander House
Twickenham Hamiltons **(L)**
Uckfield Horsted Place
Ullswater Leeming House
Ullswater Old Church Hotel **(D)**
Ullswater Rampsbeck Country House Hotel
Ullswater Sharrow Bay
Ulverston Bay Horse Inn & Bistro
Upper Slaughter Lords of the Manor
Uppingham The Lake Isle **(L)**
Veryan Nare Hotel
Wadhurst Spindlewood
Wansford-in-England Haycock Hotel
Wareham Priory Hotel
Warminster Bishopstrow House
Waterhouses Old Beams **(L)**
Wath-in-Nidderdale Sportsman's Arms
Watlington Well House **(L)**
Wells Ritcher's **from 11.30**
Weston-under-Penyard Wharton Lodge
Wetherby Sheba **(D)**
Weybridge Casa Romana
Weymouth Perry's
Whimple Woodhayes Hotel **(D)**
Whitstable Whitstable Oyster Fishery Co
Williton White House **(D)**
Wilmslow Harry's **(D)**
Wilmslow Stanneylands **(L)**
Windermere Holbeck Ghyll **(D)**
Windsor Oakley Court
Witherslack Old Vicarage **(D at 8)**
Wiveliscombe Langley House **(D at 8.30)**
Woburn Paris House **(L)**
Woodstock Bear Hotel
Woodstock Feathers Hotel
Woolton Hill Hollington House Hotel
Worcester Brown's **(L)**
Worfield Old Vicarage
Wymondham Number Twenty Four **(L)**
Yattendon Royal Oak
York Grange Hotel
York Melton's **(L)**
York Middlethorpe Hall

Scotland

Aberfeldy Farleyer House **(D at 8.30)**
Aberfoyle Braeval Old Mill **(L)**
Achiltibuie Summer Isles **(D at 8)**
Alexandria Cameron House
Arisaig Arisaig House
Auchterarder Auchterarder House
Auchterhouse Old Mansion House
Ayr Fouters Bistro **(D)**
Ayr The Stables **(L from 1)**
Ballater Tullich Lodge
Banchory Raemoir House
Bearsden Fifty Five BC
Blairgowrie Kinloch House
Cairndow Loch Fyne Oyster Bar **from 9am**
Canonbie Riverside Inn **(D at 8.30)**
Craigellachie Craigellachie Hotel
Crinan Crinan Hotel **(D)**
Dalguise Kinnaird
Drumnadrochit Polmaily House **(D)**
Dulnain Bridge Auchendean Lodge **(D)**
Dunblane Cromlix House
Edinburgh L'Auberge
Edinburgh The Balmoral: Bridges Brasserie **from 7am**
Edinburgh Caledonian: Carriages
Edinburgh Indian Cavalry Club
Edinburgh Shamiana **(D)**
Edinburgh Szechuan House **(D)**
Eriska Isle of Eriska **(D)**
Fort William Crannog Seafood Restaurant
Fort William The Factor's House **(D)**
Fort William Inverlochy Castle
Glamis Castleton House
Glasgow Amber
Glasgow Ashoka West End **(D to 12.30am)**
Glasgow D'Arcy's **(L from 11)**
Glasgow Glasgow Hilton **(D)**
Glasgow Loon Fung
Glasgow One Devonshire Gardens
Glasgow Rogano **(D)**
Glasgow Ubiquitous Chip
Glenborrodale Glenborrodale Castle
Glenelg Glenelg Inn **from 8:30am**
Gullane Greywalls Hotel
Gullane La Potiniere **(L from 1)**
Inverness Culloden House
Inverness Dunain Park **(D)**
Kentallen of Appin Ardsheal House
Kilchrenan Ardanaiseig
Kilchrenan Taychreggan Hotel
Kilfinan Kilfinan Hotel **(D)**
Kilmore Glenfeochan House **(D at 8)**
Kinclaven by Stanley Ballathie House
Kingussie The Cross
Kirknewton Dalmahoy Hotel, Golf & Country Club
Linlithgow Champany Inn Chop & Ale House
Maybole Ladyburn **(D)**
Muir-of-Ord Dower House **(D)**
Nairn Clifton Hotel **(D)**
Newton Stewart Kirroughtree Hotel
Newtonmore Ard-na-Coille Hotel **(D at 7.45)**
Oban Knipoch Hotel **(D)**
Onich Allt-nan-Ros Hotel
Peebles Cringletie House
Port Appin Airds Hotel
Portpatrick Knockinaam Lodge **(D)**
Quothquan Shieldhill
Scarista Scarista House **(D at 8)**
Scone Murrayshall House
Sleat Kinloch Lodge **(D at or to 8.30)**
Tiroran Tiroran House **(D at 7.45)**
Turnberry Turnberry Hotel
Ullapool Altnaharrie Inn **(D at 8)**
Whitebridge Knockie Lodge **(D at 8)**

Wales

Aberkenfig New Garden **(D)**
Abersoch Porth Tocyn Hotel

Cardiff Champers **(D)**
Cardiff Quayles **(L from 11.30)**
Chepstow Beckfords **(L)**
Chepstow Leadon's Brasserie **(D)**
Chirk Starlings Castle
Clydach Drum & Monkey
Coychurch Coed-y-Mwstwr Hotel
Eglwysfach Ynyshir Hall
Gowerton Cefn Goleu Park **(L)**
Harlech The Cemlyn **(D)**
Llanberis Y Bistro **(D)**
Llandrillo Tyddyn Llan
Llandudno Bodysgallen Hall
Llandudno St Tudno Hotel
Llangammarch Wells Lake Country House Hotel **(D)**
Llangefni Tre-Ysgawen Hall
Llansanffraid Glan Conwy Old Rectory **(D at 8)**
Llyswen Llangoed Hall
Mumbles Norton House **(D)**
Northop Soughton Hall
Penally Penally Abbey **(D)**
Portmeirion Hotel Portmeirion
Pwllheli Plas Bodegroes **(D)**
Reynoldston Fairyhill
Talsarnau Maes-y-Neaudd
Trellech Village Green **(L)**
Welsh Hook Stone Hall **(D)**
Whitebrook Crown at Whitebrook

Channel Islands

Alderney First & Last
Guernsey La Grande Mare Hotel
L'Eree Taste of India
Rozel Bay Chateau la Chaire
St Anne Georgian House
St Anne Inchalla Hotel **(L from 1)**
St Brelade Hotel Chateau Valeuse
St Brelade Sea Crest
St Brelade Taj Mahal
St Helier Grand Hotel **(L)**
St Ouen The Lobster Pot
St Peter Port Louisiana
St Saviour Longueville Manor
Sark Aval Du Creux
Sark Dixcart Hotel **(D)**
Sark La Sablonnerie
Sark Stocks Hotel

Isle of Man

Ballasalla La Rosette **(L)**
Ramsey Harbour Bistro

Northern Ireland

Annalong Glassdrumman Lodge **(D at 8)**
Belfast Bengal Brasserie **(D)**
Belfast Manor House
Belfast Strand Restaurant
Belfast Welcome Restaurant **(D)**
Holywood Culloden Hotel

Republic of Ireland

Adare Adare Manor
Ahakista Shiro **(D)**
Aughrim Aughrim Schoolhouse Restaurant **(L)**
Ballina Mount Falcon Castle **(D at 8)**
Ballyhack Neptune Restaurant
Ballylickey Sea View Hotel
Ballyvaughan Gregans Castle
Baltimore Chez Youen
Blacklion MacNean Bistro
Blackrock Ayumi-Ya **(D)**
Boyle Cromleach Lodge **(D at 8)**
Bray Tree of Idleness **(D)**
Caherdaniel Loaves & Fishes **(D)**
Carlingford Jordan's Bar & Restaurant
Carne Lobster Pot **(D)**
Cashel Cashel House
Castledermot Doyle's School House Country Inn **(L)**
Castledermot Kilkea Castle
Castletownshend Mary Ann's Bar & Restaurant **(L)**
Clifden Ardagh Hotel **(D)**
Clifden Destry Rides Again **from 11am**
Clifden O'Grady's Seafood Restaurant
Cong Ashford Castle
Cork Bully's
Cork Flemings
Cork Huguenot **(D)**
Cork Isaacs **(D)**
Dalkey Il Ristorante **(D)**
Dingle Beginish Restaurant
Dingle Half Door
Dingle Lord Baker's Bar & Restaurant
Dublin Chapter One
Dublin Cooke's Café
Dublin Hibernian Hotel
Dublin Oisins **(D)**
Dublin Roly's Bistro
Dublin Shalimar **(D)**
Dublin The Westbury
Dunderry Dunderry Lodge Restaurant **(L from 1)**
Dunlavin Rathsallagh House
Dunworley Dunworley Cottage
Enniskerry Curtlestown House **(L)**
Enniskerry Enniscree Lodge
Galway Casey's Westwood Restaurant & Bars
Glasson Glasson Village Restaurant **(L)**
Gorey Marlfield House
Greystones The Hungry Monk
Howth Adrian's **(L)**
Kanturk Assolas Country House **(D at 8)**
Kenmare The Old Bank House **(D)**
Kenmare Park Hotel
Kenmare Sheen Falls Lodge
Kilkenny Kilkenny Kitchen **from 10am**
Killarney Cahernane Hotel **(D)**
Killorglin Nick's Restaurant

Kinsale Blue Haven Hotel **(D)**
Kinsale Man Friday **(D)**
Kinsale Max's Wine Bar
Leighlinbridge The Lord Bagenal Inn
Letterfrack Rosleague Manor
Mallow Longueville House
Maynooth Moyglare Manor
Monkstown Mr Hung's **to 12:30am**
Mountrath Roundwood House
Mullingar Crookedwood House **(L)**
Navan Ardboyne Hotel
Newmarket-on-Fergus Dromoland Castle
Newport Newport House **(D)**
Oughterard Currarevagh House **(D)**
Oysterhaven The Oystercatcher **(D)**
Rathnew Hunter's Hotel
Rathnew Tinakilly House
Riverstown Coopershill House **(D)**
Roundwood Roundwood Inn **(L from 1)**
Shanagarry Ballymaloe House
Skerries Red Bank Restaurant **(L)**
Sligo Truffles Restaurant **(D)**
Spiddal Boluisce Seafood Bar **(D)**
Stillorgan China-Sichuan Restaurant
Stillorgan Mr Hung's Sawadee Thai Restaurant
Straffan Kildare Hotel
Swords Le Chateau
Thomastown Mount Juliet Hotel
Waterford Waterford Castle
Wicklow Old Rectory **(D)**
Youghal Aherne's Seafood Restaurant

Seafood Restaurants

England

Barnstaple Lynwood House
Bridport Riverside Restaurant
Broadhembury Drewe Arms
Dartmouth Carved Angel
Elton Loch Fyne Oyster Bar
Falmouth Seafood Bar
Great Yarmouth Seafood Restaurant
Harrogate Drum & Monkey
Harwich Pier at Harwich
Helford Riverside
Hull Ceruttis
Kingston Restaurant Gravier
Lympstone River House
Newcastle-upon-Tyne Fisherman's Lodge
Norwich Greens Seafood Restaurant
Nottingham Loch Fyne Oyster Bar
Padstow Seafood Restaurant
St Ives Pig'n'Fish
Salcombe Spinnakers
Tuckenhay Floyd's Inn (Sometimes)
Weymouth Perry's

Scotland

Aberdeen Atlantis
Aberdeen Silver Darling
Anstruther Cellar
Cairndow Loch Fyne Oyster Bar
Colbost Three Chimneys Restaurant
Crinan Crinan Hotel
Fort William Crannog Seafood Restaurant
Glasgow Rogano

Wales

Cardiff Le Monde (see under La Brasserie)

Channel Islands

St Peter Port Absolute End
St Peter Port Le Nautique
Sark Aval Du Creux

Northern Ireland

Portrush Ramore

Republic of Ireland

Caherdaniel Loaves & Fishes
Carne Lobster Pot
Clifden Ardagh Hotel
Cork Lovetts
Dingle Doyle's Seafood Bar & Townhouse
Dingle Lord Baker's Bar & Restaurant
Dublin Chapter One
Dun Laoghaire Restaurant Na Mara
Howth King Sitric
Killarney Gaby's Seafood Restaurant
Kinsale Chez Jean-Marc
Kinsale Man Friday
Spiddal Boluisce Seafood Bar
Youghal Aherne's Seafood Restaurant

Outstanding Desserts

England

Applethwaite Underscar Manor
Baslow Fischer's Baslow Hall
Bath Bath Spa Hotel
Bath The New Moon
Bath Royal Crescent Hotel
Battle Netherfield Place
Birmingham Sloans
Bowness-on-Windermere Gilpin Lodge
Bradford Restaurant 19
Braunton Otters Restaurant
Bray-on-Thames The Waterside Inn
Bristol Harveys Restaurant
Broadway Lygon Arms
Broxted Whitehall
Bury Normandie Hotel
Calstock Danescombe Valley Hotel
Cambridge Midsummer House
Chadlington The Manor
Chagford Gidleigh Park
Cheltenham Le Champignon Sauvage
Cheltenham Epicurean
Cheltenham Redmond's
Chester Chester Grosvenor
Corse Lawn Corse Lawn House
Dartmouth Carved Angel
Dedham Le Talbooth
Duxford Duxford Lodge
East Grinstead Gravetye Manor
Eastbourne Grand Hotel
Felsted Rumbles Cottage
Gillingham Stock Hill House
Gloucester Hatton Court
Grasmere Michael's Nook
Great Milton Le Manoir aux Quat'Saisons
Gulworthy Horn of Plenty
Hampton Wick Le Petit Max
Harrogate Old Swan Hotel
Harvington The Mill
Haslemere Morel's
Highclere The Yew Tree
Kendal The Moon
Kingston Restaurant Gravier
Leamington Spa Mallory Court
Longridge Paul Heathcote's Restaurant
Lower Slaughter Lower Slaughter Manor
Malvern Croque-en-Bouche
Manchester Victoria & Albert Hotel
Mawnan Smith Nansidwell
Melbourn Pink Geranium
Midhurst Angel Hotel
Moulsford-on-Thames Beetle & Wedge
Nantwich Rookery Hall
New Milton Chewton Glen
Newcastle-upon-Tyne 21 Queen Street
Norwich Adlard's
Oakham Hambleton Hall
Padstow Seafood Restaurant
Plymouth Chez Nous
Pool-in-Wharfedale Pool Court
Prestbury White House
Richmond Petersham Hotel
Ridgeway Old Vicarage
Ripley Michels'
Shinfield L'Ortolan
Silverton Silverton Inn & Restaurant
South Molton Whitechapel Manor
Staddle Bridge McCoy's
Ston Easton Ston Easton Park
Stonham Mr Underhill's
Storrington Manley's
Stow-on-the-Wold Wyck Hill House
Stratford-upon-Avon Billesley Manor
Stroud Oakes
Sutton Coldfield New Hall
Taplow Cliveden
Taunton Castle Hotel
Thornton-le-Fylde River House
Tunbridge Wells Thackeray's House
Uckfield Horsted Place
Ullswater Rampsbeck Country House Hotel
Ullswater Sharrow Bay
Warminster Bishopstrow House
Windsor Oakley Court
Witherslack Old Vicarage
Woolton Hill Hollington House Hotel
Worfield Old Vicarage
York Melton's
York Middlethorpe Hall

Scotland

Arisaig Arisaig House
Colbost Three Chimneys
Cupar Ostlers Close
Dalguise Kinnaird
Dunoon Chatters
Edinburgh The Balmoral
Edinburgh Martin's
Edinburgh Vintners Room
Fort William Inverlochy Castle
Maybole Ladyburn
Ullapool Altnaharrie Inn

Wales

Abergavenny Walnut Tree Inn
Reynoldston Fairyhill

Northern Ireland

Belfast Roscoff
Portrush Ramore

Republic of Ireland

Blacklion MacNean Bistro
Boyle Cromleach Lodge

Caherdaniel Loaves & Fishes
Cork Arbutus Lodge
Cork Clifford's
Dingle Beginish Restaurant
Dingle Half Door
Dunderry Dunderry Lodge Restaurant
Kinsale Chez Jean-Marc
Moycullen Drimcong House Restaurant
Rathnew Tinakilly House
Waterford Duryer's
Youghal Aherne's Seafood Restaurant

Restaurants offering a good cheeseboard

England

Alderley Edge Alderley Edge Hotel
Alston Lovelady Shield
Amberley Amberley Castle
Ambleside Rothay Manor Hotel
Appleby-in-Westmorland Appleby Manor Hotel
Applethwaite Undersear Manor
Ascot Royal Berkshire
Aston Clinton Bell Inn
Aylesbury Hartwell House
Barnsley Armstrongs
Barnsley Restaurant Peano
Baslow Fischer's Baslow Hall
Basingstoke Audleys Wood
Bath Bath Spa Hotel
Bath Priory Hotel
Bath Royal Crescent Hotel
Beckingham Black Swan
Berwick-upon-Tweed Funnywayt'mekalivin
Bibury The Swan
Bilbrough Bilbrough Manor
Birmingham Swallow Hotel: Langtry's
Bishop's Tawton Halmpstone Manor
Blackpool September Brasserie
Bowness-on-Windermere Gilpin Lodge
Bowness-on-Windermere Linthwaite House
Bracknell Coppid Beech Hotel
Bradford Restaurant 19
Bradford-on-Avon Woolley Grange
Brampton Farlam Hall
Braunton Otters Restaurant
Brighton Hospitality Inn
Brighton Langan's Bistro
Brimfield Poppies Restaurant
Bristol Harveys
Bristol Hunt's
Bristol Restaurant Lettonie
Bristol Markwick's
Broadway Collin House
Broadway Lygon Arms
Brockenhurst Le Poussin
Buckland Buckland Manor
Bury Normandie Hotel & Restaurant
Calstock Danescombe Valley Hotel
Cambridge Midsummer House
Canterbury County Hotel
Cartmel Uplands
Castle Cary Bond's
Castle Combe Manor House
Cawston Grey Gables
Chaddesley Corbett Brockencote Hall
Chagford Gridleigh Park
Chapeltown Greenhead House
Charingworth Charingworth Manor
Chedington Chedington Court
Cheltenham Le Champignon Sauvage
Cheltenham Greenway
Cheltenham Redmond's
Chester Chester Grosvenor
Chichester The Droveway
Chiseldon Chiseldon House
Clanfield The Plough at Clanfield
Claygate Les Alouettes
Cockermouth Quince & Medlar
Colerne Lucknam Park
Corse Lawn Corse Lawn House
Cowan Bridge Cobwebs
Darlington Victor's Restaurant
Dartmouth Carved Angel
Dedham Le Talbooth
Dorking Partners West Street
Dorrington Country Friends
Dulverton Ashwick House
Dunbridge Mill Arms Inn
Duxford Duxford Lodge
East Boldon Forsters
East Buckland Lower Pitt
Eastbourne Grand Hotel
Elcot Elcot Park Resort Hotel
Ely Old Fire Engine House
Erpingham Ark
Evershot Summer Lodge
Eversley New Mill
Evesham Riverside Hotel
Eyton Marsh Country Hotel
Faversham Read's
Felsted Rumbles Cottage
Freshford Homewood Park
Fressingfield Fox & Goose
Gillingham Stock Hill House
Gloucester Hatton Court
Goring-on-Thames The Leatherne Bottel
Grasmere Michael's Nook
Grasmere White Moss House
Grasmere Wordsworth Hotel
Great Dunmow The Starr
Great Milton Le Manoir aux Quat'Saisons
Grimston Congham Hall
Guist Tollbridge
Gulworthy Horn of Plenty
Handforth Belfry Hotel

Harrogate Old Swan Hotel
Haslemere Morel's
Hastings Roser's
Hayfield Bridge End Restaurant
Helford Riverside
Hersham The Dining Room
Highclere The Yew Tree
Hintlesham Hintlesham Hall
Hockley Heath Nuthurst Grange
Horton French Partridge
Hunstrete Hunstrete House
Huntingdon Old Bridge Hotel
Hurstbourne Tarrant Esseborne Manor
Kendal Posh Nosh
Keyston Pheasant Inn
Kintbury Dundas Arms
Kinver Berkley's Bistro
Knutsford La Belle Epoque
Lacock At The Sign of The Angel
Langar Langar Hall
Langho Northcote Manor
Lavenham Great House
Lavenham The Swan
Leamington Spa Mallory Court
Ledbury Hope End
Leeds Haley's Hotel
Linton Wood Hall
Liskeard Well House
Long Melford Chimneys
Longridge Paul Heathcote's Restaurant
Lower Slaughter Lower Slaughter Manor
Madingley Three Horseshoes
Maiden Newton Maiden Newton House
Maidenhead Fredrick's
Malvern Cottage in the Wood
Malvern Croque-en-Bouche
Manchester Market Restaurant
Manchester Airport Etrop Grange
Manchester Airport Moss Nook
Mawnan Smith Nansidwell
Melbourn Pink Geranium
Melmerby Village Bakery
Moreton-in-Marsh Marsh Goose
Moulsford-on-Thames Beetle & Wedge
Nantwich Rookery Hall
New Milton Chewton Glen
Newcastle-upon-Tyne 21 Queen Street
Northleach Wickens
Norwich Adlard's
Oakham Hambleton Hall
Old Burghclere Dew Pond
Oxford Bath Place
Oxford Cherwell Boathouse
Oxford Restaurant Elizabeth
Padstow Seafood Restaurant
Paulerspury Vine House
Penkridge William Harding's House
Pitton Silver Plough
Plumtree Perkins Bar Bistro
Pool-in-Wharfedale Pool Court
Porlock Oaks Hotel
Puckrup Puckrup Hall
Purton Pear Tree
Ramsbottom Village Restaurant
Richmond Petersham Hotel
Ridgeway Old Vicarage
Ripley Michels'
Roade Roadhouse
Romaldkirk Rose and Crown
Romsey Old Manor House
Ross-on-Wye Pheasants
Rotherwick Tylney Hall
Rowde George & Dragon
Rye Landgate Bistro
St Martin's St Martin's Hotel
St Mawes Idle Rocks
Salcombe Spinnakers
Sandiway Nunsmere Hall
Shepton Mallet Blostin's Restaurant
Shinfield L'Ortolan
Silverton Silverton Inn & Restaurant
South Godstone La Bonne Auberge
South Molton Whitechapel Manor
Southampton Browns Brasserie
Southwold The Swan
Staddle Bridge McCoy's
Stamford The George of Stamford
Stapleford Stapleford Park
Stilton Bell Inn
Ston Easton Ston Easton Park
Stonham Mr Underhill's
Storrington Abingworth Hall
Storrington Little Thakeham
Storrington Old Forge
Stow-on-the-Wold Wyck Hill House
Stretton Ram Jam Inn
Stroud Oakes
Sutton Partners Brasserie
Taunton Castle Hotel
Tetbury Calcot Manor
Torquay Table Restaurant
Tresco Island Hotel
Tunbridge Wells Cheevers
Tunbridge Wells Downstairs at Thackeray's
Tunbridge Wells Thackeray's House
Twickenham McClements
Ullswater Leeming House
Ullswater Old Church Hotel
Ullswater Rampsbeck Country House Hotel
Ullswater Sharrow Bay
Ulverston Bay Horse Inn & Bistro
Upper Slaughter Lords of the Manor
Uppingham The Lake Isle
Walkington Manor House
Wareham Priory Hotel
Warminster Bishopstrow House
Wath-in-Nidderdale Sportsman's Arms
Watlington Well House
Wells Ritcher's
Weston-under-Penyard Wharton Lodge
Whimple Woodhayes
Williton White House
Wilmslow Stanneylands
Windermere Roger's Restaurant
Windsor Oakley Court
Witherslack Old Vicarage
Wiveliscombe Langley House
Woburn Paris House
Woodstock Feathers
Worcester Brown's
Worfield Old Vicarage
Wylam Laburnum House
Wymondham Number Twenty Four
Yeovil Little Barwick House

York Melton's
York Middlethorpe Hall

Scotland

Alyth Drumnacree House
Arisaig Arisaig House
Auchterhouse Old Mansion House
Ayr Stables
Ballater Tullich Lodge
Banchory Raemoir House
Bearsden Fifty Five BC
Canonbie Riverside Inn
Colbost Three Chimneys Restaurant
Crinan Crinan Hotel: Westward Restaurant
Crinan Crinan Hotel
Cumbernauld Westerwood Hotel
Dalguise Kinnaird
Drumnadrochit Polmaily House
Dulnain Bridge Auchendean Lodge
Dunblane Cromlix House
Dunoon Chatters
Edinburgh L'Auberge
Edinburgh The Balmoral
Edinburgh Caledonian
Edinburgh Martin's
Eriska Isle of Eriska
Fort William Inverlochy Castle
Glasgow Glasgow Hilton
Glasgow One Devonshire Gardens
Glasgow Ubiquitous Chip
Inverness Culloden House
Kilchrenan Ardanaiseig
Kilfinan Kilfinan Hotel
Kilmore Glenfeochan House
Kinclaven by Stanley Ballathie House
Kingussie The Cross
Kirknewton Dalmahoy Hotel, Golf & Country Club
Linlithgow Champany Inn
Muir-of-Ord Dower House
Nairn Clifton Hotel
Newton Stewart Kirroughtree Hotel
Newtonmore Ard-na-Coille Hotel
Onich Allt-nan-Ros Hotel
Peat Inn Peat Inn
Scarista Scarista House
Scone Murrayshall House
Tiroran Tiroran House
Turnberry Turnberry Hotel
Ullapool Altnaharrie Inn

Wales

Abergavenny Walnut Tree Inn
Abersoch Porth Tocyn Hotel
Chirk Starlings Castle
Colwyn Bay Café Niçoise
Coychurch Coed-y-Mwstwr Hotel
Eglwysfach Ynyshir Hall
Harlech The Cemlyn
Llanberis Y Bistro
Llandrillo Tyddyn Llan
Llandudno Bodysgallen Hall
Llandudno St Tudno Hotel
Llangefni Tre-Ysgawen Hall
Llansanffraid Glan Conwy Old Rectory
Llyswen Llangoed Hall
Llyswen Llangoed Hall
Northop Soughton Hall
Pwllheli Plas Bodegroes
Swansea Number One
Talsarnau Maes-y-Neaudd
Whitebrook Crown at Whitebrook

Channel Islands

Rozel Bay Chateau la Chaire
St Saviour Longueulle Manor
Sark Stocks Hotel

Isle of Man

Ramsey Harbour Bistro

Northern Ireland

Belfast Roscoff

Republic of Ireland

Adare Adare Manor
Adare Mustard Seed
Ballina Mount Falcon Castle
Caherdaniel Loaves & Fishes
Castletownshend Mary Ann's Bar & Restaurant
Cong Ashford Castle
Cork Arbutus Lodge
Cork Clifford's
Dingle Beginish Restaurant
Dingle Doyle's Seafood Bar & Townhouse
Dingle Half Door
Dublin Old Dublin Restaurant
Enniskerry Curtlestown House
Enniskerry Enniscree Lodge
Gorey Marlfield House
Kenmare Park Hotel
Kenmare Sheen Falls Lodge
Kilkenny Lacken House
Killarney Cahernane Hotel
Killarney Gaby's Seafood Restaurant
Killorglin Nick's Restaurant
Kinsale Blue Haven Hotel
Kinsale Chez Jean-Marc
Mallow Longueville House
Moycullen Drimcong
Newmarket-on-Fergus Dromoland Castle
Skerries Red Bank Restaurant
Waterford Prendiville's Restaurant/Guesthouse

Restaurants with Outstanding Wine Lists

England

Alderley Edge Alderley Edge Hotel
Aston Clinton Bell Inn
Aylesbury Hartwell House
Bath Priory Hotel
Bray-on-Thames The Waterside Inn
Bristol Harveys Restaurant
Broxted Whitehall
Buckland Buckland Manor
Bury Normandie Hotel & Restaurant
Calstock Danescombe Valley Hotel
Castle Combe Manor House
Chadlington The Manor
Chagford Gidleigh Park
Charingworth Charingworth Manor
Chedington Chedington Court
Cheltenham Greenway
Cheltenham Redmond's
Chester Chester Grosvenor
Chilgrove White Horse Inn
Chinnor Sir Charles Napier Inn
Colerne Lucknam Park
Corse Lawn Corse Lawn House
Dartmouth Carved Angel
Dedham Fountain House & Dedham Hall
Dedham Le Talbooth
East Grinstead Gravetye Manor
Evershot Summer Lodge
Eversley New Mill Restaurant
Faversham Read's
Fressingfield Fox & Goose
Gloucester Hatton Court
Grasmere Michael's Nook
Grasmere White Moss House
Grasmere Wordsworth Hotel
Great Dunmow The Starr
Great Milton Le Manoir aux Quat'Saisons
Handforth Belfry Hotel
Haslemere Morel's
Hastings Roser's
Helford Riverside
Herstmonceux Sundial Restaurant
Hintlesham Hintlesham Hall
Hunstrete Hunstrete House
Huntingdon Old Bridge Hotel
Ixworth Theobalds
Keyston Pheasant Inn
Kintbury Dundas Arms
Ledbury Hope End
Lower Beeding South Lodge
Lower Slaughter Lower Slaughter Manor
Malvern Croque-en-Bouche
Moulsford-on-Thames Beetle & Wedge
New Milton Chewton Glen
Norwich Adlard's
Oakham Hambleton Hall
Oxford Cherwell Boathouse
Oxford Restaurant Elizabeth
Padstow Seafood Restaurant
Pool-in-Wharfedale Pool Court
Ramsbottom Village Restaurant
Ridgeway Old Vicarage
Romsey Old Manor House
Ross-on-Wye Pheasants
Shinfield L'Ortolan
Southwold The Crown
Stamford The George of Stamford
Stapleford Stapleford Park
Ston Easton Ston Easton Park
Stonor Stonor Arms
Stuckton The Three Lions
Sutton Coldfield New Hall
Taplow Cliveden
Taunton Castle Hotel
Ullswater Sharrow Bay
Ulverston Bay Horse Inn & Bistro
Uppingham The Lake Isle
Walkington Manor House
Wansford-in-England Haycock Hotel
Waterhouses Old Beams
Wath-in-Nidderdale Sportsman's Arms
Williton White House
Wilmslow Stanneylands
Windsor Oakley Court
Winteringham Winteringham Fields
Woolton Hill Hollington House
Worfield Old Vicarage

Scotland

Aberfoyle Braeval Old Mill
Anstruther Cellar
Auchterarder Auchterarder House
Blairgowrie Kinloch House
Crinan Crinan Hotel
Dalguise Kinnaird
Edinburgh L'Auberge
Glasgow One Devonshire Gardens
Glasgow Ubiquitous Chip
Gullane La Potiniere
Kingussie The Cross
Linlithgow Champany Inn
Newtonmore Ard-na-Coille Hotel
Peat Inn Peat Inn
Port Appin Airds Hotel
Turnberry Turnberry Hotel
Ullapool Altnaharrie Inn

Wales

Abergavenny Walnut Tree Inn
Llandudno Bodysgallen Hall
Llandudno St Tudno Hotel
Llyswen Llangoed Hall
Northop Soughton Hall
Portmeirion Hotel Portmeirion
Pwllheli Plas Bodegroes

Channel Islands

Castel La Grande Mare Hotel

Republic of Ireland

Bray Tree of Idleness
Cork Arbutus Lodge
Dublin Le Coq Hardi
Greystones The Hungry Monk
Howth King Sitric
Kenmare Park Hotel
Kenmare Sheen Falls Lodge
Killorglin Nick's
Maynooth Moyglare Manor
Newmarket-on-Fergus Dromoland Castle
Newport Newport House

Restaurants with a good list of California Wines

England

Alderley Edge Alderley Edge Hotel
Ambleside Rothay Manor Hotel
Ashford Eastwell Manor
Aston Clinton Bell Inn
Aylesbury Hartwell House
Barnsley Armstrongs
Basingstoke Audleys Wood
Bath Bath Spa Hotel
Bath Garlands
Bath Priory Hotel
Bath Royal Crescent Hotel
Bibury The Swan
Birmingham Hyatt Regency
Bracknell Coppid Beech Hotel
Bristol Harveys Restaurant
Bristol Markwick's
Broadway Lygon Arms
Bromsgrove Grafton Manor
Broxted Whitehall
Cambridge Midsummer House
Campsea Ash Old Rectory
Castle Combe Manor House
Cawston Grey Gables
Chagford Gidleigh Park
Chapeltown Greenhead House
Charingworth Charingworth Manor
Chedington Chedington Court
Cheltenham Le Champignon Sauvage
Cheltenham Epicurean
Cheltenham Greenway
Chester Chester Grosvenor
Chilgrove White Horse Inn
Chinnor Sir Charles Napier Inn
Chobham Quails Restaurant
Colerne Lucknam Park
Corse Lawn Corse Lawn House
Cowan Bridge Cobwebs
Dartmouth Carved Angel
Dedham Fountain House & Dedham Hall
Dedham Le Talbooth
East Grinstead Gravetye Manor
Evershot Summer Lodge
Eversley New Mill Restaurant
Evesham Riverside Hotel
Faversham Read's
Freshford Homewood Park
Fressingfield Fox & Goose
Gloucester Hatton Court
Grasmere Michael's Nook
Grasmere White Moss House
Grasmere Wordsworth Hotel
Great Milton Le Manoir aux Quat'Saisons
Great Yarmouth Seafood Restaurant
Handforth Belfry Hotel
Harwich Pier at Harwich
Hastings Roser's
Helford Riverside
Hintlesham Hintlesham Hall
Hockley Heath Nuthurst Grange
Horton French Partridge
Huntingdon Old Bridge Hotel
Huntsham Huntsham Court
Ixworth Theobalds
Keyston Pheasant Inn
Kintbury Dundas Arms
Knutsford La Belle Epoque
Leamington Spa Mallory Court
Leeds Brasserie Forty Four
Linton Wood Hall
Long Melford Chimneys
Lower Slaughter Lower Slaughter Manor
Lymington Gordleton Mill
Lympstone River House
Madingley Three Horseshoes
Maiden Newton Maiden Newton House
Maiden Newton Le Petit Canard
Malvern Cottage in the Wood
Malvern Croque-en-Bouche
Marlow Compleat Angler Hotel
Medmenham Danesfield House
Midhurst Angel Hotel
Moreton-in-Marsh Marsh Goose
New Milton Chewton Glen
Northleach Wickens
Norwich Adlard's
Oakham Hambleton Hall
Old Burghclere Dew Pond
Oxford Bath Place Hotel & Restaurant
Oxford Cherwell Boathouse
Padstow Seafood Restaurant
Pool-in-Wharfedale Pool Court
Prestbury White House
Puckrup Puckrup Hall

Purton Pear Tree
Ramsbottom Village Restaurant
Romaldkirk Rose and Crown
Romsey Old Manor House
Ross-on-Wye Pheasants
Rotherwick Tylney Hall
Sandiway Nunsmere Hall
Sevenoaks Royal Oak
Shinfield L'Ortolan
South Molton Whitechapel Manor
Southwold The Crown
Southwold The Swan
Spark Bridge Bridgefield House
Stamford The George of Stamford
Stapleford Stapleford Park
Ston Easton Ston Easton Park
Stonor Stonor Arms
Storrington Old Forge
Stow-on-the-Wold Wyck Hill House
Stratford-upon-Avon Billesley Manor
Streatley-on-Thames Swan Diplomat
Stuckton The Three Lions
Sturminster Newton Plumber Manor
Sutton Coldfield New Hall
Taplow Cliveden
Taunton Castle Hotel
Teffont Evias Howard's House
Thundridge Hanbury Manor
Tunbridge Wells Thackeray's House
Twickenham McClements
Uckfield Horsted Place
Ullswater Leeming House
Ullswater Rampsbeck Country House Hotel
Ullswater Sharrow Bay
Ulverston Bay Horse Inn & Bistro
Upper Slaughter Lords of the Manor
Uppingham The Lake Isle
Walkington Manor House
Wansford-in-England Haycock Hotel
Wareham Priory Hotel
Warminster Bishopstrow House
Waterhouses Old Beams
Wath-in-Nidderdale Sportsman's Arms
Wilmslow Stanneylands
Windermere Roger's Restaurant
Windsor Oakley Court
Winteringham Winteringham Fields
Witherslack Old Vicarage
Woburn Paris House
Worfield Old Vicarage
York Middlethorpe Hall

Scotland

Aberfoyle Braeval Old Mill
Achiltibuie Summer Isles
Anstruther Cellar
Auchterarder Auchterarder House
Auchterhouse Old Mansion House
Banchory Raemoir House
Blairgowrie Kinloch House
Colbost Three Chimneys Restaurant
Craigellachie Craigellachie Hotel
Crinan Crinan Hotel
Cumbernauld Westerwood Hotel
Dalguise Kinnaird
Drumnadrochit Polmaily House
Edinburgh Caledonian Hotel
Edinburgh Martin's
Edinburgh Vintners Room
Fort William Inverlochy Castle
Glasgow Glasgow Hilton
Glasgow One Devonshire Gardens
Glasgow Ubiquitous Chip
Gullane Greywalls Hotel
Gullane La Potiniere
Kentallen of Appin Ardsheal House
Kingussie The Cross
Linlithgow Champany Inn
Nairn Clifton Hotel
Newtonmore Ard-na-Coille Hotel
Oban Knipoch Hotel
Peat Inn Peat Inn
Port Appin Airds Hotel
Quothquan Shieldhill
Ullapool Altnaharrie Inn

Wales

Abergavenny Walnut Tree Inn
Abersoch Porth Tocyn Hotel
Llandudno Bodysgallen Hall
Llandudno St Tudno Hotel
Llyswen Llangoed Hall
Northop Soughton Hall
Portmeirion Hotel Portmeirion
Pwllheli Plas Bodegroes
Talsarnau Maes-y-Neaudd
Whitebrook Crown at Whitebrook

Channel Islands

Castel La Grande Mare Hotel

Northern Ireland

Belfast Roscoff
Portrush Ramore

Republic of Ireland

Adare Adare Manor
Ballyvaughan Gregans Castle
Bray Tree of Idleness
Cong Ashford Castle
Cork Arbutus Lodge
Cork Lovetts
Dublin Le Coq Hardi
Dublin Patrick Guilbaud
Greystones The Hungry Monk
Kenmare Park Hotel
Kenmare Sheen Falls Lodge
Killarney Cahernane Hotel
Killarney Gaby's Seafood
Leighlinbridge Lord Bagenal Inn
Newport Newport House
Rathnew Tinakilly House
Waterford Waterford Castle

Restaurants offering a good range of wines by the glass

England

Alderley Edge Alderley Edge Hotel
Aston Clinton Bell Inn
Aylesbury Hartwell House
Barnstaple Lynwood House
Bath Bath Spa Hotel
Bath The New Moon
Bath Royal Crescent Hotel
Birmingham Sloans
Botley Cobbett's
Bracknell Coppid Beech Hotel
Brightling Jack Fuller's
Brighton Hospitality Inn
Bristol Browns Restaurant & Bar
Bristol Harveys Restaurant
Broadway Lygon Arms
Brockenhurst Le Poussin
Buckland Buckland Manor
Cambridge Browns
Cambridge Midsummer House
Cartmel Uplands
Chagford Gidleigh Park
Chapeltown Greenhead House
Charingworth Charingworth Manor
Cheltenham Epicurean
Cheltenham Greenway
Cheltenham Redmond's
Chester Chester Grosvenor
Chilgrove White Horse Inn
Chinnor Sir Charles Napier Inn
Chobham Quails Restaurant
Clitheroe Browns Bistro
Colerne Lucknam Park
Corse Lawn Corse Lawn House
Cowan Bridge Cobwebs
Dartmouth Carved Angel
Dedham Le Talbooth
Dorking Partners West Street
Dorrington Country Friends
East Grinstead Gravetye Manor
Eastbourne Grand Hotel
Erpingham Ark
Eversley New Mill Restaurant
Evesham Riverside Hotel
Freshford Homewood Park
Fressingfield Fox & Goose
Goring-on-Thames The Leatherne Bottel
Grasmere Michael's Nook
Grasmere White Moss House
Great Dunmow The Starr
Grimston Congham Hall
Guist Tollbridge
Gulworthy Horn of Plenty
Harrogate Tannin Level
Harwich Pier at Harwich
Helford Riverside
Highclere The Yew Tree
Hintlesham Hintlesham Hall
Hockley Heath Nuthurst Grange
Huntingdon Old Bridge Hotel
Keyston Pheasant Inn
Lavenham Great House
Leamington Spa Mallory Court
Leeds Brasserie Forty Four
Leeds Haley's Hotel
Lymington Gordleton Mill
Lympstone River House
Madingley Three Horseshoes
Maiden Newton Maiden Newton House
Malvern Cottage in the Wood
Malvern Croque-en-Bouche
Manchester Market Restaurant
Marlow Compleat Angler Hotel
Medmenham Danesfield House
Melbourn Pink Geranium
Moulsford-on-Thames Beetle & Wedge
New Alresford Hunters
New Milton Chewton Glen
Northleach Wickens
Oxford Browns
Pitton Silver Plough
Polperro Kitchen at Polperro
Poole Haven Hotel: La Roche Restaurant
Prestbury White House
Puckrup Puckrup Hall
Purton Pear Tree
Ramsbottom Village Restaurant
Reigate La Barbe
Ridgeway Old Vicarage
Ripley Michels'
Ross-on-Wye Pheasants
Rowde George & Dragon
Sevenoaks Royal Oak
Southwold The Crown
Southwold The Swan
Spark Bridge Bridgefield House
Stamford The George of Stamford
Storrington Old Forge
Stratford-upon-Avon The Opposition
Stuckton The Three Lions
Sutton Coldfield New Hall
Taunton Castle Hotel
Taunton Porters Wine Bar
Teffont Evias Howard's House
Thundridge Hanbury Manor
Tunbridge Wells Downstairs at Thackeray's
Ullswater Leeming House
Ullswater Old Church Hotel
Ullswater Rampsbeck Country House Hotel
Ullswater Sharrow Bay
Ulverston Bay Horse Inn & Bistro
Upper Slaughter Lords of the Manor
Wadhurst Spindlewood
Wansford-in-England Haycock Hotel
Waterhouses Old Beams
Wath-in-Nidderdale Sportsman's Arms
Williton White House
Winchester Wykeham Arms
Windsor Oakley Court
Winteringham Winteringham Fields

Witherslack Old Vicarage
Woodstock Feathers Hotel
Worfield Old Vicarage
York Melton's

Scotland

Aberfeldy Farleyer House
Anstruther Cellar
Ayr Stables
Cairndow Loch Fyne Oyster Bar
Cupar Ostlers Close
Drybridge Old Monastery
Edinburgh Atrium
Edinburgh Kelly's
Edinburgh Vintners Room
Glasgow Café Gandolfi
Glasgow Glasgow Hilton
Glasgow Ubiquitous Chip
Linlithgow Champany Inn
Nairn Clifton Hotel
Newtonmore Ard-na-Coille Hotel

Wales

Abergavenny Walnut Tree Inn
Chepstow Beckfords
Coychurch Coed-y-Mwstwr Hotel
Eglwysfach Ynyshir Hall
Llandudno St Tudno Hotel
Llyswen Llangoed Hall
Mumbles PA's Winebar
Portmeirion Hotel Portmeirion
Pwllheli Plas Bodegroes
Whitebrook Crown at Whitebrook

Channel Islands

Castel La Grande Mare Hotel

Northern Ireland

Annalong Glassdrumman Lodge
Belfast Roscoff

Republic of Ireland

Ballyvaughan Gregans Castle
Dublin Il Primo
Enniskerry Enniscree Lodge
Newmarket-on-Fergus Dromoland Castle
Oughterard Currarevagh House
Roundwood Roundwood Inn
Wicklow Old Rectory

Hotel Groups and Hotels with Conference and Banqueting Facilities

Overleaf is a listing of major hotel groups each of which has to a lesser or greater extent a definable corporate identity. We have included budget hotel chains (some coming under the banner of the major groups) which, while not given our normal percentage grading in the main gazetteer section of the Guide, nevertheless offer the businessman or overnight traveller a convenient stop-over.

A brief description of the main characteristics of each group is given as well as head office addresses, and phone and fax numbers for general enquiries and central reservations.

In the subsequent tables we list those hotels (in groups or privately owned) which offer conference and banqueting facilities. The numbers quoted are for the maximum number of delegates for a theatre-style conference or diners at a banquet in one room. Leisure centres are listed if they are part of the hotel and feature at least an indoor heated swimming pool, sauna, solarium, whirlpool bath and keep-fit equipment.

These conference and banqueting facilities have not been evaluated by our inspectors.

Also included for the first time are the hotel's grading, its category (eg **HR** or **H** – indicatng whether or not the restaurant is recommended in the Guide – a useful indicator when selecting banqueting facilities) and golf amenities.

Campanile Hotels

Head Office:

Unit 8 Red Lion Court
Alexandra Road
Hounslow
Middx TW3 1JS
Tel 081-569 5757

Central Reservations (from UK):
Tel 010 33 1 64 62 46 46
Fax 010 33 1 64 62 46 61
Weekdays 8am-7pm, Saturdays 9am-12pm French time.

A chain of 14 modern, purpose-built, functional hotels. All are open 365 days. Liverpool has 24hr reception. All bedrooms are either twin or double, have remote-control colour TV, fully fitted bathrooms, radio-alarms. Each hotel has rooms designed for the disabled. A standard tariff of £35.75 per room applies though there is a third person supplement of £7.50. Buffet breakfasts, either Continental or full English, are £4.25 per person. Each hotel has conference facilities for 30.

Copthorne Hotels

Head Office:

Victoria House
Horley
Surrey RH6 7AF
Tel 0293 772288
Fax 0293 772345

Reservations: Freephone 0800 41 47 41

Standard rooms (Classics) offer good-sized bedrooms each with a double bed, colour TV with movie and/or satellite channel, en-suite bath and shower as well as the other usual facilities that are expected of a modern hotel. Executive rooms (Connoisseur) have larger more comfortable bedrooms and, usually, a better outlook. Extras include fresh fruit and magazines, while bathrooms offer bathrobes and better-quality toiletries.

De Vere Hotels

Head Office:

De Vere House
Chester Road
Daresbury
Warrington
Cheshire WA4 4BN

Central Enquiries and Conference Desk North:
Tel 0925 265050
Fax 0925 601264
Conference Desk South:
Tel 0753 64505

On the whole, these are quite distinctive hotels, some grand, others not so, each with its own style and character based on comfort and tradition. Standards of service are generally high. Leisure clubs are free to guests.

Edwardian Hotels

Head Office:

140 Bath Road
Hayes, Middlesex UB3 5AW

Central Reservations:
Tel 081-564 8888
Fax 081-759 8422
Conference Line: 081-564 7474

A London-based group of hotels ranging from the Hampshire in Leicester Square and the Edwardian International at London Heathrow to the more modest but still comfortable Kenilworth and Grafton Hotels.

Forte Hotels

Head Office:

Forte UK Ltd
St Martin's House
20 Queensmere
Slough, Berkshire SL1 1YY
Tel 0753 573266
Fax 0753 577227

Sales Office:
Forte House
80 Gatehouse Road
Aylesbury
Buckinghamshire HP19 3EB
Tel 0296 393939
Fax 0296 395419
Reservations (local call cost): 0345 40 40 40 (leisure breaks)
Business Guarantee Line: Freephone 0800 404040

Trusthouse Forte was rebranded a couple of years ago and this vast network of hotels now offers six categories of hotels ranging from the Exclusive brand to the budget Travelodges. We feel that the brands Forte Crest and Forte Posthouse are the two primarily aimed at the businessman as these offer the best deals in terms of value. However, we also list the other hotels in the group as these often have good conference facilities, though the package can be more expensive. Heritage hotels are mid-priced and of mixed appeal; they are generally situated in small towns and more rural locations and are suitable for smaller meetings.

Forte Exclusive, Grand & Heritage

Reservations: (local call cost) 0345 40 40 40

Forte Crest

Reservations: (local call cost) 0345 40 40 40

Incorporating some of the best former Posthouses and most of the original Crests, this is a chain of around 28 modern business-orientated hotels. Over half have fully-equipped business centres. All offer 24hr room service for both executive and standard rooms.

Forte Posthouse

Reservations: Freephone 0800 40 40 40

A leading UK chain of around 65 mostly purpose-built modern hotels. Many have health and fitness centres. Rooms have lost the starkness of the early 80s but currently the chief attribute of this chain is the room rate – from Sunday to Thursday the daily 'room only' rate is £53.50, dropping to £39.50 for Friday and Saturday. The midweek room price including cooked breakfast for two people is £67.40.

Forte Travelodge

Reservations: Freephone 0800 850 950

Roadside budget accommodation offering simple but modern rooms in 93 locations conveniently sited along major routes. Room rates, payable in advance, are currently £31.95 per room. All have en-suite bathrooms with shower, colour television, radio/alarms and tea and coffee-making facilities. Rooms sleep three adults, a child under 12 and a baby in a cot. Every Travelodge has a room equipped for the disabled. The lodges have either 27 or 56 bedrooms.

Granada Lodges

Head Office:

Toddington Service Area
M1 Service Area Southbound
Toddington
Near Dunstable
Bedfordshire LU5 6HR
Tel 0525 873881
Fax 0525 875358

Central Reservations: Freephone 0800 555 300

A chain of around 21 budget hotels located close to major routes. All rooms have private bath and shower, colour TV, radio/alarm and tea and coffee making facilities. In-room continental breakfast is available, otherwise meals are taken in the adjacent service area restaurant. Family rooms are available and 2 children under 16 sharing with 2 adults are accommodated free (excluding breakfast). Every lodge has rooms for the disabled. Prices are from £37.95 (Sun-Thurs, £34.95 Fri & Sat) for single, twin and double or family rooms; exceptions are Heston (London Heathrow) and Thurrock (Dartford Crossing) which are £46.95 (Sun-Thurs, £43.95 Fri & Sat). Payment is on arrival.

Hilton Hotels

Head Office:

Hilton International Hotels (UK) Ltd
Chancel House
Neasden Lane
London NW10 2XE

Hilton UK Reservations
PO Box 137
Watford, Herts WD1 1DN
Tel 0923 238877
Fax 0923 249271
Conference Reservations Tel 0923 250222

Hilton International and Hilton National hotels have superior rooms designated either Executive or Plaza, these are to a higher specification than standard rooms. They include large teletext TVs, a welcome tray with miniature spirits, chocolates, bathrobes, additional toiletries and lounge seating. Apart from all but one of the London hotels (the London Hilton on Park Lane), the majority of Hilton hotels have leisure centres that include swimming pools, fitness rooms and saunas.

Holiday Inns

European Head Office:

Woluwe Office Park 1
Rue Neerveld 101
1200 Brussels
Belgium
Tel 010 32 2 773 5511
Fax 010 32 2 772 0272

Holiday Inn Reservations: Freephone Tel 0800 897 121
Fax: Tel 010 31 20 606 5454

After starting off in the 70s and early 80s as a leader in the field of luxury business hotels, Holiday Inns haven't kept up the momentum and so some of the newer hotel groups have now caught up and even overtaken them. Under Bass plc the original concept has been expanded to include Holiday Inn Garden Courts, an economy version. Large beds and good bathrooms are a feature as well as the free accommodation of children (including teenagers) when sharing with parents. All have good leisure facilities and well-equipped conference rooms.

Jarvis Hotels

Head Office:

Wye House
London Road
High Wycombe
Buckinghamshire HP11 1LH
Tel 0494 473800
Fax 0494 471666

Linkline Reservations: (local call cost) Tel 0345 581 237
Fax 071-589 8193
Conference Reservations: Tel 071-581 3466
Fax 071-589 8193

A nationwide network of 39 dependable middle-range hotels. A few have leisure clubs (free to guests) and 27 have purpose-built Summit meeting rooms. Trouser presses and hair dryers are standard to all rooms, Executive bedrooms having a better standard of decor and additional amenities such as fruit and chocolates plus extra toiletries in the bathrooms.

Marriott Hotels

Scott's Hotels Limited
Executive Offices
Ditton Road
Langley
Berkshire SL3 8PT
Tel 0753 544255
Fax 0753 585484

Worldwide Reservations: Freephone (UK) Tel 0800 221 222
Fax 071-287 0271
Conferences & Groups 071-434 2299

The Marriott Corporation run the London Marriott and Cheshunt Marriott, while the remainder are operated under franchise by Scott's Hotels who relinquished their association with Holiday Inns in July 1992. Many millions of pounds have since been spent upgrading all aspects - from landscaping, exteriors and interiors, to staff uniforms of the former Holiday Inns. Staff have been trained to the exacting standards demanded by Marriott, the aim of the group being to attract senior management, with the family and leisure business geared more to the weekends. Bedrooms are spacious, with large desks and comfortable sofas. The Bristol, Heathrow/Slough, Marble Arch and new Leeds Marriott (due to open as we go to press) have Executive floors with private lounges and complimentary canapés. There are currently 18 hotels including four Courtyard by Marriott which offer more moderately priced accommodation but still have good-sized rooms with separate seating and dressing areas, plus mini-gyms.

Mount Charlotte Thistle Hotels

Head Office:

Mount Charlotte Investments plc
2 The Calls, Leeds
West Yorkshire LS2 7JU
Tel 0532 439111
Fax 0532 445555

Central Reservations:
Tel 071-937 8033
Highlife Shortbreaks Reservations:
Freephone 0800 700 400
National Conference Sales:
Tel 071-938 1755

Next to the Forte Hotels group, Mount Charlotte Thistle hotels are the most widespread throughout the country with hotels from Plymouth to Wick, and including 24 in London. Overall, the quality of bedroom accommodation is good and many of the hotels appear in the main gazetteer. Most hotels have a main meeting room with capacity for at least 100 delegates. Selected hotels have boardrooms that seat between 10 to 15 people for small meetings and senior management gatherings. The majority of hotels offer Executive bedrooms: these are larger rooms, more recently decorated and each having a number of useful extras. Lady guests have specially designated rooms.

Novotel

Head Office:

Novotel UK
1 Shortlands
Hammersmith
London W6 8DR
Tel 081-748 4580
Fax 081-741 0672

Resinter Reservations: 071-724 1000

A multinational hotel chain with properties located on the outskirts of cities and close to motorway junctions. Rooms, if somewhat plainly decorated, are large and functional. The standard is identical in all and is designed for practical comfort and rest. Each has a bed/settee as well as a double bed. There is ample writing space among the usual modern facilities offered. Accommodation and breakfast are free for two children under 16 sharing their parents' room. Food and efficient room service are available at any time from 6am to midnight and the bar follows the same hours.

Principal Hotels

Head Office:

Principal House
11 Ripon Road
Harrogate
North Yorkshire HG1 1TS
Tel 0423 530797
Fax 0423 500086

A group of 23 hotels, most located in town or city centres, that are characterised by an attractive, traditional style and decor. Standard rooms are well equipped, with all the usual amenities. Executive rooms have bathrobes and a trouser press.

Queens Moat Houses

Head Office:

Queens Court
9 Eastern Road
Romford
Essex RM1 3NG
Tel 0708 730522
Fax 0708 762691

Reservations:
Tel 0708 766677
Fax 0708 761033
Freephone (UK only): 0800 289 330

With properties as diverse as the Royal Crescent in Bath, Eastwell Manor in Ashford, the Rose and Crown in Salisbury and the Newmarket Moat House, there is no longer a characteristic pattern to the 102 UK hotels currently in the Queens Moat Houses directory (one of the largest three hotel groups, alongside Forte and Mount Charlotte Thistle). It was only a relatively short time ago that the group name was synonymous with pleasant enough but, on the whole, rather lacklustre hotels offering acceptable standards of accommodation. With its newest acquisitions Queens Moat Houses has moved firmly into the luxury hotel league as well.

Resort Hotels

Head Office:

Resort House
Edward Street
Brighton
East Sussex BN2 2HW
Tel 0273 676717
Fax 0273 608306

Central Reservations (local call charge):
Tel 0345 313 213

Currently based in the South of England there are now 46 hotels in this group. They vary from a 12th-century coaching inn near Maidenhead to modern purpose-built hotels, some with leisure clubs. These clubs are free to overnight guests.

Stakis Hotels

Head Office:

3 Atlantic Quay
York Street
Glasgow G2 8GH
Tel 041-221 0000
Fax 041-204 1111

Hotel Reservations: Freephone 0800 262 626
Conference Call: Freephone 0800 833 900

Located close to major business centres and trunk routes as well as in country settings, the hotels offer spacious, comfortable accommodation and 10 currently have a self-contained business centre. Guests have free use of the sports and leisure facilities. Originally based in Scotland but now with over 30 hotels scattered throughout the UK.

Swallow Hotels

Head Office:

Swallow House
19 Parsons Road
Washington
Tyne & Wear NE37 1ES
Tel 091-419 4545
Fax 091-415 1888

Central Reservations:
Tel 091-419 4666
Fax 091-415 1777

Based in the North East but with new hotels and acquisitions in the south this is a chain of hotels that is striving hard to improve its image. Hotels of the standing of the Birmingham Swallow and Bristol Swallow Royal are to be much admired. 29 of the 35 current hotels have leisure clubs; most include an indoor heated swimming pool, sauna and/or steam room, solarium and spa bath. Mini-gyms also feature in many. The facilities are free to overnight guests. Children of 14 years and under sharing a room with two adults are accommodated and served a cooked breakfast free of charge.

Whitbread

Head Office:

Whitbread House
Park Street West
Luton
Bedfordshire LU1 3BG
Tel 0582 422994
Fax 0582 400024

Country Club Hotels

Reservations:
Tel 0582 396969
Fax 0582 400024

A feature of the 10 hotels currently in this group is that all but two have at least one 18-hole golf course. Additionally, all feature a comprehensive range of leisure and sports facilities including swimming pools, saunas, solarium, tennis and squash courts and fitness studios.

Lansbury Hotels

Reservations:
Tel 0582 400158
Fax 0582 400024

A chain of 43 small hotels with a maximum of about 60 bedrooms. The character is fairly formal and traditional. All differ in style ranging from a mock-Georgian folly to up-to-date, purpose-built hotels.

Travel Inns

Reservations:
Tel 0582 482224
Fax 0582 405680

There are 37 Travel Inns, all located next to separate popular themed eating chains. All rooms have bath and shower, always a double bed with duvet, remote control TV, tea and coffee making facilities, radio/alarm and adequate writing/work space. Travel Inns currently operate a price of £32.50 per room irrespective of whether taken as a single, double or for family occupancy. Two children under 16 are accommodated free when sharing with adults. Payment is on arrival and reception closes at 11pm. Every Travel Inn has a specially adapted room for the disabled. At some, adjacent meeting rooms are available.

HOTELS LISTED BY COUNTY

LONDON

Swimming pool refers to indoor swimming pools only. See page 14 How to use this Guide for explanation of percentage rating system, room pricing and categories.

Key: QMH (Queens Moat Houses), MtCT (Mount Charlotte Thistle). See under England for London Airport, Heathrow and Gatwick.

Location	*Hotel*	*Group*	*%*	*Room Price*	*Cat*	*Tel*	*Rooms*	*Conf*	*Banq*	*Leisure Centre*	*Swim Pool*	*Golf*
E1	Tower Thistle	MtCT	66%	£176	H	071-481 2575	808	250	250			
E14	Britannia International Hot		68%	£113	H	071-515 1551	445	1000	500	yes	yes	
EC1	New Barbican Hotel	MtCT	51%	£100	H	071-251 1565	470	100	150			
N1	Great Northern Hotel	Compass	60%	£83	H	071-837 5454	89	100	100			
NW1	Dorset Square Hotel		74%	£142	H	071-723 7874	37					
NW1	Kennedy Hotel	MtCT	63%	£102	H	071-387 4400	360	100	85			
NW1	The Regent London		83%	£238	HR	071-631 8000	309	330	360	yes	yes	
NW1	White House	Rank	71%	£136	H	071-387 1200	576	120	100			
NW3	Charles Bernard Hotel		60%	£65	H	071-794 0101	57					
NW3	Clive Hotel	Hilton	64%	£64	H	071-586 2233	96	350	250			
NW3	Forte Posthouse	Forte	65%	£68	H	071-794 8121	140	25	25			
NW3	Regent's Park Marriott	Marriott	73%	£192	H	071-722 7711	303	400	270	yes	yes	
NW3	Swiss Cottage Hotel		62%	£140	H	071-722 2281	81	60	75			
NW4	Hendon Hall	MtCT	63%	£106	H	081-203 3341	52	330	240			
NW8	Hilton International Regent's Park	Hilton	73%	£148	HR	071-722 7722	377	150	130			
SE16	Scandic Crown Nelson Dock	Scandic	69%	£119	H	071-231 1001	390	410	300	yes	yes	
SE3	Bardon Lodge		56%	£84	H	081-853 4051	37	50	40			
SE9	Yardley Court			£52	H	081-850 1850	9					
SW1	The Berkeley	Savoy Group	86%	£252	HR	071-235 6000	160	220	200		yes	
SW1	Cadogan Hotel	Historic House	74%	£170	H	071-235 7141	75	40	40			

Location	Hotel	Group	%	Room Price	Cat	Tel	Rooms	Conf	Banq	Leisure Centre	Swim Pool	Golf
SW1	Chelsea Hotel		63%	£155	H	071-235 4377	225	120	120			
SW1	Collin House			£54	H	071-730 8031	13					
SW1	Dukes Hotel		79%	£238	HR	071-491 4840	64	55	70			
SW1	Durley House		74%	£275	H	071-235 5537	11					
SW1	Elizabeth Hotel			£70	H	071-828 6812	40	25	40			
SW1	Forte Crest St James's	Forte	68%	£119	H	071-930 2111	256	90	75			
SW1	The Goring		79%	£192	HR	071-936 9000	82	70	52			
SW1	Grosvenor Thistle Hotel	MtCT	64%	£138	H	071-834 9494	366	200	150			
SW1	Halkin Hotel		86%	£239	HR	071-333 1000	41	42	26			
SW1	Hyatt Carlton Tower		88%	£240	HR	071-235 5411	224	260	300			
SW1	Hyde Park Hotel	Forte	82%	£244	H	071-235 2000	185	250	250			
SW1	Knightsbridge Green Hotel			£117	PH	071-584 6274	24					
SW1	The Lanesborough		89%	£290	HR	071-259 5599	95	70	50			
SW1	The Lowndes Hyatt Hotel		76%	£233	H	071-823 1234	78	25	20			
SW1	Royal Horseguards Thistle	MtCT	71%	£110	H	071-839 3400	376	75	700			
SW1	Royal Court Hotel	QMH	68%	£145	H	071-730 9191	102	40	22			
SW1	Royal Westminster Thistle	MtCT	71%	£146	H	071-834 1821	134	160	200			
SW1	Rubens Hotel		66%	£141	H	071-834 6600	189	75	25			
SW1	St James Court		73%	£179	HR	071-821 1899	390	250	200			
SW1	Scandic Crown Victoria	Scandic	66%	£154	H	071-834 8123	210	200	210	yes	yes	
SW1	Sheraton Park Tower	Sheraton	79%	£270	HR	071-235 8050	295	60	150			
SW1	Sheraton Belgravia	Sheraton	75%	£250	HR	071-235 6040	89	40	22			
SW1	The Stafford		74%	£240	H	071-493 0111	74	20	30			
SW1	Stakis St Ermin's	Stakis	71%	£159	H	071-222 7888	290	200	200			
SW1	Tophams Ebury Court		60%	£100	HR	071-730 8147	46	24	24			
SW1	22 Jermyn Street			£200	PH	071-734 2353	18	30	12			
SW1	Wilbraham Hotel		55%	£86	H	071-730 8296	52					
SW1	Willett Hotel			£97	H	071-824 8415	18					
SW3	Basil Street Hotel		71%	£178	H	071-581 3311	92	55	80			

SW3	The Beaufort			£135	PH	071-584 5252	28				
SW3	Blair House Hotel			£85	H	071-581 2323	17				
SW3	The Capital		81%	£235	HR	071-589 5171	48	20	24		
SW3	The Draycott			£235	PH	071-730 6466	25				
SW3	Egerton House			£185	PH	071-589 2412	30		14		
SW3	The Fenja			£156	PH	071-589 7333	13	12			
SW3	L'Hotel			£133	HR	071-589 6286	12				
SW5	Concord Hotel			£60	H	071-370 4151	40				
SW5	Hogarth Hotel		59%	£85	H	071-370 6831	85	50			
SW5	Kensington Court Hotel			£59	H	071-370 5151	35				
SW5	Hotel 167			£77	H	071-373 0672	19				
SW5	Swallow International Hotel	Swallow	64%	£130	H	071-370 4200	417	200	180	yes	yes
SW5	Terstan Hotel			£50	H	071-835 1900	50				
SW6	Earls Court Park Inn International		69%	£109	H	071-385 1255	501	1750	1750		
SW6	La Reserve		62%	£90	H	071-385 8561	40		60		
SW7	Adelphi Hotel		62%	£112	H	071-373 7177	68	80			
SW7	Alexander Hotel		64%	£116	H	071-581 1591	37				
SW7	Aster House			£91	H	071-581 5888	12				
SW7	Blakes Hotel		78%	£215	HR	071-370 6701	52				
SW7	Embassy House Hotel	Jarvis	59%	£106	H	071-584 7222	69				
SW7	Forum Hotel	Inter-Continental	62%	£144	H	071-370 5757	910	400	300		
SW7	The Gloucester		74%	£160	H	071-373 6030	548				
SW7	The Gore		65%	£145	H	071-584 6601	54	12			
SW7	Harrington Hall		72%	£117	H	071-396 9696	200	140	180		
SW7	Holiday Inn Kensington	Holiday Inns	68%	£185	H	071-373 2222	162	150	200		
SW7	Kensington Manor			£94	H	071-370 7516	15				
SW7	Norfolk Hotel	QMH	69%	£125	H	071-589 8191	96	60	60		
SW7	Number Sixteen			£135	PH	071-589 5232	36				
SW7	Pelham Hotel		74%	£160	H	071-589 8288	37				
SW7	The Periquito Queen's Gate			£81	H	071-370 6111	63				
SW7	Prince Hotel			£71	H	071-589 6488	20				
SW7	Regency Hotel		68%	£133	H	071-370 4595	210	100	180		
SW7	Rembrandt Hotel		67%	£144	H	071-589 8100	195	250	180	yes	yes
SW7	Vanderbilt Hotel	Edwardian	62%	£139	H	071-589 2424	223	120	100		

Location	Hotel	Group	%	Room Price	Cat	Tel	Rooms	Conf	Banq	Leisure Centre	Swim Pool	Golf
SW10	Hotel Conrad		85%	£225	H	071-823 3000	160	150	200	yes	yes	
SW19	Cannizaro House	MtCT	76%	£138	H	081-879 1464	46	45	80			
W1	The Athenaeum		78%	£230	HR	071-499 3464	144	60	36			
W1	Bentinck House Hotel			£76	H	071-935 9141	20					
W1	Berkshire Hotel	Edwardian	72%	£185	H	071-629 7474	147	45	26			
W1	Berners Park Plaza		72%	£150	H	071-636 1629	229	160	160			
W1	Britannia Inter-Continental	Inter-Continental	77%	£210	H	071-629 9400	317	100	80			
W1	Brown's Hotel	Forte	74%	£239	H	071-493 6020	120	35	70			
W1	Bryanston Court		61%	£102	H	071-262 3141	54					
W1	Chesterfield Hotel		70%	£190	H	071-491 2622	110	120	120			
W1	Churchill Hotel	Inter-Continental	80%	£242	HR	071-486 5800	414	40	250			
W1	Claridge's	Savoy Group	88%	£304	HR	071-629 8860	190	450	220	yes	yes	
W1	The Clifton-Ford	Doyle	72%	£196	H	071-486 6600	212	150	128			
W1	Concorde Hotel			£84	H	071-402 6169	27					
W1	The Connaught	Savoy Group	91%	£278	HR	071-499 7070	90					
W1	Cumberland Hotel	Forte	69%	£140	H	071-262 1234	890	475	560			
W1	The Dorchester		91%	£278	HR	071-629 8888	197	550	550	yes	yes	
W1	Durrants Hotel		65%	£112	H	071-935 8131	96	50	35			
W1	Forte Crest Regent's Park	Forte	64%	£121	H	071-388 2300	320	650	300			
W1	47 Park Street		86%	£326	H	071-491 7282	52					
W1	Four Seasons Hotel		89%	£316	HR	071-499 0888	227	500	400			
W1	Grafton Hotel	Edwardian	63%	£160	H	071-388 4131	324		110			
W1	Green Park Hotel		70%	£163	H	071-629 7522	161	66	80			
W1	Grosvenor House	Forte	83%	£256	HR	071-499 6363	454	1500	1500	yes	yes	
W1	Holiday Inn Mayfair	Holiday Inns	72%	£199	H	071-493 8282	185	70	60			
W1	Hospitality Inn Piccadilly	MtCT	64%	£149	H	071-930 4033	92		16			
W1	Inter-Continental Hotel	Inter-Continental	84%	£307	HR	071-409 3131	467 1	000	750			
W1	The Langham	Hilton	75%	£222	HR	071-636 1000	411	320	280			
W1	London Marriott Hotel	Marriott	77%	£279	H	071-493 1232	223	800	550			

W1	London Mews Hilton on Park	Hilton	67%	£139	H	071-493 7222	72	45	25		
W1	London Hilton on Park Lane	Hilton	75%	£212	H	071-493 8000	448	1200	1000		
W1	Mandeville Hotel		62%	£130	H	071-935 5599	165				
W1	Marble Arch Marriott	Marriott	68%	£177	H	071-723 1277	239	100	160		yes
W1	May Fair Inter-Continental	Inter-Continental	79%	£271	HR	071-629 7777	293	292	300		yes
W1	Le Meridien		84%	£271	HR	071-734 8000	263	250	250	yes	yes
W1	Merryfield House			£48	H	071-935 8326	8				
W1	Montcalm Hotel		74%	£230	H	071-402 4288	116	80	60		
W1	Mostyn Hotel		62%	£124	H	071-935 2361	122	150	100		
W1	The Park Lane Hotel		77%	£195	HR	071-499 6321	320	500	600		
W1	Rathbone Hotel		69%	£161	H	071-636 2001	72	12			
W1	The Ritz		86%	£249	HR	071-493 8181	129	80	63		
W1	St George's Hotel	Forte	65%	£147	H	071-580 0111	86	50	50		
W1	SAS Portman Hotel		77%	£193	H	071-486 5844	272	400	400		
W1	The Selfridge	MtCT	75%	£181	H	071-408 2080	296	300	240		
W1	Sherlock Holmes Hotel	Hilton	61%	£132	H	071-486 6161	125				
W1	Washington Hotel		70%	£199	H	071-499 7000	173	80	60		
W1	The Westbury	Forte	75%	£203	H	071-629 7755	244	120	100		
W2	Abbey Court			£148	PH	071-221 7518	22				
W2	Coburg Resort Hotel	Resort	64%	£122	H	071-221 2217	132				
W2	Columbia Hotel			£55	H	071-402 0021	102	200	120		
W2	Craven Gardens Hotel			£66	H	071-262 3167	43				
W2	Hospitality Inn Bayswater	MtCT	60%	£102	H	071-262 4461	175	40	20		
W2	London Metropole Hotel		69%	£182	H	071-402 4141	747	1000	1000	yes	yes
W2	London Embassy	Jarvis	68%	£132	H	071-229 1212	193				
W2	Mornington Hotel		63%	£96	H	071-262 7361	68				
W2	Parkwood Hotel			£65	H	071-402 2241	18				
W2	Pembridge Court Hotel		65%	£140	H	071-229 9977	21				
W2	Royal Lancaster Hotel	Rank	75%	£179	H	071-262 6737	418	1400	1500		
W2	Whites Hotel	MtCT	77%	£198	H	071-262 2711	54	30			
W5	Carnarvon Hotel		58%	£125	H	081-992 5399	145				
W6	Novotel	Novotel	65%	£97	H	081-741 1555	640	900	900		
W8	Apollo Hotel			£64	H	071-835 1133	59	20			
W8	Atlas Hotel			£64	H	071-835 1155	66	20			

Location	*Hotel*	*Group*	*%*	*Room Price*	*Cat*	*Tel*	*Rooms*	*Conf*	*Banq*	*Leisure Centre*	*Swim Pool*	*Golf*
W8	Copthorne Tara	Copthorne	69%	£114	H	071-937 7211	829	500	400			
W8	Kensington Palace Thistle	MtCT	67%	£131	H	071-937 8121	298	250	160			
W8	Kensington Close Hotel	Forte	59%	£99	H	071-937 8170	530	170	140			
W8	Kensington Park Thistle	MtCT	67%	£166	H	071-937 8080	332	100	80			
W8	Hotel Lexham			£63	H	071-373 6471	66					
W8	The Milestone		78%	£237	H	071-917 1000	56		60			
W8	Royal Garden Hotel	Rank	82%	£191	HR	071-937 8000	398	900	600			
W9	Colonnade Hotel		60%	£80	H	071-286 1052	49					
W11	The Halcyon		79%	£261	HR	071-727 7288	43	20	60			
W11	Hilton International Kensington	Hilton	67%	£150	HR	071-603 3355	603	250	250			
W11	Portobello Hotel		60%	£120	H	071-727 2777	25					
W14	London Olympia Hilton	Hilton	66%	£149	H	071-603 3333	406	90	60			
WC1	Bonnington Hotel		61%	£108	H	071-242 2828	215	250	150			
WC1	Euston Plaza Hotel		67%	£129	H	071-383 4105	150	110	100			
WC1	Forte Crest Bloomsbury	Forte	65%	£120	H	071-837 1200	284	550	700			
WC1	George Hotel			£50	H	071-387 8777	75					
WC1	Holiday Inn Kings Cross/Bloomsbury	Holiday Inns	69%	£135	H	071-833 3900	405	220	180	yes	yes	
WC1	Kenilworth Hotel	Edwardian	63%	£172	H	071-637 3477	192	120	150			
WC1	The Marlborough	Edwardian	69%	£190	H	071-636 5601	169	200	200			
WC1	Montague Park Hotel		64%	£149	H	071-637 1001	109					
WC1	President Hotel			£64	H	071-837 8844	447					
WC1	Hotel Russell	Forte	68%	£141	H	071-837 6470	328	450	350			
WC1	St Giles Hotel			£108	H	071-636 8616	600	45	110	yes		
WC2	Hampshire Hotel	Edwardian	77%	£220	HR	071-839 9399	124	120	100			
WC2	Howard Hotel		81%	£254	HR	071-836 3555	137	120	120			
WC2	Moat House	QMH	65%	£148	H	071-836 6666	153	100	90			
WC2	Mountbatten Hotel	Edwardian	70%	£193	H	071-836 4300	127	80	60			
WC2	Royal Trafalgar Thistle	MtCT	65%	£135	H	071-930 4477	108					
WC2	The Savoy	Savoy Group	91%	£242	HR	071-836 4343	202	500	500			
WC2	The Waldorf	Forte	83%	£206	HR	071-836 2400	292	600	400			

ENGLAND

Avon

Location	Hotel	Group	%	Room Price	Cat	Tel	Rooms	Conf	Banq	Leisure Centre	Swim Pool	Golf
Alveston	Alveston House		65%	£80	H	(0454) 415050	30	100	75			
Alveston	Forte Posthouse	Forte	62%	£68	H	(0454) 412521	74	100	120			
Bath	Apsley House		67%	£105	H	(0225) 336966	12					
Bath	Bath Spa Hotel	Forte	87%	£183	HR	(0225) 444424	100	120	120	yes	yes	
Bath	Fountain House			£120	PH	(0225) 338622	14					
Bath	Francis Hotel	Forte	67%	£125	H	(0225) 424257	93	80	70			
Bath	Hilton National	Hilton	67%	£120	H	(0225) 463411	150	230	200	yes	yes	
Bath	Lansdown Grove		65%	£105	H	(0225) 315891	45	100	80			
Bath	Newbridge House		63%	£110	H	(0225) 446676	12					
Bath	Priory Hotel	Select	79%	£164	HR	(0225) 331922	21	25	60			
Bath	Queensberry Hotel		75%	£123	HR	(0225) 447928	22	18				
Bath	Royal Crescent Hotel	QMH	84%	£170	HR	(0225) 319090	42	60	80			
Bristol	Aztec Hotel	Shire Inns	74%	£96	H	(0454) 301090	88	100	180	yes	yes	
Bristol	Berkeley Square Hotel		69%	£104	H	(0272) 254000	43	16	50			
Bristol	Bristol Marriott Hotel	Marriott	73%	£136	H	(0272) 294281	289	600	500	yes	yes	
Bristol	Forte Crest	Forte	67%	£107	H	(0272) 564242	197	500	425	yes	yes	
Bristol	Grand Hotel	MtCT	62%	£96	H	(0272) 291645	170	500	500			
Bristol	Hilton Hotel	Hilton	69%	£110	H	(0272) 260041	201	400	280	yes	yes	
Bristol	Holiday Inn Crowne Plaza	QMH	72%	£105	H	(0272) 255010	132	200	150			
Bristol	Redwood Lodge	Country Club	64%	£85	H	(0275) 393901	108	175	250	yes	yes	
Bristol	Rodney Hotel		64%	£87	H	(0272) 735422	31					
Bristol	Stakis Bristol Hotel	Stakis	61%	£109	H	(0454) 201144	111	80	100	yes	yes	
Bristol	Swallow Royal Hotel	Swallow	77%	£118	HR	(0272) 255100	242	250	230	yes	yes	

Location	Hotel	Group	%	Room Price	Cat	Tel	Rooms	Conf	Banq	Leisure Centre	Swim Pool	Golf
Bristol	Unicorn Hotel	Rank	63%	£70	H	(0272) 230333	245	360	280			
Chelwood	Chelwood House		63%	£75	HR	(0761) 490730	11	40	40			
Dunkirk	Petty France Hotel		65%	£94	H	(0454) 238361	20	25	80			
Freshford	Homewood Park		79%	£115	HR	(0225) 723731	15	12	50			
Gordano	Forte Travelodge	Forte		£42	L	(0275) 373709	40					
Hinton	Hinton Grange		62%	£89	HR	(0272) 372916	17	24	60		yes	yes
Hunstrete	Hunstrete House	Clipper	72%	£150	HR	(0761) 490490	24					
Monkton Combe	Combe Grove Manor		71%	£168	H	(0225) 834644	41	40	60	yes	yes	
Sedgemoor	Forte Travelodge	Forte		£42	L	(0934) 750831	40					
Ston Easton	Ston Easton Park		88%	£152	HR	(0761) 241631	21	36	24			
Thornbury	Thornbury Castle		80%	£150	H	(0454) 281182	18					
Weston-super-Mare	Grand Atlantic	Forte	64%	£95	H	(0934) 626543	76	250	250			
Winterbourne	Grange Resort Hotel	Resort	68%	£100	H	(0454) 777333	52	150	150		yes	

Bedfordshire

Location	Hotel	Group	%	Room Price	Cat	Tel	Rooms	Conf	Banq	Leisure Centre	Swim Pool	Golf
Aspley Guise	Moore Place		70%	£75	H	(0908) 282000	54	60	40			
Bedford	Moat House	QMH	65%	£70	H	(0234) 355131	100	400	365			
Bedford	Woodlands Manor		70%	£97	H	(0234) 363281	25	50	85			
Dunstable	Forte Travelodge	Forte		£42	L	(0525) 211177	28					
Dunstable	Old Palace Lodge		66%	£100	H	(0582) 662201	49					
Flitwick	Flitwick Manor		73%	£135	HR	(0525) 712242	15	40	60			
Leighton Buzzard	The Swan	Resort	64%	£80	H	(0525) 372148	38	50	35			
Luton	Forte Crest	Forte	60%	£90	H	(0582) 575911	93	250	220			
Luton	Forte Posthouse	Forte	57%	£68	H	(0582) 575955	117	80				
Luton	Hotel Ibis		60%	£40	H	(0582) 424488	98	100	70			
Luton	Leaside Hotel		55%	£55	H	(0582) 417643	15					
Luton	Strathmore Thistle	MtCT	63%	£106	H	(0582) 34199	150	300	250			

Marston	Forte Travelodge	Forte		£42	L	(0234) 766755	32				
Toddington	Granada Lodge	Granada		£45	L	(0525) 873881	43				
Woburn	Bedford Arms	MtCT	63%	£104	H	(0525) 290441	55	60	60		
Woburn	Bell Inn		57%	£65	H	(0525) 290280	27	35	25		

Berkshire

Ascot	Berystede Hotel	Forte	67%	£129	H	(0344) 23311	91	120	120		
Ascot	Royal Berkshire	Hilton	76%	£168	HR	(0344) 23322	63	75	70		yes
Bracknell	Coppid Beech Hotel		72%	£140	HR	(0334) 303333	205	375	225		yes
Bracknell	Hilton National	Hilton	69%	£126	H	(0344) 424801	167	300	220		
Donnington	Donnington Valley Hotel		74%	£95	H	(0635) 551199	58	200	150		
Elcot	Elcot Park Resort Hotel	Resort	67%	£100	HR	(0488) 58100	75	100	180	yes	yes
Eton	Christopher Hotel			£76	I	(0753) 852359	34	60	50		
Hungerford	Bear Hotel	Resort	63%	£72	H	(0488) 682512	41	80	60		
Hurley	Ye Olde Bell	Resort	65%	£100	H	(0628) 825881	36				
Kintbury	Dundas Arms			£65	IR	(0488) 58263	5				
Maidenhead	Fredrick's		75%	£155	HR	(0628) 35934	38	70	140		
Maidenhead	Holiday Inn	Holiday Inns	66%	£147	H	(0628) 23444	189	400	350		yes
Newbury	Chequers Hotel	Forte	66%	£113	H	(0635) 38000	56	65	120		
Newbury	Foley Lodge		71%	£125	H	(0635) 528770	69	250	220		yes
Newbury	Hilton National	Hilton	69%	£85	H	(0635) 529000	104	200	150	yes	yes
Newbury	Millwaters		67%	£75	H	(0635) 528838	32	25	90		
Newbury	Regency Park Hotel		70%	£103	H	(0635) 871555	50	60	60		
Newbury	Stakis Newbury Hotel	Stakis	67%	£108	H	(0635) 247010	112	60	40	yes	yes
Pingewood	Kirtons Farm Country Club	Resort	60%	£100	H	(0734) 500885	81	120	120		yes
Reading	Forte Posthouse	Forte	64%	£68	H	(0734) 875485	138	100	100	yes	yes
Reading	Forte Travelodge	Forte		£42	L	(0734) 750618	36				
Reading	Holiday Inn	QMH	71%	£119	H	(0734) 391818	112	250	180		yes
Reading	Ramada Hotel		68%	£109	H	(0734) 586222	194	220	150	yes	yes
Sindlesham	Reading Moat House	QMH	70%	£132	H	(0734) 351035	96	80	80		
Slough	Copthorne Hotel Slough	Copthorne	71%	£135	H	(0753) 516222	219	200	180	yes	yes
Slough	Courtyard by Marriott		60%	£70	H	(0753) 551551	148	50			

Location	Hotel	Group	%	Room Price	Cat	Tel	Rooms	Conf	Banq	Leisure Centre	Swim Pool	Golf
Slough	Heathrow/Slough Marriott	Marriott	73%	£135	H	(0753) 544244	352	400	350	yes	yes	
Streatley-on-Thames	Swan Diplomat		72%	£134	HR	(0491) 873737	46	90	80			
Taplow	Cliveden		91%	£210	HR	(0628) 668561	31	42	42	yes	yes	
Windsor	Castle Hotel	Forte	67%	£146	H	(0753) 851011	104					
Windsor	Oakley Court	QMH	78%	£168	HR	(0628) 74141	92	160	200			yes
Wokingham	Stakis St Anne's Manor	Stakis	69%	£130	H	(0734) 772550	130	250	300		yes	
Woolton Hill	Hollington House Hotel		79%	£110	HR	(0635) 255100	20	38	45			
Yattendon	Royal Oak			£80	IR	(0635) 201325	5					

Buckinghamshire

Location	Hotel	Group	%	Room Price	Cat	Tel	Rooms	Conf	Banq	Leisure Centre	Swim Pool	Golf
Aston Clinton	Bell Inn		78%	£176	HR	(0296) 630252	21	250	300			
Aylesbury	Forte Posthouse	Forte	69%	£68	H	(0296) 393388	94	100	80		yes	
Aylesbury	Hartwell House	Historic House	86%	£157	HR	(0296) 747444	47	90	60		yes	
Beaconsfield	Bellhouse Hotel	De Vere	67%	£115	H	(0753) 887211	136	450	300	yes	yes	
Burnham	Burnham Beeches Moat House	QMH	68%	£110	H	(0628) 603333	75	180	140		yes	
Burnham	Grovefield Hotel		63%	£55	H	(0628) 603131	38	50	120			
Chenies	Bedford Arms Thistle	MtCT	64%	£108	H	(0923) 283301	10	30	65			
Gerrards Cross	Bull Hotel	De Vere	63%	£125	H	(0753) 885995	95	200	160			
High Wycombe	Forte Posthouse	Forte	65%	£68	H	(0494) 442100	106	100	90			
Marlow	Compleat Angler Hotel	Forte	73%	£164	HR	(0628) 484444	64	150	100			
Medmenham	Danesfield House		78%	£150	HR	(0628) 891010	93	120	100			
Milton Keynes	Forte Crest	Forte	68%	£107	H	(0908) 667722	151	150	110	yes	yes	

Cambridgeshire

Location	Hotel	Group	%	Room Price	Cat	Tel	Rooms	Conf	Banq	Leisure Centre	Swim Pool	Golf
Cambridge	Arundel House		60%	£57	H	(0223) 67701	88	35	100			
Cambridge	Cambridge Lodge		58%	£80	H	(0223) 352833	11	16				

Cambridge	Cambridgeshire Moat House	QMH	63%	£78	H	(0954) 780555	100	180	180		yes	yes
Cambridge	Forte Posthouse	Forte	67%	£68	H	(0223) 237000	118	70	50	yes	yes	
Cambridge	Garden House	QMH	69%	£135	H	(0223) 63421	118	250	200			
Cambridge	Gonville Hotel		62%	£82	H	(0223) 66611	64	200	170			
Cambridge	Holiday Inn	Holiday Inns	68%	£115	H	(0223) 464466	199	150	100		yes	
Cambridge	University Arms	De Vere	65%	£110	H	(0223) 351241	117	300	250			
Duxford	Duxford Lodge		65%	£88	HR	(0223) 836444	15	30	36			
Ely	Forte Travelodge	Forte		£42	L	(0353) 668499	39					
Ely	Lamb Hotel	QMH	62%	£75	H	(0353) 663574	32	65	65			
Fenstanton	Forte Travelodge	Forte		£42	L	(0954) 30919	40					
Huntingdon	Old Bridge Hotel	Poste Hotels	68%	£90	HR	(0480) 52681	26	50	100			
Lolworth	Forte Travelodge	Forte		£42	L	(0954) 781335	20					
Peterborough	Butterfly Hotel		63%	£70	H	(0733) 64240	70	80	50			
Peterborough	Forte Travelodge	Forte		£42	L	(0733) 231109	32					
Peterborough	Forte Posthouse	Forte	60%	£68	H	(0733) 240209	90	50	40		yes	
Peterborough	Moat House	QMH	64%	£92	H	(0733) 260000	125	400	400	yes	yes	
Peterborough	Swallow Hotel	Swallow	69%	£99	H	(0733) 371111	163	300	280	yes	yes	
St Ives	Slepe Hall		61%	£60	H	(0480) 463122	16	220	220			
Six Mile Bottom	Swynford Paddocks		74%	£107	H	(063 870) 234	15	30	50			
Stilton	Bell Inn			£62	IR	(0733) 241066	19	100	90			
Swavesey	Forte Travelodge	Forte		£42	L	(0954) 789113	36					
Wansford-in-England	Haycock Hotel	Poste Hotels	70%	£90	HR	(0780) 782223	51	200	220			

Cheshire

Alderley Edge	Alderley Edge Hotel		72%	£117	HR	(0625) 583033	32	120	100			
Alsager	Manor House	Compass	65%	£70	H	(0270) 884000	57	250	150		yes	
Altrincham	Bowdon Hotel		65%	£79	H	061-928 7121	82	150	150			
Altrincham	Cresta Court		61%	£72	H	061-927 7272	139	400	350			
Altrincham	George & Dragon		60%	£52	H	061-928 9933	47					
Bramhall	Moat House	QMH	63%	£85	H	061-439 8116	65	110	170			
Bucklow Hill	The Swan		62%	£52	H	(0565) 830295	70	40	70			

Location	Hotel	Group	%	Room Price	Cat	Tel	Rooms	Conf	Banq	Leisure Centre	Swim Pool	Golf
Bunbury	Wild Boar	Rank	67%	£78	H	(0829) 260309	37	60	70			
Burtonwood	Forte Travelodge	Forte		£42	L	(0925) 710376	40					
Chester	Abbots Well	Jarvis	62%	£85	H	(0244) 332121	127	230	180	yes	yes	
Chester	Blossoms Hotel	Forte	63%	£107	H	(0244) 323186	64	100	50			
Chester	Chester International	QMH	69%	£145	H	(0244) 322330	152	420	400			
Chester	Chester Grosvenor		84%	£196	HR	(0244) 324024	86	250	220			
Chester	Chester Resort Hotel	Resort	62%	£60	H	(0244) 851551	113	180	200			
Chester	Crabwall Manor		76%	£125	H	(0244) 851666	48	100	100			
Chester	Forte Posthouse	Forte	62%	£68	H	(0244) 680111	105	115	80	yes	yes	
Chester	Mollington Banastre	Ambassador	67%	£95	H	(0244) 851471	66	250	200	yes	yes	
Chester	Rowton Hall		64%	£88	H	(0244) 335262	42	200	160	yes	yes	
Crewe	Forte Travelodge	Forte		£42	L	(0270) 883157	42					
Handforth	Belfry Hotel		71%	£102	HR	061-437 0511	81					
Knutsford	Cottons Hotel	Shire Inns	65%	£112	H	(0565) 650333	82	200	150	yes	yes	
Knutsford	Forte Travelodge	Forte		£42	L	(0565) 652187	32					
Macclesfield	Sutton Hall			£85	I	(0260) 253211	10	30	16			
Mottram St Andrew	Mottram Hall	De Vere	70%	£140	H	(0625) 828135	133	275	180		yes	yes
Nantwich	Rookery Hall	Select	79%	£118	HR	(0270) 610016	45	80	80			
Northwich	Hartford Hall		63%	£70	H	(0606) 75711	20	30	25			
Parkgate	Ship Hotel	Forte	58%	£60	H	051-336 3931	26					
Prestbury	Bridge Hotel		63%	£84	H	(0625) 829326	23	100	100			
Prestbury	White House Manor			£112	PH	(0625) 829376	9					
Puddington	Craxton Wood		70%	£95	HR	051-339 4717	14	35	50			
Runcorn	Campanile Hotel	Campanile		£44	L	(0928) 581771	53					
Runcorn	Forte Posthouse	Forte	62%	£70	H	(0928) 714000	136	500	450		yes	
Sandbach	Chimney House	Lansbury	62%	£81	H	(0270) 764141	48	90	90			
Sandiway	Nunsmere Hall		77%	£120	HR	(0606) 889100	32	48	60			
Stockport	Forte Travelodge	Forte		£42	L	(0625) 875292	32					
Stockport	Travel Inn	Travel Inns		£43	L	061-499 1944	41					

Warrington	Holiday Inn Garden Court	Holiday Inns	65%	£77	H	(0925) 838779	100					
Warrington	Lord Daresbury Hotel	De Vere	67%	£115	H	(0925) 267331	141	400	300	yes	yes	
Warrington	Travel Inn	Travel Inns		£43	L	(0582) 482224	40					
Wilmslow	Moat House	QMH	58%	£96	H	(0625) 529201	125	300	250	yes	yes	
Wilmslow	Stanneylands		70%	£106	HR	(0625) 525225	33	100	100			

Cleveland

Crathorne	Crathorne Hall		72%	£110	H	(0642) 700398	37	160	120			
Easington	Grinkle Park		70%	£80	H	(0287) 640515	20					
Hartlepool	Grand Hotel		59%	£63	H	(0429) 266345	47	200	160			
Middlesbrough	Hotel Baltimore		62%	£80	H	(0642) 224111	31	25	90			
Middlesbrough	Hospitality Inn	MtCT	59%	£92	H	(0642) 232000	180	400	400			
Stockton-on-Tees	Swallow Hotel	Swallow	67%	£92	H	(0642) 679721	124	300	250		yes	
Thornaby-on-Tees	Forte Posthouse	Forte	60%	£68	H	(0642) 591213	135	120	80			

Cornwall

Calstock	Danescombe Valley Hotel		72%	£175	HR	(0822) 832414	5					
Carlyon Bay	Carlyon Bay Hotel		68%	£122	H	(0726) 812304	73	200	250		yes	yes
Carlyon Bay	Porth Avallen Hotel		60%	£79	H	(0726) 812802	24	100	100			
Constantine Bay	Treglos Hotel		65%	£138	H	(0841) 520727	44	15	120		yes	
Falmouth	Falmouth Hotel		63%	£92	H	(0326) 312671	72	200	190	yes	yes	
Falmouth	Greenbank Hotel		69%	£105	H	(0326) 312440	61					
Falmouth	Royal Duchy Hotel		66%	£99	H	(0326) 313042	47	150	200		yes	
Falmouth	St Michael's Hotel		63%	£86	H	(0326) 312707	66	175	200	yes	yes	
Golant	Cormorant Hotel		62%	£84	H	(0726) 833426	11	20	20		yes	
Helland Bridge	Tredethy Country Hotel		56%	£68	H	(020 884) 262	11	60	40			
Lamorna Cove	Lamorna Cove Hotel		65%	£95	H	(0736) 731411	16					
Land's End	State House		67%	£70	H	(0736) 871844	34	240	200			
Liskeard	Well House		74%	£105	HR	(0579) 342001	7					

Location	*Hotel*	*Group*	*%*	*Room Price*	*Cat*	*Tel*	*Rooms*	*Conf*	*Banq*	*Leisure Centre*	*Swim Pool*	*Golf*
Looe	Talland Bay Hotel		66%	£107	H	(0503) 72667	24	30	30			
Mawnan Smith	Budock Vean Hotel		65%	£144	H	(0326) 250288	58	30			yes	
Mawnan Smith	Meudon Hotel		69%	£120	H	(0326) 250541	32					
Mawnan Smith	Nansidwell		70%	£140	HR	(0326) 250340	12					
Mousehole	Lobster Pot		57%	£76	H	(0736) 731251	25					
Mullion	Polurrian Hotel		66%	£164	H	(0326) 240421	40	100	120	yes	yes	
Newlyn	Higher Faugan Country House		62%	£84	H	(0736) 62076	12					
Newquay	Hotel Bristol		64%	£90	H	(0637) 875181	76	180	265		yes	
Newquay	Hotel Riviera		63%	£78	H	(0637) 874251	50	120	150			
Penzance	Abbey Hotel		67%	£75	HR	(0736) 66906	7					
Portloe	Lugger Hotel		59%	£98	H	(0872) 501322	19					
St Austell	Boscundle Manor		65%	£110	H	(0726) 813557	10					
St Austell	White Hart			£63	I	(0726) 72100	18	60	60			
St Ives	Garrack Hotel		62%	£91	H	(0736) 796199	18	30	30		yes	
St Mawes	Idle Rocks Hotel		64%	£108	HR	(0326) 270771	24					
St Mawes	Rising Sun		62%	£90	H	(0326) 270233	12					
St Mawes	Hotel Tresanton		69%	£70	H	(0326) 270544	21					
Saltash	Granada Lodge	Granada		£45	L	(0752) 848408	31					
Tintagel	Trebrea Lodge		66%	£60	HR	(0840) 770410	7					
Truro	Alverton Manor		70%	£90	H	(0872) 76633	25	200	150			
Veryan	Nare Hotel		70%	£124	HR	(0872) 501279	39	40	100			
Isles of Scilly:												
St Martin's	St Martin's Hotel		69%	£178	HR	(0720) 22092	24	100	48	yes		
St Mary's	Hotel Godolphin		58%	£92	H	(0720) 22316	31					
St Mary's	Tregarthen's Hotel		60%	£110	H	(0720) 22540	29					
Tresco	Island Hotel		67%	£170	HR	(0720) 22883	40					

Cumbria

Alston	Lovelady Shield		69%	£76	H	(0434) 381203	12	12	50		
Ambleside	Kirkstone Foot		65%	£99	H	(053 94) 32232	16				
Ambleside	Nanny Brow		62%	£90	H	(053 94) 32036	19	30	20		
Ambleside	Rothay Manor Hotel		71%	£104	HR	(053 94) 33605	18	20	55		
Ambleside	Wateredge Hotel		63%	£118	HR	(053 94) 32332	23				
Appleby-in-Westmorland	Appleby Manor Hotel		66%	£98	HR	(076 83) 51571	30	26	26		yes
Appleby-in-Westmorland	Tufton Arms		66%	£75	H	(076 83) 51593	19	120	120		
Applethwaite	Underscar Manor		74%	£100	HR	(076 87) 75000	11	16			
Bassenthwaite	Armathwaite Hall		65%	£100	H	(076 87) 76551	42	100	120	yes	yes
Bassenthwaite Lake	Pheasant Inn		65%	£92	H	(076 87) 76234	20				
Borrowdale	Borrowdale Hotel		60%	£88	H	(076 87) 77224	34	30			
Borrowdale	Stakis Lodore Swiss Hotel	Stakis	71%	£120	H	(076 87) 77285	70	70	55	yes	yes
Bowness-on-Windermere	Belsfield Hotel	Forte	62%	£112	H	(053 94) 42448	64	130	180	yes	yes
Bowness-on-Windermere	Gilpin Lodge		64%	£80	HR	(053 94) 88818	9	20	20		
Bowness-on-Windermere	Linthwaite House		72%	£118	HR	(053 94) 88600	18	20	40		
Bowness-on-Windermere	Old England Hotel	Forte	65%	£136	H	(053 94) 42444	79	100	250		
Braithwaite	Ivy House		66%	£62	H	(076 87) 78338	12				
Brampton	Farlam Hall		75%	£150	HR	(069 77) 46234	13				
Carlisle	Granada Lodge	Granada		£45	L	(069 74) 73131	39				
Carlisle	Swallow Hilltop	Swallow	59%	£70	H	(0228) 29255	92	500	500	yes	yes
Cartmel	Aynsome Manor		60%	£102	H	(053 95) 36653	13				
Coniston	Sun Hotel		63%	£70	H	(053 94) 41248	11	20	75		
Cowan Bridge	Hipping Hall		64%	£69	H	(052 42) 71187	7		10		
Crook	Wild Boar Hotel		60%	£110	H	(053 94) 45225	36	30			
Crooklands	Crooklands Hotel		60%	£84	H	(053 95) 67432	30	160	100		
Crosby-on-Eden	Crosby Lodge		66%	£85	HR	(0228) 573618	11	25	12		
Faugh	String of Horses Inn			£65	I	(022 870) 297	14				
Grasmere	Michael's Nook		79%	£152	HR	(053 94) 35496	14	20	36		
Grasmere	The Swan	Forte	65%	£148	H	(053 94) 35551	36	30	40		
Grasmere	White Moss House		69%	£128	HR	(053 94) 35295	6				
Grasmere	Wordsworth Hotel		72%	£100	HR	(053 94) 35592	37	130	115	yes	yes

Location	Hotel	Group	%	Room Price	Cat	Tel	Rooms	Conf	Banq	Leisure Centre	Swim Pool	Golf
Grizedale	Grizedale Lodge		61%	£68	HR	(053 94) 36532	9					
Kendal	Woolpack Hotel		59%	£70	H	(0539) 723852	54	150	120			
Keswick	Keswick Hotel	Principal	60%	£70	H	(076 87) 72020	66	80	150			
Langdale	Langdale Hotel		71%	£130	H	(053 94) 37302	65	90	130	yes	yes	
Newby Bridge	The Swan		61%	£86	H	(053 95) 31681	36	65				
Penrith	Forte Travelodge	Forte		£42	L	(0768) 66958	32					
Penrith	North Lakes Hotel	Shire Inns	71%	£108	H	(0768) 68111	85	200	200	yes	yes	
Ravenstonedale	Black Swan Inn			£62	I	(053 96) 23204	16		50			
Silloth-on-Solway	Skinburness Hotel		67%	£55	H	(069 73) 32332	25	200	170			
Spark Bridge	Bridgefield House		60%	£70	HR	(0229) 885239	5					
Troutbeck	Mortal Man Inn			£100	I	(053 94) 33193	12					
Ullswater	Leeming House	Forte	75%	£164	HR	(076 84) 86622	40	20				
Ullswater	Old Church Hotel		67%	£90	HR	(076 84) 86204	10					
Ullswater	Rampsbeck Country House Hotel		65%	£90	HR	(076 84) 86442	20	20				
Ullswater	Sharrow Bay		82%	£160	HR	(076 84) 86301	28					
Wetheral	The Crown	Shire Inns	70%	£106	H	(0228) 561888	51	175	120	yes	yes	
Windermere	Holbeck Ghyll		68%	£130	HR	(053 94) 32375	14	40	38			
Windermere	Merewood Hotel		66%	£75	H	(053 94) 46484	20	200	100			
Windermere	Miller Howe		70%	£169	H	(053 94) 42536	13	10				
Witherslack	Old Vicarage		68%	£78	HR	(053 95) 52381	15	12	12			

Derbyshire

Location	Hotel	Group	%	Room Price	Cat	Tel	Rooms	Conf	Banq	Leisure Centre	Swim Pool	Golf
Ashbourne	Ashbourne Lodge Hotel		66%	£69	H	(0335) 46666	50	250	170			
Ashbourne	Callow Hall		69%	£99	H	(0335) 343403	13	40	30			
Ashford-in-the-Water	Riverside Hotel		65%	£85	H	(0629) 814275	15	30	18			
Bakewell	Hassop Hall		74%	£93	H	(0629) 640488	13	60	100			
Baslow	Cavendish Hotel		71%	£117	H	(0246) 582311	24	20	50			

Castle Donington	Donington Thistle	MtCT	70%	£118	H	(0332) 850700	110	200	180		yes	
Chesterfield	Chesterfield Hotel		59%	£70	H	(0246) 271141	73	200	230	yes	yes	
Chesterfield	Forte Travelodge	Forte		£42	L	(0246) 455411	20					
Derby	Forte Posthouse	Forte	61%	£68	H	(0332) 514933	62	60	50			
Derby	International Hotel		62%	£60	H	(0332) 369321	62	60	180			
Dovedale	Izaak Walton Hotel		59%	£95	H	(033 529) 555	34	60	100			
Dovedale	Peveril of the Peak	Forte	60%	£102	H	(033 529) 333	47	95	60			
Grindleford	Maynard Arms			£60	I	(0433) 630321	13	200	120			
Hathersage	Hathersage Inn			£68	I	(0433) 650259	15	20	12			
Matlock	Riber Hall		71%	£107	HR	(0629) 582795	11	14	24			
Matlock Bath	New Bath Hotel	Forte	63%	£118	H	(0629) 583275	55	130	200		yes	
Morley	Breadsall Priory	Country Club	69%	£108	H	(0332) 832235	91	150	80	yes	yes	yes
Newton Solney	Newton Park	Jarvis	67%	£111	H	(0283) 703568	51	140	100			
Renishaw	Sitwell Arms		61%	£60	H	(0246) 435226	30	160	150			
Rowsley	Peacock Hotel	Jarvis	64%	£116	H	(0629) 733518	14	28	24			
South Normanton	Swallow Hotel	Swallow	69%	£96	H	(0773) 812000	161	250	220	yes	yes	

Devon

Barnstaple	Imperial Hotel	Forte	60%	£87	H	(0271) 45861	56	80	80		
Bigbury-on-Sea	Burgh Island Hotel		66%	£168	H	(0548) 810514	14	100	100		
Bishop's Tawton	Halmpstone Manor		68%	£100	HR	(0271) 830321	5				
Branscombe	Masons Arms		64%	£54	H	(029 780) 300	21	100	100		
Brixham	Quayside Hotel		59%	£76	H	(0803) 855751	29	30	30		
Chagford	Gidleigh Park		82%	£260	HR	(0647) 432367	15				
Chagford	Great Tree Hotel		61%	£76	H	(0647) 432491	12	30	30		
Chagford	Mill End		63%	£80	H	(0647) 432282	17				
Chittlehamholt	Highbullen		60%	£105	H	(0769) 540561	35				yes
Clawton	Court Barn		61%	£70	H	(040 927) 219	8	30	30		
Dartmouth	Royal Castle Hotel			£74	I	(0803) 833033	25	100	80		
Dartmouth	Stoke Lodge		60%	£67	H	(0803) 770523	24	100	100	yes	yes
Exeter	Buckerell Lodge		66%	£87	H	(0392) 52451	54	60	120		

Location	*Hotel*	*Group*	*%*	*Room Price*	*Cat*	*Tel*	*Rooms*	*Conf*	*Banq*	*Leisure Centre*	*Swim Pool*	*Golf*
Exeter	Forte Crest	Forte	69%	£100	H	(0392) 412812	110	150	100		yes	
Exeter	Rougemont Hotel	MtCT	63%	£79	H	(0392) 54982	90	300	208			
Exeter	Royal Clarence	QMH	71%	£98	H	(0392) 58464	56	150	120			
Exeter	White Hart		61%	£78	H	(0392) 79897	61	70	60			
Exmouth	Imperial Hotel	Forte	60%	£116	H	(0395) 274761	57					
Fairy Cross	Portledge Hotel		62%	£67	H	(0237) 451262	35					
Gittisham	Combe House		73%	£92	H	(0404) 42756	15	34	22			
Hatherleigh	George Hotel			£65	I	(0837) 810454	11	50	75			
Hawkchurch	Fairwater Head Hotel		65%	£109	H	(029 77) 349	21					
Haytor	Bel Alp House		72%	£126	H	(0364) 661217	9					
Holbeton	Alston Hall		65%	£75	H	(075 530) 555	20	70	120	yes	yes	
Hope Cove	Cottage Hotel		56%	£114	H	(0548) 561555	35	50	90			
Hope Cove	Lantern Lodge		59%	£70	H	(0548) 561280	14				yes	
Huntsham	Huntsham Court		68%	£110	HR	(039 86) 365	17	50	30			
Lewdown	Lewtrenchard Manor		73%	£125	HR	(056 683) 256	8	80	60			
Lifton	Arundell Arms		65%	£88	H	(0566) 784666	29	100	110			
Lynmouth	Rising Sun Inn			£79	I	(0598) 53223	16					
Lynton	Lynton Cottage		65%	£70	H	(0598) 52342	17	30	20			
Moretonhampstead	White Hart Inn			£63	I	(0647) 40406	20	80	90			
Newton Abbot	Passage House		65%	£75	H	(0626) 55515	40	60	100	yes	yes	
Okehampton	Forte Travelodge	Forte		£42	L	(0837) 52124	32					
Paignton	Palace Hotel	Forte	60%	£100	H	(0803) 555121	52	50	40			
Paignton	Redcliffe Hotel		60%	£90	H	(0803) 526397	59	150	200			
Parkham	Penhaven Country House		64%	£98	H	(0237) 451388	12					
Plymouth	Boringdon Hall		70%	£65	H	(0752) 344455	40	140	110		yes	
Plymouth	Campanile Hotel	Campanile		£44	L	(0752) 601087	50					
Plymouth	Copthorne Hotel	Copthorne	70%	£118	H	(0752) 224161	135	50	50		yes	
Plymouth	Forte Posthouse		65%	£68	H	(0752) 662828	106	100	140			
Plymouth	Moat House	QMH	70%	£118	H	(0752) 662866	217	400	350		yes	

Plymouth	Novotel	Novotel	62%	£70	H	(0752) 221422	100	240	180		
Salcombe	Marine Hotel		68%	£142	H	(0548) 844444	51	75	120	yes	yes
Salcombe	Soar Mill Cove		66%	£128	H	(0548) 561566	14		30		yes
Salcombe	South Sands Hotel		60%	£136	H	(0548) 843741	30				yes
Salcombe	Tides Reach		71%	£162	H	(0548) 843466	38			yes	yes
Saunton	Saunton Sands		67%	£120	H	(0271) 890212	96	200	250		yes
Sidmouth	Belmont Hotel		63%	£106	H	(0395) 512555	54	50	110		
Sidmouth	Fortfield Hotel		59%	£91	H	(0395) 512403	55	100	120		yes
Sidmouth	Hotel Riviera		65%	£112	H	(0395) 515201	29	90	90		
Sidmouth	Victoria Hotel		67%	£120	H	(0395) 512651	65	100	120	yes	yes
Sourton	Collaven Manor		65%	£79	HR	(0837) 86522	7	20	20		
South Molton	Whitechapel Manor		76%	£130	HR	(0769) 573377	10	24	24		
Teignmouth	Thomas Luny House			£60	PH	(0626) 772976	4				
Thurlestone	Thurlestone Hotel		69%	£160	H	(0548) 560382	68	100	150	yes	yes
Tiverton	Forte Travelodge	Forte		£42	L	(0884) 821087	40				
Torquay	Grand Hotel		69%	£108	H	(0803) 296677	112	300	300	yes	yes
Torquay	Homers Hotel		63%	£98	H	(0803) 213456	15	50	45		
Torquay	Imperial Hotel	Forte	81%	£160	H	(0803) 294301	167	350	350	yes	yes
Torquay	Livermead Cliff Hotel		60%	£80	H	(0803) 299666	64	60	80		
Torquay	Livermead House		60%	£88	H	(0803) 294361	64	100	140		
Torquay	Osborne Hotel		65%	£110	H	(0803) 213311	23	90	80		yes
Torquay	Palace Hotel		68%	£110	H	(0803) 200200	140	450	600		yes
Whimple	Woodhayes Hotel		75%	£85	HR	(0404) 822237	6				
Wilmington	Home Farm		58%	£56	H	(040 483) 278	13				
Woody Bay	Woody Bay Hotel		59%	£66	H	(059 83) 264	15	16			
Woolacombe	Woolacombe Bay Hotel		65%	£172	H	(0271) 870388	61	200	200	yes	yes
Yelverton	Moorland Links		65%	£70	H	(0822) 852245	30	120	200		

Dorset

Bournemouth	Carlton Hotel		78%	£150	H	(0202) 552011	70	160	120		
Bournemouth	Chine Hotel		65%	£80	H	(0202) 396234	97	150	180		yes

Location	*Hotel*	*Group*	*%*	*Room Price*	*Cat*	*Tel*	*Rooms*	*Conf*	*Banq*	*Leisure Centre*	*Swim Pool*	*Golf*
Bournemouth	Forte Posthouse	Forte	59%	£68	H	(0202) 553262	98	100	100			
Bournemouth	Langtry Manor		62%	£79	H	(0202) 553887	27	100	100			
Bournemouth	Norfolk Royale		70%	£138	H	(0202) 551521	95	80	100		yes	
Bournemouth	Palace Court		71%	£108	H	(0202) 557681	110	250	250		yes	
Bournemouth	Royal Bath Hotel	De Vere	73%	£140	HR	(0202) 555555	131	450	450	yes	yes	
Bournemouth	Swallow Highcliff Hotel	Swallow	70%	£120	H	(0202) 557702	157	450	275			
Chedington	Chedington Court		71%	£140	HR	(0935) 891265	10	30	20			yes
Chedington	Hazel Barton			£95	PH	(0935) 891613	4	12	20			
Christchurch	Travel Inn	Travel Inns		£43	L	(0202) 485376	38					
Corfe Castle	Mortons House Hotel		62%	£80	H	(0929) 480988	17	45	45			
East Stoke	Kemps Country House Hotel		56%	£64	H	(0929) 462563	15	60	120			
Evershot	Summer Lodge		72%	£125	HR	(0935) 83424	17	25	20			
Ferndown	Dormy Hotel	De Vere	71%	£105	H	(0202) 872121	128	250	270	yes	yes	
Gillingham	Stock Hill House		74%	£190	HR	(0747) 823626	9		12			
Longham	Bridge House		61%	£60	H	(0202) 578828	37	120	100			
Lyme Regis	Alexandra Hotel		58%	£90	H	(0297) 442010	26					
Maiden Newton	Maiden Newton House		73%	£90	HR	(0300) 20336	6	30	14			
Mudeford	Avonmouth Hotel	Forte	59%	£99	H	(0202) 483434	41	60	120			
Poole	Haven Hotel		66%	£145	H	(0202) 707333	95	180	160		yes	
Poole	Hospitality Inn	MtCT	63%	£78	H	(0202) 666800	68	65	50			
Poole	Mansion House		74%	£110	HR	(0202) 685666	28	40	32			
Poole	Sandbanks Hotel		59%	£110	H	(0202) 707377	105	170	180		yes	
Shaftesbury	Grosvenor Hotel	Forte	62%	£87	H	(0747) 52282	35	150	120			
Shaftesbury	Royal Chase Hotel		60%	£84	H	(0747) 53355	35	190	160		yes	
Sherborne	Eastbury Hotel	Clipper	67%	£98	H	(0935) 813131	15	60	80			
Sherborne	Forte Posthouse	Forte	59%	£68	H	(0935) 813191	59	100	70			
Studland Bay	Knoll House		63%	£165	H	(0929) 44251	80					
Wareham	Priory Hotel		72%	£75	HR	(0929) 551666	19					
Wareham	Springfield Country Hotel		59%	£90	H	(0929) 552177	32			yes	yes	

West Bexington	Manor Hotel		59%	£76	H	(0308) 897785	13	40	60		
Winkton	Fisherman's Haunt Hotel			£55	I	(0202) 477283	20		80		

Durham

Barnard Castle	Jersey Farm Hotel		59%	£50	H	(0833) 38223	22	200	150		
Blanchland	Lord Crewe Arms		63%	£98	H	(0434) 675251	18	24	70		
Chester-le-Street	Lumley Castle		69%	£98	H	091-389 1111	65	150	200		
Coatham Mundeville	Hall Garth		68%	£90	H	(0325) 300400	40	300	250		
Darlington	Blackwell Grange Moat House	QMH	62%	£98	H	(0325) 380888	99	300	250		
Darlington	St George Thistle	MtCT	56%	£79	H	(0325) 332631	59	160	120		
Darlington	Swallow King's Head	Swallow	57%	£86	H	(0325) 380222	85	250	250		
Durham	Royal County Hotel	Swallow	67%	£110	H	091-386 6821	150	150	120	yes	yes
Greta Bridge	Morritt Arms			£66	I	(0833) 27232	17				
Middleton-in-Teesdale	Teesdale Hotel		58%	£61	H	(0833) 40264	14				
Neasham	Newbus Arms		62%	£80	H	(0325) 721071	15	120	80		
Romaldkirk	Rose and Crown			£74	IR	(0833) 50213	12				

Essex

Basildon	Campanile Hotel	Campanile		£44	L	(0268) 530810	98				
Basildon	Forte Posthouse	Forte	59%	£68	H	(0268) 533955	110	300	250		
Basildon	Travel Inn	Travel Inns		£43	L	(0268) 522227	42				
Brentwood	Forte Travelodge	Forte		£42	L	(0277) 810819	22				
Brentwood	Forte Posthouse	Forte	61%	£68	H	(0277) 260260	111	120	120		yes
Brentwood	Moat House	QMH	67%	£118	H	(0277) 225252	33	50	85		
Broxted	Whitehall		72%	£105	HR	(0279) 850603	25	120	120		
Coggeshall	White Hart		69%	£82	HR	(0376) 561654	18	35	24		
Colchester	Butterfly Hotel		61%	£61	H	(0206) 230900	50	80	50		
Dedham	Dedham Vale Hotel		67%	£70	H	(0206) 322273	6	60	120		
Dedham	Maison Talbooth		78%	£133	H	(0206) 322367	10	60	80		

Location	*Hotel*	*Group*	*%*	*Room Price*	*Cat*	*Tel*	*Rooms*	*Conf*	*Banq*	*Leisure Centre*	*Swim Pool*	*Golf*
Epping	Forte Posthouse	Forte	63%	£68	H	(0992) 573137	79	100	85			
Great Baddow	Pontlands Park		70%	£135	H	(0245) 476444	17	40	200	yes	yes	
Great Dunmow	Saracen's Head	Forte	58%	£97	H	(0371) 873901	24	60	50			
Harlow	Green Man	Forte	60%	£102	H	(0279) 442521	55	75	64			
Harlow	Moat House	QMH	68%	£72	H	(0279) 422441	120	220	180			
Ingatestone	Heybridge Moat House	QMH	68%	£85	H	(0277) 355355	22	600	500			
Maldon	Blue Boar	Forte	59%	£97	H	(0621) 852681	28	30	80			
North Stifford	Moat House	QMH	61%	£103	H	(0375) 390909	126	120	150			
Old Harlow	Travel Inn	Travel Inns		£43	L	(0279) 442545	38					
Saffron Walden	Saffron Hotel		57%	£55	H	(0799) 522676	19	100	80			
Thurrock	Granada Lodge	Granada		£55	L	(0708) 891111	35					
Waltham Abbey	Swallow Hotel	Swallow	66%	£110	H	(0992) 717170	163	240	230			
Woodford Bridge	Prince Regent Hotel		63%	£85	H	081-505 9966	51	350	300			

Gloucestershire

Amberley	Amberley Inn		57%	£74	H	(0453) 872565	14					
Bibury	The Swan		78%	£128	HR	(0285) 740695	18	12	12			
Bourton-on-the-Water	Dial House		61%	£68	H	(0451) 22244	10					
Charingworth	Charingworth Manor		79%	£110	HR	(038 678) 555	24	38		yes	yes	
Cheltenham	Cheltenham Park	Park Hotels	68%	£115	H	(0242) 222021	153	350	300			
Cheltenham	Golden Valley Thistle	MtCT	69%	£90	H	(0242) 232691	124	220	300		yes	
Cheltenham	Greenway		80%	£120	HR	(0242) 862352	19	35	28			
Cheltenham	Hotel de la Bere	Forte	64%	£98	H	(0242) 237771	57	80	80	yes		
Cheltenham	On The Park		68%	£64	H	(0242) 518898	12	16	20			
Cheltenham	Queen's Hotel	Forte	69%	£119	H	(0242) 514724	74	200	180			
Cheltenham	Travel Inn	Travel Inns		£43	L	(0242) 233847	40					

Chipping Campden	Cotswold House		69%	£90	H	(0386) 840330	15	30	20			
Chipping Campden	Noel Arms		61%	£78	H	(0386) 840317	26	60	60			
Chipping Campden	Seymour House		66%	£91	H	(0386) 840429	15	40	85			
Cirencester	Fleece Hotel	Resort	64%	£80	H	(0285) 658507	30	60	60			
Cirencester	Stratton House		62%	£66	H	(0285) 651761	41	180	150			
Clearwell	Clearwell Castle		69%	£85	H	(0594) 832320	16	40	140			
Corse Lawn	Corse Lawn House		71%	£90	HR	(0452) 780479	19	40	70			
Fairford	Bull Hotel		60%	£43	H	(0285) 712535	20	60	36			
Fossebridge	Fossebridge Inn		65%	£55	H	(0285) 720721	9					
Gloucester	Forte Crest		66%	£109	H	(0452) 613311	123	100	100	yes	yes	
Gloucester	Hatherley Manor		65%	£78	H	(0452) 730217	55	200	150			
Gloucester	Hatton Court		75%	£90	HR	(0452) 617412	46	60	80			
Gloucester	Travel Inn	Travel Inns		£43	L	(0452) 862521	40					
Gloucester	Travel Inn	Travel Inns		£43	L	(0452) 523519	40					
Lower Slaughter	Lower Slaughter Manor		77%	£200	HR	(0451) 20456	19	26	26		yes	
Lower Swell	Old Farmhouse			£60	I	(0451) 830232	14		8			
Mickleton	Three Ways Hotel		59%	£68	H	(0386) 438429	40	130	90			
Moreton-in-Marsh	Manor House		66%	£83	H	(0608) 50501	39	75	75		yes	
Painswick	Painswick Hotel		70%	£95	H	(0452) 812160	19	30	80			
Puckrup	Puckrup Hall		70%	£78	HR	(0684) 296200	16	200	180			
Stonehouse	Stonehouse Court	Clipper	68%	£98	H	(0453) 825155	37	120	120			
Stow-on-the-Wold	Fosse Manor		60%	£95	H	(0451) 30354	20					
Stow-on-the-Wold	Grapevine Hotel		63%	£98	H	(0451) 830344	23	70				
Stow-on-the-Wold	Unicorn Hotel	Forte	59%	£100	H	(0451) 830257	20	15				
Stow-on-the-Wold	Wyck Hill House		74%	£90	HR	(0451) 831936	30	40	80			
Tetbury	Calcot Manor		74%	£107	HR	(0666) 890391	14	25	50			
Tetbury	The Close		75%	£75	HR	(0666) 502272	15	40	22			
Tetbury	Snooty Fox Hotel		69%	£80	H	(0666) 502436	12	30	16			
Tewkesbury	Bell Hotel		60%	£80	H	(0684) 293293	25					
Tewkesbury	Royal Hop Pole	Forte	66%	£105	H	(0684) 293236	29	12				
Tewkesbury	Tewkesbury Park	Country Club	62%	£98	H	(0684) 295405	78	150	156	yes	yes	yes
Upper Slaughter	Lords of the Manor		75%	£135	HR	(0451) 820243	29					
Westonbirt	Hare & Hounds		59%	£75	H	(0666) 880233	30	40	150			

Location	*Hotel*	*Group*	*%*	*Room Price*	*Cat*	*Tel*	*Rooms*	*Conf*	*Banq*	*Leisure Centre*	*Swim Pool*	*Golf*
Greater Manchester												
Bolton	Egerton House	Rank	63%	£85	H	(0204) 307171	32	150	150			
Bolton	Forte Posthouse	Forte	58%	£68	H	(0204) 651511	96	120	90			
Bolton	Pack Horse Hotel	De Vere	62%	£60	H	(0204) 27261	73	375	230			
Bury	Normandie Hotel & Restaurant		64%	£83	HR	061-764 3869	24	18	14			
Manchester	Britannia Hotel		66%	£123	H	061-228 2288	362	300	250		yes	
Manchester	Charterhouse Hotel	Hidden	72%	£114	H	061-236 9999	58	180	130			
Manchester	Copthorne Hotel	Copthorne	70%	£121	H	061-873 7321	166	150	132	yes	yes	
Manchester	Forte Posthouse	Forte	60%	£68	H	061-998 7090	190	150	100			
Manchester	Granada Lodge	Granada		£45	L	061-410 0076	37					
Manchester	Holiday Inn Crowne Plaza	Holiday Inns	73%	£124	H	061-236 3333	303	700	700	yes	yes	
Manchester	Novotel	Novotel	62%	£80	H	061-799 3535	119	220	160			
Manchester	Hotel Piccadilly	Jarvis	73%	£138	H	061-236 8414	271	800	700		yes	
Manchester	Portland Thistle	MtCT	69%	£120	H	061-228 3400	205	300	250	yes	yes	
Manchester	Ramada Hotel		73%	£115	H	061-835 2555	200	350	400			
Manchester	Sachas Hotel		64%	£110	H	061-228 1234	223	600	650	yes	yes	
Manchester	Victoria & Albert Hotel	Granada	73%	£136	HR	061-832 1188	132	250	200			
Manchester Airport	Etrop Grange		67%	£110	HR	061-499 0500	40		80			
Manchester Airport	Forte Crest	Forte	65%	£107	H	061-437 5811	292	200	200	yes	yes	
Manchester Airport	Four Seasons Hotel		68%	£102	H	061-904 0301	94	150	140			
Manchester Airport	Hilton International	Hilton	71%	£159	H	061-436 4404	223	200	150	yes	yes	
Standish	Almond Brook Moat House	QMH	63%	£95	H	(0257) 425588	126	150	100		yes	
Stockport	Alma Lodge	Jarvis	61%	£94	H	061-483 4431	56	250	220			
Hampshire												
Alton	Forte Travelodge	Forte		£42	L	(0420) 62659	31					
Alton	Grange Hotel		61%	£61	H	(0420) 86565	34	40	90			

Alton	The Swan	Forte	58%	£80	H	(0420) 83777	36	120	125		
Ampfield	Potters Heron Hotel	Lansbury	60%	£87	H	(0703) 266611	54	140	100		
Andover	White Hart Inn	Forte		£82	I	(0264) 352266	20	65	65		
Barton Stacey	Forte Travelodge	Forte		£42	L	(0264) 72260	20				
Basingstoke	Audleys Wood	MtCT	75%	£123	HR	(0256) 817555	71	50	40		
Basingstoke	Forte Travelodge	Forte		£42	L	(0256) 843566	32				
Basingstoke	Forte Posthouse	Forte	64%	£68	H	(0256) 468181	84	180	160		
Basingstoke	Hilton National	Hilton	66%	£87	H	(0256) 460460	144	150	120		yes
Basingstoke	The Ringway	Hilton	65%	£64	H	(0256) 20212	134	160	120		yes
Basingstoke	Travel Inn	Travel Inns		£43	L	(0256) 811477	49				
Beaulieu	Montagu Arms		68%	£96	H	(0590) 612324	24	45	120		
Brockenhurst	Balmer Lawn Hotel	Hilton	65%	£90	H	(0590) 23116	58	100	90		yes
Brockenhurst	Careys Manor		67%	£89	H	(0590) 23551	80	100	150	yes	yes
Brockenhurst	Rhinefield House		68%	£95	H	(0590) 22922	34	150	110		
Buckler's Hard	Master Builder's House			£80	I	(0590) 616253	23	50	100		
Burley	Burley Manor		61%	£70	H	(0425) 403522	30	80	75		
Eastleigh	Forte Travelodge	Forte		£42	L	(0703) 616813	32				
Eastleigh	Forte Crest Southampton	Forte	66%	£95	H	(0703) 619700	120	300	250		
Fareham	Forte Posthouse	Forte	61%	£68	H	(0329) 844644	126	140	120	yes	yes
Fareham	Red Lion	Lansbury	57%	£65	H	(0329) 822640	43	80	100		
Fareham	Solent Hotel	Shire Inns	75%	£101	H	(0489) 880000	90	250	200	yes	yes
Farnborough	Forte Crest	Forte	66%	£119	H	(0252) 545051	110	200	180	yes	yes
Fleet	Forte Travelodge	Forte		£42	L	(0252) 815578	40				
Havant	Bear Hotel	Lansbury	59%	£77	H	(0705) 486501	42	120	100		
Havant	Forte Posthouse	Forte	62%	£68	H	(0705) 465011	92	180	120	yes	yes
Hurstbourne Tarrant	Esseborne Manor		72%	£95	HR	(0264) 76444	12	12	28		
Lymington	Gordleton Mill		65%	£70	HR	(0590) 682219	7		50		
Lymington	Passford House		70%	£101	H	(0590) 682398	56	80	150	yes	yes
Lymington	Stanwell House	Clipper	65%	£98	H	(0590) 677123	35	16	60		
Lyndhurst	The Crown		65%	£97	H	(0703) 282922	40	50	50		
Lyndhurst	Lyndhurst Park		61%	£70	H	(0703) 283923	59	400	300		
Lyndhurst	Parkhill Hotel		67%	£94	H	(0703) 282944	20	60	85		

Location	*Hotel*	*Group*	*%*	*Room Price*	*Cat*	*Tel*	*Rooms*	*Conf*	*Banq*	*Leisure Centre*	*Swim Pool*	*Golf*
Middle Wallop	Fifehead Manor		61%	£85	H	(0264) 781565	16	30	20			
Milford-on-Sea	South Lawn		66%	£84	H	(0590) 643911	24					
New Milton	Chewton Glen		89%	£206	HR	(0425) 275341	58	110	120	yes	yes	
Odiham	George Hotel			£68	I	(0256) 702081	18					
Petersfield	Langrish House		63%	£63	H	(0730) 66941	18	60	100			
Portsmouth	Forte Posthouse	Forte	65%	£68	H	(0705) 827651	163	220	180		yes	
Portsmouth	Hilton National	Hilton	66%	£93	H	(0705) 219111	122	230	200			
Portsmouth	Hospitality Inn	MtCT	61%	£79	H	(0705) 731281	115	280	250			
Portsmouth	Pendragon Hotel	Forte	59%	£87	H	(0705) 823201	49	60	90			
Portsmouth	Portsmouth Marriott Hotel	Marriott	73%	£127	H	(0705) 383151	170	600	300	yes	yes	
Romsey	White Horse Hotel	Forte	63%	£101	H	(0794) 512431	33	40	90			
Rotherwick	Tylney Hall		77%	£114	HR	(0256) 764881	91	100	100		yes	
Silchester	Romans Hotel		64%	£80	H	(0734) 700421	23	50	50			
Southampton	Dolphin Hotel	Forte	60%	£82	H	(0703) 339955	73	100	90			
Southampton	Forte Posthouse	Forte	58%	£68	H	(0703) 330777	128	200	200	yes	yes	
Southampton	Hilton National	Hilton	68%	£94	H	(0703) 702700	135	180	140			
Southampton	Novotel	Novotel	62%	£85	H	(0703) 330550	121	450	350			
Southampton	Polygon Hotel	Forte	65%	£77	H	(0703) 330055	119	500	400			
Southampton	Southampton Park Hotel		64%	£66	H	(0703) 223467	71	200	150	yes	yes	
Stockbridge	Grosvenor Hotel	Lansbury	57%	£77	H	(0264) 810606	25	80	70			
Stratfield Turgis	Wellington Arms			£68	I	(0256) 882214	35	70	70			
Sutton Scotney North	Forte Travelodge	Forte		£42	L	(0962) 761016	31					
Sutton Scotney South	Forte Travelodge	Forte		£42	L	(0962) 760779	40					
Wickham	Old House Hotel		66%	£85	HR	(0329) 833049	12	12	14			
Winchester	Forte Crest	Forte	69%	£68	H	(0962) 861611	94	100	85			
Winchester	Lainston House		75%	£145	H	(0962) 863588	38	120	90			
Winchester	Royal Hotel		67%	£65	H	(0962) 840840	76	120	100			
Winchester	Wykeham Arms			£70	IR	(0962) 853834	7	10				

Hereford & Worcester

Abberley	Elms Hotel	QMH	71%	£97	H	(0299) 896666	25	60	75		
Abbot's Salford	Salford Hall		66%	£95	H	(0386) 871300	33	50	50		
Broadway	Broadway Hotel		60%	£86	H	(0386) 852401	20	25			
Broadway	Collin House		65%	£88	HR	(0386) 858354	7				
Broadway	Dormy House		69%	£110	HR	(0386) 852711	49	200	160		
Broadway	Lygon Arms	Savoy Group	78%	£171	HR	(0386) 852255	65	80	80		yes
Bromsgrove	Grafton Manor		70%	£105	HR	(0527) 579007	9	12	40		
Bromsgrove	Perry Hall	Jarvis	56%	£93	H	(0527) 579976	58	70	42		
Bromsgrove	Stakis Country Court	Stakis	69%	£116	H	021-447 7888	141	80	60	yes	yes
Buckland	Buckland Manor		79%	£145	HR	(0386) 852626	11				
Chaddesley Corbett	Brockencote Hall			£90	HR	(0562) 777876	17	30	50		
Droitwich	Forte Travelodge	Forte		£42	L	(0527) 86545	32				
Droitwich Spa	Chateau Impney		70%	£80	H	(0905) 774411	114	500	400		
Droitwich Spa	Raven Hotel		66%	£140	H	(0905) 772224	72	150	250		
Evesham	Evesham Hotel		62%	£94	H	(0386) 765566	40	12	12		yes
Evesham	Riverside Hotel		68%	£72	HR	(0386) 446200	7				
Eyton	Marsh Country Hotel		67%	£100	HR	(0568) 613952	5				
Hartlebury	Forte Travelodge	Forte		£42	L	(0299) 250553	32				
Harvington	The Mill		67%	£85	HR	(0386) 870688	15	20	15		
Hereford	Moat House	QMH	63%	£70	H	(0432) 354301	60	400	250		
Hereford	Travel Inn	Travel Inns		£43	L	(0432) 274853	40				
Kidderminster	Stone Manor		65%	£65	H	(0562) 777555	52	150	250		
Ledbury	The Feathers			£85	I	(0531) 635266	11	150	125		
Ledbury	Hope End		70%	£119	HR	(0531) 633613	9				
Malvern	Abbey Hotel	De Vere	62%	£70	H	(0684) 892332	107	150	200		
Malvern	Colwall Park Hotel		62%	£77	H	(0684) 40206	20	100	100		
Malvern	Cottage in the Wood		65%	£93	HR	(0684) 573487	20	20	14		
Malvern	Foley Arms		61%	£88	H	(0684) 573397	28	120	90		
Much Birch	Pilgrim Hotel		64%	£60	H	(0981) 540742	20	45	36		
Redditch	Campanile Hotel	Campanile		£44	L	(0527) 510710	50				
Ross-on-Wye	Chase Hotel		64%	£80	H	(0989) 763161	39	300	300		

Location	Hotel	Group	%	Room Price	Cat	Tel	Rooms	Conf	Banq	Leisure Centre	Swim Pool	Golf
Ross-on-Wye	Pengethley Manor		67%	£100	H	(098 987) 211	24	90	75			
Ruckhall	Ancient Camp Inn			£58	I	(0981) 250449	5					
Stourport-on-Severn	Moat House	QMH	62%	£49	H	(0299) 827733	68	450	300			
Weobley	Olde Salutation Inn			£53	I	(0544) 318443	5					
Weston-under-Penyard	Wharton Lodge		73%	£85	HR	(0989) 750795	9	14	60			
Worcester	Fownes Resort Hotel	Resort	70%	£100	H	(0905) 613151	61	120	100			
Worcester	Giffard Hotel	Forte	61%	£62	H	(0905) 726262	103	130	180			

Hertfordshire

Location	Hotel	Group	%	Room Price	Cat	Tel	Rooms	Conf	Banq	Leisure Centre	Swim Pool	Golf
Baldock	Forte Travelodge	Forte		£42	L	(0462) 835329	40					
Broxbourne	Cheshunt Marriott Hotel	Marriott	66%	£93	H	(0992) 451245	150			yes	yes	
Dane End	Green End Park		62%	£95	H	(0920) 438344	10	100	60			
Hadley Wood	West Lodge Park		66%	£106	H	081-440 8311	50	75	65			
Harpenden	Glen Eagle Hotel		63%	£85	H	(0582) 760271	50	80	150			
Harpenden	Moat House	QMH	68%	£95	H	(0582) 764111	53	150	120			
Hatfield Heath	Down Hall		71%	£138	H	(0279) 731441	103	200	180		yes	
Hertingfordbury	White Horse Hotel	Forte	63%	£90	H	(0992) 586791	42	60	20			
Letchworth	Broadway Toby Hotel		59%	£60	H	(0462) 480111	35	180	180			
Markyate	Hertfordshire Moat House	QMH	57%	£94	H	(0582) 840840	89	450	300			
Rushden	Forte Travelodge	Forte		£42	L	(0933) 57008	40					
St Albans	Noke Thistle	MtCT	68%	£107	H	(0727) 854252	111	55	50			
St Albans	St Michael's Manor		63%	£80	H	(0727) 864444	22	36	110			
St Albans	Sopwell House		65%	£108	H	(0727) 864477	92	400	380	yes	yes	
Sawbridgeworth	Manor of Groves		74%	£90	H	(0279) 600777	39	35	150			yes
South Mimms	Forte Posthouse	Forte	60%	£68	H	(0707) 643311	120	170	120	yes	yes	
South Mimms	Forte Travelodge	Forte		£42	L	(0707) 665440	52					
Stanstead Abbots	Briggens House	QMH	70%	£106	H	(0279) 792416	54	100	100			

Stevenage	Novotel	Novotel	60%	£80	H	(0438) 742299	100	150	110			
Thundridge	Hanbury Manor		79%	£180	HR	(0920) 487722	96	180	100	yes	yes	yes
Tring	Travel Inn	Travel Inns		£43	L	(0442) 824819	30					
Watford	Hilton National	Hilton	64%	£109	H	(0923) 235881	198	400	350	yes	yes	

Humberside

Beverley	Beverley Arms	Forte	62%	£90	H	(0482) 869241	57	80	65			
Bridlington	Expanse Hotel		60%	£59	H	(0262) 675347	48	40	120			
Cleethorpes	Kingsway Hotel		62%	£80	H	(0472) 601122	50		24			
Driffield	Bell Hotel			£91	I	(0377) 46661	14	300	200		yes	
Grimsby	Forte Crest	Forte	64%	£67	H	(0472) 350295	52	250	200			
Hull	Campanile Hotel	Campanile		£44	L	(0482) 25530	50					
Hull	Forte Posthouse	Forte	62%	£68	H	(0482) 645212	97	100	120			
Hull	Forte Crest	Forte	69%	£89	H	(0482) 225221	99	140	120		yes	
Pocklington	Feathers Hotel			£48	I	(0759) 303155	12	30	60			
South Cave	Forte Travelodge	Forte		£42	L	(0430) 424455	40					
Tickton	Tickton Grange		62%	£56	H	(0964) 543666	16	86	86			
Walkington	Manor House		72%	£93	HR	(0482) 881645	6	30	24			
Willerby	Grange Park		67%	£87	H	(0482) 656488	104	550	450	yes	yes	
Willerby	Willerby Manor		62%	£97	H	(0482) 652616	36	500	400			

Isle of Wight

Bonchurch	Winterbourne Hotel		64%	£94	H	(0983) 852535	19					
Calbourne	Swainston Manor		66%	£76	H	(0983) 521121	17	150	100		yes	
Freshwater	Farringford Hotel		57%	£88	H	(0983) 752500	19	30	20			
Ryde	Hotel Ryde Castle		61%	£79	H	(0983) 563755	17	170	200			
Seaview	Seaview Hotel		62%	£73	HR	(0983) 612711	16					
Shanklin	Cliff Tops Hotel		64%	£99	H	(0983) 863262	88	250	200	yes	yes	
Ventnor	Royal Hotel	Forte	60%	£66	H	(0983) 852186	54	36	120			

Location	Hotel	Group	%	Room Price	Cat	Tel	Rooms	Conf	Banq	Leisure Centre	Swim Pool	Golf
Kent												
Ashford	Ashford International	QMH	71%	£107	H	(0233) 611444	200	400	400	yes	yes	
Ashford	Eastwell Manor	QMH	82%	£110	HR	(0233) 635751	23	85	80			
Ashford	Forte Posthouse	Forte	66%	£68	H	(0233) 625790	60	120	100			
Ashford	Holiday Inn Garden Court	Holiday Inns	65%	£70	H	(0233) 713333	104	25				
Ashford	Travel Inn	Travel Inns		£43	L	(0223) 712571	40					
Bearsted	Tudor Park	Country Club	67%	£109	H	(0622) 34334	120	275	216	yes	yes	yes
Bexley	Forte Crest	Forte	56%	£68	H	(0322) 526900	102	80	60			
Bexleyheath	Swallow Hotel	Swallow	71%	£94	H	081-298 1000	142	250	250		yes	
Boughton Monchelsea	Tanyard Hotel		63%	£76	H	(0622) 744705	6					
Brands Hatch	Brands Hatch Thistle	MtCT	70%	£97	H	(0474) 854900	137	300	250			
Bromley	Bromley Court		66%	£89	H	081-464 5011	119	150	200			
Canterbury	Canterbury Hotel		58%	£50	H	(0227) 450551	27	40	25			
Canterbury	Chaucer Hotel	Forte	61%	£98	H	(0227) 464427	42	100	100			
Canterbury	County Hotel		68%	£105	HR	(0227) 766266	74	180	150			
Canterbury	Ebury Hotel		59%	£60	H	(0227) 768433	15				yes	
Canterbury	Falstaff Hotel			£85	I	(0227) 462138	25	50	50			
Canterbury	Howfield Manor		68%	£85	H	(0227) 738294	13	80	80			
Canterbury	Slatters Hotel	QMH	57%	£75	H	(0227) 463271	31	100	100			
Chartham	Thruxted Oast			£73	PH	(0227) 730080	3					
Cranbrook	Hartley Mount		62%	£70	H	(0580) 712230	7					
Cranbrook	Kennel Holt Hotel		66%	£98	H	(0580) 712032	10	35	30			
Dover	Forte Posthouse	Forte	63%	£67	H	(0304) 821222	67	40	20			
Dover	Moat House	QMH	66%	£75	H	(0304) 203270	79	150	120	yes	yes	
Dover	Travel Inn	Travel Inns		£43	L	(0304) 213339	30					
Fawkham	Brandshatch Place		66%	£90	HR	(0474) 872239	29	150	120	yes	yes	
Golden Green	Goldhill Mill			£60	PH	(0732) 851626	3					
Goudhurst	Star & Eagle Inn			£40	I	(0580) 211512	11	20	60			

Hawkhurst	Tudor Court		61%	£78	H	(0580) 752312	18	80	70			
Hollingbourne	Great Danes	Jarvis	64%	£65	H	(0622) 30022	126	600	320	yes	yes	
Hythe	Hythe Imperial		71%	£117	H	(0303) 267441	100	200	280	yes	yes	yes
Hythe	Stade Court		62%	£75	H	(0303) 268263	42	60	100		yes	
Lenham	Chilston Park		71%	£95	H	(0622) 859803	40	120	80			
Maidstone	Larkfield Priory	Forte	62%	£71	H	(0732) 846858	52	70	70			
Maidstone	Stakis Country Court Hotel	Stakis	67%	£93	H	(0622) 34322	138	90	60	yes	yes	
Rochester	Bridgewood Manor Hotel		68%	£100	H	(0634) 201333	100	200	180	yes	yes	
Rochester	Forte Posthouse	Forte	62%	£68	H	(0634) 687111	105	40	80		yes	
St Margaret's	Wallett's Court		60%	£45	H	(0304) 852424	7	30				
Sevenoaks	Royal Oak		66%	£99	HR	(0732) 451109	39	45				
Shorne	Inn on the Lake		61%	£70	H	(0474) 823333	78	700	500			
Tonbridge	Rose & Crown	Forte	59%	£97	H	(0732) 357966	50	110	80			
Tunbridge Wells	Royal Wells Inn		64%	£80	H	(0892) 511188	22	100	90			
Tunbridge Wells	Spa Hotel		72%	£84	HR	(0892) 520331	76	350	180	yes	yes	
Wateringbury	Wateringbury Hotel		59%	£61	H	(0622) 812632	40	80	100			
Wrotham Heath	Forte Posthouse Maidstone	Forte	67%	£68	H	(0732) 883311	106		60	yes	yes	
Wrotham Heath	Travel Inn	Travel Inns		£43	L	(0732) 884214	40					

Lancashire

Blackburn	Moat House	QMH	58%	£69	H	(0254) 264441	98	350	300		
Blackpool	Imperial Hotel	Forte	64%	£114	H	(0253) 23971	183	500	450	yes	yes
Blackpool	Pembroke Hotel		67%	£129	H	(0253) 23434	274	900	600		yes
Bolton	Last Drop Village Hotel	Rank	68%	£88	H	(0204) 591131	83	200	200	yes	yes
Broughton	Broughton Park	Country Club	65%	£94	HR	(0772) 864087	98	220	180		yes
Burnley	Forte Travelodge	Forte		£42	L	(0282) 416039	32				
Burnley	Oaks Hotel	Shire Inns	63%	£88	H	(0282) 414141	56	200	120		yes
Chipping	Gibbon Bridge Country House		70%	£76	H	(0955) 61456	30	100	160		
Clayton-le-Woods	Pines Hotel		67%	£65	H	(0772) 38551	39	100	200		
Lancaster	Forte Posthouse	Forte	69%	£68	H	(0524) 65999	110	120	100	yes	yes
Langho	Northcote Manor		67%	£65	HR	(0254) 240555	13	100	100		

Location	Hotel	Group	%	Room Price	Cat	Tel	Rooms	Conf	Banq	Leisure Centre	Swim Pool	Golf
Lytham	Clifton Arms	Lansbury	63%	£87	H	(0253) 739898	41					
Lytham St Annes	Dalmeny Hotel		60%	£68	HR	(0253) 712236	90	250	200		yes	
Mellor	Millstone Hotel	Shire Inns		£84	I	(0254) 813333	21					
Preston	Forte Posthouse	Forte	63%	£68	H	(0772) 259411	126	120	100			
Preston	Novotel	Novotel	62%	£69	H	(0772) 313331	100	240	130			
Preston	Travel Inn	Travel Inns		£43	L	(0772) 720476	40					
Samlesbury	Swallow Trafalgar	Swallow	64%	£72	H	(0772) 877351	78	25	180	yes	yes	
Samlesbury	Tickled Trout		63%	£85	H	(0772) 877671	72	100	90		yes	
Slaidburn	Hark to Bounty Inn			£45	I	(0200) 446246	8	100	70			
Whitewell	Inn at Whitewell			£63	I	(020 08) 222	9	40	160			
Worthington	Kilhey Court	Principal	65%	£90	H	(0257) 472100	55	150	200		yes	

Leicestershire

Location	Hotel	Group	%	Room Price	Cat	Tel	Rooms	Conf	Banq	Leisure Centre	Swim Pool	Golf
Hinckley	Hinckley Island Hotel		64%	£89	H	(0455) 631122	276	400	400	yes	yes	
Leicester	Belmont Hotel		65%	£80	H	(0533) 544773	68	120	100			
Leicester	Forte Posthouse	Forte	64%	£68	H	(0533) 630500	172	100	100			
Leicester	Granada Lodge	Granada		£45	L	(0530) 244237	39					
Leicester	Grand Hotel	Jarvis	66%	£102	H	(0533) 555599	92	450	320			
Leicester	Holiday Inn	Holiday Inns	72%	£114	H	(0533) 531161	188	300	280	yes	yes	
Leicester	Leicester Forest Moat House	QMH	58%	£73	H	(0533) 394661	34	65	60			
Leicester	Park International		61%	£82	H	(0533) 620471	209	450	320			
Leicester	Stakis Country Court	Stakis	69%	£104	H	(0533) 630066	141	90	70	yes	yes	
Lockington	Hilton National E Midlands	Hilton	69%	£113	H	(0509) 674000	151	220	200	yes	yes	
Loughborough	King's Head	Jarvis	58%	£96	H	(0509) 233222	78	120	120			
Lutterworth	Denbigh Arms	Resort	66%	£65	H	(0455) 553537	34	60	50			
Market Harborough	Three Swans Hotel		65%	£72	H	(0858) 466644	36	75	95			
Melton Mowbray	George Hotel		57%	£58	H	(0664) 62112	22	35	78			

Oakham	Barnsdale Lodge		65%	£70	H	(0572) 724678	17	64	220			
Oakham	Hambleton Hall		84%	£120	HR	(0572) 756991	15	30	60			
Oakham	Whipper-In Hotel		70%	£80	H	(0572) 756971	25	50	60			
Quorn	Quorn Grange		67%	£94	HR	(0509) 412167	17	80	120			
Quorn	The Quorn		72%	£102	H	(0509) 415050	19	120	120			
Rothley	Rothley Court	Forte	67%	£100	H	(0533) 374141	36	100	100			
Stapleford	Stapleford Park		86%	£142	HR	(057 284) 522	35	300	200			
Stretton	Ram Jam Inn			£59	IR	(0780) 410776	10	40				
Thrussington	Forte Travelodge	Forte		£42	L	(0664) 424525	32					
Uppingham	Forte Travelodge	Forte		£42	L	(0572) 87719	40					

Lincolnshire

Belton	Belton Woods Hotel	De Vere	72%	£115	H	(0476) 593200	96	275	240	yes	yes	yes
Boston	New England Hotel	Forte	56%	£78	H	(0205) 365255	25					
Colsterworth	Forte Travelodge	Forte		£42	L	(0476) 861181	32					
Grantham	Forte Travelodge	Forte		£42	L	(0476) 77500	40					
Grantham	Granada Lodge	Granada		£45	L	(0476) 860686	38					
Lincoln	D'Isney Place			£60	PH	(0522) 538881	17					
Lincoln	Forte Posthouse	Forte	63%	£68	H	(0522) 520341	70	80	80			
Lincoln	White Hart	Forte	69%	£90	H	(0522) 526222	50					
Sleaford	Forte Travelodge	Forte		£42	L	(0529) 414752	40					
South Witham	Forte Travelodge	Forte		£42	L	(057 283) 586	32					
Stamford	The George of Stamford	Poste Hotels	72%	£100	HR	(0780) 55171	47	50	90			
Woodhall Spa	Dower House		62%	£60	H	(0526) 52588	7	24	24			

London Airport Heathrow

Heathrow Airport	Berkeley Arms Hotel	Jarvis	67%	£111	H	081-897 2121	56	150	140		
Heathrow Airport	Edwardian International	Edwardian	76%	£206	H	081-759 6311	459	450	330	yes	yes
Heathrow Airport	Excelsior Hotel	Forte	71%	£128	H	081-759 6611	839	800	800	yes	yes

Location	Hotel	Group	%	Room Price	Cat	Tel	Rooms	Conf	Banq	Leisure Centre	Swim Pool	Golf
Heathrow Airport	Forte Crest	Forte	68%	£99	H	081-759 2323	572	200	160			
Heathrow Airport	Forte Posthouse Ariel Hotel	Forte	65%	£68	H	081-759 2552	180	50	30			
Heathrow Airport	Granada Lodge	Granada		£55	L	081-574 5875	46					
Heathrow Airport	Heathrow Hilton Hotel	Hilton	76%	£162	H	081-759 7755	400	140	200	yes	yes	
Heathrow Airport	Holiday Inn Crowne Plaza	Holiday Inns	74%	£164	H	(0895) 445555	375	200	180	yes	yes	yes
Heathrow Airport	Park Hotel	MtCT	61%	£111	H	081-759 2400	306	600	400			
Heathrow Airport	Ramada Hotel Heathrow		66%	£115	H	081-897 6363	636	500	500		yes	
Heathrow Airport	Sheraton Heathrow Hotel	Sheraton	70%	£103	H	081-759 2424	415	80	70			
Heathrow Airport	Sheraton Skyline	Sheraton	73%	£164	H	081-759 2535	353	500	450		yes	

London Airport Gatwick

Location	Hotel	Group	%	Room Price	Cat	Tel	Rooms	Conf	Banq	Leisure Centre	Swim Pool	Golf
Gatwick Airport	Chequers Thistle	MtCT	63%	£106	H	(0293) 786992	78	85	60		yes	
Gatwick Airport	Copthorne London Gatwick	Copthorne	69%	£128	H	(0342) 714971	227	110	160			
Gatwick Airport	Copthorne Effingham Park	Copthorne	72%	£126	H	(0342) 714994	122	500	500	yes	yes	
Gatwick Airport	Europa Gatwick		68%	£117	H	(0293) 886666	211	150	100		yes	
Gatwick Airport	Forte Crest Gatwick	Forte	74%	£99	H	(0293) 567070	474	550	500	yes	yes	
Gatwick Airport	Forte Posthouse	Forte	63%	£68	H	(0293) 771621	210	150	120			
Gatwick Airport	Gatwick Hilton International	Hilton	72%	£159	H	(0293) 518080	550	500	400	yes	yes	
Gatwick Airport	Gatwick Concorde Hotel	QMH	61%	£104	H	(0293) 533441	116	60	120			
Gatwick Airport	Holiday Inn Gatwick	Holiday Inns	68%	£118	H	(0293) 529991	223	200	200	yes	yes	
Gatwick Airport	Moat House	QMH	62%	£74	H	(0293) 785599	121	180	150			
Gatwick Airport	Ramada Hotel Gatwick		70%	£134	H	(0293) 820169	255	150	150	yes	yes	
Horley	Langshott Manor		71%	£106	HR	(0293) 786680	5	15	12			

Merseyside

Location	Hotel	Group	%	Room Price	Cat	Tel	Rooms	Conf	Banq	Leisure Centre	Swim Pool	Golf
Bebington	Forte Travelodge	Forte		£42	L	051-327 2489	31					

Birkenhead	Bowler Hat Hotel		65%	£70	H	051-652 4931	32	240	240			
Gayton	Travel Inn	Travel Inns		£43	L	051-342 1982	37					
Haydock	Forte Posthouse	Forte	65%	£68	H	(0942) 717878	136	170	130	yes	yes	
Haydock	Forte Travelodge	Forte		£42	L	(0942) 272055	40					
Haydock	Haydock Thistle	MtCT	67%	£107	H	(0942) 272000	139	200	180	yes	yes	
Liverpool	Atlantic Tower	MtCT	65%	£103	H	051-227 4444	226	140	120			
Liverpool	Britannia Adelphi Hotel		68%	£105	H	051-709 7200	391	900	600	yes	yes	
Liverpool	Campanile Hotel	Campanile		£44	L	051-709 8104	82					
Liverpool	Gladstone Hotel	Forte	58%	£90	H	051-709 7050	154	600	400			
Liverpool	Moat House	QMH	67%	£116	H	051-709 0181	251	450	300	yes	yes	
Liverpool	St George's Hotel	Forte	60%	£70	H	051-709 7090	155	300	280			
Southport	New Bold Hotel		58%	£51	H	(0704) 532578	23					
Southport	Prince of Wales Hotel	Forte	65%	£74	H	(0704) 536688	104	450	350			

Middlesex

Hayes	Travel Inn	Travel Inns		£43	L	081-573 7479	40					
Heathrow Airport – *see under* **London Airports**												
Kenton	Travel Inn	Travel Inns		£43	L	081-907 1671	43					
Shepperton	Moat House	QMH	61%	£103	H	(0932) 241404	180	300	280			
Shepperton	Warren Lodge			£72	I	(0932) 242972	52	12				
Wembley	Hilton National	Hilton	65%	£129	H	081-902 8839	300	250	300			

Norfolk

Acle	Forte Travelodge	Forte		£42	L	(0493) 751970	40					
Barnham Broom	Barnham Broom Hotel		62%	£82	H	(060 545) 393	52	200	250		yes	yes
Blakeney	Blakeney Hotel		64%	£112	H	(0263) 740797	60	200	140		yes	
Blakeney	Manor Hotel		58%	£68	H	(0263) 740376	36	20	60			
East Dereham	King's Head			£48	I	(0362) 693842	15	60	45			
East Dereham	Phoenix Hotel	Forte	59%	£77	H	(0362) 692276	23	140	160			

Location	Hotel	Group	%	Room Price	Cat	Tel	Rooms	Conf	Banq	Leisure Centre	Swim Pool	Golf
Great Snoring	Old Rectory		61%	£84	H	(0328) 820597	6					
Great Yarmouth	Carlton Hotel	Waveney	67%	£79	H	(0493) 855234	90					
Grimston	Congham Hall		76%	£97	HR	(0485) 600250	14		50			
Hethersett	Park Farm		64%	£90	H	(0603) 810264	38	160	120		yes	
King's Lynn	Butterfly Hotel		62%	£67	H	(0553) 771707	50	50	15			
King's Lynn	Duke's Head	Forte	60%	£93	H	(0553) 774996	71	240	230			
King's Lynn	Forte Travelodge	Forte		£42	L	(0406) 362230	40					
Morston	Morston Hall		73%	£120	H	(0263) 741041	4					
Norwich	Airport Ambassador Hotel		65%	£76	H	(0603) 410544	108	450	350		yes	
Norwich	Forte Posthouse	Forte	63%	£68	H	(0603) 56431	113	100	65	yes	yes	
Norwich	Friendly Hotel		60%	£94	H	(0603) 741161	80	200	200		yes	
Norwich	Hotel Nelson		65%	£83	H	(0603) 760260	121	90	44			
Norwich	Norwich Sport Village Hotel		63%	£65	H	(0603) 788898	55	5000	2000	yes	yes	
Norwich	Hotel Norwich		62%	£62	H	(0603) 787260	108	340	260	yes	yes	
Norwich	Sprowston Manor		69%	£88	H	(0603) 410871	97	120	90	yes	yes	
Ormesby St Margaret	Ormesby Lodge		58%	£46	H	(0493) 730910	9	40	100			
Scole	Scole Inn			£60	I	(0379) 740481	23	50	50			
Shipdham	Shipdham Place		64%	£65	H	(0362) 820303	8	20	20			
South Wootton	Knights Hill Hotel		64%	£94	H	(0553) 675566	52	300	200	yes	yes	
Thetford	The Bell	Forte	62%	£97	H	(0842) 754455	47	90	65			
West Runton	The Links Country Park Hotel		62%	£150	H	(0263) 838383	40				yes	

Northamptonshire

Location	Hotel	Group	%	Room Price	Cat	Tel	Rooms	Conf	Banq	Leisure Centre	Swim Pool	Golf
Castle Ashby	Falcon Inn			£72	I	(0604) 696200	14	25				
Crick	Forte Posthouse Northampton	Forte	64%	£68	H	(0788) 822101	88	185	120	yes	yes	
Daventry	Daventry Resort Hotel	Resort	70%	£100	H	(0327) 301777	138	600	400			
Desborough	Forte Travelodge	Forte		£42	L	(0536) 762034	32					

Kettering	Kettering Park Hotel	Shire Inns	71%	£105	H	(0536) 416666	90	280	240		
Milton Keynes	Friendly Hotel		57%	£79	H	(0908) 561666	88	120	100		yes
Northampton	Courtyard by Marriott	Marriott	65%	£77	H	(0604) 22777	104	30			
Northampton	Forte Travelodge	Forte		£42	L	(0604) 758395	40				
Northampton	Moat House	QMH	63%	£93	H	(0604) 22441	138	600	500		
Northampton	Stakis Country Court	Stakis	68%	£107	H	(0604) 700666	139	320	320		yes
Northampton	Swallow Hotel	Swallow	72%	£99	H	(0604) 768700	122	250	180	yes	yes
Northampton	Travel Inn	Travel Inns		£43	L	(0604) 832340	51				
Northampton	Westone Moat House	QMH	59%	£79	H	(0604) 406262	66	140	180		
Oundle	Talbot Hotel	Forte	62%	£96	H	(0832) 273621	40	100	100		
Thrapston	Forte Travelodge	Forte		£42	L	(0801) 25199	40				
Towcester	Forte Travelodge	Forte		£42	L	(0327) 359105	33				
Weedon	Crossroads Hotel		63%	£52	H	(0327) 40354	48	50	120		

Northumberland

Allendale	Bishop Field		59%	£76	H	(0434) 683248	11	20			
Alnwick	White Swan		58%	£75	H	(0665) 602109	43	150	100		
Bamburgh	Lord Crewe Arms		58%	£62	H	(066 84) 243	25				
Belford	Blue Bell Hotel		63%	£66	H	(0668) 213543	17	120	80		
Berwick-upon-Tweed	Kings Arms		59%	£75	H	(0289) 307454	36	200	120		
Chollerford	George Hotel	Swallow	59%	£95	H	(0434) 681611	50	60	36		yes
Cornhill-on-Tweed	Tillmouth Park		68%	£86	H	(0890) 882255	13				
Hexham	Beaumont Hotel		58%	£75	H	(0434) 602331	23	80	100		
Langley-on-Tyne	Langley Castle		65%	£70	H	(0434) 688888	8	180	130		
Longhorsley	Linden Hall		73%	£115	H	(0670) 516611	52	200	300		
Powburn	Breamish House		67%	£65	H	(066 578) 266	11				
Seahouses	Olde Ship Hotel			£64	I	(0665) 720200	15	40	40		

Nottinghamshire

Barnby Moor	Ye Olde Bell	Principal	60%	£80	H	(0777) 705121	55	250	200		

Location	Hotel	Group	%	Room Price	Cat	Tel	Rooms	Conf	Banq	Leisure Centre	Swim Pool	Golf
Blyth	Forte Travelodge	Forte		£42	L	(0909) 591775	32					
Blyth	Granada Lodge	Granada		£45	L	(0909) 591836	39					
Langar	Langar Hall		70%	£80	HR	(0949) 60559	11					
Newark	Forte Travelodge	Forte		£42	L	(0636) 703635	30					
Newark	Grange Hotel		58%	£53	H	(0636) 703399	15	20	24			
Nottingham	Forte Crest	Forte	70%	£92	H	(0602) 470131	130	600	496			
Nottingham	Forte Posthouse	Forte	61%	£68	H	(0602) 397800	91	70	50			
Nottingham	Holiday Inn Garden Court	Holiday Inns	65%	£70	H	(0602) 500600	100	40	20			
Nottingham	Moat House	QMH	59%	£88	H	(0602) 602621	172	180	160			
Nottingham	Novotel	Novotel	62%	£70	H	(0602) 720106	108	200	150			
Nottingham	Royal Moat House	QMH	70%	£101	H	(0602) 414444	201	600	500			
Nottingham	Rutland Square Hotel		72%	£72	H	(0602) 411114	104	200	140			
Nottingham	Stakis Victoria Hotel	Stakis	62%	£72	H	(0602) 419561	166	200	200			
Nottingham	Strathdon Thistle	MtCT	66%	£106	H	(0602) 418501	69	150	120			
Retford	Forte Travelodge	Forte		£42	L	(0777) 838091	40					
Southwell	Saracen's Head	Forte	62%	£80	H	(0636) 812701	27	120	120			
Worksop	Forte Travelodge	Forte		£42	L	(0909) 501528	40					

Oxfordshire

Location	Hotel	Group	%	Room Price	Cat	Tel	Rooms	Conf	Banq	Leisure Centre	Swim Pool	Golf
Abingdon	Abingdon Lodge	Four Pillars	61%	£80	H	(0235) 553456	63	180	120			
Abingdon	Upper Reaches	Forte	62%	£106	H	(0235) 522311	25	80	65			
Banbury	Moat House	QMH	62%	£79	H	(0295) 259361	48	70	80			
Banbury	Whately Hall	Forte	65%	£105	H	(0295) 263451	74	130	90			
Burford	Bay Tree	Select	67%	£105	H	(0993) 822791	22					
Burford	Lamb Inn			£75	IR	(0993) 823155	15					
Chadlington	The Manor		76%	£100	HR	(0608) 76711	7	10	10			
Charlbury	Bell Hotel			£75	I	(0608) 810278	14	55	55			

Chipping Norton	Crown & Cushion			£75	I	(0608) 642533	40	200	170	yes	yes
Clanfield	The Plough at Clanfield			£80	IR	(036 781) 222	6	8	12		
Dorchester-on-Thames	George Hotel			£75	I	(0865) 340404	18	40	40		
Frilford Heath	Dog House Hotel			£63	I	(0865) 390830	19	25	115		
Great Milton	Le Manoir aux Quat'Saisons		85%	£184	HR	(0844) 278881	19	36	45		
Hailey	The Bird In Hand			£55	I	(0993) 868321	16				
Henley-on-Thames	Red Lion		62%	£111	H	(0491) 572161	26	75	30		
Horton-cum-Studley	Studley Priory		64%	£98	H	(0865) 351203	19	35	55		
Kingham	Mill House		66%	£100	H	(0608) 658188	24	30	60		
Middleton Stoney	Jersey Arms			£70	I	(0869) 89234	16	12	50		
Minster Lovell	Old Swan		67%	£90	HR	(0993) 774441	60	50	41		
Moulsford-on-Thames	Beetle & Wedge		69%	£95	HR	(0491) 651381	10	50	50		
North Stoke	Springs Hotel		70%	£100	H	(0491) 36687	37	50	36		
Oxford	Eastgate Hotel	Forte	61%	£123	H	(0865) 248244	43	100	80		
Oxford	Forte Travelodge	Forte		£42	L	(0867) 75705	24				
Oxford	Moat House	QMH	62%	£105	H	(0865) 59933	155	150	110	yes	yes
Oxford	Old Parsonage		70%	£125	H	(0865) 310210	30				
Oxford	Randolph Hotel	Forte	68%	£161	H	(0865) 247481	109	300	250		
Steeple Aston	Hopcrofts Holt Hotel	MtCT	63%	£80	H	(0869) 40259	88	150	250		
Thame	Spread Eagle		63%	£84	H	(0844) 213661	33	250	200		
Wallingford	George Hotel	MtCT	62%	£106	H	(0491) 836665	39	120	120		
Wallingford	Shillingford Bridge Hotel		58%	£70	H	(0867) 328567	42	80	150		
Wantage	Bear Hotel		58%	£58	H	(0235) 766366	34	80	60		
Weston-on-the-Green	Weston Manor	Hidden	61%	£100	H	(0869) 50621	37	50	65		
Witney	Witney Lodge		62%	£84	H	(0993) 779777	74	150	120		yes
Woodstock	Bear Hotel	Forte	66%	£120	HR	(0993) 811511	45	150	80		
Woodstock	Feathers Hotel		73%	£105	HR	(0993) 812291	17	35	60		
Wroxton St Mary	Wroxton House Hotel		66%	£98	H	(0295) 730482	32	60	50		

Shropshire

All Stretton	Stretton Hall Hotel		59%	£54	H	(0694) 723224	13	20			

Location	Hotel	Group	%	Room Price	Cat	Tel	Rooms	Conf	Banq	Leisure Centre	Swim Pool	Golf
Alveley	Mill Hotel		66%	£73	H	(0746) 780437	21	200	250			
Ludlow	Dinham Hall		66%	£90	H	(0584) 876464	13	30	30			
Ludlow	Feathers Hotel		69%	£104	H	(0584) 875261	40	80	80			
Ludlow	Forte Travelodge	Forte		£42	L	(0584) 72695	32					
Market Drayton	Corbet Arms			£55	I	(0630) 652037	11	140	140			
Market Drayton	Goldstone Hall		60%	£75	H	(0630) 86202	8	90	70			
Oswestry	Forte Travelodge	Forte		£42	L	(0691) 658178	40					
Oswestry	Wynnstay Hotel		68%	£83	H	(0691) 655261	27	200	110			
Shifnal	Park House	Rank	71%	£85	H	(0952) 460128	54	250	250		yes	
Shrewsbury	Lion Hotel	Forte	62%	£92	H	(0743) 353107	59	200	140			
Shrewsbury	Prince Rupert Hotel	QMH	64%	£85	H	(0743) 236000	65	110	90			
Telford	Forte Travelodge	Forte		£42	L	(0952) 251244	40					
Telford	Holiday Inn Telford/Ironbridge	Holiday Inns	68%	£108	H	(0952) 292500	100	240	180		yes	
Telford	Madeley Court		67%	£90	H	(0952) 680068	47	200	200			
Telford	Moat House	QMH	67%	£95	H	(0952) 291291	148	400	350	yes	yes	
Telford	Telford Hotel		64%	£89	H	(0952) 585642	86	300	220	yes	yes	yes
Weston-under-Redcastle	Hawkstone Park		61%	£75	H	(0939) 200611	59	200	180			yes
Worfield	Old Vicarage		67%	£85	HR	(074 64) 497	14	30	30			

Somerset

Location	Hotel	Group	%	Room Price	Cat	Tel	Rooms	Conf	Banq	Leisure Centre	Swim Pool	Golf
Axbridge	Oak House			£51	I	(0934) 732444	10					
Castle Cary	Bond's		63%	£60	HR	(0963) 350464	7					
Dulverton	Ashwick House		68%	£78	HR	(0398) 23868	6					
Dulverton	Carnarvon Arms		60%	£90	H	(0398) 23302	25	120	80			
Dunster	Luttrell Arms	Forte	64%	£107	H	(0643) 821555	27					
Hatch Beauchamp	Farthings Hotel		70%	£94	H	(0823) 480664	6					
Ilminster	Forte Travelodge	Forte		£42	L	(0460) 53748	32					

Kilve	Meadow House		70%	£80	H	(0278) 741546	10	24	20		
Lympsham	Batch Farm Country Hotel		56%	£56	H	(0934) 750371	8	70	80		
Middlecombe	Periton Park		66%	£88	H	(0643) 706885	8	24	20		
Montacute	King's Arms Inn			£64	I	(0935) 822513	11				
North Petherton	Walnut Tree Inn		65%	£68	H	(0278) 662255	28	90	65		
Podimore	Forte Travelodge	Forte		£42	L	(0935) 840074	31				
Porlock	Oaks Hotel		65%	£75	HR	(0643) 862265	10				
Seavington St Mary	The Pheasant		69%	£70	H	(0460) 40502	10		40		
Simonsbath	Simonsbath House		64%	£90	H	(0643) 83259	7				
Somerton	Lynch Country House Hotel		69%	£45	H	(0458) 72316	6				
Street	Bear Hotel		63%	£60	H	(0458) 42021	17	80	110		
Taunton	Castle Hotel		76%	£102	HR	(0823) 272671	35	90	90		
Taunton	County Hotel	Forte	61%	£97	H	(0823) 337651	66	400	350		
Taunton	Forte Posthouse	Forte	66%	£68	H	(0823) 332222	97	200	170		
Taunton	Travel Inn	Travel Inns		£43	L	(0823) 321112	40				
Winsford	Royal Oak Inn			£90	I	(0643) 85455	14				
Wiveliscombe	Langley House		66%	£95	HR	(0984) 23318	8	24	18		
Yeovil	The Manor	Forte	63%	£97	H	(0935) 231161	41	60	70		

Staffordshire

Barton-under-Needwood	Forte Travelodge (N)	Forte		£42	L	(0283) 716343	20				
Barton-under-Needwood	Forte Travelodge (S)	Forte		£42	L	(0283) 716784	40				
Burton-on-Trent	Dovecliffe Hall		68%	£85	H	(0283) 31818	7				
Burton-on-Trent	Riverside Inn			£68	I	(0283) 511234	22	150	150		
Cannock	Travel Inn	Travel Inns		£43	L	(0543) 572721	38				
Eccleshall	St George Hotel			£55	I	(0785) 850300	10				
Hanchurch	Hanchurch Manor		74%	£75	H	(0782) 643030	9	12			
Lichfield	George Hotel	Jarvis	59%	£90	H	(0543) 414822	38	100	100		
Newcastle-under-Lyme	Clayton Lodge	Jarvis	60%	£84	H	(0782) 613093	50	240	200		
Newcastle-under-Lyme	Forte Posthouse	Forte	60%	£68	H	(0782) 717171	119	70	100	yes	yes
Rolleston-on-Dove	Brookhouse Hotel		62%	£85	H	(0283) 814188	19	14			

Location	Hotel	Group	%	Room Price	Cat	Tel	Rooms	Conf	Banq	Leisure Centre	Swim Pool	Golf
Rugeley	Forte Travelodge	Forte		£42	L	(0889) 570096	32					
Stafford	Tillington Hall	De Vere	63%	£80	H	(0785) 53531	90	200	174	yes	yes	
Stoke-on-Trent	Haydon House Hotel		65%	£62	H	(0782) 711311	30	80	80			
Stoke-on-Trent	North Stafford Hotel	Principal	61%	£90	H	(0782) 744477	69	450	475			
Stoke-on-Trent	Stakis Grand Hotel	Stakis	68%	£96	H	(0782) 202361	128	300	250	yes	yes	
Stoke-on-Trent	Stoke-on-Trent Moat House	QMH	70%	£99	H	(0782) 219000	147	550	500	yes	yes	
Swinfen	Swinfen Hall		70%	£85	H	(0543) 481494	19	200	150			
Tamworth	Granada Lodge	Granada		£45	L	(0827) 260123	63					
Tutbury	Ye Olde Dog & Partridge Inn			£70	I	(0283) 813030	17					
Uttoxeter	Forte Travelodge	Forte		£42	L	(0889) 562043	32					
Uttoxeter	White Hart			£54	I	(0889) 562437	26	40	50			

Suffolk

Location	Hotel	Group	%	Room Price	Cat	Tel	Rooms	Conf	Banq	Leisure Centre	Swim Pool	Golf
Aldeburgh	Brudenell Hotel	Forte	60%	£107	H	(0728) 452071	47	50	80			
Aldeburgh	Uplands		60%	£59	H	(0728) 452420	20					
Aldeburgh	Wentworth Hotel		68%	£80	H	(0728) 452312	31					
Barton Mills	Forte Travelodge	Forte		£42	L	(0638) 717675	32					
Beccles	Waveney House		59%	£60	H	(0502) 712270	13	100	120			
Brome	Oaksmere		67%	£80	H	(0379) 870326	11	40	70			
Bury St Edmunds	Angel Hotel		70%	£99	H	(0284) 753926	42	150	120			
Bury St Edmunds	Butterfly Hotel		62%	£61	H	(0284) 760884	66	50	30			
Bury St Edmunds	Suffolk Hotel	Forte	59%	£93	H	(0284) 753995	33	35	35			
Copdock	Ipswich Moat House	QMH	64%	£68	H	(0473) 730444	74	500	400	yes	yes	
Felixstowe	Orwell Moat House	QMH	69%	£85	H	(0394) 285511	58	200	180			
Framlingham	The Crown	Forte	62%	£103	H	(0728) 723521	14					
Hintlesham	Hintlesham Hall		82%	£110	HR	(0473) 652334	33	80	80		yes	yes
Ipswich	Belstead Brook Hotel		68%	£67	H	(0473) 684241	92	70	60			

Ipswich	Forte Posthouse	Forte	63%	£68	H	(0473) 690313	112	120	90			
Ipswich	Marlborough Hotel		65%	£75	H	(0473) 257677	22		74			
Ipswich	Novotel	Novotel	61%	£78	H	(0473) 232400	101	200	180			
Lavenham	The Swan	Forte	71%	£120	HR	(0787) 247477	47					
Long Melford	Black Lion		65%	£65	H	(0787) 312356	9	16	120			
Long Melford	Bull Hotel	Forte	65%	£102	H	(0787) 378494	25	60	100			
Needham Market	Pipps Ford		60%	£59	H	(044 979) 208	6	20	30			
Newmarket	Moat House	QMH	62%	£78	H	(0638) 667171	47	150	100			
Newmarket	White Hart		60%	£49	H	(0638) 663051	23	120	200			
Southwold	The Crown			£63	IR	(0502) 722275	12					
Southwold	The Swan		65%	£88	HR	(0502) 722186	45	50	85			
Stowmarket	Forte Travelodge	Forte		£42	L	(0449) 615347	40					
Sudbury	Mill Hotel		58%	£89	H	(0787) 375544	50	80	80			
Woodbridge	Seckford Hall		68%	£90	H	(0394) 385678	35	100	100		yes	
Yoxford	Satis House		63%	£65	H	(072 877) 418	7					

Surrey

Bagshot	Pennyhill Park		75%	£134	H	(0276) 471774	76	60	80			
Bramley	Bramley Grange		64%	£105	H	(0483) 893434	46	80	120			
Camberley	Frimley Hall	Forte	68%	£122	H	(0276) 28321	66	60	130			
Chessington	Travel Inn	Travel Inns		£43	L	(0372) 744060	42					
Chiddingfold	Crown Inn			£57	I	(0428) 682255	8					
Churt	Frensham Pond Hotel		62%	£68	H	(0252) 795161	53	200	130	yes	yes	
Cobham	Hilton National	Hilton	65%	£110	H	(0932) 864471	152	300	250		yes	
Cobham	Woodlands Park	Select	69%	£147	H	(0372) 843933	58	300	270			
Croydon	Croydon Park		69%	£126	H	081-680 9200	214	300	200	yes	yes	
Croydon	Forte Posthouse	Forte	61%	£68	H	081-688 5185	83	170	170			
Croydon	Hilton National	Hilton	69%	£105	H	081-680 3000	168	300	250			
Croydon	Selsdon Park		68%	£120	H	081-657 8811	170	150	200	yes	yes	yes
Croydon	Travel Inn	Travel Inns		£43	L	081-686 2030	40					
Dorking	Forte Travelodge	Forte		£42	L	(0306) 740361	29					

Location	*Hotel*	*Group*	*%*	*Room Price*	*Cat*	*Tel*	*Rooms*	*Conf*	*Banq*	*Leisure Centre*	*Swim Pool*	*Golf*
Dorking	White Horse	Forte	62%	£80	H	(0306) 881138	68	60				
East Horsley	Thatchers Resort Hotel	Resort	63%	£100	H	(0483) 284291	59	100	100			
Egham	Great Fosters		67%	£99	H	(0784) 433822	45	100	220			
Egham	Runnymede Hotel		74%	£145	H	(0784) 436171	171	400	350		yes	
Farnham	Bishop's Table Hotel		62%	£81	H	(0252) 710222	18	30	55			
Farnham	Bush Hotel	Forte	62%	£103	H	(0252) 715237	66	60	90			
Farnham	Trevena House		59%	£59	H	(0252) 716908	20	14				
Godalming	Inn on the Lake			£75	H	(0483) 415575	20	120	100			
Guildford	The Angel		71%	£122	H	(0483) 64555	11	80	70			
Guildford	Forte Crest	Forte	68%	£108	H	(0483) 574444	111	200	150		yes	
Haslemere	Lythe Hill Hotel		67%	£110	H	(0428) 651251	40	60	130			
Horley, Gatwick Airport – *see under* **London Airports**												
Morden	Forte Travelodge	Forte		£42	L	081-640 8227	32					
Nutfield	Nutfield Priory	Hidden	70%	£110	H	(0737) 822066	52	60	110	yes	yes	
Reigate	Bridge House		61%	£83	H	(0737) 246801	37	40	200			
Richmond	Petersham Hotel		64%	£120	HR	081-940 7471	54	50	34			
Richmond	Richmond Gate Hotel		65%	£105	H	081-940 0061	64	70	50			
Seale	Hog's Back Hotel	Jarvis	64%	£108	H	(0252) 782345	89	140	120	yes	yes	
Sutton	Holiday Inn		70%	£129	H	081-770 1311	116	200	160	yes	yes	
Weybridge	Oatlands Park		69%	£128	H	(0932) 847242	117	300	220			
Weybridge	Ship Thistle	MtCT	63%	£116	H	(0932) 848364	39	140	130			

Sussex, East

Battle	Netherfield Place		78%	£90	HR	(042 46) 4455	14	50	40			
Boreham Street	White Friars Hotel		57%	£75	H	(0323) 832355	20	30	60			
Brighton	Bedford Hotel		66%	£128	H	(0273) 329744	129	450	350			

Brighton	Brighton Metropole		70%	£160	H	(0273) 775432	328	1800	*1200	yes	yes	
Brighton	Grand Hotel	De Vere	74%	£160	H	(0273) 321188	200	820	600	yes	yes	
Brighton	Hospitality Inn	MtCT	77%	£155	HR	(0273) 206700	204	300	250		yes	
Brighton	Old Ship Hotel		65%	£105	H	(0273) 329001	152	350	250			
Brighton	Topps Hotel		69%	£79	HR	(0273) 729334	14					
Brighton (Hove)	Sackville Hotel		61%	£75	H	(0273) 736292	45	100	70			
Brigthon (Hove)	Whitehaven Hotel		56%	£70	H	(0273) 778355	17					
Cooden	Cooden Resort Hotel	Resort	60%	£75	H	(0424) 842281	41	200	150	yes	yes	
Eastbourne	Cavendish Hotel	De Vere	68%	£70	H	(0323) 410222	112	150	350			
Eastbourne	Grand Hotel	De Vere	75%	£150	HR	(0323) 412345	164	350	400	yes	yes	
Eastbourne	Queen's Hotel	De Vere	67%	£80	H	(0323) 22822	108	300	230			
Eastbourne	Wish Tower Hotel	Principal	66%	£80	H	(0323) 722676	65	60	120			
Hailsham	Forte Travelodge	Forte		£42	L	(0323) 844556	40					
Hastings	Cinque Ports Hotel		66%	£73	H	(0424) 439222	40	320	275			
Hastings	Royal Victoria Hotel	Resort	70%	£75	H	(0424) 445544	52	120	120			
Lewes	Shelleys Hotel	MtCT	60%	£118	H	(0273) 472361	21	50	40			
Rye	George Hotel	Forte	62%	£97	H	(0797) 222114	22	80	100			
Rye	Mermaid Inn		60%	£98	H	(0797) 223065	30	90	80			
Sedlescombe	Brickwall Hotel		56%	£54	H	(0424) 870253	23					
Uckfield	Horsted Place		79%	£140	HR	(0825) 750581	17	60	22		yes	yes
Wadhurst	Spindlewood		60%	£83	HR	(0580) 200430	9	20	60			

Sussex, West

Amberley	Amberley Castle		81%	£130	HR	(0798) 831992	14	40	48			
Arundel	Norfolk Arms		60%	£70	H	(0903) 882101	34	100	100			
Ashington	Mill House Hotel			£74	I	(0903) 892426	10	40				
Billingshurst	Forte Travelodge	Forte		£42	L	(0403) 782711	26					
Bognor Regis	Royal Norfolk	Forte	60%	£70	H	(0243) 826222	51	65	65			
Bosham	Millstream Hotel		63%	£99	H	(0243) 573234	29	35	23			
Chichester	Dolphin & Anchor	Forte	63%	£102	H	(0243) 785121	49	180	180			

Location	Hotel	Group	%	Room Price	Cat	Tel	Rooms	Conf	Banq	Leisure Centre	Swim Pool	Golf
Climping	Bailiffscourt		69%	£125	H	(0903) 723511	20	36	80			
Crawley	George Hotel	Forte	64%	£76	H	(0293) 524215	86	40	30			
Cuckfield	Ockenden Manor		71%	£98	H	(0444) 416111	22	50	75			
East Grinstead	Gravetye Manor		84%	£200	HR	(0342) 810567	18	15	18			
East Grinstead	Woodbury House		67%	£65	H	(0342) 313657	14		20			
Findon	Findon Manor		61%	£60	H	(0903) 872733	10	40	26			
Fontwell	Forte Travelodge	Forte		£42	L	(0243) 543972	32					
Gatwick Airport – *see under* **London Airports**												
Goodwood	Goodwood Park	Country Club	67%	£94	H	(0243) 775537	89	120	120	yes	yes	
Horsham	Travel Inn	Travel Inns		£43	L	(0403) 50141	40					
Lower Beeding	Cisswood House		67%	£97	HR	(0403) 891216	34	150	130		yes	
Lower Beeding	South Lodge		76%	£130	HR	(0403) 891711	39	80	80			
Midhurst	Angel Hotel			£55	IR	(0730) 812421	17	70	90			
Midhurst	Spread Eagle		69%	£78	H	(0730) 816911	41	50	100			
Pulborough	Chequers Hotel		61%	£69	H	(0798) 872486	11	20	20			
Rusper	Ghyll Manor	Forte	68%	£80	H	(0293) 871571	22	100	80			
Storrington	Abingworth Hall		71%	£96	HR	(0798) 813636	20	50	55			
Storrington	Little Thakeham		78%	£150	HR	(0903) 744416	9		80			
Turners Hill	Alexander House		79%	£185	HR	(0342) 714914	14	50	55			
Walberton	Avisford Park		66%	£106	H	(0243) 551215	126	250	300	yes	yes	
West Chiltington	Roundabout Hotel		61%	£80	H	(0798) 813838	24	30	55			
Worthing	Beach Hotel		64%	£82	H	(0903) 234001	82	70	200			
Worthing	Chatsworth Hotel		57%	£77	H	(0903) 236103	105	150	140			

Tyne & Wear

Location	Hotel	Group	%	Room Price	Cat	Tel	Rooms	Conf	Banq	Leisure Centre	Swim Pool	Golf
Gateshead	Forte Travelodge	Forte		£42	L	(0748) 3768	41					
Gateshead	Newcastle Marriott Hotel	Marriott	70%	£129	H	091-493 2233	150	500	300		yes	

Gateshead	Springfield Hotel	Jarvis	63%	£88	H	091-477 4121	60		100			
Gateshead	Swallow Hotel	Swallow	60%	£88	H	091-477 1105	103	350	350	yes	yes	
Newcastle-upon-Tyne	Copthorne Hotel	Copthorne	73%	£116	H	091-222 0333	156				yes	
Newcastle-upon-Tyne	County Thistle	MtCT	68%	£105	H	091-232 2471	115	130	200			
Newcastle-upon-Tyne	Forte Crest	Forte	61%	£93	H	091-232 6191	166	400	350			
Newcastle-upon-Tyne	Holiday Inn	Holiday Inns	70%	£121	H	091-236 5432	150	400	280	yes	yes	
Newcastle-upon-Tyne	Moat House	QMH	59%	£68	H	091-262 8989	147	400	300	yes		
Newcastle-upon-Tyne	Novotel	Novotel	63%	£81	H	091-214 0303	126	200	160		yes	
Newcastle-upon-Tyne	Swallow Gosforth Park	Swallow	73%	£120	H	091-236 4111	178	600	500		yes	
Newcastle-upon-Tyne	Swallow Hotel	Swallow	63%	£88	H	091-232 5025	93	100	85			
Newcastle-upon-Tyne Airport	Moat House	QMH	62%	£79	H	(0661) 24911	100	400	350			
Sunderland	Swallow Hotel	Swallow	70%	£95	H	091-529 2041	65			yes	yes	
Washington	Campanile Hotel	Campanile		£44	L	091-416 5010	77					
Washington	Forte Posthouse	Forte	59%	£68	H	091-416 2264	138	120	100			
Washington	Granada Lodge	Granada		£45	L	091-410 0076	35					
Washington	Moat House	QMH	66%	£93	H	091-417 2626	106	200	180		yes	yes

Warwickshire

Alcester	Arrow Mill			£72	I	(0789) 762419	18	100	100			
Ansty	Ansty Hall	Hidden	71%	£108	H	(0203) 612222	31	70	80			
Barford	Glebe Hotel		68%	£105	H	(0926) 624218	41	150	120	yes	yes	
Bodymoor Heath	Marston Farm		65%	£80	H	(0827) 872133	37	45	95			
Brandon	Brandon Hall	Forte	65%	£107	H	(0203) 542571	60	100	120			
Charlecote	Charlecote Pheasant	QMH	62%	£85	H	(0789) 470333	67	120	140			
Hockley Heath	Nuthurst Grange		74%	£117	HR	(0564) 783972	15	80	95			
Kenilworth	Clarendon House		60%	£77	H	(0926) 57668	31	200	130			
Kenilworth	De Montfort Hotel	De Vere	63%	£100	H	(0926) 55944	96	350	200			
Leamington Spa	Courtyard by Marriott	Marriott	65%	£70	H	(0926) 425522	97	50	35			
Leamington Spa	Inchfield Hotel		63%	£78	H	(0926) 883777	22	35	60			
Leamington Spa	Mallory Court		80%	£162	HR	(0926) 330214	10		50			
Leamington Spa	Regent Hotel		68%	£89	HR	(0926) 427231	80	100	250			

Location	*Hotel*	*Group*	*%*	*Room Price*	*Cat*	*Tel*	*Rooms*	*Conf*	*Banq*	*Leisure Centre*	*Swim Pool*	*Golf*
Nuneaton	Forte Travelodge	Forte		£42	L	(0203) 382541	40					
Nuneaton	Travel Inn	Travel Inns		£43	L	(0203) 343584	30					
Stratford-upon-Avon	Alveston Manor	Forte	65%	£115	H	(0789) 204581	108	180	120			
Stratford-upon-Avon	Billesley Manor	QMH	76%	£135	HR	(0789) 400888	41	100	100		yes	
Stratford-upon-Avon	Dukes Hotel		65%	£65	H	(0789) 269300	22					
Stratford-upon-Avon	Ettington Park		76%	£140	H	(0789) 450123	48	65	48		yes	
Stratford-upon-Avon	Falcon Hotel	QMH	63%	£94	H	(0789) 205777	73	200	180			
Stratford-upon-Avon	Forte Posthouse	Forte	59%	£68	H	(0789) 266761	60	120	100			
Stratford-upon-Avon	Moat House International	QMH	71%	£125	H	(0789) 414411	247	450	450	yes	yes	
Stratford-upon-Avon	Shakespeare Hotel	Forte	69%	£127	H	(0789) 294771	63	120	100			
Stratford-upon-Avon	Stratford House		62%	£82	H	(0789) 268288	11					
Stratford-upon-Avon	Welcombe Hotel		74%	£140	H	(0789) 295252	76	120	180			yes
Stratford-upon-Avon	White Swan	Forte	62%	£112	H	(0789) 297022	37	40	20			
Stratford-upon-Avon	Windmill Park		64%	£98	H	(0789) 731173	100	350	300	yes	yes	
Warwick	Hilton National	Hilton	66%	£140	H	(0926) 499555	181	500	350		yes	
Wishaw	The Belfry	De Vere	73%	£110	H	(0675) 470301	219	300	300	yes	yes	yes

West Midlands

Aldridge	Fairlawns		62%	£78	H	(0922) 55122	35	80	80			
Birmingham	Birmingham Metropole		72%	£190	H	021-780 4242	802	2000	1440			
Birmingham	Campanile Hotel	Campanile		£44	L	021-622 4925	50					
Birmingham	Copthorne Hotel	Copthorne	70%	£127	H	021-200 2727	212	200	150	yes	yes	
Birmingham	Forte Crest	Forte	68%	£97	H	021-643 8171	253	630	560		yes	
Birmingham	Forte Posthouse	Forte	60%	£68	H	021-357 7444	192	150	150	yes	yes	
Birmingham	Granada Lodge	Granada		£45	L	021-550 3261	60					
Birmingham	Holiday Inn	Holiday Inns	70%	£124	H	021-631 2000	288	160	200	yes	yes	
Birmingham	Hyatt Regency		77%	£162	HR	021-643 1234	319	240	200	yes	yes	

Birmingham	Midland Hotel		67%	£99	H	021-643 2601	111	200	170			
Birmingham	Norton Place		75%	£115	HR	021-433-5656	10	150	120			
Birmingham	Novotel	Novotel	61%	£100	H	021-643 2000	148	300	180			
Birmingham	Plough & Harrow	Forte	59%	£107	H	021-454 4111	44	70	80			
Birmingham	Royal Angus Thistle	MtCT	65%	£102	H	021-236 4211	133	180	180			
Birmingham	Strathallan Thistle	MtCT	63%	£103	H	021-455 9777	167	200	170			
Birmingham	Swallow Hotel	Swallow	77%	£120	HR	021-452 1144	98	28	21		yes	
Birmingham Airport	Forte Posthouse	Forte	61%	£68	H	021-782 8141	136	150	130			
Birmingham Airport	Novotel	Novotel	65%	£92	H	021-782 7000	195	40	30			
Brierley Hill	Copthorne Hotel	Copthorne	71%	£118	H	(0384) 482882	138	200	150	yes	yes	
Coventry	Chace Hotel		61%	£98	H	(0203) 303398	67	120	90			
Coventry	De Vere Hotel	De Vere	69%	£85	H	(0203) 633733	190	450	400			
Coventry	Forte Crest	Forte	66%	£98	H	(0203) 613261	147	450	450	yes	yes	
Coventry	Forte Posthouse	Forte	60%	£68	H	(0203) 402151	184	120	150			
Coventry	Novotel	Novotel	62%	£78	H	(0203) 365000	100	200	100			
Coventry (North)	Campanile Hotel	Campanile		£44	L	(0203) 622311	50					
Coventry (South)	Campanile Hotel	Campanile		£44	L	(0203) 639922	50					
Dudley	Forte Travelodge	Forte		£42	L	(0384) 481579	32					
Dunchurch	Forte Travelodge	Forte		£42	L	(0788) 521528	40					
Hagley	Travel Inn	Travel Inns		£43	L	(0562) 883120	40					
Meriden	Forest of Arden Hotel	Country Club	70%	£110	H	(0676) 22335	152	180	200	yes	yes	yes
Meriden	Manor Hotel	De Vere	64%	£85	H	(0676) 22735	74	275	275			
Oldbury	Forte Travelodge	Forte		£42	L	021-552 2967	33					
Solihull	George Hotel	Jarvis	66%	£116	H	021-711 2121	130	200	180			
Solihull	Moat House	QMH	69%	£108	H	021-711 4700	115	200	200	yes	yes	
Solihull	Regency Hotel		64%	£90	H	021-745 6119	112	180	180			
Solihull	St John's Swallow Hotel	Swallow	63%	£97	H	021-711 3000	177	800	650	yes	yes	
Solihull	Travel Inn	Travel Inns		£43	L	021-744 2942	40					
Stourbridge	Talbot Hotel		59%	£50	H	(0384) 394350	25	650	120			
Sutton Coldfield	Forte Travelodge	Forte		£42	L	021-355 0017	32					
Sutton Coldfield	Moor Hall		62%	£90	H	021-308 3751	75	200	250		yes	
Sutton Coldfield	New Hall	MtCT	78%	£129	HR	021-378 2442	60	50	40			
Sutton Coldfield	Penns Hall	Jarvis	66%	£132	H	021-351 3111	114	700	600	yes	yes	

Location	*Hotel*	*Group*	*%*	*Room Price*	*Cat*	*Tel*	*Rooms*	*Conf*	*Banq*	*Leisure Centre*	*Swim Pool*	*Golf*
Walsall	Forte Posthouse	Forte	61%	£68	H	(0922) 33555	98	45	25			
Walsall Wood	Baron's Court Hotel		62%	£55	H	(0543) 452020	100	110	90	yes	yes	
West Bromwich	Moat House	QMH	59%	£89	H	021-553 6111	172	180	140			
Wolverhampton	Goldthorn Hotel		62%	£65	H	(0902) 29216	93	130	112			
Wolverhampton	Mount Hotel	Jarvis	60%	£102	H	(0902) 752055	56	200	160			
Wolverhampton	Victoria Hotel Periquito	Park Hotels	67%	£73	H	(0902) 29922	117	200	150			

Wiltshire

Location	*Hotel*	*Group*	*%*	*Room Price*	*Cat*	*Tel*	*Rooms*	*Conf*	*Banq*	*Leisure Centre*	*Swim Pool*	*Golf*
Amesbury	Forte Travelodge	Forte		£42	L	(0980) 624966	32					
Beanacre	Beechfield House	Hidden	70%	£80	H	(0225) 703700	24	50	50			
Bradford-on-Avon	Woolley Grange		75%	£130	HR	(0225) 864705	20	40	40			
Castle Combe	Manor House		79%	£135	HR	(0249) 782206	36					
Chippenham	Granada Lodge	Granada		£45	L	(0666) 837097	35					
Chiseldon	Chiseldon House		67%	£85	HR	(0793) 741010	21		20		yes	
Colerne	Lucknam Park		83%	£150	HR	(0225) 742777	42	60	100	yes	yes	
Corsham	Methuen Arms			£65	I	(0249) 714867	25	20	120			
Corsham	Rudloe Park		64%	£80	H	(0225) 810555	11	80	80			
Easton Grey	Whatley Manor		73%	£112	H	(0666) 822888	29	65	80			
Lacock	At The Sign of The Angel			£75	IR	(0249) 730230	10					
Malmesbury	Old Bell Hotel	Clipper	64%	£98	H	(0666) 822344	37	30	90			
Marlborough	Ivy House		61%	£55	H	(0672) 515333	32	70	70			
Melksham	King's Arms Hotel			£59	I	(0225) 707272	14	50	50			
Mere	Old Ship Hotel			£52	I	(0747) 860258	23	30	70			
Purton	Pear Tree		74%	£92	HR	(0793) 772100	18	60	50			
Salisbury	Rose & Crown	QMH	56%	£98	H	(0722) 327908	28	95	60			
Salisbury	White Hart	Forte	63%	£106	H	(0722) 327476	68	80	62			
Stanton St Quintin	Stanton Manor		64%	£82	HR	(0666) 837552	10	30	60			

Swindon	Blunsdon House		69%	£93	H	(0793) 721701	88	300	250	yes	yes
Swindon	De Vere Hotel	De Vere	69%	£100	H	(0793) 878785	154			yes	yes
Swindon	Forte Posthouse	Forte	63%	£68	H	(0793) 524601	100	80	60	yes	yes
Swindon	Forte Crest	Forte	62%	£100	H	(0793) 831333	91	80	80		
Swindon	Swindon Marriott Hotel	Marriott	71%	£123	H	(0793) 512121	153	280	200	yes	yes
Swindon	Wiltshire Hotel	MtCT	62%	£100	H	(0793) 528282	95	230	200		
Teffont Evias	Howard's House		68%	£90	HR	(0722) 716392	8				
Warminster	Bishopstrow House		79%	£123	HR	(0985) 212312	32	60	60		yes
Warminster	Granada Lodge	Granada		£45	L	(0985) 219639	31				

Yorkshire, North

Bainbridge	Rose & Crown Inn			£64	I	(0969) 50225	12	75	100		
Bilbrough	Bilbrough Manor		75%	£105	HR	(0937) 834002	12	20	15		
Bolton Abbey	Devonshire Arms		73%	£110	H	(0756) 710441	40	150	120		
Boroughbridge	The Crown		63%	£50	H	(0423) 322328	42	200	140		
Goathland	Mallyan Spout		61%	£60	H	(0947) 86206	24	70			
Great Ayton	Ayton Hall		73%	£85	H	(0642) 723595	11	30	60		
Hackness	Hackness Grange		61%	£118	H	(0723) 882345	28	20	80		yes
Harome	Pheasant Hotel		68%	£110	H	(0439) 71241	18				yes
Harrogate	The Crown	Forte	67%	£98	H	(0423) 567755	121	450	300		
Harrogate	Hospitality Inn	MtCT	61%	£98	H	(0423) 564601	71	150	100		
Harrogate	Imperial Hotel	Principal	65%	£95	H	(0423) 565071	85	200	200		
Harrogate	Majestic Hotel	Forte	64%	£114	H	(0423) 568972	156	450	700	yes	yes
Harrogate	Moat House	QMH	64%	£125	H	(0423) 500000	214	400	250		
Harrogate	Old Swan Hotel		69%	£128	HR	(0423) 500055	135	500	600		
Harrogate	Hotel St George	Swallow	63%	£105	H	(0423) 561431	93	300	180	yes	yes
Harrogate	Studley Hotel		66%	£90	H	(0423) 560425	36				
Helmsley	Black Swan	Forte	69%	£111	H	(0439) 70466	44	40	30		
Helmsley	Feversham Arms		66%	£70	H	(0439) 70766	18	30	24		
Jervaulx	Jervaulx Hall		70%	£130	H	(0677) 60235	10				
Knaresborough	Dower House		63%	£66	H	(0423) 863302	32	60	110		yes

Location	*Hotel*	*Group*	*%*	*Room Price*	*Cat*	*Tel*	*Rooms*	*Conf*	*Banq*	*Leisure Centre*	*Swim Pool*	*Golf*
Markington	Hob Green		70%	£80	H	(0423) 770031	12	12				
Monk Fryston	Monk Fryston Hall		65%	£90	H	(0977) 682369	28	40	80			
Newby Wiske	Solberge Hall		69%	£60	H	(0609) 779191	25	110	100			
Nidd	Nidd Hall		77%	£120	H	(0423) 771598	59	250	150		yes	
Reeth	Burgoyne Hotel		65%	£60	H	(0748) 84292	8					
Ripon	Ripon Spa Hotel		62%	£70	H	(0765) 602172	40	250	180			
Rosedale Abbey	Milburn Arms		60%	£70	H	(075 15) 312	11		65			
Scalby	Wrea Head		65%	£90	H	(0723) 378211	21	60	60			
Scarborough	The Crown	Forte	63%	£97	H	(0723) 373491	78	200	100			
Scotch Corner	Forte Travelodge	Forte		£42	L	(0748) 3768	40					
Skipton	Forte Travelodge	Forte		£42	L	(0756) 798091	32					
Skipton	Randell's Hotel		65%	£78	H	(0756) 700100	61	400	350		yes	
South Milford	Forte Posthouse Leeds/Selby		65%	£68	H	(0977) 682711	105	120	100		yes	
Staddle Bridge	McCoy's		70%	£99	HR	(060 982) 671	6	25	25			
Stokesley	Chapters		65%	£59	HR	(0642) 711888	13	54	54			
York	Abbey Park Resort Hotel	Resort	57%	£75	H	(0904) 658301	85	140	120			
York	Dean Court		63%	£95	H	(0904) 625082	42	30	30			
York	Forte Travelodge	Forte		£42	L	(0973) 531823	40					
York	Forte Posthouse	Forte	65%	£68	H	(0904) 707921	139	120	65			
York	Grange Hotel		74%	£98	HR	(0904) 644744	29	45	60			
York	Judges Lodging		64%	£110	H	(0904) 638733	13	25	28			
York	Middlethorpe Hall		79%	£149	HR	(0904) 641241	30	68	68			
York	Mount Royale		68%	£75	H	(0904) 628856	23	20				
York	Novotel	Novotel	62%	£85	H	(0904) 611660	124	210	150		yes	
York	Royal York Hotel	Principal	65%	£100	H	(0904) 653681	145	180	260			
York	Stakis York	Stakis	68%	£130	H	(0904) 648111	128	150	140			
York	Swallow Hotel	Swallow	64%	£105	H	(0904) 701000	113	180	120	yes	yes	
York	Viking Hotel	QMH	69%	£113	H	(0904) 659822	188	300	300			

Yorkshire, South

Barnsley	Ardsley Moat House	QMH	65%	£60	H	(0226) 289401	73	300	300		
Barnsley	Forte Travelodge	Forte		£42	L	(0226) 298799	32				
Bawtry	The Crown	Forte	64%	£88	H	(0302) 710341	57				
Carcroft	Forte Travelodge	Forte		£42	L	(0302) 330841	40				
Dinnington	Dinnington Hall		65%	£45	H	(0909) 569661	10	60	60		
Doncaster	Campanile Hotel	Campanile		£44	L	(0302) 370770	50				
Doncaster	Danum Swallow Hotel	Swallow	64%	£86	H	(0302) 342261	66	300	300		
Doncaster	Grand St Leger		64%	£80	H	(0302) 364111	20	70	70		
Doncaster	Moat House	QMH	68%	£88	H	(0302) 310331	100	400	350	yes	yes
Rotherham	Campanile Hotel	Campanile		£44	L	(0709) 700255	50				
Rotherham	Moat House	QMH	69%	£68	H	(0709) 364902	83	280	200		
Rotherham	Travel Inn	Travel Inns		£43	L	(0709) 543216	37				
Sheffield	Charnwood Hotel		67%	£90	H	(0742) 589411	21	100	80		
Sheffield	Forte Crest	Forte	65%	£93	H	(0742) 670067	136	300	210	yes	yes
Sheffield	Grosvenor House	Forte	67%	£77	H	(0742) 720041	103	500	40		
Sheffield	Holiday Inn Royal Victoria	Holiday Inns	67%	£107	H	(0742) 768822	100	300	300		
Sheffield	Moat House	QMH	71%	£100	H	(0742) 375376	95	500	400	yes	yes
Sheffield	St George Swallow Hotel	Swallow	64%	£96	H	(0742) 583811	141	250	250		yes

Yorkshire, West

Bingley	Bankfield Hotel	Jarvis	61%	£105	H	(0274) 567123	103	300	250		
Bradford	*Novotel	Novotel	60%	£70	H	(0274) 683683	132	250	200		
Bradford	Stakis Norfolk Gardens	Stakis	65%	£106	H	(0274) 734734	120	700	700		
Bradford	Victoria Hotel	Forte	61%	£77	H	(0274) 728706	59	150	200		
Bramhope	Forte Crest	Forte	66%	£98	H	(0532) 842911	126	160	120	yes	yes
Bramhope	Parkway Hotel	Jarvis	63%	£122	H	(0532) 672551	103	250	300		yes
Brighouse	Forte Crest	Forte	68%	£98	H	(0484) 400400	94			yes	yes
Ferrybridge	Granada Lodge	Granada		£45	L	(0977) 670488	35				
Garforth	Hilton National	Hilton	61%	£94	H	(0532) 866556	144	350	300	yes	yes

Location	Hotel	Group	%	Room Price	Cat	Tel	Rooms	Conf	Banq	Leisure Centre	Swim Pool	Golf
Halifax	Holdsworth House		69%	£87	H	(0422) 240024	40	100	100			
Hartshead Moor	Forte Travelodge	Forte		£42	L	(0274) 851706	40					
Huddersfield	George Hotel	Principal	62%	£85	H	(0484) 515444	60	200	260			
Huddersfield	Pennine Hilton National	Hilton	66%	£95	H	(0422) 375431	118	400	330	yes	yes	
Ilkley	Rombalds Hotel		60%	£100	HR	(0943) 603201	15	80	50			
Leeds	42 The Calls			£120	PH	(0532) 440099	39	55				
Leeds	Haley's Hotel		74%	£112	HR	(0532) 784446	22	30	25			
Leeds	Hilton International	Hilton	69%	£105	H	(0532) 442000	206	400	290			
Leeds	Holiday Inn Crowne Plaza	Holiday Inns	71%	£150	H	(0532) 442200	125	200	150	yes	yes	
Leeds	Merrion Thistle Hotel	MtCT	65%	£101	H	(0532) 439191	109	80	70			
Leeds	Queen's Hotel	Forte	70%	£119	H	(0532) 431323	190	700	650			
Linton	Wood Hall		80%	£89	HR	(0937) 587271	44	140	110		yes	
Otley	Chevin Lodge		64%	£87	H	(0943) 467818	52	130	130			
Wakefield	Campanile Hotel	Campanile		£44	L	(0924) 201054	77					
Wakefield	Cedar Court		59%	£90	H	(0924) 276310	151	400	400			
Wakefield	Forte Posthouse	Forte	64%	£68	H	(0924) 276388	99	150	120			
Wakefield	Granada Lodge	Granada		£45	L	(0924) 830569	31					
Wakefield	Swallow Hotel	Swallow	58%	£86	H	(0924) 372111	63	250	190			
Wentbridge	Forte Travelodge	Forte		£42	L	(0977) 620711	56					
Wentbridge	Wentbridge House	Select	63%	£75	H	(0977) 620444	12	120	120			

SCOTLAND

Swimming pool refers to indoor swimming pools only. See page 14 How to use this Guide for explanation of percentage rating system, room pricing and categories.

Key: QMH (Queens Moat Houses), MtCT (Mount Charlotte Thistle).

Borders

Location	*Hotel*	*Group*	*%*	*Room Price*	*Cat*	*Tel*	*Rooms*	*Conf*	*Banq*	*Leisure Centre*	*Swim Pool*	*Golf*
Dryburgh	Dryburgh Abbey		58%	£130	H	(0835) 22261	30	150	120			
Ettrickbridge	Ettrickshaws Hotel		62%	£76	H	(0750) 52229	6		24			
Kelso	Ednam House		64%	£72	H	(0573) 224168	32	200	200			
Kelso	Sunlaws House		72%	£128	H	(0573) 450331	22	25	20			
Melrose	Burts Hotel			£68	I	(089 682) 2285	21					yes
Melrose	George & Abbotsford Hotel		56%	£66	H	(089 682) 2308	30	160	140			
Peebles	Cringletie House		65%	£86	HR	(0721) 730233	13					
Peebles	Park Hotel		62%	£89	H	(0721) 720451	24	80	120			
Peebles	Peebles Hotel Hydro		70%	£103	H	(0721) 720602	137	400	350	yes	yes	
Peebles	Tontine Hotel	Forte	57%	£80	H	(0721) 720892	37	40	90			
Selkirk	Philipburn House		60%	£99	H	(0750) 20747	16	30	20			
Tweedsmuir	Crook Inn		59%	£52	H	(089 97) 272	7					

Central

Location	*Hotel*	*Group*	*%*	*Room Price*	*Cat*	*Tel*	*Rooms*	*Conf*	*Banq*	*Leisure Centre*	*Swim Pool*	*Golf*
Airth	Airth Castle		68%	£100	H	(0324) 831411	75	400	280		yes	
Alloa	Gean House		77%	£140	HR	(0259) 219275	10	80	50			
Bridge of Allan	Royal Hotel		59%	£66	H	(0786) 832284	32	150	120			

Location	Hotel	Group	%	Room Price	Cat	Tel	Rooms	Conf	Banq	Leisure Centre	Swim Pool	Golf
Drymen	Buchanan Highland Hotel		62%	£128	H	(0360) 60588	50	200	130		yes	
Dunblane	Cromlix House		82%	£160	HR	(0786) 822125	14	40	40			
Dunblane	Stakis Dunblane Hydro	Stakis	61%	£131	H	(0786) 822551	214	500	400	yes	yes	
Falkirk	Hotel Cladhan		60%	£82	H	(0324) 27421	37	200	200			
Stirling	Granada Lodge	Granada		£45	L	(0786) 815033	37					
Strathblane	Kirkhouse Inn			£72	I	(0360) 70621	15	25	50			

Dumfries & Galloway

Location	Hotel	Group	%	Room Price	Cat	Tel	Rooms	Conf	Banq	Leisure Centre	Swim Pool	Golf
Annan	Warmanbie Hotel		59%	£74	H	(0461) 204015	7	40	50			
Beattock	Auchen Castle		65%	£70	H	(068 33) 407	25	25	80			
Gatehouse of Fleet	Cally Palace		69%	£89	H	(0557) 814341	56	80			yes	yes
Gatehouse of Fleet	Murray Arms Inn			£79	I	(0557) 814207	13	140	100			
Gretna Green	Forte Travelodge	Forte		£42	L	(0461) 37566	41					
Newton Stewart	Kirroughtree Hotel		75%	£116	HR	(0671) 2141	22	20	20			
Port William	Corsemalzie House		61%	£75	H	(098 886) 254	14		70			
Portpatrick	Knockinaam Lodge		75%	£100	HR	(077 681) 471	10					
Rockcliffe	Baron's Craig		65%	£90	H	(055 663) 225	27					
Stranraer	North West Castle		68%	£70	H	(0776) 4413	72	150	150	yes	yes	

Fife

Location	Hotel	Group	%	Room Price	Cat	Tel	Rooms	Conf	Banq	Leisure Centre	Swim Pool	Golf
Dunfermline	King Malcolm Thistle	MtCT	65%	£93	H	(0383) 722611	48	150	120			
Glenrothes	Balgeddie House		65%	£87	H	(0592) 742511	18	70	70			
Letham	Fernie Castle		60%	£75	H	(033 781) 381	15	160	140			
Markinch	Balbirnie House		74%	£125	H	(0592) 610066	30	150	120			
North Queensferry	Queensferry Lodge		63%	£68	H	(0383) 410000	32	150	200			
St Andrews	Rufflets Country House		65%	£104	H	(0334) 72594	26	50	100			

St Andrews	Rusacks Hotel	Forte	74%	£150	H	(0334) 74321	50	150	150		
St Andrews	St Andrews Old Course Hotel		82%	£200	H	(0334) 74371	125	300	300	yes	yes

Grampian

Aberdeen	Ardoe House		70%	£108	H	(0224) 867355	71	150	200		
Aberdeen	Caledonian Thistle	MtCT	68%	£125	H	(0224) 640233	80	45	30		
Aberdeen	Copthorne Hotel	Copthorne	68%	£129	H	(0224) 630404	89	220	200		
Aberdeen	Holiday Inn Crowne Plaza	Holiday Inns	69%	£112	H	(0224) 713911	144	540	420	yes	yes
Aberdeen	Stakis Tree Tops	Stakis	63%	£127	H	(0224) 313377	110	620	400	yes	yes
Aberdeen	Travel Inn	Travel Inns		£43	L	(0224) 821217	40				
Aberdeen Airport	Aberdeen Marriott Hotel	Marriott	70%	£141	H	(0224) 770011	154	400	380	yes	yes
Aberdeen Airport	Airport Skean Dhu Hotel	MtCT	65%	£110	H	(0224) 725252	148	600	460		
Ballater	Craigendarroch Hotel		74%	£135	H	(033 97) 55858	50	100	120		yes
Ballater	Tullich Lodge		71%	£160	HR	(033 97) 55406	10				
Banchory	Invery House		78%	£125	H	(033 02) 4782	14	30	30		
Banchory	Raemoir House		71%	£110	HR	(033 02) 4884	25	60	30		
Banchory	Tor-na-Coille Hotel		66%	£85	H	(033 02) 2242	25	80	90		
Chapel of Garioch	Pittodrie House		65%	£110	H	(0467) 681444	27	130	130		
Craigellachie	Craigellachie Hotel		68%	£91	HR	(0340) 881204	30	40	40		
Elgin	Mansion House		67%	£100	H	(0343) 548811	23	200	200	yes	yes
Kildrummy	Kildrummy Castle		70%	£104	H	(097 55) 71288	16				
Maryculter	Maryculter House		65%	£73	H	(0224) 732124	24	60	150		
Newburgh	Udny Arms Hotel		60%	£76	H	(035 86) 89444	26				
Peterhead	Waterside Inn		67%	£89	H	(0779) 71121	110	250	240	yes	yes
Rothes	Rothes Glen Hotel		65%	£110	H	(034 03) 254	16				

Highland

Achiltibuie	Summer Isles		64%	£73	HR	(085 482) 282	11				
Advie	Tulchan Lodge		77%	£350	H	(0807) 510200	11				

Location	Hotel	Group	%	Room Price	Cat	Tel	Rooms	Conf	Banq	Leisure Centre	Swim Pool	Golf
Altnaharra	Altnaharra Hotel		60%	£112	H	(054 981) 222	20					
Appin	Invercreran Country House Hotel		67%	£108	H	(063 173) 414	9	50	20			
Arisaig	Arisaig House		75%	£135	HR	(068 75) 622	15					
Aviemore	Aviemore Highlands Hotel	Principal	61%	£70	H	(0479) 810771	103	175	220			
Aviemore	Stakis Aviemore Four Season	Stakis	70%	£100	H	(0479) 810681	89	100	180	yes	yes	
Aviemore	Stakis Coylumbridge Resort	Stakis	62%	£96	H	(0479) 810661	175	750	600	yes	yes	
Ballachulish	Ballachulish Hotel		60%	£75	H	(085 52) 606	30	100	50			
Ballachulish	Isles of Glencoe Hotel		59%	£79	H	(085 52) 603	39	70	120			
Contin	Craigdarroch Lodge		56%	£98	H	(0997) 421265	13				yes	
Drumnadrochit	Polmaily House		63%	£100	HR	(0456) 450343	9					
Dulnain Bridge	Auchendean Lodge		62%	£64	HR	(0479) 851347	7					
Dulnain Bridge	Muckrach Lodge		63%	£78	H	(047 985) 257	12	70	80			
Duror	Stewart Hotel		59%	£80	H	(063 174) 268	19					
Fort William	Inverlochy Castle		90%	£240	HR	(0397) 702177	16					
Fort William	Mercury Hotel	MtCT	58%	£79	H	(0397) 703117	86					
Gairloch	Creag Mor		66%	£77	H	(0445) 2068	17		60			
Garve	Inchbae Lodge		57%	£56	H	(099 75) 269	12					
Glenborrodale	Glenborrodale Castle		75%	£173	HR	(097 24) 266	16					
Glenelg	Glenelg Inn			£120	IR	(059 982) 273	6					
Helmsdale	Navidale House		60%	£60	H	(043 12) 258	14	60				
Inverness	Bunchrew House		70%	£115	H	(0463) 234917	11					
Inverness	Caledonian Hotel	Jarvis	69%	£99	H	(0463) 235181	106	300	220	yes	yes	
Inverness	Culloden House		73%	£150	HR	(0463) 790461	23	34	51			
Inverness	Dunain Park		69%	£130	HR	(0463) 230512	14				yes	
Inverness	Kingsmills Hotel	Swallow	67%	£110	H	(0463) 237166	84	70	40	yes	yes	
Inverness	Mercury Hotel	MtCT	62%	£85	H	(0463) 239666	118	250	160			
Isle of Raasay	Isle of Raasay Hotel		57%	£64	H	(0478) 660222	12	23				
Kentallen of Appin	Ardsheal House		67%	£160	HR	(063 174) 227	13					
Kentallen of Appin	Holly Tree		65%	£75	H	(063 174) 292	11	12				

Kinlochbervie	Kinlochbervie Hotel		64%	£84	H	(0971) 521275	14				
Kyle of Lochalsh	Lochalsh Hotel		63%	£87	H	(0599) 4202	40				
Lochinver	Inver Lodge Hotel		70%	£130	H	(057 14) 496	20				
Nairn	Carnach House		60%	£90	H	(0667) 52094	9	22	40		
Nairn	Clifton Hotel		70%	£96	HR	(0667) 53119	12		30		
Nairn	Golf View Hotel	Rank	65%	£99	H	(0667) 52301	47	140	120		
Nairn	Newton Hotel		65%	£90	H	(0667) 53144	44	60	60		
Newtonmore	Ard-na-Coille Hotel		67%	£120	HR	(0540) 673214	7				
Onich	Allt-nan-Ros Hotel		63%	£133	HR	(085 53) 250	21				
Onich	Lodge on the Loch		63%	£131	H	(085 53) 237	18				
Onich	Onich Hotel		61%	£74	H	(085 53) 214	27				
Portree	Rosedale Hotel		54%	£70	H	(0478) 613131	24				
Scarista	Scarista House		67%	£90	HR	(0859) 550238	8				
Scourie	Eddrachilles Hotel		60%	£68	H	(0971) 502080	11				
Scourie	Scourie Hotel		60%	£68	H	(0971) 2396	21				
Skeabost Bridge	Skeabost House		60%	£86	H	(047 032) 202	26				
Sleat	Kinloch Lodge		67%	£100	HR	(047 13) 214	10		30		
Spean Bridge	Letterfinlay Lodge		55%	£68	H	(039 781) 622	13				
Stornoway	Cabarfeidh Hotel		64%	£85	H	(0851) 702604	46				
Talladale	Loch Maree Hotel			£70	I	(044 584) 288	18	40	36		
Uig	Uig Hotel		59%	£75	H	(047 042) 205	16	12			
Ullapool	Ceilidh Place			£90	I	(0854) 612103	13	60	30		
Whitebridge	Knockie Lodge		67%	£150	HR	(0456) 486276	10				

Lothian

Bonnyrigg	Dalhousie Castle		62%	£130	H	(0875) 820153	25	150	120		
Dirleton	Open Arms Hotel		67%	£110	H	(0620) 85241	7	100	80		
Edinburgh	The Balmoral	Forte	83%	£190	HR	031-556 2414	189	400	350	yes	yes
Edinburgh	Barnton Thistle	MtCT	63%	£85	H	031-339 1144	50	130	100		
Edinburgh	Braid Hills Hotel		61%	£89	H	031-447 8888	68	200	120		
Edinburgh	Caledonian Hotel	QMH	79%	£192	HR	031-225 2433	240	300	228		

Location	*Hotel*	*Group*	*%*	*Room Price*	*Cat*	*Tel*	*Rooms*	*Conf*	*Banq*	*Leisure Centre*	*Swim Pool*	*Golf*
Edinburgh	Carlton Highland		68%	£138	H	031-556 7277	199	350	290	yes	yes	
Edinburgh	Channings			£115	PH	031-315 2226	48					
Edinburgh	Forte Travelodge	Forte		£42	L	031-441 4296	40					
Edinburgh	Forte Posthouse	Forte	62%	£68	H	031-334 0390	200	120	100			
Edinburgh	George Inter-Continental		74%	£186	H	031-225 1251	195	220	170			
Edinburgh	Granada Lodge	Granada		£45	L	031-653 2427	44					
Edinburgh	Hilton National	Hilton	68%	£152	H	031-332 2545	144	115	90			
Edinburgh	Holiday Inn Garden Court	Holiday Inns	65%	£93	H	031-332 2442	119	70	50			
Edinburgh	Howard Hotel	Select	75%	£180	H	031-557 3500	16	35	35			
Edinburgh	King James Thistle	MtCT	70%	£126	H	031-556 0111	147	250	250			
Edinburgh	Roxburghe Hotel		64%	£90	H	031-225 3921	75	300	225			
Edinburgh	Royal Terrace Hotel		70%	£151	H	031-557 3222	95	90	60	yes	yes	
Edinburgh	Scandic Crown Hotel		68%	£155	H	031-557 9797	238	220	120		yes	
Edinburgh	Sheraton Grand Hotel	Sheraton	79%	£199	H	031-229 9131	263	485	485	yes	yes	
Edinburgh	Stakis Grosvenor Hotel	Stakis	64%	£115	H	031-226 6001	136	300	450			
Edinburgh	Swallow Royal Scot	Swallow	65%	£120	H	031-334 9191	259	250	250	yes	yes	
Gullane	Greywalls Hotel		76%	£150	HR	(0620) 842144	23	30	50			
Ingliston	Norton House		66%	£115	H	031-333 1275	47	300	150			
Kirknewton	Dalmahoy Hotel	Country Club	78%	£125	HR	031-333 1845	115	190	140	yes	yes	yes
North Berwick	Marine Hotel	Forte	62%	£100	H	(0620) 2406	84	350	250			
North Middleton	Borthwick Castle		66%	£95	H	(0875) 20514	10	60	80			
South Queensferry	Forth Bridges Moat House	QMH	61%	£114	H	031-331 1199	108	200	200		yes	
Uphall	Houstoun House		68%	£110	H	(0506) 853831	30	65	200			

Orkney

Harray Loch	Merkister Hotel		57%	£59	H	(085 677) 366	15		80			

Shetland

Lerwick	Shetland Hotel		62%	£74	H	(0595) 5515	66	350	200		yes	

Strathclyde

Abington	Forte Travelodge	Forte		£42	L	(0864) 2782	54					
Alexandria	Cameron House		81%	£150	HR	(0389) 55565	68	300	168	yes	yes	
Ardentinny	Ardentinny Hotel		59%	£78	H	(036 981) 209	11		30			
Arduaine	Loch Melfort Hotel		63%	£90	H	(085 22) 233	27					
Ayr	Caledonian Hotel	Jarvis	64%	£99	H	(0292) 269331	114	175	200	yes	yes	
Craignure	Isle of Mull Hotel		56%	£84	H	(068 02) 351	60					
Crinan	Crinan Hotel		69%	£110	HR	(054 683) 261	22	60				
Cumbernauld	Travel Inn	Travel Inns		£43	L	(0236) 725339	37					
Cumbernauld	Westerwood Hotel		73%	£90	HR	(0236) 457171	47	250	180		yes	yes
Dumbarton	Forte Travelodge	Forte		£42	L	(0389) 65202	32					
East Kilbride	Bruce Swallow Hotel	Swallow	59%	£75	H	(035 52) 29771	79					
East Kilbride	Stuart Hotel		62%	£70	H	(035 52) 21161	39	200	150			
East Kilbride	Westpoint Hotel		74%	£125	H	(035 52) 36300	74			yes	yes	
Eriska	Isle of Eriska		73%	£145	HR	(063 172) 371	17					
Erskine	Forte Posthouse	Forte	62%	£68	H	041-812 0123	166	600	450	yes	yes	
Giffnock	Macdonald Thistle	MtCT	64%	£102	H	041-638 2225	56	150	100			
Glasgow	Copthorne Hotel	Copthorne	64%	£122	H	041-332 6711	140	100	100			
Glasgow	Devonshire Hotel			£120	PH	041-339 7878	15	50	30			
Glasgow	Forte Crest	Forte	74%	£117	H	041-248 2656	254	800	800			
Glasgow	Glasgow Hilton		78%	£140	HR	041-204 5555	321	1100	950	yes	yes	
Glasgow	Glasgow Marriott Hotel	Marriott	73%	£136	H	041-226 5577	298	850	750	yes	yes	
Glasgow	Hospitality Inn	MtCT	67%	£130	H	041-332 3311	307	1,500	1,000			
Glasgow	Jurys Pond Hotel	Jurys	59%	£78	H	041-334 8161	137	150	120	yes	yes	
Glasgow	Kelvin Park Lorne Hotel	QMH	63%	£81	H	041-334 4891	99	350	240			
Glasgow	Moat House International	QMH	69%	£126	H	041-204 0733	282	600	500	yes	yes	
Glasgow	One Devonshire Gardens		82%	£155	HR	041-339 2001	27	50	50			

Location	Hotel	Group	%	Room Price	Cat	Tel	Rooms	Conf	Banq	Leisure Centre	Swim Pool	Golf
Glasgow	Stakis Grosvenor	Stakis	66%	£99	H	041-339 8811	95	400	400			
Glasgow	Swallow Hotel	Swallow	61%	£92	H	041-427 3146	119	380	280	yes	yes	
Glasgow	Tinto Firs Hotel	MtCT	62%	£85	H	041-637 2353	30	200	130			
Glasgow	Town House	Hidden	70%	£110	H	041-332 3320	34	140	140			
Glasgow Airport	Forte Crest	Forte	68%	£95	H	041-887 1212	300	500	300			
Glasgow Airport	Stakis Normandy	Stakis	61%	£102	H	041-886 4100	141	1,000	750			
Gourock	Stakis Gantock Hotel	Stakis	64%	£95	H	(0475) 34671	99	200	136	yes	yes	
Irvine	Hospitality Inn	MtCT	68%	£86	H	(0294) 74272	128	320	220		yes	yes
Kilchrenan	Ardanaiseig		74%	£192	HR	(086 63) 333	14			yes		
Kilchrenan	Taychreggan Hotel		66%	£72	HR	(086 63) 211	15					
Kilfinan	Kilfinan Hotel			£68	IR	(070 082) 201	11	40	26			
Kilmelford	Cuilfail Hotel		52%	£56	H	(085 22) 274	12					
Kilmore	Glenfeochan House		70%	£124	HR	(063 177) 273	3					
Kilwinning	Montgreenan Mansion		70%	£92	H	(0294) 57733	21	100	100			
Langbank	Gleddoch House		68%	£130	H	(047 554) 711	33	80	120			yes
Maybole	Ladyburn		73%	£130	HR	(065 54) 585	8					
Milngavie	Black Bull Thistle	MtCT	59%	£70	H	041-956 2291	27	100	120			
Newhouse	Travel Inn	Travel Inns		£43	L	(0698) 860277	40					
Oban	Alexandra Hotel		57%	£90	H	(0631) 62381	60	80	120			
Oban	Columba Hotel		60%	£53	H	(0631) 62183	49	400	400			
Oban	Knipoch Hotel		72%	£125	HR	(085 26) 251	17					
Port Appin	Airds Hotel		76%	£220	HR	(063 173) 236	13					
Quothquan	Shieldhill		75%	£98	HR	(0899) 20035	11	16	32			
Skelmorlie	Manor Park		61%	£75	H	(0475) 520832	23	100	130			
Stewarton	Chapeltoun House		71%	£90	H	(0560) 482696	8	60	50			
Strachur	Creggans Inn		61%	£98	H	(036 986) 279	21	36	80			
Tarbert	Stonefield Castle		58%	£122	H	(0880) 820836	33	60	120			
Tiroran	Tiroran House		70%	£186	HR	(068 15) 232	9					
Tobermory	Tobermory Hotel		57%	£60	H	(0688) 2091	17					

Troon	Marine Highland Hotel		67%	£138	H	(0292) 314444	72	150	220	yes	yes	
Troon	Piersland House		64%	£85	H	(0292) 314747	19	100	150			
Turnberry	Turnberry Hotel		84%	£190	HR	(0655) 31000	132	160	240	yes	yes	yes

Tayside

Aberfeldy	Farleyer House		70%	£90	HR	(0887) 820332	11	20				
Alyth	Lands of Loyal Hotel		62%	£65	H	(082 83) 3151	14	35	25			
Auchterarder	Auchterarder House		75%	£130	HR	(0764) 63646/7	15	50	50			
Auchterarder	Gleneagles Hotel		86%	£205	H	(0764) 662231	236	360	260	yes	yes	yes
Auchterhouse	Old Mansion House		68%	£95	HR	(082 626) 366	6		20			
Blairgowrie	Kinloch House		70%	£138	HR	(0250) 884237	21	15	30			
Callander	Roman Camp		70%	£80	H	(0877) 30003	14	30	50			
Cleish	Nivingston House		65%	£90	H	(0577) 850216	17	30	60			
Crieff	Crieff Hydro		64%	£104	H	(0764) 655555	199	350	300	yes	yes	
Dalguise	Kinnaird		76%	£170	HR	(0796) 482440	9		25			
Dundee	Angus Thistle	MtCT	69%	£108	H	(0382) 26874	58	500	450			
Dundee	Invercarse Hotel		59%	£80	H	(0382) 69231	38	200	280			
Dundee	Travel Inn	Travel Inns		£43	L	(0382) 561115	40					
Forfar	Royal Hotel		57%	£65	H	(0307) 62691	19	220	160	yes	yes	
Glamis	Castleton House		71%	£90	HR	(0307) 840340	6					
Glencarse	Newton House Hotel		58%	£	H	(073 886) 250	10					
Kenmore	Kenmore Hotel		62%	£88	H	(0887) 830205	38	30	75			yes
Killiecrankie	Killiecrankie Hotel		64%	£92	H	(0796) 473220	11					
Kinclaven by Stanley	Ballathie House		74%	£120	HR	(0250) 883268	27					
Kinross	Granada Lodge	Granada		£45	L	(0577) 64646	35					
Kinross	Windlestrae Hotel		62%	£85	H	(0577) 863217	45	250	200	yes	yes	
Kirkmichael	Log Cabin Hotel		59%	£50	H	(0250) 881288	13	40	90			
Perth	Royal George Hotel	Forte	62%	£95	H	(0738) 24455	42	100	80			
Perth	Stakis City Mills Hotel	Stakis	59%	£90	H	(0738) 28281	76	235	130			
Pitlochry	Green Park Hotel		58%	£76	H	(0796) 473248	37	100	120			

Location	*Hotel*	*Group*	*%*	*Room Price*	*Cat*	*Tel*	*Rooms*	*Conf*	*Banq*	*Leisure Centre*	*Swim Pool*	*Golf*
Pitlochry	Pitlochry Hydro		64%	£98	H	(0796) 472666	62	100	60		yes	
St Fillans	Four Seasons Hotel		60%	£70	H	(0764) 685333	18					
Scone	Murrayshall House		72%	£125	HR	(0738) 51171	19	60	80			yes
Strathtummel	Port-an-Eilean Hotel		65%	£58	H	(0882) 634233	8					

WALES

Location	Hotel	Group	%	Room Price	Cat	Tel	Rooms	Conf	Banq	Leisure Centre	Swim Pool	Golf
Clwyd												
Colwyn Bay	Hotel Seventy Degrees		61%	£53	H	(0492) 516555	43					
Ewloe	St David's Park Hotel		69%	£107	H	(0244) 520800	121	270	220	yes	yes	
Halkyn	Forte Travelodge	Forte		£42	L	(0352) 780952	31					
Llanarmon Dyffryn Ceiriog	Hand Hotel			£58	I	(069 176) 666	13					
Llanarmon Dyffryn Ceiriog	West Arms Hotel			£78	I	(069 176) 665	14	70	55			
Llandrillo	Tyddyn Llan		65%	£84	HR	(049 084) 264	10	50	90			
Llangollen	Hand Hotel	MtCT	55%	£66	H	(0978) 860303	57	80	90			
Llangollen	Royal Hotel	Forte	59%	£82	H	(0978) 860202	33	60	80			
Northop	Soughton Hall		79%	£99	HR	(0352) 840811	12	30	16			
Northop Hall	Forte Travelodge	Forte		£42	L	(0244) 816473	40					
Rossett	Llyndir Hall		71%	£110	H	(0244) 571648	38	150	90	yes	yes	
Ruthin	Ruthin Castle		62%	£79	H	(0824) 702664	58	200	140			
Wrexham	Forte Travelodge	Forte		£42	L	(0978) 365705	32					
Dyfed												
Aberystwyth	Conrah Country Hotel		63%	£79	H	(0970) 617941	20				yes	
Brechfa	Ty Mawr		60%	£68	H	(0267) 202332	5					
Carmarthen	Ivy Bush Royal	Forte	59%	£60	H	(0267) 235111	75	200	200			
Cross Hands	Forte Travelodge	Forte		£42	L	(0269) 845700	32					
Fishguard	Fishguard Bay Hotel		59%	£60	H	(0348) 873571	62	200	300			
Gwbert-on-Sea	Cliff Hotel		60%	£79	H	(0239) 613241	73	200	200			

Location	Hotel	Group	%	Room Price	Cat	Tel	Rooms	Conf	Banq	Leisure Centre	Swim Pool	Golf
Lamphey	Court Hotel		59%	£99	H	(0646) 672273	31	100	80		yes	
Llandeilo	Cawdor Arms		65%	£57	H	(0558) 823500	17	80	130			
Penally	Penally Abbey		65%	£86	HR	(0834) 843033	11				yes	
St David's	St Non's Hotel		56%	£73	H	(0437) 720239	24					
St David's	Warpool Court		62%	£111	H	(0437) 720300	25	100	100		yes	

Gwent

Location	Hotel	Group	%	Room Price	Cat	Tel	Rooms	Conf	Banq	Leisure Centre	Swim Pool	Golf
Abergavenny	Llanwenarth Arms Hotel			£59	I	(0873) 810550	18					
Chepstow	Castle View Hotel			£60	I	(0291) 620349	11					
Chepstow	St Pierre Hotel		66%	£100	H	(0291) 625261	147	220	200	yes	yes	yes
Llangybi	Cwrt Bleddyn Hotel		71%	£100	H	(0633) 49521	36	200	170	yes	yes	
Llanvihangel Gobion	Llansantffraed Court		66%	£70	H	(0873) 840678	21	80	120			
Monmouth	King's Head		64%	£65	H	(0600) 712177	29	200	180			
Newport	Celtic Manor		75%	£117	H	(0633) 413000	73	350	200		yes	
Newport	Hilton National	Hilton	61%	£93	H	(0633) 412777	119	500	400	yes	yes	
Newport	Kings Hotel		62%	£51	H	(0633) 842020	47	200	220			
Newport	Stakis Country Court Hotel	Stakis	69%	£112	H	(0633) 413733	141	95	72	yes	yes	
Tintern	Beaufort Hotel	Jarvis	60%	£92	H	(0291) 689777	24	50	100			
Tintern Abbey	Royal George		59%	£67	H	(0291) 689205	19	150	120			

Gwynedd

Location	Hotel	Group	%	Room Price	Cat	Tel	Rooms	Conf	Banq	Leisure Centre	Swim Pool	Golf
Aberdovey	Plas Penhelig		62%	£83	H	(0654) 767676	11	40	45			
Aberdovey	Trefeddian Hotel		58%	£88	H	(0654) 767213	46				yes	
Abersoch	Porth Tocyn Hotel		69%	£94	HR	(0758) 713303	17					
Abersoch	Riverside Hotel		59%	£80	H	(0758) 712419	12				yes	

Beaumaris	Bulkeley Arms		59%	£77	H	(0248) 810415	43	160	135		
Beddgelert	Royal Goat Hotel		60%	£68	H	(076 686) 224	34	150			
Betws-y-Coed	Royal Oak		59%	£74	H	(0690) 710219	27	25	90		
Bontddu	Bontddu Hall		62%	£90	H	(0341) 49661	20	30	100		
Conwy	Sychnant Pass Hotel		60%	£60	H	(0492) 596868	14				
Llandderfel	Pale Hall		68%	£110	H	(067 83) 285	17	55	30		
Llandudno	Bodysgallen Hall	Historic House	77%	£155	HR	(0492) 584466	28	50	40		
Llandudno	Empire Hotel		69%	£70	H	(0492) 860555	58	48	48	yes	
Llandudno	St George's Hotel		61%	£72	H	(0492) 877544	86	250	250		
Llandudno	St Tudno Hotel		69%	£104	HR	(0492) 874411	21	10	50	yes	
Llangefni	Tre-Ysgawen Hall		79%	£107	HR	(0248) 750750	19	120	150		
Llanrug	Seiont Manor		71%	£97	H	(0286) 673366	28	100	100	yes	
Llansanffraid Glan Conwy	Old Rectory		73%	£89	HR	(0492) 580611	6				
Llanwnda	Stables Hotel		57%	£49	H	(0286) 830711	14	100	120		
Penmaenpool	George III Hotel			£88	I	(0341) 422525	12				
Portmeirion	Hotel Portmeirion		74%	£84	HR	(0766) 770228	34	100	100		yes
Talsarnau	Maes-y-Neaudd		72%	£109	HR	(0766) 780200	16	20	50		
Talyllyn	Tynycornel Hotel		59%	£80	H	(0654) 782282	15	25			

Powys

Crickhowell	Bear Hotel			£48	I	(0873) 810408	28	50	60
Crickhowell	Gliffaes Country House Hotel		63%	£59	H	(0874) 730371	22		90
Eglwysfach	Ynyshir Hall		70%	£110	HR	(0654) 781209	8	35	30
Lake Vyrnwy	Lake Vyrnwy Hotel		64%	£70	H	(069 173) 692	30	150	150
Llangammarch Wells	Lake Country House Hotel		68%	£98	HR	(059 12) 202	19		50
Llyswen	Llangoed Hall		80%	£145	HR	(0874) 754525	23	45	150
Machynlleth	Wynnstay Arms		57%	£53	H	(0654) 702941	20	30	98
Pantmawr	Glansevern Arms			£55	I	(055 15) 240	7		
Presteigne	Radnorshire Arms	Forte	61%	£124	H	(0544) 267406	16	25	

Location	Hotel	Group	%	Room Price	Cat	Tel	Rooms	Conf	Banq	Leisure Centre	Swim Pool	Golf
Mid Glamorgan												
Abercynon	Llechwen Hall			£60	I	(0443) 742050	11	80	80			
Bridgend	Forte Travelodge	Forte		£42	L	(0656) 659218	40					
Coychurch	Coed-y-Mwstwr Hotel		70%	£95	HR	(0656) 860621	24	220	150			
Merthyr Tydfil	Baverstock Hotel		57%	£55	H	(0685) 386221	53	400	250			
Miskin	Miskin Manor	Select	70%	£107	H	(0443) 224204	32	150	100	yes	yes	
Pencoed	Forte Travelodge	Forte		£42	L	(0656) 864404	40					
South Glamorgan												
Barry	Mount Sorrel Hotel		59%	£85	H	(0446) 740069	50	150	150		yes	
Cardiff	Angel Hotel	QMH	66%	£114	H	(0222) 232633	91	350	300			
Cardiff	Campanile Hotel	Campanile		£44	L	(0222) 549044	50					
Cardiff	Cardiff International		67%	£82	H	(0222) 341441	143	40	120			
Cardiff	Cardiff Marriott Hotel	Marriott	69%	£131	H	(0222) 399944	182	300	300	yes	yes	
Cardiff	Copthorne Hotel	Copthorne	70%	£119	H	(0293) 599100	135	300	200	yes	yes	
Cardiff	Forte Posthouse	Forte	63%	£68	H	(0222) 731212	139	140	120	yes	yes	
Cardiff	Forte Crest	Forte	69%	£93	H	(0222) 388681	155	150	180			
Cardiff	Forte Travelodge	Forte		£42	L	(0222) 549564	32					
Cardiff	Moat House	QMH		£103	H	(0222) 732520	135	300	255	yes	yes	
Cardiff	Park Hotel	MtCT	70%	£108	H	(0222) 383471	119	300	200			
Cardiff	Travel Inn	Travel Inns		£43	L	(0633) 680070	49					
Porthkerry	Egerton Grey		73%	£85	H	(0446) 711666	10	30	36			
West Glamorgan												
Gowerton	Cefn Goleu Park		69%	£80	HR	(0792) 873099	6	20	20			

Mumbles	Norton House		65%	£70	HR	(0792) 404891	15	20	16		
Port Talbot	Travel Inn	Travel Inns		£43	L	(0639) 813017	40				
Reynoldston	Fairyhill		64%	£75	HR	(0792) 390139	15				
Swansea	Forte Crest	Forte	69%	£95	H	(0792) 651074	99	230	180	yes	yes
Swansea	Hilton National	Hilton	65%	£88	H	(0792) 310330	120	200	140		
Swansea	Langland Court Hotel			£78	I	(0792) 361545	21				
Swansea	Swansea Marriott Hotel	Marriott	67%	£123	H	(0792) 642020	118	250	180	yes	yes

CHANNEL ISLANDS & ISLE OF MAN

Location	Hotel	Group	%	Room Price	Cat	Tel	Rooms	Conf	Banq	Leisure Centre	Swim Pool	Golf
Alderney												
Alderney	Chez Andre		63%	£62	H	(0481) 822777	11					
St Anne	Inchalla Hotel		64%	£73	HR	(0481) 823220	10					
Guernsey												
Castel	La Grande Mare Hotel		73%	£134	HR	(0481) 56577	27		100			yes
Castel	Hougue du Pommier			£71	I	(0481) 57100	38					yes
Forest	Mallard Hotel		67%	£63	H	(0481) 64164	47	100				
Pleinmont	Imperial Hotel			£57	I	(0481) 64044	17					
St Martin	Hotel Bon Port		66%	£90	H	(0481) 39249	14					
St Martin	St Margaret's Lodge		63%	£76	H	(0481) 35757	47	120	120			
St Martin	La Trelade Hotel		61%	£70	H	(0481) 35454	45					
St Peter Port	Braye Lodge		56%	£63	H	(0481) 723787	25	250	120			
St Peter Port	Duke of Richmond		63%	£75	H	(0481) 726221	74	120	200			
St Peter Port	La Fregate		64%	£111	H	(0481) 724624	13					
St Peter Port	Old Government House		68%	£109	H	(0481) 724921	72	150	150			
St Peter Port	St Pierre Park		71%	£130	H	(0481) 728282	134	200	330	yes	yes	
Herm												
Herm	White House		64%	£116	H	(0481) 722159	38					

Jersey

Bouley Bay	Water's Edge Hotel		64%	£104	H	(0534) 862777	51		120		
Gorey	Moorings Hotel		62%	£96	H	(0534) 853633	16	25	65		
Gorey	Old Court House		64%	£89	H	(0534) 854444	58				
Grouville	Grouville Bay Hotel		62%	£80	H	(0534) 51004	56				
Havre des Pas	Hotel de la Plage		66%	£84	H	(0534) 23474	78	25	20		
Havre des Pas	Ommaroo Hotel		58%	£75	H	(0534) 23493	85				
Portelet Bay	Portelet Hotel		66%	£100	H	(0534) 41204	86	60	120		
Rozel Bay	Chateau la Chaire		74%	£105	HR	(0534) 863354	14				
St Aubin	Old Court House Inn			£80	I	(0534) 46433	9				
St Brelade	Atlantic Hotel		70%	£130	H	(0534) 44101	50	60	60	yes	yes
St Brelade	Hotel Chateau Valeuse		65%	£74	HR	(0534) 46281	33		70		
St Brelade	La Place Hotel		67%	£110	H	(0534) 44261	40				
St Brelade	Sea Crest		64%	£84	HR	(0534) 46353	7				
St Brelade's Bay	Hotel L'Horizon	Clipper	72%	£160	H	(0534) 43101	107	150	200		yes
St Brelade's Bay	St Brelade's Bay Hotel		70%	£140	H	(0534) 46141	82				
St Clement's Bay	Hotel Ambassadeur		63%	£70	H	(0534) 24455	69				
St Helier	Apollo Hotel		63%	£88	H	(0534) 25441	85	80	60		yes
St Helier	Beaufort Hotel		60%	£92	H	(0534) 32471	54	60	40		yes
St Helier	Grand Hotel	De Vere	68%	£120	HR	(0534) 22301	115	180	250	yes	yes
St Helier	Hotel de France		71%	£120	H	(0534) 38990	320			yes	yes
St Helier	Pomme d'Or Hotel		65%	£90	H	(0534) 78644	148	300	300		
St Peter	Mermaid Hotel		64%	£92	H	(0534) 41255	68	80	60		yes
St Saviour	Longueville Manor		80%	£144	HR	(0534) 25501	32		70		
St Saviour	Merton Hotel & Leisure Centre		60%	£86	H	(0534) 24231	330				yes

Sark

Sark	Aval Du Creux		57%	£63	HR	(0481) 832036	12				
Sark	Dixcart Hotel		64%	£90	HR	(0481) 832015	18				
Sark	Hotel Petit Champ		61%	£68	H	(0481) 832046	16				

Location	Hotel	Group	%	Room Price	Cat	Tel	Rooms	Conf	Banq	Leisure Centre	Swim Pool	Golf
Sark	La Sablonnerie		66%	£64	HR	(0481) 832061	22					
Sark	Stocks Hotel		61%	£102	HR	(0481) 832001	25	60	60			

Isle of Man

Location	Hotel	Group	%	Room Price	Cat	Tel	Rooms	Conf	Banq	Leisure Centre	Swim Pool	Golf
Douglas	Palace Hotel		65%	£95	H	(0624) 662662	135	350	270	yes	yes	
Douglas	Sefton Hotel		63%	£70	H	(0624) 626011	80	100	90	yes	yes	
Ramsey	Grand Island Hotel		67%	£90	H	(0624) 812455	54	500	250	yes	yes	

NORTHERN IRELAND

Swimming pool refers to indoor swimming pools only. See page 14 How to use this Guide for explanation of percentage rating system, room pricing and categories.

Key: QMH (Queens Moat Houses); MtCT (Mount Charlotte Thistle).

Location	*Hotel*	*Group*	*%*	*Room Price*	*Cat*	*Tel*	*Rooms*	*Conf*	*Banq*	*Leisure Centre*	*Swim Pool*	*Golf*
Co Antrim												
Belfast	Dukes Hotel		67%	£92	H	(0232) 236666	21	130	160			
Belfast	Plaza Hotel		64%	£76	H	(0232) 333555	83	100	60			
Belfast	Wellington Park		59%	£90	H	(0232) 381111	50	150	150			
Bushmills	Bushmills Inn			£68	I	(026 57) 32339	11	50	90			
Dunadry	Dunadry Inn		64%	£98	H	(084 94) 32474	67	350	300	yes	yes	
Dunmurry	Forte Crest Belfast	Forte	67%	£95	H	(0232) 612101	82	450	350			
Larne	Magheramorne House		63%	£66	H	(0574) 279444	22	200	180			
Portballintrae	Bayview Hotel		58%	£65	H	(026 57) 31453	16	150	180		yes	
Templepatrick	Templeton Hotel		66%	£100	H	(084 94) 32984	20	400	350			
Co Down												
Annalong	Glassdrumman Lodge		69%	£85	HR	(039 67) 68451	10	16	60			
Comber	La Mon House		59%	£85	H	(0232) 448631	38 1	100	450	yes	yes	
Crawfordsburn	Old Inn Crawfordsburn			£80	I	(0247) 853255	33	100	86			
Holywood	Culloden Hotel		72%	£140	HR	(0232) 425223	91	500	300		yes	
Newtownards	Strangford Arms		58%	£88	H	(0247) 814141	40	120	120			
Co Londonderry												
Londonderry	Everglades Hotel		59%	£76	H	(0504) 46722	52	350	250			

REPUBLIC OF IRELAND

Location	Hotel	Group	%	Room Price	Cat	Tel	Rooms	Conf	Banq	Leisure Centre	Swim Pool	Golf

Swimming pool refers to indoor swimming pools only. See page 14 How to use this Guide for explanation of percentage rating system, room pricing and categories.

Key: QMH (Queens Moat Houses), MtCT (Mount Charlotte Thistle).

Co Cavan

Location	Hotel	Group	%	Room Price	Cat	Tel	Rooms	Conf	Banq	Leisure Centre	Swim Pool	Golf
Ballyconnell	Slieve Russell Hotel		78%	£110	H	(049) 264444	150	1,000	500	yes	yes	yes

Co Clare

Location	Hotel	Group	%	Room Price	Cat	Tel	Rooms	Conf	Banq	Leisure Centre	Swim Pool	Golf
Ballyvaughan	Gregans Castle		71%	£88	HR	(065) 77005	22					
Bunratty	Fitzpatricks Shannon Shamro		60%	£125	H	(061) 361177	115	200	200	yes	yes	
Ennis	Auburn Lodge		61%	£65	H	(065) 21247	100		400			
Ennis	Old Ground Hotel	Forte	66%	£98	H	(065) 28127	58	250	180			
Ennis	West County Inn	Lynch	59%	£77	H	(065) 28421	110	200	500			
Newmarket-on-Fergus	Clare Inn Hotel		64%	£70	H	(061) 368161	121	400	350		yes	yes
Newmarket-on-Fergus	Dromoland Castle		78%	£208	HR	(061) 368144	75	450	450			yes
Shannon	Great Southern	Great Southern	64%	£110	H	(061) 471122	115	150	130			
Shannon	Oakwood Arms Hotel		63%	£75	H	(061) 361500	42	280	250			

Co Cork

Location	Hotel	Group	%	Room Price	Cat	Tel	Rooms	Conf	Banq	Leisure Centre	Swim Pool	Golf
Ballylickey	Ballylickey Manor House		67%	£150	H	(027) 50071	12					

Ballylickey	Sea View Hotel		69%	£100	HR	(027) 50462	17				
Cork	Arbutus Lodge		65%	£72	HR	(021) 501237	19	150	180		
Cork	Fitzpatrick Silver Springs		64%	£107	H	(021) 507533	110	800	700	yes	yes
Cork	Forte Travelodge	Forte		£42	L	(021) 310722					
Cork	Imperial Hotel		69%	£110	H	(021) 274040	101	600	350		
Cork	Jurys Hotel	Jurys	66%	£133	H	(021) 276622	185	700	520	yes	yes
Cork	Morrisons Island Hotel		69%	£111	H	(021) 275858	40	15			
Cork	Rochestown Park Hotel		67%	£85	H	(021) 892233	63	200	300		yes
Cork	Seven North Mall			£50	PH	(021) 397191	5				
Innishannon	Innishannon House Hotel		63%	£85	H	(021) 775121	13	150	150		
Kanturk	Assolas Country House		66%	£108	HR	(029) 50015	9	20			
Kinsale	Actons Hotel	Forte	60%	£100	H	(021) 772135	57	400	300	yes	yes
Kinsale	Blue Haven Hotel			£84	IR	(021) 772209	10				yes
Kinsale	The Old Bank House			£53	PH	(021) 774075	9				
Kinsale	Scilly House			£80	PH	(021) 772413	7	25			
Mallow	Longueville House		72%	£110	HR	(022) 47156	16	20			
Shanagarry	Ballymaloe House		63%	£108	HR	(021) 652531	30				

Co Donegal

Rathmullan	Rathmullan House		62%	£72	H	(074) 58188	23	20			yes
Rossnowlagh	Sand House		68%	£88	H	(072) 51777	40	75			

Co Dublin

Dublin	Berkeley Court	Doyle	76%	£182	H	(01) 601711	207	225	275		yes
Dublin	Blooms Hotel		60%	£120	H	(01) 671 5622	86				
Dublin	Burlington Hotel	Doyle	70%	£152	H	(01) 660 5222	500	1,000	1,000		
Dublin	Central Hotel		58%	£120	H	(01) 679 7302	72	150	80		
Dublin	Hotel Conrad		73%	£210	H	(01) 676 5555	190	300	250		
Dublin	Davenport Hotel		76%	£177	H	(01) 661 6799	120	400	300		

Location	Hotel	Group	%	Room Price	Cat	Tel	Rooms	Conf	Banq	Leisure Centre	Swim Pool	Golf
Dublin	Doyle Montrose Hotel	Doyle	63%	£134	H	(01) 269 3311	180	80				
Dublin	Grafton Plaza Hotel		64%	£85	H	(01) 475 0888	75		36			
Dublin	Gresham Hotel	Ryan	64%	£140	H	(01) 874 6881	200	325	250			
Dublin	Grey Door			£99	PH	(01) 676 3286	7					
Dublin	Hibernian Hotel		75%	£120	HR	(01) 668 7666	30	40	55			
Dublin	Jurys Hotel and Towers	Jurys	76%	£158	H	(01) 660 5000	400	850	600		yes	
Dublin	Jurys Christchurch Inn		55%	£43	H	(01) 475 0111	183					
Dublin	Mont Clare Hotel		64%	£155	H	(01) 661 6799	74	150	120			
Dublin	Royal Dublin Hotel		63%	£98	H	(01) 873 3666	117	250	230			
Dublin	Sachs Hotel		62%	£98	H	(01) 680995	20	170	120			
Dublin	Shelbourne Hotel	Forte	74%	£174	H	(01) 676 6471	164	400	300			
Dublin	Stephen's Hall Hotel		65%	£103	HR	(01) 661 0585	37					
Dublin	The Westbury	Doyle	79%	£180	HR	(01) 679 1122	205	300	200			
Dublin Airport	Forte Crest	Forte	57%	£134	H	(01) 844 4211	188	150	130		yes	
Dun Laoghaire	Royal Marine Hotel	Ryan	67%	£85	H	(01) 280 1911	104	600	400			
Killiney	Court Hotel		68%	£97	H	(01) 285 1622	86	300	300			
Killiney	Fitzpatrick's Castle		68%	£147	H	(01) 285 1533	90	550	400	yes	yes	
Swords	Forte Travelodge	Forte		£42	L							

Co Galway

Ballynahinch	Ballynahinch Castle		71%	£94	H	(095) 31006	28	25				
Cashel	Cashel House		76%	£120	HR	(095) 31001	32					
Cashel	Zetland House		65%	£99	H	(095) 31111	20					
Clifden	Abbeyglen Castle		60%	£102	H	(095) 21201	40	230	200			
Clifden	Ardagh Hotel		60%	£75	HR	(095) 21384	21					
Clifden	Rock Glen Manor		61%	£88	H	(095) 21035	29					

Galway	Ardilaun House		66%	£90	H	(091) 21433	90	400	250			
Galway	Brennans Yard		64%	£70	H	(091) 68166	24					
Galway	Corrib Great Southern Hotel	Great Southern	68%	£109	H	(091) 55281	180	850	850		yes	
Galway	Glenlo Abbey		66%	£110	H	(091) 26666	20	48	75			
Galway	Great Southern	Great Southern	69%	£113	H	(091) 64041	116	450	350		yes	
Galway	Jurys Galway Inn		55%	£49	H	(091) 66444	128					
Letterfrack	Rosleague Manor		72%	£90	HR	(095) 41101	20					
Moycullen	Cloonabinnia House Hotel		61%	£50	H	(091) 85555	14					
Oughterard	Connemara Gateway Hotel		65%	£100	H	(091) 82328	62	200	150		yes	
Oughterard	Currarevagh House		65%	£78	HR	(091) 82312	15					
Oughterard	Sweeny's Oughterard House		59%	£98	H	(091) 82207	20					
Renvyle	Renvyle House		64%	£109	H	(095) 43511	74	120	150			
Spiddal	Bridge House Inn			£65	I	(091) 83118	14					

Co Kerry

Beaufort	Dunloe Castle		71%	£92	H	(064) 44111	120	800	400		yes	
Caragh Lake	Hotel Ard-na-Sidhe		70%	£110	H	(066) 69105	20					
Caragh Lake	Caragh Lodge		65%	£72	H	(066) 69115	10					
Dingle	Dingle Skellig Hotel		61%	£86	H	(066) 51144	115		120		yes	
Kenmare	Park Hotel		85%	£210	HR	(064) 41200	50	35	50			yes
Kenmare	Sheen Falls Lodge		86%	£220	HR	(064) 41600	40	120	120			
Killarney	Aghadoe Heights Hotel		70%	£136	H	(064) 31766	60	100	130	yes	yes	
Killarney	Cahernane Hotel		66%	£110	HR	(064) 31895	52					
Killarney	Hotel Europe		72%	£95	H	(064) 31900	210	500	650		yes	
Killarney	Great Southern	Great Southern	69%	£129	H	(064) 31262	183	1,000	700	yes	yes	
Killarney	Killarney Towers Hotel		57%	£80	H	(064) 31038	102					
Killarney	Killarney Park Hotel		73%	£110	H	(064) 35555	55	150	160		yes	
Killarney	Torc Great Southern	Great Southern	65%	£85	H	(064) 31611	96				yes	
Parknasilla	Great Southern	Great Southern	72%	£151	H	(064) 45122	83	80	75	yes	yes	
Tralee	Ballyseede Castle Hotel		60%	£85	H	(066) 25799	15	180	80			

Location	*Hotel*	*Group*	*%*	*Room Price*	*Cat*	*Tel*	*Rooms*	*Conf*	*Banq*	*Leisure Centre*	*Swim Pool*	*Golf*
Co Kildare												
Castledermot	Kilkea Castle		73%	£118	HR	(0503) 45156	45	300	250		yes	
Maynooth	Moyglare Manor		77%	£110	HR	(01) 628 6351	17	40	70			
Newbridge	Hotel Keadeen		68%	£85	H	(045) 31666	37	500	600			
Straffan	Kildare Hotel		86%	£245	HR	(01) 6273333	45	70	50	yes	yes	yes
Co Kilkenny												
Kilkenny	Newpark Hotel		58%	£90	H	(056) 22122	60	500	400	yes	yes	
Thomastown	Mount Juliet Hotel		81%	£240	HR	(056) 24455	32	50	140	yes		yes
Co Laois												
Mountrath	Roundwood House		58%	£64	HR	(0502) 32120	6	12				
Co Limerick												
Adare	Adare Manor		79%	£201	HR	(061) 396566	64		220		yes	
Adare	Dunraven Arms		65%	£120	H	(061) 396209	47	350	300			
Limerick	Castletroy Park Hotel		73%	£124	H	(061) 335566	107	450	300	yes	yes	
Limerick	Greenhills Hotel		60%	£69	H	(061) 53033	60	350	300	yes	yes	
Limerick	Jurys Hotel	Jurys	66%	£113	H	(061) 327777	96	150	120	yes	yes	
Limerick	Limerick Inn	Ryan	66%	£115	H	(061) 326666	153	800	800	yes	yes	
Limerick	Two Mile Inn		60%	£78	H	(061) 326255	125	250	300			

Co Louth

Dundalk	Ballymascanlon House	59%	£73	H	(042) 71124	36	250	300	yes	yes	

Co Mayo

Ballina	Downhill Hotel	65%	£110	H	(096) 21033	52	500	450	yes	yes	
Ballina	Mount Falcon Castle	60%	£88	HR	(096) 21172	10					
Cong	Ashford Castle	86%	£199	HR	(092) 46003	83	40	140			
Crossmolina	Enniscoe House	63%	£88	H	(096) 31112	6					
Newport	Newport House	67%	£116	HR	(098) 41222	20					

Co Meath

Navan	Ardboyne Hotel	60%	£75	HR	(046) 23119	27	700	400			

Co Monaghan

Carrickmacross	Nuremore Hotel	62%	£120	H	(042) 61438	69	200	400	yes	yes	yes
Scotshouse	Hilton Park		£111	PH	(047) 56007	5					yes

Co Offaly

Birr	Dooly's Hotel	60%	£50	H	(0509) 20032	18					
Birr	Tullanisk		£60	PH	(0509) 20572	7					

Co Roscommon

Hodson Bay	Hodson Bay Hotel	65%	£90	H	(0902) 92444	46	500	400		yes	

Location	Hotel	Group	%	Room Price	Cat	Tel	Rooms	Conf	Banq	Leisure Centre	Swim Pool	Golf
Co Sligo												
Ballymote	Temple House			£60	PH	(071) 83329	5					
Boyle	Cromleach Lodge		78%	£118	HR	(071) 65155	10					
Collooney	Markree Castle		61%	£96	H	(071) 67800	15	40	100			
Riverstown	Coopershill House		68%	£80	HR	(071) 65108	7					
Sligo	Sligo Park		58%	£95	H	(071) 60291	89			yes	yes	
Co Tipperary												
Clonmel	Clonmel Arms		61%	£82	H	(052) 21233	31	450	400			
Dundrum	Dundrum House		66%	£96	H	(062) 71116	55	400	350			yes
Glen of Aherlow	Aherlow House		63%	£56	H	(062) 56153	10	280	220			
Kilcoran	Kilcoran Lodge	Waveney	58%	£66	H	(052) 41288	23	300	220	yes	yes	
Co Waterford												
Waterford	Granville Hotel		69%	£79	H	(051) 55111	74	300	200			
Waterford	Jurys Hotel	Jurys	60%	£103	H	(051) 32111	99	700	600		yes	
Waterford	Tower Hotel		57%	£124	H	(051) 75801	141	600	500	yes	yes	
Waterford	Waterford Castle		80%	£193	HR	(051) 78203	19	16			yes	yes
Co Wexford												
Ferrycarrig Bridge	Ferrycarrig Hotel		61%	£90	H	(053) 22999	40	400	400	yes		

Gorey	Marlfield House		81%	£147	HR	(055) 21124	19	20	30		
Newbawn	Cedar Lodge		62%	£75	H	(051) 28386	18	100	70		
Newbay	Newbay Country House		65%	£60	H	(053) 42779	6				
Rosslare	Great Southern	Great Southern	62%	£76	H	(053) 33233	99	150	180	yes	yes
Rosslare	Kelly's Strand Hotel		71%	£84	H	(053) 32114	99	20			yes
Wexford	White's Hotel		60%	£69	H	(053) 22311	82	600	350		

Co Wicklow

Blessington	Downshire House		57%	£63	H	(045) 65199	25	100	250		
Delgany	Glenview Hotel		63%	£70	H	(01) 287 3399	42	300	200		
Dunlavin	Rathsallagh House		67%	£110	HR	(045) 53112	14	50			yes
Rathnew	Hunter's Hotel		60%	£75	HR	(0404) 40106	17	20	30		
Rathnew	Tinakilly House		70%	£100	HR	(0404) 69274	29	150	100		
Wicklow	Old Rectory		59%	£84	HR	(0404) 67048	6				

Special Features

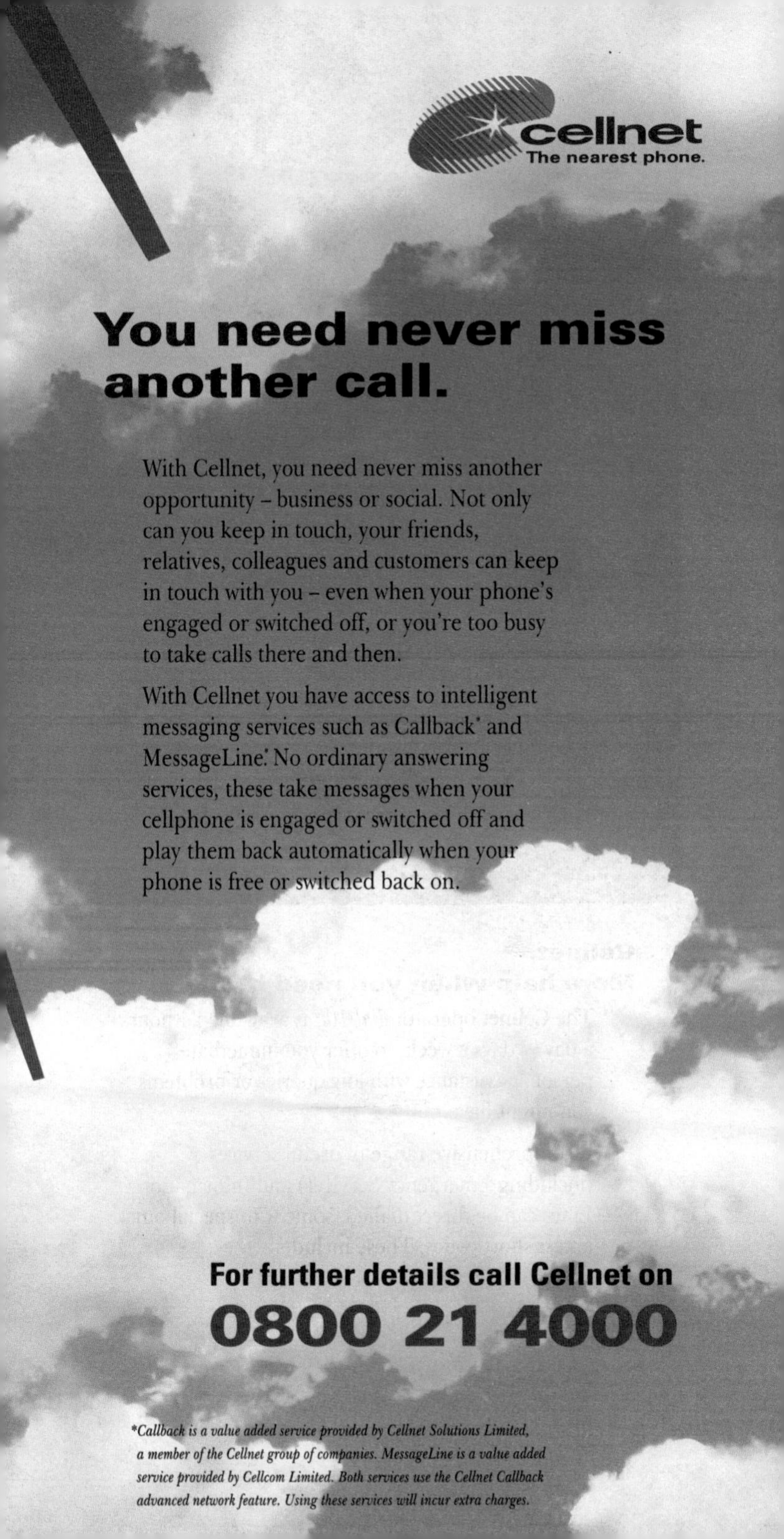
cellnet
The nearest phone.
You need never miss another call.
With Cellnet, you need never miss another opportunity – business or social. Not only can you keep in touch, your friends, relatives, colleagues and customers can keep in touch with you – even when your phone's engaged or switched off, or you're too busy to take calls there and then.
With Cellnet you have access to intelligent messaging services such as Callback* and MessageLine.* No ordinary answering services, these take messages when your cellphone is engaged or switched off and play them back automatically when your phone is free or switched back on.
For further details call Cellnet on
0800 21 4000
*Callback is a value added service provided by Cellnet Solutions Limited, a member of the Cellnet group of companies. MessageLine is a value added service provided by Cellcom Limited. Both services use the Cellnet Callback advanced network feature. Using these services will incur extra charges.

Cellnet.
More help when you need it.

The Cellnet operator *dial 100* is available 24 hours a day, 7 days a week, to offer you immediate personal assistance with any queries or problems you might have.

A comprehensive range of useful services (including Emergency Services) and Information Lines can be direct dialled, some with special quick access short codes. These include:-

cellnet
The nearest phone.

Directory Enquiries.

Specially developed for the mobile phone user, Cellnet's Directory Enquiries *dial 192* is contactable while you're on the move. Having found your number, the operator will dial your call for you if you wish, so that you do not have to pull off the road to make your call.

Talking Pages.

This national classified business information services, Talking Pages *dial 888* offers fast easy access to a vast national database covering businesses, shops and services – 24 hours a day.

For further details call Cellnet on

0800 21 4000

*Talking Pages is a service mark of British Telecommunications plc in the UK.

NATURAL
Britvic
ORANGE JUICE

BALLYGOWAN
Sparkling
IRISH SPRING
WATER
Enjoyed for over 800 years. 250 ml

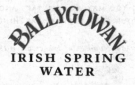

PAINT THE TOWN ROUGE.

LYONS, FRANCE. YOU MAY AS WELL TAKE ANOTHER SIP OF CORDON ROUGE DE MUMM. YOUR CHEF IS STILL SEARCHING FOR THE PERFECT ONION

CHAMPAGNE MUMM. REIMS. FRANCE. DEPUIS 1827

Wedgwood®
for fine Hotels and Restaurants
Wedgwood Hotel & Restaurant Division
Park Street · Fenton · Stoke-on-Trent · ST4 3JB
Telephone: 0782 744221 Fax: 0782 744491

THE NEV

FOR FURTHE

TELEPHON

SAAB 900

FORMATION

800 626556

EXTRA QUALITY
MURPHY'S
IRISH STOUT
LADY'S WELL BREWERY
MURPHY'S
IRISH STOUT

BRITANNIA FOOD SAFETY SERVICE LTD

NEW RECIPE FOR HYGIENE

Britannia Food Safety Service Ltd, with the support of Egon Ronay's Guide, has launched a new Award Scheme for the food industry which aims to help raise standards of hygiene and create greater consumer confidence in catering establishments.

When you see the Britannia Food Safety and Hygiene Award Certificate displayed, you know that the premises operate to high standards of hygiene and food safety.

The Dorchester leads the way
The Dorchester Hotel, Park Lane, London was the first establishment to receive the Britannia Food Safety Award.

Egon Ronay makes the presentation to general manager Ricci Obertelli.

Food Minister, the Hon. Nicholas Soames at the launch of the Britannia Food Safety and Hygiene Award Scheme said "I welcome this initiative. It will heighten awareness among both providers and consumers of the importance of high standards of hygiene in the food industry."

Once you have savoured Martell, the smoothest of French Cognac, mere words seem superfluous.
MARTELL
V.S
MARTELL

PAINT THE TOWN **R**OUGE.

<u>PARIS.</u> DRESS UP AS MUCH AS YOU PLEASE, BUT WEAR AS LITTLE AS YOU LIKE. AND ALWAYS HAVE A LITTLE CORDON ROUGE DE MUMM UP YOUR SLEEVE.

CHAMPAGNE MUMM, REIMS, FRANCE, DEPUIS 1827

Britvic
5
SPARKLING
ORANGE JUICE DRINK

Stoves: the perfect dinner companion

The success of a dinner party often depends on the ability of a cooker to fulfil the demands of the gourmet cook. There is nothing more frustrating than attempting to recreate a fantastic dish you experienced in a hotel or restaurant, only to discover that the souffle lacks sophistication and the dessert is a disaster.

One British cooker company, Stoves, faced this challenge by investing in an extensive consumer research programme which asked cooks what they really wanted.

Stoves' research revealed that cooks need a wide variety of cookers to meet their creative demands. As a result, Stoves' range – thought to be the most comprehensive and technologically advanced in the world – includes fanned and non-fanned gas and electric ovens, in built-in, slide-in and free-standing versions, as well as hobs and hoods. Each model is designed to produce perfect cooking results every time.

A special selection of models is also finished in a stunning range

STOVES

Maps

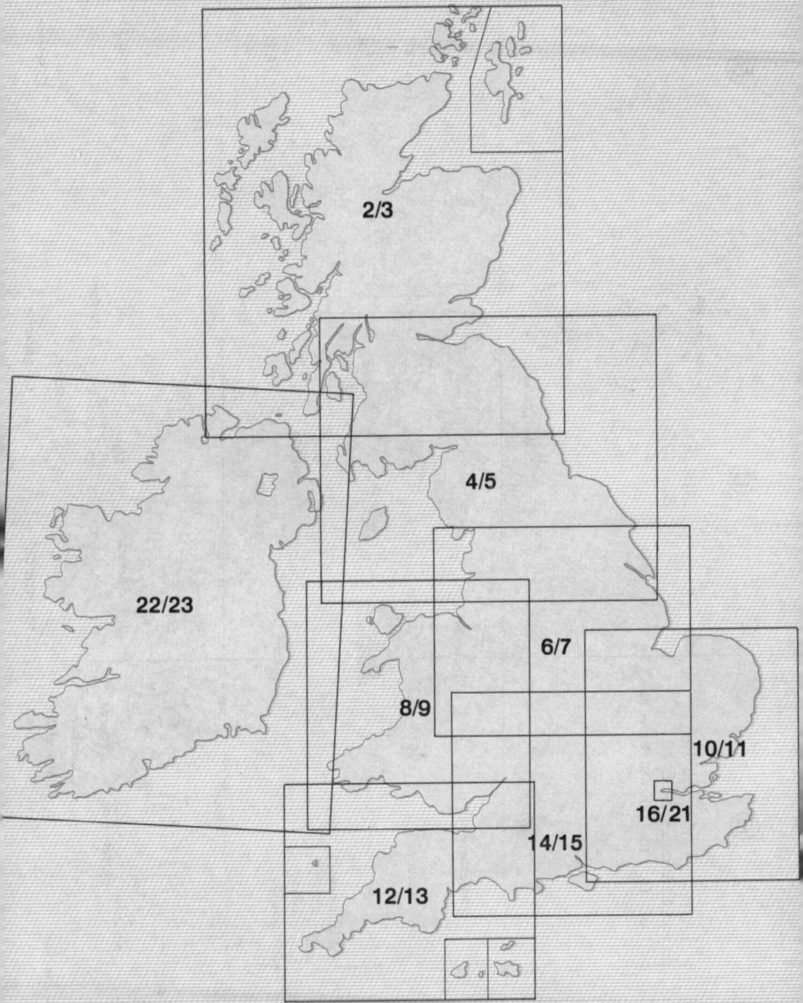

	Motorways	□	Hotel
	Primary Routes	●	Restaurant
	Other Roads	▣	Hotel and Restaurant
	County Boundaries	■	London hotels

Leading Guides Ltd.

Designed and Produced by
European Map Graphics Ltd. Pangbourne, Berks.

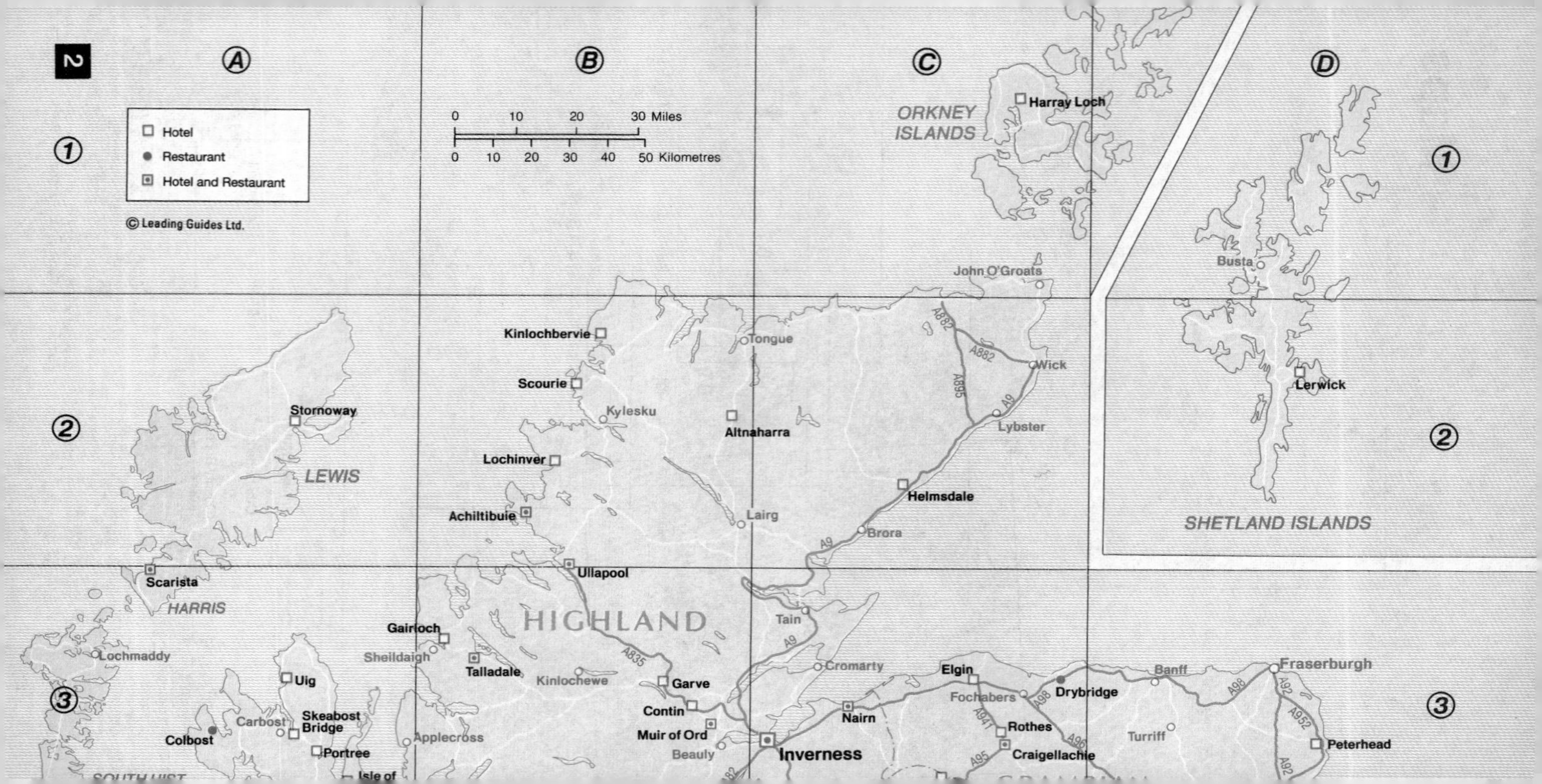
2
A
B
C
D
1
2
3
Hotel
Restaurant
Hotel and Restaurant
© Leading Guides Ltd.
0 10 20 30 Miles
0 10 20 30 40 50 Kilometres
ORKNEY ISLANDS
Harray Loch
SHETLAND ISLANDS
Busta
Lerwick
John O'Groats
Wick
A882
A895
A9
Lybster
Helmsdale
Brora
Tongue
Altnaharra
Lairg
Kinlochbervie
Scourie
Kylesku
Lochinver
Achiltibuie
Ullapool
LEWIS
Stornoway
Scarista
HARRIS
HIGHLAND
A835
Gairloch
Sheildaigh
Talladale
Kinlochewe
Garve
Contin
Muir of Ord
Beauly
Inverness
Tain
Cromarty
Nairn
Elgin
Fochabers
A941
Rothes
A95
Craigellachie
A96
A98
Drybridge
Banff
Turriff
Fraserburgh
A92
A952
Peterhead
Lochmaddy
Uig
Skeabost Bridge
Carbost
Colbost
Portree
Applecross
Isle of
SOUTH UIST

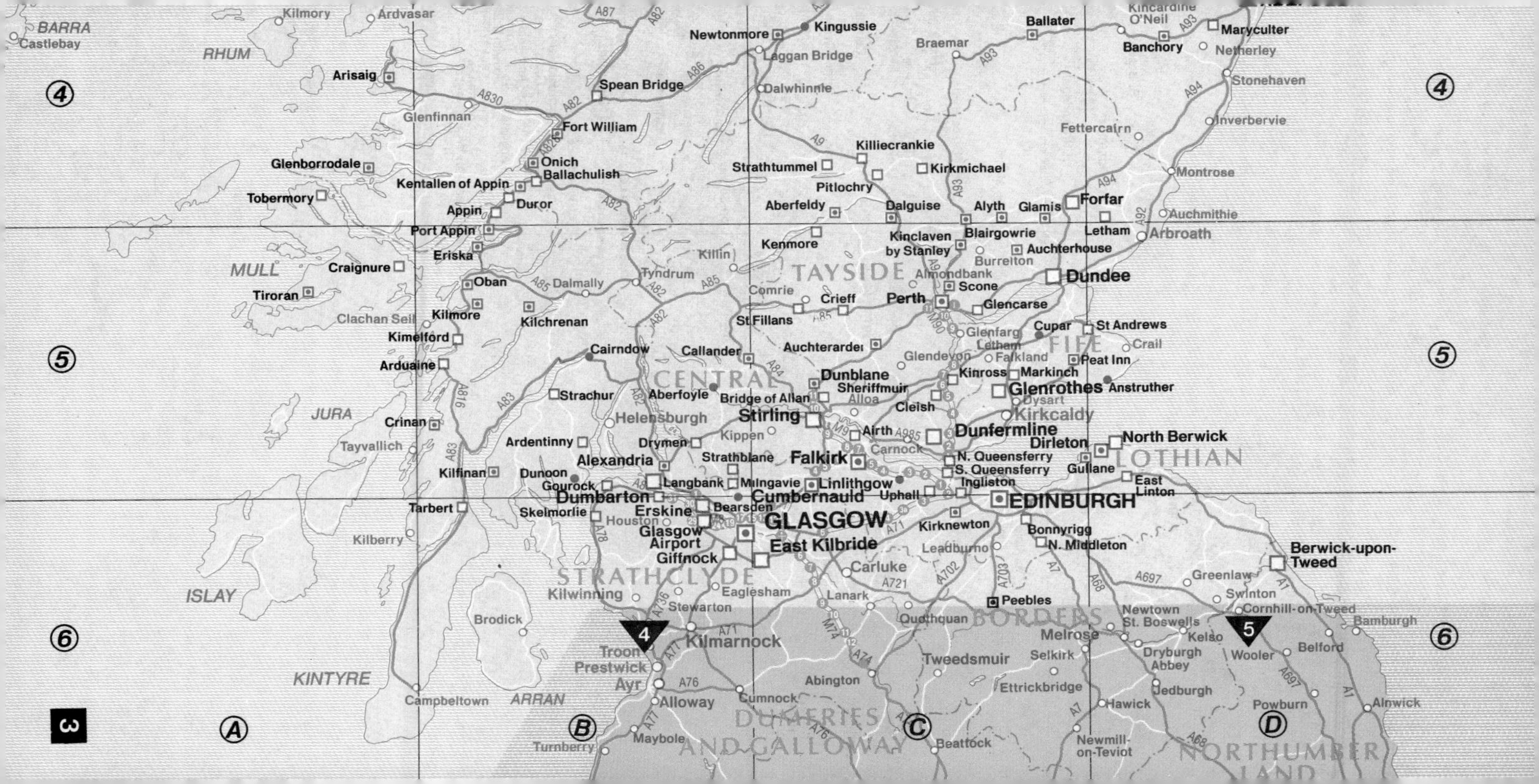
3
4
5
6
A
B
C
D
BARRA
Castlebay
RHUM
Kilmory
Ardvasar
Arisaig
Glenfinnan
Spean Bridge
Fort William
Newtonmore
Kingussie
Laggan Bridge
Dalwhinnie
Braemar
Ballater
Banchory
Maryculter
Netherley
Stonehaven
Inverbervie
Montrose
Auchmithie
Arbroath
Fettercairn
Glenborrodale
Tobermory
Onich
Ballachulish
Kentallen of Appin
Duror
Appin
Port Appin
Eriska
Killiecrankie
Strathtummel
Kirkmichael
Pitlochry
Aberfeldy
Dalguise
Alyth
Glamis
Forfar
Letham
Kinclaven by Stanley
Blairgowrie
Auchterhouse
Burrelton
MULL
Craignure
Tiroran
Oban
Kilmore
Clachan Seil
Kimelford
Arduaine
Kilchrenan
Dalmally
Tyndrum
Killin
Kenmore
TAYSIDE
Almondbank
Scone
Dundee
Perth
Comrie
Crieff
Glencarse
St Fillans
Cupar
St Andrews
Crail
FIFE
Cairndow
Callander
Auchterarder
Glenfarg
Letham
Glendevon
Falkland
Peat Inn
CENTRAL
Kinross
Markinch
Anstruther
Dunblane
Sheriffmuir
Glenrothes
Strachur
Aberfoyle
Bridge of Allan
Alloa
Dysart
Kirkcaldy
JURA
Crinan
Tayvallich
Helensburgh
Stirling
Cleish
Airth
Dunfermline
Kippen
Ardentinny
Drymen
Carnock
North Berwick
Dirleton
Alexandria
Strathblane
Falkirk
N. Queensferry
S. Queensferry
Gullane
LOTHIAN
Kilfinan
Dunoon
Gourock
Langbank
Milngavie
Linlithgow
Ingliston
East Linton
Tarbert
Dumbarton
Cumbernauld
Uphall
EDINBURGH
Skelmorlie
Erskine
Bearsden
Houston
GLASGOW
Glasgow Airport
Kirknewton
Bonnyrigg
N. Middleton
Kilberry
Giffnock
East Kilbride
Leadburn
Carluke
Berwick-upon-Tweed
STRATHCLYDE
Greenlaw
ISLAY
Kilwinning
Eaglesham
Lanark
Peebles
Swinton
Stewarton
Cornhill-on-Tweed
Brodick
Quothquan
BORDERS
Newtown St. Boswells
Kelso
Bamburgh
Kilmarnock
Melrose
Troon
Prestwick
Tweedsmuir
Selkirk
Dryburgh Abbey
Wooler
Belford
KINTYRE
Ayr
Abington
Ettrickbridge
Jedburgh
Alloway
Cumnock
Hawick
Powburn
Alnwick
Campbeltown
ARRAN
DUMFRIES AND GALLOWAY
Turnberry
Maybole
Beattock
Newmill-on-Teviot
NORTHUMBERLAND
A87
A82
A86
A830
A93
A94
A92
A9
A85
A84
A83
A816
A82
M90
M9
A985
M8
A71
A78
A736
A77
A76
A74
M74
A721
A702
A703
A7
A68
A697
A1

TAYSIDE
FIFE
CENTRAL
Inveraray
Strachur
A
B
C
A83
A82
A811
Dunblane
Bridge of Allan
Alva
Alloa
Clelsh
Dollar
Kinross
Glenrothes
Leslie
Leven
Anstru
Cowdenbeath
Kirkcaldy
Kinghorn
Burntisland
Gullane
Dunfermline
Rosyth
Airth
Grangemouth
N. Queensferry
Stirling
Garelochead
Lochgilphead
Drymen
Helensburgh
Alexandria
Strathblane
Falkirk
Kilfinan
M9
A80
Linlithgow
Greenock
Dumbarton
Erskine
EDINBURGH
Ingliston
Port Glasgow
Cumbernauld
LOTHIAN
Tranent
Tarbert
1
Skelmorlie
Glasgow Airport
Clydebank
GLASGOW
M8
Kirknewton
Bonnyrigg
STRATHCLYDE
Johnstone
Paisley
Rutherglen
Motherwell
Shotts
Penicuik
N. Middleton
Barrhead
Hamilton
Wishaw
East Kilbride
Carluke
A78
A77
A702
A703
A7
A68
3
Ardrossan
Kilwinning
Strathaven
Lanark
Quothquan
Peebles
Kilmarnock
A71
A72
Brodick
Irvine
Galston
Biggar
Innerleithen
Newton St Boswick
ARRAN
Troon
Mauchline
Prestwick
Abington
Tweedsmuir
Ayr
Cumnock
BORDERS
Alloway
Ettrickbridge
Hawick
A76
Sanquhar
A74
Maybole
Turnberry
Moffat
Beattock
Girvan
Thornhill
Eskdalemuir
DUMFRIES AND GALLOWAY
Newcastleton
2
Barrhill
New Galloway
Lochmaben
Lockerbie
Langholm
Dumfries
Canonbie
Newton Stewart
Castle Douglas
A75
New Abbey
Annan
Gretna Green
Brampton
Stranraer
Glenluce
Gatehouse of Fleet
Dalbeattie
Metal Bridge
Kirkbean
Carlisle
Crosby
Eden
Portpatrick
Wigtown
Rockcliffe
Kirkcudbright
Auchencairn
Silloth-on-Solway
A596
Southwaite
Port William
Whithorn
Isle of Whithorn
Hesket Newmarket
M6
A6
Maryport
Braithwaite
Cockermouth
Bassenthwaite Lake
3
Loweswater
Keswick
Ullswater
CUMBRIA
Workington
Buttermere
Borrowdale
Wasdale Head
Grasmere
Egremont
Elterwater
Ambleside
Gosforth
A595
Langdale
Troutbeck
Skelwith Bridge
Eskdale Green
Windermere
Coniston
Bowness-on-Windermere
Grizedale
Broughton-in-Furness
Spark Bridge
Cartmel Fell
Lowick Green
Crooklands
Ulverston
Kirkby Lonsdale
Grange-over-Sands
A590
Barrow-in-Furness
Dalton-in-Furness
Morecambe
6
Lancaster
LANCASHIRE
4
Ramsey
Fleetwood
Great Eccleston
Cleveleys
ISLE OF MAN
Peel
BLACKPOOL
M55
Kirkham
Douglas
Lytham-St.-Annes
Preston
Leyland
Chorley
Ballasalla
Southport
Formby
Burscough
Skelmersdale
MERSEYSIDE
4
A
B
C

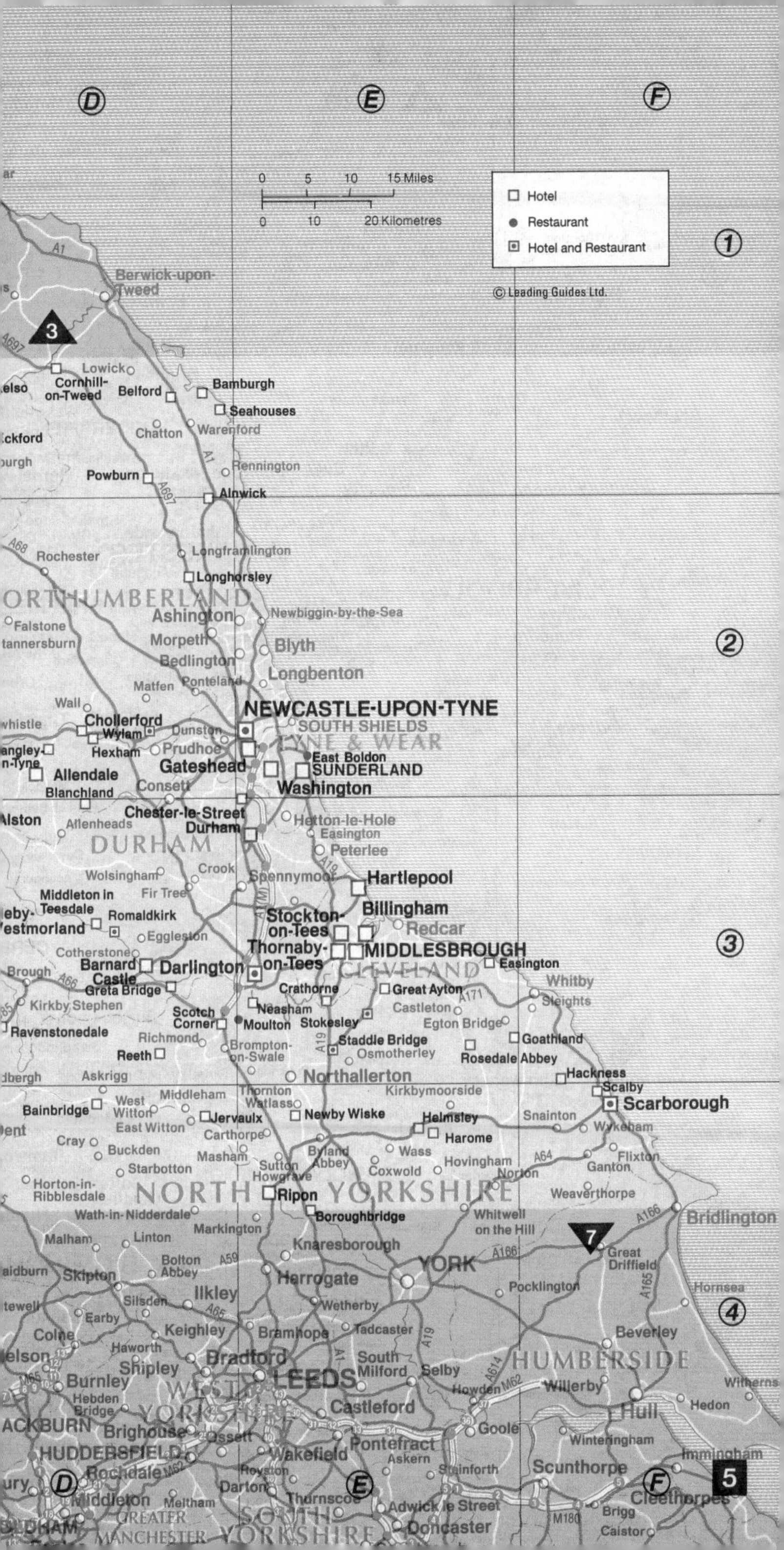

D
E
F
0 5 10 15 Miles
0 10 20 Kilometres
Hotel
Restaurant
Hotel and Restaurant
© Leading Guides Ltd.
1
2
3
4
A1
Berwick-upon-Tweed
3
A697
Lowick
Cornhill-on-Tweed
Belford
Bamburgh
Seahouses
Chatton
Warenford
A1
Rennington
Powburn
A697
Alnwick
A68
Rochester
Longframlington
Longhorsley
NORTHUMBERLAND
Ashington
Newbiggin-by-the-Sea
Falstone
Morpeth
Blyth
Bedlington
Longbenton
Matfen
Ponteland
Wall
NEWCASTLE-UPON-TYNE
Chollerford
SOUTH SHIELDS
Wylam
Dunston
TYNE & WEAR
Hexham
Prudhoe
East Boldon
Gateshead
SUNDERLAND
Allendale
Consett
Washington
Blanchland
Chester-le-Street
Alston
Allenheads
Hetton-le-Hole
Durham
Easington
DURHAM
Peterlee
Crook
Wolsingham
Spennymoor
A19
Hartlepool
Middleton in Teesdale
Fir Tree
Billingham
Romaldkirk
A1(M)
Stockton-on-Tees
Redcar
Eggleston
Thornaby-on-Tees
MIDDLESBROUGH
Cotherstone
Barnard Castle
Darlington
CLEVELAND
Easington
Brough
A66
Greta Bridge
Crathorne
Great Ayton
Whitby
A171
Kirkby Stephen
Neasham
Castleton
Sleights
Scotch Corner
Moulton
Stokesley
Egton Bridge
Ravenstonedale
Richmond
Staddle Bridge
Goathland
Brompton-on-Swale
A19
Osmotherley
Reeth
Rosedale Abbey
Askrigg
Northallerton
Hackness
Kirkbymoorside
Scalby
Thornton Watlass
Middleham
Bainbridge
West Witton
Scarborough
Jervaulx
Newby Wiske
Helmsley
East Witton
Snainton
Harome
Wykeham
Carthorpe
Cray
Byland Abbey
Wass
Buckden
Masham
Flixton
A64
Sutton Howgrave
Coxwold
Hovingham
Starbotton
Norton
Ganton
Horton-in-Ribblesdale
Ripon
NORTH YORKSHIRE
Weaverthorpe
Wath-in-Nidderdale
Boroughbridge
Whitwell on the Hill
Bridlington
A166
Markington
7
Malham
Linton
Knaresborough
Great Driffield
Bolton Abbey
A59
YORK
A166
Skipton
Harrogate
Pocklington
A165
Ilkley
Silsden
Hornsea
Wetherby
A65
Earby
Keighley
Tadcaster
Colne
Bramhope
A19
Beverley
Haworth
Bradford
South Milford
Shipley
HUMBERSIDE
LEEDS
Selby
A614
Burnley
WEST YORKSHIRE
Howden
M62
Willerby
Hebden Bridge
Castleford
Hull
Hedon
Goole
Brighouse
Ossett
Pontefract
Winteringham
HUDDERSFIELD
Wakefield
Askern
Immingham
Rochdale
M62
Royston
Stainforth
Scunthorpe
5
Middleton
Darton
Meltham
Thurnscoe
Cleethorpes
Adwick le Street
M180
Brigg
GREATER MANCHESTER
SOUTH YORKSHIRE
Doncaster
Caistor

Ulverston
Grange-over-Sands
Cowan Bridge
Furness
Ripon
Carnforth
Wath-in-Nidderdale
Boroughbridge
Markington
Morecambe
Heysham
Lancaster
Malham
Bolton Abbey
Knaresborough
Skipton
Slaidburn
Harrogate
LANCASHIRE
Ilkley
Fleetwood
Barnoldswick
Whitewell
Earby
Silsden
Otley
Wharfe
Thornton le Fylde
Cleveleys
Clitheroe
Keighley
Guiseley
Colne
Chipping
Nelson
Haworth
Bingley
Shipley
Longridge
Brierfield
BLACKPOOL
Broughton
Samlesbury
Langho
Mellor
Burnley
Bradford
Kirkham
Preston
Hebden Bridge
WEST YORKSHIRE
Lytham-St.-Annes
BLACKBURN
Accrington
Todmorden
Halifax
Batley
Haslingden
Bacup
Brighouse
Hartshead Moor
Leyland
Darwen
Rawtenstall
Sowerby Bridge
Ossett
Wakefield
Clayton-le-Woods
Ramsbottom
Southport
Chorley
Rochdale
HUDDERSFIELD
Worthington
Standish
Bolton
Norden
Manchester (Birch)
Burscough
Formby
Ormskirk
Bury
Meltham
Barnsley
Wigan
Heywood
Middleton
Skelmersdale
Radcliffe
Atherton
OLDHAM
Maghull
Rainford
Leigh
SALFORD
Stocksbridge
Kirkby
Haydock
Eccles
Ashton-under-Lyne
Urmston
MANCHESTER
MERSEYSIDE
St. Helens
Bootle
Prescot
Burton Wood
Hyde
Glossop
Wallasey
LIVERPOOL
Warrington
STOCKPORT
Chapeltown
Hoylake
Birkenhead
Widnes
Manchester Airport
Marple
Hayfield
SHEFFIELD
Altrincham
Bramhall
New Mills
Heswall
Runcorn
Wilmslow
Handforth
Hope
Bamford
Prestatyn
Gayton
Parkgate
Ellesmere Port
Bucklow Hill
Knutsford
Mottram St Andrew
Whaley Bridge
Hathersage
Prestbury
Grindleford
Bebington
Puddington
Holywell
Frodsham
Alderley Edge
Bollington
Flint
Northwich
Buxton
Baslow
Connah's Quay
Queensferry
CHESHIRE
Macclesfield
Ashford in the Water
Chesterfield
Northop
Sandiway
Bakewell
Rowsley
Denbigh
Ewloe
Chester
Winsford
Mold
Buckley
Congleton
DERBYSHIRE
Sandbach
Matlock
Ruthin
Bunbury
Biddulph
Crewe
Alsager
Leek
Matlock Bath
CLWYD
Rossett
Kidsgrove
Waterhouses
Wirksworth
Nantwich
Wrexham
Newcastle-under-Lyme
STOKE-ON-TRENT
Dovedale
Ashbourne
Rhosllanerchrugog
Llangollen
Whitchurch
Hanchurch
Chirk
DERBY
Market Drayton
Stone
Uttoxeter
Ellesmere
Eccleshall
Tutbury
Whittington
Wem
Weston under Redcastle
STAFFORDSHIRE
Oswestry
Burton-upon-Trent
Stafford
Swadlincote
Newport
Barton-under-Needwood
Penkridge
Rugeley
Ashby de la Zouch
Shrewsbury
Cannock
Lichfield
Welshpool
Telford
Brownhills
Swinfen
Shifnal
SHROPSHIRE
Walsall Wood
Tamworth
POWYS
Dorrington
WOLVERHAMPTON
Aldridge
Bodymore Heath
Much Wenlock
Walsall
Sutton Coldfield
Montgomery
All Stretton
Church Stretton
Nuneaton
Bridgnorth
Worfield
Wishaw
WEST MIDLANDS
Newtown
DUDLEY
WEST BROMWICH
Brierley Hill
Bishop's Castle
Stourbridge
Oldbury
BIRMINGHAM
WARLEY
Birmingham Airport
Alveley
Kinver
Halesowen
Clun
Solihull
Kidderminster
Hagley
Frankley
Bewdley
Hockley Heath
COVENTRY
Ludlow
Stourport-on-Severn
Chaddesley Corbett
Kenilworth
Brimfield
Bromsgrove
Leamington Spa
Hartlebury
Redditch
Presteigne
Abberley
Warwick
Droitwich
Studley
Llandrindod Wells
Eyton
Barford
Kington
Leominster
Alcester
WARWICKSHIRE
HEREFORD AND WORCESTER
Worcester
Charlecote
Bromyard
Abbot's Salford
Stratford-upon-Avon
Pershore
0 5 10 15 Miles
0 5 10 15 20 25 Kilometres
4
8
14
A
B
C
1
2
3
4

Hotel
Restaurant
Hotel and Restaurant
© Leading Guides Ltd.
D
E
F
1
2
3
4
5
10
15
7
YORKSHIRE
HUMBERSIDE
NOTTINGHAMSHIRE
LINCOLNSHIRE
LEICESTERSHIRE
NORTHAMPTONSHIRE
CAMBRIDGESHIRE
BEDFORDSHIRE
Norton
Bridlington
Driffield
YORK
Pocklington
Hornsea
Bilbrough
Tadcaster
Beverley
Tickton
Walkington
Cottingham
South Milford
Selby
Willerby
Hull
Monk Fryston
Howden
South Cave
Hessle
Hedon
Withernsea
Pontefract
Goole
Barton-upon-Humber
Ferrybridge
Winteringham
Wentbridge
Askern
Stainforth
Scunthorpe
Immingham
Grimsby
Cleethorpes
Carcroft
Adwick le Street
Brigg
Doncaster
Caistor
Conisbrough
Maltby
Bawtry
Gainsborough
Market Rasen
Dinnington
Louth
Mablethorpe
Blyth
Barnby Moor
East Retford
Worksop
Clowne
Bolsover
Lincoln
Horncastle
Retford
Woodhall Spa
Skegness
Mansfield
Sutton-in-Ashfield
Kirkby in Ashfield
Newark-on-Trent
Beckingham
Southwell
Hucknall
Eastwood
Arnold
Sleaford
Boston
Carlton
Hunstanton
NOTTINGHAM
Great Gonerby
Belton
Beeston
Grantham
Long Eaton
Plumtree
Colsterworth
Keyworth
Langar
South Witham
Castle Donington
Holbeach
South Wootton
Grimsthorpe
Spalding
Thrussington
Melton Mowbray
King's Lynn
Bourne
Loughborough
Quorn
Stapleford
Rothley
Stretton
Wisbech
Oakham
Stamford
LEICESTER
Wansford in England
Uppingham
PETERBOROUGH
Elton
Oadby
Old Fletton
Whittlesey
March
Magna
Fotheringhay
Stilton
Market Harborough
Corby
Oundle
Littleport
Chatteris
Desborough
Rothwell
Kettering
Ely
Thrapston
Soham
Rugby
Keyston
Huntingdon
St. Ives
Crick
Burton Latimer
Irthlingborough
Godmanchester
Fenstanton
Wellingborough
Higham Ferrers
Swavesey
Lolworth
Staverton
Madingley
Priors Marston
Six Mile Bottom
Weedon
NORTHAMPTON
St. Neots
Cambridge
Horton
Roade
Towcester
Bedford
Kempston
Sandy
Sawston
Biggleswade
A64
A165
A166
A59
A163
A19
A614
M62
A63
M18
A18
M180
A15
A159
A46
A180
A16
A631
A1
A57
A60
A158
A1028
A52
A17
A47
A10
A606
A1101
A1122
A141
A427
A6
A142
A43
A604
A45
A5
M1
A508
A14
M11
A11
A509
A428
A1(M)

8
A
B
C
D
1
2
3
Hotel
Restaurant
Hotel and Restaurant
© Leading Guides Ltd.
0 5 10 15 Miles
0 5 10 15 20 25 Kilometres
ANGLESEY
GWYNEDD
CLWYD
CHESHIRE
SHROPSHIRE
MERSEYSIDE
Holyhead
Amlwch
Llangefni
Red Wharf Bay
Penmaenmawr
Beaumaris
Menai Bridge
Bangor
Bethesda
Llanrug
Caernarfon
Llanberis
Llanwnda
Beddgelert
Pwllheli
Abersoch
Porthmadog
Portmeirion
Talsarnau
Harlech
Blaenau Ffestiniog
Ffestiniog
Llandudno
Conwy
Colwyn Bay
Llansanffraid Glan Conwy
Llanrwst
Betws-y-Coed
Rhyl
Abergele
Prestatyn
Denbigh
Ruthin
Ty-nant
Bala
Llandderfel
Llandrillo
Llanarmon Dyffryn Ceiriog
Lake Vyrnwy
Llanfyllin
Bontddu
Barmouth
Penmaenpool
Dolgellau
Talyllyn
Machynlleth
Aberdovey
Eglwysfach
Welshpool
Montgomery
Holywell
Flint
Halkyn
Connah's Quay
Northop
Ewloe
Mold
Buckley
Queensferry
Parkgate
Gayton
Heswall
Hoylake
West Kirby
Wallasey
Bootle
Formby
Skelmersdale
Ormskirk
Burscough
Maghull
Kirkby
Prescot
Rainford
St. Helens
Wigan
Standish
Bolton
Bury
Radcliffe
Atherton
Leigh
Haydock
Eccles
LIVERPOOL
Birkenhead
Widnes
Runcorn
Warrington
Altrincham
Wilmslow
Bucklow Hill
Ellesmere Port
Puddington
Frodsham
Northwich
Sandiway
Winsford
Chester
Rossett
Wrexham
Rhosllanerchrugog
Llangollen
Chirk
Oswestry
Whittington
Ellesmere
Whitchurch
Bunbury
Nantwich
Crewe
Sandbach
Market Drayton
Wem
Weston under Redcastle
Newport
Shrewsbury
Telford
Shifnal
Dorrington
Much Wenlock
All Stretton
Church Stretton
A5
A55
A470
A487
A494
A458
A483
A495
A49
A41
A51
A525
A53
A56
A570
A556
A533
A534
M6
M53
M56
6

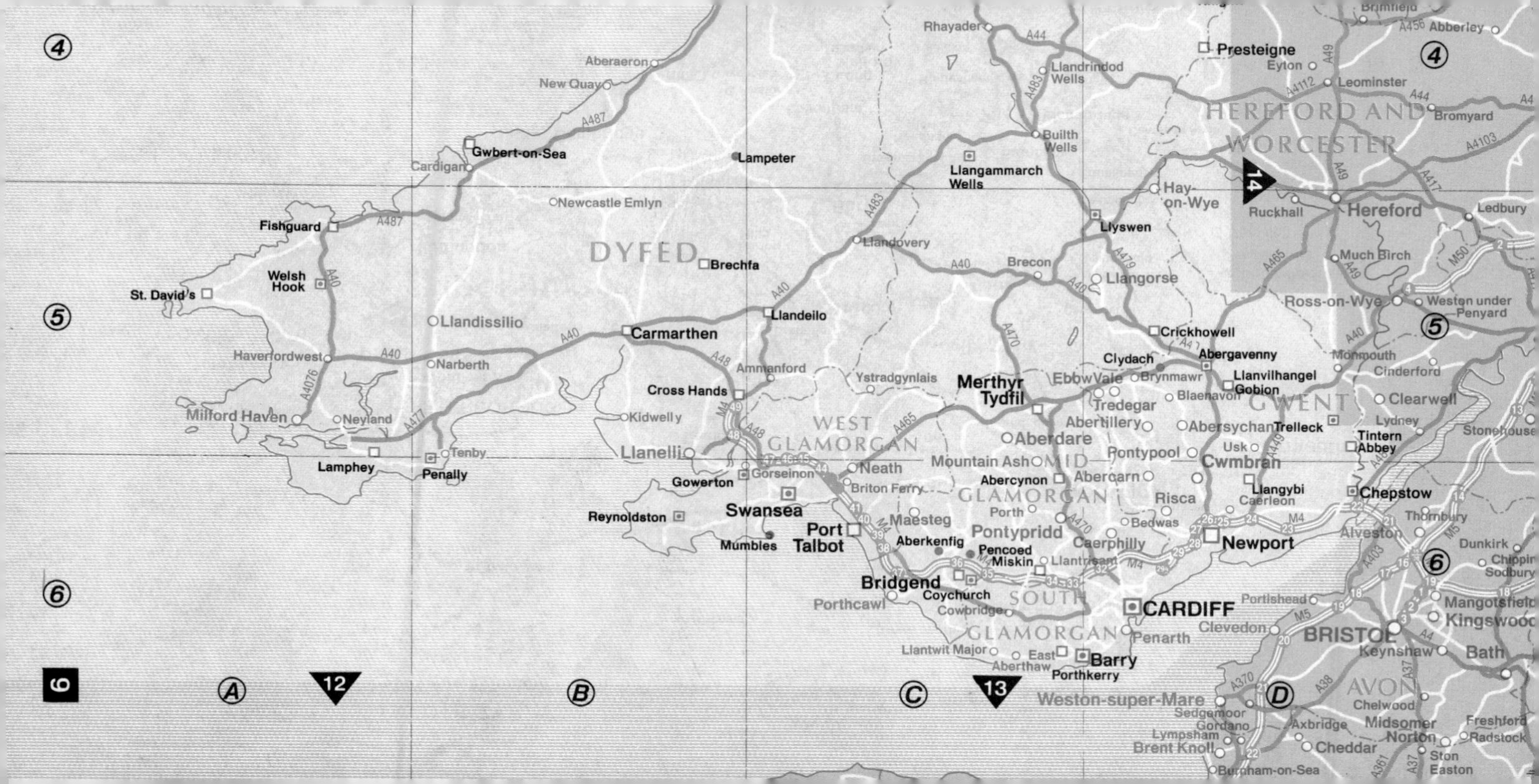
DYFED
WEST GLAMORGAN
MID GLAMORGAN
SOUTH GLAMORGAN
GWENT
HEREFORD AND WORCESTER
AVON
St. David's
Fishguard
Welsh Hook
Haverfordwest
Milford Haven
Neyland
Lamphey
Penally
Tenby
Narberth
Llandissilio
Cardigan
Gwbert-on-Sea
New Quay
Aberaeron
Newcastle Emlyn
Lampeter
Brechfa
Carmarthen
Llandeilo
Llandovery
Ammanford
Cross Hands
Kidwelly
Llanelli
Gowerton
Gorseinon
Reynoldston
Swansea
Mumbles
Port Talbot
Neath
Briton Ferry
Maesteg
Aberkenfig
Bridgend
Porthcawl
Coychurch
Cowbridge
Llantwit Major
East Aberthaw
Barry
Porthkerry
Pencoed
Miskin
Llantrisant
Pontypridd
Porth
Mountain Ash
Aberdare
Abercynon
Abercarn
Caerphilly
Bedwas
Risca
CARDIFF
Penarth
Newport
Caerleon
Llangybi
Cwmbran
Pontypool
Usk
Abersychan
Trelleck
Blaenavon
Abertillery
Tredegar
Ebbw Vale
Brynmawr
Clydach
Merthyr Tydfil
Ystradgynlais
Abergavenny
Llanvihangel Gobion
Crickhowell
Llangorse
Brecon
Llyswen
Hay-on-Wye
Llangammarch Wells
Builth Wells
Llandrindod Wells
Rhayader
Presteigne
Eyton
Leominster
Bromyard
Abberley
Ruckhall
Hereford
Much Birch
Ledbury
Ross-on-Wye
Weston under Penyard
Monmouth
Cinderford
Clearwell
Lydney
Tintern Abbey
Chepstow
Stonehouse
Thornbury
Alveston
Dunkirk
Chipping Sodbury
Mangotsfield
Kingswood
BRISTOL
Keynshaw
Bath
Portishead
Clevedon
Weston-super-Mare
Sedgemoor
Gordano
Lympsham
Brent Knoll
Burnham-on-Sea
Axbridge
Cheddar
Chelwood
Midsomer Norton
Freshford
Radstock
Ston Easton
A40
A48
A477
A4076
A487
A483
A470
A465
A479
A44
A49
A4112
A4103
A417
A456
A466
A449
A403
A4
A370
A38
A37
A361
M4
M5
M50
4
5
6
A
B
C
D
12
13
14

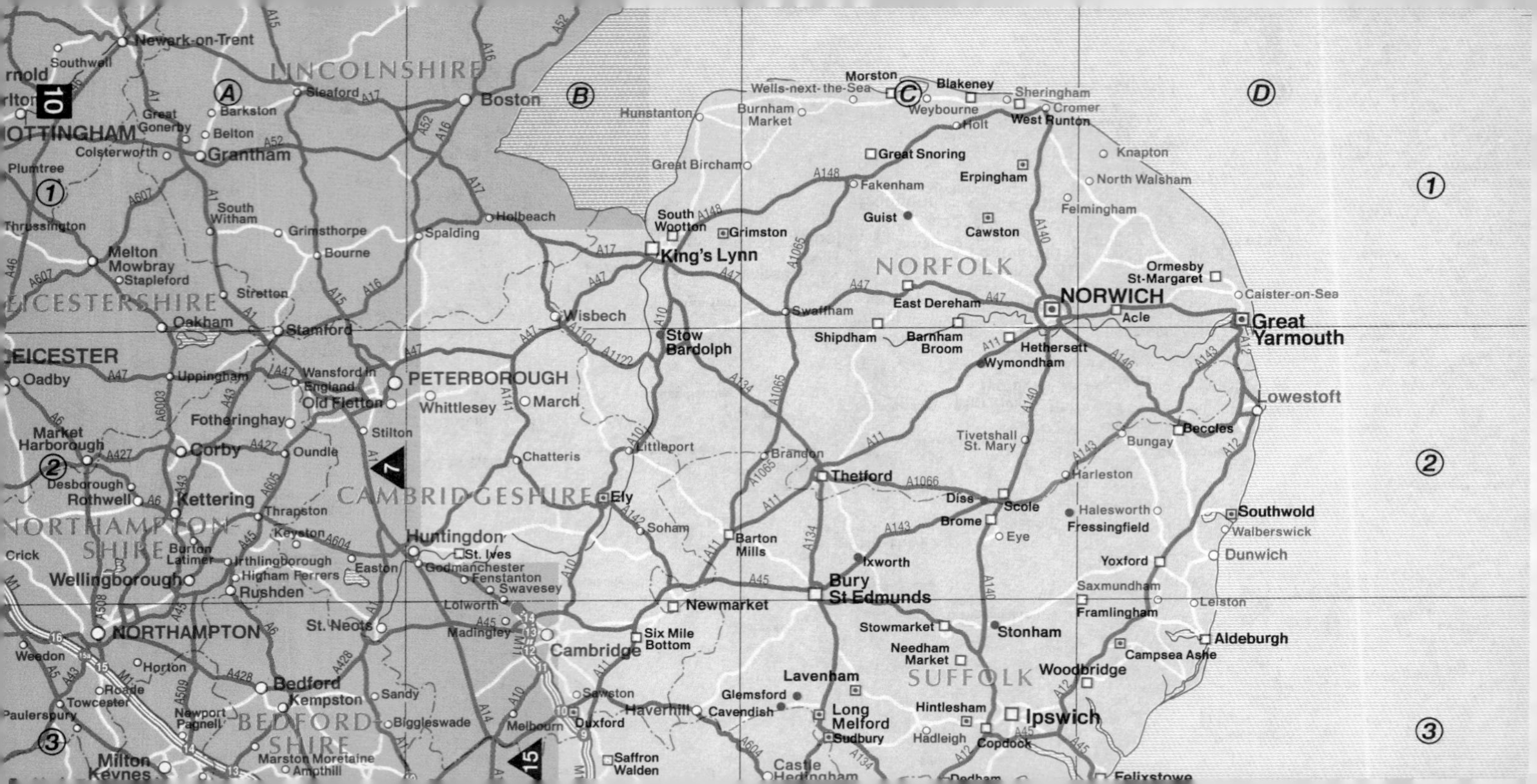
10
A
B
C
D
1
2
3
LINCOLNSHIRE
LEICESTERSHIRE
NORTHAMPTONSHIRE
CAMBRIDGESHIRE
BEDFORDSHIRE
NORFOLK
SUFFOLK
Newark-on-Trent
Southwell
NOTTINGHAM
Grantham
Sleaford
Boston
Barkston
Belton
Great Gonerby
Colsterworth
Plumtree
Melton Mowbray
Stapleford
South Witham
Grimsthorpe
Bourne
Spalding
Holbeach
Stretton
Oakham
Stamford
LEICESTER
Oadby
Uppingham
Wansford in England
Old Fletton
PETERBOROUGH
Whittlesey
March
Wisbech
Fotheringhay
Market Harborough
Corby
Oundle
Stilton
Desborough
Rothwell
Kettering
Thrapston
Keyston
Burton Latimer
Irthlingborough
Higham Ferrers
Rushden
Wellingborough
Crick
NORTHAMPTON
Weedon
Horton
Roade
Towcester
Paulerspury
Newport Pagnell
Milton Keynes
Bedford
Kempston
Marston Moretaine
Ampthill
Sandy
Biggleswade
St. Neots
Huntingdon
St. Ives
Godmanchester
Fenstanton
Swavesey
Lolworth
Madingley
Easton
Chatteris
Ely
Soham
Littleport
Cambridge
Sawston
Duxford
Melbourn
Saffron Walden
Six Mile Bottom
Newmarket
Haverhill
Cavendish
Glemsford
Castle Hedingham
Hunstanton
Great Bircham
Burnham Market
Wells-next-the-Sea
Morston
Blakeney
Weybourne
Sheringham
Cromer
West Runton
Holt
Great Snoring
Fakenham
Erpingham
Knapton
North Walsham
Felmingham
Guist
Cawston
South Wootton
Grimston
King's Lynn
Stow Bardolph
Swaffham
East Dereham
Shipdham
Barnham Broom
NORWICH
Acle
Ormesby St-Margaret
Caister-on-Sea
Great Yarmouth
Hethersett
Wymondham
Lowestoft
Beccles
Bungay
Tivetshall St. Mary
Harleston
Brandon
Thetford
Diss
Scole
Brome
Eye
Halesworth
Fressingfield
Southwold
Walberswick
Dunwich
Barton Mills
Ixworth
Bury St Edmunds
Yoxford
Saxmundham
Leiston
Framlingham
Aldeburgh
Stonham
Stowmarket
Needham Market
Campsea Ashe
Woodbridge
Lavenham
Long Melford
Sudbury
Hintlesham
Hadleigh
Copdock
Ipswich
Dedham
Felixstowe

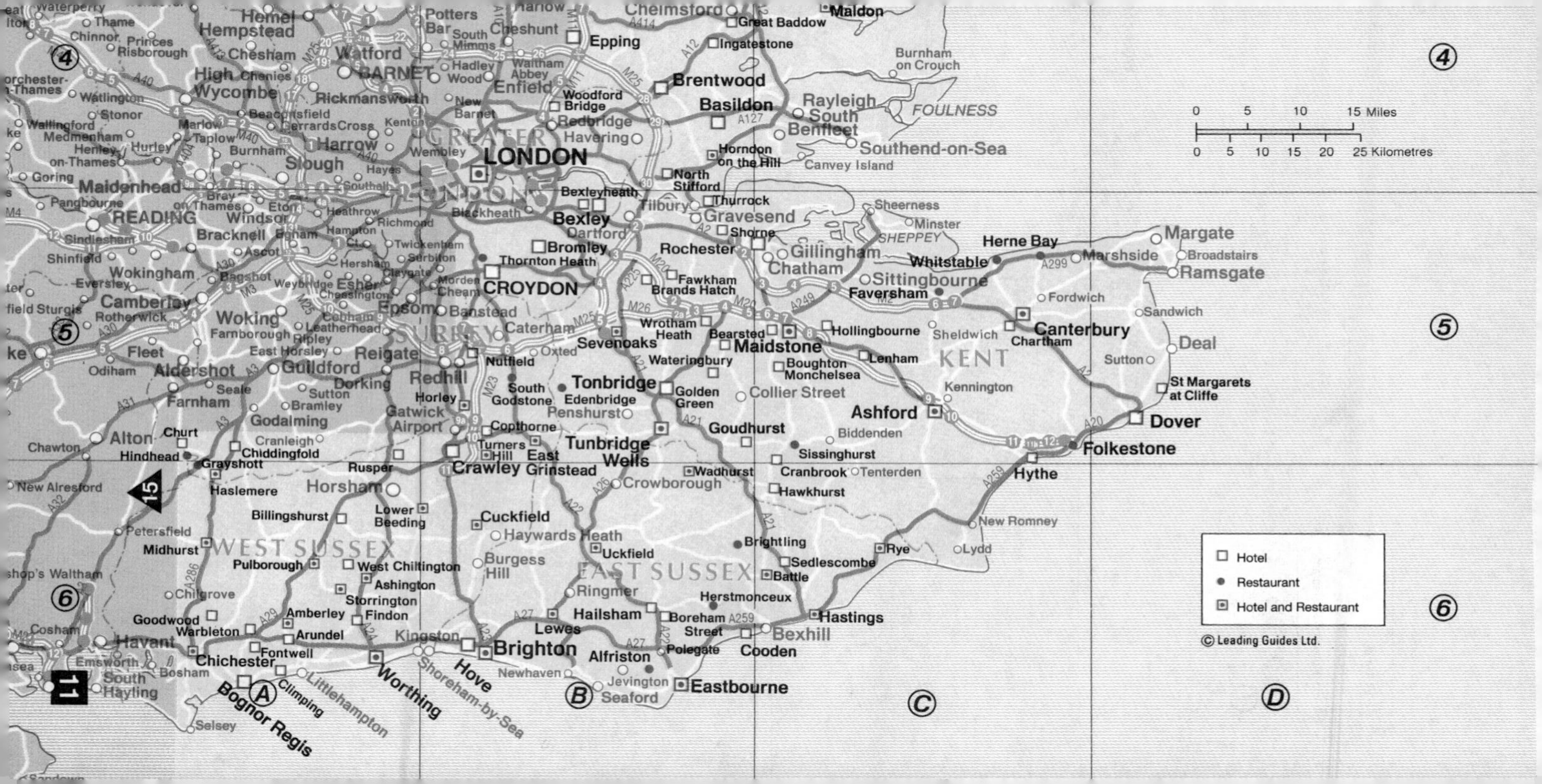
Hotel
Restaurant
Hotel and Restaurant
© Leading Guides Ltd.
0 5 10 15 Miles
0 5 10 15 20 25 Kilometres
11
15
4
5
6
A
B
C
D
LONDON
GREATER LONDON
CROYDON
READING
BARNET
SURREY
KENT
WEST SUSSEX
EAST SUSSEX
FOULNESS
SHEPPEY
Hemel Hempstead
Chesham
High Wycombe
Watford
Rickmansworth
Potters Bar
South Mimms
Cheshunt
Harlow
Chelmsford
Maldon
Great Baddow
Ingatestone
Epping
Brentwood
Basildon
Rayleigh
South Benfleet
Southend-on-Sea
Canvey Island
Burnham on Crouch
Thame
Chinnor
Princes Risborough
Waterperry
Dorchester-on-Thames
Watlington
Stonor
Wallingford
Medmenham
Henley-on-Thames
Hurley
Marlow
Taplow
Burnham
Beaconsfield
Gerrards Cross
Chenies
Harrow
Slough
Goring
Maidenhead
Bray on Thames
Pangbourne
Eton
Windsor
Heathrow
Hayes
Southall
Wembley
Kenton
Hadley Wood
Waltham Abbey
Enfield
New Barnet
Woodford Bridge
Redbridge
Havering
Horndon on the Hill
North Stifford
Thurrock
Tilbury
Gravesend
Shorne
Bexleyheath
Bexley
Dartford
Blackheath
Bromley
Thornton Heath
Richmond
Twickenham
Surbiton
Hampton Ct.
Egham
Bracknell
Ascot
Sindlesham
Shinfield
Wokingham
Eversley
Bagshot
Camberley
Sheffield Sturgis
Rotherwick
Weybridge
Hersham
Esher
Claygate
Chessington
Morden
Cheam
Epsom
Banstead
Cobham
Leatherhead
Woking
Farnborough
Ripley
East Horsley
Fleet
Odiham
Aldershot
Guildford
Reigate
Redhill
Caterham
Oxted
Nutfield
South Godstone
Dorking
Sutton
Seale
Farnham
Bramley
Godalming
Alton
Chawton
Churt
Hindhead
Grayshott
Chiddingfold
Cranleigh
Haslemere
New Alresford
Petersfield
Midhurst
Bishop's Waltham
Billingshurst
Horsham
Rusper
Lower Beeding
Horley
Gatwick Airport
Copthorne
Turners Hill
Crawley
East Grinstead
Cuckfield
Haywards Heath
Burgess Hill
Pulborough
West Chiltington
Ashington
Storrington
Findon
Amberley
Arundel
Fontwell
Chilgrove
Goodwood
Warbleton
Cosham
Havant
Emsworth
South Hayling
Bosham
Chichester
Selsey
Bognor Regis
Climping
Littlehampton
Worthing
Kingston
Shoreham-by-Sea
Hove
Brighton
Newhaven
Lewes
Ringmer
Uckfield
Hailsham
Alfriston
Jevington
Seaford
Polegate
Eastbourne
Boreham Street
Herstmonceux
Cooden
Bexhill
Hastings
Battle
Sedlescombe
Brightling
Rye
Lydd
New Romney
Hythe
Folkestone
Dover
St Margarets at Cliffe
Sutton
Deal
Sandwich
Ramsgate
Broadstairs
Margate
Marshside
Herne Bay
Whitstable
Fordwich
Canterbury
Chartham
Sheldwich
Faversham
Sittingbourne
Minster
Sheerness
Gillingham
Chatham
Rochester
Fawkham
Brands Hatch
Wrotham Heath
Sevenoaks
Bearsted
Maidstone
Hollingbourne
Lenham
Boughton Monchelsea
Wateringbury
Collier Street
Tonbridge
Edenbridge
Penshurst
Golden Green
Goudhurst
Tunbridge Wells
Crowborough
Wadhurst
Cranbrook
Tenterden
Sissinghurst
Biddenden
Hawkhurst
Ashford
Kennington
M25
M4
M40
M3
M23
M26
M20
M2
M11
A404
A413
A40
A30
A31
A3
A286
A32
A29
A24
A23
A27
A22
A26
A21
A259
A20
A2
A299
A249
A229
A225
A127
A12
A414
A10

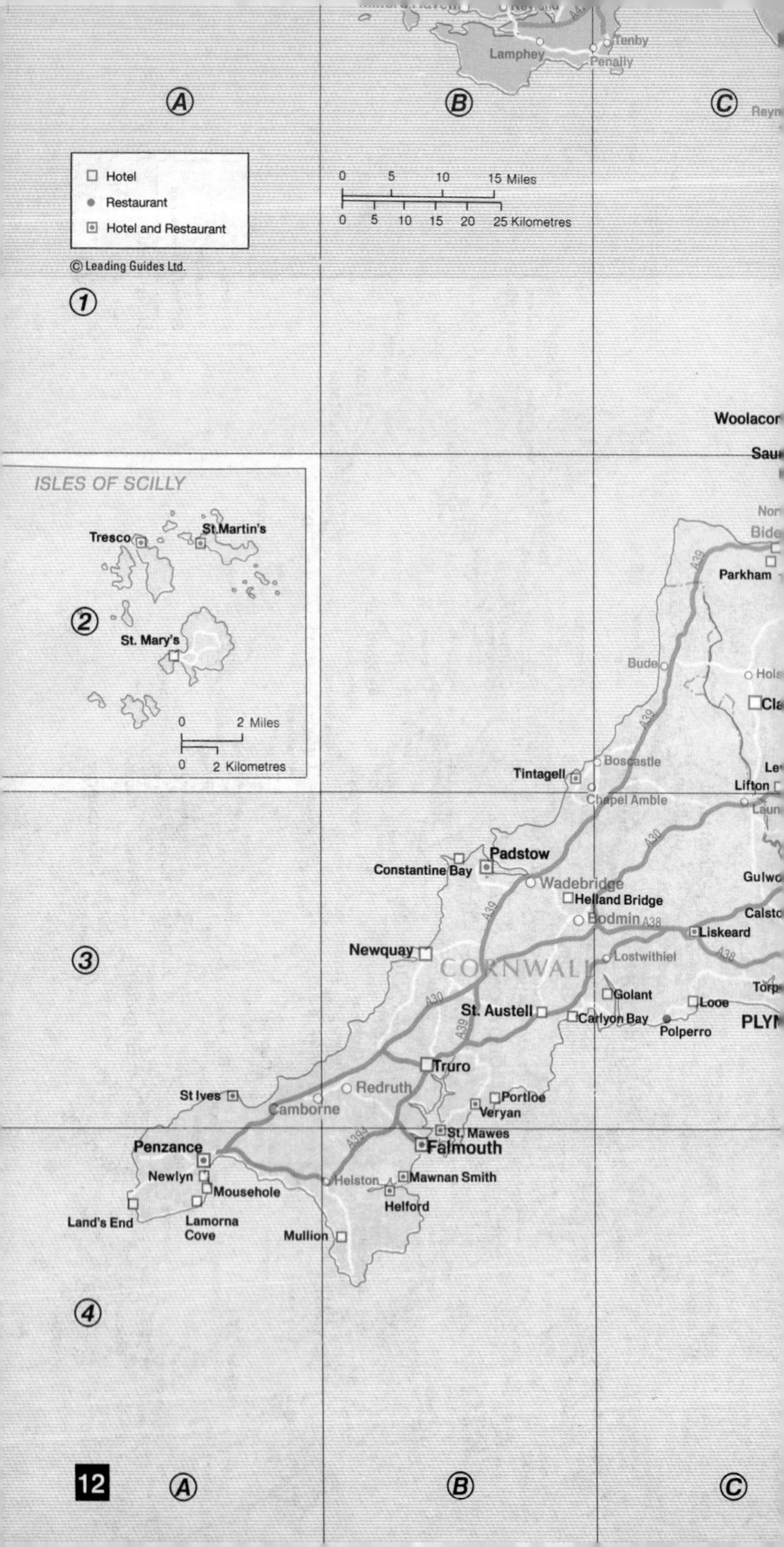

Lamphey
Tenby
Penally
A
B
C
Hotel
Restaurant
Hotel and Restaurant
© Leading Guides Ltd.
0 5 10 15 Miles
0 5 10 15 20 25 Kilometres
1
Woolacor
ISLES OF SCILLY
Tresco
St.Martin's
St. Mary's
0 2 Miles
0 2 Kilometres
2
Parkham
A39
Bude
Hols
Cla
Boscastle
Tintagell
Lifton
Chapel Amble
A30
Padstow
Constantine Bay
Wadebridge
Helland Bridge
Bodmin
A38
Liskeard
Gulwo
Calsto
Newquay
CORNWALL
Lostwithiel
3
Golant
Looe
St. Austell
Carlyon Bay
Polperro
Truro
Redruth
Camborne
St Ives
Portloe
Veryan
St. Mawes
Falmouth
A394
Penzance
Newlyn
Mousehole
Helston
Mawnan Smith
Helford
Land's End
Lamorna Cove
Mullion
4

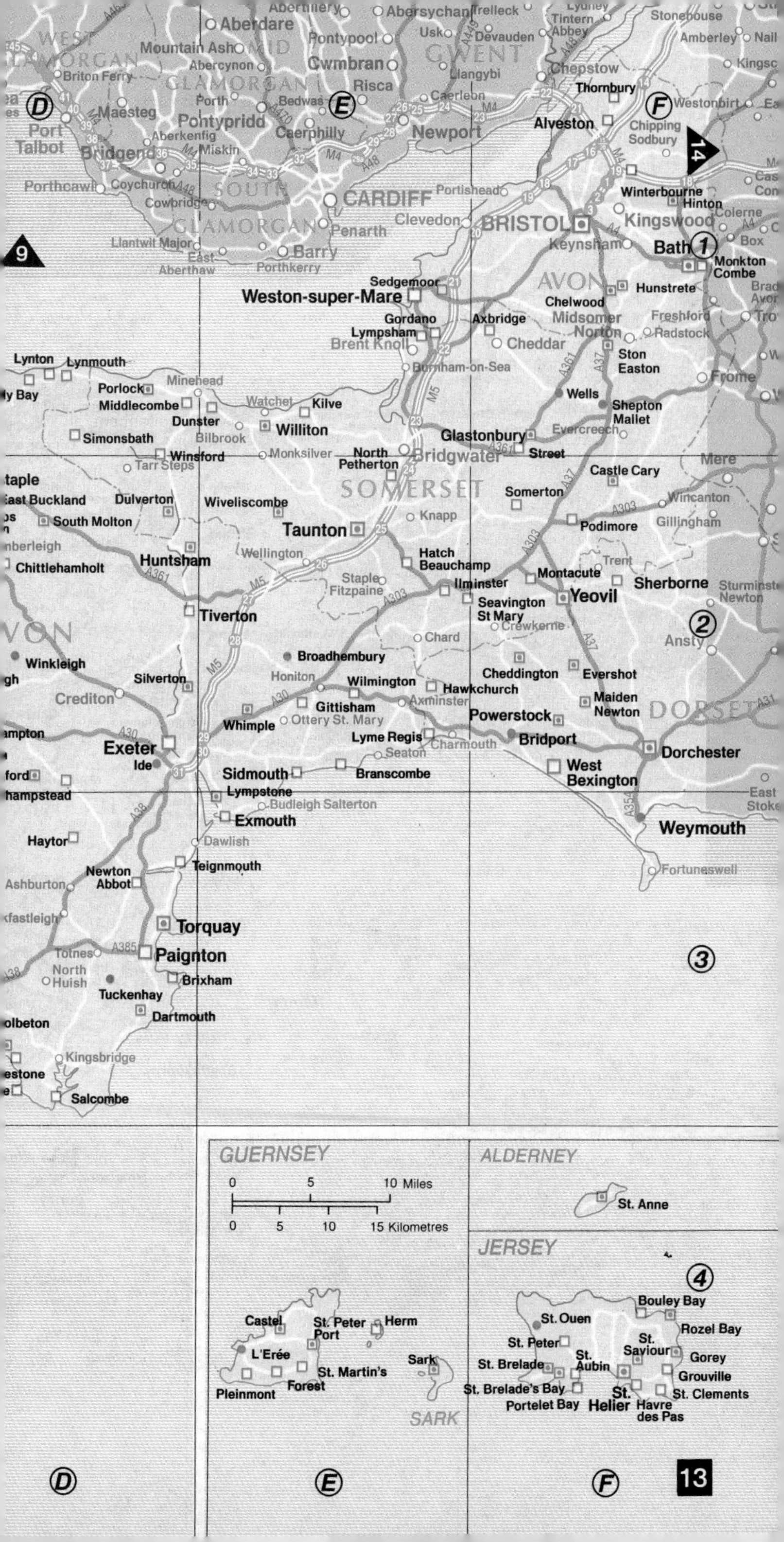

Aberdare
Abersychan
Trelleck
Tintern Abbey
Stonehouse
WEST GLAMORGAN
Mountain Ash
MID GLAMORGAN
Pontypool
Usk
Devauden
GWENT
Amberley
Nailsworth
Briton Ferry
Abercynon
Cwmbran
Llangybi
Chepstow
Kingscote
D
Maesteg
Porth
Bedwas
E
Risca
Caerleon
Thornbury
F
Westonbirt
Port Talbot
Pontypridd
Aberkenfig
Caerphilly
Newport
Alveston
Chipping Sodbury
14
Bridgend
Miskin
Porthcawl
Coychurch
Cowbridge
SOUTH GLAMORGAN
CARDIFF
Portishead
Winterbourne
Hinton
Penarth
Clevedon
BRISTOL
Kingswood
Colerne
Llantwit Major
East Aberthaw
Barry
Porthkerry
Keynsham
Bath
1
Box
Monkton Combe
9
Sedgemoor
AVON
Hunstrete
Weston-super-Mare
Chelwood
Gordano
Axbridge
Midsomer Norton
Freshford
Lympsham
Radstock
Brent Knoll
Cheddar
Ston Easton
Lynton
Lynmouth
Burnham-on-Sea
Minehead
Frome
Porlock
Wells
Middlecombe
Watchet
Kilve
Shepton Mallet
Dunster
Simonsbath
Bilbrook
Williton
Evercreech
Glastonbury
Winsford
Monksilver
North Petherton
Bridgwater
Street
Tarr Steps
Mere
Castle Cary
SOMERSET
East Buckland
Dulverton
Wiveliscombe
Somerton
Wincanton
South Molton
Knapp
Gillingham
Taunton
Podimore
Chittlehamholt
Huntsham
Wellington
Hatch Beauchamp
Trent
Staple Fitzpaine
Montacute
Sherborne
Ilminster
Yeovil
Sturminster Newton
Tiverton
Seavington St Mary
Crewkerne
2
Chard
Ansty
Winkleigh
Broadhembury
Cheddington
Evershot
Silverton
Honiton
Wilmington
Hawkchurch
Crediton
Gittisham
Axminster
Maiden Newton
DORSET
Whimple
Ottery St. Mary
Powerstock
Lyme Regis
Bridport
Exeter
Charmouth
Seaton
Dorchester
Ide
West Bexington
Sidmouth
Branscombe
Lympstone
East Stoke
Budleigh Salterton
Exmouth
Weymouth
Haytor
Dawlish
Fortuneswell
Newton Abbot
Teignmouth
Ashburton
Torquay
Totnes
Paignton
3
North Huish
Brixham
Tuckenhay
Dartmouth
Kingsbridge
Salcombe
GUERNSEY
0
5
10 Miles
0
5
10
15 Kilometres
ALDERNEY
St. Anne
JERSEY
4
Castel
St. Peter Port
Herm
Bouley Bay
St. Ouen
Rozel Bay
L'Erée
St. Peter
St. Saviour
Gorey
Sark
St. Brelade
St. Aubin
St. Martin's
Grouville
Forest
St. Brelade's Bay
St. Helier
St. Clements
Pleinmont
SARK
Portelet Bay
Havre des Pas
D
E
F

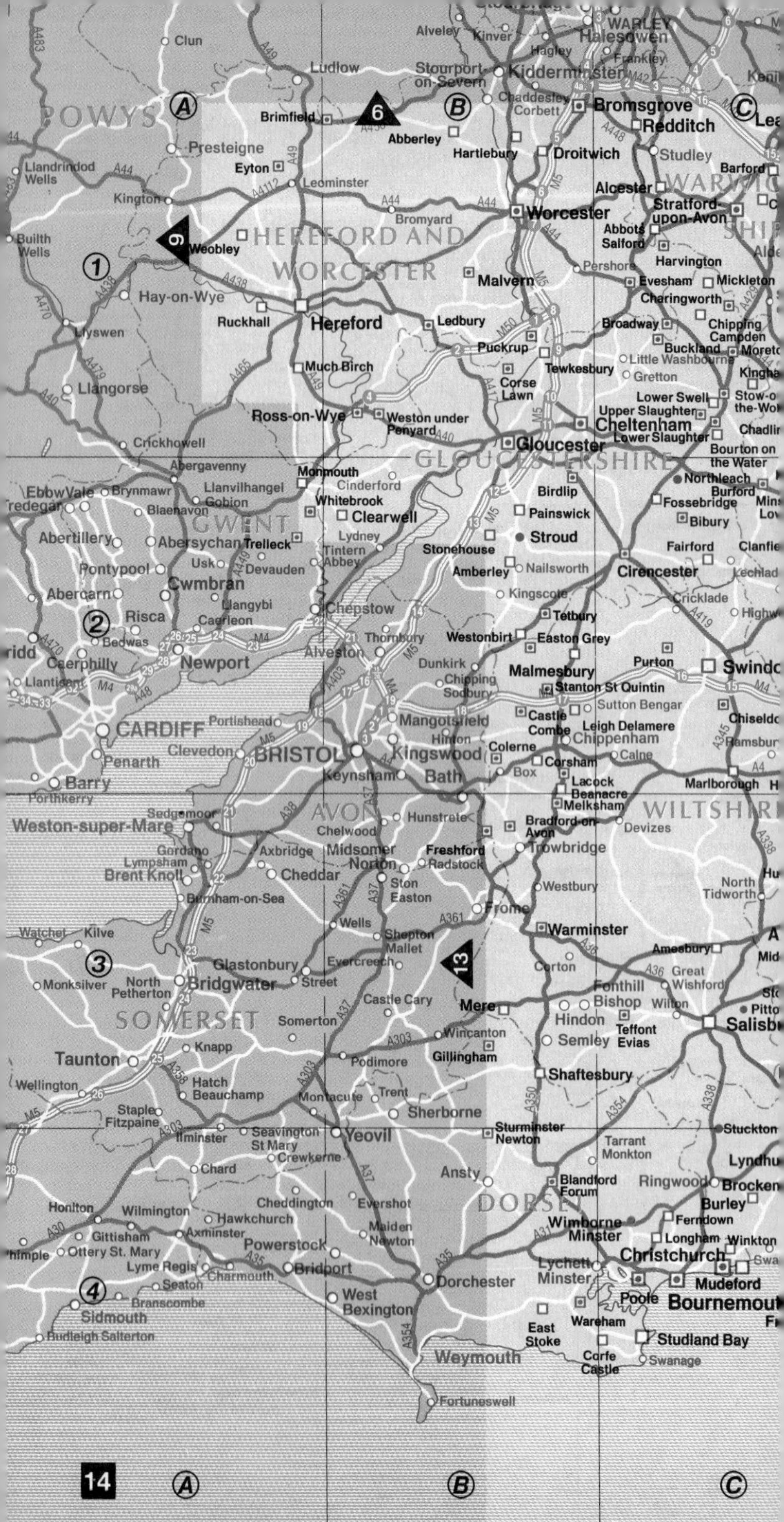

POWYS
HEREFORD AND WORCESTER
GLOUCESTERSHIRE
GWENT
AVON
WILTSHIRE
SOMERSET
DORSET
WARLEY
Halesowen
Frankley
Alveley
Kinver
Hagley
Clun
Ludlow
Stourport-on-Severn
Kidderminster
Chaddesley Corbett
Bromsgrove
Redditch
Brimfield
Abberley
Hartlebury
Droitwich
Studley
Presteigne
Eyton
Leominster
Llandrindod Wells
Kington
Bromyard
Worcester
Alcester
Stratford-upon-Avon
Barford
Abbots Salford
Harvington
Builth Wells
Weobley
Pershore
Evesham
Mickleton
Malvern
Charingworth
Hay-on-Wye
Llyswen
Ruckhall
Hereford
Ledbury
Broadway
Chipping Campden
Buckland
Puckrup
Tewkesbury
Little Washbourne
Gretton
Much Birch
Corse Lawn
Llangorse
Lower Swell
Stow-on-the-Wold
Upper Slaughter
Lower Slaughter
Cheltenham
Ross-on-Wye
Weston under Penyard
Gloucester
Bourton on the Water
Crickhowell
Abergavenny
Monmouth
Cinderford
Northleach
Burford
Llanvilhangel Gobion
Birdlip
Whitebrook
Ebbw Vale
Brynmawr
Blaenavon
Clearwell
Painswick
Fossebridge
Bibury
Tredegar
Stroud
Lydney
Abertillery
Abersychan
Trelleck
Tintern Abbey
Stonehouse
Fairford
Usk
Devauden
Pontypool
Amberley
Nailsworth
Cirencester
Cwmbran
Abercarn
Kingscote
Cricklade
Llangybi
Chepstow
Risca
Caerleon
Tetbury
Bedwas
Thornbury
Westonbirt
Easton Grey
Newport
Alveston
Caerphilly
Dunkirk
Purton
Swindon
Malmesbury
Llantisant
Chipping Sodbury
Stanton St Quintin
Sutton Bengar
Castle Combe
Mangotsfield
Leigh Delamere
CARDIFF
Portishead
Hinton
Chippenham
Clevedon
BRISTOL
Kingswood
Colerne
Corsham
Calne
Penarth
Keynsham
Box
Bath
Barry
Porthkerry
Lacock
Beanacre
Melksham
Marlborough
Sedgemoor
Hunstrete
Weston-super-Mare
Chelwood
Bradford-on-Avon
Devizes
Gordano
Axbridge
Midsomer Norton
Freshford
Radstock
Trowbridge
Lympsham
Brent Knoll
Cheddar
Ston Easton
Westbury
North Tidworth
Burnham-on-Sea
Wells
Frome
Watchet
Kilve
Shepton Mallet
Warminster
Amesbury
Glastonbury
Evercreech
Corton
Great Wishford
Monksilver
North Petherton
Bridgwater
Street
Fonthill Bishop
Castle Cary
Wilton
Mere
Hindon
Salisbury
Somerton
Teffont Evias
Wincanton
Semley
Knapp
Gillingham
Taunton
Podimore
Shaftesbury
Wellington
Hatch Beauchamp
Montacute
Trent
Staple Fitzpaine
Sherborne
Sturminster Newton
Stuckton
Ilminster
Seavington St Mary
Yeovil
Tarrant Monkton
Crewkerne
Chard
Ansty
Lyndhurst
Blandford Forum
Ringwood
Brockenhurst
Cheddington
Evershot
Burley
Honiton
Wilmington
Hawkchurch
Wimborne Minster
Ferndown
Gittisham
Axminster
Maiden Newton
Longham
Winkton
Ottery St. Mary
Powerstock
Christchurch
Lyme Regis
Charmouth
Bridport
Lychett Minster
Mudeford
Seaton
Dorchester
Poole
Bournemouth
Branscombe
West Bexington
Sidmouth
Wareham
East Stoke
Studland Bay
Budleigh Salterton
Weymouth
Corfe Castle
Swanage
Fortuneswell
A B C
1 2 3 4
6 9 13

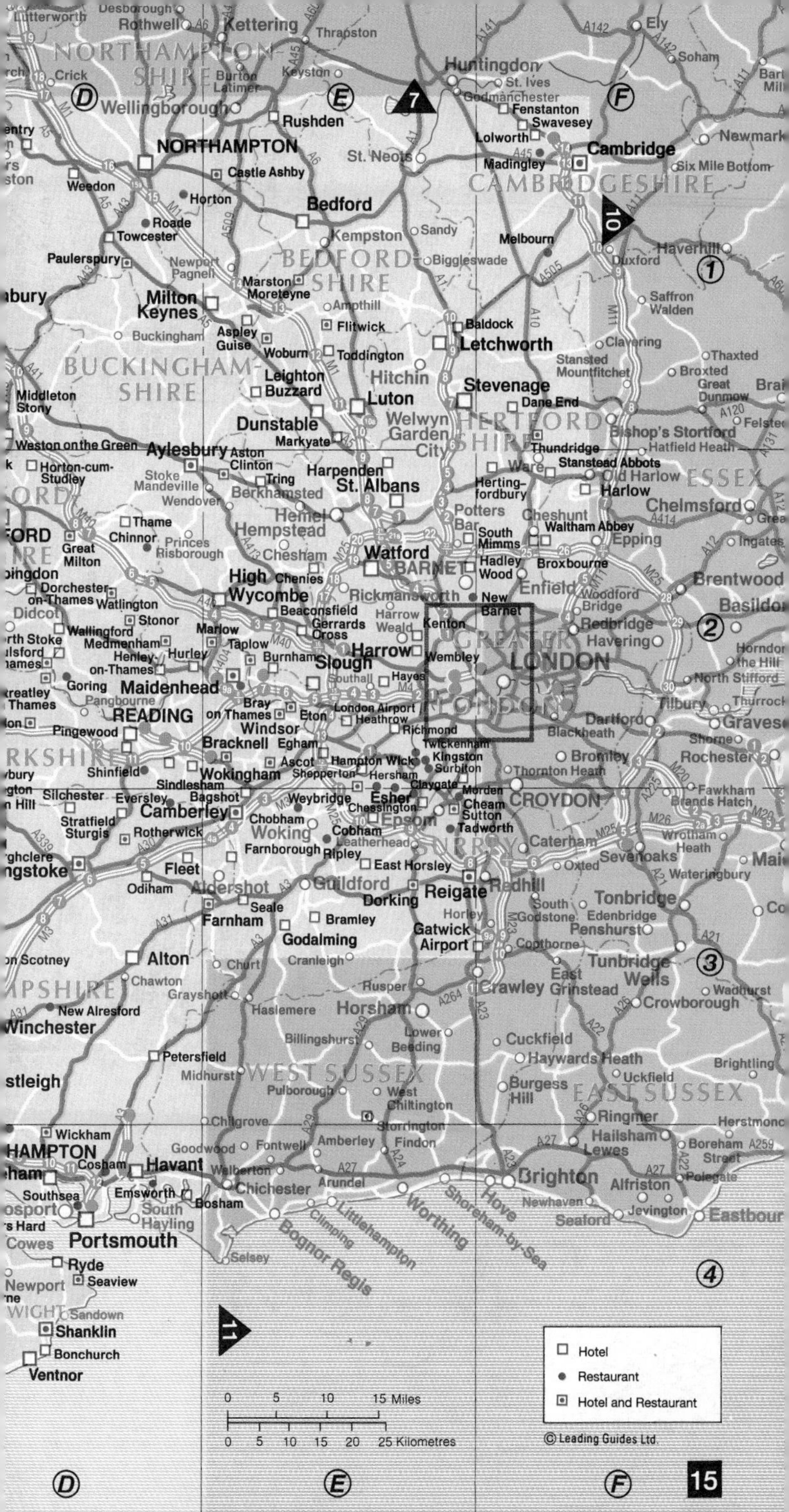
Kettering
Rothwell
Desborough
Thrapston
NORTHAMPTONSHIRE
Crick
Wellingborough
Burton Latimer
Keyston
Rushden
Huntingdon
St. Ives
Godmanchester
Fenstanton
Swavesey
Ely
Soham
Newmarket
Cambridge
Lolworth
Madingley
Six Mile Bottom
CAMBRIDGESHIRE
NORTHAMPTON
St. Neots
Castle Ashby
Weedon
Horton
Bedford
Roade
Towcester
Kempston
Sandy
Melbourn
Haverhill
Paulerspury
Newport Pagnell
BEDFORDSHIRE
Biggleswade
Duxford
Marston Moreteyne
Saffron Walden
Milton Keynes
Ampthill
Flitwick
Baldock
Letchworth
Clavering
Buckingham
Aspley Guise
Woburn
Toddington
Stansted Mountfitchet
Thaxted
BUCKINGHAMSHIRE
Leighton Buzzard
Hitchin
Stevenage
Broxted
Great Dunmow
Middleton Stony
Luton
Dane End
Dunstable
Welwyn Garden City
HERTFORDSHIRE
Bishop's Stortford
Felsted
Markyate
Thundridge
Hatfield Heath
Weston on the Green
Aylesbury
Aston Clinton
Horton-cum-Studley
Stoke Mandeville
Tring
Harpenden
St. Albans
Ware
Stanstead Abbots
Old Harlow
ESSEX
Wendover
Berkhamsted
Hertingfordbury
Harlow
Chelmsford
Hemel Hempstead
Potters Bar
Cheshunt
Thame
Chinnor
Princes Risborough
South Mimms
Waltham Abbey
Epping
Great Milton
Chesham
Watford
BARNET
Hadley Wood
Broxbourne
Ingatestone
High Wycombe
Chenies
Enfield
Brentwood
Dorchester-on-Thames
Watlington
Rickmansworth
New Barnet
Woodford Bridge
Basildon
Didcot
Stonor
Beaconsfield
Harrow Weald
Kenton
Redbridge
Wallingford
Marlow
Gerrards Cross
GREATER LONDON
Havering
Medmenham
Taplow
Harrow
Wembley
LONDON
Henley-on-Thames
Hurley
Burnham
Slough
Horndon on the Hill
Goring
Maidenhead
Southall
Hayes
North Stifford
Pangbourne
Bray on Thames
London Airport Heathrow
Tilbury
Thurrock
READING
Eton
Windsor
Richmond
Dartford
Gravesend
Pingewood
Bracknell
Egham
Blackheath
Twickenham
Kingston
Shorne
Ascot
Hampton Wick
Surbiton
Bromley
Rochester
Shinfield
Wokingham
Shepperton
Hersham
Thornton Heath
Sindlesham
Claygate
Morden
Fawkham
Silchester
Eversley
Bagshot
Weybridge
Esher
Cheam
CROYDON
Brands Hatch
Chessington
Sutton
Stratfield Sturgis
Camberley
Chobham
Epsom
Tadworth
Rotherwick
Woking
Cobham
Leatherhead
Caterham
Wrotham Heath
Farnborough
Ripley
SURREY
Sevenoaks
East Horsley
Oxted
Basingstoke
Fleet
Waterinbury
Odiham
Aldershot
Guildford
Reigate
Redhill
Tonbridge
Dorking
Seale
South Godstone
Farnham
Bramley
Horley
Edenbridge
Penshurst
Godalming
Gatwick Airport
Copthorne
Alton
Cranleigh
Tunbridge Wells
Churt
East Grinstead
Chawton
HAMPSHIRE
Rusper
Crawley
Grayshott
Wadhurst
Crowborough
Horsham
New Alresford
Haslemere
Winchester
Lower Beeding
Billingshurst
Cuckfield
Haywards Heath
Petersfield
Brightling
Midhurst
WEST SUSSEX
Uckfield
Pulborough
West Chiltington
Burgess Hill
EAST SUSSEX
Chilgrove
Storrington
Ringmer
Herstmonceux
Wickham
Amberley
Findon
Hailsham
Goodwood
Fontwell
Boreham Street
Cosham
Havant
Walberton
Arundel
Brighton
Lewes
Alfriston
Polegate
Southsea
Emsworth
Bosham
Chichester
Newhaven
Seaford
Jevington
Eastbourne
South Hayling
Littlehampton
Worthing
Shoreham-by-Sea
Hove
Gosport
Portsmouth
Climping
Bognor Regis
Cowes
Ryde
Selsey
Seaview
Newport
Sandown
Shanklin
Bonchurch
Ventnor
0 5 10 15 Miles
0 5 10 15 20 25 Kilometres
Hotel
Restaurant
Hotel and Restaurant
© Leading Guides Ltd.
D
E
F
1
2
3
4
7
10
11

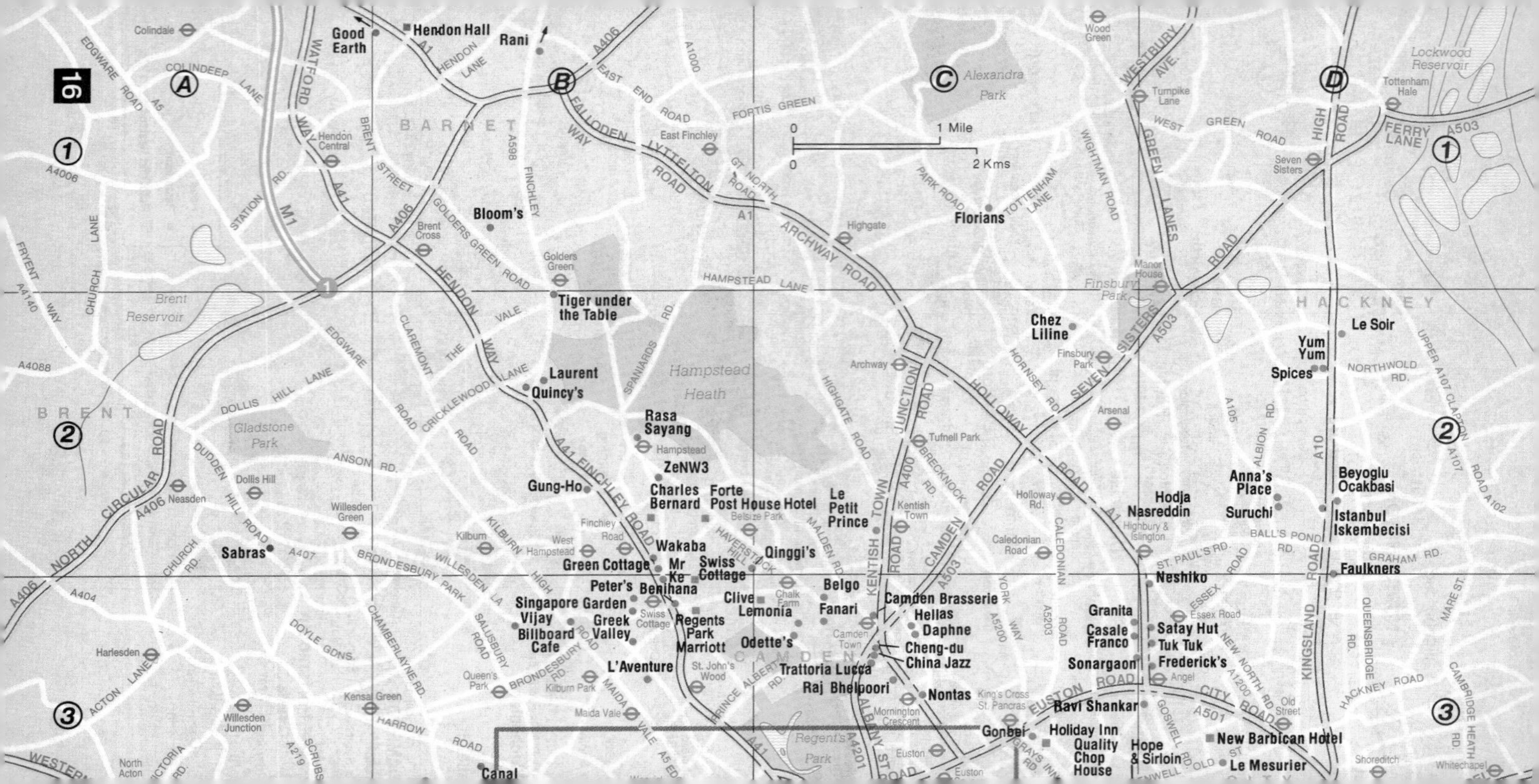
16
A
B
C
D
1
2
3
0 1 Mile
0 2 Kms
BARNET
BRENT
HACKNEY
CAMDEN
Good Earth
Hendon Hall
Rani
Bloom's
Tiger under the Table
Laurent
Quincy's
Rasa Sayang
ZeNW3
Gung-Ho
Charles Bernard
Forte Post House Hotel
Le Petit Prince
Wakaba
Green Cottage
Mr Ke
Swiss Cottage
Qinggi's
Peter's
Benihana
Singapore Garden
Vijay
Billboard Cafe
Greek Valley
Regents Park Marriott
Clive
Lemonia
Belgo
Fanari
Odette's
L'Aventure
Trattoria Lucca
Raj Bhelpoori
Camden Brasserie
Hellas
Daphne
Cheng-du
China Jazz
Nontas
Florians
Chez Liline
Hodja Nasreddin
Anna's Place
Suruchi
Le Soir
Yum Yum
Spices
Beyoglu Ocakbasi
Istanbul Iskembecisi
Faulkners
Neshiko
Granita
Casale Franco
Sonargaon
Satay Hut
Tuk Tuk
Frederick's
Ravi Shankar
Gonbei
Holiday Inn
Quality Chop House
Hope & Sirloin
New Barbican Hotel
Le Mesurier
Canal
Sabras
Hampstead Heath
Alexandra Park
Gladstone Park
Brent Reservoir
Lockwood Reservoir
Finsbury Park
Regent's Park

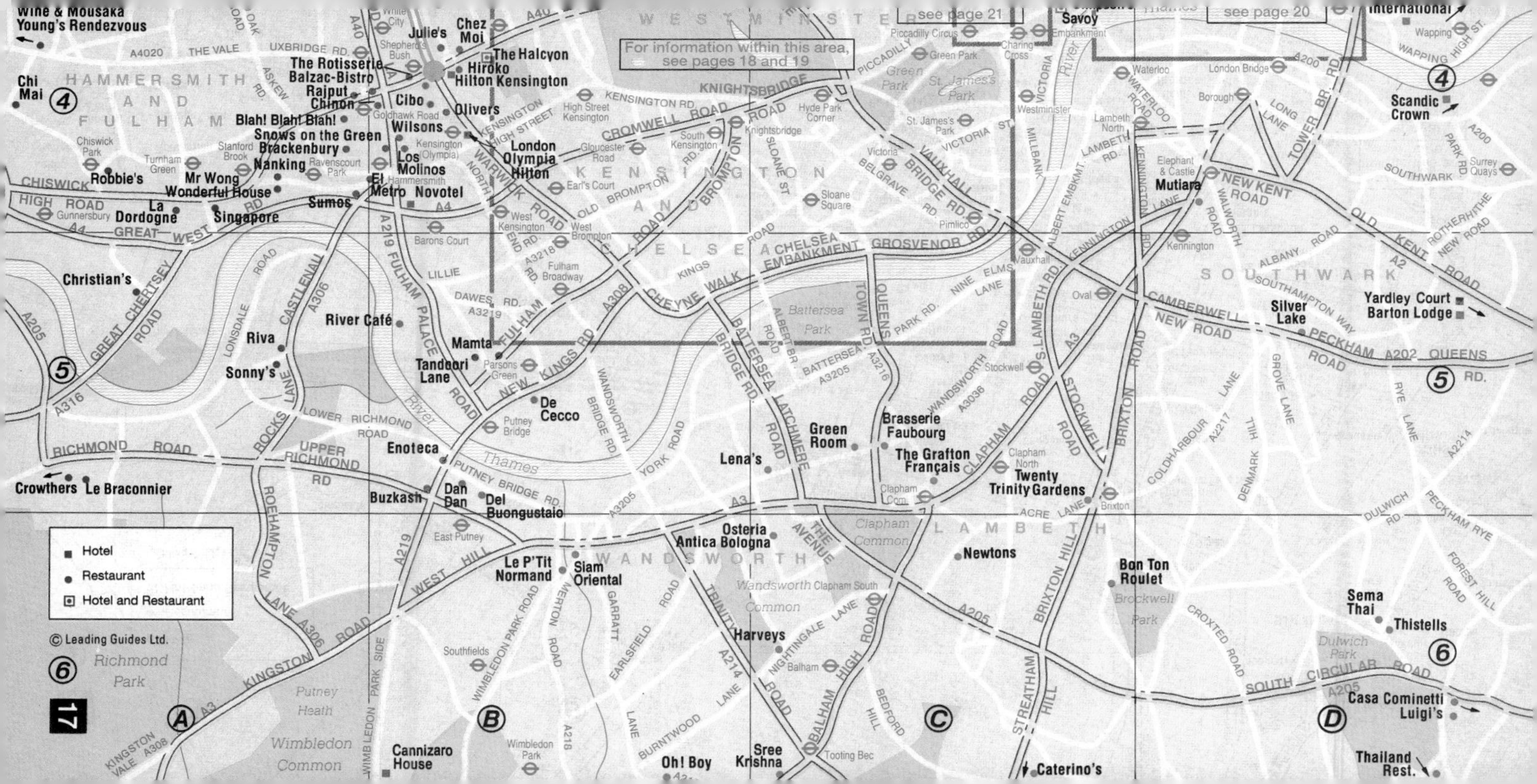

For information within this area, see pages 18 and 19
see page 21
see page 20
Hotel
Restaurant
Hotel and Restaurant
© Leading Guides Ltd.
17
Wine & Mousaka
Young's Rendezvous
Chi Mai
Robbie's
La Dordogne
Mr Wong
Wonderful House
Singapore
Nanking
Brackenbury
Snows on the Green
Blah! Blah! Blah!
Chinon
Rajput
Balzac-Bistro
The Rotisserie
Julie's
Chez Moi
The Halcyon
Hiroko
Hilton Kensington
Cibo
Olivers
Wilsons
Los Molinos
El Metro
Novotel
Sumos
London Olympia Hilton
Christian's
River Café
Riva
Sonny's
Mamta
Tandoori Lane
De Cecco
Enoteca
Buzkash
Dan Dan
Del Buongustaio
Crowthers
Le Braconnier
Le P'Tit Normand
Siam Oriental
Cannizaro House
Oh! Boy
Sree Krishna
Harveys
Osteria Antica Bologna
Lena's
Green Room
Brasserie Faubourg
The Grafton Français
Newtons
Twenty Trinity Gardens
Caterino's
Bon Ton Roulet
Savoy
Mutiara
Silver Lake
Yardley Court
Barton Lodge
Scandic Crown
International
Sema Thai
Thistells
Casa Cominetti
Luigi's
Thailand Rest.
HAMMERSMITH AND FULHAM
KENSINGTON AND CHELSEA
WESTMINSTER
SOUTHWARK
LAMBETH
WANDSWORTH
Richmond Park
Putney Heath
Wimbledon Common
Battersea Park
Clapham Common
Wandsworth Common
Brockwell Park
Dulwich Park
Green Park
St. James's Park
River Thames

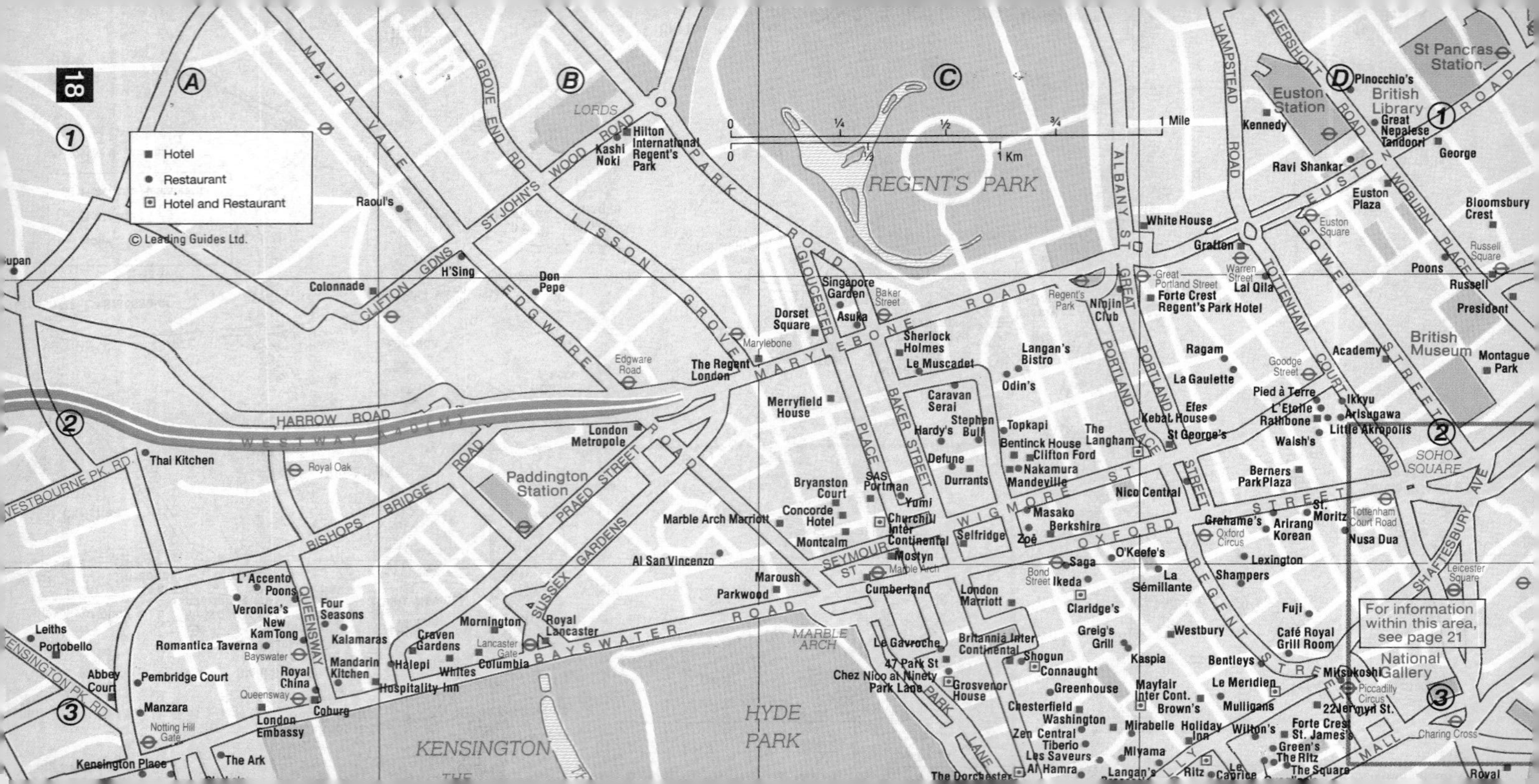

Hotel
Restaurant
Hotel and Restaurant
© Leading Guides Ltd.
A
B
C
D
1
2
3
0
1/4
1/2
3/4
1 Mile
1 Km
REGENT'S PARK
HYDE PARK
KENSINGTON
MARBLE ARCH
LORDS
SOHO SQUARE
MAIDA VALE
GROVE END RD
ST JOHN'S WOOD ROAD
PARK ROAD
LISSON GROVE
EDGWARE ROAD
CLIFTON GDNS
HARROW ROAD
WESTWAY
WESTBOURNE PK. RD.
KENSINGTON PK. RD
BISHOPS BRIDGE ROAD
PRAED STREET
SUSSEX GARDENS
BAYSWATER ROAD
QUEENSWAY
MARYLEBONE ROAD
GLOUCESTER PLACE
BAKER STREET
SEYMOUR ST
WIGMORE ST
OXFORD STREET
REGENT STREET
PORTLAND PLACE
GREAT PORTLAND STREET
ALBANY ST
HAMPSTEAD ROAD
EVERSHOLT ROAD
EUSTON ROAD
WOBURN PLACE
GOWER STREET
TOTTENHAM COURT ROAD
SHAFTESBURY AVE
PARK LANE
PICCADILLY
MALL
St Pancras Station
Euston Station
Paddington Station
British Library
British Museum
National Gallery
Euston Square
Warren Street
Great Portland Street
Regent's Park
Baker Street
Marylebone
Edgware Road
Royal Oak
Bayswater
Queensway
Notting Hill Gate
Lancaster Gate
Marble Arch
Bond Street
Oxford Circus
Goodge Street
Tottenham Court Road
Leicester Square
Piccadilly Circus
Charing Cross
Russell Square
For information within this area, see page 21
Pinocchio's
Kennedy
Great Nepalese Tandoori
George
Ravi Shankar
Euston Plaza
Bloomsbury Crest
Poons
Russell
President
Montague Park
White House
Grafton
Lal Qila
Forte Crest Regent's Park Hotel
Ragam
La Gaulette
Academy
Pied à Terre
Ikkyu
L'Etoile
Arisugawa
Rathbone
Little Akropolis
Walsh's
Efes Kebab House
St George's
Ninjin Club
Langan's Bistro
Odin's
The Langham
Topkapi
Bentinck House
Clifton Ford
Nakamura
Mandeville
Nico Central
Berners Park Plaza
Grehame's
Arirang Korean
St. Moritz
Nusa Dua
Lexington
Shampers
Masako
Berkshire
Zoë
O'Keefe's
La Sémillante
Saga
Ikeda
Claridge's
Fuji
Café Royal Grill Room
Westbury
Greig's Grill
Kaspia
Bentleys
Mitsukoshi
Le Meridien
Mulligans
22 Jermyn St.
Mayfair Inter Cont.
Brown's
Mirabelle
Holiday Inn
Wilton's
Forte Crest St. James's
Green's
The Ritz
The Square
Ritz
Le Caprice
Langan's
Miyama
Connaught
Greenhouse
Shogun
Chesterfield
Washington
Zen Central
Tiberio
Les Saveurs
Al Hamra
The Dorchester
Royal
Britannia Inter Continental
London Marriott
Grosvenor House
47 Park St
Chez Nico at Ninety Park Lane
Le Gavroche
Cumberland
Mostyn
Churchill Inter Continental
Selfridge
Yumi
SAS Portman
Bryanston Court
Concorde Hotel
Montcalm
Durrants
Defune
Hardy's
Stephen Bull
Caravan Serai
Sherlock Holmes
Le Muscadet
Merryfield House
Dorset Square
Singapore Garden
Asuka
The Regent London
Marble Arch Marriott
Al San Vincenzo
Maroush
Parkwood
London Metropole
Royal Lancaster
Mornington
Craven Gardens
Halepi
Whites
Columbia
Hospitality Inn
Mandarin Kitchen
Four Seasons
Kalamaras
L'Accento
Poons
Veronica's
New Kam Tong
Romantica Taverna
Royal China
Coburg
London Embassy
Leiths
Portobello
Abbey Court
Pembridge Court
Manzara
Kensington Place
The Ark
Thai Kitchen
H'Sing
Don Pepe
Colonnade
Raoul's
Kashi Noki
Hilton International Regent's Park

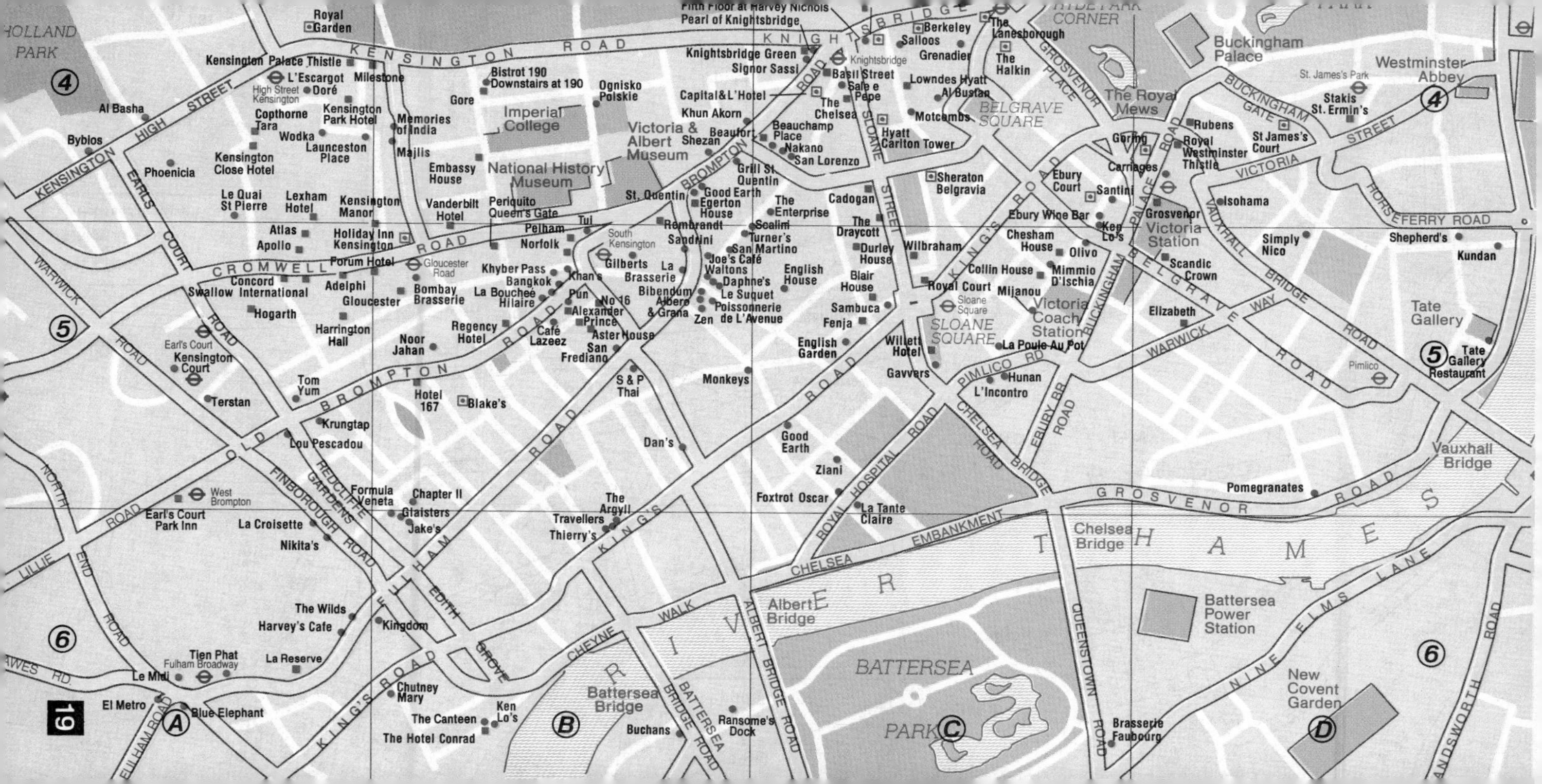
HOLLAND PARK
KENSINGTON ROAD
KNIGHTSBRIDGE
HYDE PARK CORNER
Buckingham Palace
Westminster Abbey
St. James's Park
Royal Garden
Fifth Floor at Harvey Nichols
Pearl of Knightsbridge
Berkeley
Salloos
Grenadier
The Lanesborough
The Halkin
Knightsbridge Green
Signor Sassi
Knightsbridge
Basil Street
Sale e Pepe
The Chelsea
Lowndes Hyatt
Al Bustan
Motcombs
BELGRAVE SQUARE
The Royal Mews
GROSVENOR PLACE
BUCKINGHAM GATE
St James's Court
Stakis St. Ermin's
Rubens
Royal Westminster Thistle
Goring
Carriages
VICTORIA STREET
Kensington Palace Thistle
L'Escargot
High Street Kensington
Doré
Milestone
Bistrot 190
Downstairs at 190
Gore
Ognisko Polskie
Imperial College
Victoria & Albert Museum
Capital & L'Hotel
Khun Akorn
Beaufort
Shezan
Beauchamp Place
Nakano
San Lorenzo
Hyatt Carlton Tower
SLOANE STREET
Al Basha
Bybios
HIGH STREET
KENSINGTON
Copthorne Tara
Wodka
Kensington Park Hotel
Launceston Place
Memories of India
Majlis
Embassy House
National History Museum
Kensington Close Hotel
Phoenicia
EARLS COURT ROAD
Le Quai St Pierre
Lexham Hotel
Kensington Manor
Vanderbilt Hotel
Periquito Queen's Gate
St. Quentin
Good Earth
Egerton House
Grill St Quentin
BROMPTON ROAD
Sheraton Belgravia
Cadogan
The Enterprise
Ebury Court
Santini
Ebury Wine Bar
Ken Lo's
Grosvenor
Victoria Station
PALACE ROAD
Isohama
VAUXHALL BRIDGE ROAD
HORSEFERRY ROAD
Simply Nico
Shepherd's
Kundan
Atlas
Apollo
Holiday Inn Kensington
CROMWELL ROAD
Forum Hotel
Gloucester Road
Pelham
Tui
Norfolk
South Kensington
Rembrandt
Sandrini
Scalini
Turner's
San Martino
The Draycott
Durley House
Wilbraham
Chesham House
Olivo
Collin House
Mimmio D'Ischia
Scandic Crown
Tate Gallery
Concord
Swallow International
Adelphi
Gloucester
Khyber Pass
Bangkok
Bombay Brasserie
La Bouchée
Hilaire
Khan's
Gilberts
La Brasserie
Joe's Café
Waltons
Daphne's
English House
Blair House
Royal Court
Mijanou
Victoria Coach Station
BUCKINGHAM PALACE ROAD
BELGRAVE ROAD
WARWICK WAY
Elizabeth
Hogarth
Harrington Hall
Regency Hotel
Pun
No 16
Alexander
Prince
Bibendum
Albero & Grana
Le Suquet
Poissonnerie de L'Avenue
Zen
Sambuca
Fenja
Sloane Square
SLOANE SQUARE
La Poule Au Pot
Tate Gallery Restaurant
Pimlico
WARWICK ROAD
Earl's Court
Kensington Court
Noor Jahan
Café Lazeez
Aster House
San Frediano
English Garden
Willett Hotel
Gavvers
PIMLICO RD
Hunan
L'Incontro
Tom Yum
Terstan
BROMPTON ROAD
Hotel 167
Blake's
S & P Thai
Monkeys
Krungtap
Lou Pescadou
Dan's
Good Earth
Ziani
ROYAL HOSPITAL ROAD
CHELSEA BRIDGE ROAD
EBURY BR ROAD
Vauxhall Bridge
GROSVENOR ROAD
Pomegranates
NORTH END ROAD
West Brompton
Earl's Court Park Inn
REDCLIFFE GARDENS
FINBOROUGH ROAD
Formula Veneta
Chapter II
Glaisters
Jake's
The Argyll
Travellers
Thierry's
KING'S ROAD
Foxtrot Oscar
La Tante Claire
CHELSEA EMBANKMENT
Chelsea Bridge
THAMES
La Croisette
Nikita's
LILLIE ROAD
FULHAM ROAD
EDITH GROVE
Albert Bridge
RIVER
Battersea Power Station
NINE ELMS LANE
The Wilds
Harvey's Cafe
Kingdom
CHEYNE WALK
ALBERT BRIDGE ROAD
QUEENSTOWN ROAD
Tien Phat
Fulham Broadway
La Reserve
Le Midi
BATTERSEA
New Covent Garden
El Metro
Blue Elephant
Chutney Mary
The Canteen
The Hotel Conrad
Ken Lo's
Battersea Bridge
BATTERSEA BRIDGE ROAD
Buchans
Ransome's Dock
PARK
Brasserie Faubourg
WANDSWORTH ROAD
A
B
C
D
4
5
6

Hotel
Restaurant
Hotel and Restaurant
© Leading Guides Ltd.
Bubb's
The Howard
Miyama
Corney & Barrow
Whittingtons
Sri Siam City
Corney & Barrow
Imperial City
Luc's
Poons in the City
Namaste
Manzi's
Tower Thistle
RSJ
Smithfield Markets
National Postal Museum
Holborn Viaduct Sta.
St. Paul's Cathedral
Museum of London
Barbican
Guildhall Sch. of Music and Drama
Liverpool Street Station
Stock Exchange
Bank of England
Mansion House
Cannon Street Stn.
Fenchurch St. Station
Blackfriars Stn.
Royal Courts of Justice
Old Billingsgate Market
Customs House
The Tower of London
World Trade Ctre
Southwark Cathedral
L.W.T. Centre
National Theatre
RIVER THAMES
HOLBORN
FLEET STREET
CHEAPSIDE
QUEEN VICTORIA STREET
UPPER THAMES STREET
VICTORIA EMBANKMENT
LONDON WALL
BISHOPSGATE
LEADENHALL STREET
FENCHURCH STREET
CANNON STREET
LOWER THAMES STREET
LONDON BRIDGE
SOUTHWARK BRIDGE
BLACKFRIARS BRIDGE
TOWER BRIDGE APPROACH
0 220 440 yards
0 200 400 metres

British Museum
Kenilworth
Museum Street Café
Wagamama
St. Giles
Marlborough Crest
Drury Lane Moat House
Ajimura
Bhatti
Gay Hussar
Au Jardin des Gourmets
Bistrot Bruno
Rasa Sayang
Dell'ugo
Soho Soho
L'Escargot
Miyako
Est
Alastair Little
Bahn Thai
Chiang Mai
Sri Siam
La Reash
Lindsay House
Panda
Ming
French House Dining Room
New World
Lok Ho Fook
Dragon Inn
New Fook Lam Moon
Harbour City
Lido
Dragons Nest
Chuen Cheng ku
Hong Kong
Fung Shing
Jade Garden
Manzi's
Joy King Lau
Poons
Thai Pavilion
Rasa Sayang
Hospitality Inn
The Hampshire Hotel
Café Fish
Royal Trafalgar Thistle
Mon Plaisir
Neal Street
Mountbatten
Kagura
The Ivy
Tageen
Now And Zen
Le Palais du Jardin
Arts Theatre Café
Poons
Sheekey's
Giovannis
Café Pelican
Bertorelli's
Royal Opera House
Poons of Covent Garden
L'Estaminet
Covent Garden Market
Boulestin
Nat. Portrait Gallery
National Gallery
Nelson's Column
Charing Cross Station
Admiralty Arch
Design Centre
Tottenham Court Road
Leicester Square
Covent Garden
Charing Cross
Tottenham Court Road
New Oxford Street
Oxford Street
Bloomsbury Street
Great Russell Street
Bedford Square
Bedford Avenue
Bainbridge Street
Streatham Street
Bucknall Street
Earnshaw Street
Dyott Street
Shaftesbury Avenue
St Giles High Street
Princes Circus
High Holborn
Endell Street
Charing Cross Road
Denmark Street
Monmouth Street
Upper St Martins Lane
Neal Street
Earlham Street
Mercer St
Long Acre
Garrick Street
King Street
Henrietta Street
Maiden Lane
Bedford Street
Chandos Place
William IV Street
Strand
Duncannon Street
Trafalgar Square
Pall Mall East
Pall Mall
Cockspur Street
Northumberland Avenue
Whitehall
Villiers Street
Craven Street
John Adam Street
Irving Street
Orange Street
Panton Street
Gerrard Street
Lisle Street
Leicester St
Old Compton Street
Greek St
Frith Street
Dean Street
Romilly Street
Soho Sq.
110
220yards
100
200metres
Hotel
Restaurant
Hotel and Restaurant
Leading Guides Ltd.

A
B
C
D
1
2
3
Hotel
Restaurant
Hotel and Restaurant
© Leading Guides Ltd.
Bushmills
Portrush
Portballintrae
Rosapenna
Rathmullan
Coleraine
Limavady
Garvagh
Londonderry
ANTRIM
LONDONDERRY
Ballymena
Larne
DONEGAL
Strabane
Carrickfergus
Bangor
Dunadry
Antrim
Templepatrick
Holywood
Crawfordsburn
BELFAST
Newtownards
Dunmurry
Comber
Lisburn
Saintfield
Donegal
TYRONE
Cookstown
Omagh
Rossnowlagh
Ballyshannon
Dungannon
Enniskillen
Lurgan
Portadown
FERMANAGH
Armagh
DOWN
Downpatrick
Sligo
Blacklion
Monaghan
ARMAGH
Newcastle
Newry
Collooney
Riverstown
Clones
MONAGHAN
Annalong
Ballina
Crossmolina
SLIGO
Ballyconnell
Scotshouse
Boyle
Carlingford
MAYO
LEITRIM
Dundalk
Cavan
Carrick-on-Shannon
Carrickmacross
Newport
Charlestown
Castlebar
CAVAN
LOUTH
ROSCOMMON
LONGFORD
Longford
Drogheda
Ceanannas Mor
Claremorris
Navan
Renvyle
Roscommon
Dunderry

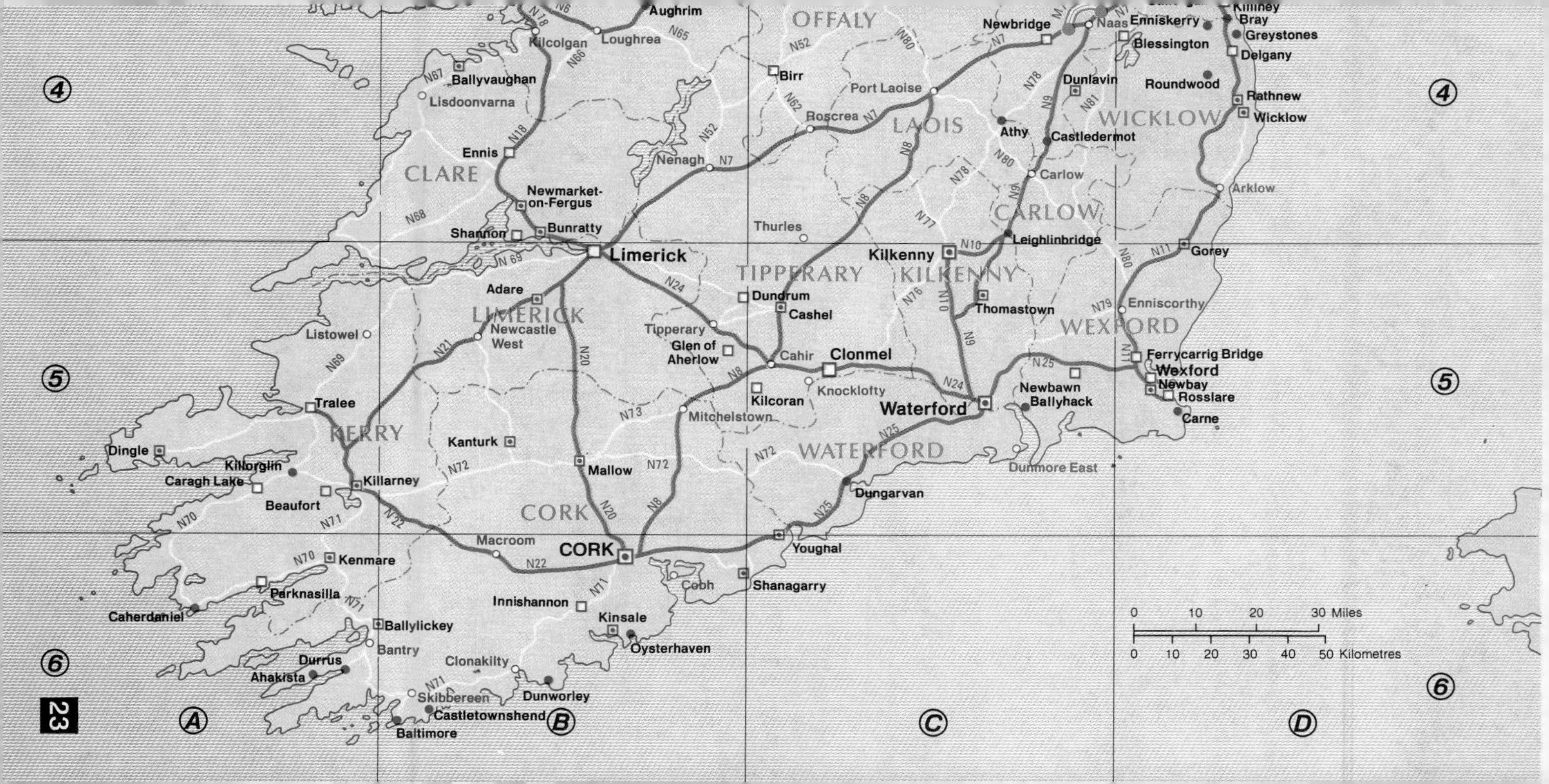
OFFALY
CLARE
LAOIS
WICKLOW
CARLOW
TIPPERARY
KILKENNY
LIMERICK
WEXFORD
KERRY
WATERFORD
CORK
Aughrim
Loughrea
Kilcolgan
Ballyvaughan
Lisdoonvarna
Ennis
Newmarket-on-Fergus
Shannon
Bunratty
Limerick
Nenagh
Birr
Port Laoise
Roscrea
Newbridge
Naas
Enniskerry
Blessington
Killiney
Bray
Greystones
Delgany
Roundwood
Rathnew
Wicklow
Dunlavin
Athy
Castledermot
Carlow
Arklow
Leighlinbridge
Gorey
Thurles
Kilkenny
Thomastown
Enniscorthy
Ferrycarrig Bridge
Wexford
Newbay
Rosslare
Carne
Adare
Newcastle West
Listowel
Dundrum
Cashel
Tipperary
Glen of Aherlow
Cahir
Clonmel
Knocklofty
Kilcoran
Mitchelstown
Waterford
Newbawn
Ballyhack
Dunmore East
Dungarvan
Tralee
Dingle
Killorglin
Caragh Lake
Beaufort
Killarney
Kanturk
Mallow
Macroom
CORK
Youghal
Cobh
Shanagarry
Kenmare
Parknasilla
Caherdaniel
Innishannon
Kinsale
Oysterhaven
Ballylickey
Bantry
Durrus
Ahakista
Clonakilty
Dunworley
Skibbereen
Castletownshend
Baltimore
N18
N6
N65
N66
N67
N68
N69
N52
N62
N7
N80
N78
N9
N81
N8
N77
N10
N11
N79
N76
N24
N25
N21
N20
N13
N72
N22
N70
N71
N 69
0 10 20 30 Miles
0 10 20 30 40 50 Kilometres
4
5
6
A
B
C
D

THE VIBRANT SPIRIT OF ROME
First distilled in 1875 by the Pallini family, Romana can be served in many different ways - Con Mosca (with three coffee beans), neat over ice or long with your favourite mixer.
ROMANA
ROMANA SAMBVCA
LIQUORE CLASSICO
Liqueur
PRODUCT OF ITALY

Index

READERS' COMMENTS

Please use this sheet, and the continuation overleaf, to recommend hotels or restaurants of **really outstanding quality.**

Complaints about any of the Guide's entries will be treated seriously and passed on to our inspectorate, but we would like to remind you always to take up your complaint with the management at the time.

We regret that owing to the volume of readers' communications received each year, we will be unable to acknowledge all these forms, but they will certainly be seriously considered.

Please post to: **Egon Ronay's Guides, 73 Uverdale Road, London SW10 0SW**

Please use an up-to-date Guide. We publish annually. (H&R 1994)

Name and address of establishment	**Your recommendation or complaint**

Readers' Comments continued

Name and address of establishment	**Your recommendation or complaint**

Your Name (BLOCK LETTERS PLEASE)

Address

READERS' COMMENTS

Please use this sheet, and the continuation overleaf, to recommend hotels or restaurants of **really outstanding quality.**

Complaints about any of the Guide's entries will be treated seriously and passed on to our inspectorate, but we would like to remind you always to take up your complaint with the management at the time.

We regret that owing to the volume of readers' communications received each year, we will be unable to acknowledge all these forms, but they will certainly be seriously considered.

Please post to: **Egon Ronay's Guides, 73 Uverdale Road, London SW10 0SW**

Please use an up-to-date Guide. We publish annually. (H&R 1994)

Name and address of establishment	**Your recommendation or complaint**

Readers' Comments continued

Name and address of establishment	**Your recommendation or complaint**

Your Name (BLOCK LETTERS PLEASE)

Address

READERS' COMMENTS

Please use this sheet, and the continuation overleaf, to recommend hotels or restaurants of **really outstanding quality.**

Complaints about any of the Guide's entries will be treated seriously and passed on to our inspectorate, but we would like to remind you always to take up your complaint with the management at the time.

We regret that owing to the volume of readers' communications received each year, we will be unable to acknowledge all these forms, but they will certainly be seriously considered.

Please post to: **Egon Ronay's Guides, 73 Uverdale Road, London SW10 0SW**

Please use an up-to-date Guide. We publish annually. (H&R 1994)

Name and address of establishment	**Your recommendation or complaint**

Readers' Comments continued

Name and address of establishment	**Your recommendation or complaint**

Your Name (BLOCK LETTERS PLEASE)

Address

READERS' COMMENTS

Please use this sheet, and the continuation overleaf, to recommend hotels or restaurants of **really outstanding quality.**

Complaints about any of the Guide's entries will be treated seriously and passed on to our inspectorate, but we would like to remind you always to take up your complaint with the management at the time.

We regret that owing to the volume of readers' communications received each year, we will be unable to acknowledge all these forms, but they will certainly be seriously considered.

Please post to: **Egon Ronay's Guides, 73 Uverdale Road, London SW10 0SW**

Please use an up-to-date Guide. We publish annually. (H&R 1994)

Name and address of establishment	Your recommendation or complaint

Readers' Comments continued

Name and address of establishment	**Your recommendation or complaint**

Your Name (BLOCK LETTERS PLEASE)

Address

READERS' COMMENTS

Please use this sheet, and the continuation overleaf, to recommend hotels or restaurants of **really outstanding quality.**

Complaints about any of the Guide's entries will be treated seriously and passed on to our inspectorate, but we would like to remind you always to take up your complaint with the management at the time.

We regret that owing to the volume of readers' communications received each year, we will be unable to acknowledge all these forms, but they will certainly be seriously considered.

Please post to: **Egon Ronay's Guides, 73 Uverdale Road, London SW10 0SW**

Please use an up-to-date Guide. We publish annually. (H&R 1994)

Name and address of establishment	**Your recommendation or complaint**

Readers' Comments continued

Name and address of establishment	**Your recommendation or complaint**

Your Name (BLOCK LETTERS PLEASE)

Address

READERS' COMMENTS

Please use this sheet, and the continuation overleaf, to recommend hotels or restaurants of **really outstanding quality.**

Complaints about any of the Guide's entries will be treated seriously and passed on to our inspectorate, but we would like to remind you always to take up your complaint with the management at the time.

We regret that owing to the volume of readers' communications received each year, we will be unable to acknowledge all these forms, but they will certainly be seriously considered.

Please post to: **Egon Ronay's Guides, 73 Uverdale Road, London SW10 0SW**

Please use an up-to-date Guide. We publish annually. (H&R 1994)

Name and address of establishment	Your recommendation or complaint

Readers' Comments continued

Name and address of establishment	**Your recommendation or complaint**

Your Name (BLOCK LETTERS PLEASE)

Address

READERS' COMMENTS

Please use this sheet, and the continuation overleaf, to recommend hotels or restaurants of **really outstanding quality.**

Complaints about any of the Guide's entries will be treated seriously and passed on to our inspectorate, but we would like to remind you always to take up your complaint with the management at the time.

We regret that owing to the volume of readers' communications received each year, we will be unable to acknowledge all these forms, but they will certainly be seriously considered.

Please post to: **Egon Ronay's Guides, 73 Uverdale Road, London SW10 0SW**

Please use an up-to-date Guide. We publish annually. (H&R 1994)

Name and address of establishment	**Your recommendation or complaint**

Readers' Comments continued

Name and address of establishment	Your recommendation or complaint

Your Name (BLOCK LETTERS PLEASE)

Address

READERS' COMMENTS

Please use this sheet, and the continuation overleaf, to recommend hotels or restaurants of **really outstanding quality.**

Complaints about any of the Guide's entries will be treated seriously and passed on to our inspectorate, but we would like to remind you always to take up your complaint with the management at the time.

We regret that owing to the volume of readers' communications received each year, we will be unable to acknowledge all these forms, but they will certainly be seriously considered.

Please post to: **Egon Ronay's Guides, 73 Uverdale Road, London SW10 0SW**

Please use an up-to-date Guide. We publish annually. (H&R 1994)

Name and address of establishment	**Your recommendation or complaint**

Readers' Comments continued

Name and address of establishment	**Your recommendation or complaint**

Your Name (BLOCK LETTERS PLEASE)

Address

READERS' COMMENTS

Please use this sheet, and the continuation overleaf, to recommend hotels or restaurants of **really outstanding quality.**

Complaints about any of the Guide's entries will be treated seriously and passed on to our inspectorate, but we would like to remind you always to take up your complaint with the management at the time.

We regret that owing to the volume of readers' communications received each year, we will be unable to acknowledge all these forms, but they will certainly be seriously considered.

Please post to: **Egon Ronay's Guides, 73 Uverdale Road, London SW10 0SW**

Please use an up-to-date Guide. We publish annually. (H&R 1994)

Name and address of establishment	Your recommendation or complaint

Readers' Comments continued

Name and address of establishment	**Your recommendation or complaint**

Your Name (BLOCK LETTERS PLEASE)

Address

READERS' COMMENTS

Please use this sheet, and the continuation overleaf, to recommend hotels or restaurants of **really outstanding quality.**

Complaints about any of the Guide's entries will be treated seriously and passed on to our inspectorate, but we would like to remind you always to take up your complaint with the management at the time.

We regret that owing to the volume of readers' communications received each year, we will be unable to acknowledge all these forms, but they will certainly be seriously considered.

Please post to: **Egon Ronay's Guides, 73 Uverdale Road, London SW10 0SW**

Please use an up-to-date Guide. We publish annually. (H&R 1994)

Name and address of establishment	**Your recommendation or complaint**

Readers' Comments continued

Name and address of establishment	**Your recommendation or complaint**

Your Name (BLOCK LETTERS PLEASE)

Address

READERS' COMMENTS

Please use this sheet, and the continuation overleaf, to recommend hotels or restaurants of **really outstanding quality.**

Complaints about any of the Guide's entries will be treated seriously and passed on to our inspectorate, but we would like to remind you always to take up your complaint with the management at the time.

We regret that owing to the volume of readers' communications received each year, we will be unable to acknowledge all these forms, but they will certainly be seriously considered.

Please post to: **Egon Ronay's Guides, 73 Uverdale Road, London SW10 0SW**

Please use an up-to-date Guide. We publish annually. (H&R 1994)

Name and address of establishment	**Your recommendation or complaint**

Readers' Comments continued

Name and address of establishment	**Your recommendation or complaint**

Your Name (BLOCK LETTERS PLEASE)

Address